INVERTEBRATE ZOOLOGY

INVERTEBRATE ZOOLOGY

For B. Sc. and B. Sc. (Hons.) classes of all Indian Universities

E.L. JORDAN

M.Sc., M.A. (Toronto)

Formerly Head of Zoology Department
Lucknow Christian College, Lucknow

P.S. VERMA

M.Sc., Ph.D., F.E.S.I., F.A.Z.

Department of Zoology,
Meerut College, Meerut

2002

S. CHAND & COMPANY LTD.

RAM NAGAR, NEW DELHI - 110 055

S. CHAND & COMPANY LTD.

(An ISO 9002 Company)

Head Office : 7361, RAM NAGAR, NEW DELHI - 110 055
Phones : 3672080-81-82; Fax : 91-11-3677446

Shop at: **schandgroup.com**

E-mail: **schand@vsnl.com**

Branches :

No. 6, Ahuja Chambers, 1st Cross, Kumara Krupa Road, **Bangalore**-560 001. Ph: 2268048
152, Anna Salai, **Chennai**-600 002. Ph : 8460026
Pan Bazar, **Guwahati**-781 001. Ph : 522155
Sultan Bazar, **Hyderabad**-500 195. Ph : 4651135, 4744815
Mai Hiran Gate, **Jalandhar** - 144008 . Ph. 401630
613-7, M.G. Road, Ernakulam, **Kochi**-682 035. Ph : 381740
285/J, Bipin Bihari Ganguli Street, **Kolkata**-700 012. Ph : 2367459, 2373914
Mahabeer Market, 25 Gwynne Road, Aminabad, **Lucknow**-226 018. Ph : 226801, 284815
Blackie House, 103/5, Walchand Hirachand Marg , Opp. G.P.O., **Mumbai**-400 001. Ph : 2690881, 2610885
3, Gandhi Sagar East, **Nagpur**-440 002. Ph : 723901
104, Citicentre Ashok, Govind Mitra Road, **Patna**-800004. Ph:671366

First Edition 1963
Subsequent Editions and Reprints 1964, 65, 66, 67, 68, 69, 70, 71, 72, 74 (Twice), 76, 78, 79, 81, 82, 83, 85, 87, 88, 89, 91, 92 (Twice), 93, 95 (Twice), 97, 98, 99, 2000, 2001
Reprint 2002

ISBN : 81-219-0367-X

PRINTED IN INDIA

By Rajendra Ravindra Printers (Pvt.) Ltd., 7361, Ram Nagar, New Delhi-110 055 and published by S. Chand & Company Ltd., 7361, Ram Nagar, New Delhi-110 055

DEDICATED
to
My Parents
Who could not see the fruits of this labour
P.S.Verma

PREFACE TO THE FOURTEENTH EDITION

The dimensions of biology are fast increasing with more and more emphasis on cell biology, molecular biology, genetics, biochemistry, physiology, electron microscopy and biotechnology, etc. Many Indian universities have already introduced some topics of these disciplines in their under-graduate syllabi. The importance of basic zoology, however, cannot be ignored; most teachers and researchers rightly feel the need for a strong base in general zoology as a prerequisite for all fields of specializations. Jordan's "Invertebrate Zoology" has served a great deal towards the fulfilment of this aim. It has been a national best seller for more than three decades. It was, therefore, found necessary to bring out the same book in a more useful and enlarged form. The book has been thoroughly revised and enlarged in this edition. In this New Edition I have retained all that was judged good and useful in the previous edition. However, a number of changes have been made in this edition. Subject matter have been updated in the light of recent researches and new topics have been added at appropriate places keeping in view the changes in the syllabi of various Indian universities.

New chapters which have been added in this edition are : General Principles of Systematics and Animal Classification, *Polystoma, Ancylostoma* (The hookworm), *Wuchereria* (The filaria worm), Helminths and Diseases, *Bombyx* (The silkworm), *Cimex* (The bedbug), Termites (The white ants), *Peripatus* and Glossary. Comparative account of certain selected systems of Phylum Mollusca and Phylum Annelida is an additional feature of this edition. In addition to this, general topics, which are usually asked in the examinations, have been thoroughly revised and some new topics have also been added in all the phyla.

The examination oriented text is written for all the students, even for those who do not have a good background in the subject. The language is simple, explanations are clear, and presentation is very systematic. To improve scientific accuracy, about 900 well-labelled diagrams have been included at appropriate places. Important words are given in bold face and definitions in italics. Subject matter is error-free.

Thanks are due to Dr. P.C. Srivastava, K.K. College, Etawah for his help in the revision of this book. Thanks are also due to Shri Ravindra K.Gupta, Director and Shri T.N. Goel, M/s. S. Chand and Company Ltd., New Delhi for their wholehearted cooperation during the preparation and publication of this book.

Constructive suggestions for further improvement of the book will be always welcomed and entertained wholeheartedly.

"PREETI"   P.S. VERMA
121, New Mohanpuri Colony
Meerut - 250 001

PREFACE TO THE FIRST EDITION

Invertebrate Zoology has been written to meet the requirements of B.Sc. students. It is intended for those who have already completed an elementary course in Zoology. The book covers the courses laid down in the Universities of the Punjab, Delhi, U.P., Madhya Pradesh and Rajasthan. There are many books in the market which are used in these Universities, but the majority of these books are either out of date and often erroneous, or they do not deal with the selected types of animals.

Tremendous researches have been made in Zoology in the last few years; this book includes material from all recent researches and investigations in describing one to several animal types from each major phylum, keeping in mind not only the anatomy and physiology of animals, but also the relationship of structure to functional requirements of the environment. Besides the precise and up-to-date descriptions of selected types this book has three special features: 1. It deals with fair detail the animals included in the practical courses. 2. Illustrations have been used profusely with labels printed on the diagrams, so that they not only supplement the descriptions, but make it easier for the student to clearly grasp the text. 3. In each phylum several important topics are discussed which are difficult to find in one place or in any single book. With these features it is hoped that the book will be a complete guide in meeting the needs of the student.

Lucknow,   **E.L. JORDAN**
Ist January, 1963

CONTENTS

Introduction

Zoology (Gr., *zoion*=animal+*logos* = study) is the branch of life sciences that deals with the animal organism as contrasted to botany, the science that is concerned with the plant organism. Zoology and botany make up the science of biology (Gr., *bios* = life + *logos* = study) or the study of living things. Biology is the branch of science which investigates the origin,structure,functions and distribution of life in all its forms. Both zoology and botany seek to establish exact and quantitative principles for the basic organisation of living system.

RELATION OF ZOOLOGY TO OTHER SCIENCES

All the sciences are inter-related. Although biology uses physics, chemistry and other physical sciences in explaining its phenomena, biological principles are not merely an application of physico-chemical laws. The laws of many life processes have no counterparts in physics or chemistry. Many biological concepts can be expressed mathematically but others cannot. Biological sciences at present are often restricted to mere descriptive statements of general phenomena without quantitative connotation. Biological systems are represented by many levels of organisation, not all of which have been resolved into concise concepts and testable theories. Many branches of study serve to connect biology to other sciences, such as palaeontology, biophysics and biochemistry. There has been a marked trend for some time toward a synthesis of the biological sciences with other sciences.

SUBDIVISIONS OF ZOOLOGY

Zoology is such a vast subject that advanced workers in the field tend to specialize in one or more of the subdivisions in which they can hope to become very proficient. The subdivisions are grouped according to two types of approach.

Subdivisions According to Subject Matter

1. **Morphology** (Gr., *morphe*=form; *logos*=study). The study of the physical structure of organisms.

(i) **External morphology.** The study of external features of animals.

(ii) **Anatomy** (Gr., *ana*=up; *tome*=cutting). The study of gross structure of the internal organs by dissection, that which can be seen with the naked eyes.

(iii) **Comparative anatomy.** The study of gross structure emphasizing similarities and differences between animals.

(iv) **Histology** (Gr., *histos* = tissue; *logos* = study). The study of fine (microscopic) structure of tissues,which include the cells and their intercellular materials.

(v) **Cytology** (Gr., *kytos* = hollow vessel; *logos* = study). The study of the detailed structure of individual cells and their components.

2. **Physiology** (Gr., *physis* = nature; *logos*=study). The study of functional mechanism of animals. The method of digestion of food in the human body and the way in which cells construct new protoplasm are typical physiological aspects of zoology.

(i) **Cellular physiology.** The study of internal functions of cells and their components.

(ii) **Comparative physiology.** The study of the similarities and differences between functional mechanisms of different animals.

(iii) **Physiological chemistry.** The study of animal functions involving chemical reactions.

(iv) **Systematic physiology.** The study of the functions of organs and organ systems.

(v) **Pathological physiology.** The study of disturbances that occur in various functions of the organism during certain diseases.

(vi) **Clinical physiology.** The study of the problems that come during fundamental task of clinical practice.

(vii) **Ecological physiology.** The study of the peculiarities of physiological processes in various species of animals in relation to the various conditions of their existence.

3. **Taxonomy** (Gr., *taxis*=organisation; *nomos*=law). The study of the classification of animals into logical groups; the study of the evolutionary relationship of animals with one another.

4. **Endocrinology** (Gr.,*endon*=within; *krinein*=to separate; *logos*=study). The study of endocrine glands and the hormone actions in animals.

5. **Embryology** (Gr., *embryon*=embryo; *logos*=study).The study of development of organism from its beginning until it reaches a form of recognisable as the adult type. Since most animals have their beginning as single cells, embryology starts when the single cell begins divisions and continues with the formation of the various body parts until all the basic adult characteristics are present. This termination is at birth if the animal is a mammal, or at the hatching of the egg for most other forms of animal life.

6. **Ecology** (Gr., *oikos*=house; *logos*=study). The study of organisms in relation to their environment. An example would be how a certain animal gets its food, what animals threaten it, how it protects itself from those animals and how it survives unfavourable climatic conditions.

7. **Genetics** (Gr., *genesis*=origin). The study of heredity and variations. It seeks to find the explanation for similarities and differences between parents and their offspring. Since the basic unit of the heredity is gene, genetics involves a study of nature of the genes and chromosomes and how they control the growth and development of living organisms.

8. **Evolution** (L.,*e*=out; *volvere*=develop). The study of evolution is a study of how living organisms develop inherited characteristics which better adapt them to their surroundings, the progress of these adaptive changes in the present and the course of such changes in the past. This study extends back into the possible origin of living things.

9. **Palaeontology** (Gr., *palaios*=ancient; *onto*=existing; *logos*=study). The study of life as it existed in the past. It is closely related to the study of evolution. Palaeontology must be based on fossil remains of prehistoric animals, although certain other evidences are also used.

10. **Zoogeography** (Gr., *zoois*=animal; *ge*=earth; *graphein*=to write).The study of distribution of animals on the surface of the earth.

Subdivisions According to Animal Studied

1. **Protozoology** (Gr., *protos* = first; *zoios* = animal; *logos* = study). The study of one-celled animals,the Protozoa.

2. **Helminthology** (Gr., *helmins* = worm ; *logos* = study). The study of parasitic worms or helminthes.

3. **Parasitology** (Gr., *para*=beside; *sitos* =foods; *logos* = study). The study of parasitic animals.

4. **Entomology** (Gr., *enton* = insect; *logos* = study). The study of insects.

5. **Malacology** (Gr., *malakos* = soft; *logos* = *study*). The study of molluscs.

6. **Ichthyology** (Gr., *ichtys* = fish; *logos* = study). The study of fishes.

7. **Herpetology** (Gr., *herpein* = to creep; *logos* = to study). The study of amphibians and reptiles.

8. **Ornithology** (Gr., *ornis* = bird; *logos* = study). The study of birds.

9. **Mammalogy** (Gr., *mamma* = breast; *logos* = study). The study of mammals.

Besides the above. the following branches concern with the practical applications of zoology:

1. **Animal husbandry.** The cultivation of domesticated animals, such as cattle.

2. **Piggery.** The cultivation of pigs.

3. **Poultry.** The cultivation of fowl.

4. **Aquaculture.** The cultivation of fish and other aquatic animals.

5. **Apiculture.** The cultivation of honeybees.

6. **Sericulture.** The cultivation of silkworms.

IMPORTANCE OF STUDY OF ZOOLOGY

Zoology is a complex science having immense number of problems yet to solve. This alone is a challenge to an enquiring mind, but there are also other motives for zoological study.

1. Man is the product of the biological heritage. He is a part of the animal kingdom and a product of the evolutionary process. He is limited by the potentialities of living matter, for his roots are found in his biological background. No group of animals stands alone and isolated from other groups; all are linked in a sequence of life patterns, many of which have been displaced by other patterns in the long evolutionary process. Much information about man is obtained by studying other animals, for there is an underlying unity of structure and function throughout the animal kingdom.

2. The study of zoology is necessary for preprofessional work in medicine, dentistry, nursing, veterinary science, dietetics, agriculture, fishery, poultry, sericulture, apiculture, conservation of wildlife, sanitary engineering and many other fields. Medical sciences have profited from zoological discoveries, for concepts formed by studying one group of animals can be applied also to other groups, including man.

3. Zoology is of practical importance because of our dependence upon animals for many products and uses, such as food, clothing, sources of drugs, subjects of experimentation, etc. Genetics, one of the branches of zoology, has been a factor in producing better domestic animals and even promises some progress in the improvement of human stock.

4. Zoological study furnishes the basis for psychological and sociological studies. At present there is a lively study of animal behaviour and its implications of human application, which is indicative of this interest. Animal sociology is rapidly becoming a branch of zoology in its own right.

5. An interest in living forms is basic. Primitive man followed the chase from necessity; modern man does it as a relief from the tension of organised society and for the sheer love of hunting and fishing.

6. Animals influence man's welfare in harmful ways. Parasites injure man and his domestic animals. Many animals carry disease (vectors) and others themselves disease agents, such as those causing malaria. Destruction of crops and fruits by insect pests is a problem for agriculture everywhere.

7. All animals, including man, fit into a balance of nature. This is the web of life in which all plant and animal life fits into a pattern of environmental relationship.

8. The study of zoology is an excellent discipline for your mind. This is true for all sciences, but it is particularly true of life sciences that have a unique role in man's cultural pattern. Biological concepts influence your thinking in every realm of human interest. For instance, the concept of evolution or the transformation of organisms from one type to another during geological eras, has affected concepts in philosophy, psychology, sociology, religion and many other disciplines. One of the fascinating facets of biological study is the ever changing nature of its concepts. Much biological investigation may be done with practical objectives in mind, but a greater amount is motivated by curiosity and an urge to explain what lies beyond our present knowledge of life process.

9. There are aesthetic values in a study of biology as well. A student can expect to learn all or even many of the names and characteristics of the vast variety of plants and animals but a knowledge of the structure and functions of the major types will greatly increase the pleasure of a stroll in the woods or an excursion to the sea shore. The average city dweller gets only a small glimpse of vast panorama of living things, for so many of them live in places from where they cannot easily see the sea, or parts of the earth that are not easily visited. Trips to botanical gardens, zoos, aquariums and museums will help give one an appreciation of tremendous variety of living things.

REVISION QUESTIONS

1. Define the terms biology and zoology.
2. Discuss the relationship of zoology to other sciences.
3. Name and describe the subdivisions of zoology.
4. Name the specialized branches of zoology for the study of various animal groups.
5. Write an essay on the importance of study of zoology in relation to human welfare.

2

General Principles of Systematics (Taxonomy) and Animal Classification

This world comprises a great number of living and non-living objects. The group of living organisms of the world exhibits a great diversity and variations. Living world or animate objects are animals and plants. The variations in plants and animals have posed a great problem to human being for their study, *i.e.*, how to recognise them with their differences and similarities. Therefore, from the beginning of the human civilization people felt the necessity of arranging them by studying not only the morphological aspects but up to some extent their anatomy also. With the development of world civilization and various discoveries including the apparatuses, subcellular structures and subatomic particles have created another problem in the methods of systematic arrangement of animate objects. Now, their arrangement includes their anatomical, histological, embryological, physiological, cytological, cytochemical, genetical, ecological, palaeontological, geographical and evolutionary aspects also.

The term systematics is derived from Latinised Greek word–*systema*–as applied to the systems of classification developed by early naturalists, notably Linnaeus (*Systema Naturae*, First Edition, 1935).

According to Simpson, "*Systematics is the scientific study of kinds and diversity of organisms and of any and all relationships among them.*"

Systematics includes taxonomy, identification, classification and nomenclature and all other aspects of dealing with different kinds of organisms and data accumulated about them is also included in systematics.

ORIGIN AND DEVELOPMENT OF SYSTEMATICS

The origin and development of systematics and human civilization started simultaneously, *i.e.*, civilization of human being is the systematics or in other words we say that in our daily life those people who maintain their houses systematically that means they are civilized. As the knowledge developed they started naming the plants and animals according to their own choice.

The clue for the earliest classification comes from Vedas and Upanishads (1500 BC to 600 BC). In Vedas and Upanishads, several technical terms are used in the description of plants and plant parts, both morphologically and anatomically. Plants of medicinal importance were collected and studied. Charaka and Susruta, the two eminent ancient Indian scholars and ayurvedic physicians, contributed a lot to our knowledge of diversity and utility of organisms. One of the remotest works dealing with plant-life in a scientific manner is the Vrikshayurveda (science of plants and plant-life) compiled by Parasara, even before the beginning of Christian era, which formed the basis of botanical teaching and medical studies in ancient India.

Several early Greek scholars notably Hippocrates (460–377 B.C) and Democritus (465–370 B.C.) made observations on animals but their classification was not useful. Later on Aristotle (384–322 B.C.) also studied the living organisms, *viz.*, plants and animals and gave statement on classification that "*animals may be characterized according to their way of living, their action, their habit and their bodily parts*". He classified the major groups of animals as birds, fishes, insects and whales. Aristotle is called the "Father of biological taxonomy." Theophrastus (370–385 B.C.) who was the student of Plato and then of Aristotle, is known as the "Father of Botany", classified all plants on the basis of form and texture and divided them into trees, shrubs. under-shrubs and herbs. His classification was strictly artificial and in his "Historia Plantarum" he has classified and described 480 plants. Albertus Magnus (1193–1280) recognised the differences with the help of crude lenses in between the monocotyledons and dicotyledons and recognised the classification of

Theophrastus. Otto Brunfels (1464–1554), a German, first recognised the Perfecti and Imperfecti group of plants based on the presence or absence of flowers respectively. Jerome Bock (1498–1554), another German, classified the plants into trees, shrubs and herbs. Andrea Cesalpino (1519–1603) taxonomically classified plants on the basis of habit and subdivided them on the characters of fruits and seeds.

Gaspard Bauhin (1560–1624) classified the plants on the basis of texture and form. He was first to find out the binomial nomenclature although it is usually credited to Linnaeus. In the history of systematics John Ray (1627–1705) has done a great job. Before him the classification was baseless and there was not any strong scientific background. John Ray travelled widely in Europe with Francis Willougby (1635–1672). They not only observed and collected plants and animals, but also planned to classify them. Unfortunately, Willougby died prematurely and later John Ray published

his Historia Generalis Plantarum in three volumes between 1668 and 1704. In this book John Ray described accurately and in meticulous detail and catalogued over 18,000 plants. He was the first person who recognised the difference between genus and species, and through valuation of both similarities and dissimilarities in animals arrived at a more natural higher classification than of the former persons. After John Ray, the most remarkable man in the field of taxonomy was Carolus Linnaeus (1707–1778) who is often referred to as the "Father of Taxonomy" for his outstanding contribution in this field. Linnaeus visited many European countries and made careful observations on the plants and animals. He published his scheme of classification in his famous book Systema Naturae in 1753. The 10th Edition of this book was published in 1758 and the 1st January of that year marks the beginning of the consistent application of what is known as the "binomial system of

Fig. 2.1. Carolus Linnaeus (1704—1778).

nomenclature". This system which introduces the principles of naming an organism by two words, was first proposed by Linnaeus and is universally followed today. This work of Linnaeus became the foundation of systematics. He also laid down the clear delimitations for species.

Jean Baptiste Monet de Lamarck (1744–1829) wrote Flore Francoise in 1778 in which he laid down the principles of his concept of natural classification. Charles Darwin (1809–1882) a great evolutionist, on the basis of his extensive studies and with the help of convincing evidences gathered on the Voyage of the Beagle, explained the origin of species through natural selection. The evolution theories of Lamarck and Darwin not only greatly influenced Linnaean classical systematics but also totally rejected the pre-Lamarckian idea of the fixity of species. Ernst Haeckel (1866) introduced the method of representing phylogeny by means of trees or branching diagrams.

Sir Julian Huxley (1940) introduced the new term "New Systematics" which incorporates the results of recent studies in various branches of life sciences in systematics which modify some of the older ideas of classical systematics. Today the definition of species is based on population because the development of population genetics which in turn influenced the further development of population systematics.

UTILITY OF SYSTEMATICS (TAXONOMY)

No scientific ecological survey can be carried out without the most painstaking identification of all the species of ecological significance. A similar dependence on systematics is true for other areas of science. Even the experimental biologists have learned to appreciate the necessity for sound taxonomy. The systematists can fill many gaps in our knowledge. There are more than one million species of animals and more than half million species of plants described in the biosphere. In addition, there must be a large number of plant and animal species yet to be described. Without the knowledge of systematics the discovery of new species of plants and animals is not possible and we cannot know much about the organisms of our surroundings. Therefore, there is a great necessity or utility of systematics.

SYSTEMS OF CLASSIFICATION

There are three different systems of classifications which have been proposed so far by different taxonomists. They are: (i) Artificial; (ii) Natural;(iii) Phylogenetic.

Artificial System of Classification

This type of classification is based upon characters of convenience without relation to phylogenetic significance; classification based upon characters erroneously presented to indicate phylogenetic relationship; also classification based on a single arbitrarily chosen criterion, instead of an evolution of the totality of characters known as artificial classification. This system of classification was adopted by Pliny in the first century A.D. for animals on the basis of habitats, *e.g.,* land, air and water. Accordingly animals were classified into two categories on the basis of their flying ability: (i) animals that can fly and (ii) animals that cannot fly. In the first group unrelated animals like butterflies, birds and bats were placed together.

The classification of plants on the basis of habit into (i) herbs, (ii) undershrubs, (iii) shrubs and (iv) trees is also an artificial one. The criteria used in this classification, although very simple and easy to follow are arbitrary and do not reflect any natural relationship existing among the organisms. Moreover, it leads to heterogeneous assemblage of unrelated organisms under one heading and does not do justice to the totality of characteristics of an organism.

The system adopted by Linnaeus was also artificial in which the plants were classified on the basis of number and arrangement of stamens and carpels. Closely related species of organisms are kept far apart in this system of classification.

Natural System of Classification

The natural classification may be defined as "*Classification based on characters which indicate natural relationships*".The organisms of a natural systematic category agree with one another in so many characters because they are descendants of one common ancestor. The natural system of classification is based on similarity.

Zoologists and botanists differ in their interpretation of the implication of this system of classsification. According to zoologists, the natural system of classification includes the phylogenetic and evolutionary trends which are evident in the word "natural". Botanists hold the opinion that the natural system does not necessarily include phylogenetic trends of plants. Here they proposed the "phylogenetic system" of classsification separate from the "natural system" to include the evolutionary trends in plants. The "natural system" of classification of the plant kingdom was proposed by George Bentham (1800–1844) and Joseph Dalion Hooker (1817–1911).

Phylogenetic System of Classification

The phylogenetic system is based on the evolutionary and genetic relationship of the organisms. It enables us to find out the ancestors or derivatives of any taxon. Our present-day knowledge is insufficient to construct a perfect phylogenetic classification and all the present phylogenetic systems are formed by the combination of natural and phylogenetic evidences. This system is adopted by Adolph Engler (1844–1930) and Karl A.E. Prantl and John Hutchinson (1884–1974) in classifying the plants.

NOMENCLATURE

Nomenclature is defined as the system of naming of plants, animals and other objects or groups of plants, animals and other objects. Scientific names are the language of taxonomists. When a taxonomist identifies and describes the natural group of animals, he gives appropriate scientific names to the groups. Common names do not serve the purpose because a particular animal is known by different names in different parts of the world. For example, the bird that we know as gauraiya in India and Pakistan, is known by different names in other countries, house sparrow in England; Pardal in Spain; Musch in Holland; Suzune in Japan and so on. Moreover the common name may be used for different kinds of animals. For example, the name kenchua is used both for the earthworm and *Ascaris.* On the other hand, a scientfic name is universally used for a particular species or particular group of animals. For example, gauraiya or house sparrow is termed *Passer domesticus* by zoologists throughout the world.

To ensure that one scientific name stands for one particular kind of animal everywhere and is the only name for that organism, the taxonomist must see the following: (1) The name chosen for an animal has not been already given to some other animal or plant. (2) The animals and plants have been described in such detail that another taxonomist can determine from the description exactly the kind of animal to which the name has been given. (3) The animal or plant has been duly placed in the system of classification establishing its relationships.

Binomial Nomenclature

The history of binomial system of nomenclature is very long. Two centuries before Christ, Cato used two names for plants in his De Re Rustica. But he had no knowledge that genera were usually composed of several species. Later, two ideas developed with the evolution of the idea of nomenclature. One was to translate the descriptive Greek nouns used for genera into Latin. As a result of this translation into Latin the generic name consists of two words. These were called binary generic names. The other tendency was to use descriptive phrases for specific names. These tendencies in conjunction gave rise to a polynomial system of nomenclature. According to this system the name of a plant was composed of several words in a series which bore a brief description of the plant. For example, Bentham used the name Caryophyllum saxatilis, folis gramineus umbellatis corymbis to represent the Caryophyllum which grew on rocks, with grass-like leaves and flowers in umbellate corymbs. This was the system of cumbersome.

In the middle of the sixteenth century, a number of binary generic names were changed by Brunfels to single ones. Dodonaeus and Gaspard Bauhin later followed in general the binomial system but it is usually credited to Linnaeus who used it more than hundred years later in his Species Plantarum. According to this binomial nomenclature, long names were cut short so that they could be used with greater convenience. This system postulates that every individual of plant and animal kingdom consists of only two words in Latin; the first word designating the genus and the second, the additional epithet, that signifies the particular species with that genus. It is also known as two naming system or binary system. For example, the genus of modern horse is *Equus*. Among its species are *Equus caballus* and *Equus asinus*. The word *caballus* and *asinus* standing above have no meaning in taxonomy ; they are not names of species or any thing else. Only when they are part of a binomial combination, they are meaningful taxonomically and then it is the combination that is the name of the species. Often, specific names of animals and plants are given in honour of some persons. If the person honoured is a man the specific name ends in "i". For example, the earthworm, *Lumbricus friendi* is named after Rev. H. Friend. If the person honoured is a woman, the specific name ends "ae". Sometimes, the specific name indicates a locality (*e.g.,* indica for Indian) or colour (*e.g.,* niger for black),

In scientific literature, it is a general practice to write a specific name followed by the name of the person who first described the species and the year when he did so. For example, the scientfic name of man is written as *Homo sapiens* Linnaeus, 1758. If the species, after its publication, is transferred to any other genus or the generic name is changed the first author's name is written in brackets (parenthesis). For example, *Panthera leo* (Linnaeus) means that species *leo* was originally assigned by Linnaeus to some other genus (*Felis*).

Trinomial Nomenclature

This system of nomenclature is employed to name the subspecies. In classification the sub-species is a category below the species. The subspecies name is also a Latin or Latinised word and follows the name of the species to which it belongs. For example, the specific name of the house crow, which occurs throughout India, Pakistan, Burma and Ceylon is *Corvus splendens.* The house crows of India and Pakistan, Burma and Ceylon differ with each other in minute morphological features and are, thus, separated as distinct subspecies. The Indian and Pakistani house crow has been assigned the subspecific name *Corvus splendens splendens,* the Burmese house crow, *Corvus splendens insolens* and the Ceylonese house crow, *Corvus splendens protegatus.* The full scientific name of subspecies is, therefore, a trinomial name consisting of three names: the names of genus, the species and subspecies itself.

Rules of Nomenclature

In 1898, the International Congress of Zoology organised an International Commission on Zoological Nomenclature to formulate a set of rules, which would be binding for all taxonomical publications. The aim of International Code of Nomenclature is to make the stability in naming the taxa, avoiding the use of names which may cause error, ambiguity or confusion.

The standardisation and legislation of nomenclatural practices are usually made at International Botanical and Zoological Congresses. This is done in order to put the nomenclature of the past in order and to provide guidelines for that of the future.

A few commonly followed rules and recommendations which may be considered as the essentials of a code of nomenclature are given below :

1. The system of nomenclature adopted is the binomial system to indicate the specific name and trinomial for subspecific name.
2. The name of the genus is a single word in a nominative singular and must begin with a capital letter. The name of the species may be a single or compound word and must begin with a small letter.
3. The name of the author, who first publishes the name when describing it, should follow the species name and should rarely be abbreviated and is printed in roman type.
4. The scientific names of animals and plants must be different.
5. The names must be in Latin or Latinised form and are usually printed in italic type.
6. Within the animal and plant kingdom, no two genera can have the same name, and whithin a genus, no two species can have the same name.
7. The generic or specific name first published is the only one recognised. All duplicate names are synonyms.
8. When the name of the genus is not the one under which a species is placed by the original author, or if the generic name is changed the original author's name is written in parenthesis.
9. The formation of family and subfamily names follow rules which are different in the Zoological and Botanical Codes.
10. A name must retain its original spelling,obvious errors and misprints may be corrected; diacritic marks are dropped.
11. A name may be based on any part of an animal or a plant, or on any stage of an organism's life history.

RECOMMENDATIONS

To make new names the following suggestions are followed :

1. A name should be in Latin or easily converted into Latin form.
2. A name should not contain less than three and more than twelve letters.
3. A name should be easy to pronounce.
4. The name given should preferably describe some characteristics of the organism.
5. A name should not be derived from two languages.
6. A name should not be frivolous.

FAMILIARITY WITH TAXA

According to Darwin (1850), "All organic beings are found to resemble each other in descending degree, so that they can be classed in groups under groups". All major groups of animals can individually be subdivided into smaller and smaller subgroups. Within the vertebrates we can distinguish subgroups such as birds and mammals; within the mammals, carnivores and rodents; within the carnivores, those that are dog-like, those that are cat-like and so forth. If one wants to construct a classification of these species, this classification is not arbitrary. The task of classification then is the delimitation of these groups and their arrangement in an orderly sequence, *i.e.,* hierarchy.

SYSTEMATIC HIERARCHY

Since the number of animal and plant species is very large, it is not possible to either know them individually by their names or to refer them in the literature. This necessitated arranging them into categories and taxa of different grades. Then arranging these categories and taxa in an ascending order so that a higher category includes one or more lower categories and higher taxa include one or more lower taxa.

Linnaeus was the first taxnomist to establish a definite hierarchy of taxonomic categories recognised within the animal kingdom. These are classes, order, genus, species and varieties. The varieties, used by Linnaeus as an optional category of various types of intraspecific variants, was, eventually discarded or replaced by the species. These few categories sufficed to cope with small number of animals and plants known at that time. However, as the number of known species increased and with it our knowledge of the degrees of relationship of these species, the need arose for a more precise indication of the taxonomic position of species and inserting additional ones among them. Most are formed by combining the original category names with the prefixes super or sub. Thus, there are superorder, superfamilies and subfamilies, etc. The most frequently used additional new category name is perhaps the term tribe for a category between genus and family. Vertebrate palaeontologists also used in routine the category cohort between order and class. Some authors used terms for additional subdivisions, such as cladus, legio, and sectio. Some used infraclass below the subclass and infraorder below the suborder. The generally accepted categories are the following :

> Kingdom
> Phylum
> Subphylum
> Superclass
> Class
> Subclass
> Infraclass
> Cohort
> Superorder
> Order
> Suborder
> Infraorder
> Superfamily (-oidea)
> Family (-idae)
> Subfamily(-inae)
> Tribe(-ini)
> Subtribe
> Genus
> Subgenus
> Species
> Subspecies

Indicated in the parenthesis are the standardized endings for the names of tribes, subfamilies, families and superfamilies.

The systematic hierarchy or Linnaean hierarchy as it is commonly known, with its need for arbitrary ranking has often been attacked as an unscientific system of classification. Alternate methods, such as numerical scheme have been proposed but have not found favour among taxonomists, primarily for following two reasons :

(i) Assigning definite numerical values to taxa demands a far greater knowledge of the relationships of taxa than can be inferred from available evidences.

(ii) An assignment of such values would freeze the system into a family which would preclude any further improvement.

It is the very subjectivity of the Linnaean hierarchy which gives it the flexibility required by the incompleteness of our knowledge of relationships. It permits the proposal of alternate models of relationships and gives different authors an opportunity to test which particular balance between splitting and lumping permits the presentation of maximum amount of information. Like any other scientific theory it will for ever be provisional.

TAXON AND CATEGORY

Taxon (Plural : Taxa.). The taxa are the groups of animals generally groups of species. The words insects, fishes, birds, mammals in animals; algae, fungi, ferns, mosses, grasses, etc., in plants are the groups of organisms. These are the concrete objects of classification. Any such group of such population is called taxon. But in ordinary usage only the so called basic categories (genus, family, order, class, phylum, kingdom), are treated as such groups. The supertaxa at all lelvels are treated as groups of the basic taxa (a superclass as a group of classes) and the subtaxa at all levels as a subdivision of the basic taxa (a suborder as a section of the order).

According to **Simpson,** " *A taxon is a group of real organisms recognised as a formal unit at any level of a hierarchic classification.*"

According to **Mayr** (1964), "*A taxon is a taxonomic group of any rank that is sufficiently distinct to be worthy of being assigned to a definite category.*"

Category. The group of animals are taxa. Each taxon is placed at some level in hierarchy. A category designates rank or level in a hierarchic classification. It is a class, the members of which are all the taxa assigned a given rank.

A category can be higher or lower than some other one, so we may speak of a higher category. The categories have names, but these are terms and not names in biological nomenclature. They are kingdom, phylum, class and so on. It is an error to state "this animal belongs to category Mammalia", Mammalia is the name of taxon not of category.

TAXONOMIC CATEGORIES

Species. Species is the most important category in the taxonomic hierarchy. It is the basic unit in taxonomy and also in evolution. Its definition has long been one of the major problems of taxonomy. Several definitions and aspects are discussed about the definition of species.

According to **Blackweldler,** the species can be defined as follows: (i) One of the groups,the one placed in the category called the species level (a species group), (ii) The category or level at which the species groups are placed (the species level).

Two main definitions are given for species. These are as follows :

Biological species. Biological species are usually defined as groups of actually or potentially interbreeding natural populations, which are reproductively isolated from other such groups. This gives theoretical groups which can seldom be distinguished in practice.

Simpson has pointed out that all the definitions of animal species give us biological species. He, therefore, prefers the name genetical species for this and cites also biospecies. (It should be noted that populations do not interbreed, only individual animals and plants interbreed).

Genetical species. Genetical species are groups of interbreeding populations which are reproductively isolated from each other. They are, thus, the same as biological species. For example, in *Homo sapiens*, the *sapiens* is a species of *Homo.*

Genus. The taxa placed in the genus category are the genera. These are groups of species brought together by the taxonomists as evidenced by the fact that generic name is a part of each name of each of the included species.

The genus is involved from naming of the first species of whose name it forms the first part. Again it is possible to say that a genus is any group of species included under the one generic name by any taxonomist. This is completely subjective, but it is approximately the working definition which is the basis of most taxonomic work. The genus cannot properly be described as the next higher level above the species, because it is common and always possible to use subgenera between the genus and species, and to use also sections or other informal categories.

A pragmatic definition of the genus states, "*A genus is a taxonomic category containing a single species or a monophyletic group of species, which is separated from other taxa of the same rank (other genera) by a decided gap.*"

The genus *Felis* includes the golden cat (*Felis temincki*) the fishing cat (*Felis viverrina*) and the leopard cat (*Felis bengalensis*).

Family. This is a taxonomic category containing one or more related genera and which is separated from other related families by important and characteristic differences.

The family Felidae which includes the lion, the leopard, the tiger and all types of cats belonging to different genera. This family is distinctly separate from the family Canidae which includes dogs and foxes.

Order. The order is the basic category of what has been called the order group which includes also superorders, the suborders, the infraorders and taxa at any other levels interpolated between superfamily and infraclass. In many phyla, orders are very well known groups, but in some phyla they are less well known than the classes, whereas classes do have a fairly evident uniformity throughout the animal kingdom. The orders of vertebrates, for example, are scarcely comparable to families in insects and levels vary in other groups. For example, the order Carnivora includes families Felidae and Canidae.

Class. The class is the basic category of what has been called the class group which included also superclasses and infraclasses, as well as any others interpolated among these. In the animal kingdom as a whole, the classes are undoubtedly the best known taxa, even the phyla being subject to more differences of the opinion. A class is generally a subdivision of a phylum. For example, the order Carnivora includes the lion, the cat, etc., are included in the class Mammalia.

Phylum. The taxa placed in the phylum category are the phyla, subdivisions of the kingdom. They may be assembled into superphyla or subdivided into subphyla. The phylum Porifera includes three classes such as Calcarea, Hexactinellida and Demospongia.

Kingdom. This is the highest taxonomic category. All animals are included in the animal kingdom and all plants are included in the plant kingdom.

SPECIES AS A CATEGORY

The importance of the term species in all fields of biology is so immense that it deserves special consideration. It has already been stated that individual organisms which have many features in common and are able to breed only amongst themselves are encompassed by the term species.

The definition of species is not restricted only to the taxonomists. Nowadays the other fields of biology also consider the species to a great extent. Cytologists, geneticists, ecologists, biochemists and others have also defined the species. The definitions given by different workers are as follows :

Allopatric species. The species inhabiting different geographical areas.

Sympatric species. The species normally occupying the same geographical areas.

Morphospecies. "These are ones established by the morphological similarity regardless of other considerations" (Simpson).

Biospecies and genetical species. A group of inter-breeding populations which are reproductively isolated from other such group.

Sibling species. It is a term applied to pairs or groups of very similar and closely related species. When applied to closely related species (in phylogenetic sense) this expression refers to hypothetical species, these cannot be dealt with in taxonomy but can be useful in speculations on evolution.

Taxonomic species. A species which has been provided a specific name under the International Rules of Nomenclature.

Evolutionary species. These are lineages (ancestral descendent sequences of populations) evolving separately from each other and with their own unitary evolutionary roles and tendencies.

Polytypic species. Polytypic species are those which consist of two or more subspecies.

Monotypic species. Monotypic species consist of a single subspecies.

OUTLINE CLASSIFICATION OF ANIMALS

The animals have been classified in various ways by different authors. The classification which follows is based on the classification proposed by Meglitsch, P.A. (1972). In this classification, only larger groups have been taken into consideration.

KINGDOM ANIMALIA

This is the largest group of animal classification. It includes the entire animal population (fauna) of the world. It is divided into two subkingdoms : Protozoa and Metazoa.

Subkingdom A. Protozoa

About 50,000 species. Acellular microscopic animals. Solitary or colonial. Specialized cell organelles. Single to many nuclei. Nutrition holozoic, holophytic or saprozoic or parasitic. Freshwater, marine or moist terrestrial.

MAJOR GROUPS IN ANIMAL CLASSIFICATION

Kingdom - Animalia

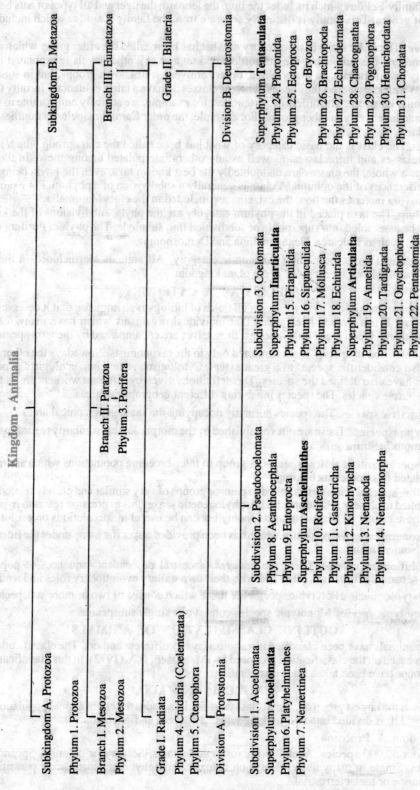

Subkingdom A. Protozoa
Phylum 1. Protozoa

Subkingdom B. Metazoa

Branch I. Mesozoa
Phylum 2. Mesozoa

Branch II. Parazoa
Phylum 3. Porifera

Branch III. Eumetazoa

Grade I. Radiata
Phylum 4. Cnidaria (Coelenterata)
Phylum 5. Ctenophora

Grade II. Bilateria

Division A. Protostomia

Subdivision 1. Acoelomata
Superphylum Acoelomata
Phylum 6. Platyhelminthes
Phylum 7. Nemertinea

Subdivision 2. Pseudocoelomata
Phylum 8. Acanthocephala
Phylum 9. Entoprocta
Superphylum Aschelminthes
Phylum 10. Rotifera
Phylum 11. Gastrotricha
Phylum 12. Kinorhyncha
Phylum 13. Nematoda
Phylum 14. Nematomorpha

Subdivision 3. Coelomata
Superphylum Inarticulata
Phylum 15. Priapulida
Phylum 16. Sipunculida
Phylum 17. Mollusca
Phylum 18. Echiurida
Superphylum Articulata
Phylum 19. Annelida
Phylum 20. Tardigrada
Phylum 21. Onychophora
Phylum 22. Pentastomida
Phylum 23. Arthropoda

Division B. Deuterostomia
Superphylum Tentaculata
Phylum 24. Phoronida
Phylum 25. Ectoprocta
or Bryozoa
Phylum 26. Brachiopoda
Phylum 27. Echinodermata
Phylum 28. Chaetognatha
Phylum 29. Pogonophora
Phylum 30. Hemichordata
Phylum 31. Chordata

Phylum 1. Protoza (First animals). Characters as those of the subkingdom.

Subkingdom B. Metazoa

Multicellular animals. Body comprises many cells, usually arranged in layers or tissues. It is divided into three branches: Mesozoa, Parazoa, Eumetazoa.

Branch I. Mesozoa

Cellular animals having the structure of a stereoblastula, composed of surface layer of somatic cells and interior reproductive cells.

Phylum 2. Mesozoa (Middle animals). About 50 species. Worm-like, small. Symmetry bilateral. An external layer of ciliated digestive cells surrounding one or several reproductive cells. Parasitic in cephalopods and other invertebrates.

Examples : *Dicyema, Rhopalura,* etc.

Branch II. Parazoa

Animals of cellular grade of organization with incipient tissue formation. Interior cells of several different kinds. There is no mouth or digestive tract and no organ systems are pressent. The body is porous with one to many internal cavities lined by choanocytes. Sessile, marine, a few freshwater. Solitary or colonial.

Phylum 3. Porifera (Pore-bearers). About 5,000 species. Characters as those of the branch.

Examples : *Scypha or Sycon, Euplectella, Hyalonema, Euspongia,* etc.

Branch III. Eumetazoa

Animals of tissue or organ-system grade of organisation with mouth and digestive tract (except when lost by parasitic degeneration). Interior cells of several kinds. Body not porous and without cavities lined by choanocytes.

Grade I. Radiata

Eumetazoa with primary radial symmetry. Tissues are present and organ-systems are incipient. Mesoderm, usually derived from the ectoderm, is present as an incipient tissue, without a high degree of cellular specialisation. The only body space is the digestive cavity, which has a mouth, but no anus.

Phylum 4. Cnidaria (Coelenterata). About 10,000 species. Symmetry radial, biradial or radio-bilateral. The mouth is encircled by tentacles bearing nematocysts. No rows of ciliated plates. Body cavity as coelenteron. Sessile or free swimming. Solitary or colonial. Marine or freshwater.

Examples : *Hydra, Obelia, Aurelia, Metridium,* Corals, etc.

Phylum 5. Ctenophora (Comb-bearers or Comb-jellies). About 90 species. Symmetry is biradial. Tentacles when present, do not encircle the mouth. No nematocysts. Eight radial rows of ciliated swimming plates. Free-swimming and marine.

Examples : *Pleurobrachia, Coeloplana, Ctenoplana,* etc.

Grade II. Bilateria

Eumetazoa with bilateral symmetry, or those with embryonic bilateral symmetry later modified into radial symmetry. Organ-system grade of organisation. Mostly with a well-developed mesoderm of endodermal origin. Mostly with body spaces other than the digestive cavity. Mouth and anus generally present. Bilateria is divided into two divisions: Protostomia and Deuterostomia.

Division A. Protostomia

Bilateria in which the mouth arises from the blastopore or from the anterior margin of the blastopore. Protostomia is subdivided into three subdivisions : Acoelomata, Pseudocoelomata, and Coelomata.

Subdivision 1. Acoelomata

No body cavity or coelom. Space between the body wall and digestive tract is filled with mesenchyme. Excretory system of protonephrida with flame bulbs.

Superphylum Acoelomata

Bilateria without a coelom. With mesenchyme between the body wall and digestive tract. Excretory system of protonephridia with flame bulbs. Body unsegmented or consisting of a strobila, with youngest segment toward the head.

Phylum 6. Platyhelminthes (Flatworms). About 12,700 species. Body dorsoventrally flat-tened. Anus and circulatory system absent. Free living or parasitic. Terrestrial, freshwater or marine.

Examples : *Planaria, Fasciola, Taenia,* etc.

Phylum 7. Nemertinea or Rhynchocoela (Ribbon worms). About 750 species. Body slender, soft, very elastic and covered with cilia. No segmentation. Mouth anterior with a long eversible proboscis. Digestive tract complete with anus. Circulatory system present. Free-living. Mostly marine, few terrestrial and freshwater.

Examples : *Cerebratulus, Stichostemma,*etc.

Subdivision 2. Pseudocoelomata

Space present between digestive tract and body wall but this space is a pseudocoel (remnant of the blastocoel) and not a coelom. Anus present with or without protonephridia, flame bulbs present or absent.

Phylum 8. Acanthocephala (Spiny-headed worms). About 500 species. Minute parasitic worms. Proboscis protrusible (eversible) with recurved spines. No digestive tract.

Examples : *Echinorhynchus, Gigantorhynchus,* etc.

Phylum 9. Entoprocta (Moss animals). About 60 species. Digestive tube U-shaped. Mouth and anus close together lying within a region surrounded by ciliated tentacles. Sessile. Mostly marine, few freshwater. Solitary or colonial .

Examples : *Pedicellina, Loxosoma, Urnatella,* etc.

Superphylum Aschelminthes

An assemblage of pseudocoelomates. All have anterior mouth, posterior anus and straight digestive tube.

Phylum 10. Rotifera (Wheel animalcule). About 1,500 species. Microscopic. Anterior end with a ciliated corona. Pharynx with internal jaws known as trophi. Protonephridial system with terminal flame bulbs. Mostly freshwater, some marine.

Examples : *Brachionus, Philodina, Rotatoria,* etc.

Phylum 11. Gastrotricha (Hairy stomach worms). About 150 species. Microscopic. Ventral surface flattened and ciliated. Cuticle with spines, plates or scales and unsegmented. Pharynx tubular devoid of trophi. Freshwater and marine.

Examples : *Chaetonotus, Macrodasys,* etc.

Phylum 12. Kinorhyncha (Jaw-moving worms). About 60 species. Small. More or less spiny without superficial cilia. Body unsegmented with the anterior end an introvert. Marine.

Examples : *Echinoderes, Pycnophyses,* etc.

Phylum 13. Nematoda (Round worms). About 10,000 species. Body rounded, slender, covered by a continuous cuticle, often tapered at ends. Cilia absent. Epidermis divided into four or more chords. Only longitudinal muscles in the body wall. Long muscular pharynx having triradiate lumen. Free-living or parasitic. Freshwater or marine or in soil.

Examples : *Ascaris, Rhabditis, Enterobius, Ancylostoma, Wuchereria,* etc.

Phylum 14. Nematomorpha (Horse-hair worms). About 230 species. Body long slender, cylindrical with dorsal and ventral epidermal chords. Gonoducts joining the intestine. Larval stages parasitic and adults free-living.

Examples : *Gordius, Nectonema,* etc.

Subdivision 3. Coelomata

Animals with a true coelom and usually well-developed ectomesoderm. Excretory organs are protonephridia with or without nephrostome. Anus present.

Superphylum Inarticulata

Unsegmented, coelomate protostomes.

Phylum 15. Priapulida. About 8 species. Body surface covered with spines and tubercles. Proboscis anterior. Urinogenital pores separate from the digestive tube in both sexes. Protonephridia terminating in solenocytes joining the gonoducts. Marine.

Example : *Priapulus.*

Phylum 16. Sipunculida (Peanut worms). About 275 species. Body elongated and cylindrical with retractile anterior introvert. Short hollow tentacles around the mouth. No segmentation or setae. Anus dorsal. Marine.

Examples : *Sipunculus, Phascolosoma,* etc.

Phylum 17. Mollusca (Soft-bodied animals). About 1,28,000 species. Body soft covered by mantle usually with an anterior head and a ventral muscular foot. Mantle secretes shell. Shell sometimes vestigial and sometimes in several pieces. Coelom reduced. Terrestrial, freshwater and marine.

Examples : *Chiton, Pila* (Snail), *Unio* (Mussel), *Sepia, Loligo* (Squid), *Nautilus*, etc.

Phylum 18. Echiurida (Adder-tailed worms). About 150 species. Body cylindrical with trough- shaped elastic proboscis (non- retractile). Mouth ventral. Trunk with setae. Coelom spacious. Marine.

Examples : *Echiurus, Urechis,* etc.

Superphylum Articulata

Segmented coelomate animals. Characterised by segmentation of embryonic stages, even though the adult may have secondarily lost its metameric organisation.

Phylum 19. Annelida (Ringed or Segmented worms). About 8,700 species. Body elongated and metamerically segmented. Coelom spacious, typically divided into metameric compartments. Terrestrial, freshwater and marine.

Examples : *Nereis* (Clamworm), *Pheretima* (Earthworm), *Hirudinaria* (Leech), etc.

Phylum 20. Tardigrada (Water bears or Bear animalcules) Minute. Body cylindrical and segmented with four pairs of unsegmented legs terminating in claws. Coelom transitory replaced by a haemocoel. No appendages associated with mouth.

Examples : *Echiniscus, Hypsibius,* etc.

Phylum 21. Onychophora (Claw-bearers). About 73 species. Body worm-like, elongated and unsegmented. Thin unsegmented cuticle covers the body. Many pairs of short unsegmented legs. Head with three pairs of appendages, two of which are associated with mouth. Tracheal system for respiration. Moist terrestrial.

Example : *Peripatus.*

Phylum 22. Pentastomatida (Tongue worms). About 70 species. Worm-like body with two pairs of claws or short appendages at the sides of the mouth. Respiratory system absent. Parasitic in vertebrates.

Examples : *Porocephalus, Cephalobaena.* etc.

Phylum 23. Arthropoda (Joint-footed animals). About 9,00,000 species. Body segmented with jointed appendages usually terminating in claws. Exoskeleton chitinous. Coelom greatly reduced and replaced by a haemocoel. Terrestrial, freshwater and marine.

Examples : Prawns, Scorpions, Flies, Centipedes, etc.

Division B. Deuterostomia

Bilateria in which the mouth does not arise from the blastopore or near its anterior margin. Coelom arise from the primitive gut.

Superphylum Tentaculata (Lophophorates)

Animals with a circular, crescentic or double spirally coiled edge bearing ciliated tentacles and known as a lophophore. Mouth and anus near together. Intestine forming a loop.

Phylum 24. Phoronida. About 15 species. Solitary worm-like animals. Body enclosed in a chitinous tube. Closed circulatory system. One pair of metanephridia. Marine.

Examples : *Phoronis, Phoronopsis,* etc.

Phylum 25. Ectoprocta or Bryozoa (Moss animals). About 4,000 species. Sessile or colonial animals with a lophophore. Body enclosed in a gelatinous, chitinous or calcareous covering. Anus outside of the lophophore region. Mostly marine, few freshwater.

Examples : *Bugula, Plumatella,* etc.

Phylum 26. Brachiopoda (Lamp shells). About 260 species. Solitary animals with a lopho-phore. Body enclosed in a bivalve shell. One or two pairs of metanephridia. Marine.

Examples : *Lingula, Crania, Hemithyris,* etc.

Phylum 27. Echinodermata (Spiny-skinned animals) . About 6,000 species. Animals with secondary radial symmetry. Water vascular system present. Locomotion by tube-feet.

Examples : Starfish, Brittle star, Sea urchins, Sea lilies, etc.

Phylum 28. Chaetognatha (Arrow worms). About 50 species. Small, slender, elongated, transparent animals. Body divided into head, trunk and tail. Hooks or bristles near mouth, paired fins on trunk and a terminal tail fin. Digestive tube complete. Planktonic and marine. Free-living.

Examples : *Sagitta, Spadella,* etc.

Phylum 29. Pogonophora (Beard worms). About 43 species. Body elongated in a chitinous tube. Anterior end with one to many tentacles. Endoskeleton, gill-slits, and digestive tube absent. Deep water and marine.

Examples : *Siboglinum, Polybrachia, Spirobrachia,* etc.

Phylum 30. Hemichordata (Acorn worms). About 80 species. Animals permanently bilateral with gill-slits. Endoskeleton poor. Embryo lacking a tyical notochord. Marine.

Examples : *Balanoglossus* (Acorn worm), *Cephalodiscus,* etc.

Phylum 31. Chordata. About 45,000 species. Animals permanently bilateral. A dorsal tubular nerve cord, a notochord and paired pharyngeal gill-slits present at some stage in life-history. Terrestrial, freshwater, marine.

Examples : Ascidians, *Amphioxus,* Fishes, Frogs and Toads, Lizards and Snakes, Birds and Mammals, etc.

REVISION QUESTIONS

1. What is taxonomy? What does it offer to Zoology?
2. Define systematics. What do you know about the origin and development of systematics?
3. Discuss the necessity of systemtics.
4. What are different types of classifications?
5. What is nomenclature? What do you know about binomial nomenclature?
6. Describe the aims and rules of International Code of Nomenclature.
7. What do you know about systematic hierarchy?
8. Describe briefly Linnaeus' system of classification.
9. Describe briefly taxonomic categories.
10. What is a species ? Give an account of species concept.
11. Discuss the role of John Ray in the field of taxonomy.
12. What do you know about trinomial nomenclature? Give some examples.
13. Give the recent outline classification of animals enumerating characteristic features of different groups with common examples.
14. Distinguish between :
    (i) Protozoa and Metazoa; (ii) Acoelomata and Coelomata; (iii) Radiata and Bilateria; (iv) Protostomia and Deuterostomia; (v) Diploblastic and Triploblastic; (vi) Species and Subspecies; (vii) Artificial and Natural classsification; (viii) Biological species and Genetical species.
15. Write short notes on:
    (i) Carolus Linnaeus; (ii) Binomial nomenclature; (iii) Trinomial nomenclature; (iv) Taxonomic hierarchy; (v) Species; (vi) Subspecies.

3

Protoplasm

The term protoplasm (Gr., *protos* = first+plasma = anything formed) was first coined in 1840 by Purkinje who used the word to designate the living substance in the embryo of animals. Earlier the protoplasm was first of all observed by Corti (1772) and the French zoologist Dujardin (1935) first of all recognised its significance and called it "sarcode". Later, Hugo Von Mohl applied this term to embryonic cells of plants. In 1861 Schultze established the similarity which exists in the protoplasm of animal and plant cells, thus, offering a theory which was later called the "protoplasm theory" which states that the cell is an accumulation of living substances having a nucleus and limiting cell membrane. Gradually, protoplasm came to mean all living matter out of which plants and animals are formed. Huxley (1868) referred to protoplasm as the "physical basis of life". It was first thought that protoplasm was a definite chemical substance, but investigations have shown that it is not a single chemical substance but is made up of different compounds and that it differs in every species of plant and animal life and probably in every different kind of cell.

For quite a long time, the protoplasm and cytoplasm were regarded to be synonyms. However, after recent investigations the protoplasm is a term used for the transparent, homogeneous and colloidal substance found in whole of the cell. The cytoplasm (Gr., *kytos* = hollow+*plasma* = form)is defined as the part of the cell which occurs between the plasma membrane and nuclear envelope.

PHYSICAL NATURE OF PROTOPLASM

The protoplasm is a polyphasic colloidal system. The colloidal (Gr., *kolla*=glue) system of protoplasm contains abundance of water in which certain solutes remain dissolved and certain solute particles of various sizes remain suspended in it. The suspended particles may be of 0.001μ to $0.1\ \mu$ diameter. These particles are of two kinds : hydrophilic and hydrophobic. The hydrophilic or water loving substances are the carbohydrates, proteins and inorganic salts and the hydrophobic or water repulsive substances are the lipids, etc.

The colloidal system of the protoplasm may be in semisolid or liquid state. The semisolid state is known as gel phase or gelly-like state, while the liquid state is known as sol phase. In gel phase the molecules of solutes remain held together by various types of chemical bonds or bond between H–H, C–H or C–N. The stability of gel depends on the nature and strength of chemical bonds. The colloidal system of the matrix usually changes its phase according to various metabolic and other physiological activities of the cell. A gel can change into sol by solation and a sol can change into gel by gelation. This property of colloid is known as phase reversal. The property of phase reversal provides many shapes or phases to the colloidal system of protoplasm.

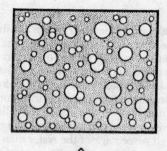 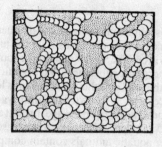

A   B

Fig. 3.1. Protoplasm. A—In sol; B—In gel state.

In the past, there has been a lot of controversy about the physical nature of protoplasm. Different workers advanced different theories about the physical characteristics of the protoplasm. These theories have been represented as follows :

1. **Reticular theory** suggests that the protoplasm is composed of reticulum of fibres or particles in the ground substance (Fig. 3.2 A).

2. **Alveolar theory** was proposed by **Butschili** in 1892 and according to it the protoplasm consists of many suspended droplets or alveoli or minute bubbles resembling the foams of emulsion (Fig. 3.2 B).

3. **Granular theory** was propounded by **Altmann** in 1893. This theory supports the view that the protoplasm contains many granules of smaller and larger size arranged differently. These granules were known as **bioplasts** (Fig. 3.2 C).

4. **Fibrillar theory** was proposed by **Flemming** very recently after the electron microscopical observations of the protoplasm. It holds that the protoplasm is fibrillar in nature. It is the most accepted view now-a-days (Fig. 3.2 D).

5. **Colloidal theory** has been forwarded very recently after the electron microscopical observations of the protoplasm. According to the recent concept, the protoplasm is partly a true **solution** and partly a **colloidal** system.

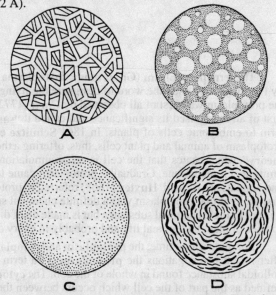

Fig. 3.2. Physical appearance of protoplasm. A—Reticular; B—Alveolar; C—Granular; and D—Fibrillar.

CHEMICAL NATURE OF PROTOPLASM

The protoplasm is found to consist of about thirty-six (36) chemical elements out of the total ninety-two (92) elements. Out of 36 elements only 12 are predominant in the protoplasm. These 12 elements are the carbon (C), hydrogen (H), nitrogen (N), oxygen (O), phosphorus (P), potassium (K), sulphur (S), chlorine (Cl), sodium (Na), calcium (Ca), magnesium (Mg) and iron (Fe). Of these first four (C, H, N and O) form the 99 per cent of the protoplasm, while the remaining elements form only one per cent of the matrix. Some elements, *e.g.*, copper (Cu), cobalt Co), manganese (Mn), zinc (Zn), iodine (I), molybednum (Mb), boron (B), vanadium (Vd) and silicon (Si) occur as tracer elements. In the protoplasm these elements occur in the form of inorganic and the organic compounds.

Inorganic Compounds of Protoplasm

The inorganic components of the protoplasm mostly occur in the form of water, minerals and salts which are as follows :

Water

The most abundant inorganic constituent of the protoplasm is the water. Water constitutes about 65 to 80 per cent of the protoplasm. In the protoplasm the water occurs in two forms, *viz.*, **free water** and **bound water**. The 95 per cent of the total cellular water is used by the protoplasm as the solvent for various inorganic substances and organic compounds and is known as **free water.** The remaining 5 per cent of the total cellular water remains loosely linked with protein molecules by hydrogen bonds or other forces and is known as **bound water.** The water contents of the cellular protoplasm of an organism depend directly on the age, habitat and metabolic activities. For instance, the cells of embryo have 90 to 95 per cent water which decreases progressively in the cells of the adult organism. The cells of lower aquatic animals contain comparatively high percentage of the water than the cells of higher terrestrial animals. Further, the percentage of water in the protoplasm also varies from cell to cell according to the rate of the metabolism.

The water is the best biological solvent for inorganic substances such as mineral ions, salts, etc., and organic compounds such as carbohydrates and proteins. It forms the good dispersion medium for the colloidal system of the protoplasm. Because the water has high specific heat and high heat of vaporization, so it prevents drastic temperature changes in the cell. The temperature of cell remains relatively constant. The water is a good conductor of the electricity, therefore, it dissociates various molecules which remain dissolved in it into ions. It has high surface tension. The water has greater importance for the various metabolic functions because most of them require exclusively the aqueous media. The water is used by the cell as a transporting media for the food, nitrogen wastes and other necessary substances. The water is immiscible with the non-polar liquids as the lipids, so its molecules remain stable and unmixed with the lipid contents of the plasma membrane and other intra-cellular membranes.

Minerals

The minerals are the inorganic chemical substances which occur in the crust of the earth. In the protoplasm the minerals usually occur in the form of salts and in combination with the organic compounds.

The mineral salts occur in the form of ions in the protoplasm. An ion is an atom or group of atoms which carries one or more positive or negative charge. The positively charged ions are known as cations and the negatively charged ions are known as anions. For example, when sodium chloride (NaCl) is dissolved in water, it is ionized to form a sodium cation (Na^+) and a chlorine anion (Cl^-). The inorganic compounds which by dissolving in water become ionized are known as electrolytes but those which do not dissociate in the solvent but remain as such in the molecular state are known as non-electrolytes. The protoplasm contains both electrolytes and non-electrolytes.

Electrolytes. The electrolytes play a vital role in the maintenance of osmotic pressure and acid base equilibrium in the protoplasm. Certain ions such as the magnesium (Mg^+), etc., are essential for many enzymatic activities because these ions act as cofactor. The phosphate (PO_4) ion is the important constituent of the adenosine triphosphate (ATP) which is the chief supplier of energy for most of the life processes. Other important ions of the protoplasm are sodium(Na^+), potassium (K^+), calcium (Ca^+), chlorine (Cl^-), carbonate (CO_3), sulphate (SO_2), and amino acids.

Non-electrolytes. Some of the minerals occur in protoplasm in non-ionising state. The non-electrolytes of the protoplasm are Na, K, Ca, Mg, Cu, I, Fe, Mn, Fl, Mo, Cl, Zn, Co, Ni, etc. The iron (Fe) occurs in the haemoglobin, ferritin cytochromes and some enzymes as catalase and cytochrome oxidase. The calcium (Ca) occurs in the blood, protoplasm and the bones. The copper (Cu), manganese (Mn), molybdenum (Mo) and zinc (Zn) are useful as cofactors for enzymatic actions. The iodine and fluorine are essential for the thyroid and the enamel metabolism respectively.

Organic Compounds of Protoplasm

The chemical substances which contain carbon (C) in combination with one or more other elements as hydrogen (H), nitrogen (N), sulphur (S), etc., are called organic compounds. The organic compounds usually contain large molecules which are formed by the similar or dissimilar unit structures known as the monomers. A monomer (Gr., *mono* = one; *meros* = part) is a simplest unit of the organic molecule which can exist freely. Some organic compounds such as carbohydrates occur in the protoplasm as the monomers. The monomers usually link with other monomers to form oligomers (Gr., *oligo* = few or little; *meros* = part) and polymers (Gr., *poly* = man ; *meros* = part). The oligomers contain small numbers of monomers, while the polymers contain large number of monomers. The oligomers and polymers contain large-sized molecules or macromolecules. When a polymer contains similar kinds of monomers in its macromolecule it is known as homopolymer and when the polymer is composed of different kinds of monomers it is known as the heteropolymer. The main organic compounds of the protoplasm are the carbohydrates, lipids, proteins and nucleotides.

Carbohydrates

The carbohydrates (L., *carbo* = carbon or coal; Gr., *hydro* = water) are the compounds containing the carbon, hydrogen and oxygen. The carbohydrates form the main source of the energy for all living beings. Only green plants and certain microbes have the power of synthesizing the carbohydrates from the water and CO_2 in the presence of sunlight and chlorophyll by the process of photosynthesis. All the animals, non-green plants (*e.g.*, fungi, bacteria and viruses) depend on green plants for the supply of carbohydrats. Chemically the carbohydrates are the polyhydroxy aldehydes or ketones and they are classified as follows :

1. Monosaccharides (Monomers);
2. Oligosaccharides (Oligomers); and
3. Polysaccharides (Polymers).

1. **Monosaccharides.** The monosaccharides are the simple sugars with empirical formula $C_n(H_2O)_n$. They are classified and named according to the number of carbon atoms in their molecules as follows :

(i) **Trioses** contain three carbon atoms in their molecules, *e.g.*, Glyceraldehyde and Dihydroxy acetone.

(ii) **Tetroses** contain four carbon atoms in their molecules, *e.g.*, Erythrulose.

(iii) **Pentoses** contain five carbon atoms in their molecules, *e.g.*, Ribose, Deoxyribose, Arabinose and Xylulose.

(iv) **Hexoses** contain six carbon atoms in their molecules, *e.g.*, Glucose, Fructose and Galactose.

(v) **Heptoses** contain seven carbon atoms in their molecules, *e.g.*, Sedoheptulose.

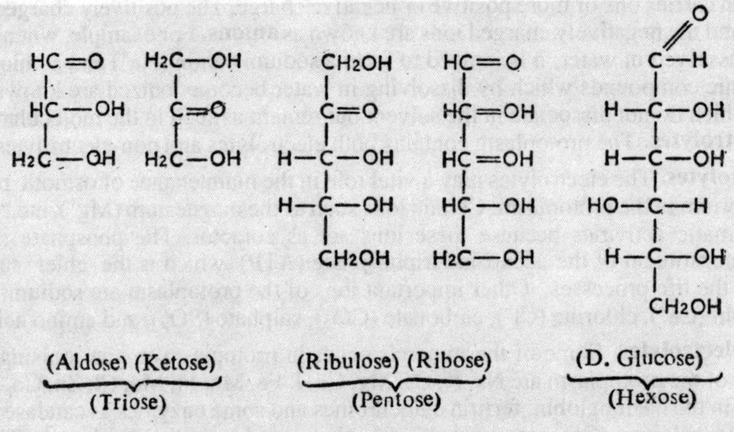

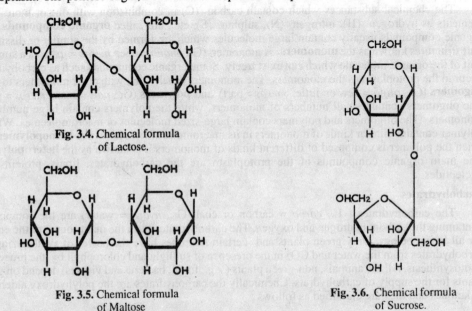

Fig. 3.3. Structure of some monosaccharides.

The monosaccharides are the monomers and cannot split further (or hydrolysed) into the simpler compounds. The pentoses and hexoses are the most abundantly found monosaccharides in the protoplasm. The pentose sugar, ribose is the important compound of ribonucleic acid (RNA), and

Fig. 3.4. Chemical formula
of Lactose.

Fig. 3.5. Chemical formula
of Maltose

Fig. 3.6. Chemical formula
of Sucrose.

certain coenzymes as nicotinamide adenine dinucleotide (NAD), NAD phosphate (NADP), adenosine triphosphate (ATP) and coenzyme A(CoA). Another pentose sugar the deoxyribose is the important constituent of the deoxyribonucleic acid (DNA). The ribulose is a pentose which is necessary for photosynthesis mechanism. The glucose, a hexose sugar is the primary source of the energy for the cell. The other important hexose sugars of the protoplasm are the fructose and galactose.

2. **Oligosaccharides.** The oligosacchrides contain 2 to 10 monosaccharides (monomers) in their molecules. The monomers remain linked with each other by the glycosidic linkages. Certain important oligosaccharides are as follows :

(i) **Disaccharides** contain two monomers, *e.g.,* Sucrose, Maltose, Lactose, etc.

(ii) **Trisaccharides** contain three monomers, *e.g.,* Raffinose, Mannotriose, Rabinose, Rhaminose, Gentianose and Melezitose.

(iii) **Tetrasaccharides** contain four monomers, *e.g.,* Stachyose and Scordose.

(iv) **Pentasaccharides** contain five monomers, *e.g.,* Verbascose.

The most abundant oligosaccharides are the disaccharides, *viz.,* sucrose, maltose and lactose. The sucrose and maltose occur mainly in the protoplasm of plant cells, while lactose occurs exclusively in the protoplasm of animal cells. The molecules of sucrose are composed of D-glucose and D-fructose. The moleclues of maltose consist of D-glucose. The lactose is composed of two monomers, *viz.,* D-glucose and D-galactose.

3. **Polysaccharides.** The polysaccharides are composed of ten to many thousands monosaccharides as the monomers in their macromolecules. Their empirical formula is $(C_6H_{10}O_5)_n$. The molecules of the polysaccharides are of collodial size having high molecular weights. The polysaccharides can be hydrolysed into simpler sugars. The protoplasm contains two kinds of polysaccharides, *viz.,* homopolysaccharides and heteropolysaccharides.

(i) **Homopolysaccharides.** The homopolysaccharides have similar kinds of monosaccharides in their molecules. The most important homopolysaccharides of the protoplasm are the starch, glycogen and cellulose.

(a) **Starch.** The molecules of the starch are composed of several units of amyloses and amylopectins. The starch is the storage food material of the plant cells.

(b) **Glycogen.** The glycogen is a polymer of glucose molecules. It is the important storage food material of animal cells. The glycogen though occurs in most animal cells in smaller amount but the cells of molluscs, liver and muscles are rich in glycogen contents.

(c) **Cellulose.** The cellulose is the polymer of the cellobiose $(C_{12}H_{22}O_{11})$ which in turn contains many glucose molecules in its molecule. The cellulose forms the cell wall of the plant cells and provides mechanical support to the cell. The plant cells beside starch and the cellulose contain other polysaccharides as xylan, alginic acids (algae), pectic acids, inulin, agar-agar and hemicellulose out of which some provide mechanical support, while others are used as stored food material.

(ii) **Heteropolysaccharides.** The polysaccharides which are composeed of different kinds of the monosaccharides and aminonitrogen or sulphuric or phosphoric acids are known as heteropolysaccharides. The most important heteropolysaccharides are as follows : .

(a) **Neutral heteropolysaccharides.** The neutral heteropolysaccharides contain monosaccharides and the acetylated amino-nitrogen in their molecules and are known as acetyl glucosamines. The most important acetyl glucosamine of the animal cells is the chitin which is an important constituent of the cells of the crustaceans and some insects. The chitin provides mechanical support to the cells.

(b) **Acidic heteropolysaccharides.** The acidic heteropolysaccharides contain different kinds of monosaccharides and sulphuric or other acids in their molecules. The most important acidic heteropolysaccharides of the protoplasm of the animal cells are the hyluronic acid, chondroitin sulphate and heparin.

The hyluronic acid forms the cementing material of the connective tissues. It occurs in the skin, connective tissues and synovial fluid of the joints. The chondroitin sulphate occurs in the cells of the cartilage, skin, cornea, umbilical cord and it serves as a matrix for the bone formation. The heparin is a blood anticoagulant and is found in the liver, lung, thymus, spleen and blood.

(c) **Mucoproteins and Glycoproteins.** When the acetyl glucosamines, monosaccharides and proteins unite together they form **mucoproteins** and **glycoproteins.** These include the blood group polysaccharides and occur in the red blood corpuscles, saliva, gastric mucin, ovomucoids, ovalbumins, cerum and albumins, etc.

Lipids (Fats)

The lipids (Gr., *lipos* = fat) are the organic compounds which are insoluble in water but soluble in ether, chloroform, benzene, hot alcohol and petroleum ether. They contain long chains of aliphatic hydrocarbons or benzene ring in their molecules. The lipids are non-polar and hydrophobic. They are important constituents of the cellular membranes, hormones and vitamins of the cells and are the source of energy for the cells. The lipids contain carbon (C), hydrogen (H) and oxygen (O) and are classified into following types :

1. Simple lipids. Simple lipids are the esters of the alcohols or the triglycerides containing fatty acids and alcohols.

$$\text{Triglyceride} \xrightarrow[\text{H}_2\text{O}]{\text{Lipase}} \text{Glycerol} + 3 \text{ Fatty acids.}$$

The constituent fatty acids may be saturated, *e.g.,* palmatic, stearic acids or unsaturated, *e.g.,* oleic, linoleic, linolenic, arachedonic and clupanadonic acids. The lipids of the animal cell protoplasm contain the fatty acids, *viz.,* palmatic, stearic, palmitoleic, oleic, linoleic and linolenic acids. The simple lipids of the protoplasm are as follows :

(i) **Natural fats.** The natural fats are the naturally occurring fats which occur in animal and plant cells as stored food substances.

(ii) **Wax.** The waxes are the simple lipids and are the esters of fatty acids of high molecular weight with the alcohols except the glycerol. The most important constituent alcohol of the molecules of wax is the **cholesterol,** *e.g.,* bees wax.

2. Compound lipids. The compound lipids contain fatty acids, alcohols and other compounds as phosphorus, amino-nitrogen carbohydrates, etc., in their molecules. The most important compound lipids of the protoplasm of amimal and plant cells are as follows :

(i) **Steroids.** These lipids contain a common cyclic nucleus of cyclopentano-perhydro- phenanthrene. The common steroids of the protoplasm of animal cells are the sex hormones, adrenocortical hormones, vitamin D and bile acids. The steroids which possess – OH group in their molecules are known as **sterols.** The sterol alcohol **cholesterol** occurs in the bile, brain, adrenal gland, blood and other animal cells. The plant cells usually contain no cholesterol in their cellular protoplasm.

(ii) **Phospholipids.** The phospholipids or phosphotids contain in their molecules, the glycerol, fatty acids and phosphoric acids. The phospholipids are the main component of the lipids of the unit membranes of the cells. In animal cells the phospholipids occur along with the choline, ethanolamine or serine. For instance, the phosphotidyl-cholines or lecithins occur in most animal cells and are important for the metabolism of fats in the liver cells. The phosphotidyl ethanolamine and phosphatidyl serine are commonly called **cephalins.** The other important phospholipids of the matrix are the phosphoinositides (occur mostly in the cells of liver, brain, muscle and soyabean), plasmogen and isositides.

(iii) **Sphingolipids.** The sphingolipids occur mostly in the cells of the brain and instead of the glycerol they contain in their molecules amine alcohol, sphingol or sphingosine. For instance, the mylein sheaths of the nerve fibres contain a lipid known as **sphingomyelin** which contains sphingosine and phosphatides in its molecules.

(iv) **Glycolipids.** The glycolipids contain in their molecules the carbohydrates and the lipids. The protoplasm of the animal cells contain two kinds of glycolipids, *viz.,* cerebrosides and gangliosides.

(a) **Cerebrosides.** The cerebrosides contain in their molecules sphingosine, fatty acids and galactose or glucose. The cerebrosides are the important lipids of the white matter of the cells of brain and the myelin sheath of the nerve. The important cerebrosides are the **kerasin, cerebron, nervon** and **oxynervons.**

(b) **Gangliosides.** The gangliosides have complex molecules which are composed of sphingosine, fatty acids and one or more molecules of glucose, lactose, galactosamine and neuraminic acid.

The gangliosides occur in the grey matter of the brain, membrane of erythrocytes and cells of the spleen.

(v) **Lipoproteins.** The lipoproteins contain lipids and proteins in their molecules and occur in blood of mammals in association with plasma proteins. In lipoproteins cholesterol and α and β globulins are found.

(vi) **Carotenoids.** The carotenoids are the compound lipids and they form pigments of the animal and plant cells. There are about 70 carotenoids occurring in both types of cells. The important carotenoids of cells are the α, β and γ carotenes, retineve, xanthophylls, lactoflavin in milk, riboflavin (vitamin B$_2$), xanthocyanins, coenzyme Q, anthocyanin flavones, flavonols and flavonones, etc. Chemically carotenoids are porphyrins. The porphyrin (Gr., *porphyra* = purple) are the carotenoids (a lipid). These are the cyclic compounds formed by four pyrrole (CH$_4$NH) rings linked by methylene bridges. The porphyrins linked with metals and proteins forming the important pigments of animal and plant cells as the chlorophyll and haemoglobin. The chlorophyll is a porphyrin containing magnesium. Many pigments of animal cells such as haemoglobin, myoglobin and cytochromes contain porphyrins in their molecules.

Proteins

The proteins (Gr., *proteno* = occupy first place) are the most important constituents of the protoplasm. All proteins are composed of carbon (C), hydrogen (H), oxygen (O), nitrogen (N) and some of them in addition contain sulphur (S) and phosphorus (P). The protoplasm is dependent almost entirely upon proteins for its supply of nitrogen, sulphur and phosphorus. The proteins are the polymers of the amino acids. An organic compound containing one or more amino groups (–NH$_2$) and one or more carboxyl groups (–COOH) is known as amino acid. The amino acids occur freely in the protoplasm and constitute the so called amino acid pool. The amino acids are derived from the organic acids in which the hydrogen in alpha position is replaced by the amino groups. For example, glycine is formed by the acetic acid and alanine derived from propionic acid as shown by following reactions :

Acetic acids + Amino group ——>Glycine

Propionic acids + Amino group ——> Alanine

The molecular formula of an amino acid is as follows :

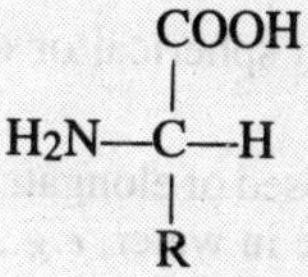

$$
\begin{array}{c}
COOH \\
| \\
H_2N—C—H \\
| \\
R
\end{array}
$$

Here the NH$_2$ is the amino group, –COOH is the carboxylic group, while the 'R' represents variety of chemical combinations which occur in different types of amino acids. The protoplasm contains about 22 amino acids, *e.g.*, glycine, alanine, valine, leucine, isoleucine, glutamic acid, aspartic acid, arginine, lysine, threonine, serine, cysteine, cystine, methionine, phenyl alanine, tyrosine, tryptophan, proline, hydroxy proline, histidine, glutamine and aspargine, etc.

Formation of proteins. Because molecule of the amino acid contains both amino (–NH$_2$) and acidic or carboxyl (–COOH) group, it can behave as an acid and base at a time. The molecules of such organic compounds which contain both acidic and basic properties are known as amphoteric molecules. Due to amphoteric molecules, the amino acids unite with one another to form complex and large protein molecules. When two molecules of amino acids are combined then the basic group (–NH$_2$) of one amino acid molecule combines with the carboxylic (–COOH) group of other amino acid and the loss of a water molecule takes place. This sort of condensation of two amino acid

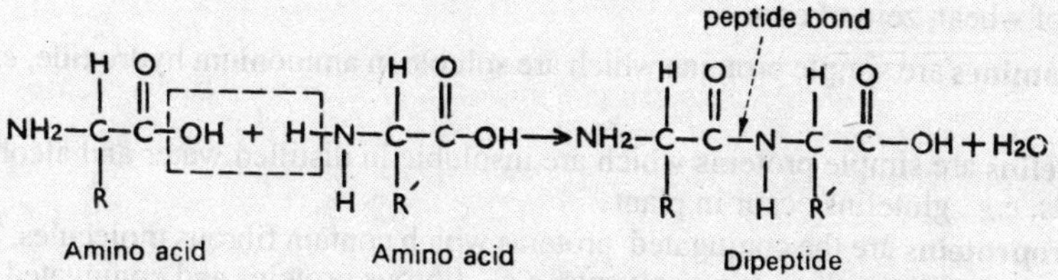

Fig. 3.7. A chemical reaction showing formation of a dipeptide.

molecules by –NH–CO linkage or bond is known peptide linkage or peptide bond. A combination of two amino acids by the peptide bond is known as dipeptide, when three amino acids are united by two peptide bonds they form tripeptide. Likewise, by condensation of few or many amino acids by the peptide bonds the oligopeptides and polypeptides are formed respectively. Various molecules of polypeptides unite to form the peptones, proteases and proteins. Thus, protein macromolecules are the polymers of many amino acid monomers. The macromolecules of proteins comparatively have high molecular weights.

Classification of proteins. The proteins are the organic compounds of immense biological importance. Various methods have been adopted for the classification of the proteins. Some of the simple and important methods of classification of proteins are as follows :

Classification on the Basis of Chemical Composition of the Proteins

1. Simple proteins. The proteins which contain only amino acids in their molecules are known as simple proteins, *e.g.,* albumins, globulins, histones, prolamines and protamines.

2. Conjugated proteins. The proteins which contain amino acids and other chemical compounds in their molecules are known as conjugated proteins and are of the following types :

(i) Chromoproteins contain amino acids and coloured pigments in their molecules, *e.g.,* haemocyanin, haemoglobin, flavoproteins and cytochromes.

(ii) Glycoproteins and mucoproteins containing carbohydrates and proteins in their molecules, *e.g.,* mucin of saliva.

(iii) Phosphoproteins contain proteins and phosphoric acid in their molecules, *e.g.,* casein of the milk.

(iv) Lipoproteins contain amino acids and lipids in their molecules, *e.g.,* lipovitellin of egg yolk, serum, protein of brain and nerve tissues.

(v) Nucleoproteins contain amino acids and nucleic acids in their molecules, *e.g.,* the viruses and nucleic acid proteins.

(vi) Metalloproteins contain amino acids and metal ions in their molecules, *e.g.,* the enzyme carbonic anhydrase contains zinc and amino acids in its molecules.

Classification on the Basis of the Molecular Shapes of the Proteins

1. Globular proteins. These proteins contain spherical or oval molecules and are generally soluble in water.

2. Fibrous proteins. These proteins are composed of elongated molecules of coiled polypeptide chains and are fibrous in shape. These are insoluble in water, *e.g.,* keratin of skin, hair and feathers, the collagens of cartilage and tendons, the elastins of ligaments and silk fibroin of silk fibres.

Classification on the Basis of the Solubility of the Proteins

1. Albumins are simple proteins which are soluble in the distilled water, dilute salt solutions, dilute acids and bases, *e.g.,* egg albumin, serum albumin and milk albumin.

2. Globulins are simple proteins which are insoluble in distilled water but soluble in neutral salt solutions, *e.g.,* globulins of egg white, serum and globulins of many seeds as squash, soyabean, hemp and others.

3. Globins are simple proteins which are insoluble in distilled water but soluble in ammonium hydroxide, *e.g.,* haemoglobins.

4. Histones are simple proteins and are insoluble in ammonium hydroxide, *e.g.,* nucleoproteins.

5. Prolamines are simple proteins which are insoluble in water but soluble in 70% ethyl alcohol, *e.g.,* gliadin of wheat, zein of corn.

6. Protamines are simple proteins which are soluble in ammonium hydroxide, *e.g.,* proteins of fish sperms.

7. Glutelins are simple proteins which are insoluble in distilled water and alcohol but soluble in dilute acids, *e.g.,* glutelins occur in plants.

8. Scleroproteins are the conjugated proteins which contain fibrous molecules. These proteins are insoluble in water as well as other solvents, *e.g.,* fibrous proteins and conjugated proteins.

Classification of the Proteins According to the Arrangement of the Peptide Chains in the Molecules

1. Primary proteins. In primary proteins many amino acids occur but all remain arranged in a single linear chain by the peptide bonds, *e.g.*, insulin, ribonuclease.

2. Secondary proteins. The secondary proteins contain spirally or helically arranged chains of hundreds of the amino acids in their molecules. These proteins contain H bonds, *e.g.*, fibrous or scleroproteins as keratin, collagen, etc.

3. Tertiary proteins. The tertiary proteins are composed of many polypeptidic chains which remain held together by –S–S– bonds in their molecules. These molecules contain compactly arranged helix which assumes ellipsoid or other form, *e.g.*, globular proteins.

4. Quaternary proteins. The quaternary proteins contain two to many polypeptidic chains of similar or different nature which remain bound together by weak covalent bonds, *e.g.*, haemoglobin.

Properties of the proteins. The proteins are amphoteric compounds and, therefore, act as acids and bases. The solubility of proteins depends on the pH value of the solvent. The proteins can bind salts by forming ionic bonds. The proteins are precipitated by salts of heavy metals and by high temperature. Certain proteins are specific for a particular species and they possess antigen properties. Proteins coagulate on heating.

Uses of proteins. The **functional proteins** or **enzymes** function as specific catalysts in most biosynthetic and metabolic activities of the cell and the **structural proteins** form various structures of the cell.

Enzymes

The protoplasm and many cellular organelles contain very important organic compounds known as the **enzymes** (Gr., *en* =in+*zyme* = leaven). The enzymes are the specialized proteins having the capacity to act as catalysts in chemical reactions. Like other catalysts of the chemical world, the enzymes are the catalysts of the biological world and they influence the rate of a chemical reaction, while themselves remain quite unchanged at the end of the reaction. The substance on which the enzymes act is known as **substrate**. The enzymes play a vital role in various metabolic and biosynthetic activities of the cell such as synthesis of DNA, RNA and protein molecules and metabolism of carbohydrates, lipids, fats and other chemical substances. The enzymes of the protoplasm and cellular organelles are classified as follows :

1. Oxireductases. The enzymes catalyzing the oxidation and reduction reactions of the cell are known as oxireductases. These enzymes transfer the electrons and hydrogen ions from the substrates, *e.g.*, hydrogenases or reductases, oxidases, oxygenases and peroxidases.

2. Transferases. The enzymes which transfer following groups from one molecule to other are known as transferases : one carbon, aldehydic or ketonic residues, acyl, glycosyl, alkyl, nitrogenous. phosphorus containing groups and sulphur containing groups.

3. Hydrolases. These enzymes hydrolyse a complex molecule into two compounds by adding the element of water across the bond which is cleaved. These enzymes act on the following bonds : ester, glycosyl, ether, peptide, other C–N bonds, acid anhydride, C–C, halide and P–N bonds. Certain important hydrolase enzymes are the proteases, esterases, phosphatases, nucleases and phosphorylases.

4. Lysases. The lysases enzymes add or remove group to or from the chemical compounds containing the double bonds. The lysases act on C–C, C–O, C–N, C–S and C– halide bonds.

5. Isomerases. These enzymes catalyze the reaction involving in the isomerization or intramolecular rearrangements in the substrates, *e.g.*, intramolecular oxidoreductases, intramolecular transferases, intramolecular lysases, cis-trans-isomerases, racemerases and epimerases.

6. Ligases or Synthetases. These enzymes catalyze the linkage of two molecules by splitting a phosphate bond. The synthetases enzymes form C–O, C–S, C–N and C–C bonds.

Classification of Enzymes on the Basis of Chemical Nature of Substrate

According to the chemical nature of the substrate, the enzymes have been classified as follows :

1.Carbohydrases, 2. Proteases (endopeptidases and exopeptidases), 3. Amidases, 4. Esterases,5. Dehydrogenases, 6. Oxidases, 7. Decarboxylases, 8. Hydrases, 9.Transferases, and 10. Isomerases.

The enzymes are specific in action and many factors such as pH, temperature and concentration of the substrate effect the rate of the activity of enzymes. Certain enzymes, *viz.*, zymogens occur in the inactive form and these are activated by other enzymes known as kinases to perform catalytic activities. For instance, the enzyme trypsinogen of the pancreatic cells is activated in the intestine by the enzyme enterokinases and the enzyme pesinogen of the Chief cells of the stomach is activated by the hydrochloric acid which is secreted by parietal cells.

Prosthetic groups and coenzymes. Certain enzymes such as cytochromes are the conjugated proteins and contain prosthetic groups a: metalloporphyrins complex in their molecules. Certain enzymes cannot function singly but they can function only by the addition with the small molecules of other chemical substances which are known as coenzymes. The inactive enzyme (which cannot function singly) is known as the apoenzyme.The apoenzyme and coenzyme are collectively known as holoenzyme. For instance, the enzyme hydrogenase is an apoenzyme which can function either with the coenzyme NAD$^+$ or NADP. Some important coenzymes or cofactors are nicotinamide adenine dinucleotide (NAD) or diphosphopyridine nucleotide (DPN), nicotinamide adenine dinucleotide phosphate (NADP) or triphosphopyridine nucleotide (TPN), flavin adenine mononucleotide (FMN), flavin adenine dinucleotide (FAD), ubiquinone (coenzyme Q) (Q), lipoic acid (LIP or S$_2$), adenosine triphosphate (ATP), pyridoxyl phosphate (PALP), tetrahydrofolic acid (COF), adenosyl-methionine, biotin, coenzyme A (CoA), thiamine phyrophosphate (TPP) and uridine diphosphate (UDP).

Isoenzymes

Recently it has been investigated that some enzymes have similar activities and almost similar molecular structures. These enzymes are known as isoenzymes. The isoenzymes in the cell, *e.g.*, lactic dehydrogenase (LDH) occur in five identical isoenzymes.

Vitamins

The vitamins are complex organic compounds of diverse chemical nature which are required in minute amounts for normal growth, functioning and reproduction of cells. The vitamins play an important role in the cellular metabolism and they act as the enzymes or other biological catalysts in the various chemical activities of the cell. Their importance for the animal has been reported by Hopkins, Osborne, Mendel and McCollum (1912–1913).Funk (1912) demonstrated the presence of basic nitrogen in them and gave the name vitamins, *i.e.*, vital amines to them. The cell cannot synthesise the vitamins from the standard food and so they are taken along with the food. Their deficiency in the cell causes metabolic disorders and leads to various diseases. The vitamins of utmost biological importance have been tabulated in the following table :

TABLE 3.1 : CLASSIFICATION AND OTHER CHARACTERS OF VITAMINS

Vitamin	Chemical Nature	Sources	Diseases due to Deficiency	Cellular Functions
Fat Soluble Vitamins				
A	Carotenoid	Milk, butter, liver, fish, carrots and vegetables.	Xerophthalmia, hardening of cornea, night blindness and growth interference.	Maintains the integrity of epithelial cells, forming the part of the visual purple (rhodopsin) of retinal cells and necessary for growth.
D	Sterol	Fish liver oils, steroid containing food, ultra violet light, butter, eggs.	Bone defects, *e.g.*, rickets and osteo-malacia.	Regulates calcium and phosphorus metabolism.
E	Tocopherol	Green salad, vegetable oils, egg yolk and meat.	Sterility in male rats.	Rapid cell proliferation.

Vitamin	Chemical Nature	Sources	Diseases due to Deficiency	Cellular Functions
K	1-4 naphthaqui-none acetate.	Green leafy vege-tables, spinach, liver and eggs.	Haemorrhage.	Forms prothrombin in the liver which is necessary for clotting of blood.
Water Soluble Vitamins				
B₁	Thiamine	Unpolished cereal grains, yeast, egg yolk, liver, nuts, pork.	Beriberi and loss of appetite.	Coenzyme for pyru-vate metabolism in cel-lular respiration and metabolism of carbo-hydrates. Promotes appetite.
B₂	Riboflavin	Liver, cheese, milk, egg white, meat, kidney and green leaves.	Cataract, form lesions in the mouth, tongue, nose, and eyes, cheiosis.	Cellular respiration and growth.
Niacin	Nicotinic acid	Milk, liver, kidney, meat, legumes, coffee, tea, egg, vegetable, etc.	Pellagra.	Part of dehydrogenase coenzymes (NAD and NADA₂). Controls cellular functions.
B₆	Pyridoxine	Yeast, polished rice, cereal grains, egg yolk, royal jelly (bee).	Anemia, skin lesions.	Coenzyme in the meta-bolism of amino acids.
Pantothenic acid	Pantothenic acid	Yeast, liver, kidney, eggs, wheat, rice bran, peanuts and peas.	Dermatitis and spectacle eye.	Part of coenzyme A.
Biotin (H)	Biotin	Egg yolk, liver, kidney, milk, yeast and royal jelly (bee).	Dermatitis (rat, pig, fowl), paralysis, muscle pain.	Coenzyme in CO₂ fixation.
Folic acid	Pteroylglutamic acid	Green leafy veget-ables, yeast, beef, wheat and soyabean.	Anemia.	Part of coenzymes of nucleic acid meta-bolism and essential for growth and formation of blood cells.
Vit. B₁₂	Cyanocobalamin	Liver, eggs, milk, meat and fish.	Pernicious anemia.	Coenzyme of an enzyme involved in methyl transfer and nucleic acid meta-bolism and red blood cell formation.
Protogen	Thioctic acid or α-Lipoic acid.	Yeast and liver.		Coenzyme in pyruvate oxidation.
C	Ascorbic acid.	Tomatoes, citrus fruits, green vegetables, flowers, and pepper.	Scurvy.	Maintains optimal oxi-dation reduction pot-ential, capillary walls and normal growth of bones and teeth.
P	Eriodictin, hesperidin, rutin.	—	Capillary fragility.	Maintains cement of capillary walls.

Hormones

Hormones are the complex organic compounds which occur in traces in the protoplasm and regulate the synthesis of mRNA, enzymes and various other intracellular physiological activities. The most important hormones are growth hormone, estrogen, androgen, insulin, thyroxine, cortisone, adrenocortical hormones, etc. These hormones are synthesized by the endocrine glands and transported to various cells of multicellular organisms. In cells they regulate various metabolic activities. For example, the ecdysone hormone has been found to form puffs (Balbiani rings) in the giant chromosomes of insects.

In mammalian liver cells, the enzymes which convert glucose into glycogen are regulated by the hormone insulin which is synthesized by the islets of Langerhans in the pancreas. Moreover, the hormone thyroxine, secretion of thyroid gland, activates the enzyme phosphorylase to form glucose phosphate from glycogen. Adrenalin produced by adrenal medulla maintains the tone of involuntary muscles. Pituitary gland produces many important hormones, prolactin starts and maintains secretions of milk, intermedian controls expansion of pigments and oxytocin helps in child birth. Gonads produce androgens and estrogens which control the development of sex organs and secondary sexual characters. Hormones have been studied largely in vertebrates, but in the head of insects is a pair of small endocrine glands called corpora allata which produce hormones which control metamorphosis, moulting and egg production.

Nucleic Acids

The nucleic acids are the complex macromolecular compounds of immense biological importance. They control the important biosynthetic activities of the cell and carry hereditary informations

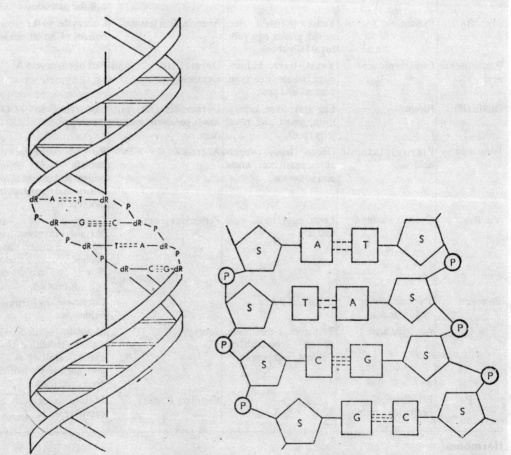

Fig. 3.8. DNA molecule (Spiral arrangement of two chains).

Fig. 3.9. Two chains showing nucleotides. P=phosphates, S=deoxyribose sugar, A=adenine, C=cytosine, G=guanine, T=thymine, = or ≡ hydrogen bonds.

from generation to generation. There occur two types of nucleic acids in living organisms, *viz.*, ribonucleic acid (RNA)and deoxyribonucleic acid(DNA). Both types of nucleic acids are the polymers of nucleotides. A nucleotide is composed of nucleoside and phosphoric acid. Even the nucleoside is composed of the pentose sugar (ribose or deoxyribose) and nitrogen bases (purines and pyrimidines). The purines are adenine and guanine and pyrimidines are cytosine, thymine and uracil.

Deoxyribonucleic acid (DNA). Deoxyribonucleic acid (DNA) molecule was first of all isolated by F. Miescher in 1869 from the nuclei of pus cells, spermatozoa and red blood cells of the birds. DNA is found only in the nucleus from where it controls and guides the activities of a cell. DNA is a compound of very high molecular weight (over one million), it has a giant molecule made of smaller molecules linked together, but its molecular weight is variable. The DNA molecule consists of a pentose sugar called deoxyribose, and phosphoric acid to which are joined four bases of pyrimidines and purines. The bases of purine are adenine (A) and guanine (G), while those of pyrimidine are cytosine (C) and Thymine (T). The bases are always paired, G is always paired with C in equal quantities, and A is always paired with T in equal amounts, these pairs are tied to each other by hydrogen bonds. When a sugar molecule is linked to a phosphate and a pyrimidine or purine base is attached to this sugar, then this new molecule made of three parts is called nucleotide. A nucleotide is a single structural unit of nucleic acid, it is made of pentose sugar, a nitrogenous base, and phosphoric acid. Only four kinds of nucleotides are possible in DNA, because there are four kinds of bases (A, C, G and T). All four kinds of nucleotides are very similar and they differ only in the kind of purine or pyrimidine base they contain. But a DNA molecule is made of a very large number of nucleotides linked together serially forming two chains. The sugar and phosphate constituents of nucleic acid hardly vary, but the four bases of purine and pyrimidine show great variety in their arrangement, sequence, and possible variations. The ratio of the four bases differs widely in different organisms, but there are always equal numbers of cytosine and guanine, and also equal numbers of adenine and thymine.

In 1953 Watson and Crick presented a model of a DNA molecule, according to their model all the units or nucleotides of the long DNA molecule are joined by phosphates and arranged in two single chains wound together in a coiled helix and cross-linked between the bases, thus, the molecule is in the form of a spiral ladder. Each upright part of the ladder is made of a series of phosphates and sugars, and the cross-linked rungs of the ladder are the base pairs of purines and pyrimidines linked together by hydrogen; each rung has either an adenine paired with thymine or cytosine paired with guanine. A molecule of DNA may have 20,000 such purine-pyrimidine base pairs. The two chains of a DNA molecules are complementary and each chain is capable of enormous variety due to the numbers and arrangement of base pairs. The two chains may form thousands of coils of the helix. The sequence of base pairs along the two chains represents coded information.

The quantity of DNA in a nucleus is constant in nearly all conditions. DNA never leaves the nucleus, it directs the activities of a cell from the nucleus. It has the power of self-duplication by splitting longitudinally into two chains along its hydrogen bonds, after separation each of the two chains builds another exactly like its partner from which it has separated. Thus, it can make a copy of itself due to which a cell divides into two. DNA molecules have the unique property of adhering to each other forming an orderly structural pile. When these molecules come together they influence other molecules in their environment to arrange themelves in a template or mould so that an order is introduced among smaller organic molecules.

Ribonucleic acid (RNA). Ribonucleic acid (RNA) has the same constituents as DNA except that it contains **ribose sugar** which has one more atom of oxygen than in deoxyribose sugar of DNA, and its bases are adenine, cytosine, guanine and uracil (its pyrimidine base is uracil in place of thymine). There are four kinds of nucleotides in RNA because there are only four bases (A, C, G, and U). According to present evidence RNA is made of a single chain of nucleotide rather than the double chain of DNA. RNA is first formed by DNA in the nucleus where it may be stored in the nucleolus, but most of it passes out into the cytoplasm either directly or after being stored in the nucleolus. It lies within particles which either float freely in the cytoplasm or line the membranes in a cell, it is active in ribosomes and microsomes. Some RNA is believed to be a messenger (mRNA) carrying information from DNA to the sites of protein synthesis in the cytoplasm, while some other kinds of RNA pick up particular kinds of amino acids to form the molecules of proteins. The quantitiy of RNA varies with the nutritional conditions of a cell.

Nucleic acids play a major role in various protoplasmic activities and together with proteins they form the foundation of all living phenomena, they transmit instructions from one cell to another, they also bring about cell division, they form the core of viruses because a particle of any virus is composed of a protein linked intimately with DNA, and studies on nucleic acids have shown how viruses work. DNA controls and guides the synthesis of proteins in the cytoplasm through various types of RNA in association with ribosomes. In this synthesis of proteins the DNA in the nucleus controls the formation of specific RNA, in other words the DNA serves as a template or mould for

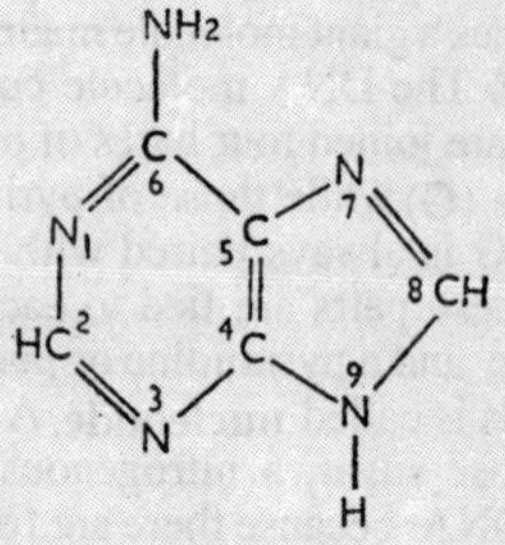

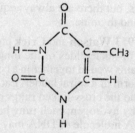

Fig. 3.10. Chemical formula of Adenine. 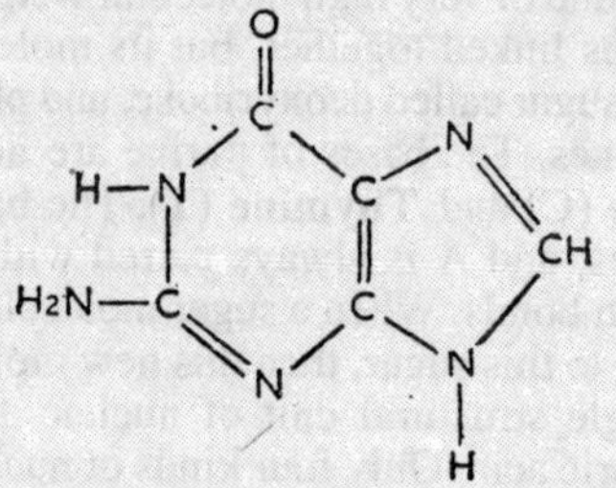   **Fig. 3.11.** Chemical formula of Guanine.

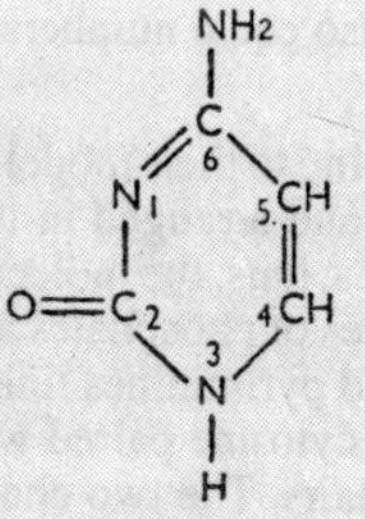

Fig. 3.12. Chemical formula   **Fig. 3.13.** Chemical formula   **Fig. 3.14.** Chemical formula
of Cytosine.   of Uracil.   of Thymine.

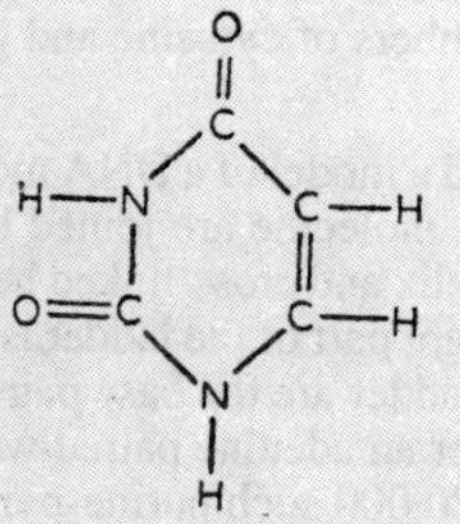

synthesis of RNA. This is known as **messenger RNA (mRNA)** which passes out through the pores of the nuclear membrane into the cytoplasm and becomes associated with ribosomes, then this messenger RNA becomes a template. Other kinds of RNA called **transfer RNA (tRNA)** which are already present in the cytoplasm now pick up individual amino acids and take them to the ribosomes. Various transfer RNAs along with their amino acids get aligned on the RNA of ribosomes in a specific order to form a new polypeptide chain which is a part of a protein molecule. This process is repeated until the synthesis of a protein is completed. The kind of protein produced is determined by its particular sequence of amino acids. The transfer RNA molecules are now freed and each becomes available to again pick up an amino acid of a particular kind. Such a control of nucleic acids over synthesis of proteins is an indirect control over all the chemical reactions of a cell. Some proteins are used directly to form parts of a cell, while other proteins function as enzymes which control the types of chemical reactions that can take place in cells. Many enzymes also contain nucleic acids, such as the energy-carrier **adenosine triphosphate (ATP)** which is present in all living organisms and plays the role of storing and supplying energy. Nucleic acids control the genes of a chromosome which are made of DNA. The genes are responsible for determination of hereditary characters. The DNA content of a cell is constant and it passes intact from the parent cells to the daughter cells. In mitosis the DNA content becomes doubled so that the daughter cells receive DNA identical to that of parent cells. In a cell the DNA may be dispersed or condensed with proteins to form nucleoproteins, the nucleoproteins then are the components of chromosomes and genes. The DNA content is directly connected with chromosomes and genes, that is with the hereditary content of cell. The chromatin of chromosomes resolves itself into four major molecules, they are histone, a protamine, DNA and RNA, but DNA is the key molecule because it is the chemical basis of heredity and one molecule of DNA may be the seat of many genes, each gene serves as the source of hereditary information. DNA is the main part of hereditary genes, in fact some authorities believe that each gene is a single molecule of nucleoprotein. The genes pass exact replicas of themselves to all cells descending from the original zygote, secondly the genes control each and every step of development of an organism, thus, DNA controls and guides heredity and development .

PROPERTIES OF PROTOPLASM

The protoplasm is a living substance and it has following physical and biological properties :

Physical Properties

The most of the physical properties of the protoplasm are due to its colloidal nature and these are as follows :

1. Tyndall's effect. When a beam of strong light is passed through the colloidal system of the protoplasm at right angles in the dark room, then the small colloidal particles which remain suspended in the colloidal system, reflect the light. The path of the light appears like a cone. This light cone is known as Tyndall's cone because this phenomenon was first of all reported by Tyndall (1820–1893) in colloids.

2. Brownian movement. The suspended colloidal particles of the protoplasm always move in zig-zag fashion. This movement of molecules is caused by moving water molecules which strike with the colloidal molecules to provide motion to them. This type of movement was first of all observed by Scottish botanist Robert Brown in 1827 in the colloidal solution. Therefore, such movements are known as Brownian movement. The Brownian movement is the peculiarity of all colloidal solutions and depends on the size of the particles and temperature.

3. Cyclosis and amoeboid movement. Due to the phase reversal property of the protoplasm, the intracellular streaming or movement of the protoplasm takes place. This property of intracellular movement of protoplasm is known as the cyclosis. The cyclosis usually occurs in the sol-phase of the protoplasm and is effected by the hydrostatic pressure, temperature, pH, viscocity, etc. The intracel-lular movements of the pinosomes, phagosomes and various cytoplasmic organelles such as lysosomes, mitochondria, chromosomes, centrioles, etc., occur only due to cyclosis of the protoplasm. The cyclosis has been observed in most animal and plant cells.

The amoeboid movement depends directly on the cyclosis. The amoeboid movement occurs in the protozoans, leucocytes, epithelial, mesenchymal and other cells. In the amoeboid movement the cell changes its shape actively and gives out cytoplasmic projections known as pseudopodia. Due to cyclosis protoplasm moves these pseudopodia and this causes forward motion of the cell.

4. Surface tension. The molecules in the interior of a homogeneous liquid are free to move and are attached by surrounding molecules equally in all directions. At the surface of the liquid where it touches air or some other liquid, however, they are attached downward and sideways or inward, more than upward consequently they are subjected to unequal stress and are held together to form a membrane. The force by which the molecules are bound is called the surface tension of the liquid. The protoplasm being a liquid has the property of surface tension. The proteins and lipids of protoplasm have less surface tension, therefore, occur at the surface and form the membrane, while the chemical substances such as NaCl have high surface tension, therefore, occur in deeper part of the protoplasm.

5. Adsorption. The increase in the concentration of a substance at the surface of a solution is known as adsorption (L., *ad* = to; *sorbex* = to draw in). The phenomenon of adsorption helps the protoplasm to form protein boundaries.

6. Other mechanical properties of protoplasm. Besides surface tension and adsorption the protoplasm possesses other mechanical properties, *e.g.*, elasticity, contractility, rigidity and viscosity which provide the protoplasm many physiological utilities.

7. Polarity of the egg. The colloidal system due to its stable phase determines the polarity of the cell protoplasm which cannot be altered by centrifugation or other mechanical means.

8. Buffers and pH. The protoplasm has a definite pH value and it does not tolerate significant variations in its pH balance. Yet various metabolic activities produce small amount of excess acids or bases. Therefore, to protect itself from such pH variation the protoplasm contains certain chemical compounds as carbonate bicarbonate system known as buffers which maintain a constant state of pH in the protoplasm.

Biological Properties

The protoplasm is a living substance and it has follwoing biological properties :

1. **Irritability.** The irritability is the fundamental and inherent property of protoplasm. It possesses a sensitivity to stimulation, an ability to transmission of excitation and ability to react according to stimuli. The heat, light, chemical substances and other factors stimulate the protoplasm to contract.

2. **Conductivity.** The conductivity is the process of conduction or transmission of excitation from the place of its origin to the region of its reaction. The protoplasm of many cells possesses the property of the conductivity.

3. **Movement.** The protoplasm possesses movement due to cyclosis. The cyclosis depends on the age, water contents, heredity factors and composition of the cells.

4. **Metabolism.** The protoplasm is the seat of various chemical activities. These activities may be either constructive or destructive in nature. The constructive processes such as biosynthesis of proteins, lipids, carbohydrates and nucleic acids are known as anabolic processes, while the destructive processes such as oxidation of foodstuffs, etc., are known as catabolic processes. The anabolic and catabolic processes are collectively known as metabolic process.

5. **Nutrition.** Nutrition involves taking in of the food, its digestion and assimilation. Protoplasm exhibits the power of nutrition.

6. **Respiration.** The gaseous exchange, *i.e.*, intake of oxygen and giving out of carbon dioxide is an important property of protoplasm. The oxidation of the food materials for the production of energy needed for various activities of life.

7. **Excretion.** Protoplasm possesses the power of excretion. Waste products are passed out of body of the organisms.

8. **Growth.** Due to the secretory activities of the cell, new protoplasm continuously increases in its volume. The increase in the volume of the protoplasm causes into the growth of the cell which ultimately divides into daughter cells by the cell divisions.

9. **Reproduction.** The protoplasm has the property of asexual and sexual reproduction and producing exactly similar substannces.

REVISION QUESTIONS

1. What is protoplasm ? Describe various theories regarding the physical nature of the protoplasm.
2. Describe the physical properties and chemical nature of protoplasm.
3. Justify the statement *"protoplasm is the physical basis of life."*
4. What properties of water make it an essential component of living matter.
5. What is a colloidal system ? Why does the protoplasm constitute a colloidal system?
6. What is the structural basis for the unique properties of the water molecules ? How do the properties of water make it of importance to living systems ?
7. How would you define an enzyme ? Describe some main types of enzymes.
8. How would you define carbohydrates ? What are the major classes of carbohydrates ? How do the polysaccharides differ from the protein molecules ?
9. What are the major classes of lipids and what types of functions are served by them ?
10. What are nucleic acids ? Discuss their biological importance.
11. Give an account of the structure and biological significance of DNA.
12. Write short notes on the following :
    (i) Brownian movement; (ii) Reversible and irreversible colloids; (iii) Sol-gel states; (iv) Amino acids; (v) ATP; (vi) Vitamins, (vii) Hormones; (viii) RNA and its kinds; (ix) Tyndall's effect; (x) Cyclosis.

4

Cell–Structure and Function

Cells were first seen and described by Robert Hooke, the English scientist in 1665. The cells he saw were the box-like cavities he found in cork. In the next hundred years or so many other scientists made observations on the cell and some of its components. Among these were Lamarck (1809), Detrochet (1824) and Turpin (1826). Brown (1831) noticed that the nucleus was a regular constituent in all plant cells. In 1838 Schleiden, a German botanist studied the plant cells and emphasized that "cells are organisms and entire animals and plants are aggregations of these organisms arranged according to definite laws". In 1839 Schwann, a German zoologist stated, "we have seen that all organisms are composed of essentially like parts namely of cells". The deductions of two microscopists (Schleiden and Schwann) formed the basis of what came to be known as the cell theory. The cell theory holds that "*all living matter, from the simplest of unicellular organisms to very complex higher plants and animals, is composed of cells and that each cell can act independently but functions as an integral part of the complete organism.*" In 1841 A. Kollikar suggested that sperms and ova are histological elements originating in the organisms. In 1858 Virchow reported, "where a cell exists there must have been a pre-existing cell, just as the animal arises only from an animal and the plant only from a plant."

According to cell theory and organismal theory, the cell may be considered as a smallest mass of protoplasm having permeable plasma membrane and nucleus which is capable of energy transformation, biosynthesis and self-reproduction. But certain primitive units of life such as viruses do not fulfil the fundamental requirements of the cell as suggested by the cell theory, therefore, in the present state of knowledge *the cell has been defined as the smallest but complete expression of the fundamental organization and functions of all living organisms, delimited by a permeable plasma membrane and capable of reproducing in a medium free of other living systems unlike the viruses.* The body of all living organisms except the viruses are composed of one or many cells. The organisms may have two types of cells, *viz.*, prokaryotic cells and eukaryotic cells.

1.**Prokaryotic cells.** The prokaryotic (*Gr., pro*= before, primitive; *karyon*=nucleus) cells are the most primitive cells from morphological point of view. These cells have primitive nuclei without nuclear membrane and the nuclear contents as proteins, nucleic acids (DNA and RNA), etc., and have direct contact with the cytoplasm. The prokaryotic cells also lack in well defined cytoplasmic organelles. The prokaryotic cells occur in viruses, bacteria and blue green algae.

2.**Eukaryotic cells.** The eukaryotic (*Gr., eu*=good or well; *karyotic*=nucleus) cells are the true cells which occur in the plants (from algae to angiosperms) and the animals (from Protozoa to mammals). Though the eukaryotic cells have different shape, size, and physiology but all the cells typically composed of plasma membrane, cytoplasm and its organelles, *viz.*, mitochondria, endoplasmic reticulum, ribosomes, Golgi complex, etc., and a true nucleus. Here the nuclear contents such as DNA, RNA and nucleoproteins remain concentrated and separated from the cytoplasm by the thin, perforated nuclear membranes. Before going into the details of cell and its various components, it will be advisable to consider the general features of different types of cells which are as follows :

SHAPE OF CELLS

The plant and animal cells exhibit various forms and shapes. Typically the animal cell is spherical in shape but the shape of the cell may be irregular, triangular, tubular, cuboidal, polygonal, cylindrical, oval, rounded or elongated in different animals and plants. The shape of the cells may vary from animal to animal and from organ to organ. Even the cells of the same organ may display variations in the shape. Generally the shape of the cell remains correlated with its functions. For example, the epithelial cells have flat shape and the muscles are elongated. Moreover, external or internal environment may also cause shape variations in the cell due to internal or mechanical stress or pressure and surface tension, etc.

SIZE OF CELLS

Mostly the eukaryotic cells are microscopic in size but definitely they are larger in size than the bacterial cells. The size of cells varies from 1 μ to 1,75,000 μ (175 mm). The ostrich egg cell is usually considered as largest cell (175 mm in diameter) but certain longest nerve cells have been found to have the length of 92 cm to 1.06 metre.

NUMBER OF CELLS

The unicellular or acellular animals (protozoans) consist of single cell. Most of the animals and plants have many cells in the body and are known as multicellular animals or plants. The number of cells in the multicellular organisms usually remain correlated with size of the organism and, therefore, small-sized organisms have less number of cells in comparison to large-sized organisms.

STRUCTURE OF CELL

Recently with the introduction of electron microscope and the use of new biological techniques for an analysis of the parts of a cell, the finer detailed structures, properties and functions of the cell have come to light. Although the animal cells differ greatly in shape, size, structure and function, yet all types of cells have some common features. A generalized animal cell is a transluscent speck of protoplasm containing an inner nucleus and an outer cytoplasm enclosed within an external plasma membrane. The cell consists of the following parts :

1. Plasma membrane ; 2. Cytoplasm; and 3. Nucleus.

Plasma Membrane

The plasma membrane is a living, ultra-thin, elastic, porous and semi-permeable membranous covering of the cell. The plasma membrane is a trilaminar (three-layered) membrane of lipoprotein. The trilaminar nature of plasma membrane was proposed by Danielli and Davson in 1935. In 1938 Harvey and Danielli produced a hypothetical model of plasma membrane which has shown a bimolecular lipid structure sandwiched by two (outer and inner) layers of protein molecules. The electron microscopic studies have confirmed this protein-lipid-protein arrangement in plasma membrane. The plasma membrane of most cells varies from 100 to $215A^0$ in thickness. The plasma membrane of most cells composed of mainly carbohydrates, lipids and proteins.

Molecular structure of the plasma membrane. The plasma membrane composed of two layers of protein molecules and two layers of lipid molecules. The lipid molecules occur in chains. In plasma membrane two molecular chains of lipids remain parallel to each other and form a bimolecular or double-layered structure. Both lipid layers remain linked with each other by the inner ends of lipid molecules which are non-polar and hydrophobic (Gr., hydr=water; phobe=hate) in nature. Both the layers of lipids are able to be held together due to Vanderwaal's forces at these non-polar ends. The lipid layers are enclosed by an outer and inner layer of proteins. The lipid molecules remain linked with the molecules of protein layers by their outer, polar and hydrophilic (Gr., hydr = water; phil=loving) ends. In the hydrogen bonds, ionic linkages or electrostatic forces bind the molecules of lipids and proteins together. The carbohydrate molecules occur in the association of protein molecules and provide stability to lipoprotein complex. The protein layers provide elasticity and mechanical resistance to the plasma membrane.

Intercellular space. In the tissues of multicellular animals, the plasma membrane of two adjacent cells usually remains separated by a space of 110 to $150A^0$ wide. This intercellular space is uniform and contains a material of low electron density which can be considered as a cementing substance. The exact chemical nature of this substance is still unknown.

Specialized structures of plasma membrane. The cell surface of certain cells performs various physiological activities such as absorption, secretion, transportation, etc. To perform such sort of specialized functions certain modifications are inevitable in the plasma membrane of such cells. The most important specialized structures of plasma membrane are microvilli, desmosomes, hemides-mosomes, septate desmosomes, terminal bars, inter-digitations, tight junctions, gap junctions and infoldings.

Primarily the plasma membrane provides mechanical support and external form to the protoplasm and it also delimits the protoplasm from the exterior, checks the entry or exit of undesirable substances and due to its semi-permeability it transmits necessary material to and from the cell. Though the plasma membrane is a limiting barrier around the cell but it performs various important physiological functions which are as follows :

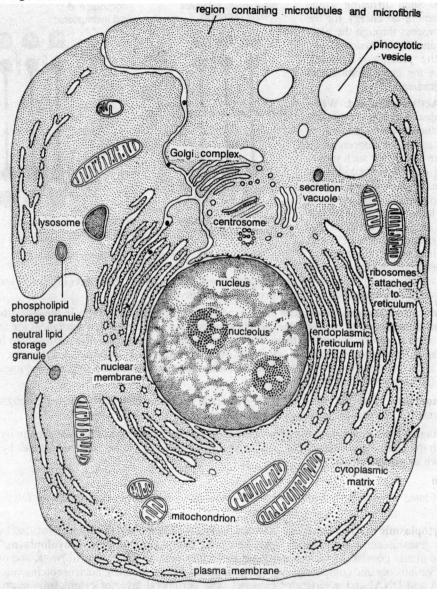

Fig. 4.1. An animal cell as seen under electron microscope (After **Brachet**, 1961).

1. Permeability. The plasma membrane is a thin, elastic membrane around the cell which usually allows the movement of small ions and molecules of various substances through it. This nature of plasma membrane is termed as permeability.

2. Osmosis. The plasma membrane is permeable to water molecules. To and fro movement of water molecules through the plasma membrane occurs due to the differences in the concentration of the solutes on its either side. The process by which the water molecules pass through a membrane from a region of higher water concentration to the region of lower water concentration is known as osmosis (*Gr., osmos* = pushing). The process in which the water molecules enter into the cell is known as endosmosis, while the reverse process which involves the exit of the water molecules from the cell is known as exosmosis.

3. Diffusion or passive transport. When molecules of two kinds are placed together they tend to mix with each other by a process known as diffusion. The diffusion of certain solutes or substances takes place through the plasma membrane. Such diffusing solute particles require no energy for the diffusion process through the plasma membrane. The diffusion of ions through the plasma membrane depends on the concentration and electrical gradients.

4. Active transport. When the molecules or ions move through the plasma membrane from low concentration to higher concentration they require energy for such movement. The energy is provided by adenosine triphosphate (ATP) which is produced by the oxidative phosphorylation in the mitochondria. The active transport of the molecules occurs in nerve cells and kidney cells. Through the pores of plasma membrane some chemical compounds such as urea, formamide and glycerol could pass actually. Brachet (1957) has shown that sometimes large molecules of certain proteins penetrate the cell.

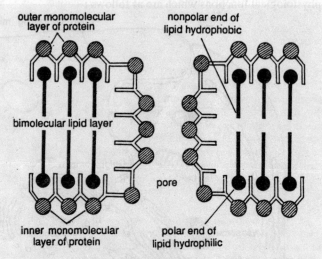

Fig. 4.2. Molecular structure of plasma membrane.

5.Endocytosis and exocytosis. The plasma membrane participates actively in the ingestion of certain large-sized foreign or food substances. The process by which the foreign substances are taken in and digested is known as endocytosis. In the process of exocytosis the cells which have secretory function such as pancreatic cells pass out their enzymatic secretions outside the cell. According to the nature of the food or foreign substances the endocytosis may be classified into two types, *viz.,* (i) pinocytosis and, (ii) phagocytosis.

(i)Pinocytosis. When the ingestion of fluid material in bulk takes place by the cell through the plasma membrane, the process is known as pinocytosis.

(ii)Phagocytosis. Sometimes the large-sized solid food or foreign particles are taken in by the cell through the plasma membrane. The process of ingestion of large-sized solid substances by the cell is known as phagocytosis.

Cytoplasm

The plasma membrane is followed by the cytoplasm which is distinguished into following structures :

A. Cytoplasmic matrix. The space between plasma membrane and the nucleus is filled by an amorphous, transluscent, homogeneous liquid known as cytoplasmic matrix or hyaloplasm. The cytoplasmic matrix consists of various inorganic molecules such as water, salts of Na, K and other metals and various organic compounds, *viz.*, carbohydrates, lipids, proteins, nucleoproteins, nucleic acids (RNA and DNA) and a variety of enzymes. The peripheral layer of cytoplasmic matrix is relatively non-granular, viscous, clear and rigid and is known as the plasmagel, or cortex or cortical layer or ectoplasm (*Gr., ecto* = outside; *plasm*= form). The inner portion of the cytoplasmic matrix is granular, less viscous and is known as endoplasm (*Gr., endo*=inner; *plasm*=form).

B. Cytoplasmic structures. In the cytoplasmic matrix certain non-living and living structures are suspended. The non-living structures are called paraplasm, deutoplasm or inclusions, while the living structures are membrane bounded and are called organoids or organelles. Both kinds of cytoplasmic structures can be studied under the following headings :

(a) Cytoplasmic inclusions. The cytoplasmic matrix contains many refractile granules of various sizes and shapes known as trophoplasm. These granules in animal cells are known as cytoplasmic inclusions or deutoplasm (*Gr., deuteros* =second) or paraplasm. The cytoplasmic inclusions include oil drops, yolk granules, pigments, secretory granules and glycogen granules.

(b) **Cytoplasmic organoids or organelles.** Besides the cellular inclusions and plastids, the cytoplasmic matrix contains many large-sized living structures known as cytoplasmic organelles or organoids which perform various important biosynthetic and metabolic activities such as respiration, storage, synthesis, transportation, support and reproduction. These cytoplasmic organelles are the endoplasmic reticulum, ribosomes, Golgi complex, lysosomes, mitochondria, plastids, centrioles, cilia, etc.

1. **Endoplasmic reticulum.** The cytoplasmic matrix is traversed by a vast reticulum or network of inter-connecting tubules and vesicles which is known as **endoplasmic reticulum** or ER. The endoplasmic reticulum has a single vast and interconnected cavity which is usually bounded by a single membrane. The membrane of endoplasmic reticulum is supposed to be originated by inpushings of plasma membrane in the matrix because like the plasma membrane it has an outer and inner layer of protein molecules sandwiching the middle layer of lipid molecules. The membrane of endoplasmic reticulum may be either smooth when they do not have attached ribosomes or rough when they have attached ribosomes with them. The membranes of endoplasmic reticulum are found to be continuous with the nuclear membrane and plasma membrane. The endoplasmic reticulum forms the ultrastructural skeletal framework of the cytoplasmic matrix and it provides mechanical support to it. It also acts as an intracellular circulatory system and it circulates various substances into and outside the cell by membrane flow mechanism. Further, the endoplasmic reticulum acts as a storage and synthetic organ. For example, it synthesizes lipids, glycogen, cholesterol, glycerides and hormones, etc.

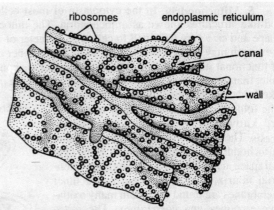

Fig. 4.3. Three-dimensional model (diagrammatic) of a part of the cytoplasm to show endoplasmic reticulum and ribosomes.

2. **Ribosomes.** Many minute spherical structures known as ribosomes remain attached to membranes of endoplasmic reticulum and form granular or rough type of endoplasmic reticulum. The ribosomes also occur scattered freely in the cytoplasm. The ribosomes are originated in the nucleolus and consist of mainly the ribonucleic acid (RNA) and proteins. Each ribosome is composed of two structural units, a smaller subunit known as 40 S subunit and a larger subunit known as 60 S subunit. The ribosomes remain attached with the membranes of endoplasmic reticulum by the 60 S subunit. The 40 S subunits occur on the larger unit and form a cap-like structure. The ribosomes consist of 3 types of RNA's known as ribosomal RNA's or rRNA, viz., 5 S, 18 S and 28 S RNA's. The 28 S and 5 S rRNA occur in large (60 S) subunit, while 18 S rRNA occurs in the smaller ribosomal subunit. Ribosomes are the sites of protein synthesis.

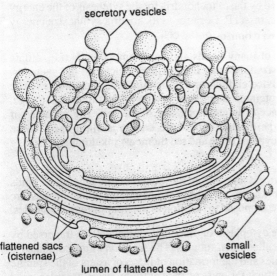

Fig. 4.4. Three-dimensional view of Golgi complex.

3. **Golgi complex.** In cytoplasm a stack of flattened membrane bounded, parally arranged organelles occurs in the association of endoplasmic reticulum and is known as Golgi complex. The Golgi complex is a disc-shaped organelle. Each Golgi complex is composed of many lamellae (flattened sacs or cisternae), tubules, vesicles and vacuoles. The membranes of Golgi complex are of lipoproteins and

these are supposed to be originated from the membranes of endoplasmic reticulum. The function of Golgi complex is the storage of proteins and enzymes which are secreted by ribosomes and transported by endoplasmic reticulum to them. Further, the Golgi complex has the most important secretory function. It secretes many secretory granules and lysosomes.

4. **Lysosomes.** The cytoplasm of animal cells contains many tiny spherical or irregular-shaped membrane bounded vesicles known as lysosomes. The lysosomes are originated by Golgi complex and contain many digestive enzymes. Their function is the digestion of food material which comes in the cell by pinocytosis and phagocytosis. During starvation lysosomes digest the stored food contents of cytoplasm. Further the lysosomes also do the extracellular digestion.

5. **Mitochondria.** In the cytoplasm of most cells occur large-sized filamentous, rounded or rod-like structures known as mitochondria. The mitochondria occur singly or in groups and their shape and size vary from cell to cell. The diameter of mitochondria ranges from 0.2 μ to 2.0 μ and the length may range from 0.3 μ to 40 μ. The number of mitochondria in a cell depends on the type of functional state of the cell. The mitochondria are bounded by two membranes of lipoproteins. The outer membrane forms a bag-like structure around the inner membrane which gives out many finger-like folds in the lumen of the mitochondria.

The folds of inner mitochondrial membrane are known as cristae or mitochondrial crests. The space between the outer and inner mitochondrial membranes as well as the central space is filled up by a viscous mito- chondrial matrix. The matrix, outer and inner membranes are found to contain many oxidative enzymes and coenzymes. The mitochondria perform most important functions such as oxidation, dehydrogenation, oxidative phosphorylation and respiratory chain of the cell. Their structure and enzymatic system are fully adapted for their different functions. They are the actual respiratory organs of the cells where the foodstuffs, *i.e.*, carbohydrates and fats are completely oxidised into CO_2 and H_2O. During the biological oxidation of the carbohydrates and fats

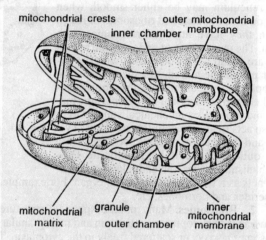

Fig. 4.5. Detailed structure of a typical mitochondrion.

large amount of energy is released which is utilized by the mitochondria for the synthesis of the energy rich compound known as adenosine triphosphate or ATP. Because mitochondria synthesize energy rich compound ATP, they are also known as power houses of the cell.

6. **Cytoplasmic vacuoles.** The cytoplasm of many plants and some animal cells (*i.e.*, ciliate protozoans) contains numerous small or large-sized, hollow, liquid-filled structures, the vacuoles. These vacuoles are supposed to be greatly expanded endoplasmic reticulum or Golgi complex. The vacuoles of animal cells are bounded by a lipoproteinous membrane and their function is the storage, transmission of the materials and the maintenance of internal pressure of the cell. The vacuoles of the plant cells are bounded by a single, semi-permeable membrane known as tonoplast. These vacuoles contain water, phenol, flavonols, anthocyanins (blue and red pigment), alkaloids and storage products such as sugars and proteins.

7. **Sphaerosomes.** In plant cells certain cytoplasmic organelles contain large amount of lipids (98%) and certain hydrolytic enzymes and are known as sphaerosomes. The sphaerosomes are bounded by the lipoproteinous membrane and are supposed to function as the lipid storage organelles.

8. **Microtubules and microfilaments.** The cytoplasm of plant and animal cells is traversed by numerous ultra-fine tubules of tubulin protein, called microtubules. The function of microtubules is the transportation of water, ions or small molecules and the formation of fibres or asters of the spindle during cell division. Moreover, they form the structural units of the centriole, basal granules, cilia and flagella.

The cytoplasm of most animal cells also contains many ultra-fine proteinous, solid microfilaments which maintain the structure of the cell and form contractile components of the muscle cells.

9. Centrosomes. The centrosome contains dense cytoplasm and is located near the nucleus of animal cells. During the cell division the centrosome is found to contain two rod-shaped granules known as centrioles. The centrioles consist of nine fibrillar units and each fibrillar unit is found to contain three microtubules. At the time of cell division the centrioles form the spindle of microtubules which help in the separation movement of chromosomes during last stages of cell division.

10. Basal granules or kinetosomes. The animal or plant cells which are having locomotory organelles such as the cilia or flagella, contain spherical bodies known as basal granules or kinetosomes at the base of the cilia or flagella. The kinetosomes are embedded in the ectoplasm and are composed of nine outer fibrils and two central fibrils. Each outer fibril consists of three microtubules, out of which two enters in the cilia or flagella. Each central fibril contains single microtubule.

11. Cilia and flagella. The cells of many unicellular organisms and ciliated epithelium of multicellular organisms consist of some hair-like cytoplasmic projections outside the surface of the cell. These are known as cilia or flagella and they help in locomotion of the cell. The cilia and flagella consist of nine outer fibrils around the two large central fibrils. Each outer fibril consists of two microtubules. The cilia and flagella are originated from the basal bodies and chemically consist of proteins and adenosine triphosphate (ATP).

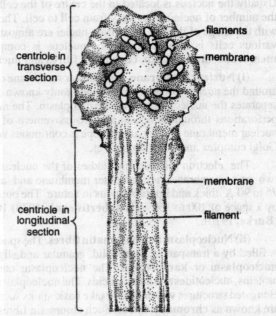

Fig. 4.6. A centriole in transvere and longitudinal section.

12. Tonofibrils. The cytoplasm of most cells contains bundles of fibrils rannging from 30 A^0 to 60 A^0 long in the region of desmosomes. The desmosomes are the apertures of the plasma membrane by which cells of a tissue remain in direct contact with each other.

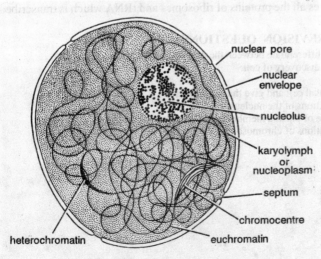

Fig. 4.7. Structure of a metaphase nucleus.

13. Plastids. The plastids occur commonly in plant cells and their diameter varies from 4 microns to 6 microns. They may be colourless or coloured. The colourless plastids are known as leucoplastids or leucoplasts, and coloured plastids as chromoplastids or chromoplasts. The leucoplasts usually have storage function and store starch and lipids and may be called amyloplasts and lipoplasts respectively. The chromoplasts may have many forms and pigments, but those having the chlorophyll are most important. These are known as chloroplasts. They contain DNA, ribosomes and complete synthetic machinery. The chloroplasts help in the biosynthesis of foodstuffs by the process of photosynthesis.

Nucleus

The nucleus (Fig. 4.7) is a centrally located and spherical cellular component. It is most significant component of the cell which controls various metabolic activities of the cell and contains the genetic material DNA. The nucleus is found in all the eukaryotic cells of the animals and plants. The location of the nucleus in a cell usually is the characteristic of the cell type and it is often variable. Usually the nucleus is located in the centre of the cell. Usually the cells contain single nucleus but the number of nucleus may vary from cell to cell. The shape of the nucleus usually remains related with the shape of the cell but certain nuclei are almost irregular in shape. The size of the nucleus of various cells is also variable. The nucleus is composed of following structures, *viz.*, nuclear membrane, nucleoplasm, chromatin fibres and nucleolus.

(i) **Nuclear membrane.** The nuclear membrane or karyotheca forms an envelope-like structure around the nuclear contents and is commonly known as the nuclear envelope. The nuclear envelope separates the nucleoplasm from the cytoplasm. The nuclear envelope also contains many pore-like perforations through which to and fro movement of chemical substances takes place. The outer nuclear membrane of nuclear envelope is continuous with the membranes of endoplasmic reticulum, Golgi complex and mitochondria, etc.

The electron microscopic studies of the nuclear envelope have shown that it is composed of two unit membranes, *viz.*, an outer membrane and an inner membrane. Each membrane is about 75 to 90 A^0 thick and lipoproteinous in nature. The outer and inner nuclear membranes are separated by a space of 100 to 150 A^0 (Robertis *et al.,* 1970) 100 to 300 A^0 (Cohn, 1970), or 400 to 700 A^0 (Burke, 1970).

(ii) **Nucleoplasm and chromatin fibres.** The space between the nuclear envelope and nucleolus is filled by a transparent, semi-solid, granular and slightly acidophilic ground substance known as nucleoplasm or karyolymph. The nucleoplasm contains dissolved phosphorus, ribose sugars, proteins, nucleotides and nucleic acids. The nucleoplasm also contains many thread-like, coiled, much elongated structures which readily take basic stains such as basic fuchsin. These thread-like structures are known as chromatin fibres. Such chromatin fibres are observed only in the interphase nucleus. During cell division (mitosis and meiosis) chromatin fibres become thick ribbon-like structures which are known as the chromosomes. The chromatin granules or chromosomes fundamentally consist of large molecules of deoxyribonucleic acid (DNA) and many proteins.

(iii) **Nucleolus.** The nucleoplasm contains a conspicuous darkly stained spherical body known as the nucleolus. The position of nucleolus in the nucleus is accentric. Chemically nucleolus is composed of large amount of ribosomal proteins and ribosomal RNA. The nucleolus plays a very important role in the process of protein synthesis and cell division. The main function of nucleolus is the biogenesis of ribosomes. It stores all the proteins of ribosomes and rRNA which is transcribed by rDNA of nucleolar organizer.

REVISION QUESTIONS

1. Define the cell. How will you differentiate between the prokaryotic and eukaryotic cells?
2. Outline the brief history of the discovery of cell.
3. Discuss the cell theory.
4. Describe various parts of a typical cell and give their functions.
5. Describe the structure and functions of the nucleus.
6. Give an account of the structure of plasma membrane and mention its functions.
7. Describe the structure and functions of chromosome.
8. Write short notes on :
   (i)   Cell membrane;
   (ii)   Plasma membrane;
   (iii)   Golgi apparatus;
   (iv)   Mitochondria;
   (v)   Ribosomes;
   (vi)   Lysosomes;
   (vii)   Nucleolus;
   (viii) Endoplasmic reticulum.

5

Cell Division

The growth and development of every organism depend exclusively on the multiplication and enlargement of its cells. All cells of the body arise from the division of pre-existing cells. The development of a multicellular organism from the unicellular zygote is achieved by the cell division, growth and differentiation. The asexual and sexual reproduction of the organisms also depends on the cell division.

The division of the nucleate cells is achieved by two integral activities such as the division of the nucleus (kayrokinesis)and the division of the cytoplasm (cytokinesis).Usually the kayrokinesis is followed by the cytokinesis and results into the multinucleate cells.

In animals and plants following three types of cell division have been distinguished :

1. Direct cell division or amitosis; 2. Indirect cell division or mitosis; 3. Reduction division or meiosis.

AMITOSIS

The amitosis or direct cell division is the means of asexual reproduction in unicellular organisms like bacteria and protozoans and also a method of multiplication or growth in foetal membranes of some vertebrates. In amitosis type of cell division the splitting of nucleus is followed by cytoplasmic constriction.

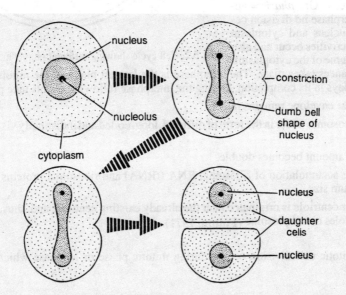

Fig. 5.1. Diagrammatic representation of amitosis.

During amitosis the nucleus elongates first and then assumes dumb-bell-shaped appearance. The depression or constriction increases in size and ultimately divides the nucleus into two nuclei. The division of nucleus is followed by the constriction of cytoplasm which divides the cell into two equal or approximately similar halves. Therefore, without the occurrence of any nuclear events two daughter cells are formed.

MITOSIS

The mitosis (Gr., *mitos*=thread) occurs in the somatic cells and it is meant for the multiplication of cell number during embryogenesis and blastogenesis of plants and animals. Fundamentally it is related with the growth of an individual from zygote to adult stage.

One of the basic characteristics of mitotic cell division which is meant for growth due to multiplication is that it gives rise to two daughter cells, which resemble each other and also the parent cell qualitatively and quantitatively (*i.e.*, the chromosome number of mitotic product cells remain the same like the parent cell). The mitosis composed of two apparatuses, *viz.*, chromatic apparatus which includes the chromosomes and the nucleolus and the achromatic apparatus which in its turn includes the centrioles and spindle.

The basic outline of mitosis is the same in all living organisms. It includes four phases namely G_1 phase, S phase, G_2 phase and mitotic phase which occur in succession and forming the so called cell cycle. The G_1 phase, S phase and G_2 phase are collectively forming the interphase. Thus, in continuously dividing cells, an individual cell passes through following two main phases of cell or mitotic cycle :

A. Interphase ; B Mitotic phase.

A. Interphase

The resting phase or stage between the two mitotic divisions is known as the intermitotic phase or interphase (*L., inter* = between, Gr., *phasis* = appearance). In interphase no division occurs but in the nucleus and cytoplasm active metabolic activities occur and also increase in the volume of the cytoplasmic and nuclear substances takes place. The interphase is the longest phase of the mitotic cycle and it takes one or two days in its completion. During the interphase following events take place :

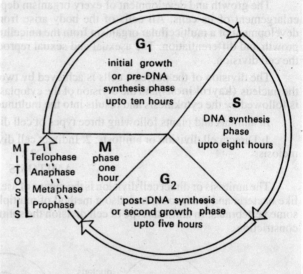

Fig. 5.2. Cell cycle showing different phases in a growing cell.

1. The nuclear envelope remains intact.

2. The chromosomes occur in the form of diffused, long, coiled and indistinctly visible chromatin fibres.

3. The DNA amount becomes double.

4. Due to the accumulation of ribosomal RNA (rRNA) and ribosomal proteins the nucleolus attains the maximum size.

5. A daughter centriole is originated near the already existing centriole and, thus, an interphase cell has two centrioles or a diplosome (Fulton, 1971).

B. Mitotic Phase

The main mitotic cell division occurs during mitotic phase or M phase which includes the following phases :

Prophase

The prophase (Gr., *pro*=before; *phasis*=appearance) is the actual first phase of the mitosis. During the prophase following events take place in the cell :

1. The cell becomes spheroid, refractive and viscous.

2. The disintegration of nuclear envelope starts.

3. Due to the DNA duplication in the interphase each chromosome now possesses two chromatids. Each chromatid consists of a single DNA molecule wrapped in the nucleoproteins.

4. Both chromatids remain connected with each other by the centromere and both remain closely associated along their entire lengths.

5. The chromatids become shortened and thickened.

6. The nucleolus starts to disappear.

7. Each centriole separates and migrates towards the opposite poles of the cell. Each centriole duplicates, so that both poles of the cell contain paired centrioles or diplosome.

8. The centrosome forms an elongated body or bridge known as the centrodesmus in between the two centrioles.

9. From the centrodesmus delicate filaments (microtubules) or asters arise and form the spindle.

Prometaphase

In prometaphase (Gr., *pro*=before; *meta*=after; *phasis*=appearance) following changes usually occur in the cell :

1. The nuclear membrane completely disintegrates.

2. A clear zone known as the equator appears in between the mid-line of the spindle and the nucleus.

3. The chromosomes move towards the equator.

Metaphase

The metaphase (Gr., *meta*=after ; *phasis*=appearance) follows the prometaphase and during this phase following events occur in the cell :

1. Each chromosome reaches to the equator and all arrange themselves radially at the periphery of the spindle.

2. The smaller chromosomes usually remain towards the interior, while the larger chromosomes remain at the periphery.

3. Some of the fibres of microtubules of the spindle attach with the centromere of each chromosome and are known as the chromosomal fibres.

4. Some of the fibres or microtubules of the spindle remain attached from one end to the other end with the centrioles and are known as continuous fibres.

5. Certain fibres occur in between the chromosomes and are known as interzonal fibres or interchromosomal fibres.

Anaphase

In the anaphase (Gr., *ana*=up; *phasis*=appearance) following changes occur in the cell :

1. The centromere of each chromosome divides into two.

2. The chromatids of the each chromosome are separated and form two chromosomes.

3. The chromosomes become shorter and thicker and migrate towards the opposite poles of the cell.

4. The migration of the daughter chromosomes towards the opposite poles is achieved by the contraction of chromosomal fibres and the stretching of interchromosomal or interzonal fibres. The interzonal fibres push the daughter chromosomes towards the opposite poles.

Telophase

The telophase is the final stage of mitosis and during this phase following events occur :

1. The chromosomes which reach at the opposite poles of the cells now elongate, the coils of DNA protein fibres loosen and the chromosomes become thread-like.

2. The nucleolus reappears.

3. The endoplasmic reticulum forms the new nuclear envelope around the chromosomes and the nucleolus.

4. The microtubules of the aster and mitotic spindle rearrange and disappear.

Thus, after the telophase two daughter nuclei are formed due to the karyokinesis. The karyokinesis is followed by the cytokinesis.

Cytokinesis

In the process of cytokinesis the cytoplasm splits from the equatorial region and the two daughter halves of the cytoplasm are separated. Soon after a unit membrane of lipoprotein develops in between the two daughter cells. The cytokinesis of animal cells involves the cyclosis of the cytoplasm, formation of a contractile ring, the expansion of the cell membrane, ATP and interaction of the spindle and asters with the cell surface, while in the plant cells the cytokinesis involves the movement of the endoplasmic reticulum and dicytosomes to the equator where they fuse to form the primary cell wall.

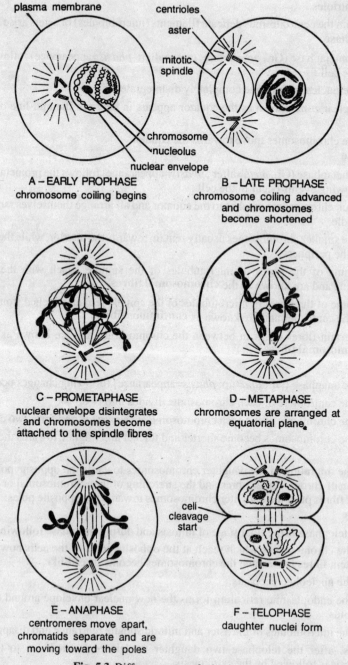

A – EARLY PROPHASE
chromosome coiling begins

B – LATE PROPHASE
chromosome coiling advanced
and chromosomes
become shortened

C – PROMETAPHASE
nuclear envelope disintegrates
and chromosomes become
attached to the spindle fibres

D – METAPHASE
chromosomes are arranged at
equatorial plane.

E – ANAPHASE
centromeres move apart,
chromatids separate and are
moving toward the poles

F – TELOPHASE
daughter nuclei form

Fig. 5.3. Different stages of mitosis.

Significance of Mitosis

The importance of the mitosis for the organisms has been summarized in the following points :

1. In mitotic division, the chromosome number in each daughter cell remains the same like the parent cell.

2. The mitosis helps the cell in maintaining its proper size.

3. Through the process of the mitosis an equilibrium is maintained in the amount of DNA and RNA contents.

4. The mitosis provides the opportunity for the growth and development of organs and the body of the organisms.

5. Due to the mitosis the old decaying and dead cells are replaced by the new cells.

6. The mitosis helps the organisms in the asexual reproduction.

7. The gonads and the sex cells also depend on the mitosis for the increase in their number.

MEIOSIS

The term meiosis (Gr., *meioum* = to reduce) was coined by J.B. Farmer in 1905. The meiotic division is of utmost importance for those organisms in which the union of the haploid gametes takes place during the sexual reproduction. By reducing the number of chromosomes of the diploid germ cells into the haploid gametes the meiosis maintains a constant number of the chromosomes in the species. Thus, meiosis helps in alternation of generation of haploidic generations of plants and animals. In the process of meiosis the chromosomes divide once and the nucleus and cytoplasm divide twice. Due to the meiosis four haploid cells are formed from the single diploid cell. The process of meiosis is fundamentally same in all the animals and plants but certain biologists recognised following three types of meiotic divisions according to their occurrence at different stages of the life cycle of the organisms.

1. **Sporogenetic meiosis.** The meiosis occurring at the time of spore formation is referred to as the sporogenetic meiosis. This type of meiosis is commonly found in plants.

2. **Gametic meiosis.** In most animals and lower plants the meiosis occurs at the time of gametogenesis (spermatogenesis and oogenesis) and is known as gametic meiosis.

3. **Zygotic meiosis.** In certain lower plants, sometimes the meiosis occurs immediately after the fertilization of the egg by a sperm. This type of meiosis is known as zygotic meiosis.

Meiocytes. The cells in which the meiosis takes place are known as the meiocytes. The meiocytes of the testes or male gonads are known as the spermatocytes and the meiocytes of the ovaries or female gonads are termed as oocytes. The meiocytes of the plant sporangium are known as sporocytes.

Chemical substances initiating meiosis. The process of meiosis seems to depend on the balance of nucleic acids in the nucleus or on certain hormones. For instance, insect moulting hormone, the ecdysone is found to initiate the meiosis in certain parasitic flagellate protozoans. Further, when in the cell the amount of the DNA material is increased in comparison to the RNA, meiosis is found to occur in the cell. However, till now no information is available about the exact chemical substances which may initiate the meiosis.

Process of Meiosis

The meiotic division includes two complete divisions of a diploid cell resulting into four haploid nuclei. The first meiotic division includes a long prophase in which the homologous chromosomes become closely associated to each other and interchange of hereditary material takes place between them. Further, in the first meiotic division the reduction of chromosome number takes place and, thus, two haploid cells are resulted by this division. The first meiotic division is also known as the heterotypic division. In the second meiotic division, the haploid cell divides mitotically and results into four haploid cells. The second meiotic division is also known as the homotypic division. In the homotypic division pairing of chromosomes, exchange of the genetic material and reduction of the chromosome number do not occur.

Both the meiotic divisions occur continuously and each includes the usual stages of the mitosis, *viz.,* prophase, metaphase, anaphase and telophase. The prophase of first meiotic division is very significant phase because the most cytogenetical events such as synapsis, crossing over, etc., occur during this phase. The prophase is the longest meiotic phase, therefore, for the sake of convenience it is divided into six substages, *viz.,* proleptonema (proleptotene), leptonema (leptotene), zygonema (zygotene), pachynema (pachytene), diplonema (diplotene) and diakinesis. The successive meiotic substages can be represented as follows :

Division I or Heterotypic division	(i) —Prophase I	Proleptotene Leptotene Zygotene Pachytene Diplotene Diakinesis
Meiosis	(ii) —Prometaphase I (iii) —Metaphase I (iv) —Anaphase I (v) —Telophase I	
Interphase		
Division II or Homotypic division	(i) — Prophase II (ii) —Metaphase II (iii) — Anaphase II (iv) —Telophase II	

Heterotypic Division or First Meiotic Division

In the beginning of the first meiotic division the nucleus of the meiocyte starts to swell up by absorbing the water from the cytoplasm and the nuclear volume increases about three folds. This increase in the volume of the nucleus causes modification of nuclear components. After these changes the cell passes to the first stage of first meiotic division which is known as prophase.

First Prophase

The first prophase is the longest stage of the meiotic division. During this stage the amount of DNA becomes double. Most of the synthesis of DNA occurs at the beginning of this phase. It includes following substages :

1. **Preleptotene or Preleptonema.** The preleptotene stage closely resembles with the early mitotic prophase. In this stage the chromosomes are extremely thin, long, uncoiled, longitudinally single and slender thread-like structures.

2. **Leptotene or Leptonema.** In the leptotene stage the chromosomes become more uncoiled and assume a long thread-like shape. The chromosomes at this stage take up a specific orientation inside the nucleus; the ends of the chromosomes converge toward one side of the nucleus, that side where the centrosome lies (the bouquet stage). The centriole duplicates and each daughter centriole migrates towards the opposite pole of the cell. On reaching at the poles, each centriole duplicates and, thus, each pole of the cell possesses two centrioles or a single diplosome.

3. **Zygotene or Zygonema.** In the zygotene stage, the pairing of homologous chromosomes takes place. The homologous chromosomes which come from the mother (by ova) and father (by sperm) are attracted towards each other and their pairing takes place. The pairing of the homologous chromosomes is known as synapsis (Gr., *synapsis*=union). The synapsis begins at one or more points along the length of the homologous chromosomes. Three types of synapsis have been recognised.

(i) **Proterminal synapsis.** In proterminal type of synapsis, the pairing in homologous chromosomes starts from the end and continues towards their centromeres.

(ii) **Procentric synapsis.** In procentric synapsis the homologous chromosomes start pairing from their centromeres and the pairing progresses towards the ends of the homologous chromosomes.

(iii) **Localized pairing or Random synapsis.** The random type of synapsis occurs at various points of the homologous chromosomes.

The pairing of the homologous chromosomes is very exact and specific. The bouquet is supposed to maintain a regularity in the synapsis mechanism.

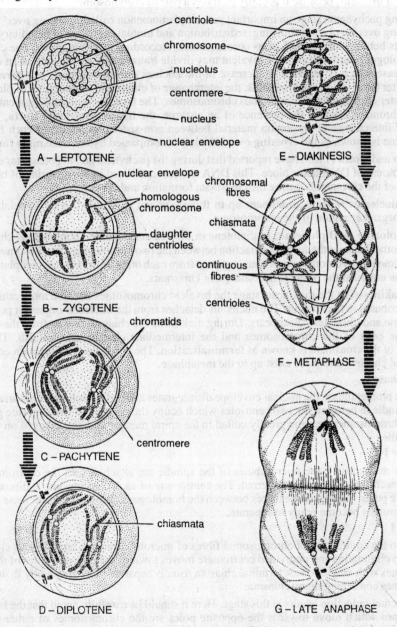

Fig. 5.4. Diagrams of early stages of meiosis.

4. Pachytene or Pachynema. In the pachytene or pachynema stage, the pair of chromosomes become twisted spirally around each other and cannot be distinguished separately. In the middle of the pachynema stage each homologous chromosome splits lengthwise to form two chromatids. Actually, the doubling of the DNA molecule strands, which is necessary for the subsequent duplication of the chromosomes, occurs earlier, before the beginning of meiotic prophase. Through the earlier part of the meiotic prophase, however, the DNA molecule in each chromosome behaves as a single body. In the pachynema stage, this is now changed, the two chromatids of each chromosome containing half of the DNA present in the chromosome at start, become partially independent of one another although they still continue to be linked together by their common centromere. The pachynema chromosome, thus, consists of four chromatids closely joined together in one complex unit called a bivalent, because it actually contains a pair of chromosomes.

During pachynema stage an important genetic phenomenon called "crossing over" takes place. The crossing over involves reshuffling, redistribution and mutual exchange of hereditary material of two parents between two homologous chromosomes. According to recent views, one chromatid of each homologous chromosome of a bivalent may divide transversely by the help of an enzyme, the endonuclease which is reported to increase in the nucleus during this stage by Stern and Hotta (1969). After the division of chromatids, the interchange of chromatid segments takes place between the non-sister chromatids of homologous chromosomes. The broken chromatid segments are united with the chromatids due to the presence of an enzyme, the ligase (Stern and Hotta, 1969). This process of interchange of chromatin material between non-sister chromatids of each homologous chromosome is known as the crossing over which is accompanied by the chiasmata formation.

Stern and Hotta (1969) have reported that during the pachytene and zygotene stages, synthesis of small amount of DNA takes place. This DNA amount is utilized in the repairing of broken DNA molecules of the chromatids during the chiasmata formation and crossing over.

The nucleolus remains prominent up to this stage and it is found to be associated with the nucleolar organizer region of the chromosome.

5. Diplotene or Diplonema. In diplotene or diplonema stage, the homologous chromosomes repel each other because the force of attraction between the two homologous chromosomes decreases. The two homologous chromosomes, thus, separate from each other, however, not completely because both remain united at the point of interchange or chiasmata.

6. Diakinesis. In the diakinesis stage the bivalent chromosomes become more condensed and evenly distributed in the nucleus. The nucleolus detaches from the nucleolar organizer portion of the chromosome and ultimately disappears. During diakinesis the chiasma moves from the centromere towards the ends of the chromosomes and the intermediate chiasmatas diminish. This type of movement of the chiasmata is known as terminalization. The chromatids still remain connected by the terminal chiasma and these exist up to the metaphase.

Prometaphase I

In the prometaphase the nuclear envelope disintegrates and the microtubules get arranged in the form of spindle in between the two centrioles which ocupy the position of two opposite poles of the cell. The chromosomes become greatly coiled in the spiral manner and get arranged on the equator of the spindle.

Metaphase I

In the metaphase I, the microtubules of the spindle are attached with the centromeres of the homologous chromosomes of each tetrad. The centromere of each chromosome is directed towards the opposite poles. The repulsive forces between the homologous chromosomes increase greatly and the chromosomes become ready to separate.

Anaphase I

Due to the contraction of chromosomal fibres of microtubules each homologous chromosome with its two chromatids and undivided centromere moves towards the opposite poles of the cell. The chromosomes with single or few terminal chiasma usually separate more frequently than the longer chromosomes containing many chiasma.

The actual reduction occurs at this stage. Here it should be carefully noted that the homologous chromosomes which move towards the opposite poles are the chromosomes of either paternal or maternal origin. Moreover, because during the chiasma formation out of two chromatids of a chromosome, one has changed its counterpart, therefore, the two chromatids of a chromosome do not resemble with each other in the genetical terms.

Telophase I

In telophase I, the endoplasmic reticulum forms the nuclear envelope around the chromosomes and the chromosomes become uncoil. The nucleolus reappears and, thus, two daughter chromosomes are formed. After the karyokinesis, cytokinesis occurs and two haploid cells are formed.

Both cells pass through a short resting phase or interphase. In case of *Trillium,* telophase I and interphase do not occur and the anaphase I is followed by prophase II directly.

Homotypic or Second Meiotic Division

The homotypic or second meiotic division is actually the mitotic division which divides each haploid meiotic cell into two haploid cells. The second meiotic division includes following four stages :

Prophase II

In the prophase second, each centriole divides into two and, thus, two pairs of centrioles are formed. Each pair of centrioles migrate to the opposite pole. The microtubules of fibres get arranged in the form of spindle at the right angle of the spindle of first meiosis. The nuclear membrane and the nucleolus disappear. The chromosomes with two chromatids become short and thick.

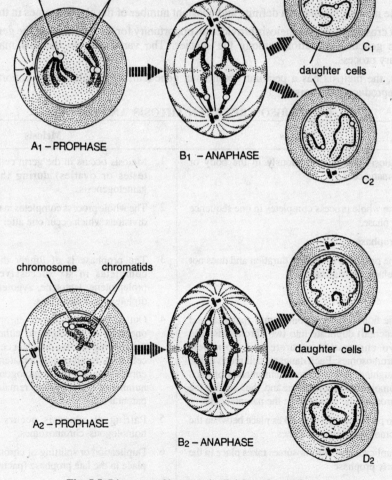

Fig. 5.5. Diagrams of homotypic division of meiosis.

Metaphase II

During the metaphase II, the chromosomes get arranged on the equator of the spindle. The centromere divides into two and, thus, each chromosome produces two monads or daughter chromosomes. The microtubules of the spindle are attached with the centromere of the chromosomes.

Anaphase II

The daughter chromosomes move towards the opposite poles due to the contraction of chromosomal microtubules and stretching of interzonal microtubules of the spindle.

Telophase II

The chromatids migrate to the opposite poles and now known as chromosomes. The endoplasmic reticulum forms the nuclear envelope around the chromosomes and the nucleolus reappears due to synthesis of ribosomal RNA (rRNA) by ribosomal DNA (rDNA) and also due to accumulation of ribosomal proteins.

After the karyokinesis in each haploid meiotic cell the cytokinesis occurs and, thus, four haploid cells are resulted. These cells have different types of chromosomes due to the crossing over in the prophase I.

Significance of Meiosis

The meiosis has the greatest significance for the biological world because of its following uses :

1. The meiosis maintains a definite and constant number of the chromosomes in the organisms.

2. By crossing over, the meiosis provides an opportunity for the exchange of the genes and, thus, causes the genetical variations among the species. The variations are the raw material of the evolutionary process.

Thus, the meiosis has a peculiar taxonomic, genetical, and evolutionary importance for the sexually reproducing organisms.

COMPARISON BETWEEN MITOSIS AND MEIOSIS

Mitosis	Meiosis
1. Mitosis occurs continuously in the body or somatic cells.	1. Meiosis occurs in the germ cells (the cells of testes or ovaries) during the process of gametogenesis.
2. The whole process completes in one sequence or phase.	2. The whole process completes in two successive divisions which occur one after the other.
Prophase	
3. The prophase is of short duration and does not include any substage.	3. The prophase is of longer duration and it completes in six successive stages, *viz.,* proleptotene, leptotene, zygotene, pachytene, diplotene and diakinesis.
4. The homologous chromosomes (paternal and maternal) duplicate into two chromatids. The two chromatids separate and form new chromosomes. Each daughter cell receives the daughter chromosome or chromatids of each homologous chromosome and, thus, having the chromosome number like the parental cells.	4. Out of two homologous chromosomes only one type of chromosome either maternal or paternal move to the daughter cells. A daughter cell, thus, receives only a maternal or paternal chromosome of the homologous pair and the number of chromosomes remain half than the parental cells.
5. No pairing or synapsis takes place between the homologous chromosomes.	5. Pairing or synapsis occurs between the homologous chromosomes.
6. Duplication of chromosomes takes place in the early prophase.	6. Duplication or splitting of chromosomes takes place in the late prophase (pachytene stage).
7. No chiasma formation or crossing over takes place.	7. Chiasma formation or crossing over takes place.
8. The exchange of the genetic material between the homologous chromosomes does not occur.	8. The exchange of the genetic material takes place between the non-sister chromatids of homologous chromosomes.

Mitosis	Meiosis
Metaphase	
9. The chromatids occur in the form of dyads.	9. The chromatids of two homologous chromosomes occur as the tetrads.
10. The centromeres of the chromosomes remain directed towards the equator and the arms of the chromosomes remain directed towards the poles.	10. The centromeres of the chromosomes remain directed towards the poles and the chromosomal arms remain directed towards the equator.
Anaphase	
11. The chromosomes are the monads, *i.e.*, having single chromatid.	11. The chromosomes are the dyads, *i.e.*, having two chromatids and single centromere.
12. The chromosomes are long and thin.	12. The chromosomes are short and thick.
13. The telophase always occurs.	13. The first telophase is sometimes omitted.
Significance	
14. In mitotic division the chromosome number in each daughter cell remains the same like the parent cell.	14. In meiotic division the chromosome number is reduced to half in the daughter cells than the parental cells.
15. A diploid cell produces two diploid cells by a mitotic division.	15. A diploid cell produces four haploid cells by a meiotic division.

REVISION QUESTIONS

1. What is cell division? Why does a cell divide?
2. How many types of cell divisions occur in living organisms? Discuss the use and biological significance of each type of cell division.
3. Define mitosis. Outline briefly the events which take place in each stage of mitosis. What is its significance?
4. Give an account of meiosis.
5. What is meiosis? Describe the major features of each meiotic phase. Also discuss, why is meiosis needed for the production of gametes.
6. Summarize the events of first meiotic prophase.
7. Which phases of meiosis are the same as the corresponding phases of mitosis and which are different? In what ways do they differ.
8. Compare the stages of mitosis and meiosis.
9. What is cytokinesis? Describe the process of cytokinesis in animal cells.
10. Write short notes :
    (i) Amitosis; (ii) Cytokinesis; (iii) Interphase; (iv) Chiasmata; (v) Cell cycle; (vi) Importance of mitosis.

6
Reproduction

This is the inherent property of the living organisms to continue their race by the mechanism of reproduction. The reproduction is a process by which the living beings propagate or duplicate their own kinds. The reproduction may be of following two types :

1. Asexual reproduction; 2. Sexual reproduction.

ASEXUAL REPRODUCTION

The development of new individuals without the fusion of the male and female gametes is known as asexual reproduction.The asexual reproduction usually includes amitotic or mitotic divisions of the nucleus and the cytoplasm of the body (somatic) cells, therefore, it is also known as somatogenic or blastogenic reproduction. The asexual reproduction is common only in lower plants and animals and it may be of following types :

1. By fission ;   3. By gemmule formation ;

2. By budding;   4. By regeneration.

1. Asexual reproduction by the fission. The fission is the most widely occurring type of asexual reproduction of the protozoans and various metazoans. In this method the nuclear and cytoplasmic contents of the cell divide or split completely into smaller-sized daughter individuals. The fission itself may be of following types :

A. Binary fission. In the binary fission the animal body splits or divides in such a plane that two equal and identical halves are produced. It is most common in protozoans but it also occurs in certain lower metazoans. First of all the nucleus divides by amitotic or mitotic division and the division of the nucleus is followed by the division of the cytoplasm. According to the plane of fission following types of binary fission have been recognized in the organisms.

(i) Simple or orthodox type of binary fission. The simple or orthodox type of binary fission occurs in the irregular shaped organism, e.g., Amoeba in which the plane of division is difficult to observe.

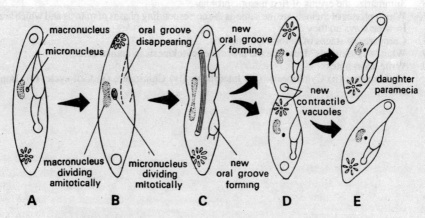

Fig. 6.1. Transverse binary fission in *Paramecium.*

(ii) Transverse binary fission.

transverse binary fission the plane of the division is always transverse to the longitudinal axis of the body of the organisms.

(iii) **Longitudinal binary fission.** The longitudinal binary fission occurs in certain ciliates and flagellates, *e.g.; Vorticella* and *Euglena* (Fig. 6.2) (Protozoa) and some corals (Anthozoa). In longitudinal binary fission the nucleus and the cytoplasm divide in the longitudinal plane.

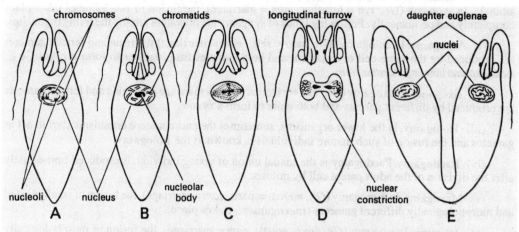

Fig. 6.2. Longitudinal binary fission in *Euglena*.

(iv) **Oblique binary fission.** The oblique binary fission coccurs in most dinoflagellates. In this type of fission the cell or body of the organism divides by the oblique division.

(v) **Strobilation.** In certain metazoan animals a special type of transverse fission known as the strobilation occurs. In the process of strobilation several transverse fissions occur simultaneously and giving rise to a number of individuals which often do not separate from each other immediately. The strobilation occurs in the scyphozoan (*Aurelia*), certain polychaets and ascidians. In *Aurelia*, for instance, the strobilation occurs during the formation of ephyra larva.

B. Asexual reproduction by multiple fission. In the multiple fission, the nucleus of the cell divides very rapidly into many nuclei. Each daughter nucleus in later stage is surrounded by the little mass of the cytoplasm and forms the asexually reproducting body such as schizogont, gamont, spore, etc. The multiple fission occurs in most algae, fungi and some protozoans, *e.g., Amoeba, Plasmodium* and *Monocystis,* etc.

2. Asexual reproduction by the budding or gemmation. In certain multicellular animals such as *Hydra* (coelenterates) and certain tunicates, the body gives out a small outgrowth known as the

The bud is supported by the parent body and it ultimately develops into a new individual. The process of development of a bud into an adult animal is called blastogenesis. The developing individual gets its food from the body of the parent and when it becomes fully mature it is detached from the parent and leads an individual existence.

3. Asexual reproduction by gemmule formation. In certain metazoan animals the asexual reproduction is carried on by certain peculiar asexual bodies known as the gemmules and statoblasts. The gemmules occur in freshwater sponges (Family–Spongillidae) and the statoblasts occur in the bryozoans. The gemmules and the statoblasts are composed of a group of undifferentiated cells which contain stored food material. These cells are enclosed and protected by the monaxon spicules in the gemmules and by the chitinous covering in the statoblasts. Both (gemmules and statoblasts) are set free by the destruction of the parental body and they develop into a new individual in the favourable conditions.

4. Asexual reproduction by regeneration. The regeneration is a process by which the organisms develop or regenerate their lost or worn out parts. The regeneration is the best means of asexual reproduction in certain protozoans, sponges, coelenterates, planarians and echinoderms.

SEXUAL REPRODUCTION

In the sexual reproduction, the development of the new individual takes place by the fusion of the sex cells or female gametes. The sexual reproduction is the most common type of reproduction among the plants and animals. It may be of following types :

1. **Syngamy.** The syngamy is the most common type of sexual reproduction in the plants and animals. In syngamy (*Gr., syn* = together; *gam* = marriage), the fusion of two gametes takes place completely and permanently. Following kinds of syngamy are prevalent among the living organisms:

(i) **Autogamy.** In autogamy (*Gr., auto* = self; *gam* = marriage) the male and female gametes are produced by the same cell or organism and both gametes fuse together to form a zygote, *e.g., Actinosphaerium* and *Paramecium.*

(ii) **Exogamy.** In exogamy (*Gr., exo* = external; *gam* = marriage) the male and female gametes are produced by different parents and both unite to form a zygote.

(iii) **Hologamy.** In the lower organisms, sometimes the entire mature organisms start to act as gametes and the fusion of such mature individuals is known as the hologamy.

(iv) **Paedogamy.** Paedogamy is the sexual union of young individuals produced immediately after the division of the adult parent cell by mitosis.

(v) **Merogamy.** In merogamy (*Gr., meros* = part; *gam* = marriage), the fusion of smaller-sized and morphologically different gametes (merogametes) takes place.

(vi) **Isogamy.** In isogamy (*Gr., iso* = equal; *gam* = marriage), the fusion of morphologically and physiologically identical gametes (isogametes) takes place.

(vii) **Anisogamy.** Some organisms produce two types of gametes. Both types of gametes differ from each other in their shape, size and behaviour and are collectively known as the anisogametes or heterogametes. The male gametes are motile and small in size and known as the microgametes. The female gametes are passive and have comparatively large size and known as the macro- or megagametes. The union of micro-and macrogametes is known as the anisogamy (*Gr., an* = without; *is* = equal; *gam* =marriage). The anisogamy occurs in higher animals and plants but it is customary to use the term fertilization in them instead of the anisogamy or syngamy.

(viii) **Macrogamy.** The syngamy or fusion of the macrogametes is known as macrogamy (*Gr., macro* = large; *gam* = marriage).

(ix) **Microgamy.** The microgamy (*Gr., micro* = small; *gam* = marriage) is common in certain protozoans, *e.g.,* forminiferans and *Arcella.* In microgamy the fusion of microgametes takes place.

2. **Conjugation.** The conjugation is the temporary union of the two individuals of same species. During the union both individuals known as conjugants exchange certain amount of nuclear (DNA) materials and after this conjugants are separated. The conjugation is most common among the ciliates, *e.g., Paramecium.*

3. **Automixis (Autogamy).** When the gamete nuclei of the same cell unite togehther to form new individuals, this phenomenon is known as the automixis or autogamy, *e.g., Paramecium.*

4. **Parthenogenesis.** The parthenogenesis (*Gr., parthenos* = virgin; *genesis* = birth) is the special type of sexual reproduction. In parthenogenesis, the eggs of an organism develop into the young individuals without the fertilization of the eggs by the sperms. The parthenogenesis occurs in certain insects (wasps, and bees, etc.) and rotifers.

REVISION QUESTIONS

1 What is reproduction ? How many kinds of reproduction occur in the living organisms?
2. What is asexual reproduction ? Describe various kinds of asexual reproduction in animals.
3. How sexual reproduction occurs in animals.
4. Describe different kinds of sexual reproduction in animals.
5. Write an essay on reproduction in animals.
6. Write short notes on:
    (i) Budding; (ii) Gemmule formation ; (iii)Regeneration ; (iv) Binary fission.

7

Gametogenesis

The gametogenesis (Gr., *gamos* = marriage; *genesis* = origin) is the process of gamete formation in the sexually reproducing animals. The sexually reproducing animals contain two types of cells in their body, *e.g.*, somatic cells and the germinal cells. Both types of cells have diploid number of chromosomes but each type has its different destiny. The somatic cells form various organs of the body and provide a phase for the maturation, development and formation of the germinal cells. The somatic cells always multiply by mitotic divisions. The germinal cells form the gonads (testes and ovaries) in the animal body. These cells produce the gamete cells by successive mitotic and meiotic divisions. The male gamete is known as spermatozoon sperm and the female gamete is known as ovum or egg. The process of sperm production is known as the spermatogenesis (Gr., *sperma* = sperm or seed; *genesis* = origin) and the process of production of ovum is known as oogenesis (Gr., *oon* = egg; *genesis* = origin). Both the processes can be studied in detail under separate headings.

SPERMATOGENESIS.

The process of spermatogenesis occurs in the male gonads or testes. The testes of the vertebrates are composed of many seminiferous tubules which are lined by the cells of germinal epithelium. The cells of the germinal epithelium form sperms by the process of spermatogenesis. But in certain animals, *e.g.*, mammals and molluscs, etc., there are somatic cells lying in between germinal cells, these somatic cells are known as Sertoli cells. The Sertoli cells anchor the differentiating cells and provide nourishment to the developing sperms. The insects do not possess Sertoli cells. The spermatogenesis is a continuous process and for the sake of convenience this process can be studied in two different stages.

1. Formation of spermatids; 2. Spermiogenesis.

Formation of Spermatids

The male germinal cells which produce the sperms are known as the primary germinal cells or primordial cells. The primordial cells pass through following three phases for the formation of spermatids.

(i) **The multiplication phase.** The undifferentiated germ cells or primordial cells contain large-sized and chromatin rich nuclei. These cells multiply by repeated mitotic divisions and produce the cells which are known as the spermatogonia (Gr., *sperma* = sperm or seed; *gone* = offspring). Each spermatogonium is diploid and contains 2X number of chromosomes.

(ii) **The growth phase.** In the growth phase, the spermatogonial cells accumulate large amount of nutrition and chromatin material. Now each spermatogonial cell is known as the primary spermatocyte.

(iii) **The maturation phase.** The primary spermatocytes are ready for first meiotic or maturation division. The homologous chromosomes start pairing (synapsis), each homologous chromosome splits logitudinally and by the chiasma formation the exchange of genetic material or crossing over takes place between the chromatids of the homologous chromosomes. The DNA amount is duplicated in the beginning of the division. By first meiotic division or homotypic division two secondary spermatocytes are formed. Each secondary spermatocyte is haploid and contains X number of chromosomes. Each secondary spermoatocyte passes through the second maturation or second meiotic or heterotypic division and produces two spermatids. Thus, by a meiotic or maturation division a diploid spermatogonium produces four haploid spermatids. These spermatids cannot act directly as the gametes so they have to pass through the next phase the spermiogenesis.

2. Spermiogenesis

The metamorphosis or differentiation of the spermatids into the sperms is known as **spermiogenesis.** Because the sperm or spermatozoon is a very active and mobile cell so as to provide great amount of mobility to the sperm, the superfluous material of the developing sperms is discarded. For the reduction of the weight of the sperms following changes occur in the spermatids.

(i) Changes in the nucleus. The nucleus loses water from the nuclear sap, shrinks and assumes different shapes in the different animals. The sperm nucleus in man and bull becomes ovoid and laterally flattened. In rodents and amphibians the sperm nucleus becomes scimitar-shaped with pointed tip. In birds and molluscs the nucleus becomes spirally twisted like a cork screw. The bivalve molluscs have the round sperm nucleus. The shape of the nucleus also determines the shape of the sperm head which becomes fully adapted for the active propulsion through the water. The RNA contents of the nucleus and the nucleolus are greatly reduced, The DNA becomes more concentrated and the chromatin material becomes closely packed into small volume.

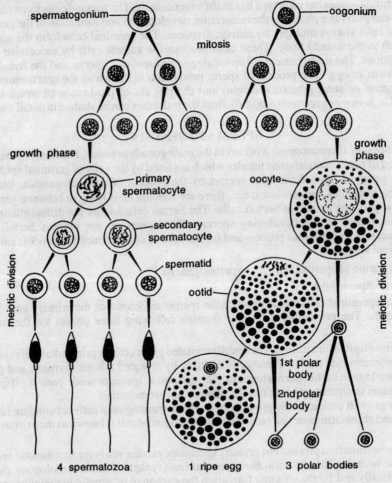

Fig. 7.1. Spermatogenesis and oogenesis. A—Spermatogenesis; B—Oogenesis.

(ii) Acrosome formation. The acrosome occurs at the anterior side of the sperm nucleus and contains proteases enzymes which help it in the easy penetration inside the egg. The acrosome is formed by the Golgi complex. The Golgi complex is concentrated near the anterior end of the sperm nucleus to form the acrosome. One or two vacuoles of the complex become large and occupy the place between the tubes of Golgi complex. Soon after a dense granule known as the **proacrosomal**

granule develops inside the vacuole. Leblond (1955) found the proacrosomal granule rich in the mucopolysaccharides. The proacrosomal granule attaches with the anterior end of the nucleus and enlarges into the **acrosome.**The membranes of Golgi vacuoles form the double membrane (unit membrane of lipoprotein) sheath around the acrosome and forms the cap-like structure of the spermatozoon. The rest of the Golgi complex becomes reduced and discarded from the sperm as **Golgi rest.** In the sperms of certain animals an **acrosomal cone** or **axial body** also develops in between the acrosome and the nucleus.

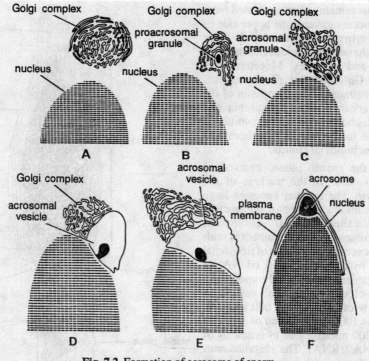

Fig. 7.2. Formation of acrosome of sperm.

(iii) **Centrioles.** The two centrioles of the spermatids become arranged one after the other behind the nucleus. The anterior one is known as the **proximal centriole** and posterior one is known as the **distal centriole.** The distal centriole changes into the basal bodies and gives rise to the **axial filament** of the sperm. The axial filament or the flagellum is composed of a pair of central longitudinal fibres and nine peripheral fibres. The distal centriole and the basal part of the axial filament occur in the middle piece of the spermatozoa. The mitochondria of the spermatids fuse together and twist spirally around the axial filament.

Thus, most of the cytoplasmic portion of the spermatid except the nucleus, acrosome, centriole, mitochondria and axial filament, is discarded during the spermiogenesis.

OOGENESIS

The process of oogenesis occurs in the cells of the germinal epithelium of the ovary; such cells are known as **primordial germinal cells.** The oogenesis is completed in following three successive stages :

1. Multiplication phase ; 2. Growth phase; 3. Maturation phase.

1. Multiplication Phase

The primordial germinal cells divide repeatedly to form the **oogonia** (Gr., *oon* = egg). The oogonia multiply by the mitotic divisions and form the primary **oocytes** which pass through the growth phase.

2. Growth Phase

The growth phase of the oogenesis is comparatively longer than the growth phase of the spermatogenesis. In the growth phase, the size of the primary oocyte increases enormously. For instance, the primary oocyte of the frog in the beginning has the diameter about 50 μ but after growth phase the diameter of the mature egg reaches about 1000 μ to 2000 μ. In the primary oocyte, large amount of fats and proteins becomes accumulated in the form of yolk and due to its heavy weight (or gravity) it is usualy concentrated towards the lower portion of the egg forming the vegetative pole.

The portion of the cytoplasm containing the egg pronucleus remains often separated from the yolk and occurs towards the upper side of the egg forming the animal pole. The cytoplasm of the oocyte becomes rich in RNA, DNA, ATP and enzymes. Moreover, the mitochondria, Golgi complex, ribosomes, etc., become concentrated in the cytoplasm of the oocyte. In certain oocytes (Amphibia and birds) the mitochondria become accumulated at some place in the occyte cytoplasm and form the mitochondrial clouds.

During the growth phase, tremendous changes also occur in the nucleus of the primary oocyte. The nucleus becomes large due to the increased amount of the nucleoplasm and is called germinal vesicle. The nucleolus becomes large or its number is multiplied due to excessive synthesis of ribosomal RNA(rRNA) by ribosomal DNA (rDNA) of nucleolar organizer region of chromosomes. Thus, the nucleus or germinal vesicle of primary oocyte of *Triturus* has 600 nucleoli, of *Siredon* has 1000 nucleoli and of *Xenopus* has 600 to 1200 nucleoli due to synthesis of ribosomal RNA (rRNA). The chromosomes change their shape and become giant lampbrush chromosomes which are directly related with increased transcription of messenger RNA (mRNA) molecules and active protein synthesis in the cytoplasm. When the growth of the cytoplasm and nucleus of the primary oocyte is completed it becomes ready for maturation phase.

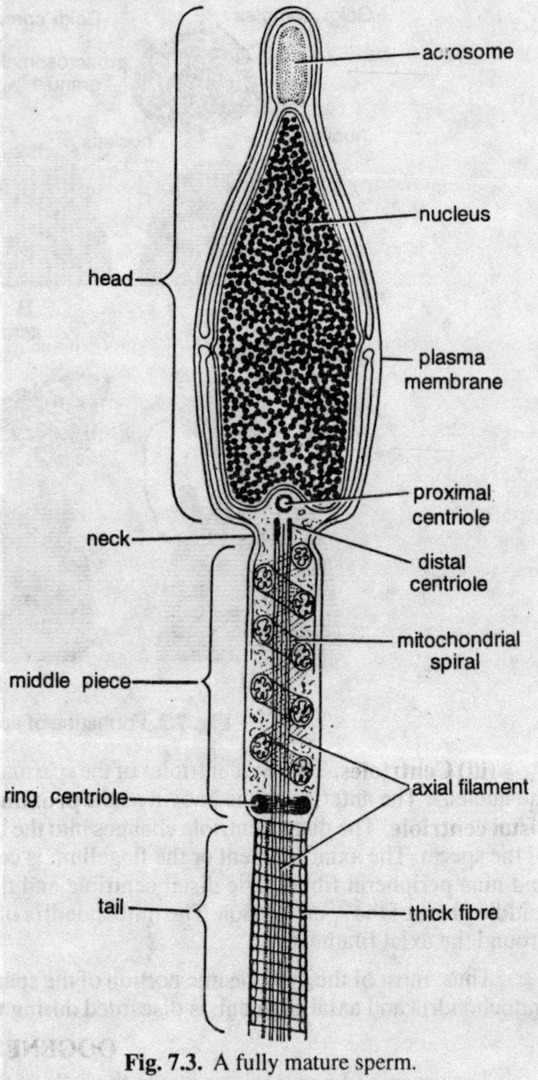

Fig. 7.3. A fully mature sperm.

3. Maturation Phase

The maturation phase is accompanied by the maturation or meiotic division. The maturation division of the primary oocyte differs greatly from the maturation division of the spermatocyte. Here after the meiotic division of the nucleus, the cytoplasm of the oocyte divides unequally to form a single large-sized haploid egg and three small haploid polar bodies polocytes at the end. This type of unequal division has the great significance for the egg. If the equal divisions of the primary oocyte might have been resulted, the stored food amount would have been distributed equally to the four daughter cells and which might prove insufficient for the developing embryo. Therefore, these unequal divisions allow one cell out of the four daughter cells to contain most of the cytoplasm and reserve food material which is sufficient for the developing embryo.

(i) **First maturation division.** During the first maturation division or first meiosis, the homologous chromosomes of the primary oocyte nucleus pass through the pairing or synapsis, duplication, chiasma formation and crossing over. Soon after the nuclear membrane breaks and the bivalent chromosomes move towards the opposite poles due to contraction of chromonemal fibres. A new nuclear envelope is developed around the daughter chromosomes by the endoplasmic reticulum. After the karyokinesis the unequal cytokinesis occurs and a small haploid polar body or polocyte and a large haploid secondary oocyte or ootid are formed.

(ii) **Second meiotic division.** The haploid secondary oocyte and first polocyte pass through the second meiotic division. Due to the second meiotic division the secondary oocyte forms a mature egg and a second polocyte. By the second meiotic division the first polocyte also divides into two secondary polocytes. These polocytes ooze out from the egg and degenerate while the haploid egg cell becomes ready for the fertilization.

Structure of Mature Egg

The mature egg has a cell-like structure and composed of the following parts :

1. **Plasma membrane.** The mature egg is covered by a plasma membrane which is the unit membrane. It is composed of an outer and an inner layer of protein. Both the layers are 50 Å in thickness. Between the proteinous layers there occurs a lipidous layer of 60 Å thickness.

2. **Primary egg membranes.** In addition to the plasma membrane the eggs of most animals except the sponges and certain coelenterates consist of certain other additional egg membranes. These membranes are known as the primary and secondary membranes. The primary egg membrane is secreted around the plasma membrane by the follicle cells of the ovary or by oocyte itself. In the insects, molluscs, amphibians and birds the primary egg membrane is known as the vitelline membrane, while in tunicates and fishes this membrane is known as the chorion. The mammalian eggs contain similar membrane and in them this is known as the zona pellucida. The vitelline membrane is composed of microproteins and fibrous proteins. The vitelline membrane usually remains closely adhered to the plasma membrane but in later stages a space is developed between the plasma membrane and the vitelline membrane and this space is known as the perivitelline space.

3. **Secondary egg membranes.** The secondary egg membranes are secreted by the ovarian tissues around the primary egg membranes. The secondary egg membrane may be composed of either jelly-like substance in the eggs of the amphibians and most invertebrates, hard shell in the eggs of sharks and rays or shell membrane and calcareous shell in the eggs of the birds. The secondary egg membranes provide protection to the developing embryo.

4. **Ooplasm.** The cytoplasm of the egg cell is known as the ooplasm. The ooplasm consists of large amount of reserve food material in the form of yolk. The yolk is composed of a lipoprotein, pigment granules, water, RNA, ribosomes, mitochondria and various other cellular inclusions. The peripheral layer of the ooplasm is known as the cortex and it contains many microvilli and cortical granules. The microvilli are formed by the outpushings of the plasma membrane and they help in the transportation of the substances from the follicle cells to the egg during the development of the egg. The cortical granules are spherical bodies of various diameters, *e.g.*, 0.8 μ in the sea urchin eggs and 2.0 μ in the eggs of frog. The cortical granules are surrounded by the unit membranes and are originated from the Golgi complex. The cortical granules contain homogeneous and granular acid mucopolysaccharides. The cortical granules are present in the eggs of sea urchins, frogs, fishes, bivalve molluscs, some annelids and certain mammals but they do not occur in man, rat, guinea pig, gastropod molluscs, urodele amphibians, insects and birds.

Yolk contents of the ooplasm. The amount of the yolk in the ooplasm varies from species to species. According to the amount of the yolk following types of egg cells have been recognised :

1. **Alecithal.** The eggs without the yolk are known as alecithal eggs, *e.g.*, eutherian mammals.

2. **Microlecithal.** The eggs with very little amount of yolk are known as the microlecithal eggs, *e.g.*, *Amphioxus*.

3. **Macrolecithal.** The eggs with large amount of the yolk are known as the macrolecithal eggs. The macrolecithal eggs can be grouped into two types on the basis of the distribution of the yolk in the ooplasm :

(a) **Homolecithal.** The eggs with evenly distributed yolk contents in the ooplasm are known as the homolecithal eggs, *e.g.*, eggs of echinoderms.

(b) **Heterolecithal.** The eggs in which the yolk is not evenly distributed in the ooplasm are known as the heterolecithal eggs. The heterolecithal eggs may be of following types :

(i) **Telolecithal.** When the amount of the yolk is concentrated in the one half of the egg to form the vegetative pole the egg is known as the telolecithal egg, *e.g.*, eggs of amphibians, etc.

(ii) **Meiolecithal.** In the meiolecithal eggs the amount of the yolk is very large and it occupies the largest portion of the egg except a small disc-shaped portion of the cytoplasm. The cytoplasm contains the zygote nucleus and is known as the germinal disc, *e.g.*, eggs of fishes, reptiles and birds.

(iii) **Centrolecithal.** In the centrolecithal eggs the yolk accumulates in the centre of the ooplasm, *e.g.*, eggs of insects.

COMPARISON OF SPERMATOGENESIS AND OOGENESIS

Spermatogenesis	Oogenesis
1. It occurs in male gonads, *i.e.*, testes.	1. It occurs in female gonads
2. Four spermatids are produced from one sperm mother cell.	2. Only one ovum is produced from one oogonium.
3. The sperm mother cell divides by meiotic cell division into four equal-sized cells and all the four cells are transformed into spermatozoa to act as reproductive units.	3. The oocyte divides unequally and produces one large-sized ovum and three small-sized polar bodies or polocytes which are sexually inert and extruded from the ovum as waste. Only ovum acts as reproductive unit.
4. Spermatozoa are produced in large number.	4. Ova are produced in small number.
5. Spermatozoa are minute, yolkless and motile.	5. Ova are much larger, often with yolk and non-motile.
6. The whole process is completed inside testes itself.	6. The process is completed outside the ovaries because egg cells are released from the ovary usually in secondary oocyte stage and second maturation division is completed later on.

REVISION QUESTIONS

1. What is gametogenesis? Summarize the stages in spermatogenesis and oogenesis.
2. Describe the events of spermiogenesis. Why it is necessary for spermatogenesis ?
3. Give an account of spermatogenesis.
4. Describe in detail the process of oogenesis.
5. What are the major features of each step of oogenesis ?
6. How acrosome of sperm is formed ?
7. Compare spermatogenesis with oogenesis.

8

Fertilization

The union of the cytoplasm and pronuclei of the male and female gametes is known as the fertilization (L., *fertilis* =to bear; *frevo*=to bear). The fertilization is the most commonly used method for the production of the diploid zygotes in the sexually reproducing organisms of Metazoa and Metaphyta.

In the process of fertilization the haploid male gamete (spermatozoon or pollen), which carries the paternal genetic information of the male parent, unites with the haploid female gamete (ovum or egg), which carries the genetic information of female parent, to form a diploid zygote. The egg carries the maternal hereditary informations in it. The zygote ultimately produces a diploid multicellular organism by the several repeated and organised mitotic divisions and cellular differentiation.

External and Internal Fertilization

The fertilization always occurs in the aquatic media such as sea water, freshwater or intra-somatic (body) fluid of the maternal individual. If the fertilization occurs outside the body of the organism it is known as external fertilization and if it occurs inside the body of the organism then it is termed as internal fertilization. The external fertilization is common in various invertebrates and chordates, while the internal fertilization occurs only in those animals which possess specialized sex organs for receiving and transmitting the sperms, *e.g.,* reptiles, birds, mammals and angiosperms, etc.

Fertilizin and Antifertilizin

The process of fertilization is very specific. The sperms of one particular species fertilize the ova of the same species. This type of specificity of male and female gametes is of utmost biological importance and is achieved by the help of certain chemical compounds. It is found that the egg and sperm both contain a chemical substance known as fertilizin (Lillie, 1919). The fertilizin is a glycoprotein which is composed of different types of amino acids and monosaccharides (glucose, fucose, fructose and galactose) according to the species. The molecular weight of the fertilizin is 300,000 and it contains large molecules. The surface layer of sperm contains another proteinous substance known as antifertilizin. The antifertilizin is a protein which is composed of acidic amino acids. It has small molecules and the molecular weight is about 10,000.

The fertilizins of the eggs are supposed to attract the sperms which contain a particular type of antifertilizin. It has been found that egg fertilizin of any species reacts efficiently with the sperm antifertilizin of the same species. It has also been reported that the fertilizin in egg-water attracts the sperms of the same species and many sperms adhere together. This type of mutual adhesion of the sperms is known as the agglutination and is most common in sea urchins.

PROCESS OF FERTILIZATION

The process of the fertilization includes two successive steps which are as follows :
1. The activation of the egg ; 2. The amphimixis.

1. Activation of the Egg

The process of activation of eggs is completed in the following stages :

(i) Movement of the sperm towards the egg. The sperms which occur in the external or internal fluid media around the egg, swim towards the egg at random. They collide with the egg by chance. The chance of colliding the sperms with the egg occurs regularly in the nature and remains fruitful only due to the large number of the sperms and enormously large size of the ovum. The fertilizins and antifertilizins become active after the chance collision of the sperms with the ova. The egg fertilizin usually occurs in the jelly surrounding the egg. It gradually dissolves in the surrounding water of the egg and forms the so called egg water.

(ii) Activation of the sperms. When a sperm with a specific antifertilizin comes in contact with the egg water of its own species then certain significant changes occur in the acrosome of the sperm. The peripheral portion of the acrosome of sperm collapses and its enzymes the lysins are extruded and dissolve in the water. The central portion of the acrosome elongates and forms a 1 to 75 μ long, thin tube known as the acrosomal filament. The acrosomal filament is the rigid tube which protrudes out from the sperm head. When the sperm possesses such an acrosomal filament it is said to be activated for the ready penetration in the unfertilized egg. When the activated sperms reach to the egg the acrosomal filaments penetrate into the egg jelly and vitelline membrane by the help of dissolving action of the sperm lysins. As soon as the tip of the acrosomal filament touches the egg membrane (plasma membrane) various important morphological and physiological changes are started in the egg.

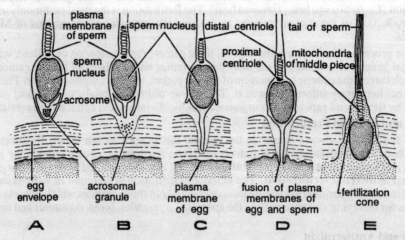

Fig. 8.1. Diagrams showing the process of fertilization in animals.

(iii) The activation of egg and insemination. As soon as the acrosomal filament touches the egg surface the ooplasm protrudes out at the point of contact into a cone-like process known as the fertilization cone. The fertilization cone may be conical, cylindrical or irregular. When the fertilization cone is irregular in shape it contains many pseudopodia-like processes of the ooplasm. The fertilization cone is composed of the plasma membrane and hyaline cytoplasm. The fertilization cone engulfs the sperm and the sperm which is surrounded by the hyaline cytoplasm moves inwards. The penetration of the sperm in the egg is known as the insemination. Immediately after the insemination a thin membrane known as the fertilization membrane is formed around the plasma membrane of the egg. The fertilization membrane prevents the entrance of further sperms in the egg.

2. Amphimixis

During the insemination the entire sperm may enter in the egg as in the mammals or the tail of the sperm remain outside the egg as in the echinoderms. In certain cases as in *Nereis*, the tail and middle piece of the sperm remain outside the egg and only the head and centrosome enter in the egg.

The nucleus of the sperm is known as the male pronucleus. The male pronucleus swells up by absorbing the water from the surrounding ooplasm and it becomes vesicular. The compactly arranged chromatin material of the male pronucleus becomes finely granular. The centriole of the sperm is surrounded by the centrosome and microtubules which form aster rays. The male pronucleus and the centriole move towards the egg pronucleus. The path is prepared by the enzymatic action of the sperm acrosome and is known as penetration path.

In the case of sea urchins and vertebrates, the two pronuclei (male and female) come close to each other and the close contact takes place between the two. The nuclear envelope is broken at the point of contact and the nuclear contents of both pronuclei are intermingled. The endoplasmic reticulum forms a new common nuclear envelope around the both pronuclei and, thus, forms a zygote nucleus. In case of *Ascaris*, annelids and molluscs this type of fusion of two pronuclei does not occur. In these animals the centrioles form the achromatic spindle from the microtubules of the ooplasm and both male and female pronuclei come close to each other, their nuclear envelopes are dissolved. The paternal and maternal homologous chromosomes get arranged on the equator of the achromatic figure and the first cleavage (mitotic) division of the egg occurs. After this division, the nuclear envelope is formed around the chromosomes of the daughter nuclei.

Post-fertilization Changes in the Egg

After the fertilization following changes occur in the egg :

1. The zygote becomes ready for the cleavage and for the formation of the embryo.

2. The oxygen consumption of the zygote increases enormously.

3. The metabolic rate of the zygote increases greatly. For instance, the amount of amino acids and the permeability of the plasma membrane of the egg increases the volume of the egg, decreases the exchange of phosphate and sodium ions between the zygote and the surrounding media, diffusion of the calcium ions from the egg starts and the hydrolysing activities of the proteolytic enzymes increase.

4. The protein synthesis is started.

KINDS OF FERTILIZATION

In the organisms following types of fertilization occur :

1. **Monospermic fertilization.** In most animals usually only one sperm enters in the egg, this type of fertilization is known as monospermic fertilization. The monospermic fertilization is common in the coelenterates, annelids, echinoderms, bony fishes, frogs and mammals.

2. **Polyspermic fertilization.** When many sperms enter in the egg, the fertilization is known as the polyspermic fertilization. It may be of two types :

(i) **Pathological polyspermy.** Under certain abnormal conditions when in a monospermic type of egg many sperms enter into the egg, the condition is known as pathological polyspermy. This type of egg does not develop further and dies soon.

(ii) **Physiological polyspermy.** In the animals with large yolky eggs such as molluscs, selachians, urodels, reptiles and birds, the polyspermic fertilization usually occurs. Such polyspermic fertilization is known as physiological polyspermy. In these cases, many sperms enter in the egg but only one unites with the egg pronucleus and rest are degenerated soon. Such eggs are viable and develop further.

3. **Polyandry.** When two male pronuclei unite with a female pronucleus, the union is known as polyandry, *e.g.*, man and rat.

4. **Polygamy.** When two egg pronuclei unite with single male pronucleus, the phenomenon is known as polygamy, *e.g.*, sea urchins, polychaete worms, urodels and rabbits.

Gynogenesis. When only sperm activates the egg but its pronucleus does not unite with the egg pronucleus, the phenomenon is known as gynogenesis, *e.g.*, planarians and nematodes.

SIGNIFICANCE OF FERTILIZATION

1. The fertilization ensures the usual specific diploidy of the organism by the fusion of the male and female pronuclei.

2. The fertilization establishes definite polarity in the eggs.

3. The fertilization provides new genetic constitution to the zygote.

4. The fertilization activates the egg for the cleavage.

5. The fertilization increases the metabolic activities and rate of the protein synthesis of the cell.

6. The fertilization initiates the egg to start cleavage and embryogenesis.

7. Fertilization combines characters of two parents, thus, introducing variations and making the resulting individuals better equipped for the struggle for existence. This happens only in cross fertilization.

REVISION QUESTIONS

1. What is fertilization? Describe the process of fertilization in animals.
2. Write a general account on fertilization.
3. Give an account of the process and kinds of fertilization.
4. What is the function of fertilization ?
5. How many kinds of fertilization occur in animals ?
6. Write short notes :
   (i) Fertilizin and antifertilizin; (ii) Polyspermy; (ii) Gynogenesis; (iv) Amphimixis.

9

Parthenogenesis

Usually an unfertilized ovum develops into a new individual only after the union with the sperm or fertilization but in certain cases the development of the egg takes place without the fertilization. This peculiar mode of sexual reproduction in which egg development occurs without the fertilization is known as the parthenogenesis (Gr., *parthenos* = virgin; *genesis* = origin). The phenomenon of parthenogenesis occurs in different groups of the animals as in certain insects (Hymenoptera, Homoptera, Coleoptera), crustaceans and rotifers. The parthenogenesis may be of two types :

1. Natural parthenogenesis ; 2. Artificial parthenogenesis.

NATURAL PARTHENOGENESIS

In certain animals the parthenogenesis occurs regularly, constantly and naturally in their life cycles and is known as the natural parthenogenesis.The natural parthenogenesis may be of two types, *viz.*, complete or incomplete.

(i) Complete parthenogenesis. Certain insects have no sexual phase and no males. They depend exclusively on the parthenogenesis for the self-reproduction. This type of parthenogenesis is known as the complete parthenogenesis or obligatory parthenogenesis.

(ii) Incomplete parthenogenesis. The life cycle of certain insects includes two generations, the sexual generation and parthenogenetic generation, both of which alternate to each other. In such cases, the diploid eggs produce females and the unfertilized eggs produce males. This type of parthenogenesis is known as the partial or incomplete or cyclic parthenogenesis.

The complete or incomplete type of natural parthenogenesis may be of following two types :

1. Haploid or arrhenotokous parthenogenesis ; 2. Diploid or thelytokous parthenogenesis.

1. Haploid or arrhenotokous parthenogenesis. In the arrhenotokous parthenogenesis, the haploid eggs are not fertilized by the sperms and develop into the haploid individuals. In these cases the haploid individuals are always males and the diploid individuals are the females, *e.g.*, 1. Insects: (i) Hymenoptera (bees and wasps), (ii) Homoptera, (iii) Coleoptera (*Micromalthus debilis*), (iv) Thysanoptera (*Anthothrips verbasi*). 2. Arachnids. *e.g.*, ticks, mites and certain spiders (*Pediculoides ventricusm*), 3. Rotifers, *e.g.*, *Asplanchne amphora*.

2. Diploid or thelytokous parthenogenesis. In the diploid parthenogenesis, the young individuals develop from the unfertilized diploid eggs. Following types of the thelytoky have been recognised.

(i) Ameiotic parthenogenesis. Sometimes during the oogenesis, first meiotic or reduction division does not occur but second meiotic division occurs as usual. Such eggs contain diploid number of chromosomes and develop into new individuals without the fertilization. This type of parthenogenesis is known as apomictic or ameiotic parthenogenesis and occurs in *Trichoniscus* (Isopoda), *Daphnia pulex* (Crustacea), *Campelona rufum* (Mollusca), weevils and long-horned grasshoppers.

(ii) Meiotic parthenogenesis. Certain eggs develop by the usual process of oogenesis but at certain stages diplosis or doubling of chromosome number and production of diploid eggs occur. Such eggs develop into the diploid individuals and this phenomenon is known as the meiotic parthenogenesis.

The diplosis of the diploid thelytoky may occur by the following methods :

(i) By autofertilization. In certain cases the oocyte divides meiotically up to the formation of ootid or ovum and secondary polocyte. But the ootid and the secondary polocyte unite together to form a diploid egg which develops into a new individual, *e.g., Artemia salina* (Crustacea) and various other organisms.

(ii) **By restitution.** Sometimes in primary oocyte karyokinesis forms a nucleus of the secondary oocyte and nucleus of the first polocyte. But the karyokinesis is not followed by the cytokinesis. The chromosomes of both daughter nuclei are arranged on the equator and undergo second meiotic division to form a diploid ootid and a diploid polocyte. The diploid ootid or ovum develops into a parthenogenetic diploid individual. This type of diplosis is known as the restitution, *e.g.,* insects of order Hymenoptera (*Nemertis conesceus*) and Leopidoptera.

ARTIFICIAL PARTHENOGENESIS

The eggs which always develop into the young individuals by the fertilization sometimes may develop parthenogenetically under certain artificial conditions. This type of parthenogenesis is known as artificial parthenogenesis. The artificial parthenogenesis may be induced by various chemical and physical means.

A. Physical means. The following physical means cause the parthenogenesis.

(i) **Temperature.** The range of temperature may induce parthenogenesis in the eggs. For instance, when the egg is transferred from the $30^{\circ}C$ to $0–10^{\circ}C$ the parthenogenesis is induced.

(ii) **Electrical shocks** can cause parthenogenesis.

(iii) **Ultraviolet light** can cause parthenogenesis.

(iv) When the eggs are pricked by the fine glass needles the development of young ones takes place parthenogenetically.

B. Chemical means. The following chemicals have been found to cause parthenogenesis in the normal eggs.

1. Chloroform;2. Strychuine; 3.Hypertonic and Hypotonic sea waters; 4. Chlorides of K^+, Ca^{++}, Na^{++}, Mg^{++} , etc.; 5. Acids such as butyric acid, lactic acid, oleic acid and other fatty acids; 6. Fat solvents, *e.g.,* toluene, alcohol, benzene and acetone ; 7. Urea and sucrose.

The artificial parthenogenesis has been induced by above mentioned physical and chemical means by various workers in the eggs of most echinoderms, molluscs, annelids, amphibians, birds and mammals.

SIGNIFICANCE OF PARTHENOGENESIS

1. The parthenogenesis serves as the means for the determination of sex in the honey bees, wasps, etc.

2. The parthenogenesis suppports the chromosome theory of inheritance.

3. The parthenogenesis is the most simple, stable and easy process of reproduction.

4. The parthenogenesis eliminates the variation from the populations.

5. The parthenogenesis is the best way of high rate of multiplication in certain insects, *e.g.,* aphids.

6. The parthenogenesis causes the polyploidy in the organisms.

7. The parthenogenesis encourages development of the advantageous mutant characters .

8. The parthenogenesis checks the non-adaptive combination of genes which may be caused due to the mutation.

9. Due to the parthenogenesis, there is no need for the organisms to waste their energy in the process of mating but it allows them to utilize that amount of energy in the feeding and reproduction.

10. The parthenogenesis avoids the sterility in the races.

However, parthenogenetic forms, *i.e.,* individuals produced due to parthenogenesis are not much successful in the struggle for existence due to the fact that no recombination of genetic material occurs, hence, variations are not produced.

REVISION QUESTIONS

1. What is parthenogenesis ? Describe various kinds of natural parthenogenesis.
2. Give a detailed account of parthenogenesis.
3. Describe artificial parthenogenesis.
4. What is the significance of parthenogenesis ?

10
The Invertebrates

The invertebrates include those animals which are without backbone as opposed to vertebrates in which a series of vertebrae constitute a backbone, but this division of the animal kingdom into invertebrates and vertebrates is largely a matter of convenience. The invertebrates constitute about 90 per cent of the known animals which number over a million. Vast and heterogeneous groups have been placed in the invertebrates. There is not even one positive character which is common to all invertebrates, and the differences between the groups are very large, each group of invertebrates has certain structural peculiarities, a special terminology, and a distinct classification. However, the life of invertebrates is as fascinating, revealing and complicated a subject as that of vertebrates. Without a thorough and careful study of invertebrates it is hardly possible to peep into the the secrets of life of animals on the whole.

PRESENT INVERTEBRATE PHYLA

Presently there are 30 invertebrate phyla, which are characterised by a unity of basic structural pattern in each of them. This means that in each phylum, though the members may differ in external features, the anatomical features are constructed on the same ground plan in many respects. The common anatomical ground plan exhibits a unique relationship among the groups of structural units which compose it. Other significant features of inter-relationships among the members of same phylum are functional. Another important feature, by which the members of the individual phylum are related with one another, is the common ancestry. Evolutionary studies have confirmed that all the members of an individual phylum have been derived directly or indirectly from a common primitive ancestral type. Thus, the 30 phyla display 30 patterns, each manifesting a characteristic, anatomical and functional integrity and common ancestry.

Table 10.1 listing the 30 invertebrate phyla with approximate number of species in each phylum is given below :

Table 10.1 : Invertebrate phyla and approximate number of species in each phylum.

S.No.	Phylum	Number of Species	S.No.	Phylum	Number of Species
1.	Protozoa	50,000	16.	Sipunculida	275
2.	Mesozoa	50	17.	Mollusca	80,000
3.	Porifera	10,000	18.	Echiurida	60
4.	Coelenterata	11,000	19.	Annelida	7,000
5.	Ctenophora	90	20.	Tardigrada	180
6.	Platyhelminthes	15,000	21.	Onychophora	65
7.	Nemertinea	750	22.	Pentastomida	70
8.	Acanthocephala	300	23.	Arthropoda	900,000
9.	Entoprocta	60	24.	Phoronida	15
10.	Rotifera	1500	25.	Ectoprocta (Bryozoa)	4,000
11.	Gastrotricha	175	26.	Brachiopoda	260
12.	Kinorhyncha	100	27.	Echinodermata	6,000
13.	Nematoda	10,000	28.	Chaetognatha	50
14.	Nematomorpha	250	29.	Pogonophora	80
15.	Priapulida	8	30.	Hemichordata	80

MAJOR AND MINOR PHYLA

Customarily the invertebrate phyla have been divided into **major** and **minor** phyla. The concept of major and minor phyla is based on two factors : (i) The number of species and individuals; (ii) Their participation in ecological communities. On the basis of the first factor, 11 phyla appear to be clearly major (as is evident from the species number in Table 10.1), these are Protozoa, Porifera, Coelenterata, Platyhelminthes, Rotifera, Nematoda, Mollusca, Annelida, Arthropoda, Ectoprocta and Echinodermata. On the basis of second factor, if the phyla are represented in great majority of ecological communities, they would be regarded as major phyla. Whereas, the minor phyla form only a fraction of animal communities. On this basis, the two phyla, Rotifera and Ectoprocta, cannot be considered as major phyla. Although they are greater in number of species, but they are included in minor phyla due to their limited participation in animal communities. Thus, keeping in view the utility of the above two factors, we can regard only nine as major phyla and the rest as minor phyla.

LOWER AND HIGHER INVERTEBRATES

The invertebrate phyla are usually referred to as lower and higher invertebrates. The lower invertebrates are simple in body organization and generally smaller in size. These are thought to have originated in the main lines of evolution, near the base of the phylogenetic tree of the Animal Kingdom. The lower invertebrates include various phyla such as Protozoa, Porifera, Coelenterata (Cnidaria), Platyhelminthes and Nematoda. On the other hand, the higher invertebrates are generally larger in size and possess a complex body organization. These occupy higher position in the phylogenetic tree of the Animal Kingdom. The higher invertebrates also include various phyla such as Mollusca, Annelida, Arthropoda and Echinodermata.

GENERAL CHARACTERISTICS OF INVERTEBRATES

1. **Habitat.** All the 30 phyla most probably originated in the sea, but not all have successfully invaded the land or its freshwater habitats. About 80 per cent are found in the terrestrial habitats. No doubt Porifera, Coelenterata and Entoprocta are represented in freshwaters but by fewer species than in the seawaters. Rotifera and Insecta are more, both in number of species and individuals, in freshwaters. Gastrotricha have about equal number of species in both fresh and seawaters. Echinodermata and Brachiopoda have never successfully colonized freshwaters. It is true that earthworm is a terrestrial animal, but most annelids are marine. There are few land snails, but most molluscs are marine. Amongst arthropods, only Crustacea is largely marine, but spiders, centipedes, millipedes and insects are mostly terrestrial. Thus, the most successful invertebrates of the land comprise arthropods.

2. **Numerical strength.** At present nearly one million living species of animals are known, out of which about 95 per cent constitute the invertebrates. It has been estimated that the number of extinct species is around seven times the number of living species and, therefore, there may have been some seven million species.

3. **Shape.** Animals of varied shapes are included amongst the invertebrates. *Amoeba* possesses an irregular ever-changing body shape, sponges and coelenterates display plant-like appearance, flatworms are leaf-like and ribbon-shaped and annelids, nemerteans and nematodes are vermiform, while the starfishes are star-shaped, etc., display spectra of body shape.

4. **Size.** The invertebrate animals exhibit a great variation in size. They range from microscopic protozoans to large-sized cephalopods. The malaria parasite is at the lowest extremity. It occupies only about one-fifth of a human red blood corpuscle (RBC). The uppermost extremity is occupied by a species of the giant squids of North Atlantic, *Architeuthis*, has been reported to have attained a total body length of 16.5 metres including tentacles.

5. **Symmetry.** Invertebrates represent all types of symmetries. Protozoans display bilateral as well as radial symmetry. Some are asymmetrical. Sponges are either asymmetrical or radially symmetrical. Coelenterates are radially symmetrical. Ctenophores exhibit biradial symmetry. The members of the remaining phyla are mostly bilaterally symmetrical. Invertebrates also represent spherical symmetry, principally in spherical protozoans such as Heliozoa and Radiolaria.

6. **Grades of organization.** Invertebrates display all grades of organization. The protoplasmic grade is seen in Protozoa, as all activities at this level are carried on within the limits of plasma

membrane (plasmalemma). The cellular grade is characteristic of sponges. In sponges only the cells exhibit division of labour for performing various specialized functions. The cell-tissue grade is observed in coelenterates as their cells are not only specialized for different functions but also certain similar cells gather together to form tissues as well. A notable example is the nerve net formed by nerve cells and their processes. The tissue-organ grade is exhibited by flatworms with arrangement of tissues to form organs. The organ-system grade organization is characteristic of all higher invertebrates. In this type of organization organs join together in a system to perform some functions.

7. **The presence or absence of germ layers.** The germ layers or embryonic cell layers are absent in Protozoa due to its unicellularity. All other invertebrates are either diploblastic, *i.e.*, they are derived form two germ layers, an outer ectoderm and an inner endoderm or triploblastic with an extra third layer, the mesoderm. Sponges and coelenterates are diploblastic, whereas other invertebrates are triploblastic.

8. **Simple integument.** The body covering of invertebrate animals is simple. In Protozoa, it is a delicate plasma membrane, while some have developed a protective covering, pellicle. Most invertebrates possess an outer protective epidermis, which is made of single layer of cells, while in others have further added a non-cellular cuticle or chitinoid covering secreted by underlying epidermis.

9. **Multiple movement devices.** Various devices for movement are found in invertebrates. Some invertebrate animals are sessile, such as sponges and corals, while others move from one place to another. Protozoa move by pseudopodia, flagella and cilia and contractile myonemes. Coelenterates and molluscs exhibit tentacular movements. Annelids move by setae, parapodia and suckers. Arthropods move with jointed legs, while echinoderms take the help of arms which are with or without tubefeet, for their movement.

10. **The presence or absence of segmentation.** The members of several invertebrate phyla are characterised by segmentation in their bodies. Certain flatworms exhibit pseudosegmentation, as their long bodies are made up of numerous sections. True segmentation is found in Annelida and Arthropoda. In them the body is divided into more or less similar segments.

11. **Absence of living endoskeleton.** The invertebrate animals do not possess any kind of rigid internal skeleton to give support to the body and provide surface for attachment of muscles. Many invertebrates are soft bodied, while some, like arthropods and molluscs, possess hard exoskeleton for supporting and protecting their body.

12. **Types of coelom.** In sponges and coelenterates, the body is a double-layered sac surrounding a single cavity, which opens to the outside through a mouth. Such animals are acoelomate as they have no coelom. Other invertebrates possess a cavity in between the body wall and the gut. This cavity is called pseudocoelom in nematodes as it is not lined by mesoderm. In higher invertebrates, the coelom is lined by mesoderm and, hence, it is the true coelom.

13. **Dorsal gut.** The alimentary canal is either absent or partially formed or complete. In case it is present, it lies dorsal to the nerve cord, and runs from the anterior terminal mouth up to the posterior terminal anus. The gill-slits are never formed in the pharyngeal wall.

14. **Intra-as well as extracellular digestion.** In invertebrates the digestion of food takes place within the cell (intracellular digestion) as well as outside the cell (extracellular digestion). In protozoans and sponges, the digestion of food takes place intracellularly. In coelenterates, the digestion of food lakes place both intracellularly as well as extracellularly. All other invertebrates exhibit extracellular digestion, which in higher invertebrates occurs within a well defined gut.

15. **Open as well as closed circulatory system.** Blood vascular system is well developed in higher invertebrates. Some, like arthropods and molluscs, possess open or lacunar circulatory system, while in others the blood flows in closed vessels, *i.e.*, closed circulatory system. The heart is always located dorsal to the gut. The hepatic portal system, carrying blood from the gut to the liver, is absent.

16. **Diversified respiratory system.** Protozoans, sponges, coelenterates and many worms have a direct diffusion of gases between the general surface of the organism and the environment. In most annelids, the exchange of gases takes place through the moist skin. Gills are common in most higher

invertebrates. Echinoderms possess branchiae and tubefeet for this purpose. Sea cucumbers have respiratory trees which act as respiratory organs. In insects the tracheal system is adapted for aerial respiration.

17. **Diversified excretory mechanisms.** In protozoans, sponges and coelenterates excretion is performed by direct diffusion through cell membranes. Flatworms possess characteristic flame cells, while annelids and molluscs possess true nephridia for the purpose. In insects, the excretory organs are Malpighian tubules. Echinoderms and some other invertebrates have amoeboid cells or phagocytes for storage and disposal of excretory products to outside.

18. **Ventral solid nervous system.** In radially symmetrical invertebrates, *e.g.*, coelenterates, the head is absent and the central nervous system is represented by a ring of nerve-tissue encircling the body. In bilaterally symmetrical invertebrates, the central nervous system comprises a pair of nerve cord running along the mid-ventral line of the body. The nerve ring and the nerve cords bear ganglia. In higher invertebrates, the head ganglia forms the brain. Invertebrate nervous system is characterized by solid nerves, these are not hollow from within.

19. **Simple sense organs.** In protozoans, the whole of the protoplasm acts as receptor, while in flagellates the stigma or eyespot acts as a photoreceptor. Coelenterates possess long sensory cells, scattered throughout the body wall, while some also possess eyespots for the reception of light, statocysts for equilibrium and sensory pits for chemoreception. Eyespots and chemoreceptors are also found in flatworms. Annelids possess various sensory receptors including simple eyes, present in the epidermis. In arthropods, compound eyes are found in addition to simple eyes. Statocysts for equilibrium, tactile receptors and chemoreceptors are common in arthropods and molluscs.

20. **Varied modes of reproduction.** In invertebrates, the modes of reproduction vary from simple asexual binary fission to most complicated sexual reproduction. In certain cases parthenogenesis has also been observed in which an unfertilized egg develops into a complete individual. It occurs in rotifers, bees, some other insects and certain crustaceans. In sexually reproducing invertebrates, hermaphrodites or bisexual forms are found, particularly in coelenterates, platyhelminthes, annelids and crustaceans. Fertilization is either external or internal. Development is direct or indirect. In the indirect development the development includes both larval stages and metamorphosis.

21. **Cold-blooded animals.** All invertebrates are cold-blooded, *i.e.*, they cannot keep body temperature constant all the time.

REVISION QUESTIONS

1. What is an invertebrate ? On what basis the animals have been classified as invertebrates and vertebrates ?
2. Name the present invertebrate phyla stating the approximate number of species contained by them.
3. What is the concept of major and minor phyla? Which invertebrate phyla are treated as major phyla and why ?
4. Describe the characteristic features of invertebrates in brief.

11
Phylum Protozoa

The name Protozoa (Gr., *protos* = first; *zoon* = animal) comes from Goldfuss (1818) who, however, used the name simply for the lower groups of zoophyta including protozoans, sponges, coelenterates, rotifers and bryozoans, It was von Siebold (1845) who, recognizing the unicellular nature of the Protozoa, first used and defined the name Protozoa in the present sense. Protozoa are generally microscopic in size, they are found in freshwater, saltwater and damp soil, while some are parasitic, symbiotic and commensals. They are called acellular or non-cellular because their bodies are not differentiated into cells; parts of their bodies are specialized for various functions, these parts are called organelles in contrast to the organs of Metazoa. Thus, Protozoa may be regarded equivalent, not to a metazoan cell, but to an entire metazoan. Protozoa have undergone cytological differentiation, whereas Metazoa have undergone histological differentiation during the course of evolution. Consequently the term unicellular used for Protozoa is unfortunate. Protozoa forms a heterogeneous group, the members display an extreme diversity of structure, different types of symmetry and adaptations to various environments. Many Protozoa are extremely complicated in structure. Some Protozoa form colonies. A colony has several individuals either attached to each other or enclosed within a gelatinous envelope and joined together by protoplasmic connections. A colony differs from a metazoan because its cells are functionally independent of each other. A protozoan, then might be defined as an organism which is made up of a mass of protoplasm not divided into cells and which carries on all the vital activities of life such as locomotion, feeding, digestion, egestion, respiration, excretion and reproduction, etc. Although it is not divided into cells, it has specialization and division of labour within its cytoplasmic mass. It is erroneous to think of protozoans as simple animals, for many have complicated structures and are physiologically complex. Inasmuch as Protozoa are not made up of cells, they represent what is called the protoplasmic level of organization. From this standpoint and others, many biologists place them close to the common ancestor of many-celled forms. Some Protozoa are quite close to the plants and may be considered as connecting link between animals and plants.

The number and variety of Protozoa is very great. About 50,000 species have been named although over 20,000 of them are fossil forms. The immense number of Protozoa have traditionally been separated by their means of locomotion into four classes : Sarcodina with pseudopodia, Mastigophora with flagella, Ciliata with cilia, and Sporozoa with no organelles for locomotion. Recently the Committee on Taxonomy and Taxonomic Problems of the Society of Protozoologists published a revised classification of the Protozoa (Honigberg *et al.*, 1964). According to Honigberg *et al.*, (1964) Protozoa have been divided into four subphyla, *viz.*, Sarcomastigophora, Sporozoa, Cnidospora and Ciliophora.

Ten representative types have been described in detail which are studied in various Indian Universities. The types described herein are : *Euglena, Trypanosoma, Amoeba, Entamoeba, Elphidium* (= *Polystomella*), *Monocystis, Eimeria, Plasmodium, Paramecium,* and *Vorticella.*

The Mastigophora(Gr., *mastix* =whip; *pherein* = to bear) or Flagellata(L., *flagrum* = a whip) are a diverse group of protozoans in which one or more elongated, whip-like flagella are found in most adults, although some have flagella present only during young stages. These structures are primarily organelles of locomotion but also may aid in food capture or serve as sensory organelles. The body form is maintained by a thin covering membrane known as pellicle. The flagellates are supposed to be one of the most primitive of all Protozoa because many of them are plant-like. A typical flagellate readily available for study in the laboratory is the free living *Euglena*. Approximately 150 species of *Euglena* are known, ranging in size from 25 to 500 microns in length and varying greatly in structure. The species commonly met in India are *Euglena viridis, E. agilis, E. orientalis, E. gracilis, E. spirogyra* and *E. fusiformis. Euglena* is a typical example and one of the commonest and largest of uniflagellate, chlorophyll-bearing Mastigophora. The most common species *Euglena viridis* is described here in detail.

EUGLENA VIRIDIS
SYSTEMATIC POSITION

Phylum	....	**Protozoa**
Subphylum	....	**Sarcomastigophora**
Superclass	....	**Mastigophora**
Class	....	**Phytomastigophora**
Order	....	**Euglenida**
Genus	....	*Euglena*
Species	....	*viridis*

HABIT AND HABITAT

Euglena viridis (Gr., *eu* =true; *glene* = eye-ball or eye-pupil; L., *viridis* =green) is a common, solitary and free living freshwater flagellate. It is found in freshwater pools, ponds, ditches and slowly running streams. It is found in abundance where there is considerable amount of vegetation. Ponds in the well maintained gardens containing decaying nitrogenous organic matter, such as twigs, leaves and faeces of animals, etc., are good source of this organism. It generally lives with the other species of the genus. They are sometimes so numerous as to give a distinct greenish colour to the water or at times forming a green film of scum on the surface of the pond water.

CULTURE

The culture of *Euglena* can be easily prepared in the laboratory by the following method. Boil some cow or horse dung in distilled water in a jar and allow it to cool for two days. Then put some weeds from a pond containing *Euglenae* into the jar and place the jar near the well lighted window. In a few days *Euglenae* will appear in this nitrogenous infusion.

STRUCTURE

Shape.*Euglena viridis* is elongated and spindle-shaped in appearance. The anterior end is blunt, the middle part is wider, while the posterior end is pointed.

Size. *Euglena viridis* is about 40–60 microns in length and 14–20 microns in breadth at the thickest part of the body.

Pellicle.The body is covered by a thin, flexible, tough and strong cuticular periplast or pellicle which lies beneath the plasma membrane. It has oblique but parallel striations called myonemes all round. But according to Chadefaud (1937), the pellicle is made of an outer thin layer epicuticle and inner thick layer cuticle. Both the layers of pellicle are present all over the body but only the epicuticle ends into an anteriorly placed cytopharynx and reservoir. The pellicle is composed of fibrous elastic protein but not of cellulose. The pel-

licle maintains a definite shape of the body, yet it is flexible enough to permit temporary changes in the body shape, these changes of shape are spoken of as metabody or euglenoid movements.

Electron strucutre of pellicle. Electron microscopic study of pellicle reveals that it is made of helically disposed strips. These strips are fused at both the ends of the cell body and each has a groove along one edge and a groove along the other. The edges of neighbouring strips overlap and articulate in a way that the ridge of one strip fits into the groove of the other. In fact, the articulating ridges give the pellicle striated appearance. Just beneath and parallel to the strips, a row of mucus-secreting muciferous bodies and bundles of microtubles are found arranged (Fig. 12.3).

Cytostome and cytopharynx. At the anterior end is a funnel-shaped cytostome or cell mouth slightly to one side of the centre. Cytostome leads into a short tubular cytopharynx or gullet which, in turn, joins a large spherical vesicle, the reservoir or flagellar   The

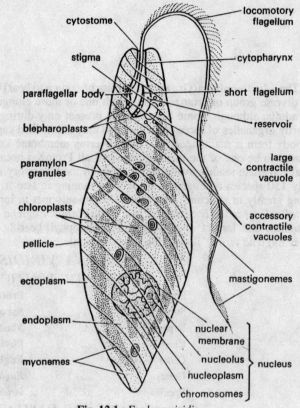

Fig. 12.1. *Euglena viridis.*

cytostome and cytopharynx are not used for ingestion of food but as a canal for escape of fluid from the reservoir.

Contractile vacuole. A large osmoregulatory body, the contractile vacuole lies near the reservoir on one side. It is surrounded by several minute accessory contractile vacuoles, which probably fuse together to form the larger vacuole. The contractile vacuole discharges the excess of water and some waste products of metabolism into the reservoir from where it goes out through the cytostome.

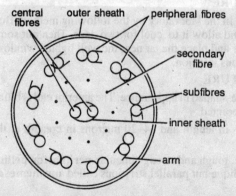

Fig. 12.2. *Euglena.* T.S. flagellum (diagrammatic).

Flagellum. A single, long, whip-like flagellum emerges out of the cytostome through cytopharynx. The length of flagellum differs in different species of *Euglena* but in *Euglena viridis* it is as long as the body of the animalcule. It arises by two roots from the base of the reservoir from the side opposite to the contractile vacuole. Each root springs from a blepharoplast (Gr., *blepharon* = eyelid; *plastos* = formed) or basal granule which lies embedded in the anterior part of the cytoplasm.

According to some workers, there are two flagella, one long and other short, each arising from a basal granule located in the cytoplasm at the base of the reservoir. The short flagellum does not extend beyond the neck of the reservoir and it often adheres to the long flagellum producing the appearance of bifurcation.

The flagellum consists of an outer contractile protoplasmic sheath and an inner elastic axial filament, the axoneme. The distal portion of the flagellum contains numerous minute fibres known as mastigonemes which project along one side of the sheath and, therefore, the flagellum is stichonematic type.

Electron structure of flagellum. Electron microscopic study of the flagellum reveals that it consists of two central and nine peripheral fibrils. Each central fibril is single, while the peripheral fibrils are paired having two sub-fibrils in each. One of the two sub-fibrils of each peripheral fibril bears a double row of short projections called arms; all the arms being directed in the same direction. The two central fibrils are found enclosed in an inner membranous sheath. All the fibrils are enclosed within an outer protoplasmic sheath continuous with the cell membrane. There are nine secondary fibrils between central and peripheral fibrils. All these fibrils fuse to join the blepharoplast or basal granule. Manton (1959) has suggested that mastigonemes, hair-like contractile fibres, arise from two of the nine peripheral fibrils.

Stigma. Near the inner end of the cytopharynx close to the reservoir is a red eye spot or stigma. It consists of a plate of lipid droplets (Leedale, 1966), a carotenoid pigment as red granules of haematochrome which stains blue with iodine. Stigma is cup-shaped with a colourless mass of oily droplets in its concavity which function as a lens. The stigma is sensitive to light.

Paraflagellar body or photoreceptor. A small swelling known as paraflagellar body lies either on one root or at the junction of two roots of the flagellum. The paraflagellar body is sensitive to light and it is regarded to be photoreceptor.

Recent studies of Chadefaud and Provasoli have shown that the stigma and paraflagellar body together form the photoreceptor apparatus.

Cytoplasm. The cytoplasm of *Euglena* is differentiated into an outer layer of ectoplasm and

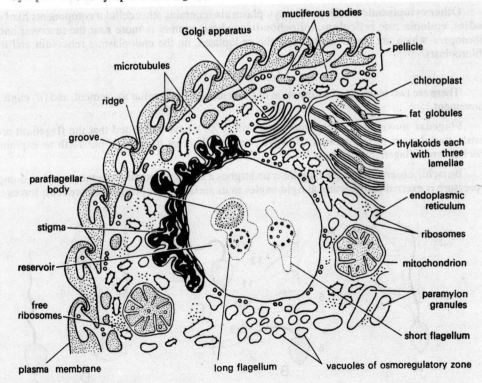

Fig. 12.3. *Euglena*. Diagrammatic representation of electron structure of a portion of body in T.S. passing through the reservoir.

inner layer of endoplasm. The ectoplasm is thin, clear or non-granular, while the endoplasm is more fluid-like and granular. The endoplasm contains nucleus, chromatophores and paramylum bodies.

Nucleus. *Euglena* has a single, large, round or oval and vesicular nucleus lying in a definite position usually near the centre or towards the posterior end of the body. There is a distinct nuclear membrane. The nucleus contains a central body known as endosome (which is also known as nucleolus or karyosome). Chromatin forms small granules in the space between nuclear membrane and the endosome. There is a large amount of nucleoplasm.

Chromatophores or chloroplasts. Radiating from the centre of the body of *Euglena*, there are several, slender, band-like elongated chromatophores. The chro-matophores contain the green pigment, chlorophyll a and b, along with β-carotene and are also known as chloroplasts. *Euglena* de-rives its green colour from these chromatophores. Chloroplasts are arranged in a stellar fashion or like the rays of the stars. Each chromatophore or chloroplast consists of a very thin central part known as pyrenophore which is enclosed by pyrenoid. The pyrenoid is enclosed between a pair of hemispherical structures made of paramylum. Paramylum is a polysaccharide (β-1, 3 glucan) starch which gives no colour with iodine. A careful observation of chloroplasts suggests the presence of groups of chlorophyll bearing lamellae or thylakoids in them. Each thylakoid bears three lamellae; the thylakoids are placed in the stroma or matrix of the chloroplasts and also contain ribosomes and fat globules. A chloroplast is bounded by a triple membrane envelope (Sleigh, 1973).

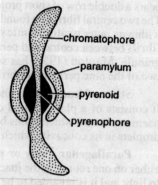

Fig. 12.4. Chromatophore of *Euglena*.

Paramylum bodies. Paramylum bodies of various shapes and sizes are found scattered throughout the endoplasm. These are refractile bodies and contain stored food material in the form of paramylum which is a product of photosynthesis.

Other cytoplasmic contents. The cytoplasm also contains other cellular components like Golgi bodies, endoplasmic reticulum, mitochondria whose number is more near the reservoir and the ribosomes which are found scattered in the endoplasm, on the endoplasmic reticulum and in the chloroplasts.

LOCOMOTION

There are two methods of locomotion in *Euglena, viz.,* (i) flagellar movement, and (ii) euglenoid movement.

Flagellar movement. Vickerman and Cox (1967) have suggested that the flagellum makes direct contribution to locomotion. However, several theories have been put forth to explain the mechanism of flagellar movement.

Butschli observed that the flagellum undergoes a series of lateral movements and in doing so, a pressure is exerted on the water at right angles to its surface. This pressure creates two forces : one

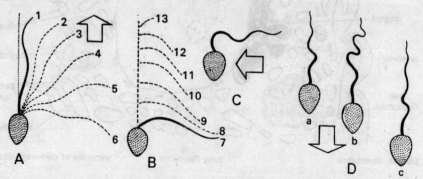

Fig. 12.5. Action of flagellum. A—Recovery stroke, successive stages from 1 to 7; B—Effective stroke, successive stages 8 to 13..

directed parallel, and the other at right angles, to the main axis of the body. The parallel force will drive the animal forward and the force acting at right angles would rotate the animal on its own axis.

Gray (1928) suggested that a series of waves pass from one end of the flagellum to the other. These waves create two types of forces, one in the direction of the movement and the other in the circular direction with the main axis of the body. The former will drive the animal forward and the latter would rotate the animal.

For quite a long time it was generally presumed that the flagellum is directed forwards during flagellar movement but now it is generally agreed that the flagellum is straight and turgid in effective stroke and dropped backwards in the recovery stroke.

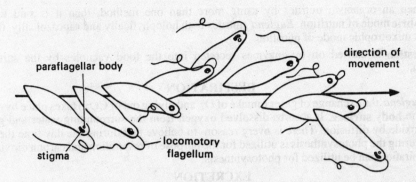

Fig. 12.6. *Euglena.* Successive stages in flagellar movement.

Recently Lowndes (1941–43) has pointed out that the flagellum is directed backwards during locomotion. According to Lowndes, a series of spiral waves pass successively from the base to the tip of the backwardly directed flagellum at about 12 per second with increasing velocity and amplitude. The waves proceed along the flagellum in a spiral manner and cause the body of the *Euglena* to rotate once in a second. Thus, in its locomotion it traces a spiral path about a straight line and moves forward. The rate of movement is 3 mm per minute.

However, movement of flagellum is related to the contraction of its all fibrils. The energy for the contraction of these fibrils is derived from ATPs formed in the mitochondria of blepharoplasts.

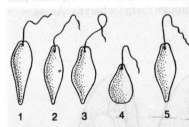

Fig. 12.7. *Euglena.* Stages of euglenoid movement.

Euglenoid movement or metaboly. *Euglena* sometimes shows a very peculiar slow wriggling movements. A peristaltic wave of contraction and expansion passes over the entire body from the anterior to the posterior end and the animal moves forward. The body becomes shorter and wider first at the anterior end, then in the middle and later at the posterior end. This type of movement is called euglenoid movement by which slow and limited movement occurs. Euglenoid movements are brought about by the contractions of cytoplasm or by the contractions of myonemes present in the cytoplasm below the pellicle.

NUTRITION

The mode of nutrition in *Euglena* is mixotrophic, *i.e.*, the nutrition is accomplished either by holophytic or saprophytic or by both the modes.

Holophytic or autotrophic nutrition. In *Euglena* the chief mode of nutrition is holophytic or plant-like. The food is manufactured photosynthetically, as in plants, with the aid of carbon dioxide, light and chlorophyll present in the chromatophores. The chlorophyll decomposes the carbon dioxide into carbon and oxygen in the presence of sunlight. The oxygen is set free and carbon is retained and combined with the elements of water to form carbohydrate (polysaccharide) like paramylum. The paramylum differs from starch because it does not become blue with iodine solution. In *Euglena* the reserve food is stored in the form of refractile paramylum bodies and their number is abundant in a well fed *Euglena*.

Saprophytic or saprozoic nutrition. In the absence of sunlight *Euglena* derives its food by another mode of nutrition known as saprophytic, osmotrophic or saprozoic. In this mode the animal absorbs through its general body surface some organic substances in solution from decaying matter in the environment of animal. They require ammonium salts, instead of nitrates, for their sources of nitrogen. *Euglena* can subsist on saprozoic nutrition when it loses its chlorophyll in complete darkness. Usually, the chlorophylls lost in darkness are regained in light. But in forms like *E. gracilis*, the change is permanent, *i.e.*, the chlorophylls once lost are not regained. The saprophytic nutrition may also supplement the normal holophytic nutrition.

Pinocytosis has also been reported to occur at the base of the reservoir for the intake of proteins and other large molecules.

When an organism nutrites by using more than one method, then it is said to exhibit mixotrophric mode of nutrition. *Euglena* nutrites both holophytically and saprozoically, therefore, it exhibits mixotrophic mode of nutrition.

Digestion is carried on by enzymes secreted into the food vacuoles by the surrounding cytoplasm.

RESPIRATION

In *Euglena* the exchange of gases (intake of O_2 and giving out of CO_2) takes place by diffusion through the body surface. It absorbs dissolved oxygen from the surrounding water and gives out carbon dioxide by diffusion. There is every reason to believe that during the day time the oxygen released during the photosynthesis is utilized for the purpose of respiration and carbon dioxide given out in respiration can be utilized for photosynthesis.

EXCRETION

The elimination of carbon dioxide and nitrogenous waste product (ammonia) takes place through the general body surface by diffusion. At least some excretion, however, is carried out by the contractile vacuole.

OSMOREGULATION

Since *Euglena* has a semi-permeable pellicle and lives in water so that water continuously enters in its body by endosmosis. The removal of excess of water from the body is known as osmoregulation. The elimination of excess of water is done by the contractile vacuole. The accessory contractile vacuoles collect excess of water from the surrounding cytoplasm and liberate their contents into the main contractile vacuole which gradually increases in size and finally bursts and forces the water into the reservoir. From the reservoir water escapes out by cytosome through the cytopharynx. Along with this water soluble wastes are also thrown out of the body.

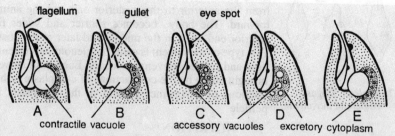

Fig. 12.8. Successive stages of contractile vacuole showing systole and diastole.

Recently Chadefaud has pointed out that the contractile vacuole is surrounded by a specialized granular and excretory cytoplasm. The contractile vacuole periodically attains its maximum size and collapses to discharge its contents into the reservoir (*i.e.*, systole). Simultaneously, several small accessory vacuoles appear in the excretory cytoplasm. These vacuoles then fuse together to form a new large vacuole (*i.e.*, diastole) which attains the maximum size and collapses to discharge the water like the former one.

BEHAVIOUR

Euglena responds to a variety of stimuli and is very sensitive to light. It swims towards an ordinary light such as that from a window and avoids strong light. If a culture of *Euglena* is examined, most of the animals will be found on the side towards the light. This is of distinct advantage to the animal, because light is necessary for the assimilation of carbon dioxide by means of its chlorophyll. *Euglena* will swim away from the direct rays of sun. Direct sunlight will kill the organism if allowed to act for a long time. If a dish containing *Euglenae* is placed in the direct sunlight and then one half of it is shaded, the animals will avoid the shady part and also the direct sunlight and will remain in a small band between the two in the light best suited for them (Fig. 12.9), that is, their optimum. A swimming *Euglena* moves in a spiral manner rotating and gyrating around its own axis but it shows a shock reaction whenever the direction of light is changed.

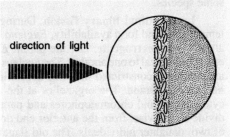

Fig. 12.9. *Euglena* showing reaction to light.

It has been found that the region in front of the eye spot is more sensitive to light than any other part of the body. *Euglena* orientates itself parallel to rays of light whenever the paraflagellar body (photoreceptor) is shaded by the stigma or eyespot. The animal adjusts its position to the direction of light moving either towards or away from it. When the animal rotates, the stigma acts as a screen, the paraflagellar body is alternately exposed or shielded when light falls on it from the side. The animal adjusts itself until the paraflagellar body is continuously exposed, this happens when the source of light is either straight in front or behind.

Euglena gives avoiding reaction to mechanical, thermal and chemical stimuli on a trial and error pattern phabotaxis). When stimulated by a change, *Euglena,* in majority of cases, stops or moves backward, turns strongly towards the dorsal surface, but continues to revolve on its long axis. The posterior end then acts as a pivot, while the anterior end traces a circle of wide diameter in the water. The animal may swim forward in a new direction from any point in this circle. This is avoiding reaction.

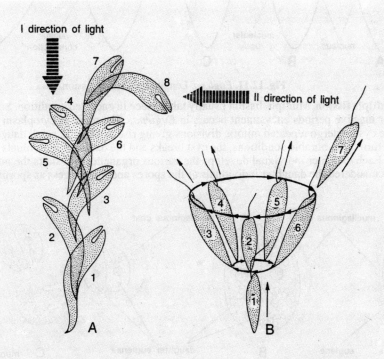

Fig. 12.10. *Euglena.* A—Shock reaction and reorientation to light; B—Avoiding reaction on a trial and error pattern.

REPRODUCTION

Euglena reproduces asexually by longitudinal binary fission and multiple fission. Encystment also takes place. Sexual reproduction does not occur, although a primitive form of it is reported in some species.

Longitudinal binary fission. During active periods, under favourable conditions of water, temperature and food availability, *Euglena* reproduces by longitudinal binary fission. The fission is always symmetrogenic, *i.e.,* the parent *Euglena* divides into two daughter *Euglenae*, which are exactly identical to one another. The nucleus divides by mitosis. The endosome elongates transversely and becomes constricted into two approximately equal parts. Nuclear division takes place within nuclear membrane. The organelles at the anterior end such as stigma, blepharoplasts, reservoir, cytopharynx and chromatophores and paramylum bodies are also duplicated. The body begins to divide lengthwise, from the anterior end downwards to the posterior end resulting in the formation of two daughter individuals. The old flagellum is retained by one half, whereas a new flagellum is developed by the other, contractile vacuole and paraflagellar body do not divide but they disappear and are made again in the daughter individuals.

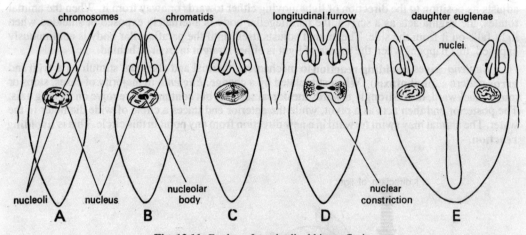

Fig. 12.11. *Euglena*. Longitudinal binary fission.

Multiple fission. Multiple fission usually takes place in encysted condition. Sometimes during resting or inactive periods encystment occurs in *Euglena*. The mass of cytoplasm and the nucleus inside the cyst undergo repeated mitotic divisions giving rise to 16 or 32 small daughter individuals. On the return of favourable conditions, the cyst breaks and the daughter individuals escape out from the cyst. Each daughter individual develops the various organelles and starts the normal life. Some workers considered the daughter individuals as the spores and this process as sporulation.

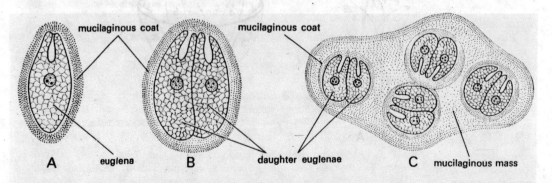

Fig. 12.12. *Euglena*. Multiple fission and encystation. A—Encysted individual; B—Fission in encysted condition; C—Palmella stage.

Palmella stage. Sometimes, usually under unfavourable conditions, large number of *Euglenae* come close together, lose their flagella and become rounded. They secrete gelatinous covering or mucilaginous matrix within which they remain embedded. This condition is called palmella stage which is often seen as green scum on the water surface of ponds. Individuals of palmella stage carry on metabolic activities and reproduce by binary fission. On the arrival of favourable conditions, the gelatinous covering swells by the absoprtion of water and the *Euglenae* are released. They regenerate their flagella and start normal active life.

ENCYSTMENT

During unfavourable conditions such as drought, extreme cold or extreme hot, scarcity of food and oxygen *Euglena* undergoes encystment. First of all *Euglena* becomes inactive, loses its flagellum and secretes a cyst around it. The cyst is secreted by the muciferous bodies lying below the pellicle. The cyst is thick-walled, rounded and red in colour due to the presence of a pigment called haematochrome. This cyst is of the protective type. During the encysted condition the periods of unfavourable conditions are successfully passed. During encystment binary fission may occur one or more times, resulting in 2 to 32 small daughter *Euglenae* within the cyst. On the return of

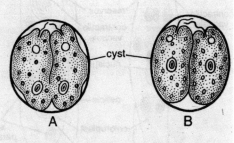

Fig. 12.13. *Euglena.* Binary fission in a cyst.

favourable conditions cyst wall breaks, the animals become active and emerge from the cyst to lead a normal free swimming life. In fact, encystment occurs only to tide over the unfavourable conditions and during this condition dispersal of *Euglena* occurs to a wide area.

POSITION OF *EUGLENA*

Euglena shows many characters of plants such as chloroplasts with chlorophyll and holophytic nutrition but it is regarded as an animal due to the following facts :

(i) Its pellicle is made of proteins and not of cellulose as in plants.

(ii) Presence of blepharoplasts, comparable to centrioles.

(iii) Presence of stigma and paraflagellar body, the photosensitive structures.

(iv) Presence of contractile vacuoles, which are not found in plants.

(v) Saprozoic mode of nutrition and also holozoic as has been claimed by certain zoologists.

(vi) Presence of longitudinal binary fission, which is not found in plants.

SOME OTHER EUGLENOID FLAGELLATES

1. *Euglena gracilis.* It is small, elongated, spindle-shaped measuring about 50 microns in length. The chloroplasts are large, flat, plate-like and about ten in number. Each chloroplast bears a protein-aceous pyrenoid. As mentioned earlier, unlike *Euglena viridis,* its chloroplasts once lost in darkness cannot be regained. Its cytoplasm contains many paramylum bodies in association with the chloroplasts (Fig. 12.14 A).

2. *Euglena spirogyra.* It is large-sized measuring about 95 microns in length and 18 microns in width. Its body is elongated, spindle-shaped and posteriorly its body is drawn out as a tail. There are numerous, small, disc-like chloroplasts without pyrenoids. It is characterised by the paramylum bodies in its cytoplasm (Fig. 12.14 B).

3. *Astasia longa.* It is a typical euglenoid form and generally supposed to be the bleached form of *Euglena gracilis.* Chloroplasts, stigma and paraflagellar body are not found. It nutrites by osmotrophy due to the absence of chloroplasts and its cytoplasm contains many paramylum bodies (Fig. 12.14 C).

4. *Paranema trichophorum.* It is an euglenoid flagellate having somewhat stumpy body. It is believed to feed holozoically by phagotrophy upon quite large microorganisms. Of its two flagella, one is locomotory and long, while the other is trailing and found attached to its body surface. The stigma and paraflagellar body are not found. Its cytoplasm contains food vacuoles and many small

paramylum bodies. It is characterised by the presence of an accessory rod-like apparatus called trichites in its cytopharynx (Fig. 12.14 D).

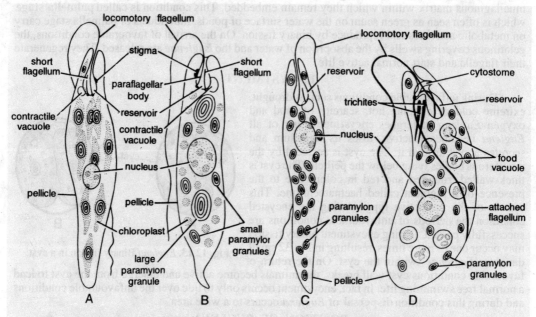

Fig. 12.14. Different forms of euglenoid flagellates. A—*Euglena gracilis*; B—*Euglena spirogyra*; C—*Astasia longa*; D—*Paranema trichophorum*.

REVISION QUESTIONS

1. Describe the structure, modes of nutrition and reproduction of *Euglena*.
2. Describe the structure and modes of reproduction in *Euglena*. Give reasons for including *Euglena* in the Animal Kingdom.
3. Describe the structure of *Euglena* as seen under electron microscope.
4. From where do you collect *Euglena* for class study? Give reasons for treating it as a plant by the botanists.
5. Describe in brief the occurrence, structure, nutrition and reproduction of *Euglena*.
6. Write short notes on the different types of euglenoid flagellates you know.
7. What do you know about different behavioural responses of *Euglena* ? How do it regulates the amount of water in its body ? What will happen if its contractile vacuole is somehow damaged ?
8. Write short notes on :
    (i) Culture of *Euglena* in laboratory; (ii) Pellicle of *Euglena*; (iii) Anterior end of *Euglena;* (iv) Flagellum; (v) Chromatophore; (vi) Flagellar movement; (vii) Metaboly; (viii) Mixotrophic nutrition; (ix) Palmella stage; (x) Osmoregulation in *Euglena*; (xi) Encystment in *Euglena;* (xii) *Peranema trichophorum;* (xiii) *Euglena gracilis.*

13

Trypanosoma

The genus *Trypanosoma* (Gr., *trypanon*= auger, *soma=body*) is parasitic in the blood of most of the vertebrates like fishes, amphibians, reptiles, birds and mammals. Many species of genus *Trypanosoma* are pathogenic, while many species are non-pathogenic. The disease caused by *Trypanosoma* is called trypanosomiasis. Of all the species of *Trypanosoma*, only three species are pathogenic in man, *viz., Trypanosoma gambiense, T. rhodesiense* and *T. cruzi. T. gambiense* and *T. rhodesiense* live as parasite in the human blood and cause a deadly disease known as sleeping sickness in Africa, while *T. cruzi* causes the chagas' disease in childern in South America. Their transmission from one vertebrate host to other takes place by invertebrate blood-sucking animals like insects and leeches. These animals are referred to as vectors. Here we shall describe the structure and life cycle of a well known parasite *Trypanosoma gambiense* which causes a very serious disease in man known as African sleeping sickness.

TRYPANOSOMA GAMBIENSE

SYSTEMATIC POSITION

Phylum	...	**Protozoa**
Subphylum	...	**Sarcomastigophora**
Superclass	...	**Mastigophora**
Class	...	**Zoomastigophorea**
Order	...	**Kinetoplastida**
Genus	...	*Trypanosoma*
Species	...	*gambiense*

HISTORICAL BACKGROUND

Valentine was the first to report *Trypanosoma* in the blood of a Trout. Gruby established the genus and Lewis reported it from the blood of rat. Evans and Bruce described *Trypanosama* from the blood of horses, camels and cattles. Forde (1901) first observed this parasite in the blood of man. It was again confirmed by Dutton (1902). Castellani reported this parasite in the cerebrospinal fluid of man. Then, Bruce and Nabarro established the relationship of the disease sleeping sickness with this parasite. Bruce also discovered that the disease is transmitted by tsetse fly.

DISTRIBUTION

The different species of *Trypanosoma* are reported from Central and West Africa, Nigeria, Congo and Central America. Commonly, areas near the rivers and lakes having low marshy land have the greatest incidence of infection because the insect vector inhabits in these areas.

HABIT AND HABITAT

Trypanosoma gambiense lives as a parasite in the blood, lymph, lymph nodes, spleen, or cerebrospinal fluid of man and in the intestine of blood-sucking fly *Glossina palpalis* (Tsetse fly).

STRUCTURE

Shape and size. *Trypanosoma gambiense* has a slender, elongated, colourless, sickle-shaped and flattened microscopic body which is tapering at both the ends. The anterior end is more pointed than the posterior end which is blunt. Its body length varies from 15 to 30 microns and width from 1 to 3 microns. The shape and size of its body vary with the form in which it exists,

Pellicle and undulating membrane. The body is covered by a thin, elastic and firm pellicle. It maintains the general shape of the body. The pellicle is made of fine fibrils which run along the whole length of the body. These fibrils are called microtubules. The pellicle is pulled out into an irregular membranous fold to one side when its flagellum beats. This fold is called undulating

membrane, which is supposed to be an adaptive structure for locomotion in a viscous environment (blood, lymph) where it lives.

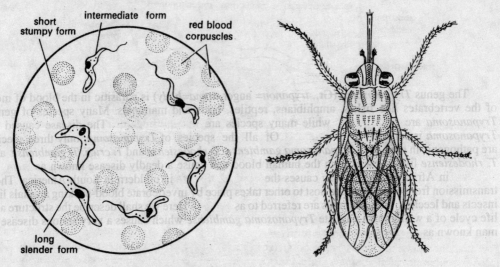

Fig. 13.1. *Trypanosoma gambiense.* Human blood smear to show its various forms.

Fig. 13.2. Tsetse fly.

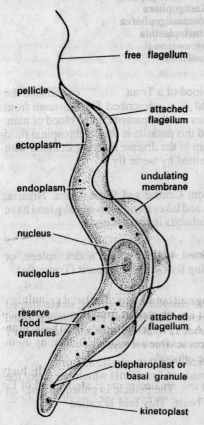

Fig. 13.3. *Trypanosoma gambiense.*

Fla

gellum. Flagellum is single in *Trypanosoma, i.e.,* it is **uni-flagellate.** The flagellum arises from the **basal granule** situated near the posterior end of the body. The flagellum runs forward and remains attached all along the length of the body marking the boundary of undulating membrane. After reaching the anterior end of the body, the flagellum becomes free and hangs freely as **free flagellum.** Structurally, the flagellum is like that of *Euglena's* and consists of the **ax-oneme** enclosed in a thin cytoplasmic sheath.

Kinetoplast. Just posterior to basal granule, there is a small, spherical or disc-shaped **parabasal body** or **kineto-plast** which contains extranuclear DNA and, hence, it is a self-duplicating body. The kinetoplast is related to locomotion.

Cytoplasm. Its cytoplasm is differentiated into ecto-plasm and endoplasm. The cytoplasm contains numerous scattered greenish refractile deep staining granules called **volutin granules.** The volutin granules are metabolic food reserves and generally consist of glycogen and phosphates. In addition, cytoplasm also contains some small **vacuoles** having hydrolytic enzymes in them and all other cellular components like Golgi body, mitochondira, endoplasmic reticulum and nucleus.

Nucleus. A single, oval or spherical and vesicular nucleus (**trophonucleus**) is seen in the middle of its body. The nucleus contains a large **endosome** surrounded by chromatin.

Electron structure of *Trypanosoma.* Vickerman (1965) has studied the structure of *Trypanosoma* under electron microscope. He has noticed a pocket-like structure at the posterior end near the basal body which is called the flagellar pocket. The flagellar pocket is believed to be the reservoir like that of *Euglena*. Its flagellum represents typical 9+2 internal fibrillar arrangement as in *Euglena*. A single, elongated, giant mitochondrion extends from its anterior to the posterior end of the body and, therefore, differentiated into anterior mitochondrion or anterior

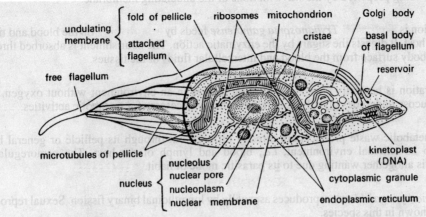

Fig. 13.4. *Trypanosoma*. An electron microscopic structure (diagrammatic).

chondriome and posterior mitochondrion or posterior chondriome. It is believed that near the basal granule, kinetoplast is formed by the posterior mitochondrion which has an extranuclear DNA. This DNA is double stranded. A single **Golgi body** is present between the flagellar pocket and the nucleus. The nucleus represents its typical structure having double layered nuclear membrane with nuclear pores. The endoplasmic reticulum is found either attached to outer nuclear membrane or free in the cytoplasm. The ribosomes are found attached to endoplasmic reticulum and also as free bodies in the cytoplasm.

POLYMORPHIC FORMS OF *TRYPANOSOMA*

Trypanosoma is a polymorphic form. Hoare (1966) has noticed as many as six morphologic stages in the life cycle of different species of *Trypanosoma* (Fig. 13.5). These forms have been named mostly on the basis of the arrangement of flagellum, its place of origin and its course through the body. However, two or more such forms occur either in one or both the hosts in the life cycle of the various species of *Trypanosoma*. Some polymorphic forms are as below :

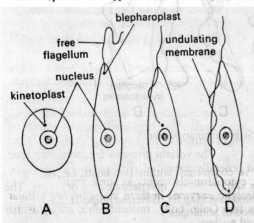

Fig. 13.5. *Trypanosoma*. Polymorphic forms.
A—Leishmanial; B—Leptomonad;
C—Crithidial; D—Trypanosome.

1. **Leishmanial (amastigote)**. It has small, oval or rounded body with a nucleus. Basal granule and kinetoplast in form of reduced dots placed in front of nucleus. Flagellum reduced, fibre-like embedded in the cytoplasm; external flagellum is not found.

2. **Leptomonad (promastigote)**. It has an elongated body with nucleus in its centre. The basal granule and kinetoplast are situated at the anterior end. A free flagellum originated from the basal granule and no undulating membrane is formed.

3. **Crithidial (epimastigote)**. Its body is short, elongated but stumpy. The basal granule and kinetoplast are situated in front of nucleus which is central. A long flagellum arises from basal granule and becomes free anteriorly. Undulating membrane ill-developed.

4. **Trypanosome (trypomastigote)**. Its body is elongated and slender. The basal granule and kinetoplast are situated at the posterior end of the body. Flagellum is large and becomes free anteriorly. The undulating membrane is well developed.

LOCOMOTION

Trypanosoma gambiense performs its locomotion by the wavy movements of the undulating membrane and by the flagellum. They swim (in blood and lymph) in the direction of the pointed end of the body, being propelled by the wave motions of the undulating membrane.

NUTRITION

Nutrition is saprozoic. *Trypanosoma gambiense* feeds by osmotrophy on the blood and tissue fluids of its host. It digests the sugars by the enzymatic action. The nourishment is absorbed through the general body surface from the blood and intercellular fluids of the tissues.

RESPIRATION

Respiration is basically anaerobic because it lives in an environment without oxygen. The absorbed glucose undergoes glycolysis to release energy necessary for metabolic activities.

EXCRETION

The metabolic waste products are directly diffused out through its pellicle or general body surface into its external environment, *i.e.,* blood and lymph of the host. The osmoregulatory mechanism is altogether wanting due to its parasitic mode of habit.

REPRODUCTION

Trypanosoma gambiense reproduces asexually by longitudinal binary fission. Sexual reproduction is not known in this species.

Longitudinal Binary Fission

In the longitudinal binary fission (Fig. 13.6), the division is initiated by basal granule (blepharoplast) and followed by the kinetoplast. Next, a new flagellum begins to grow out along the margin of the undulating membrane. The nucleus then divides and this division is followed by the longitudinal division of the cytoplasm, commencing from the anterior end and extending backwards, till the daughter individuals separate. By repeated division, the parasites increase in the blood of the vertebrate host until the blood is swarmed with them.

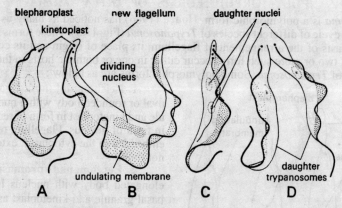

Fig. 13.6. *Trypanosoma.* Stages in binary fission.

LIFE CYCLE

The life cycle of *Trypanosoma gambiense* is completed within two hosts, *i.e.,* digenetic (Gr., *di*=double; *genos*=race), a primary vertebrate and secondary invertebrate host or vector. The vertebrate host is man and the invertebrate host is blood sucking fly, *Glassina palpalis* (Tsetse fly). *Trypanosoma gambiense* lives harmlessly in the blood of antelopes.

Part of Life Cycle in Man

When an infected fly bites a man it inoculates a few parasites in the blood of man. The parasites first live in the blood of the infected man, but later find their way into the cerebrospinal fluid. While the parasites are in the blood, the infected man develops a kind of fever termed Gambia fever, but when they reach the cerebrospinal fluid, various nervous symptoms are produced in the patient leading to a lethargic condition, which has given the name sleeping sickness to the disease. The parasites multiply by longitudinal binary fission in the blood and produce three forms of individuals, *viz.,* (i) long and thin forms with a free flagellum, (ii)short and stumpy forms with a reduced flagellum and (iii) intermediate forms. It has been observed that the parasites periodically increase and decrease in number in the blood of man. During the period of decrease the short and stumpy forms, which have great resisting power, survive the period of depression and the rest die. These short and stumpy forms are capable of development in the intermediate host, *Glossina palpalis* (Testse fly).

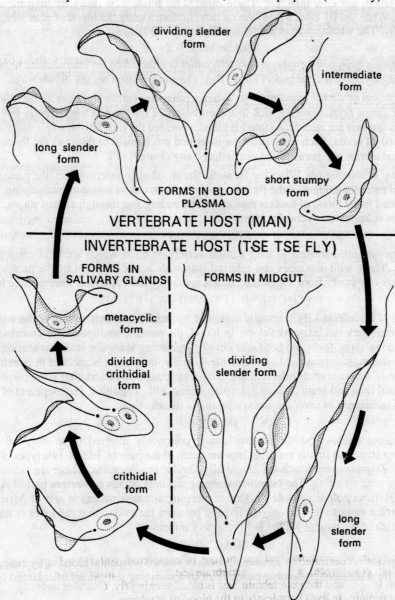

Fig. 13.7. *Trypanosoma gambiense.* Life cycle.

Part of Life Cycle in Tsetse fly

When a tsetse fly sucks the blood of an infected man, a number of parasites enter into the midgut of the fly along with the blood. These parasites remain in the midgut of the fly for a few days and start multiplying by longitudinal binary fission. After tenth to fifteenth day long slender forms appear in great numbers which move forward to the proventriculus. After several more days the trypanosomes make their way to the fly's salivary gland. In the salivary glands they become attached to the walls and undergo another rapid phase of multiplication by longitudinal binary fission and develop into crithidial forms. The crithidial forms are characterized by a shorter flagellum and undulating membrane. Flagellum and undulating membrane do not extend in the hinder part of the body. Kinetoplast and basal granule are situated above the nucleus towards the anterior end. Here the development continues for 2–5 days and the crithidial forms produce metacyclic forms (Trypanosome forms) which are now infective. These metacyclic forms pass down through the ducts and hypopharynx. When the fly bites a man, the metacyclic forms enter the blood of man along with the saliva of the fly. The whole cycle in the fly usually takes 2–30 days.

TRANSMISSION

Transmission from one vertebrate host to another is effected by an intermediate host which is a blood-sucking fly, *Glossina palpalis* (Tsetse fly). The transmission occurs in two ways.

1. **Mechanical or direct transmission.** When a tsetse fly (carrier fly) bites a man infected with *Trypanosoma*, some *Trypanosomes* stick to the proboscis of the fly and when the fly bites another man the *Trypanosomes* are introduced into his blood, provided the time between two successive bites does not exceed 24 hours. Such a transmission is termed mechanical or direct as the fly acts merely as a mechanical carrier and parasites do not undergo any changes in it.

2. **Cyclical transmission.** When the fly sucks the blood of an infected man, the parasites along with the blood enter the midgut of the fly, remain there for two days and start multiplying. Parasites can be inoculated in the blood of another man only after undergoing through a set of stages. This type of transmission is known as cyclical transmission.

RESERVOIRS

Trypanosomes are harmless to their natural vertebrate hosts which are wild antelopes, pigs, buffaloes, etc. These wild antelopes and referred mammals are not harmed by the parasite, hence, they act as reservoir hosts from which infection is spread by the **vectors** or intermediate hosts.

PATHOGENICITY AND SYMPTOMS

The bite of an infected fly is usually followed by itching and irritation near the wound, and frequently a local dark red lesion develops. In blood, the parasite multiplies and absorbs nutrients from it. After a few days, fever and headache develop, recurring at regular intervals accompanied by increasing weakness, loss of weight and anaemia. Usually, the parasites succeed in penetrating the lymphatic glands. Because of its infection, the lymphatic glands swell and after it the parasites enter the cerebrospinal fluid and brain causing a sleeping sickness like condition. Development of lethargic condition and recurrence of fever are the symptoms of its infection.

DISEASE

Trypanosoma causes trypanosomiasis; most commonly referred to as sleeping sickness leading to coma stage and finally resulting into the death of the patient. In fact, two types of diseases are caused by *Trypanosoma* which are essentially similar in symptoms. These are Gambian and Rhodesian sleeping sickness. The Gambian sleeping sickness occurs in western part of Africa and its vector is *Glossina palpalis,* while Rhodesian sleeping sickness occurs in rest of Africa and its vector is *Glossina morsitans.* The only difference between the two is that the latter is more rapid causing the death of the patient within 3–4 months of infection.

DIAGNOSIS

The diagnosis is confirmed by examining fresh or stained peripheral blood or by examining the cerebrospinal fluid obtained by lumbar puncture or by examining the extract of enlarged lymphatic glands.

TREATMENT (THERAPY)

Arsenic and antimony compounds were until recently the drugs for treatment of trypanosomiasis, but now they are rarely used except for late stages when the parasites have invaded the central nervous system. Two drugs, Bayer 205 (also called Antrypol, Germanin or Suramin and Pentamidine or Lomidine are now widely used for both treatment and prophylaxis of human infections. These drugs are low in toxicity, effective in treatment, and prevent reinfection for several months.

PREVENTION (PROPHYLAXIS)

The following measures are suggested for preventing the infection of this parasite.

1. By eradicating the vectors. The infection of this parasite can be checked by completely eradicating the secondary host (Tsetse fly). For this, the endemic areas should be kept clean and regular spray of insecticides like DDT is suggested which help in eradicating the fly.

2. Care should be taken to keep the reservoir hosts free from its infection.

3. Preventive medicines should be taken frequently and periodically which help to a great extent from its infection.

TABLE 13.1 : LIST OF SOME PATHOGENIC TRYPANOSOMES

S.No.	Name of species	Name of primary host	Site in primary host	Name of secondary host or vector	Name of disease	Distribution
1.	*Trypanosoma gambiense*	Man	Blood	*Glossina palpalis* (Tsetse fly)	African sleeping sickness	Central Africa
2.	*T. rhodesiense*	Man	Blood	*Glossina morsitans* (Tsetse fly)	Rhodesia sleeping sickness	South-eastern coastal areas of Africa
3.	*T. cruzi*	Man (children)	Blood	*Triatoma* (Bug)	Chagas' disease	South and Central America
4.	*T. brucei*	Horses, mules, donkeys, camels, cattle, swines and dogs	Blood	*Glossina morsitans* (Tsetse fly)	Nagana	Africa
5.	*T. evansi*	Horses, mules donkeys, cattle, camels, elephants	Blood	*Tabanus or Stomoxys*	Surra in horses	Widely distributed
6.	*T. equinum*	Horses	Blood	Tabanid fly	Mal de Caderas	South America
7.	*T. equiperdum*	Horses and donkeys	Blood	No intermediate host. Transmission takes place from host to host during sexual act.	Dourine	Widely distributed
8.	*T. hippicum*	Horses and mules	Blood	Flies	Murrina or Derren gadera	Panama
9.	*T. vivax*	Ruminants and horses	Blood	*Glossina* spp.	Virulent	Central and East Africa
10.	*T. simiae*	Pigs, monkeys, sheep, goats	Blood	*Glossina* spp.	Virulent	Africa

REVISION QUESTIONS

1. Describe the structure and life history of *Trypanosoma gambiense*.
2. Give an account of the structure of *Trypanosoma* as seen under electron microscope.
3. Describe the polymorphic forms, mode of transmission and pathogenic effects of *Trypanosoma*.
4. Describe some species of *Trypanosoma* in the following headings: Name of species, Name of primary host, Name of secondary host, Site of infection, Name of disease caused and distribution.
5. Write a note on various control measures of *Trypanosoma* infection.

14

Amoeba

Amoeba was first discovered by Roesel Von Rosenhof in 1775. *Amoeba* has attracted the attention of both scientists and laymen because of its everchanging shape and simple structure. It may be regarded as one of the simplest of animals since its body consists of a minute transparent asymmetrical speck of protoplasm having a nucleus but without permanent organelles. It has been studied intensively in the hope of discovering some of the fundamental features of life. In spite of its simplicity it performs all the vital activities of life such as movement, nutrition, digestion, assimilation, egestion, respiration, excretion, response to stimuli, reproduction and growth, etc. Therefore, for the study of life in its simplest form and the fundamental biological processes, *Amoeba* serves as an interesting suitable animal material. It is chosen for the study because it is easily obtained and has a transparent body which is relatively simple and large in structure and slow in locomotion. H.I. Hirschfield (1962) has given a detailed account of the biology of *Amoeba*.

AMOEBA PROTEUS
SYSTEMATIC POSITION

Phylum	...	**Protozoa**
Subphylum	...	**Sarcomastigophora**
Superclass	...	**Sarcodina**
Class	...	**Rhizopodea**
Subclass	...	**Lobosia**
Order	...	**Amoebida**
Genus	...	*Amoeba*
Species	...	*proteus*

HABIT AND HABITAT

Amoeba proteus is widely distributed. It is commonly found in the ooze or bottom mud in freshwater pools, ponds, ditches, lakes and slow streams, often in shallow water on the underside of aquatic vegetation. It is also found in damp soils. The sides of lotus ponds and the water troughs are excellent places for the collection of amoebae. It occurs in abundance in the water which contains bacteria and organic substances, such as leaves, twigs and other aquatic vegetation in abundance.

CULTURE

Amoeba may be obtained for laboratory use from a vareity of places such as organic ooze from decaying vegetation or the lower surface of the lily pads. To make a culture of *Amoeba* place some pond water, mud and leaves in 100 ml of water containing a few grains of wheat. *Amoebae* will appear after a few days, this shows the presence of cysts in the pond water. To make a pure culture boil four or five grains of wheat in 100 ml of distilled water for 10 minutes and cool for a few days; to this add some *Amoebae* from the first culture and cover with glass plate; in ten days many *Amoebae* will be formed in the pure culture.

STRUCTURE

Size and shape. *Amoeba proteus* is a one-celled microscopic animal about 0.25 mm (250 microns) in diameter and so transparent that it is invisible to the naked eyes. Under the compound microscope, it appears as an irregular, colourless, translucent mass of living animal-like jelly or protoplasm that is constantly changing its shape by sending out and withdrawing finger-like processes, the pseudopodia. The name *Amoeba* is derived from a Greek word *amoibe* which means change. The specific name *proteus* is based on the name of a mythological Greek sea-god who constantly changes his shape. Although it possesses no cell wall, it has a thin delicate outer membrane called the plasmalemma. Just beneath this is a non-granular layer, the ectoplasm which encloses the granular endoplasm. However, there is no line of demarcation between the ectoplasm and endoplasm.

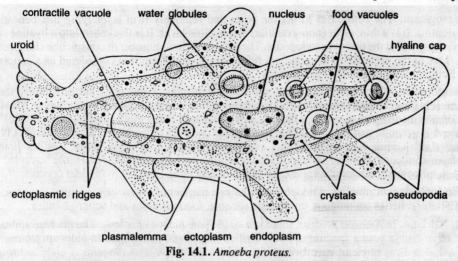

Fig. 14.1. *Amoeba proteus.*

Pseudopodia. Pseudopodia (Gr., *pseudos* = false; *podos* = foot) are temporary finger-like and blunt extensions which are constantly being given out or withdrawn by the body. They are broad to cylindrical with blunt rounded tips and are composed of both ectoplasm and endoplasm. Such pseudopodia are called lobopodia. These are formed as a result of liquefaction and flowing forward of the cytoplasm. As many pseudopodia are formed simultaneously, *Amoeba proteus* is a polypodial species.

Plasmalemma. The plasmalemma is very thin, delicate, invisible, elastic external cell membrane. The thickness of plasmalemma may be from 1/4 micron (0.00025 mm) to 2 microns. It is composed of a double layer of lipid and protein molecules. According to Schneider and Wohlfarth Batterman (1959) the plasmalemma consists of two darkly staining layers, about 200 A° thick separated by a clear layer. Other filaments, about 80 A° in diameter, extend 1100 to 1700 A° out into the medium from the plasmalemma. The outer layer of plasmalemma is supposed to contain mucoprotein. Plasmalemma can regenerate itself when broken. This membrane is selectively permeable and it regulates an exchange of substances such as water, O_2 and CO_2 between the animal and the surrounding medium. It also retains the protoplasm within the cell. Numerous fine, ridge-like projections from the outer surface of plasmalemma are supposed to be adhesive and binding the organism to its substratum.

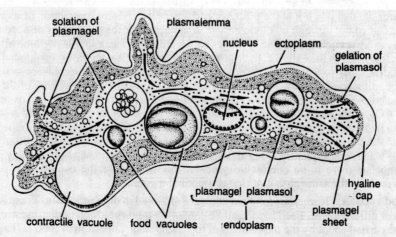

Fig. 14.2. *Amoeba proteus* showing the solation and gelation of cytoplasm during amoeboid movement. (After **Mast**).

Cytoplasm. Inside the plasmalemma, there is a dense mass of cytoplasm containing several organelles. It is differentiated fairly into two district zones, an outer ectoplasm and an inner endoplasm.

Ectoplasm. The ectoplasm forms the outer and relatively firm layer lying just beneath the plasmalemma. It is a thin, clear (non-granular) and hyaline layer. It is thickened into a hyaline cap at the advancing end at the tips of pseudopodia. The ectoplasm has a number of conspicuous longitudinal ridges. Due to the presence of longitudinal ridges in the ectoplasm it is considered as a supporting layer. Ectoplasm lends form to the cell body.

Endoplasm. The endoplasm forms the main body mass completely surrounded by the ectoplasm. It is granular heterogeneous fluid containing bipyramidal crystals. According tc Mast, the endoplasm is made up of an outer, relatively stiff plasmagel and a more fluid inner plasmasol. The plasmagel is granular and more solid but its granules show no movement. The plasmasol is highly granular fluid having various inclusions and it shows streaming movements. Besides granules endoplasm contains a number of important inclusions such as nucleus, contractile vacuole, food vacuoles, mitochondria, Golgi complex, fat globules and plate-like or bipyramidal crystals.

Endoplasmic organelles. Endoplasm contains a number of organelles or structures suspended in it. These organelles are nucleus, contractile vacuole, food vacuoles and water globules.

1. Nucleus. In *Amoeba proteus,* there is a single conspicuous nucleus. The nucleus appears as a biconcave disc in young specimens but it is often folded and convoluted in older specimens. The nucleus has a firm nuclear membrane or nuclear envelope and contains a clear achromatic substance with minute chromatin granules or chromidia distributed uniformly near the surface. The nucleoplasm is small in quantity. Such a nucleus is called massive or granular nucleus. Electron microscopic studies show a honeycomb lattice under double layered nuclear envelope. Within the nucleus are many small spherical chromosomes said to number over 500. The position of nucleus in the endoplasm is not definite, but changes during the movement of *Amoeba.* During the life of an *Amoeba,* before the period of reproduction, the nucleus plays an important role in the metabolic activities of the cell. This has been proved by experiments in which the animal was cut in two. The streaming of cytoplasm ceases within a few minutes in the piece without a nucleus but is resumed after a few hours. The enucleated *Amoeba* may attach itself to the substratum and exhibits irritability although its reponses to stumuli are modified. Food bodies are engulfed and digested in an apparently normal manner but death finally ensues. The part with the nucleus continues its life as a normal *Amoeba.* An isolated nucleus will not survive. Thus, the nucleus and cytoplasm are interdependent and their separation ultimately results in the death of both.

2. Contractile vacuole. The outer part of the endoplasm near the posterior end contains a clear, rounded and pulsating vacuole filled with a watery fluid. This vacuole, called the contractile vacuole, is enclosed by a unit membrane. It is not fixed but circulates in the endoplasm. It arises near the hind end of the animal and it grows in size probably by fusion of a number of smaller vacuoles. As it continues to grow, it comes to lie in the peripheral plasmagel layer where it remains as the endoplasm flows onwards, so that it is left at the posterior end where it bursts by contraction of its wall and the contents are forced out through no obvious pore. It appears near the point of its disappearance, then it travels towards the nucleus and finally moves backwards. The vacuole fills rhythmically with fluid and then discharges it to the exterior. In protozoans the contractile vacuole is surrounded by a crowd of mitochondria, close to which tiny vacuoles of water appear, which then coalesce to form a larger vacuole. The mitochondria provide the energy for actual formation and working of the vacuole. It expands (diastole) and contracts (systole) rhythmically and serves for excretion and osmoregulation. It removes CO_2 and waste substances from the animal, it is not only excretory and respiratory but mostly it is a hydrostatic organ because it constantly removes the water which the *Amoeba* absorbs, thus, it regulates the osmotic pressure, and it harmonizes the tension between the protoplasm and the surrounding water, consequently it regulates the weight of the animal also. In many marine and parasitic amoebae there is no contractile vacuole, this is because the osmotic pressure of their protoplasm is about the same as that of the surrounding medium.

3. Food vacuoles. Numerous food vacuoles are scattered in the endoplasm. These are non-contractile and of different size. Each food vacuole contains a morsel of food under digestion. The food vacuoles are carried about by the movements of the endoplasm. Digestion of food takes place inside the food vacuole. The endoplasm also contains some waste substances and grains of sand.

4. Water globules. These are several small, spherical, colourless and non-contractile vacuoles filled with water.

Ultrastructure or Structure by electron microscope. The electron microscopic studies have not revealed the occurrence of two colloidal phases, sol and gel, in the endoplasm. It is believed that it is the ectoplasm which is in the gel state, while endoplasm is in the sol state. De Bruyn has proposed that the protoplasm can be presumed as a "three dimensional network" of protein chains, linked together by cross linkages of side chains. The gel state is due to the fully extended protein chains and the sol state is due to the contraction of such chains. The structure of nucleus of *Amoeba proteus* is like that of a honeycomb-lattice. The nuclear membrane is double-layered having pores. The nucleoplasm contains a few nucleoli and a large number of chromosomes. Various organelles, characteristic of an animal cell, are also seen. The mitochondria are more or less oval with tubular cristae. The Golgi bodies appear as groups of sac-like tubules. The lysosomes are found scattered as minute membrane-bound spherical bodies. The endoplasmic reticulum forms a network of tubules as well as vesicles. The endoplasm contains reserve food material in the form of plate-like or bipyramidal crystals. Contractile vacuole is seen surrounded by several mitochondria and vesicles.

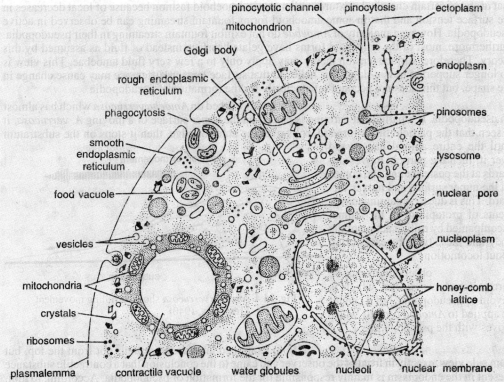

Fig. 14.3. *Amoeba.* A diagrammatic representation of the structure of a portion as revealed by electron microscope.

LOCOMOTION

Amoeba exhibits characteristic amoeboid movement by the formation of finger-like temporary processes, the pseudopodia. The pseudopodia of *Amoeba* are known as lobopodia due to their blunt, finger-like appearance and rounded tips. The ectoplasm forms a blunt projection into which the endoplasm flows to form a pseudopodium at the advancing end which is then spoken as the anterior end. Usually several small pseudopodia are formed at first, one of these enlarges and the others disappear. The protoplasm which enters pseudopodia is naturally withdrawn from other parts, so that the animal not only changes its body shape but also its position, thus, pseudopodia bring about change of shape and position of the animal. These are called amoeboid movements which occur not only in *Amoeba* but in other Protozoa and some amoeboid cells of Metazoa. How pseudopodia are formed and bring about locomotion is explained by many theories.

Theories of Amoeboid Movement

Many theories have been put forward to explain the formation of pseudopodia and the process of locomotion. A brief description of these theories is as follows :

1. Adhesion theory. According to this theory, locomotion in *Amoeba* is performed by adhesion similar to drop of water which spreads irregularly on uneven glass plate. The protoplasm flows, like the fluid of the drop, in the path of greater adhesion. Due to adhesive properties pseudopodia generally grow in the paths of adhesion. However, this explanation is not satisfactory and does not hold good as the pseudopodia are sometimes given out independently even without any contact with any surface.

2. Surface tension theory. This theory was first of all advocated by Berthold (1886) and later supported by Butschli (1894) and Rhumbler(1898). According to this theory, protoplasm is a fluid, there must exist at the surface of the protoplasmic mass a tension (surface tension) acting to make the mass spherical. Wherever on such a sphere the surface tension is locally lowered by external or internal changes, the protoplasm flows out in the form of a projection, the pseudopodium. In such a projection the protoplasm will flow forward in the centre and back along the sides. In other words there is a fountain streaming of protoplasm in the pseudopodium. This theory is supported by the facts that drops of certain chemical mixtures will move in amoeboid fashion because of local decreases in the surface tension and that in some amoeboid forms fountain streaming can be observed in active pseudopodia. However, majority of *Amoebae* do not exhibit fountain streaming in their pseudopodia. Furthermore, most of the amoeboid forms have gelated surface instead of fluid as assumed by this theory. Therefore, surface tension theory may apply only to a few very fluid amoebae. This view is no longer supported now-a-days. It is believed that surface tension difference may cause change in the shape, but this does not account satisfactorily for the formation of pseudopodia.

3. Rolling movement theory. Jennings (1904) worked on *Amoeba verrucosa* which has almost no pseudopodia. If a particle of carmine is placed on the upper surface of a moving *A. verrucosa*, it is seen that the particle flows forward, rolls over the anterior edge, then it stops on the substratum until the entire animal has passed over it, then the particle moves up-wards at the posterior end and comes on the upper surface and moves forward. This is due to streaming movements of protoplasm of the animal accompanied by rolling action of the body and these two processes bring about locomotion.

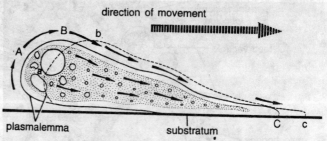

Jennings' observations may be correct for *A. verrucosa*, which is devoid of pseudopodia, but it cannot be applied to *Amoeba proteus* which moves with the pseudopodia.

Fig. 14.4. *Amoeba verrucosa* showing rolling movement (**Jennings**, 1940).

4. Contraction theory. Dellinger (1906) examined an *amoeba proteus* not from the top, but from side view, exactly in front of the observer and came to the conclusion that a contractile substance present in the endoplasm is mainly responsible for the formation of pseudopodia. According to him, the *Amoeba* extends the anterior end to form a pseudopodium, then it lifts it and places it on the substratum, then it contracts this pseudopodium which causes the body to move forward. This process is repeated. Thus, the animal is pulled from in front and pushed from behind due to contractions of a

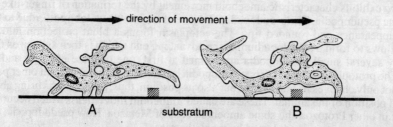

contractile substance located in the endoplasm as a coarse reticulum. In this way the *Amoeba* actually walks putting one foot out, then another. According to Dellinger, pseudopodia are formed by an exchange of water between the ectoplasm and endoplasm which causes alternate contractions and expansions. Dellinger proposed it as a walking locomotion because, in a profile, *Amoeba* appears to walk on the tips of its leg-like pseudopodia. The contraction theory is now discarded.

5. **Gel-sol theory.** Pantin (1923) studied the marine *Amoeba limax*, it forms a pseudopodium by swelling of protoplasm due to secretion of acid and absorption of water at that place. As the pseudopodium forms and extends in front, a gelatinous ectoplasmic tube is formed. At the posterior end this ectoplasmic tube changes into endoplasm. The ectoplasmic tube contracts and forces the endoplasm to stream to the front, this brings about locomotion.

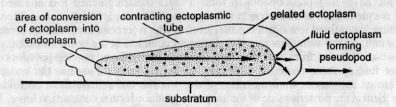

Fig. 14.6. Locomotion in *Amoeba limax* (**Pantin**). A single pseudopod is formed, the ectoplasmic tube forces endoplasm forward.

6. **Sol-gel theory or change of viscosity theory.** This theory was strongly advocated by Hyman (1917) and also adopted by Pantin (1923—1926) and Mast (1925). It is supposed to be the best to explain the locomotion in *Amoeba*. This theory is based on the reversible change of protoplasm from sol to gel state. According to Mast, amoeboid movement is brought about by four processes, (i) attachment of *Amoeba* to the substratum, (ii) gelation of plasmasol at the anterior advancing pseudopodia, (iii) solation of plasmagel at the posterior end and receding pseudopodia, (iv) contraction of plasmagel tube at the posterior end to drive the plasmasol forwards. As the plasmasol changes into plasmagel at the anterior end, the plasmagel tube extends forwards and is converted into plasmasol at the posterior end, the plasmagel tube drives the plasmasol forwards to form a pseudopodium. A thin plasmagel sheet persists intact at the anterior end and prevents the plasmasol from reaching the plasmalemma, but this sheet may break at times so that the plasmasol streams through

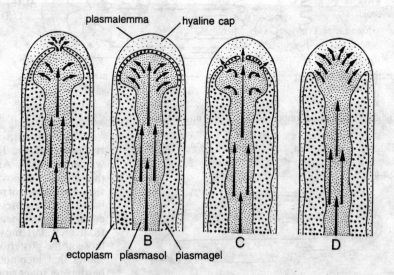

Fig. 14.7. Diagrams illustrating the idea of **Mast** about the cytoplasmic flow during the formation of pseudopodium in *Amoeba proteus*. A—Plasmagel beneath the cap dissolves and plasmasol rushes through the gap; B—Plasmasol may persist as a thin layer; C—Break only at certain points; D—Dissovle completely.

filling the hyaline cap, but soon the plasmasol gelates to form a new plasmagel sheet. Pseudopodia are formed because plasmagel is elastic and under tension, it is pushed out where the elastic strength is the lowest. During locomotion of *Amoeba* the elastic strength of plasmagel is the highest at the sides, intermediate at the posterior end, and lowest at the anterior end; this results in an elongated shape of the animal and a forward extension of the anterior end to bring about locomotion.

7. **Molecular folding-unfolding theory.** Recently, Goldacre and Lorch (1950) have explained the phenomena of solation and gelation on the molecular basis. According to Goldacre and **Lorch**, the contraction of the plasmagel tube cannot supply enough force for moving the animal. They state that all proteins gelate when their molecules unfold and they solate when their molecules fold. In the fluid endoplasm the protein molecules lie folded compactly, these molecules unfold at the tip of the advancing pseudopodia to form a layer of straightened and attached molecules. Posteriorly the protein molecules begin to fold again and they impart a contraction force. In *Amoeba* the contraction is confined towards the posterior side which forces the contracted proteins towards the anterior end. As the animal moves, the plasmagel contracts at the posterior end, it changes into plasmasol which flows in front, and then by gelation it forms the advancing pseudopod anteriorly. With further folding these posterior molecules solate and pass forward in the endoplasm. Such molecules attract substances from the sides of the *Amoeba* and release them on folding again to accumulate them at the posterior side of the animal to produce further contraction force. The rear part of the cell is squeezed like a tube of toothpaste, this drives the plasmasol to the front end where it forces out a pseudopod. Attachment of the animal to the substratum is necessary for locomotion. It is supposed that the energy for the movement of *Amoeba,* folding and unfolding of protein molecules is provided by adenosine triphosphate (ATP), a substance which has stored chemical energy and which is known to provide energy for contraction of muscles in Metazoa. This explanation of locomotion appears satisfactory since it shows that the mechanism of pseudopod formation and muscle contraction is similar.

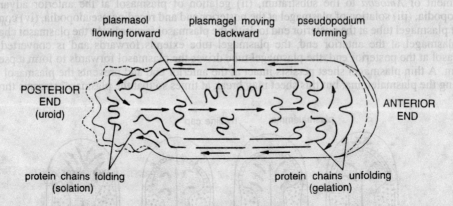

protein chains folding   protein chains unfolding
(solation)   (gelation)

Fig. 14.8. Diagram illustrating amoeboid movement on the basis of folding and unfolding of protein chains.

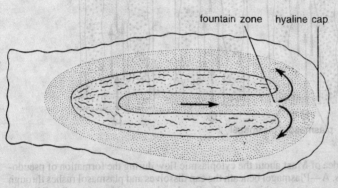

Fig. 14.9. Diagram illustrating the amoeboid movement on the basis of fountain zone theory (After **Allen**).

8. **Fountain-zone contraction theory.** This theory was proposed by Allen (1962) that amoeboid movement is a slow contraction of molecules is based on the observation that endoplasmic molecules near the front end start moving before those at the posterior end. This shows that locomotion cannot be due to squeezing from behind forwards as claimed in some other theories. The endoplasm contains long protein chains which undergo contrac-

tion at the anterior end and here the plasmasol is converted into plasmagel. In this plasmagel the protein chains are folded by which the gel state results. It is believed that at the region near the tip of the forming pseudopodium the everting plasmasol changes into plasmagel to form a wall or fountain zone, and this anterior region develops tension which is transmitted to the hinder end of the endoplasm. At the posterior end the protein chains unfold by which the plasmagel is converted into plasmasol. Thus, the animal is pulled forward by the contraction or tension at the anterior end. It is essential for the surface of the *Amoeba* to temporarily adhere to the substratum because internal streaming alone cannot cause locomotion.

9. **Views of Rinaldi and Jahn (1963).** Rinaldi and Jahn (1963) have analysed motion pictures of granule movements in advancing pseudopodia and observations given in support of theories of Mast (1925) and Allen (1962). They have strongly criticised the fountain-zone theory of Allen and supported the concept as proposed by Pantin and Mast. They have advocated that during movement when plasmagel is converted into plasmasol at the posterior end then due to contraction in the plasmagel a hydraulic pressure is exerted on the plasmasol. This pressure remains very less in the anterior end, moderate in the middle and very high in the posterior end of *Amoeba*. Due to this pressure the plasmagel in the anterior end breaks resulting into a forward flow of plasmasol which forms pseudopodium. Since, there occurs constant conversion of plasmagel into plasmasol at the posterior end and the pressure remains less at the anterior end the plasmasol flows forward and forms pseudopodium which brings about locomotion (Fig. 14.10).

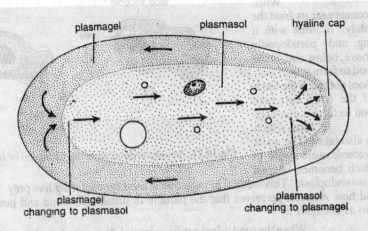

Fig. 14.10. Diagram illustrating the amoeboid movement on the basis of hydraulic pressure theory of **Rinaldi** and **Jahn** (1963).

10. **Views of Wolpert, Gingley and Garrod (1968).** Wolpert, Gingley and Garrod (1968) have again confirmed the theory of Mast with the comment that the concept of amoeboid movement as suggested by Pantin and Mast is essentially correct. However, they have said that the plasmalemma of *Amoeba* is very elastic in nature which helps in the formation of pseudopodia to affect locomotion.

Barrington (1967) has concluded that the biochemical principles involving in *Amoeba's* activity have something in common with those involved in other types of movements. The energy needed for it comes form ATPs.

NUTRITION

An *Amoeba* is unable to form its food from simple substances, but it requires ready-made organic substances for food; such a mode of nutrition in which solid organic particles are ingested is called **zootrophic** or **holozoic.** The food of *Amoeba* consists of algal cells and filaments, bacteria, other protozoans, small metazoans such as rotifers and nematodes and organic matter. Smaller flagellates and ciliates appear to constitute the favourite food of *Amoeba*. *Amoeba proteus* does not feed on diatoms, as is often claimed. *Amoeba* exhibits a choice for food and it can discriminate between inorganic particles and organic food. If a particle of carbon is fixed to the food, the animal will ingest the food and leave the carbon particle out. There is no mouth but food is ingested at any point which

96

Invertebrate Zoology

is generally at the anterior advancing end. The nutrition involves a number of processes, *viz.,* ingestion, digestion, assimilation, dissimilation and egestion.

1. Ingestion No definite regions or organelles for food intake are present. The food is captured by pseudopodia, usually by the formation of food cup, in which a pseudopodium embraces the prey from each side while a thin sheet advances over it from above pinning it to the substratum. The cup is then completed below and the food is enclosed. Food particles may be engulfed at any point on the surface of the body, but is usually taken in at what may be called the temporary anterior end, *i.e.,* the part of the body toward the direction of locomotion. According to Rhumbler (1930), ingestion in *Amoeba* takes place in many ways depending upon the nature of the food. The following methods of ingestion are employed:

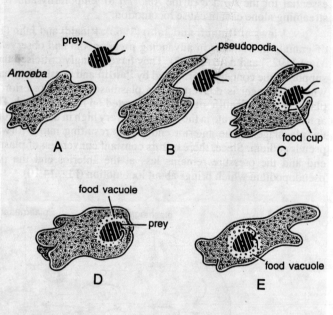

Fig.14.11. *Amoeba proteus* showing formation of food vacuole.

(i) Circumvallation. When an *Amoeba* comes near its food the part immediately in line with it stops moving, and pseudopodia are formed above, below and on the sides of the food to form a food cup, the food cup does not touch the food, but edges of the food cup fuse around the food to form a non-contractile food vacuole into which some water is also taken. The walls of the food vacuole were made of ectoplasm which becomes internal and changes into endoplasm. This method of ingestion is used for capturing live prey. It is, however, not understood how *Amoeba* perceives that the particle is suitable for food and puts forward the pseudopodia so as to engulf it.

(ii) Circumfluence. When the food is less active or immobile, a pseudopodium comes in contact with the food to form a food cup above it and pinning it down to the substratum, the cup is then completed below to enclose the food in a food vacuole. By repeating this process the *Amoeba* can ingest and roll up long filaments of algae. In other species of *Amoeba* food is ingested by import and invagination.

(iii) Import. In *Amoeba verrucosa* food comes into contact with the animal and sinks passively into the body. It absorbs and devours filamentous algae in this way.

(iv) Invagination. *Amoeba verrucosa* comes in contact with food and adheres to it, the ectoplasm along with food is invaginated as a tube into the endoplasm, and the food particle is sucked in, the plasmalemma disappears and ectoplasm changes into endoplasm.

The newly ingested organism may remain active for a time in the large primary food vacuole. Within an hour the primary food vacuoles break down into smaller secondary vacuoles, these subdivide into numerous minute vacuoles which form a large portion of the endoplasmic content.

(v) Pinocytosis. When the ingestion of fluid material in bulk takes place by the cell through the plasma membrane, the process is known as pinocytosis (Gr., *pinein* = to drink). The process of pinocytosis was first of all observed by Mast and Doyle (1934) in *Amoeba proteus.* By pinocytosis the animalcule (amoebae) absorb the high molecular compounds from the outer environment. Pinocytosis does not take place through the whole surface of the body of the amoeba. It is understood that plasmalemma along with the colloidal food material forms pinocytosis channels which run from the surface deep into the endoplasm. The internal ends of the channels then break off forming pinocytosis vesicle or pinosomes containing engulfed food material. The pinosomes, later on, are transported to the interior of the cell where they are fused with the lysosomes. It is yet to be confirmed whether pinocytosis is a normal means of ingestion in *Amoeba*.

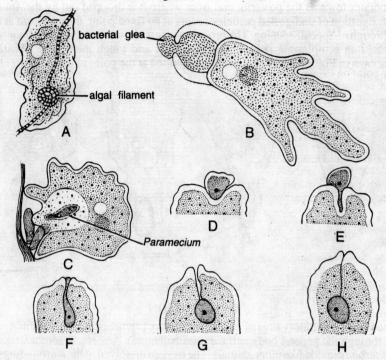

Fig. 14.12. A—*Amoeba* ingesting by import; B—*Amoeba* feeding by circumfluence; C—*Amoeba* feeding by circumvallation; D, E, F, G, and H—*Amoeba* ingesting by invagination.

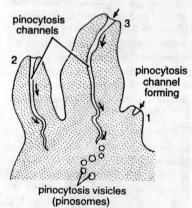

Fig. 14.13. Pinocytosis in *Amoeba*.

2. Digestion. Digestion takes place in a primary food vacuole after it gets embedded in the endoplasm. The contents of the food vacuole are at first acidic due to HCl, but later they become alkaline, living food dies in the acid phase. The protoplasm secretes enzymes into the vacuoles which convert the proteins into amino acids, starch into soluble sugar, and fats into fatty acids and glycerol. The presence of some enzymes, *e.g.*, proteases (protein-splitting enzymes), amylases (starch-digesting enzymes) and lipases (fat-splitting enzymes) have been demonstrated in *Amoeba*. When the digested food is reduced to molecular form then the food vacuole buds off smaller and smaller secondary food vacuoles which carry away the digested food.

The digestion of food in *Amoeba* is said to be intracellular in contrast to the extracellular digestion in higher animals, like earthworm and frog, taking place outside the cells in the cavity of an alimentary canal.

3. Assimilation. The digested food, water and minerals are absorbed by the surrounding protoplasm by a simple process of diffusion. In *Amoeba* the food vacuoles constantly move about in streaming endoplasm by cyclosis and directly supply nourishment to all parts of the cell. In the protoplasm, the digested food gets assimilated to build new protoplasm. The amino acids are built up to form living protoplasm; sugar, fatty acids and glycerol provide energy. This ability to form living protoplasm from simple substances is a fundamental property of living matter.

4. Dissimilation. The living protoplasm is broken down constantly by oxidation to produce heat, kinetic energy and waste products. Complex molecules of protoplasm are broken down by dissimilation to produce energy for various activities of the animal.

5. Egestion. The undigested residue of food vacuoles is waste which is heavier than protoplasm, hence, it gravitates towards the posterior end from where it is dropped out by the *Amoeba* moving away from it. Egestion of undigested particles occurs at no fixed point, they pass out at any point on the surface through no special opening. The process of egestion is not so simple in *Amoeba verrucosa*, which possesses an ectoplasmic pellicle that is a thick and tough membrane. Waste pellets are extruded as shown in Fig. 14.14. A new pellicle is formed at the point of exit to prevent the outflow of the endoplasm.

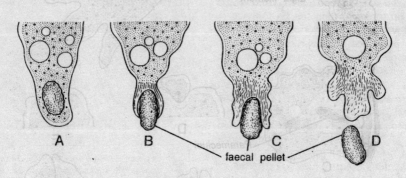

Fig. 14.14. *Amoeba verrucosa* showing various stages of egestion.

RESPIRATION

Amoeba has no respiratory organs and no respiratory pigments. Respiration in *Amoeba* occurs by diffusion through the general body surface (plasmalemma). *Amoeba* is aerobic, takes in oxygen and gives off carbon dioxide like other animals. The oxygen dissolved in the surrounding water passes into the cytoplasm of *Amoeba* by diffusion. Since the concentration of oxygen in the water is higher than that in the *Amoeba's* cytoplasm, oxygen constantly enters and is immediately used up in the burning of foods. Thus, the concentration of oxygen within the animal always remains lower than that in the outside water, and oxygen continuously enters the animal and is available for energy requirements. During metabolic activities the oxygen burns or oxidises the living matter or cytoplasm of *Amoeba* and breaks it into simpler compounds. As a result, water, carbon dioxide and urea are formed and energy is liberated which is stored in the high energy bonds of ATP and used in the life activities of the organism. Carbon dioxide diffuses to the outside because it is always at a high concentration within the body of *Amoeba* than in the surrounding water. If an *Amoeba* is placed in hydrogen instead of oxygen, then movements cease and death results, if carbon dioxide is introduced in place of oxygen then the *Amoeba* first encysts but finally dies.

EXCRETION

The oxidation of carbohydrates and fats results in the production of metabolic wastes, carbon dioxide and water. In *Amoeba,* the by-product of oxidation of proteins is ammonia and carbon dioxide and less often urea. Carbon dioxide and ammonia are soluble in water and these are excreted out through the plasmalemma by diffusion in the surrounding water or in the water discharged by the contractile vacuole.

OSMOREGULATION

Osmoregulation is a process in which the water contents of the protoplasm are controlled. The regulation of water contents in the protoplasm of *Amoeba* is performed by the contractile vacuole. The protoplasm of *Amoeba* is more concentrated than the surrounding water, so that a regular water current enters its body by osmosis through the semi-permeable plasmalemma. If the excess of water is not expelled, would lead to the rupture of the animal. This excess of water is collected by the contractile vacuole and expelled out of the protoplasm. The disappearance of one vacuole is followed by the production of a new one. The regulation of water in the protoplasm maintains an osmotic equilibrium with the surrounding water. The absence of contractile vacuole in most marine amoebae may be due to the fact that the salt concentration of the protoplasm is almost equivalent to that of the surrounding medium so that water does not accumulate in the protoplasm. Marine amoebae develop contractile vacuole when they are placed in freshwater. On the other hand, if freshwater amoebae are transferred to salt water their contractile vacuoles decrease and finally disappear altogether. Thus, it is probable that the chief function of the contractile vacuole is to regulate the water contents of *Amoeba*.

METABOLISM

Amoeba takes in food and O_2 from which it makes protoplasm, then the protoplasm is broken down into waste products and kinetic energy is produced; these processes involve many complex chemical reactions, the sum total of which is called metabolism. The processes which use energy and build up protoplasm are known as anabolism and those which break down protoplasm to release energy and produce waste products are called katabolism. The waste products of katabolism are urea, CO_2, H_2O and minerals. In metabolism the nucleus controls the assimilation of food, and the cytoplasm carries on the

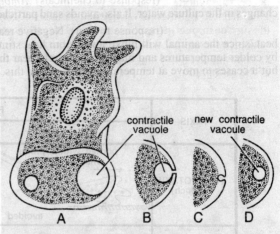

Fig.14.15. Section through the body of *Amoeba* showing contractile vacuole in systole (A, B and C) and early diastole (D).

katabolic phase. The metabolic processes exhibited by *Amoeba* (Fig. 14.16) are ingestion, digestion, egestion, absorption, circulation, assimilation, dissimilation, secretion, excretion and respiration.

BEHAVIOUR

There are no special structures for the reception of stimuli in *Amoeba* still it responds to various kinds of stimuli. The responses of *Amoeba* to stimuli or changes in its environment, either internal or external, constitute its behaviour. The responses or reactions of *Amoeba* to stimuli are due to the fundamental property of protoplasm called irritability. All changes in the environmental conditions are termed as stimuli or irritations and the property of response to stimuli is called irritability or sensibility. The behaviour of *Amoeba* involves change in shape, locomotion, food getting (ingestion of food), avoiding of unfavourable environment, hunger and so on. Its responses to different forms of sitmuli vary. The responses to stimuli are called taxes (singular, taxis). A taxis may be either positive, in which the organism moves towards the stimulus, or negative, in which the organism moves away from the

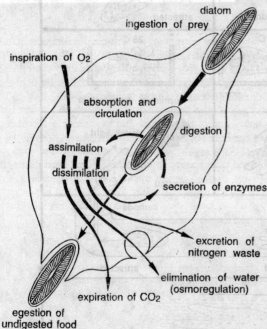

Fig.14.16. Diagram showing various steps of metabolism going on in a living *Amoeba*.

stimulus. *Amoeba proteus* exhibits both types of taxes, positive as well as negative, specifically to different stimuli. With respect to the kinds of stimuli, the taxes are classified as follows :

1. **Thigmotaxis** (response to contact or touch). The response of *Amoeba* to contact is varied. *Amoeba* reacts negatively when touched at any point with a solid object, the part affected contracts and the animal moves away. A floating *Amoeba* with spread pseudopodia, responds positively to contact with the solid object by fastening to it. Contact with the food also results positive reactions.

The creeping *Amoeba* touches lightly with a needle responds negatively by drawing back and moving away. *Amoeba*, therefore, reacts negatively to a strong mechanical stimulus and positively to a weak one.

2. Chaemotaxis (response to chemicals). *Amoeba* reacts negatively to many chemicals and changes in the culture water. It also avoids sand particles. It responds positively to the food organisms.

3. Thermotaxis (response to heat). Negative reactions result if *Amoeba* is locally affected by heat, since the animal will move away from heat stimuli. Amoeba's rate of locomotion is lessened by colder temperatures and may cease entirely near the freezing point. Its rate increases up to 30°C but it ceases to move at temperatures higher than this.

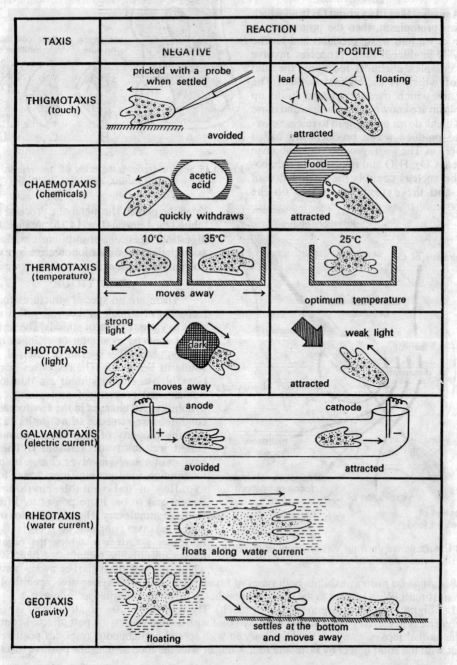

Fig. 14.17. *Amoeba*. Reactions to various stimuli. Arrows indicate the direction of movement.

4. Phototaxis (response to light). *Amoeba* moves away from strong light and may change its direction a number of times to avoid it, but it may react positively to a weak light.

5. Galvanotaxis (response to electric current). When an electric current is passed through the water containing *Amoeba,* it stops moving, withdraws its pseudopodia and becomes globular. In the weak electric current it moves towards the negative pole (cathode) and, thus, avoids positive pole (anode).

6. Rheotaxis (response to water current). *Amoeba* shows positive rheotaxis as it tends to move in line with the water current.

7. Geotaxis (response to gravity). *Amoeba* exhibits positive geotaxis since it moves toward the centre of gravity like other animals.

<h2 style="text-align:center">REPRODUCTION</h2>

Reproduction in *Amoeba* is a periodic process taking place at intervals. The duration between successive phases of reproduction essentially depends on the rate of growth of *Amoeba*. When *Amoeba* attains a maximum size, *i.e.,* 0.25 mm it starts to reproduce. Reproduction in *Amoeba* chiefly occurs by asexual method, *i.e.,* by binary fission, multiple fission and sporulation. *Amoeba* does not reproduce sexually by mating, *i.e.,* by the fusion of cells or gametes.

1. Binary fission. Binary fission is the most common mode of reproduction. It results in the division of parent amoeba into two daughter amoebae. The division involves the nuclear division followed by cytoplasmic division. *Amoeba* undergoes binary fission during favourable conditions of food and temperature. Binary fission occurs when the organism reaches a maximum limit of size, it becomes sluggish and spherical with its surface covered with small radially arranged pseudopodia. In binary fission the contractile vacuole ceases to function, the nucleus divides mitoticaily, then the cell constricts in the middle to form two daughter cells. There is a correlation between nuclear division and changes in external characters. The amoeba divides by mitosis and involves the prophase, metaphase, anaphase and telophase.

In the prophase stage, the nucleus becomes oval and numerous fine pseudopodia are formed radiating in all the directions. The cytoplasm loses its transparency to a large extent and the contractile

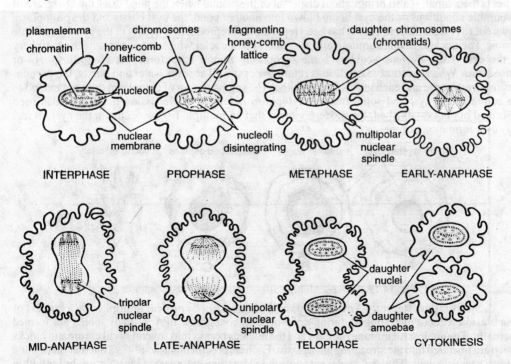

Fig. 14.18. *Amoeba.* Stages in binary fission.

vacuole disappears. The honeycomb-like lattice just below the nuclear membrane first fragments and then disappears. The nucleoli disintegrate. The chromosomes emerge in the central nucleoplasm.

The metaphase stage is marked by the arrangement of the chromosomes at the equator. Each chromosome splits longitudinally and becomes paired. The chromosomes, on each side, become attached to the spindle fibres arising from multiple poles, situated within the nuclear membrane. Externally the pseudopodia begin to thicken.

In the anaphase stage, the daughter chromosomes move towards opposite poles and the constriction of the nuclear membrane begins in the middle. The pseudopodia become thick and coarse.

In the telophase stage, the transverse constriction of the nuclear membrane is completed and the nucleus is finally divided into two daughter nuclei. In each daughter nucleus the lattice is formed just below the nuclear membrane and the nucleoli reappear. Next follows cytokinesis. *Amoeba* stretches and constricts in the middle. Numerous large pseudopodia are formed at opposite poles, drawing both the daughter amoebae in opposite directions. Ultimately the amoeba divides into two daughter amoebae. The pseudopodia become normal, then each daughter amoeba acquires a contractile vacuole and begins to grow. At about 24°C the process takes about 20 to 30 minutes.

A very interesting feature of binary fission, observed in the division of nucleus, is the existence of multipolar nuclear spindle in the metaphase, which is reduced to tripolar nuclear spindle in the mid-anaphase stage and finally reduced to unipolar nuclear spindle at the end of late anaphase.

In *Amoeba* reproducing by binary fission, the parent becomes completely merged in the offspring. Thus, there exists a continuity of life, so that *Amoeba* is potentially immortal. However, death may be due to starvation, accident or some other misfortune.

2. Multiple fission. *Amoeba* reproduces by multiple fission during unfavourable conditions of food and temperature (*i.e.,* scarcity of food and rise and fall in temperature). Pseudopodia are withdrawn, the animal becomes rounded, streaming movements of endoplasm cease, larger granules dissolve and protoplasm becomes minutely granular, distinction between ectoplasm and endoplasm is lost. The animal begins to rotate and secretes a cyst inside to which two new layers are added to complete a three-layered cyst, then the rotation of the animal stops. The cyst is a resting stage and it protects the animal, it also brings about dispersal of the animal when the pond dries up. On return of favourable conditions or the cyst being blown into another pond, the cyst bursts and the protoplasm flows out to reform the *Amoeba*. It has been reported that reproduction occurs in the cyst by multiple fission. The nucleus divides amitotically into 500 to 600 nuclei which move towards the periphery of the cell. Each nucleus acquires some cytoplasm around it to form pseudopodiospores or amoebulae. When favourable conditions return the cyst wall absorbs water and bursts, the pseudopodiospores escape and each grows into *Amoeba*. The segmentation of cytoplasm does not extend to the centre of the cyst and some residual cytoplasm is left. Multiple fission in the cyst has been described but not established, the modern view is that no multiple fission occurs in the cyst, in fact only cyst formation occurs.

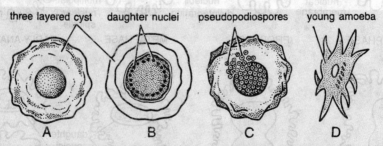

three layered cyst   daughter nuclei   pseudopodiospores   young amoeba

A   B   C   D

Fig. 14.19. *Amoeba.* Multiple fission during encysted condition.

3. Sporulation. Recently Taylor has described that *Amoeba proteus* multiplies by a process of sporulation without encystment, during unfavourable conditions. In *A. proteus* spores are formed internally. The nuclear membrane ruptures and the nucleus breaks into several small chromatin blocks which are liberated into the streaming endoplasm. Each chromatin block acquires a nuclear membrane to form a new nucleus. The new nuclei get surrounded by some cytoplasm to form amoebulae within the parent body. Each amoebula is surrounded by a spore case to form a spore. About 200 such spores may be formed within a single parent. Finally the parent body disintegrates and the spores are set free which remain inactive for some time. On the return of favourable conditions each spore forms a young *Amoeba* which soon grows to the adult size.

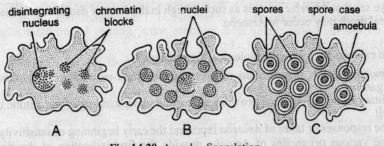

Fig. 14.20. *Amoeba.* Sporulation.

According to Johnson (1930) and Hasley (1936), multiple fission does not occur in larger free living species such as *Amoeba proteus* and *A. dubia* but it may occur in smaller forms or parasitic amoebae.

Encystment. *Amoeba* tides over unfavourable conditions by secreting a protective covering or cyst around it. This process of cyst formation is known as **encystment.** In extremes of coolness or hotness, or when the pond dries up or in the scarcity of food and in other unfavourable conditions *Amoeba* encysts. During encystment, pseudopodia are withdrawn and body becomes round. The food particles are either absorbed or thrown out and the contractile vacuole disappears. The ectoplasm secretes a tough double-walled cyst around the body. The cyst is a resting stage and it protects the animal. It may be blown off with the wind and facilitates the dispersal of *Amoeba* to long distances. On return of favourable conditions, cyst breaks and the *Amoeba* emerges out of it to lead an active life. The cyst in *Amoeba* is protective and not reproductive. Evidences in favour of *Amoeba* undergoing nuclear division in encysted condition are very rare. It is to be noted that one *Amoeba* comes out of one cyst.

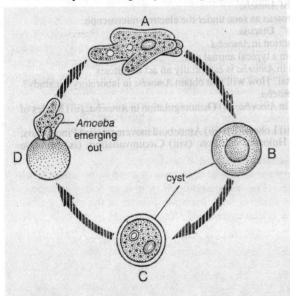

Fig.14.21. *Amoeba.* Encystment. A—*Amoeba* before encystment; B—*Amoeba* encysted; C—Section of encysted *Amoeba*; D—*Amoeba* emerging out of the cyst.

Conjugation. It has also been observed that two amoebae come closer and unite together temporarily and get separated after some time. However, its significance is not fully known.

Regeneration. Bruno and Hoger have described that if *Amoeba* is cut into pieces having a part of nucleus, each piece grows into a new *Amoeba,* but the pieces without nuclear part degenerate.

IMMORTALITY OF *AMOEBA*

Hertman (1928) first suggested that the natural death did not occur in *Amoeba,* hence, it is immortal. Weismann emphasized that the body of multicellular animals is formed of two types of cells : (i) the **somatic cells** and (ii) the **germ cells.** The somatic cells are related with the general maintenance of the body. Hence, these cells undergo wear and tear during life activities and finally they are subjected to death. The germ cells are related with reproduction, *i.e.,* the production of new individuals. Hence, these cells give something to their new individuals before their death. Therefore, the germ cells may be called immortal in contrast to the somatic cells.

Amoeba is an acellular animal without differentiation into somatic and germ cells. So, during different reproductive processes the whole body of *Amoeba* gets divided into daughter cells. Thus, the parent body is replaced by the daughter *Amoeba*. Hence, *Amoeba* is said to be immortal.

Thus, we see that *Amoeba* remains as such though in the form of daughter amoebae. However, only accidental death may occur in *Amoeba*.

BIOLOGICAL SIGNIFICANCE OF *AMOEBA*

Amoeba exhibits the following biological significance :

1. *Amoeba* depicts organization of protoplasmic mass or a single cell into a complete organism.

2. Binary fission of *Amoeba* provides a clear-cut understanding of the mitotic division of a cell.

3. The responses or taxes of *Amoeba* represent the early beginning of sensitivity in animals.

4. The various organelles of *Amoeba* provide the first indication of division of labour concerning the vital activities.

5. The large number of chromosomes present in the nucleus of *Amoeba* suggests the occurrence of isolated genes, which in higher animals are located in chromosomes.

6. *Amoeba* provides a faint idea regarding the anatomical structures of higher animals. For example, the food cup is comparable to the buccal cavity, food vacuole to gut, pseudopodia to legs, contractile vacuole to urinary bladder, and so on.

REVISION QUESTIONS

1. Describe the habit, habitat and structure of *Amoeba*.
2. Describe the physiology and behaviour of *Amoeba*.
3. Give an elaborate account of *Amoeba proteus* as seen under the electron microscope.
4. "*Amoeba* exhibits the basic life activities". Discuss.
5. Describe various views regarding locomotion in *Amoeba*.
6. How would you distinguish *Amoeba* from a typical animal cell.
7. Justify the statement that "binary fission in *Amoeba* is essentially an act of mitosis".
8. How can you say that *Amoeba* is immortal? How will you obtain *Amoeba* in laboratory for study?
9. Discuss the biological significance of *Amoeba*.
10. Write detailed notes on : (i) Locomotion in *Amoeba;* (ii) Osmoregulation in *Amoeba;* (iii) Modes of reproduction in *Amoeba*.
11. Write short notes on: (i) Plasmalemma; (ii) Lobopodia; (iii) Amoeboid movement; (iv) Pinocytosis; (v) Phagocytosis; (vi) Phototaxis; (vii) Holozoic nutrition; (viii) Circumvallation; (ix) Multiple fission; (x) Sporulation.

Certain closely related forms of *Amoeba,* known under different generic names, are found to lead a parasitic mode of life in the intestine of man and other animals. Of these, *Endamoeba, Entamoeba, Endolimax, Iodamoeba* and *Dientamoeba* are of common interest. The species of *Endamoeba* like *E. blattae* lives in the intestine of cockroaches and termites; *E. ranarum* lives in the intestine of frog; *E. bovis* lives in the intestine of cattle and *E. intestinalis* is found in the caecum and colon of horses and other animals.

The human beings may be infected by the species of *Entamoeba, Endolimax, Iodamoeba* and *Dientamoeba.* Of all species belonging to these genera, *Entamoeba histolytica* (Gr., *entos*=within; *amoeba*=change; *histos*=tissue; *lysis*=dissolve) is the most pathogenic and is responsible for the disease amoebiasis *or* amoebic dysentery in man. The other species of *Entamoeba* like *E. coli* and *E. gingivalis* are described to be non-pathogenic by Walker and Sellards (1930).

ENTAMOEBA HISTOLYTICA
SYSTEMATIC POSITION

Phylum	...	**Protozoa**
Subphylum	...	**Sarcomastigophora**
Superclass	...	**Sarcodina**
Class	...	**Rhizopodea**
Subclass	...	**Lobosia**
Order	...	**Amoebida**
Genus	...	*Entamoeba*
Species	...	*histolytica*

HISTORICAL BACKGROUND

Entamoeba histolytica was first of all reported by a Russian Zoologist, Losch (1875), as *Amoeba coli* from the faeces of a patient suffering from dysentery. The genus *Entamoeba* was established by Cosagrandi and Barbagallo (1895); it should not be confused with the genus *Endamoeba* which was established by Leidy (1879). Concilman and Loffteur (1901) worked out the pathogenecity of amoebiasis and amoebic ulcers. The species *Entamoeba histolytica* was established by Schaudinn (1903) and he differentiated the pathogenic and non-pathogenic types. But, Walker and Sellards (1930) are credited for attributing pathogenic effects of this parasite. Craig (1962) has estimated that more than 10 per cent of world population is suffering from the infection of this parasite.

DISTRIBUTION

Entamoeba histolytica is world-wide (cosmopolitan) in distribution. But it is commonly found in epidemic form in tropical and sub-tropical regions than in the temperate region. The more epidemic condition of this parasite is reported from Mexico, China, India, Philippines, South America and Thailand. Its incidence is relatively higher in rural and densely-populated urban areas particularly in those areas where the sanitary conditions are poor. In India its effect is on higher level in humid climates as compared to dry and cold climates. The children and adults are more frequently infected; surprisingly, the males are more commonly infected than the females.

HABIT AND HABITAT

Entamoeba histolytica is microscopic and lives as an endoparasite in the upper part of the large intestine, *i.e.,* colon of man. It inhabits the mucous and submucous layers of the large intestine. It feeds mainly on the tissues of the intestinal wall and often produces severe ulcers and abscesses. In chronic cases it may enter the blood circulation to reach the liver, lungs, brain and other organs. It causes a serious and often fatal disease known as amoebic dysentery or amoebiasis.

Entamoeba histolytica has also been reported from a variety of mammals, *e.g.,* Gorilla, Orang-utan, Chimpanzee, Gibbon, Baboon, Monkey, Dog, Cat, Pig and Rat, etc.

STRUCTURE

Entamoeba histolytica exists in two distinct forms : the magna or trophozoite form and the minuta or precystic form.

Trophozoite. The mature parasite or active and motile adult is known as trophozoite. The trophozoites of *E. histolytica* are large, hence, called magna, usually 20–30 microns in diameter. It is feeding form which is pathogenic to man. It resembles *Amoeba* in all structural details. The cytoplasm of trophozoite is differentiated into two distinct portions, the outer ectoplasm and inner endoplasm. The ectoplasm is clear, non-granular and hyaline, while the endoplasm is granular and fluid-like. The pseudopodia may be short, broad and rounded, long and finger-like, mainly composed of ectoplasm. During locomotion the rapidly advancing end of the body consists of a single clear pseudopodium, *i.e.,* monopodial. With this single pseudopodium, it moves in a crawling fashion like garden slug, hence, the movement is also sometimes called limax-type movement. The endoplasm

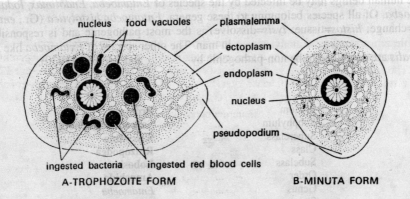

A-TROPHOZOITE FORM   B-MINUTA FORM

Fig. 15.1. *Entamoeba histolytica.* The trophozoite and minuta form.

contains the nucleus and food vacuoles containing the tissue fragments, erythrocytes, leucocytes and ingested bacteria, etc. The nucleus is rounded, 4–6 microns in diameter and vesicular. The nucleus is composed of a delicate membrane, small peripheral chromatin granules and a centrally located small dot-like nucleolus or endosome or karyosome and chromatin granules arranged in spoke-like striations. The nucleolus is surrounded by an indefinite clear area called halo. The presence of red blood corpuscles (R.B.Cs) in food vacuoles is an important characteristic feature of this parasite, as the capacity of ingesting R.B.Cs is not seen in other intestinal amoebae of man. Contractile vacuole is entirely absent because *E. histolytica* lives in an environment which is isotonic. Since, the osmotic concentration of its body remains equal to its surroundings and, hence, no water enters in its body by osmosis. Therefore, there is no need of contractile vacuole.

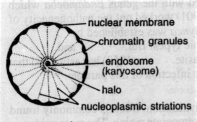

Fig. 15.2. *Entamoeba histolytica.* Vesicular nucleus.

The magna or trophozoic form of *E. histolytica* develops from small minuta form; it enters into the mucosa and submucosa layers of the intestinal wall by dissolving its tissues. Thus, it makes small wounds in the intestinal lining which later develop into ulcers. After reaching into the intestinal tissues ingests R.B.Cs and grows up to 60 microns in size.

Minuta. It is the pre-cystic form which is smaller, spherical, non-feeding, non-motile and non-pathogenic. It measures to about 7–10 microns in diameter and resembles to the trophozoite form in its structure except that it is smaller in size having no pseudopodium and contractile vacuole. It lives only in the lumen of intestine and rarely found in the tissues. It undergoes encystation and helps in the transmission of the parasite from one host to another.

NUTRITION

In *Entamoeba histolytica* the nutrition is holozoic. It feeds mainly upon the blood corpuscles, other host elements, bacteria and yeasts. It also absorbs substances saprozoically from the surrounding medium.

REPRODUCTION

The trophozoite of *Entamoeba histolytica* reproduces normally by a process of simple binary fission in the intestinal wall and by a modified form of mitosis. The exact nature of the division of the nucleus is controversial but it is believed by many authors that it is probably a modified type of mitosis. Kofoid and Swezy observed six chromosomes in it. *Entamoeba histolytica* also has the capacity to encyst. In fact, the nucleus divides by mitosis but without the disappearance of the nuclear membrane. It is, then, followed by the division of the cytoplasm (cytokinesis) resulting into two daughter entamoebae. These start feeding upon bacteria and host tissues, grow in size and again multiply by binary fission. Some of these forms may invade fresh intestinal tissues, while some of them become precystic or minuta form.

LIFE CYCLE

Entamoeba histolytica is monogenetic (Gr., *mono*=single; *genos*=race), *i.e.,* its life cycle is completed in one host only; the host being the man. Its life cycle is completed as follows :

Encystment. The precystic forms, under certain circumstances which are not well understood, remain small (7–10 microns in diameter) and live only in the intestinal lumen. They undergo encystment but before encystment, the parasites round up, eliminate food vacuoles and accumulate considerable amount of food materials in the form of glycogen and black rod-like chromatoid granules. Soon each parasite secretes a thin, rounded, resistant, colourless and transparent cyst wall around it. The cysts of *Entamoeba histolytica* vary in size from 10–20 microns (average 12 microns) in diameter. Its cytoplasm is clear and each cyst is mononucleate at this stage. Presence of chromatoid

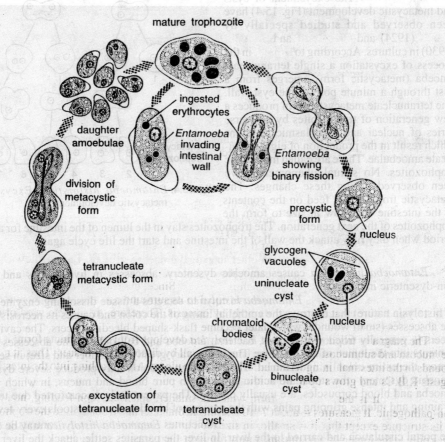

mature trophozoite

ingested erythrocytes

daughter amoebulae

Entamoeba invading intestinal wall

Entamoeba showing binary fission

division of metacystic form

precystic form

nucleus

glycogen vacuoles

tetranucleate metacystic form

uninucleate cyst

nucleus

chromatoid bodies

binucleate cyst

excystation of tetranucleate form

tetranucleate cyst

Fig. 15.3. *Entamoeba histolytica* Life cycle.

bodies is the characteristic of the cysts of *Entamoeba histolytica.* They occur either singly or in the multiples of two or more. There is a controversy about the exact nature of these bodies. Some authorities consider them as nutrient material of the cysts, while others believe them as excess of chromatin thrown off during nuclear division. The chromatoid bodies are found in the early stages of the cysts but they disappear in the mature tetranucleate cysts. Pitelka (1963) has suggested that the chromatoid bodies are made of ribonucleoprotein and Neal (1966) believes that the disappearance of chromatid granules occurs because of the dispersion of their nucleoprotein in the substance of mature tetranucleate cystic form. The nucleus of the cysts divides twice so that each cyst now becomes tetranucleate. At this stage the cyst is infective to a new host. Encysted forms pass out with the faecal matter of the host.

Transfer to new host. The infective cysts remain viable for a considerable length of time outside the human intestine, if environmental conditions are favourable. Infection of fresh human host takes place by swallowing the infective cysts with contaminated food and drinks. Contamination of food and drinks is brought about by houseflies, cockroaches and food-handlers. Houseflies generally carry the cysts from the faeces to the foods. Cockroaches have also been found to transport cysts from faeces to food. Food-handlers are also sometimes responsible for the contamination of food through touch by dirty fingers carrying the cysts under the nails. Through contaminated food or drinks, the infective cysts pass into the lower portion of the small intestine of the new host.

Excystment. The excystment of cysts and metacystic development (Fig. 15.4) have been observed and studied specially by Dobell (1924) and Cleveland and Sanders (1930) in cultures. According to Dobell, in the process of excystation a single tetranucleate amoeba (metacystic form) emerges from a cyst through a minute pore in the cyst wall. The tetranucleate metacystic form produces a new generation of trophozoites by a diverse series of nuclear and cytoplasmic divisions which result in the production of eight uninucleate amoebulae. These are called metacystic trophozoites. No sexual phenomena have been observed during these changes. The metacystic trophozoites feed on the contents of the intestine and grow in size to form the

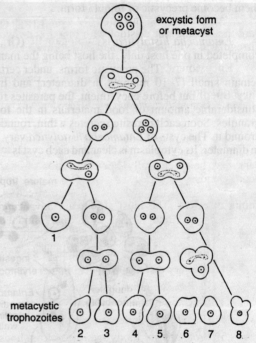

Fig. 15.4. *Entamoeba histolytica*. Excystment and metacystic development.

trophozoites of the next generation. The trophozoites stay in the lumen of the intestine for a particular period when they may attack the wall of the intestine and start the life cycle again.

PATHOGENICITY (PATHOGENIC EFFECTS)

Entamoeba histolytica causes amoebic dysentery, abscesses in liver, lungs and brain and non-dysenteric infections.

1. Amoebic dysentery. *Entamoeba histolytica* secretes a tissue dissolving enzyme (probably of histolysin nature) that destroys the epithelial lining of the colon and causes its necrosis and forms the abscesses (small wounds) which later become flask-shaped bleeding ulcers. The cavity of these ulcers is generally filled with mucus, bacteria, amoeba and cell debris. The abscesses pour their contents into the lumen of the intestine. The ulcers vary greatly in number and size; in severe cases almost the entire colon is undermined. The ulceration of colon may produce severe dysentery. In amoebic dysentery the stools are acidic and contain pure blood and mucus, in which swarms of amoeba and blood corpuscles, are usually present. The patient feels discomforted due to the rectal straining and intense gripping pains with the passage of blood and mucus stools every few minutes.

2. Abscesses in liver, lungs and brain. Sometimes *Entamoeba histolytica* may be drawn into the portal circulation and carried to the liver. In liver the parasites settle, attack the liver tissue and

form abscesses. The patient has pain in liver region, fever and high leucocyte number, a condition referred to as amoebic hepatitis. Lung abscesses are fairly frequent; these are usually caused by direct extension from a liver abscess through the diaphragm. The lung abscesses usually rupture into a bronchial tube and discharge a brown mucoid material which is coughed out with the sputum. Sometimes the parasite also forms abscesses in the brain. Abscesses elsewhere are rare.

3. Non-dysenteric infections. Although amoebiasis is usually thought of as the cause of dysentery with blood and mucus containing stools or of liver abscesses, these conditions are actually the exception rather than rule and some workers have reported that as many as 90% of dysentery cases in temperate climates are apparently symptomless. Even in tropics dysentery is exceptional. Although about 10% of the general population is infected with *Entamoeba histolytica,* yet most of them are carriers or passers. The symptoms commonly associated with chronic amoebiasis are abdominal pain, nausea, and bowel irregularity, with headaches, fatigability and nervousness in minority of cases.

SYMPTOMS

As referred, the infection of *Entamoeba histolytica* causes amoebiasis. The common symptoms are the passing out of stool with blood and mucus, abdominal pain, nausea, flatulence and bowel irregularity with headache and fatigability, etc.

DIAGNOSIS

The microscopic examination of the stool of an infected man shows the presence of trophozoites and cysts in it. The presence of stone-shaped, white coloured crystals of Charcot-Leyden suggests the infection of *Entamoeba histolytica.*

TREATMENT (THERAPY)

For prompt relief of acute or subacute dysentery the injections of Emetin are given. But certain antibiotics, such as Fumagillin, Terramycin, Erythromycin and Aureomycin are more effective and may be given orally. For eradication of intestinal infections or in chronic cases certain arsenic compounds (Carbarsone, Thiocarbarsone and Vioform) and a number of iodine compounds (Yatren Diodoquin and Vioform) are effective. For amoebiasis of liver or lungs Chloroquine is quite effective. The most significant advancement in the treatment of amoebiasis is the use of Metronidazole and Tinidazole as both luminal and tissue amoebicide.

PREVENTION (PROPHYLAXIS)

Following measures are essential in the prevention of the disease :

1. Sanitary disposal of faecal matter.
2. Perfect sanitation and protection of water and vegetables from pollution.
3. Washing of hands with antiseptic soap and water before touching the food.
4. Cleanliness in preparing the food.
5. Protection of foods and drinks from houseflies, cockroaches, etc.
6. Raw and improperly washed and cooked vegetables should be avoided.

SPECIES OF *ENTAMOEBA*

Entamoeba coli. *Entamoeba coli* is the commonest species of *Entamoeba* found in the colon and has been stated to occur probably in 50% of human popoulation. This amoeba lives in the lumen of the colon and does not enter the tissues of the wall. It is a harmless species (non-pathogenic) feeding on bacteria, particles of undigested food and other debris but never on blood cells or other lining tissues of the host, therefore, considered as endocommensal.

The trophozoite measures 15 to 40 microns (average individuals 20 to 35 microns) in diameter. The cytoplasm is not well differentiated into ecto- and endoplasm. The endoplasm is granular and contains bacteria, faecal debris of various sizes in food vacuoles. Nucleus is 5 to 8 microns in diameter containing a comparatively larger nucleolus which is not

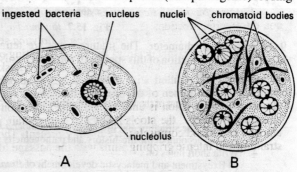

Fig. 15.5. *Entamoeba coli.* A—Mature trophozoite; B—Octonucleate cyst.

placed in the centre. The cyst is spherical or often ovoid, highly refractile; 10 to 30 microns in diameter. Immature cyst contains 1, 2 or 4 nuclei, one or more large glycogen bodies and small number of filamentous chromatoid bodies with sharply pointed ends. Mature cyst contains 8 nuclei and a few or no chromatoid bodies. Nothing is known about its life cycle in human intestine. According to Hegner, the cysts hatch as entire 8-nucleated amoeba.

Entamoeba gingivalis. *Entamoeba gingivalis* is commonly known as mouth amoeba inhabits the mouth. It lives in carious teeth, in tartar and debris accumulated arround the roots of teeth and in abscesses of gums, tonsils, etc. According to Kofoid ,75% or more people over 40 years of age harbour this amoeba.

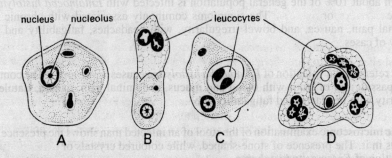

Fig. 15.6. *Entamoeba gingivalis.* A—Mature trophozoite; B—*Entamoeba* engulfing a leucocyte; C—Leucocyte engulfed in a food vacuole; D—Three leucocytes are engulfing a trophozoite.

The trophozoite is as active as that of *Entamoeba histolytica,* 8–30 microns (average 10–20 microns) in diameter. The cytoplasm is well differentiated, endoplasm hyaline but vacuolated and contains a large number of leucocytes and bacteria in food vacuoles. Nucleus is 2 to 4 microns in diameter and contains a small central nucleolus. Monopodial movements in some individuals have also been observed. This species does not form cyst since it is directly transmitted from one human mouth to another by contact during kissing or in feeding. Although *Entamoeba gingivalis* seems to occur more commonly in diseased mouths, there is no convincing evidence that the organism causes oral disease. Formerly, it was believed to cause pyorrhoea and now it is established that it is a bacterial disease but, however, *E. gingivalis* aggravates it.

Entamoeba hartmanni. *Entamoeba hartmanni* resembles the minuta form of *E. histolytica.* It lives in the lumen of the large intestine and invades the intestinal wall. Its trophozoite measures from

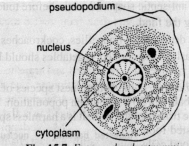

Fig. 15.7. *Entamoeba hartmanni.*

9–14 microns in diameter. The mature cysts are tetranucleate and smaller than the cysts of *E. histolytica.* The infection of this species of *Entamoeba* also causes amoebic dysentery but it is believed to be less harmful.

REVISION QUESTIONS

1. Give an account of the bionomics, morphology, life-cycle and the economic importance of *Entamoeba histolytica.*
2. Describe the structure and life-cycle of *Entamoeba histolytica.*
3. Give an account of the life-history and pathogenicity of the parasite causing amoebic dysentery in man.
4. Write short notes on :
   (i) Excystment and metacystic development of *Entamoeba;* (ii) *Entamoeba gingivalis;*
   (iii) *Entamoeba coli.*

16
Elphidium (= *Polystomella*)

All Protozoa members are not naked but some of them are found enclosed in shells. The shells of some shelled Protozoa are secreted by their own cytoplasm, while in others, the shells are made of some foreign materials which are found incorporated in a cementing matrix secreted by their cytoplasm. The foraminiferans, belonging to the order Foraminiferida (L., *forare*=pores; *ferre*=to bead) of the class Rhizopoda, are the most commonest shelled Protozoa. The shells of these Protozoa are many chambered and perforated by small pores through which their long and fine pseudopodia extend outside. Almost all such Protozoa are marine. After their death, the shells settle down at the bottom of the sea to form the ooze. Some of the common foraminiferans are *Globigerina, Microgromia, Elphidium (Polystomella)*, etc. *Elphidium* is the best studied foraminiferan having many-chambered shell and it also exhibits the phenomenon of dimorphism, *i.e.*, it exists in two distinct forms which differ in their structure, number of nuclei they possess and reproduction. However, the following account deals in detail the biology of *Elphidium*.

ELPHIDIUM
SYSTEMATIC POSITION

Phylum	...	**Protozoa**
Subphylum	...	**Sarcomastigophora**
Superclass	...	**Sarcodina**
Class	...	**Rhizopodea**
Subclass	...	**Granuloreticulosia**
Order	...	**Foraminiferida**
Genus.	...	*Elphidium (Polystomella)*

HABIT AND HABITAT

Elphidium is a marine form, found abundantly on the bottom of the ocean. It is found creeping about on sea-weeds to a depth of 300 fathoms (one fathom=1.8 meters). It also occurs in brackish waters.

STRUCTURE

Shell. Body of *Elphidium* is covered with a hard and transluscent shell made up of calcium carbonate and small amounts of silica and magnesium sulphate. The shell is biconvex, polythalamus or multilocular (many chambered) and perforated. The surface of the shell is chiselled. The chambers of the shell are V-shaped, laid down serially and arranged in a flat spiral in which each whorl of chambers overlaps the previous whorl, *i.e.*, equitant. The overlapping portions are known as alar processes. Due to the overlapping of the chambers only the last chamber is visible from outside. The hinder margin of each chamber has a row of numerous minute backwardly directed, hollow, blind protoplasmic pockets called retral processes. The adjacent chambers remain separated from each other by perforated septa. The chambers are interconnected or communicate with each other as well as with the exterior through minute pores present in the septa. The outer whorl opens to the outside by a row of large pores. The chambers of the shell originate from the initial chamber known as proloculum which may be small or large in size. The small proloculum is known as microsphere and the shell having small proloculum shall be called microspheric whereas the large proloculum is known as megalosphere and the shell having large proloculum is called megalospheric.

Cytoplasm. The cytoplasm fills all the chambers of the shell, called inner cytoplasm. Besides, a thin layer of cytoplasm covers the shell from outside, called outer cytoplasm. The cytoplasm is not differentiated into ectoplasm and endoplasm. However, the inner cytoplasm contains nucleus or nuclei, food particles, minute vacuoles, Golgi bodies, mitochondria, endoplasmic reticnlum, ribosomes and brown granules or xanthosomes which are apparently waste matter. Contractile vacuoles are not found.

Fig.16.1. *Elphidium strigilata* (After **Kudo**).

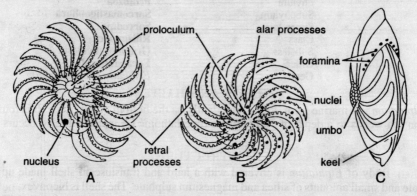

Fig. 16.2. *Elphidium*. Decalcified and stained specimens. A—Megalospheric individual; B—Microspheric individual, C—End on view of the shell.

Nucleus. The cytoplasm of megalospheric individuals contains single nucleus, while those of microsphoric individuals contains many nuclei. The nucleus is of vesicular nature and possesses many nucleoli in its nucleoplasm.

Rhizopodia. The pseudopodia of *Elphidium* are in the form of numerous fine and often very long slender thread-like structures, which are often branched and anastomosing. This type of pseudopodia are characteristically called reticulopodia, rhizopodia or myxopodia. Each rhizopodium is made of an inner fibrillar axis and the outer fluid-like cortex. The streaming circulation of cytoplasm has been observed in the rhizopodia. These are, in fact, temporary extensions of the outer cytoplasm and can be withdrawn within the shell. However, these are locomotory in function and often form feeding nets for catching diatoms on which animal feeds.

Elphidium is dimorphic and occurs in two forms, *viz.*, megalospheric and microspheric (Fig. 16.2) The two forms are outwardly indistinguishable from each other but differ in internal organisation. The megalospheric form has a large central chamber (proloculum), a large single nucleus and is relatively small in size; while the microspheric form possesses a small central chamber (proloculum), many small nuclei and is large. The megalospheric forms are said to be much more numerous than the microspheric forms.

LOCOMOTION

Elphidium creeps slowly with the help of its rhizopodia on sea-weeds at the bottom of the ocean. The rhizopodia are arranged in bundles around the shell. As referred to, rhizopodia contract and expand which bring about locomotion.

NUTRITION

Nutrition is holozoic. The food consists mostly of diatoms and algae; it also captures other Protozoa and microcrustaceans. The net-like rhizopodia are said to secrete an external mucus layer to entangle the food particles. The mucus layer also contains proteolytic secretions which help in paralysing the prey and the process of digestion soon starts. The entangled food in mucus is enclosed in a food vacuole and then the rhizopodia are withdrawn within the shell. The food is digested almost exclusively outside the shell and the digested products pass into the inner cytoplasm.

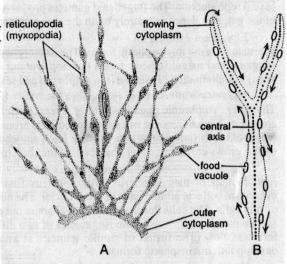

Fig. 16.3. *Elphidium*. Reticulopodia. A—A group of reticulopodia; B—A reticulopodium showing streaming circulation.

REPRODUCTION AND LIFE CYCLE

In *Elphidium*, Lister (1895) observed the development of the megalospheric form (sexual form) from the microspheric form (asexual form) by asexual reproduction. He noticed flagellated

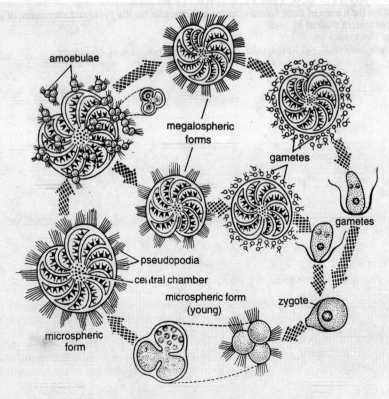

Fig. 16.4. *Elphidium crispa*. Life cycle (After **Kudo**).

swarmers in megalospheric tests and considered them as gametes which through syngamy gave rise to microspheric individuals. Recent studies by Myers (1935–1940) confirmed the correctness of this view. In *Elphidium crispa,* there is no direct association of the megalospheric individuals during sexual reproduction. The flagellated gametes produced in each are set free in the water and the fusion of the gametes depends entirely upon the chance meeting.

Elphidium exhibits an alternation of generation in its life cycle. The megalospheric forms alternate with the microspheric forms. The microspheric forms always develop by the conjugation or syngamy and megalospheric forms develop without conjugation or syngamy. That means there is always an alternation of asexual (microspheric) and sexual (megalospheric) generations in *Elphidium.*

The microspheric form reproduces asexually by fission to produce a number of amoebulae. The inner cytoplasmic mass containing several nuclei creeps out of the shell and remains as a lump around it. A small amount of cytoplasm collects around each nucleus. As a result, a large number of amoeboid cells (amoebulae) are formed. Each amoebula secretes the proloculum, forms rhizopodia, then it grows and forms other chambers of the shell to become a megalospheric form.

The megalospheric form reproduces sexually by syngamy or conjugation. During sexual reproduction in megalospheric forms, nucleus first breaks up into many small nuclei and the cytoplasm collects around each of these nuclei. The nuclei divide twice giving rise to a large number of tiny cells. The cells develop flagella and come out of the shell. The biflagellate cells are **haploid** and known as isogametes. The isogametes of two different individuals fuse (conjugate) in pairs to form zygotes. (The fusion of similar gametes is known as isogamy). The zygotes, thus, formed develop into microspheric forms.

However, the life cycle of *Elphidium* may be summarised in the following way, that the microspheric forms produce amoebulae by asexual fission which develop into megalospheric forms. The megalospheric forms produce flagellated isogametes which after syngamy produce zygotes that develop into microspheric forms. Thus, its life cycle clearly exhibits the phenomenon of alternation of asexual microspheric generation with sexual megalospheric generation.

REVISION QUESTIONS

1. Describe the structure, locomotion and nutrition of *Elphidium.*
2. Give an account of the structure and life cycle of *Elphidium.*
3. Mention the names of three foraminiferans and describe the life cycle and alternation of generation in a foraminifera studied by you.
4. Write short notes on:
   (i) *Elphidium* shell, (ii) Rhizopodia, (iii) Asexual reproduction of *Elphidium.*

Monocystis (Gr., *monos* = single; *kystis* = bladder) is a gregarine parasite of Sporozoa. Its life cycle is completed in one host only. The various species of *Monocystis* are most commonly found in the coelomic epithelial cells, gut and reproductive organs of their hosts. Usually all genera of earthworms are infected by the different species of *Monocystis* as well as by its various allied genera. The various species of *Monocystis* are *M. agilis, M. lumbrici, M. magna, M. beddardi, M. pheretimi* and *M. bengalensis,* which parasitize the common earthworms like *Pheretima, Eutyphoeus* and *Lumbricus.* However, the various allied genera of *Monocystis* are *Nematocystis, Rhabdocystis, Enterocystis, Apolocystis, Dendrocystis, Zygocystis, Dirhynchocystis, Pleurocystis, Cephalocystis, Rhynchocystis, Choanocystella,* etc. Mixed infections of the species of *Monocystis* and its allied species are of common occurrence in earthworm. In case of mixed infections of an earthworm, it becomes difficult to recognize the stages of the parasite of a respective genera, but the trophozoites of different genera are characterized by their definite form (Fig. 17.1). Here, *Monocystis* has been chosen as a typical example to represent these gregarine parasites, hence, described in detail.

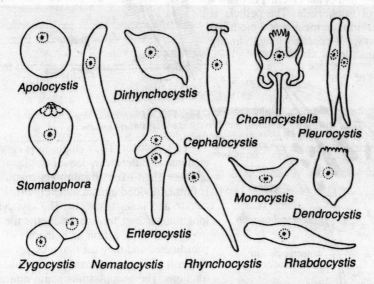

Fig. 17.1. Trophozoites of a few allied genera of *Monocystis* and their shape.

MONOCYSTIS
SYSTEMATIC POSITION

Phylum	...	**Protozoa**
Subphylum	...	**Sporozoa**
Class	...	**Telosporea**
Subclass	...	**Gregarinia**
Order	...	**Eugregarinida**
Genus	...	*Monocystis*

HABIT AND HABITAT

Monocystis lives as an intracellular parasite in its young stage when it lives in the bundle of developing sperms and becomes extracellular in its mature stage when it lives in the contents of seminal vesicles of earthworms. Its infection is so wide that practically all mature earthworms are found parasitized by this parasite.

STRUCTURE

The adult mature *Monocystis* is called trophozoite which is a feeding stage. The young trophozoite lives in the sperm morula (sperm morula is a group of developing sperms) of the host; it feeds and grows at the expense of the protoplasm of the developing sperms until all the protoplasm is exhausted. So, it is now seen to be surrounded by the tails of the dead sperms. In this stage it is sometimes mistaken to be a ciliated organism. But, soon the sperm tails are detached from its body and the trophozoite becomes free.

Shape and size. The fully grown mature trophozoite is elongated, flattened, spindle-shaped, worm-like and pointed at both the ends. It measures up to 500 microns in length and nearly 65 microns in width at its broadest portion. It is large enough to be seen with naked eyes, though its structural details can only be observed with the help of microscope.

Pellicle. It marks the external boundary of the body of trophozoite. The pellicle is thick, smooth, firm, permeable and modified in different ways. It contains longitudinally arranged contractile microtubules.

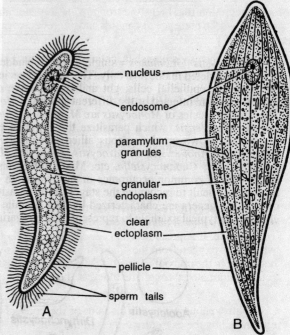

Fig. 17.2. *Monocystis*. A—Free young trophozoite; B—Mature tophozoite.

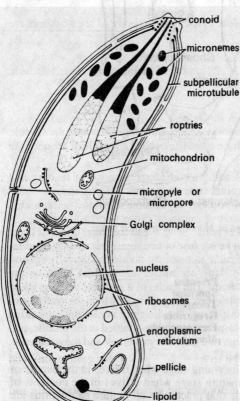

Fig. 17.3. *Monocystis*. An electron structure of sporozoite.

Cytoplasm. The cytoplasm is clearly differentiated into an outer clear, dense ectoplasm or cortex and an inner, fluid-like endoplasm or medulla. The cortex is further divided into an outer epicuticle, middle sarcocyte and inner myocyte. The myocyte consists of longitudinal and transverse contractile fibrils called myonemes. The action of both sets of myonemes is coordinated and they act like muscles and bring about sluggish gliding movements and metaboly due to contractions. The endoplasm contains numerous granules of a starch paraglycogen as reserve food, fat globules and sometimes volutin granules and nucleus.

Nucleus. The nucleus is large, vesicular, spherical or ellipsoidal in shape. It is placed more anterior in the upper half the body. The nucleus is surrounded by a nuclear membrane and the nucleoplasm contains a distinct endosome; sometimes more nucleoli or karyosomes are seen. The nucleoplasm contains four chromosomes, which represents the haploid number.

Contractile vacuoles, mouth and organelles of locomotion are absent due to a parasitic mode of life, A related genera of *Monocystis*, *Nematocystis magna* (frequently parasitizing *Pheretima*) is larger in size but narrower, it may have fine root-like cytoplasmic processes at one or both ends.

Electron structure of sporozoite. The electron structure of sporozoite (Fig. 17.3) reveals that it possesses all typical structures seen in protozoans, *i.e.*, the Golgi body, mitochondria, nuclear components, etc., are as usual. In addition, pellicle shows longitudinally arranged contractile microtubules. In the anterior end a pair of elongated reservoir-like roptries are seen which secrete some secretion that helps the trophozoite in penetrating through the host tissues. The anterior end also shows the presence of conoids and micronemes, whose functional nature is not definitely known.

LOCOMOTION

Monocys s is sluggish in locomotion. The wriggling movement is brought about by contractions and expansior of myonemes which are arranged in lines below the pellicle. These slow movements are called gregarine movements which are like euglenoid movements and are accompanied by marked circulation of the endoplasmic contents.

NUTRITION

Nutrition is saprozoic. *Monocystis* secretes digestive enzymes from its body which digest cytoplasm and developing sperms of the seminal vesicles. The digested products are absorbed by osmosis through the pellicle (osmotrophy). The excess food is stored in endoplasm as reserve paraglycogen.

RESPIRATION

In *Monocystis* respiration is performed by diffusion. Since it lives as parasite within the body of the earthworm, it has no direct contact with the exterior and the chance of getting free oxygen is very remote. It is presumed that *Monocystis* gets its oxygen supply either from the seminal vesicle which gets oxygen from the blood of earthworm or by the process of fermentation of carbohydrates occuring in the body of earthworm. The carbon dioxide produced diffuses out from the body and are finally eliminated through the blood of the host.

EXCRETION

Nitrogenous wastes diffuse out of the body of *Monocystis* into the body of the host and are eliminated by the excretory organs of the host.

REPRODUCTION

Monocystis reproduces sexually and the process is always followed by asexual reproduction. As a matter of fact, both the processes are interdependent.

LIFE CYCLE

The life cycle of *Monocystis* is completed within a single host, *i.e.*, monogenetic and characterized by the absence of asexual reproduction by schizogony. After a short free extra-cellular trophic phase, the mature trophozoite enters the reproductive phase of its life cycle. Life cycle of *Monocystis* includes gametogony, syngamy and sporogony.

Gametogony. Two adults or trophozoites, after leading a considerable period of feeding and wandering about, come together in the cavity of the seminal vesicles by their anterior ends (Hawes, 1961) or in some species side by side. The long bodies of trophozoites become shortened and rounded referred to as gamonts or gametocytes. Now they secrete a common protective two-layered cyst called gametocyst. The outer layer of the cyst is a thicker hard ectocyst and the inner thin soft layer is the endocyst. The two trophozoites in the gametocyst never fuse or conjugate but remain together in pair. This stage is known as syzygy. The nucleus of each gametocyte divides mitotically several times giving rise to numerous daughter nuclei. The daughter nuclei are haploid because the gametocytes themselves are haploid having 4 chromosomes. The nuclei of a gametocyte migrate to the periphery and project outwards so that the gametocytes look like a berry in which the endoplasm is dense and opaque and the surface projections are transparent. The daughter nuclei get surounded by some cytoplasm to form gametes, but residual cytoplasm remains unsegmented in the middle, and it contains vacuoles and paraglycogen. The walls between two gametocytes break and they coalesce.

Marshall and Williams (1972) have suggested the terms gamontogony for gametogony and gamontocyst for gametocyst.

Syngamy. All the gametes produced by both gametocytes are identical morphologically and are called isogametes M.A. Sleigh, 1973). They move about within the gametocyst and come together in pairs. Two isogametes of a pair fuse together to form a zygote. It is presumed that the two gametes uniting in pairs are from different gametocytes. This union and fusion of two gametes of the same species is called syngamy. If the two gametes are isogametes, then, their syngamy is spoken of as isogamy. Thus, numerous larger, nucleated, diploid zygotes are formed within the gametocyst by syngamy.

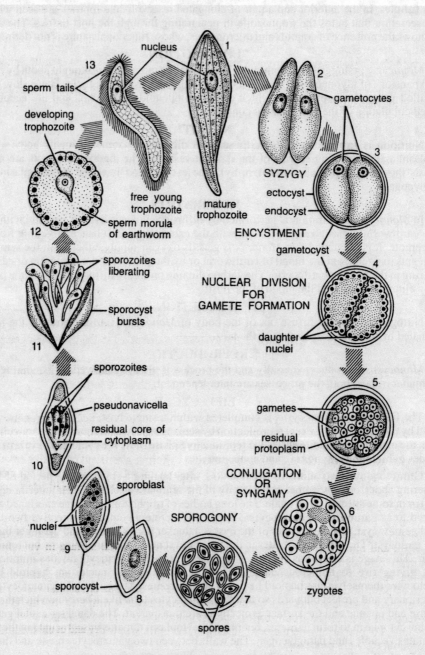

Fig. 17.4. *Monocystis.* Life cycle.

Sporogony. The developing zygotes are also called sporoblasts. A covering called sporocyst is secreted around each zygote, it is then known as spore. The spore with its sporocyst becomes spindle-shaped or boat-shaped with a mucoid plug at each end. The spore resembles a diatom *Navicella* (*Gr., navum* = boat) in shape, consequently it is often called a pseudonavicella (*Gr., pseudo*=false; *navum*=boat). The nucleus and cytoplasm of the spore divide three times, first being reduction division to form eight spindle-shaped or fusiform sporozoites which lie like flakes of an orange around a central core of residual cytoplasm. The sporozoites have been formed by asexual fission and constitute an asexual generation. The sporozoites can develop further only if the spores containing them are transferred from the host to another earthworm by oral infection. When the spores enter the intestine of a new earthworm, the sporocyst is digested and the sporozoites are set free. Most probably the sporozoites bore through the intestinal wall and come to the coelom from where they penetrate the sperm mother cells of sperm morula of the seminal vesicles. But the method by which the sporozoites find their way from the gut to the seminal vesicles is quite unknown. In the seminal vesicles the sporozoite of *Monocystis agilis* begins its intracellular phase by penetrating a cytophore (a cytophore is a cytoplasmic mass about which developing sperms are arranged). In the cytophore the parasite inhibits the development of spermatogonia which do not mature, but the testes are unaffected. In case of *Nematocystis magna* the sporozoites penetrate an epithelial cell of the ciliated funnel of vasa efferentia. In some species development is entirely extracellular in the cavity of the seminal vesicle. The sporozoite grows into a young trophozoite which is falciform or like a bent spindle. It feeds on sperms and cytoplasm, and degenerating sperms are seen attached to it. Then it grows and becomes an adult trophozoite which comes to lie freely in the cavity of the seminal vesicles.

However, the life cycle of *Monocystis* exhibits an alternation of a sexual generation of gametocytes with an asexual generation of sporozoites.

MODE OF TRANSMISSION

The transmission of sporocysts from one earthworm to another is not known with certainty. It may be brought about in one of the following ways :

By contaminated soil. When an earthworm, infested with the parasites, dies the sporocysts are released in the soil which are eaten by other earthworms.

By birds. When an infested earthworm is eaten up by a bird, the resistant sporocysts are not digested and come out to the soil along with the faeces of the bird. When the soil containing the sporocysts is eaten by other earthworms, the cyst wall is dissolved in the intestine of earthworm and the sporozoites make their way into the seminal vesicles.

During copulation. The sporocysts are transferred from one host to another during copulation or exchange of sperms from the seminal vesicles of one earthworm to another.

HOST PARASITE RELATIONSHIP

Though nearly all earthworms are found to be infected with *Monocystis,* even then they cause no appreciable damage to the earthworms. The parasite destroys the sperms of the earthworms, no doubt, but this does not affect the fertility of worms because they produce sperms in abundance. The earthworms appear to be able to combat the parasites by forming resistant protective envelope around the trophozoites and also by killing the spores by phagocytosis. On the other hand, the parasite shows various structural, physiological and reproductive adaptations so that it leads its life successfully and maintains the continuity of its race.

LABORATORY STUDY OF *MONOCYSTIS*

Monocystis can be easily obtained in laboratory and studied. For this, take a sexually mature earthworm and pin it down in a dissecting tray keeping its dorsal surface in your front. Cut the integument from segment 10 to 15 to make a slit. Whitish body will extrude out through the slit, which is seminal vesicle. Pinch it off with the help of forceps and keep it in a watch glass containing 0.7% sodium chloride solution. Stir it to make a thin paste of the contents of seminal vesicle. Make a thin smear of these pasty contents on a clean glass slide and cover it with a cover slip. Examine under microscope to observe the trophozoites, spores, gametocysts and other stages of the life cycle of *Monocystis.* For preparing a permanent slide, the smear is allowed to dry and usual method of staining, dehydration, etc., are processed.

REVISION QUESTIONS

1. Give an account of structure and life-history of *Monocystis.*
2. Classify *Monocystis* and give an account of its life history.
3. Give an account of the ultrastructure of the sporozoite of *Monocystis.* How would you obtain *Monocystis* for class study ?
4. Write short notes on:
   (i) Gregarine movement; (ii) Syzygy; (ii) Pseudonavicella; (iv) Mode of transmission of *Monocystis.*

18
Eimeria

Eimeria is a coccidian parasite of Sporozoa. The coccidians are the parasites in the cells of digestive tract of many invertebrates and vertebrates; they are, thus, typically intracellular parasites. A general diseased condition referred to as coccidiosis is caused by these parasites in their respective hosts. *Eimeria* has many species like *E. tenella* in the caecum of chicken, *E. mitis* in the anterior part of the ileum of adult birds, *E. bovis* in the intestine of cattles, *E. canis* in the small intestine of dog, *E. stiedae* in the bile duct of rabbit and *E. schubergi* in the alimentary canal of centipede arthropods. Other related genera are *Isospora* and *Adelea*. However, *Eimeria schubergi* is taken as a typical example here to be discussed in detail.

EIMERIA
SYSTEMATIC POSITION

Phylum	...	**Protozoa**
Subphylum	...	**Sporozoa**
Class	...	**Telosporea**
Subclass	...	**Coccidia**
Order	...	**Eimeriina**
Genus	...	*Eimeria*
Species	...	*schubergi*

HABIT AND HABITAT

Eimeria schubergi is an intracellular parasite in the epithelial cells of alimentary canal of centipede, *Lithobius forficatus*. The greater part of the life cycle of *Eimeria schubergi* is spent in the host and a part in open.

STRUCTURE

The full grown trophozoite is small, spherical and simple in structure. The cytoplasm is granular and contains a single nucleus. The nucleus of full grown trophozoite also contains a small endosome in its centre. Mouth, gullet, anus, contractile and locomotory organelles are absent due to parasitic mode of life.

NUTRITION

Nutrition is saprozoic. It feeds mainly on the dissolved food of the host by absorbing it, *i.e.*, osmotrophy. It also subsists on the contents of the cell of the host in which it is living.

LIFE CYCLE

Eimeria schubergi is monogenetic, *i.e.*, its life cycle is completed in one host only; the host being centipede, *Lithobius forficatus*. Its life cycle may be studied into asexual phase including schizogony, sexual phase including gamogony and the phase of spore formation, *i.e.*, sporogony. From all these three phases, first two take place either in the intestinal wall or in the intestinal lumen but the third phase takes place outside the body of the centipede in open.

Asexual Phase

Schizogony. The parasites, enclosed in spherical capsules, oocysts, find their way into the intestine of a healthy centipede, which are accidentally swallowed along with the food. In the intestine, the oocysts are digested. Each oocyst releases eight motile, falciform sporozoites. The sporozoites are sickle-shaped and tapering at both ends. Each sporozoite penetrates into an epithelial cell of the alimentary canal of the host. It grows into a large, round adult called trophozoite. The trophozoite becomes full grown in about 24 hours and it is then called a schizont. The schizont is characterised by the large vesicular nucleus containing an endosome and by the absence of reserve food material in the cytoplasm. The schizont undergoes **multiple fission** and the fission of the schizont is known as **schizogony.** The nucleus of the schizont divides into a number of nuclei which migrate to the surface. Each nucleus gets surrounded by some cytoplasm, thus, a large number of club-shaped **schizoites** or **merozoites** are formed. The portion of the cytoplasm in the centre of schizont is termed the residual cytoplasm. By this time the host cell becomes very weak because its contents have been used up by the parasite. The membrane of the host cell ruptures and the merozoites escape from the epithelial cell and become free in the lumen of the gut. The merozoites resemble with the sporozoites in form, structure and movement but differ from them in having a endosome and slightly shorter in size. The merozoites penetrate fresh epithelial cells, grow into trophozoites and repeat schizogony. This goes on for some generations. Schizogony is repeated till the greater part of the intestinal epithelium is destroyed and 'the parasites experience increasing difficulty in procuring proper nourishment.

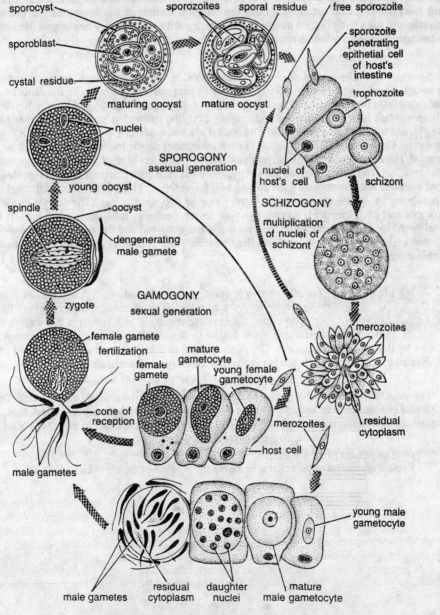

Fig. 18.1. *Eimeria schubergi.* Life cycle.

Sexual Phase

Gamogony. After several repeated cycles of asexual proliferation, some merozoites instead of forming trophozoites enter the fresh intestinal epithelial cells. After entering the epithelial cells, merozoites begin to grow slowly and differentiate to form two kinds of cells called microgametocytes or male gametocytes and macrogametocytes or female gametocytes. A male gametocyte is spherical having clear cytoplasm, while the female gemetocyte is bean-shaped having its cytoplasm crowded with darkly staining refractile granules. Male gametocyte divides to form numerous narrow, biflagellate microgametes (also called merogametes) or male gametes. The female gametocyte extrudes chromatin from its nucleus and forms single macrogamete (also called hologamete) or female gamete. The male and female gametes escape into the lumen of the gut where one male gamete fertilizes the female gamete to form a zygote by syngamy or anisogamy. In fertilization, the flagella of the male gamete are discarded. The zygote soon gets enclosed in a tough resistant cyst to form a round **oocyst.** As a rule the oocyst does not develop further in the lumen of the intestine of the centipede and the young oocyst passes to the exterior with the faeces. The oocysts are very resistant and can survive highly adverse conditions.

Phase of Spore Formation

Sporogony. The oocyst does not increase in size. The zygote nucleus divides twice to form four ovoid sporoblasts. The first division of the zygote nucleus is said to be the reduction division. Some cytoplasm remains unused during divisions of the zygote nucleus and is called cystal residue. Each sporoblast secretes a chitinous secondary cyst, the sporocyst consisting of two boat-shaped valves joined together longitudinally. The oocyst is known as tetrasporous because it contains four sporocysts. The nucleus and cytoplasm of each sporoblast divide to form two sporozoites within the sporocyst. Here also some cytoplasm remains unused which lies between two sporozoites and is called sporal residue. The sporocysts are known as dizoic because each contains two sporozoites. A mature oocyst contains four sporocysts each having two sporozoites. Thus, there is an additional generation in sporogony by which each sporocyst gives rise to two sporozoites. The oocyst containing four sporocysts and each sporocyst having two sporozoites becomes infective for the host. If the oocyst is swallowed by another centipede, the cyst walls are dissolved and the valves of the sporocysts split open and eight sporozoites escape and they penetrate the epithelial cells of the intestine and start multiplication by schizogony.

Alternation of Generation

In the life cycle of *Eimeria schubergi,* the schizogonic and sporogonic phases constitute the asexual generation as in these phases reproduction occurs by an asexual method of multiple fission. On the other hand gamogony represents the sexual generation as it involves the formation of male and female gametes and their subsequent fusion or fertilization. The sexual generation is always followed by the asexual generation. The phenomenon in which the sexual and asexual generations are followed by each other regularly is called the alternation of generations.

PATHOGENICITY

The infection of *E. schubergi* causes damage to the epithelial cells of the intestine. But, certain species of *Eimeria* are very harmful to their hosts like cattle, chicken, pig, etc., and, thus, it renders an economic damage to man. The pathogenicity of the different species of *Eimeria* varies greatly.

REVISION QUESTIONS

1. Give an account of the life cycle of *Eimeria.*
2. Explain alternation of generations by taking the example of the life cycle of *Eimeria.*

19

Plasmodium (The Malaria Parasite)

Plasmodium is an important protozoan parasite of man and the best known genus of the class Telosporea. One of the widespread diseases of man, malaria is caused by *Plasmodium*. *Plasmodium* has several species, four of which live as parasite in the red blood corpuscles (R. B. Cs) of man and the rest in those of other vertebrates such as lizards, birds and mammals. All the four species of *Plasmodium* found in the human blood (*Plasmodium vivax, P. malariae, P. falciparum* and *P. ovale*) are pathogenic parasites and cause malaria of different types. Here *Plasmodium vivax* is taken as a typical example and the salient features of structure and life cycle of other three pathogenic species are also described.

PLASMODIUM VIVAX
SYSTEMATIC POSITION

Phylum	...	**Protozoa**
Subphylum	...	**Sporozoa**
Class	...	**Telosporea**
Subclass	...	**Coccidia**
Order	...	**Eucoccidia**
Suborder	...	**Haemosporidia**
Genus	...	*Plasmodium*
Species	...	*vivax*

HISTORICAL BACKGROUND

It is very long ago that malaria was differently named as ague fever, marsh fever, intermittent fever, jungle fever, etc. The name malaria (Gr., *mala* = bad; *aria* = air) to this fever was given by Macculoch (1827) on the presumption that it was caused by the bad air of marshy localities. Laveran (1880), first reported the malaria parasites in the blood of a malarial patient. But the way of entry of the parasites in human blood remained a mystery for a long time. However, Richard Pfeiffer (1892) suggested the role of some blood-sucking insect in the transmission of malaria. Patrick Manson (1894) suggested the role of mosquitoes in the transmission of malaria. Working on this suggestion, Sir Ronald Ross (1897), an Indian army doctor, succeeded in establishing that malaria parasites are sucked up by female *Anopheles* mosquito and later on injected in the human blood. Thus, mosquito-malaria relationship was established. This historic discovery (for which Sir Ronald Ross earned Nobel Prize in medicine, 1902) was made on August 29, 1897, referred to as the 'Mosquito Day'. Then, Grassi (1898) and his associates worked out the complete life cycle of the human malaria parasite in the *Anopheles* mosquito. Shortt (1948) and Garnham (1954) have discovered that this parasite first enters the liver cells to undergo pre-erythrocytic schizogony before invading the red blood corpuscles. Rudzinska *et al.*, (1965) have studied its ultrastructure.

HABIT, HABITAT AND DISTRIBUTION

Plasmodium vivax lives as an intracellular parasite in the red blood corpuscles (R. B. Cs) of man in the form of its mature adult condition, called trophozoite. The species of *Plasmodium* are reported from reptiles, birds and various mammals. However, *Plasmodium* is widely distributed in tropical and temperate countries of the world but they are no longer a problem in the colder countries of the world. Countries like India, Sri Lanka, Bangla Desh, Nepal, Pakistan, etc., are worst affected. In our country, states like Bihar and Uttar Pradesh suffer a greater setback by the infection of this parasite. In fact, the infection of *Plasmodium* is a global problem.

123

HOSTS

Plasmodium vivax has two hosts; man and female *Anopheles* mosquito. Man is considered to be the primary host* and female *Anopheles* mosquito, the secondary or intermediate host. The common species of *Anopheles,* which transmit malaria parasite in India, are *A. maculatus, A. stephensi, A. fluvialitis* and *A. culicifacies.*

STRUCTURE

As referred to, the parasite, in its mature adult condition, is called trophozoite. The trophozoite is amoeboid, uninucleated having vacuolated and granular cytoplasm. An ultrastructure of the trophozoite is described below.

Ultrastructure of trophozoite. The ultrastructure of *Plasmodium* has been revealed by the electron microscope. According to electron microscopic studies, the *Plasmodium* in a red blood corpuscle possesses a double membrane, the plasmalemma closely applied to the cytoplasm. The cytoplasm of *Plasmodium* contains small dense particles probably containing ribonucleoproteins. The endoplasmic reticulum is not well developed and appears as vesicles of variable shapes. The vesicles are either smooth surfaced or rough surfaced and are loosely scattered in the cytoplasm. The mitochondria possess double membrane and show peripheral cristae and a structureless central region.

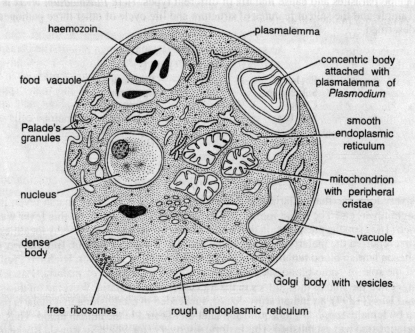

Fig. 19.1. *Plasmodium.* Ultrastructure of trophozoite in R. B. C. as seen in electron microscope.

The number of mitochondria varies with the age, the merozoite has only one mitochondrion, while the trophozoite has several mitochondria. The Golgi body is composed of small vesicles arranged in rows. A double layered concentric body is also found in the cytoplasm attached with the plasmalemma of *Plasmodium.* It appears that the concentric body originates from plasmalemma. Rudzinska *et al.,*

---

*In the life cycle of parasites having two hosts, the primary host is that in which sexual phase of the life cycle of parasite is completed and secondary or intermediate host is that in which the asexual phase of the life cycle of parasite is completed. So, technically for *Plasmodium,* man should be the secondary host because its asexual phase of life cycle is completed in man and mosquito should be the primary host because the sexual phase of the life cycle of the parasite is completed in it.

.In spite of the above fact, man is known as primary host and mosquito as secondary host in the life cycle of *Plasmodum.* This considertion is probably on the basis that the economically important vertebrate host suffers from the parasite, hence, called primary host, while the other exhibits no apparent effect due to parasite, hence, called secondary host. Only because of this exception, the arthropod host is regarded as secondary or intermediate host, and the vertebrate host is regarded as primary host, in relation to protozoan parasites, without considering the reproductive phases of the parasite.

(1965) suspect that the concentric bodies serve the function of mitochondria. One or two double membrane vacuoles with structureless matrix, also occur in the cytoplasm. The function of these vacuoles is unknown. The nucleus is large and its nucleoplasm is composed of granular and fine fibrillar material. The nuclear membrane is double, to which RNA particles are attached. The nucleolus lies eccentrally in the nucleus. Pinocytotic vacuoles are common in the cytoplasm and serve as food vacuoles. The food vaculoes may also contain hemozoin depending upon the species of *Plasmodium*.

The mode of nutrition is saprozoic, occurs by osmotrophy. Organ of locomotion, contractile vacuole, etc., are not found. Respiration takes place anaerobically. Reproduction occurs both by sexual and asexual methods.

LIFE CYCLE

The life cycle of *Plasmodium vivax* is digenetic involving two hosts as mentioned earlier. Its life cycle is completed both by asexual and sexual phases. Asexual phase of its life cycle is completed in man by schizogony (differentiated into exoerythrocytic schizogony involving pre- and post-erythrocytic schizogonic cycles, and erythrocytic schizogony) and sexual phase of its life cycle is completed in female *Anopheles* mosquito by gametogony, syngamy and sporogony.

Part of Life-Cycle of *P. vivax* in Man (Asexual Cycle)

It is completed in the following way :

Inoculation. When an infected female *Anopheles* bites a man to suck his blood, then along with its saliva it injects the sporozoite stage of *Plasmodium* into the human blood. The parasite remains always in the body of one of the two hosts, hence, the sporozoites do not possess any protective covering. The sporozoite, infective stage, is minute measuring about 11 to 12 microns in length and 0.5 to 1 micron in width, sickle-shaped cell with an oval nucleus; mosquito inoculates sporozoites in thousands. The sporozoites are capable of slight gliding movement, In about half an hour the sporozoites disappear from the blood stream, and they enter the parenchymatous cells of the liver where they undergo at least two schizogonic cycles.

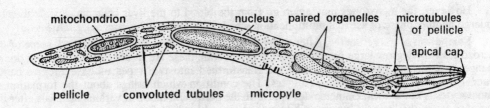

Fig. 19.2. *Plasmodium*. Ultrastructure of sporozoite as seen under electron microscope.

Ultrastructure of sporozoite. The sickle-shaped body of the sporozoite is covered externally by an elastic, firm pellicle having longitudinally arranged contractile microtubules. These microtubules help in the gliding movements shown by the sporozoite. Its anterior end bears an apical cup being made of three or more concentric rings. A pair of elongated reservoir like secretory organelles, comparable to roptries of the sporozoite of *Monocystis*, open into the apical cup. These organelles are supposed to secrete some secretion which facilitates its penetration into the liver cells. Nucleus is single and vesicular having a nucleolus in its centre. There is a single mitochondrion and a large number of convoluted tubules of unknown function. However, the micropyle represents the cytostome of other protozoans.

Schizogony in liver cells. In the liver cells the sporozoite grows to form a large, round schizont. The schizont divides by multiple fission to form about one thousand to several thousands small spindle-shaped cells called merozoites; this multiple fission is called schizogony. The schizont ruptures and merozoites are liberated into the sinusoids or venous passages of the liver. This phase of asexual multiplication is pre-erythrocytic schizogony and the merozoites produced by it are also called cryptozoites or cyptomerozoites; these cryptozoites are immune to medicines and the resistance of the host. A second phase of asexual multiplication known as an exo-erythrocytic schizogony occurs in the liver cells in which the cryptozoites enter into new liver cells and grow into schizonts, the schizont divides to form merozoites; the merozoites of the second generation are termed metacryptozoites or phanerozoites. The exo-erythrocytic schizogony may continue in more liver cells to form a reservoir of merozoites, or some merozoites after at least two cycles of schizogony may re-enter the blood stream when they invade erythrocytes. It is supposed that the merozoites of second generation, *i.e.,* metacryptozoites are of two types; the more numerous and smaller are micro-metacryptozoites, while larger and less in number are macro-metacryptozoites. In fact, the micro-metacryptozoites invade the R.B.Cs and start erythrocytic schizogony, while the macro-metacryptozoites enter fresh liver cells to continue the exo-erythrocytic schizogony. The merozoites attack only the young and immature corpuscles, (the merozoites of *P. malariae* attack only old corpuscles, while those of *P. falciparum* attack all kinds of corpuscles indiscriminately).

Pre-patent and incubation periods. The pre-patent period is the duration between the initial sporozoite infection and the first appearance of parasite in the blood. In case of *P. vivax,* it is about 8 days on an average. The incubation period is the time taken from the infection of man by sporozoites till the appearance of first malarial symptom. In case of *P. vivax,* it is about 14 days on an average ranging from 10 to 17 days. Of course, during the incubation period the host shows no symptoms of malaria.

Schizogony in erythrocytes. In the erythrocytes a third multiplication phase of schizogony occurs which is known as erythrocytic schizogony. The micro-metacryptozoite feeds on erythrocytes, a vacuole appears in it, the nucleus is pushed to one side, and the micro-metacryptozoite is changed into what is called as the ring-shaped trophozoite, the signet ring stage, which is 1/3 to 1/2 the size of the erythrocyte. The signet ring stage is not found in *P. falciparum.* The trophozoite grows to become rounded and amoeboid, this is the full grown trophozoite and is known as a schizont. The large schizont makes the erythrocyte to become very large. The schizont shows yellowish-brown pigment granules of haemozoin derived from the iron of haemoglobin of erythrocyte; the enlarged erythrocyte acquires granules called Schuffner's dots. The schizont now undergoes multiple fission to form 12 to 24 oval-shaped merozoites; this phase of asexual multiplication is erythrocytic schizogony. The much weakened erythrocyte bursts and the merozoites are liberated into the plasma from where they enter new erythrocytes, then they repeat the erythrocytic schizogony once every 48 hours.

However, the merozoites may again go from the blood to the liver cells and invade them to undergo another phase of asexual multiplication which is called post-erythrocytic schizogony.

Formation of gametocytes. After many generations of schizogony in the blood, some of the merozoites slowly grow large producing much haemozoin, these are inside erythrocytes and do not change in schizonts but they grow and are transformed into two types of gametocytes called macrogametocytes and microgametocytes. The condition which brings about the formation of gametocytes is not known. Gametocytes appear in the peripheral blood at various intervals after the oneset of fever, they remain inactive while in the human blood. The macrogametocytes are female, they are round with the food laden cytoplasm and a small eccentric nucleus. The microgametocytes are **male,** they have a clear cytoplasm and a large central nucleus. Both gametocytes contain large amounts of haemozoin; they enlarge the erythrocytes. Gametocytes remain in the human blood for several weeks, but are unable to develop any further, it is necessary for them to be taken into the body of an *Anopheles;* if this does not happen they degenerate and die.

Part of Life-Cycle of *P. vivax* in Mosquito (Sexual Cycle)

Many species of *Anopheles,* but not all species, act as intermediate hosts. If the gametocytes are sucked up along with human blood by a female *Anopheles* then they reach the stomach where corpuscles are dissolved and the gametocytes are set free.

Gametogony. The microgametocytes, after release in the stomach of mosquito, undergo the process of exflagellation. The cold-bloodedness of the mosquito is said to stimulate this process. However, the nucleus of microgametocytes divides into 6–8 haploid daughter nuclei. These nuclei migrate towards the periphery of microgometocyte. The cytoplasm pushes out forming long flagellum like structures having one daughter nuclei in each. Thus, 6–8 flagellum like male gametes or microgametes measuring from 20–25 microns in length are formed. Soon these gametes separate and start moving actively in the stomach of mosquito. On the other hand, the macrogametocytes undergo maturation process, thereby two polar bodies are pushed out and a female gamete or macrogamete is formed. The female gamete is non-motile and develops a cytoplasmic or receptive cone.

Fertilization. If microgamete happens to reach the macrogamete, then it enters into the female gamete at the point of cytoplasmic cone and finally complete fusion of nucleus and cytoplasm of the two gametes occurs. This results in the formation of rounded zygote. Several microgametes may approach a macrogamete but only one of them enters the macrogamete and others shed off. The fusion of male and female gametes is called syngamy. Here, the gametes are dissimilar (anisogametes), hence, their fusion is called anisogamy.

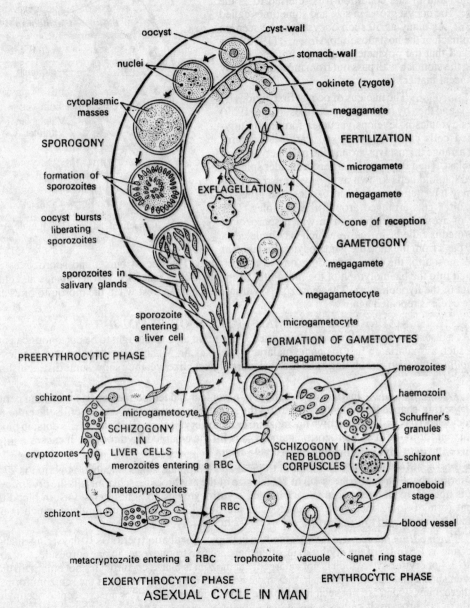

Fig. 19.3. *Plasmodium vivax.* Life cycle.

Ookinete and encystment. The zygotes, thus, formed remain rounded and motionless for 24 hours but soon they elongate to become worm-like having pointed ends and motile. The zygotes are now called ookinetes or vermicules. An ookinete measures about 15 to 22 microns in length and 3 microns in width. The ookinete moves and bores through the wall of the stomach of mosquito and

128

Invertebrate Zoology

comes to lie beneath the outer epithelial layer. (The ultrastructure of ookinete shows the presence of a central, irregular nucleus, dense cytoplasm, brown pigment granules, many mitochondria and ribosomes in it. It also shows the presence of contractile fibrils, the microtubules). However, here they become spherical and secrete a thin elastic membranous cyst. The cyst is also partly secreted by the surrounding tissues of the stomach. Thus, the ookinetes become encysted and in this condition it is referred to as the oocyst. The oocyst grows in size and sometimes called sporont. As many as 50 such oocysts can be seen on the stomach of the host mosquito. Howard (1906)) has observed that the ookinetes which do not succeed in boring the stomach wall pass out from mosquito's body with faecal matter.

Sporogony The nucleus of oocyst first divides by meiosis and then by mitosis several times Bano, 1959) and its cytoplasm develops vacuoles forming faintly-outlined cells called sporoblasts. Particles of chromatin arrange themselves around the periphery of each sporoblast. Then the cytoplasm forms slender spindle-shaped haploid cells known as sporozoites. Each oocyst may have ten thousand sporozoites, and group of sporozoites gets arranged around the vacuoles. This phase of asexual multiplication in which sporozoites are formed is called sporogony which is completed in 10–20 days from the time the gametocytes are taken in

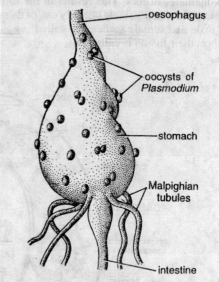

Fig. 19.4. Stomach of an infected female *Anopheles* with oocysts of *Plasmodium*.

by the mosquito, the time depending on the temperature. The oocyst bursts and sporozoites are liberated into the haemolymph of the mosquito, from where they reach its salivary glands and enter the duct of the hypopharynx. The sporozoites will infect a human host when the mosquito bites and the life cycle is repeated again.

MALARIA AND HUMAN SPECIES OF *PLASMODIUM*

As a disease malaria is known for centuries. Once night air was thought to be poisonous causing fevers such as malaria. In fact the name malaria means bad air. Malaria is caused by four species of *Plasmodium*, but their morphology and life cycles are almost alike, yet they show some distinguishing characters.

1. *Plasmodium vivax* has a wide distribution in tropical and temperate zones; incubation period is 10 days; ring-shaped trophozoite is 1/2 to 1/3 the size of the erythrocyte; schizont fills the enlarged erythrocyte and has yellowish-brown haemozoin; enlarged erythrocyte has Schuffner's dots; in blood the schizont forms 12 to 24 merozoites; gametocytes fill the enlarged erythrocytes. It causes benign tertian malaria or vivax malaria fever every 48 hours.

2. *Plasmodium malariae* is found in tropical and temperate zones; incubation period is 27 to 37 days; ring-shaped trophozoite is 1/3 to 1/2 the size of the erythrocyte; schizont fills the erythrocyte which is not enlarged; haemozoin is dark brown; erythrocyte has no Schuffner's dots; in blood the schizont forms 6 to 12 merozoites; gametocytes are round, they fill the erythrocyte which is not enlarged. It causes quartan malaria fever every 72 hours.

3. *Plasmodium falciparum* is very common in tropics; incubation period is 10 days; ring-shaped trophozoite is 1/6 to 1/5 of the erythrocyte, often there are two trophozoites in one corpuscle; schizont is 2/3 to 3/4 of erythrocyte which is not enlarged; haemozoin is black; erythrocytes not enlarged, they may even shrink and become greenish, they have no Schuffner's dots; in blood the schizont forms 8 to 36 merozoites which are not seen in peripheral circulation; gametocytes are crescentic occupying one side of erythrocyte. It causes pernicious malaria or malignant tertian malaria fever almost continuously or from 24 to 48 hours. A very serious result of falciparum infection is blackwater fever, a condition when wholesale destruction of patient's erythrocyte occurs and the liberated haemoglobin is excreted in urine.

4. *Plasmodium ovale* is sporadic in tropical and subtropical zones; incubation period is 14 days; ring-shaped trophozoite is 1/3 to 1/2 of the erythrocyte; schizont fills 3/4 of the erythrocyte

which becomes enlarged and irregular in shape; haemozoin is dark brown; the enlarged erythrocytes have Schuffner's dots; in blood the schizont forms 6 to 12 merozoites; gametocytes are round almost filling the enlarged and irregular-shaped erythrocytes. It causes ovale or mild tertian malaria fever every 48 hours.

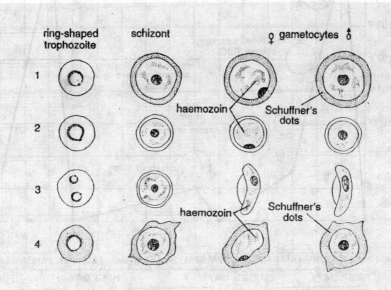

Fig. 19.5. *Plasmodium.* Species. 1. *P. vivax;* 2. *P. malariae;* 3. *P. falciparum;* 4. *P. ovale.*

SYMPTOMS AND PATHOGENICITY

The symptoms of malaria, in case of *P. vivax* infection, appear on an average after about 14 days of initial infection. In fact, it starts when the merozoites along with toxins are liberated into the blood, they are then deposited in the spleen, liver and under the skin, so that the host gets a sallow colour. The accumulated toxins cause malaria fever in which the patient suffers from chills, shivering and high temperature with convulsions followed by profuse sweating. The fever lasts from six to ten hours, then it comes on again after every 48 hours coinciding with the liberation of new generation of merozoites. The malaria caused by *P. vivax* is known as benign tertian malaria. After repeated and simultaneous schizogony, large numbers of erythrocytes are destroyed at intervals of 48 hours setting free increasing amounts of toxins into the blood, this causes the characteristic paroxysm of malaria on every third day. The paroxysm is divisible into three stages, chill or rigour stage, febrile or high temperature stage with fever over 104° F., and defervescent or sweating stage (Fig. 19.6).

Obviously, since erythrocytes are damaged in *Plasmodium* infection; hence, anaemia becomes inevitable. Anaemia develops because of the destruction of erythrocytes in large number; the infected erythrocytes become fragile, hence, easily ruptured and damaged. The enlarged spleen is said to release lysolecithin, a lytic substance, which damages erythrocytes and the parasite is believed to produce an antibody, the haemolysin, which haemolyse the normal erythrocytes.

DIAGNOSIS

Chills, shivering, muscular pain, high temperature and profuse sweating are the most apparent symptoms to diagnose the infection of *P. vivax*. In acute conditions the development of anaemia with enlargement of spleen is sufficient to diagnose its infection. However, the diagnosis must be confirmed by blood test.

CONTROL OF MALARIA

Malaria is one of the most important human diseases, since it not only kills millions of people annually, but it renders the most fertile regions of the earth unsafe for human habitation. The oldest remedy known against malaria is quinine which is very effective in killing schizont stages, but it is ineffective against gametocytes and exo-erythrocytic stages, Mepacrine is effective against merozoites, but paludrine is superior to both as it kills almost all stages, except the one in the liver.

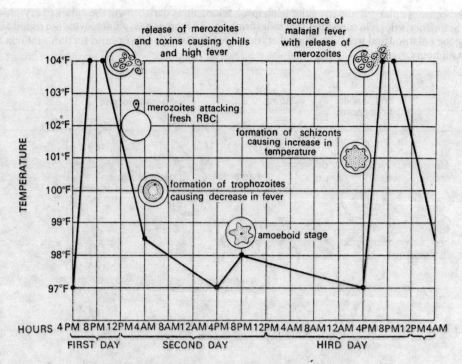

Fig. 19.6. Fever cycle in case of benign tertain malaria.

However, the control measures of malaria can be discussed in the following three headings :

1. Destruction of the secondary host (mosquito). Control of mosquitos for prevention of malaria is very important; this may be done by, (i) killing the mosquitos in human dwellings by spraying them with D.D.T., which remains toxic to mosquito for several months, (ii) by filling up ditches and ponds where mosquitos breed, and by draining swampy places to prevent breeding. In India five wet days followed by 2 to 3 dry days were found very effective in the control of mosquitos, (iii) by spraying surface of ponds with kerosene oil or with insecticides which kill larvae and pupae of mosquitos; it is easier and more effective to kill larvae than the adults; they can also be destroyed by introducing certain fish (minnow, *Gambusia, Lebistes*) which are the natural enemies of mosquitos because they feed on larvae and pupae.

2. Prevention of infection. The preventive measures are essential to adopt to avoid the infection. These usually involve the defence against mosquito bites and use of preventive drugs.

Use of insect repellents, nets, screening of windows of the house, etc., prevent mosquito bite. similarly, use of anti-malarial drugs like Quinine, Paludrine, Daraprim, etc., in definite dose periodically are effective in checking malaria infection.

3. Treatment of the infected person. Various drugs are used for the treatment of malaria. Physicians usually recommend drugs like Quinine, Atebrin, Camoquin, Chloroquine, Plasmoquine, Resochin, Pentaquine, Pamaquine, Mepacrine, Paludrine, etc., for the treatment of malaria.

ANTI-MALARIAL CAMPAIGN

Since, malaria is a global problem to some extent but certain countries like India face a widespread infection of this disease. However, with the assistance of World Health Organization (WHO), the Ministry of Health of Government of India started a National Malaria Control Programme (NMCP) in the year 1953. Under this programme effective measures were taken and malaria was almost controlled because DDT and other insecticides used were very much effective in eradicating the mosquitos. But in recent years the cases of malaria are frequently witnessed and the frequency is rapidly increasing again. It appears that the insects have developed resistance and immunity to DDT and other similar insecticides; they have also changed their behaviour. However, various research laboratories in our country like Vector Control Research Centre at Pondicherry,

Postgraduate Medical Institute at Chandigarh, National Institute of Communicable Diseases Delhi and others are engaged in finding out the measures to check malaria infection and also the way to eradicate the mosquitos.

     Monocystis and *Plasmodium* are typical sporozoan Protozoa belonging to different orders. The various stages of their life-cycle have been compared in the following table :

TABLE : 19.1. COMPARISON OF *MONOCYSTIS* AND *PLASMODIUM*

Monocystis	Plasmodium
1. Habit and Habitat	
(i) *Monocystis* lives as an **endoparasite** in the seminal vesicles of earthworms.	(i) *Plasmodium* lives as an endoparasite in the blood and liver cells of man and stomach and salivary glands of mosquito.
2. Life Cycle	
(ii) Its life-cycle is simple and involves only one host, *i.e.*, **monogenetic;** the host being **earthworm.**	(ii) Its life-cycle is complicated and involves two hosts, *i.e.*, **digenetic;** the hosts being **man,** where asexual cycle of the life cycle of parasite is completed, and female *Anopheles* mosquito, where sexual cycle of the life cycle of parasite is completed.
3. Trophozoite	
(iii) Young trophozoite is **intracellular** in sperm morula but **extracellular** in the contents of seminal vesicle when mature.	(iii) The trophozoite is always intracellular in the liver cells or R.B.Cs.
(iv) Its cytoplasm is differentiated into outer **cortex** and inner **medulla.**	(iv) No such differntiation occurs.
(v) Slow worm-like movement occurs due to contraction of myoneme fibrils, called gregarine movement.	(v) Trophozoites do not exhibit any type of movement.
(vi) Mature trophozoite is spindle-shaped, elongated, worm-like, free and motile.	(vi) Mature trophozoite is spherical and non-motile.
(vii) During growth it does not pass through signet ring and amoeboid stages.	(vii) During growth it passes through signet ring and amoeboid stages.
(viii) It does not multiply by asexual schizogony.	(viii) It multiplies by asexual schizogony producing numerous merozoites.
4. Gametocytes	
(ix) Trophozoites directly modify to become oval, called gamonts or gametocytes.	(ix) Trophozoites do not modify to become gametocytes. Some of the merozoites differentiate to become the gametocytes.
(x) The gametocytes are alike, come in pair–a stage called **syzygy,** and secrete common cyst.	(x) The gametocytes are **sexually dimorphic,** they do not pair and never secrete the cyst.
5. Gametogony	
(xi) It takes place in the same host.	(xi) It takes place in the gut of secondary host, the mosquito.
(xii) During gametogony, the nucleus of each gamont divides and arranged at the periphery and differentiated to form gametes. This all happens within the gametocyst.	(xii) During gametogony, the microgametocyte differentiates to give rise 6–8 motile sperms and macrogametocyte differentiates to give rise to two polar bodies and a single oval, non-motile female gamete. This all happens in the lumen of the stomach of mosquito.
(xiii) All gametes are alike (**isogametes**).	(xiii) The gametes are dissimilar (**anisogametes**).

Monocystis	*Plasmodium*

6. Syngamy and Zygotes

(xiv) The gametes from different gametocytes within the gametocyst fuse (syngamy) to form zygotes.	(xiv) The motile male gametes fuse with the female gametes (syngamy) to form oval zygotes.
(xv) Since the gametes are isogametes, hence, their fusion is called **isogamy.**	(xv) Since gametes are anisogametes, hence, their fusion is called anisogamy.
(xvi) The zygotes are non-motile, oval and secrete cysts around them to become **spores**.	(xvi) The zygotes elongate and motile called **ookinete.**
(xvii) The spores are many, covered in thick cysts and assume characteristic shape called **pseudonavicella** and still inside the gametocysts.	(xvii) The ookinetes pierce through the internal wall of stomach of mosquito and undergo encystment to form **oocyst** at the outer surface of mosquito's stomach.

7. Sporogony

(xviii) Each spore produces eight **sporozoites,** protected in the cyst. These are liberated when the spores reach the fresh host.	(xviii) Each oocyst forms numerous **sporozoites** and the wall of oocyst ruptures to liberate the sporozoites in the haemococl of mosquito. The sporozoites then make their way to enter the salivary gland of mosquito.

8. Mode of Transmission

(xiv) Direct, either by ingesting contaminated soil or by birds which eat up earthworms and liberate the spores containing sporozoites with their faeces in soil. When an earthworm ingests this contaminated soil; it becomes infected.	(xix) By infected female *Anopheles* mosquito; when an infected mosquito bites a man to feed on blood then it inoculates a large number of sporozoites in human blood along with its saliva.

9. Pre-patent and Incubation Periods

(xx) No such periods are noticed.	(xx) Pre-patent period 8 days; incubation period 14 days in an average.

10. Pathogenicity

(xxi) No apparent effect on host.	(xxi) Primary host (man) develops **malaria** and the secondary host (mosquito) shows no apparent effect.

REVISION QUESTIONS

1. Give an account of the habit, habitat and distribution of *Plasmodium*. Describe in detail the structure of trophozoite as seen under an electron microscope.
2. Give an account of the life history of malaria parasite.
3. What do you understand by 'intermediate host'? Give the life history of malaria parasite in mosquito. Suggest some important control measures.
4. What do you know about 'mosquito-malaria relationship'? Describe the life history of *Plasmodium* in man.
5. Describe the different species of *Plasmodium* you know. Suggest the control measures of the disease caused by this parasite.
6. Give a comparative account of *Monocystis* and *Plasmodium*.
7. Write short notes on:

    (i) Electron structure of trophozoite; (ii) Ookinete; (iii) Schizont; (iv) Schizogony; (v) Sporogony; (vi) Primary and secondary hosts.

Paramecium is a typical ciliate Protozoa. Ciliates are characterised by the presence of cilia as locomotor organelle, nuclear dimorphism and a unique type of sexual reproduction called conjugation. The two typés of nuclei are morphologically and physiologically distinct form one another; these are macronucleus and micronucleus. The number of micronuclei may be one or more in different species. However, the different species of *Paramecium* are grouped into two categories, an aurelia group which are elongated, spindle-shaped, body length more than three times the width, circular in transverse section, and the cytoproct is lateral. *P. caudatum, P. aurelia* and *P. multimicronucleatum* are common members of this group. The second is a bursaria group which are short and broad, they are flattened in transverse section, the posterior end is somewhat broad and the cytoproct is subterminal, common members of this group are *P. bursaria, P. calkinsi, P. woodruffi, P. trichium* and *P. polycaryum. Paramecium caudatum* is described here in detail.

PARAMECIUM CAUDATUM

SYSTEMATIC POSITION

Phylum	...	**Protozoa**
Subphylum	...	**Ciliophora**
Class	...	**Ciliatea**
Subclass	...	**Holotrichia**
Order	...	**Hymenostomatida**
Genus	...	*Paramecium*
Species	...	*caudatum*

HABIT AND HABITAT

Paramecium caudatum (Gr., *paramekes*=oblong; L., *caudata*=tail) is commonly found in freshwater ponds, pools, ditches, streams, lakes, reservoirs and rivers. It is specially found in abundance in stagnant ponds rich in decaying matter, in organic infusions, and in the sewage water. *Paramecium caudatum* is a free-living organism and this species is worldwide in distribution.

CULTURE

Take submerged weeds from a pond and place in a jar of distilled water, cover the jar and leave it to rot; swarms of *Paramecia* will appear in a few days. Now boil hay in water, decant the infusion and add a few grains of wheat, and let it stand till turbid with bacteria. Transfer *Paramecia* from the first jar into this liquid where they will multiply rapidly. Hay infusions alone will produce *Paramecia* showing presence of cysts, and cyst resembling sand grains have been reported, but there is no proof of *Paramecia* forming cysts, since they have never been confirmed.

STRUCTURE

Size and shape. *Paramecium caudatum* (Fig. 20.1) is a microscopic organism and visible to the naked eyes as a minute elongate body. It appears light gray or white measuring commonly between 170 to 290 microns in length and may attain a length up to 300–350 microns. *P. caudatum* looks like the sole of a slipper or shoe, hence, the animal is commonly known as slipper animalcule. It is four times as long as broad and somewhat cylindrical with distinctly different ends. The forward moving anterior part is slender with a blunt or rounded end, while the posterior end is somewhat pointed or cone-shaped. The widest part of the organism is just below the middle. The body of the animal is asymmetrical in form showing a well defined oral or ventral surface and an aboral or dorsal one.

Pellicle. The body is covered by a thin, double layered, elastic and firm pellicle made of gelatin. The pellicle holds the shape of the animal but is elastic enough to permit contractions. The pellicle

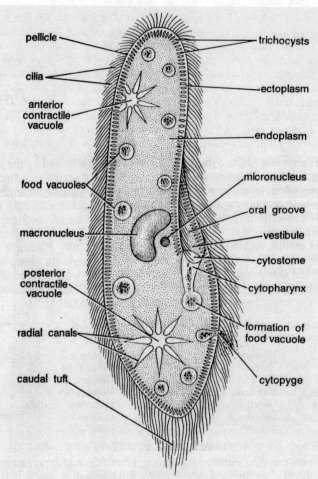

Fig. 20.1. *Paramecium caudatum.*

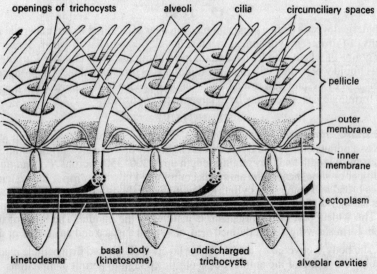

Fig. 20.2. *Paramecium.* Electron structure of pellicle and infraciliary system.

has double membrane, the outer membrane is continuous with the cilia and the inner membrane with the ectoplasm. Under the higher magnification of microscope, pellicle shows rectangular or hexagonal depressions on its surface. This arrangement is preserved on the dorsal surface of *Paramecium* but on the ventral surface the ridges converge in front and behind towards a preoral and postoral aperture. Each hexagonal depression is perforated by a central aperture through which a single cilium emerges out. The anterior and posterior margins of hexagonal depressions bear the openings of trichocysts. The electron microscopic study of pellicle (Fig. 20.2) by Ehret and Powers (1957) has revealed that the hexagonal depressions correspond to regular series of cavities, the alveoli. All alveoli collectively form a continuous alveolar layer, which is delimited by an outer alveolar and inner alveolar membranes. The outer layer lies in close contact beneath the outer cell membrane. Therefore, pellicle includes outer cell membrane, outer alveolar membrane and inner alveolar membrane.

Cilia. The entire body is covered with numerous, small, hair-like projections called cilia. Cilia occur in longitudinal rows all over the body, this condition is known as holotrichous in which the body cilia are equal. Cilia have the same structure as flagella, they have an outer protoplasmic sheath or plasma membrane with nine double longitudinal fibrils in a peripheral ring. In some cilia the nine outer fibrils are not paired. There are two central longitudinal fibrils which are thinner than the outer fibrils. Each cilium arises from a basal granule or kinetosome. The nine pairs of peripheral fibrils fuse together to form the wall of the kinetosome, thus, kinetosome is a tube which is either open or closed at its lower end, the two central fibrils stop at the level of the pellicle in most ciliates. Arising from the kinetosome is a thin rhizoplast which does not join the nucleus. Many Metazoa also have cilia, their structure is the same, except that the basal granule is different and it has fine filaments or rooting fibres extending down into the cytoplasm. But cilia differ from flagella in being generally more numerous and shorter is size. The ciliature may be conveniently divided into body or somatic cilia which are found on the body surface, and into oral ciliature which is associated with the mouth region. The body cilia are equal but they are longer at the posterior end, hence, the name *caudatum*. The cilia are organelles of locomotion and food collection, they also act as sensory receptors and detect the stimuli of the external environment.

Ultrastructure of cilia. The cilia and flagella have a fibrillar composition. At the base the cilium has the diameter of about 0.2 micron or 2,000 A^0 which may be up to 10 microns above the cell surface. The cilia are bounded by a unit membrane of 90 A^0 thickness which resembles and remains continuous with the plasma membrane. The bounded space of the cilium contains a watery substance known as the matrix. In the matrix there remain embedded eleven longitudinal fibrils or micro-tubules. Out of the eleven fibrils, two are located in the centre, while the remaining nine fibrils remain arranged peripherally around the central fibrils. Each of the nine outer fibrils is $360A^0$ in diameter and composed of two subfibrils of 180 to $250A^0$ diameter. These subfibrils are designated as the subfibril A and subfibril B. The subfibril A is slightly larger than the subfibril B. The subfibril A gives out two thick projections or arms from its one side. The arms of the subfibril A of all the outer fibrils remain directed in clockwise direction. Further, the subfibril A occurs more closely to the centre of the cilium than the subfibril B. Both the subfibrils have a common wall of 50A0 thickness. The two central fibrils do not have paired subfibrils like the peripheral nine fibrils but each contains only a single

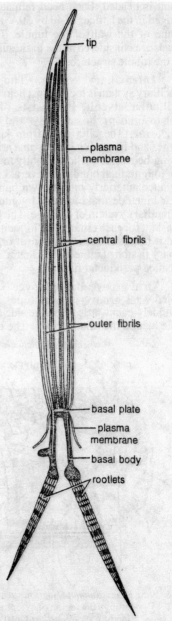

tip

plasma membrane

central fibrils

outer fibrils

basal plate

plasma membrane

basal body

rootlets

Fig. 20.3. Ultrastructure of a cilium.

tubule. Each central fibril has a diameter of about 250A⁰ and is composed of 60A⁰ thick wall. Both the central fibrils remain separated by a space of 350A⁰ and remain enveloped in a common sheath.

Gibbnos (1967) has reported that the sheath of the central fibrils gives out nine radially oriented links or spokes to each subfibril A.

The high resolution electron microscopy has revealed that each of the peripheral and central fibrils of the cilia and flagella is composed of ten to twelve filaments of 40A⁰ thickness. Each filament is beaded. Each bead remains arranged in the lattices of 40 by 50A⁰ in the plane of the wall of the tubule. These beads are considered as the basic subunit of the tubule structure.

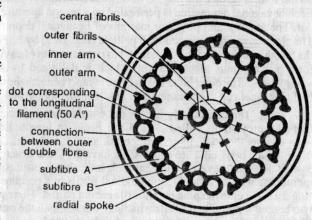

Fig. 20.4. Diagrammatic transverse section of a cilium.

Infraciliary system. The infraciliary system is located just below the pellicular alveoli. It consists of the kinetosome or basal body and kinetodesma. The cilia arise from kinetosomes and from each kinetosome arises a delicate cytoplasmic fibril called kinetodesma, (Fig. 20.2). Lying below the pellicle slightly to the right, but joined to all kinetosomes of one longitudinal row, is a longitudinal bundle of several kinetodesmata, a kinetodesmata of each kinetosome extends for a distance anteriorly into its own bundle of kinetodesmata. A longitudinal row of kinetosomes with their kinetodesmata forms a longitudinal unit called a kinety. All the kineties or kinetia make the infraciliary system of a ciliate. The kinetia lie in the cortex below the pellicle, their number is fairly constant for each ciliate. The infraciliary system controls and coordinates the movements of the cilia, and it brings about formation of organelles in cell division, *e.g.,* some kinetia form the mouth. In binary fission of ciliates the kinetia are cut transversely into two, each going to one daughter cell, this is called perikinetal fission.

Oral groove and cytopyge. On the ventrolateral side is a large oblique, shallow depression called oral groove or peristome which gives the animal an asymmetrical appearance. It runs obliquely backwards from one side (usually left to right but in some cases right to left) and ending a little behind the middle body. The oral groove leads into a short conical funnel-shaped depression called vestibule. The vestibule leads directly into the fixed, oval-shaped opening called cytostome (mouth). Extending directly from the cytostome toward the centre of the body is the wide cytopharynx. The cytopharynx then turns sharply towards the posterior side to become the slender tapering oesophagus. Thus, the oesophagus is roughly parallel to the body surface of *Paramecium* except at its posterior extremity. Here the oesophagus turns again toward the centre of the animal to lead into the forming food vacuole.

The cytopyge (also termed cell anus or anal spot or cytoproct lies on the ventral surface of the body almost vertically behind the cytostome or mouth. Undigested food particles are eliminated through the cytopyge.

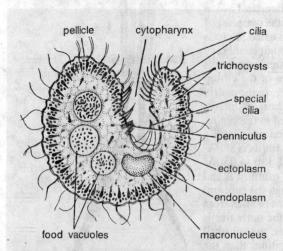

Fig. 20.5. *P. caudatum.* Diagrammatic transverse section through the region of cytopharynx showing ciliation of pharynx (After **Gelei**).

The ciliation of cytopharynx is very complicated. Gelei (1934) reported the presence of four rows and Lund (1941) observed at least four rows. A structure called penniculus is found on the left wall of the cytopharynx and spirals through approximately 90 degrees so that its posterior extremity is on the oral (ventral) surface of the oesophagus. According to Lund, the penniculus consists of eight rows of cilia arranged in two closely set blocks of each. A similar band composed of four rows of long cilia which are less compact than in the penniculus is termed as quadrulus. It spirals down the dorsal wall of buccal cavity and ends close to the penniculus. The penniculus and quadrulus have been wrongly called an undulating membrane by some workers. The quadrulus and penniculus control the passage of food. It is not known how cilia work, probably their fibrils contract in rhythmic way which causes bending. Gelei (1925) pointed out that the function of penniculus is the forcing of food elements into the body.

Cytoplasm. The cytoplasm is differentiated into a narrow, external or cortical zone called the ectoplasm and a larger, internal or medullary region called the endoplasm.

Ectoplasm. The ectoplasm (ectosarc or cortex) is a permanent part of the body, strikingly delimited from the endoplasm. Ectoplasm forms a firm, clear, thin and dense outer layer. It contains the trichocysts, cilia and fibrillar structures and is bounded externally by a covering called pellicle.

Trichocysts. Embedded in the ectoplasm at right angles to the surface are small spindle-shaped bags called trichocysts. A small spot on each anterior and posterior margin of the hexagon marks the position of a trichocyst. They are filled with a refractive, dense fluid having a swelling substance, at the outer end is a conical head or spike. The trichocysts lie perpendicular in the ectoplasm, they open by small pores on the ridges of the hexagonal areas of the pellicle. They arise from kinetosomes of cilia, then migrate and locate themselves at equal distance in the endoplasm. When the animal is irritated the trichocysts are discharged as long sticky threads. A discharged trichocyst has an opaque spike-like an inverted nail, and a long striated shaft, but the shaft is not seen in the undischarged state and is

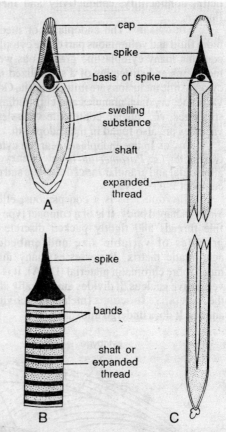

Fig. 20.6. *Paramecium.* Trichocyst. A—L.S. of hypothetical undischarged trichocyst; B—Tip of trichocyst as seen in electron microscope; C—Discharged trichocyst.

probably formed during discharge. The function of trichocysts is uncertain, but they are discharged as a reaction to local contacts and injury, they may serve as organelles of defence. But this is uncertain because the trichocysts are ineffective against *Didinium*, the chief predator on *Paramecium*, they may be for fixing the animal to a spot during feeding. In some ciliates the trichocysts act as organelles of offence. After trichocysts are discharged, new ones are regenerated from kinetosomes.

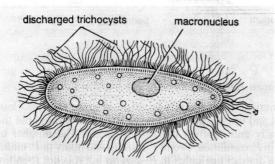

Fig. 20.7. *Paramecium* with discharged trichocysts as a result of the application of picric acid.

Neuromotorium and associated fibrils. According to Lund (1933) on the left dorsal wall of the cytopharynx at about the level of the posterior margin of the cytostome is a very small, bilobed mass, the neuromotorium. From the neuromotorium, fibrils radiate into the endoplasm. Of these four or more usually pass almost to the dorsal body wall but the rest are shorter and not definite in position. All are termed endoplasmic fibrils. Their function is unknown, but they may coordinate the feeding movements of the oral cilia. The fibrils may also give mechanical support, elasticity, contractility, conductivity and metabolic influence.

Endoplasm. The endoplasm or medulla is the more fluid and voluminous part of the cytoplasm which contains many cytoplasmic granules as well as other inclusions and structures of a specialized nature. The cytoplasmic inclusions are mitochondria, Golgi bodies, vacuome, crystals, granules and chromidia, etc. Other structures, *viz.*, nuclei, contractile vacuoles and food vacuoles are also found in the endoplasm.

Nuclei. In the endoplasm near the cytostome are two nuclei, *i.e.*, *Paramecium* is heterokaryotic, a large ellipsoidal and granular macronucleus and other small compact micronucleus.

Macronucleus is a conspicuous, ellipsoidal or kidney-shaped body. It is of a compact type containing fine threads and tightly packed discrete chromatin granules of variable size and embedded in an achromatic matrix. It possesses many nucleoli and much more chromatin material (DNA). It is somatic or vegetative nucleus. It divides amitotically and controls the vegetative functions (metabolic activities) of the animal. It does undergo mitosis.

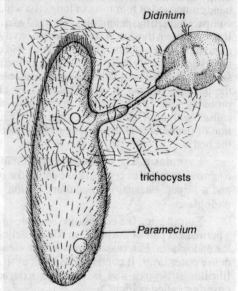

Fig. 20.8. *Paramecium.* Throwing out trichocysts when attacked by a small *Didinium.*

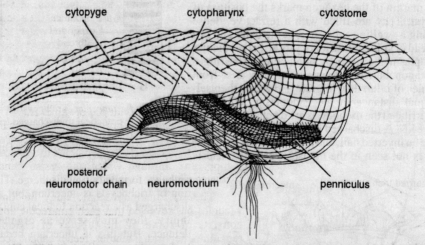

Fig. 20.9. *Paramecium multimicronucleatum.* A part of neuromotor system (After **Lund**).

Micronucleus is small, compact and spherical. It is generally found close to the macronucleus often in a concavity. Fine chromatin granules and threads are uniformly distributed throughout the structure. The micronucleus divides mitotically and controls the reproduction. The number of micronucleus varies with the species; it is one in *P. caudatum,* two in *P. aurelia* and many in *P. multimicronucleatum.* The micronucleus contains a distinct nucleolus in *P. aurelia* but it is not found in *P. caudatum.*

Moses (1949, 1950) has reported that the macronucleus and micronucleus are identical in chemical composition.

Contractile vacuoles. There are two large, liquid-filled contractile vacuoles, each situated near one end of the body close to the dorsal surface. Their position is fixed (unlike *Amoeba),* they lie between the ectoplasm and endoplasm, but they are temporary organelles disappearing periodically. In some species they appear to have a lining membrane, in which case they do not disappear entirely during systole. Connected to each contractile vacuole are five to twelve tubular radiating canals, each consisting of a terminal part long ampulla which collapses when empty, and a short injector canal which opens into the vacuole. The canals communicate with a large part of the body from where

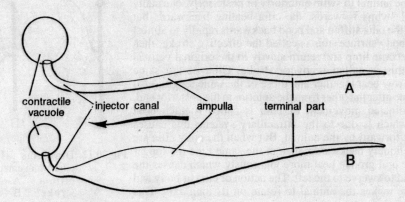

Fig. 20.10. *Paramecium.* Radial canal. A—Empty; B—Full.

they take up liquids and pour them into the vacuole which is, thus, reconstituted and grows in size, when the contractile vacuole reaches its maximum size it contracts suddenly (systole) and discharges its contents through a permanent pore in the pellicle, then the canals again form the contractile vacuoles, the canals do not disappear entirely since they are permanent structures. The two contractile vacuoles discharge irregularly, the posterior one contracts more rapidly because it is near the cytopharynx and more water comes into it. The main function of the canals and the contractile vacuoles is hydrostatic, they remove excess of water from the protoplasm, the water is partly absorbed and partly taken in while feeding. The vacuoles are probably also respiratory and excretory. The nitrogenous waste substance has ammonia compounds and some urates which are expelled from the contractile vacuoles along with CO_2 but there is no evidence of the excretory matter being secreted by the protoplasm into the canals or contractile vacuoles. There is a fixed permanent cytopyge or anus below the peristome to one side of the cytopharynx, through which undigested remains of food and urates are expelled.

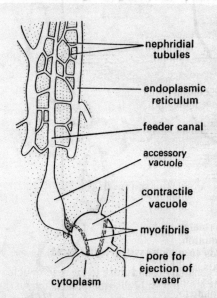

nephridial tubules

endoplasmic reticulum

feeder canal

accessory vacuole

contractile vacuole

myofibrils

pore for ejection of water

cytoplasm

The electron microscopic study of contractile vacuoles has revealed that each contractile apparatus consists of some of the tubules of endoplasmic reticulum, nephridial tubules, feeder canals, accessory vacuoles (radial canals) and main contractile vacuole. The accessory vacuoles are supposed to be the ampullae of feeder canals (Fig. 20.11).

Fig. 20.11. *Paramecium.* Contractile apparatus.

Food vacuoles. These are roughly spherical, non-contractile bodies varying in size and number lying in the endoplasm. They contain ingested food particles, principally bacteria and a small amount of fluid bounded by a thin definite membrane. Volkonsky (1934) proposed the name gastrioles for these vacuoles. Associated with the food vacuoles are the digestive granules.

LOCOMOTION

Paramecium performs locomotion by two methods, *viz.,* metaboly or body contortions and by cilia.

1. Metaboly or body contortions. The body of *Paramecium* possesses elasticity, it can squeeze itself through a passage narrower than its body, after which the body assumes its normal shape. This temporary change of body shape is metaboly, it is brought about in *Parameicum* by the protoplasm.

2. Ciliary locomotion. Locomotion brought about by cilia is the main method. The cilia can beat forwards or backwards enabling the animal to swim anteriorly or posteriorly. Normally the animal swims forwards, the cilia beating backwards but obliquely, the cilia stiffen and bend backwards rapidly to almost touch the body surface, this is called the effective stroke; then the cilia become limp and return slowly to the original vertical position, this is called recovery stroke. Cilia of the same transverse row beat together and those of the same longitudinal row beat one after the other from the anterior to the posterior end. This coordinated movement of cilia is called metachronal rhythm, which is due to the infraciliary system; this causes swimming forward by the animal. But when the body cilia are beating obliquely backwards, then at the same time the longer cilia of the oral groove beat more vigorously which causes the anterior end to swerve to the left. The action of cilia of body and oral groove makes the animal to rotate on its long axis. This

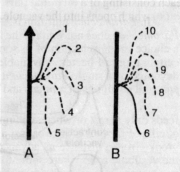

Fig.20.12. Diagrams illustrating ciliary movement of a single cilium. A—Effective stroke; B—Recovery stroke.

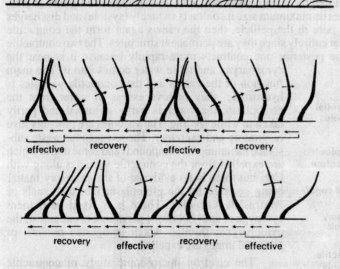

effective   recovery   effective   recovery

recovery   effective   recovery   effective

rotation is always to the left (except in *P. calkinsi* which rotates in a right hand spiral). This combination of forward motion, swerving and rotation makes the animal move forwards in a counter-clockwise spiral path. This path has a straight axis, and the same body surface of the animal remains towards the axis of the spiral path. But in swimming backwards all species rotate to the right. The ciliary beat can be reversed so that the cilia move obliquely forwards by which the animal swims backwards. By ciliary action *Paramecium* moves with a speed of 1500 microns or even more per second.

Jennings contended that the spiralling of *Paramecium* is due to the fact that while the cilia strike chiefly backward they do so obliquely to the right thereby causing the animal to roll over to the left. Also this swerving of the body toward the aboral

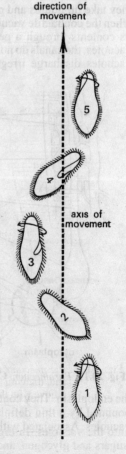

direction of movement

axis of movement

Fig. 20.15. *Paramecium.* Spiral path of movement.

surface is due largely to the greater power of the effective stroke of the oral cilia which strike more directly backward. The result—the rotation of *Paramecium* on its long axis—thereby enables the *Paramecium* to follow a more or less straight course in forming large spirals.

NUTRITION

In *Paramecium* nutrition is holozoic. The food comprises chiefly bacteria and minute Protozoa. *Paramecium* does not wait for the food but hunts for it actively. It is claimed that *Paramecium* shows a choice in the selection of its food, but there seems to be no basis for this though it engulfs only certain types of bacteria; available data suggest that 2 to 5 million individuals of *Bacillus coli* are devoured by a single *Paramecium* in 24 hours. It also feeds on unicellular plants like algae, diatoms, etc., and small bits of animals and vegetables.

Feeding mechanism. When *Paramecium* enters a region of abundant food, it comes to rest. It feeds only at rest or when swimming very slowly, it never feeds when swimming fast. The beating of cilia of the oral groove causes a cone-shaped vortex of food-laden water to be swept into the oral groove from a distance in advance of the anterior end (Fig. 20.16). The particles of food then go to the vestibule from where some food particles are rejected and thrown out, but others pass into the cytostome. At the end of the cytopharynx a food vacuole is formed which gets filled with particles of food. The quadrulus and peniculi control the passage of food into the food vacuole which is formed laterally. When the food vacuole reaches a certain size the post-buccal fibres clasp the food vacuole and it is pinched off by them and started on its course. The vacuole contains some water besides the food. Rotary streaming movements of endoplasm called cyclosis carry the food vacuoles along a definite course which is functionally equivalent to a digestive tract. The tract begins from the end of the cytopharynx, then to the posterior side, then forwards to circulate with the endoplasm, then to the dorsal surface, then towards the anterior end, then downwards to the cytopyge. Early on its journey the food vacuole decreases in size, then increases again.

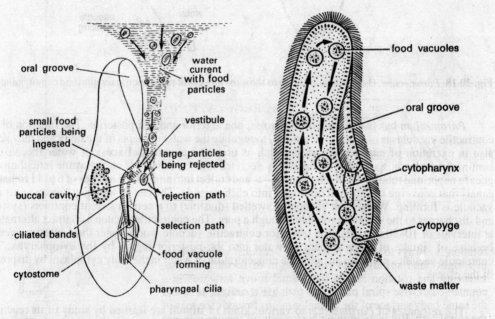

Fig. 20.16. *Paramecium*. Ciliary action creating vortex and drawing food particles into the oral groove with the water current.

Fig. 20.17. *Paramecium* showing cyclosis and the course of food vacuoles in the endoplasm.

Digestion and egestion. During cyclosis digestion occurs by enzymes secreted by protoplasm into the vacuoles. In digestion proteins are changed into amino acids, carbohydrates into soluble sugars and glycogen, and fats are probably also digested. The contents of food vacuoles are at first acidic (pH about 4) and then become alkaline, major digestion occurs during the alkaline phase. The undigested matter is egested through the cytopyge with some force.

Cyclosis can be demonstrated experimentally; if milk stained with Congo red is fed to *Paramecium,* the fat globules of milk in the food vacuoles will first turn red due to acidic reaction of enzymes, then they will change from shades of purple to blue due to alkaline reaction, the vacuoles will show the course of cyclosis.

RESPIRATION AND EXCRETION

The exchange of gases (oxygen and carbon dioxide) takes place through the semi-permeable pellicle like other freshwater protozoans by the process of diffusion. *Paramecium* obtains its oxygen from the surrounding water. Carbon dioxide and organic wastes like ammonia resulting from metabolism are probably excreted by diffusing outward into the water in the reverse direction.

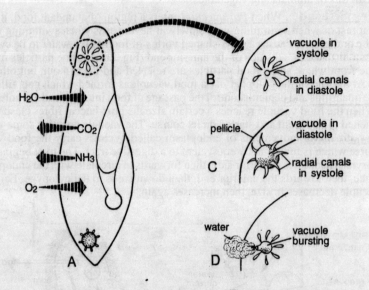

Fig. 20.18. *Paramecium.* Diagrammatic sketch to show the process of respiration, excretion and osmoregulation.

OSMOREGULATION

Paramecium has two contractile vacuoles, one anterior and one posterior. The function of the contractile vacuoles is osmoregulation, *i.e.,* to regulate the water contents of the body and may serve also in excretion of nitrogenous wastes such as urea and ammonia. Excess of water (because of continuous endosmosis) within cytoplasm is secreted into the tubules of endoplasmic reticulum and goes to nephridial tubules—> fedder canals—> and collect into ampulla of a series of 6 to 11 radiating canals that converge toward and discharge into each vacuole. The canals are most conspicuous as a vacuole is forming. When each vacuole is swelled (diastole) to a certain size, it contracts (systole) and discharges to the exterior probably through a pore. The contractile vacuoles contract alternately, at intervals of 10–20 seconds. The posterior contractile vacuole works faster than anterior vacuole because of intake of large amount of water into the posterior region by the cytopharynx. The contractile vacuoles maintain an optimum concentration of water in the body cytoplasm by disposing of the excess.

BEHAVIOUR

The responses of *Paramecium* to various kinds of stimuli are learned by study of its reactions and of the grouping or scattering of individuals in a culture. The response is positive if the animal moves toward a stimulus and negative when it moves away. To an adverse stimulus the animal continues to give the avoiding reaction until it escapes. In avoiding reaction the ciliary beat reverses, the animal moves backward a short distance, and then rotates in a conical path by swerving the anterior end aborally while pivoting on the posterior tip. All adjustments are made by trial and error. Experiments have shown that the anterior end of the animal is more sensitive than the other parts. The responses of *Paramecium* to different stimuli may be grouped as follows :

1. **Reactions to contact (Thigmotaxis).** Response to contact is varied in *Paramecium.* If the anterior end is lightly touched with a fine point, a strong avoiding reaction occurs. When a swimming

Paramecium collides with some object in the water, but if touched elsewhere there may be no response. A slow moving individual often responds positively to contact with an object by coming to rest upon it.

2. **Reactions to chemicals (Chemotaxis).** Generally *Paramecia* respond to a chemical stimuli by means of avoiding reaction. If a drop of weak salt solution (0.5 per cent) is introduced in a *Paramecium* population on a microslide, the animals respond with the avoiding reaction and none enters the drop. To acids, however, the response is positive even when the concentration is of sufficient strength to kill them.

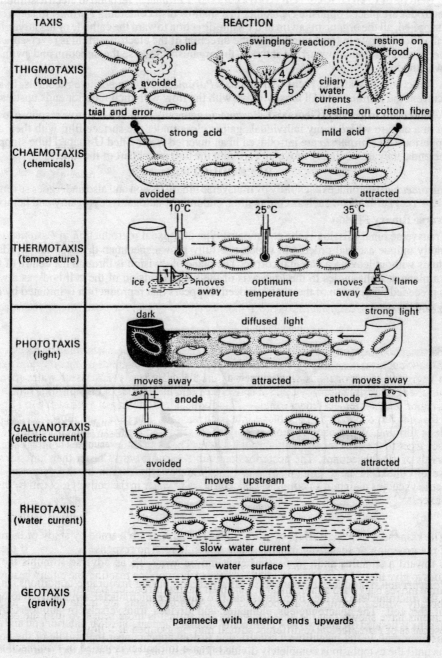

Fig. 20.19. *Paramecium*. Responses to different stimuli.

3. Reactions to temperature (Thermotaxis). *Paramecium* seeks an optimum temperature of 24 to 28^0C. When a temperature change occurs markedly above or below the optimal range, *Paramecia* show an avoiding reaction. Greater heat stimulates rapid movement and avoiding reactions until the animals escape or are killed.

4. Reactions to light (Phototaxis). With the exception of the green *Paramecium bursaria,* which is positively phototactic, other species are indifferent to ordinary light. However, when the light intensity is suddenly and sharply increased, a negative reaction generally follows. *Paramecia* exhibit an immediate negative response to ultraviolet rays.

5. Reactions to electric current (Galvanotaxis). *Paramecia* respond to electric stimuli. When two electrodes are placed opposite each other in a shallow dish containing *Paramecia* and a constant current applied, all the organisms swim in the same direction toward the cathode or negative electrode where they concentrate in large numbers. If the direction of the electric current is reversed while the *Paramecia* are swimming toward the cathode, the organisms reverse the direction and swim toward the new cathode.

6. Reactions to water current (Rheotaxis). *Paramecia* show a positive rheotaxis. In a gentle water current the *Paramecia* will mostly move with the flow with their anterior ends upstream.

7. Reactions to gravity (Geotaxis). *Paramecia* generally exhibit a negative response to gravity as seen in a culture where many individuals gather close under the surface film with their anterior ends uppermost. If *Paramecia* are introduced in an inverted water filled U-shaped tube stoppered at both the ends, they immediately move upward into the horizontal part of the tube.

REPRODUCTION

Paramecium reproduces asexually by transverse binary fission and also undergoes several types of nuclear reorganization, such as conjugation, endomixis, autogamy, cytogamy and hemixis, etc.

Transverse Binary Fission

Transverse binary fission is the commonest type of asexual reproduction in *Paramecium.* It is a distinctly unique asexual process in which one fully grown specimen divides into two daughter individuals without leaving a parental corpse. The plane of division is through the centre of the cell and in a plane at right angles to the long axis of the body. Division of the cell body as a whole is always preceded by division of the nuclei; indeed it appears that reproduction is initiated by nuclear activity and division.

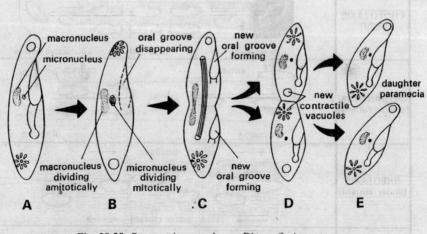

Fig. 20.20. *Paramecium caudatum.* Binary fission.

Paramecium reproduces by transverse binary fission during favourable conditions, In binary fission the micronucleus divides by mitosis into two daughter micronuclei, which move to opposite ends of the cell. The macronucleus elongates and divides transversely by amitosis. Another cytopharynx is budded off and two new contractile vacuoles appear, one near anterior end and another near posterior end. In the meantime a constriction furrow appears near the middle of the body and deepens until the cytoplasm is completely divided. The resulting two "daughter" paramecia are of equal size, each containing a set of cell organelles. Of the two daughter paramecia produced, the anterior one is called proter and the posterior one is called opisthe. They grow to full size before another division occurs. The process of binary fission requires about two hours to complete and may occur one to four times per day, yielding 2 to 16 individuals. About 600 generations are produced in a year. The rate of multiplication depends upon external conditions of food, temperature, age of the culture, and population density; also on the internal factors of heredity and physiology. Naturally, if all the descendants of one individual were to survive and reproduce, the number of paramecia produced would soon equal to the volume of the earth. The term clone is used to refer to all the individuals that have been produced from one individual by fission. All the members of a clone are hereditary alike.

Conjugation

Ordinarily *Paramecium* multiplies by binary fission for long periods of time, but at intervals this may be interrupted by the joining of two animals along their oral surfaces for the sexual process of conjugation.

Conjugation is defined as the temporary union of two individuals which mutually exchange micronuclear material. It is unique type of a sexual process in which two organisms separate soon after exchange of nuclear material. Sonneborn (1947), on the basis of mating behaviour of *Paramecium*, has reported that each species of *Paramecium* exists in a number of varieties or syngens. Further, within each syngen there are a number of mating types; usually two. The mating types remain morphologically identical but they exhibit physiological differences. In *P. aurelia*, there are 14 syngens and 28 mating types, while in *P. caudatum*, there are 16 syngens and 32 mating types. Observations have been made that usually paramecia neither conjugate with members of their own mating type nor with the other varieties, but only with the second mating type of their own variety.

Factors inducing conjugation. The factors inducing conjugation vary from species to species but some of them are given below :

1. Conjugation occurs usually under unfavourable living conditions; starvation or shortage of food and particular bacterial diet or certain chemicals are said to induce the process of conjugation in certain species of *Paramecium*.

2. Conjugation occurs after about 300 asexual generations of binary fission, or it alternates with binary fission at long intervals to rejuvenate the dying clone, *i.e.,* it occurs in the individuals which must have passed through desirable number of asexual generations, said to be the period of immaturity, and then they become sexually mature to conjugate.

3. Conjugation occurs when there is a change in the physiological condition of paramecia, then it occurs between such individuals which are somewhat smaller in size (210 microns long) and they are at a stage which may be regarded as a period of unhealthy old age; the paramecia of this condition will die if not allowed to conjugate.

4. Sudden darkness in light conditions and low temperatures are said to induce the process of conjugation in some species.

5. Conjugation does not take place during night or darkness; it starts in early morning and continues till afternoon.

6. A proteinous substance in the cilia of mating type individuals is said to induce conjugation.

Process of conjugation. The process of conjugation differs in different species of *Paramecium*, but the undernoted account relates to the conjugation process of *P. caudatum* (Fig. 20.21).

In conjugation two *Paramecium caudatum* (referred to as preconjugants) of the opposite mating types of the same variety come together with their ventral surfaces and unite by their oral grooves; their cilia produce a substance on the surface of the body which causes adhesion of the two conjugating paramecia. They stop feeding and their oral groove apparatus disappears. The pellicle and ectoplasm, at the point of contact, of both break down, and a protoplasmic bridge is formed between the two animals. Now, these individuals are called conjugants. In this condition, the conjugating pair swim actively and simultaneously a series of nuclear changes take place in each conjugant as described below :

The macronucleus begins to disintegrate, it becomes loose in texture and forms a complex twisted skein, during the latter half of the conjugation period it will finally disappear being absorbed in the cytoplasm. The micronucleus of each conjugant divides twice, one of them being a reduction division. Thus, four haploid daughter micronuclei are produced in each conjugant. Three of these four micronuclei degenerate in each, so that only one remains. The remaining micronucleus of each conjugant divides mitotically into two unequal pronuclei or gametic nuclei forming a larger **stationary female pronucleus** and a smaller, active **migratory male pronucleus.** The migratory pronucleus of one conjugant crosses over the protoplasmic bridge and fuses with the stationary

pronucleus of other conjugant to form a **synkaryon** or conjugation nucleus in which the diploid number of chromosomes is restored and there has been an exchange of hereditary material. The process has been compared with fertilization in higher animals, but this is not fertilization because no gametes are involved. The conjugants now (after about 12–48 hours) separate and are called **exconjugants.** The synkaryon of each exconjugant divides three times to form eight micronuclei in each exconjugant. Four of the eight micronuclei enlarge and become macronuclei, and three of the other four micronuclei disappear. The remaining micro- nucleus divides and at the same time the exconjugant divides by binary fission into two cells, each having two macronuclei and one micronucleus. The cells and their micronuclei divide a second time to form four paramecia from each exconjugant, so that each has one macronucleus and one micr- onucleus. The new macronucleus, as also the micronucleus, have been made of new material. These new nuclei probably contain new and different potential which is reflected in the healthy indi- viduals.

Significance of conjugation. A clone will die out if nuclear reorganization does not occur, but the clone can be **rejuvenated** to regain its former vig-

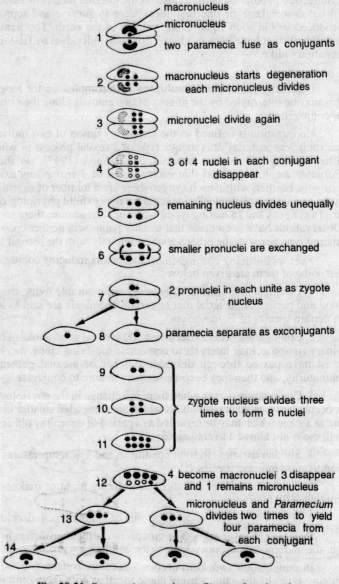

1. macronucleus / micronucleus — two paramecia fuse as conjugants
2. macronucleus starts degeneration each micronucleus divides
3. micronuclei divide again
4. 3 of 4 nuclei in each conjugant disappear
5. remaining nucleus divides unequally
6. smaller pronuclei are exchanged
7. 2 pronuclei in each unite as zygote nucleus
8. paramecia separate as exconjugants
9.
10. zygote nucleus divides three times to form 8 nuclei
11.
12. 4 become macronuclei 3 disappear and 1 remains micronucleus
13. micronucleus and *Paramecium* divides two times to yield four paramecia from each conjugant
14.

Fig. 20.21. *Paramecium caudatum.* Stages of conjugation.

our by nuclear rearrangement, this nuclear reorganization is brought about by conjugation, thus, conjugation is essential for continued binary fission. The significance of conjugation has been summarized below.

1. Conjugation serves as a process of **rejuvenation** and **reorganization** by which the vitality of the race is restored. If conjugation does not occur for long periods, the paramecia weaken and die. (**Woodruff's** claim of keeping paramecia healthy for 22,000 generations without conjugation is disproved by **Sonneborn,** because he showed that all of Woodruff's paramecia belonged to the same mating type).

2. There is no distinction of sex in conjugants though only paramecia of two different mating types of the same variety will conjugate.

3. There is no distinction of sex, yet the active migratory pronucleus is regarded as male and the stationary pronucleus as the female.

4. Conjugation is only a temporary union, there is no fusion of cytoplasm and no zygote is produced, but the nucleus of each exconjugant contains hereditary material from two conjugating individuals.

5. Conjugation brings about replacement of the macronucleus with material from the synkaryon, this is an event of fundamental importance. In binary fission the chromosomes of the macronucleus were distributed at random to the daughter cells, continued binary fission had made the clone weak with some structural abnormalities. Conjugation brings about the formation of the correct number of chromosomes in the macronucleus, so that the race is renewed in vigour. The role of the micronucleus is to restore a balanced chromosome and gene complex.

ABERRANT BEHAVIOUR IN REPRODUCTION

Paramecium shows certain variations in its nuclear behaviour during fission and conjugation, these deviations are endomixis, autogamy, cytogamy and hemixis. In the first three processes genetical recombination is effected and a new macronucleus is formed from the micronucleus.

Endomixis

Woodruff and Erdmann (1914) first of all reported a new nuclear reorganization process, endomixis (Gr., *endon*=within; *mixis* = mingling) in *Paramecium aurelia*, a bimicronucleate species (Fig. 20.22). This process was de-

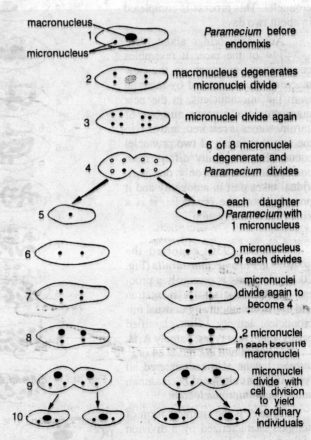

scribed as occurring periodically in which a new macronuclear apparatus is produced without synkaryon formation. Endomixis occurs within a single individual. According to Woodruff and Erdmann, the macronucleus degenerates and the micronuclei divide twice to form eight micronuclei. Six micronuclei degenerate and two remain. With only two micronuclei remaining, the animal divides by fission into two cells, each with one micronucleus. The micronucleus of each daughter cell divides twice to form four micronuclei. Two micronuclei enlarge to form macronuclei. The animal and its micronuclei divide so that two daughter individuals are formed, each having one macronucleus and two micronuclei.

Endomixis occurs in that variety of *P. aurelia* which does not conjugate, hence, the effect of endomixis may be the same as that of the conjugation since both processes bring about replacement of the macronucleus with material from the micronucleus, and both processes rejuvenate the vitality of the race. But the two processes differ because there is no fusion of pronuclei in endomixis; endomixis may be

Labels in figure:
- macronucleus
- micronucleus
- 1 — *Paramecium* before endomixis
- 2 — macronucleus degenerates micronuclei divide
- 3 — micronuclei divide again
- 4 — 6 of 8 micronuclei degenerate and *Paramecium* divides
- 5 — each daughter *Paramecium* with 1 micronucleus
- 6 — micronucleus of each divides
- 7 — micronuclei divide again to become 4
- 8 — 2 micronuclei in each become macronuclei
- 9 — micronuclei divide with cell division to yield 4 ordinary individuals
- 10

Fig. 20.22. *Paramecium aurelia.* Diagram showing nuclear changes during endomixis.

compared to parthenogenesis. However, some workers have claimed with good reasons that endomixis is not a valid process and it has been described due to faulty observation. In all probability endomixis does not take place and it may only be a specialized case of autogamy.

Later, Erdmann and Woodruff (1916) reported endomixis in *Paramecium caudatum*. Diller, however, does not believe in the validity of this process and feels that Erdmann and Woodruff have simply combined the stages of hemixis and autogamy into one scheme, endomixis.

Autogamy

Diller (1934,1936) and Sonneborn (1950) described a process of self-fertilization or autogamy occurring in single individual in *Paramecium aurelia* (Fig. 20.23). He reported that in autogamy three micronuclear (pregamic) divisions, involving maturation, produce the gametic nuclei (pronuclei). During autogamy in *P. aurelia,* the two micronuclei divide twice (once meiotically) to form eight micronuclei, six of which degenerate. Meanwhile the macronucleus grows into skein-like mass which breaks into pieces later to be absorbed in the cytoplasm. Two of the eight micronuclei, as pronuclei, enter a protoplasmic cone bulging near the cell mouth. The two pronuclei fuse to form synkaryon.

The synkaryon divides twice to form four micronuclei. Two micronuclei become macronuclei. The *Paramecium* and its micronuclei divide to form two daughter individuals, each with one macronucleus and two micronuclei. This process is completed in about two days.

Autogamy brings about rejuvenation of the race. It resembles conjugation inasmuch as the new macronucleus is formed by material from the micronucleus, in the new macronucleus correct number of chromosomes is restored; and also in the fact that fusion of two pronuclei occurs. But autogamy differs from conjugation because only one individual takes part in autogamy and it provides both the pronuclei, it is a kind of self fertilization.

Hemixis

Diller (1936) reported the hemixis in *Paramecium aurelia* (Fig. 20.24). Hemixis is primarily a process of macronuclear fragmentation and division without any unusual micronuclear activity. Diller classified hemixis into fuor types, namely A, B, C, and D as shown in Fig. 20.24 in *P. aurelia* but he also encountered all types in mass cultures of *P. caudatum* and *P. multimicronucleatum.*

Type A is the simplest form of hemixis characterized by a division of the macronucleus into two or more parts. This division is not synchronized with micronuclear division.

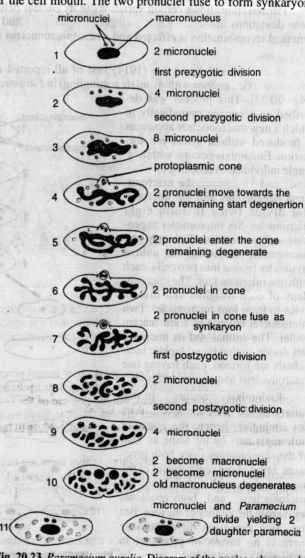

micronuclei   macronucleus

1   2 micronuclei

first prezygotic division

2   4 micronuclei

second prezygotic division

3   8 micronuclei

protoplasmic cone

4   2 pronuclei move towards the cone remaining start degenertion

5   2 pronuclei enter the cone remaining degenerate

6   2 pronuclei in cone

2 pronuclei in cone fuse as synkaryon

7   first postzygotic division

8   2 micronuclei

second postzygotic division

9   4 micronuclei

10   2 become macronuclei
2 become micronuclei
old macronucleus degenerates

micronuclei and *Paramecium* divide yielding 2 daughter paramecia

11

Fig. 20.23. *Paramecium aurelia.* Diagram of the nuclear changes during autogamy .

Type B is characterized by the extrusion of one to 20 or more chromatin balls from the macronucleus into the cytoplasm.

Type C is characterized by the simultaneous splitting of the macronucleus into two or more major portions and the extrusion of macronuclear balls into cytoplasm.

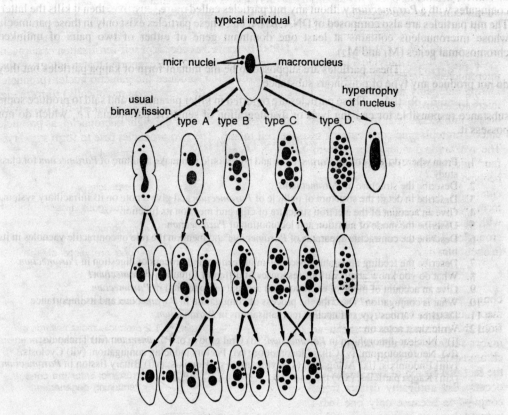

Fig. 20.24. *Paramecium aurelia.* Diagrams of the macronuclear behaviour during hemixis.

Type D is considered to represent pathologic conditions in which the macronucleus undergoes complete fragmentation into chromatin balls that eventually disappear from the cell. Micronuclei generally disappear before the dissolution of the macronucleus.

Cytogamy

Wichterman (1939) has reported another sexual process in *Paramecium caudatum,* which he termed cytogamy. In cytogamy there is no nuclear exchange. In this process two individuals come together by their ventral surfaces, but the pellicle of the two individuals does not break down. The micronucleus of each individual divides thrice to form eight micronuclei, six of which disintegrate in each individual. The two remaining micronuclei fuse to form a synkaryon in each cell. The animals now separate.

Cytogamy differs from autogamy in that there are two animals in contact with each other, but it resembles autogamy and conjugation in the fusion of two pronuclei. Cytogamy differs from conjugation in that there is no nuclear exchange between the two animals which come together.

SOME CYTOPLASMIC PARTICLES REPORTED IN *PARAMECIUM*

1. **Kappa particles.** In 1938, T.M. Sonneborn reported that some races (known as killers or killer strain) of *Paramecium* produce a poisonous substance, called paramecin which is lethal to other individuals called sensitives. The paramecin is water soluble, diffusible and depends for its production upon some particles located in the cytoplasm of the *Paramecium* (killer strain). These particles are called kappa particles. The kappa particles have DNA and RNA. A killer *Paramecium* may contain hundreds of kappa particles. The detailed study of these particles has revealed that a

dominant gene (K) in the nucleus of *Paramecium* is necessary for kappa particles to exist, multiply and produce paramecin.

2. mμ particles. R.W. Siegel (1952) reported another type of killer particles in the cytoplasm of some *Paramecium*. A *Paramecium* with mμ particles is called mate killer because when it conjugates with a *Paramecium* without any mμ particles called mate sensitive, then it kills the latter. The mμ particles are also composed of DNA, RNA, etc. These particles exist only in those paramecia whose micronucleus contains at least one dominant gene of either of two pairs of unlinked chromosomal genes (M_1 and M_2).

3. Pi particles. These particles are supposed to be the mutant form of kappa particles but they do not produce any type of poisonous substance.

4. Lambda particles. These particles are reported in killer paramecia and said to produce some substance responsible for causing lysis or disintegration of sensitive paramecia, *i.e.*, which do not possess it.

REVISION QUESTIONS

1. From where do you collect *Paramecium* and how would you make a culture of *Paramecium* for class study ?
2. Describe the structure of *Paramecium*.
3. Describe in detail the structure of pellicle of *Paramecium* and give a note on its infraciliary system.
4. Give an account of the electron structure of cilia and mention its function.
5. Describe the mode of nutrition and locomotion of *Paramecium*.
6. Describe the contractile apparatus of *Paramecium* and mention the role of contractile vacuoles in its life.
7. Describe the feeding apparatus, mechanism of feeding and process of digestion in *Paramecium*.
8. What do you know about various responses of different stimuli in *Paramecium*?
9. Give an account of mode of excretion and asexual reproduction in *Paramecium*.
10. What is conjugation? Describe the process of conjugation in *Paramecium* and its importance.
11. Describe various types of nuclear reorganisations in *Paramecium*.
12. Write short notes on :
    (i) Nuclear dimorphism in *Paramecium;* (ii) Oral groove of *Paramecium*; (iii) Trichocyst;
    (iv) Neuromotorium; (v) Ciliary locomotion; (vi) Factors inducing conjugation; (vii) Cyclosis;
    (viii) Endomixis; (ix) Autogamy; (x) Cytogamy; (xi) Hemixis; (xii) Binary fission in *Paramecium*;
    (xiii) Kappa particles; (xiv) mμ particles.

21

Vorticella

Vorticella (L., *vortex*=whirl pool) is another ciliate which is stalked and has over 200 species, most of them are found in freshwater ponds which are rich in minerals but with no putrefaction. Some species are marine, some are epizoic, and a few live within their hosts. The commonest species is *Vorticella campanula*, but *V. picta, V. monliata, V. nebulifera* and *V. microstoma* are also fairly common. *Vorticella campanula* is described here in detail.

VORTICELLA
SYSTEMATIC POSITION

Phylum	...	**Protozoa**
Subphylum	...	**Ciliophora**
Class	...	**Ciliatea**
Subclass	...	**Peritrichia**
Order	...	**Peritrichida**
Genus	...	*Vorticella*
Species	...	*campanula*

HABIT AND HABITAT

Vorticella campanula is found in freshwater ponds, lakes, rivers and streams with aquatic vegetation. It is worldwide in distribution. *Vorticella* is solitary and not colonial but usually social, several of them being found together. *Vorticella* is sedentary (fixed) form. It is commonly attached by a long highly contractile stalk to some submerged objects like weeds, animals and stones, etc. *Vorticella* is often found in large groups. All the individuals in the group, however, remain free and independent of each other. They are found in abundance in stagnant water rich in decaying organic matter and feeds largely on bacteria. But *V. campanula* and *V. nebulifera* live only in uncontaminated water where bacterial growth is not good.

CULTURE

Culture of *Vorticella* is prepared in the same way as that of *Amoeba*. Make an infusion of hay and dead leaves in rain or distilled water, let this stand for some days, a brownish scum will be formed on the surface, below which many *Vorticella* will be found; this shows the presence of cysts in *Vorticella*.

STRUCTURE

Shape, size and colour. *Vorticella* is a microscopic stalked form with an inverted bell-shaped asymmetrical body. Due to the bell-shaped body it is often called bell-animalcule. The largest species is *Vorticella campanula*, the bell of which measures up to 157 microns in length and 99 microns in width and stalk varies from 53 to 4150 microns in length which is highly contractile. The colour of the animalcule is yellowish, greenish or bluish. The smallest species is *V. microstoma*, which measures about 55 microns in length and 35 microns in width.

Body or Bell. The body of *Vorticella campanula* is like an inverted bell. The detailed structure of the bell is described below.

1. Peristome. The margin or rim of the broad free end of the bell is thickened and is termed as peristomial collar or lip. Inside the peristomial collar is a narrow, shallow, circular and marginal depression called the peristome or oral groove. The peristome surrounds a broad, slightly convex circular central disc, the peristomial disc or oral disc that seems to close the opening of the bell. The peristomial disc is fused with the collar on one side. With the result the peristome does not form a complete ring. The peristomial disc can be withdrawn when the peristome contracts and covers it.

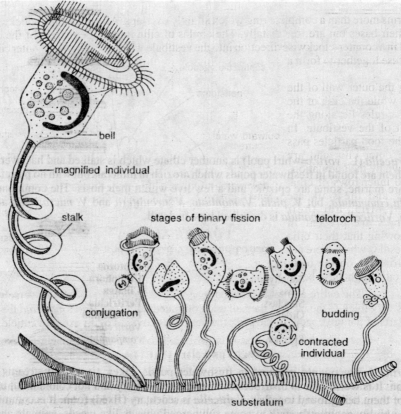

Fig. 21.1. *Vorticella.* A group of individuals in different states.

bell

magnified individual

stalk

stages of binary fission

telotroch

conjugation

budding

contracted individual

substratum

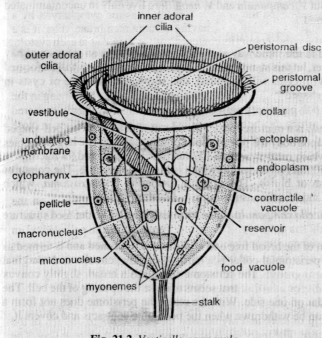

Fig. 21.2. *Vorticella campanula.*

inner adoral cilia

outer adoral cilia

peristomial disc

peristomal groove

collar

vestibule

undulating membrane

ectoplasm

endoplasm

cytopharynx

contractile vacuole

pellicle

reservoir

macronucleus

micronucleus

food vacuole

myonemes

stalk

2. Vestibule. Between the peristome and the peristomial disc is a permanently open sunken space on the left side, it is called a **vestibule** or **infundibulum.** From the vestibule a narrow **cytopharynx** leads inwards. The cytopharynx has no cilia and it opens into the endoplasm. Between the vestibule and cytopharynx is a **cytostome** which can open or close.

3. Cilia. There is an adoral wreath of cilia on the peristomial region and the rest of the body is devoid of cilia. The peristomial groove bears three concentric rows of adoral cilia arrannged into circlets. The inner circlet has two row circles of cilia which are closely associated forming a double row, its cilia standing straight up and keep up constant undulations. The outer circlet is single and has short cilia which are inclined outwards over the collar like a shelf and guide the food into the vestibule. Each cir-

of cilia forms more than a complete ring which slightly overlaps. All cilia lie anti-clockwise, they are fused at their bases but are free distally. The circles of cilia turn at the margin of the disc and are continued in a counter-clockwise direction into the vestibule where the cilia of the outer circle become

long and fuse together to form a triangular **undulating membrane** along the outer wall of the vestibule, while the cilia of the two inner circles lie along the inner wall of the vestibule. In feeding, the food particles pass along the outer cilia and are driven down by the undulations of the two inner rows of cilia. The body and the stalk are devoid of cilia, but their kinetosomes are present in circles showing that their cilia are lost, besides which there are circular striations on the body where the cilia might have been.

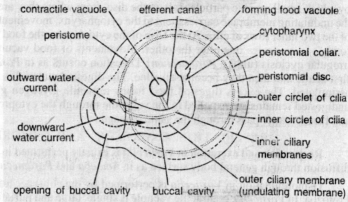

Fig. 21.3. *Vorticella.* Peristome seen from above (diagrammatic).

4. Pellicle. The entire animal is covered by a **pellicle** which is ringed transversely by parallel striae, it is very thick at the base of the bell and continued with stalk. In *V. monliata* the pellicle has nodular warts of paraglycogen. In the stalk the pellicle is covered by an external cuticle.

5. Cytoplasm. The body cytoplasm is differentiated into an outer layer of clear and firm **ectoplasm** or **cortex** and an inner fluid and granular **endoplasm** or **medulla.**

(i) **Ectoplasm.** The ectoplasm is modified to form a **myoneme system** having longitudinal, oblique and circular **myonemes,** they are more visible in the base of the bell. Longitudinal myonemes shorten the body, oblique myonemes pull the disc inwards, and the circular myonemes contract the peristome and close it over the disc.

(ii) **Endoplasm.** The endoplasm is granular and fluid-like. It contains the nuclei, contractile vacuole and food vacuoles.

Near the cytopharynx is a clear space called the **reservoir** which joins the cytopharynx by a narrow tube. Close to the reservoir is a **contractile vacuole** having a lining membrane, thus, it is a permanent vacuole which is osmoregulatory and it pours its contents into the reservoir at each systole, from where they pass out through the vestibule, (In *V. picta* and *V. monliata* there are two contractile vacuoles.) Near the reservoir is a **cytoproct** opening into the vestibule, it is a temporary or permanent aperture in different species.

There is a large, long, horse-shoe-shaped **macronucleus** and a **micronucleus,** both lying in the endoplasm. The macronucleus is highly polyploid with a large amount of chromatin material scattered in the nucleoplasm. The micronucleus, which can be seen only in a stained condition, lies in close association to macronucleus.

Stalk. The bell-shaped body of *Vorticella* is attached to weeds or stones by a long, thin, unbranched and highly contractile stalk. It is a prolongation of the pellicle and ectoplasm of the bell. The body myonemes combine and run through the centre of the stalk as a single loose spiral known as an **axial filament** or **spasmoneme.** In *V. campanula* there are **thecoplastic granules** on the spasmonema. When the stalk is contracted the spiral spasmonema coils up tightly and looks like a spring. Around the spasmoneme the stalk has a **protoplasmic sheath** covered by the pellicle and an external cuticle. *Vorticella* is extremely sensitive to any mechanical stimulus, slightest contact causes instantaneous coiling of the stalk into a tight spiral, the body becomes rounded, the disc is pulled in and the peristome closes over it.

LOCOMOTION

Vorticella does not move freely because it is usually found fixed aborally by its long highly contractile stalk. However, with the help of stalk and myonemes, the bell sways to and fro in the surrounding water like a flower in a breeze. The individuals of a group move in their own way. The detached individuals swim freely by means of cilia and are referred to as **telotrochs.**

NUTRITION

Nutrition is holozoic as in *Paramecium*. It is omnivorous but its food generally consists of small Protozoa, bacteria and organic bits. The cilia of the peristome and the disc produce a current of water by which small organic particles fall on the disc, from where they are carried into the vestibule; then the undulating membrane carries them to the cytopharynx, movement of food is aided by undulations of the two inner rows of cilia. At the base of the cytopharynx the food particles along with some water form food vacuoles one after the other. Movements of food vacuoles in the endoplasm are in an irregular cyclosis (unlike *Paramecium)*. Digestion occurs as in *Paramecium* ; the food vacuoles at first acidic and then they become alkaline. The digested material is absorbed in the endoplasm and assimilated. The excess digested food forms refractile glycogen granules in the endoplasm. The undigested remains are expelled in the vestibule through the cytoproct. Thus, in *Vorticella* the food and faecal matter pass through the same passage.

RESPIRATION, EXCRETION AND OSMOREGULATION

Respiration and excretion in *Vorticella* is exactly performed in the same way by the process of diffusion through general body surface as in *Amoeba* and *Paramecium.*

Osmoregulation in *Vorticella* is performed by the contractile vacuole, as in other freshwater Protozoa. In *Vorticella*, contractile vacuole is single, large and pulsating usually situated between the disc and vestibule in the endoplasm. The contractile vacuole opens in the vestibule by a permanent opening; it pulsates rhythmically showing diastolic and systolic phases. In fact, during diastolic phase, the excess of water drawn in the endoplasm by the process of osmosis is secreted into the contractile vacuole and during the systolic phase, the contractile vacuole expells out the excess of water into the vestibule. Thus, contractile vacuole helps in maintaining the water content in the body.

BEHAVIOUR

Vorticella exhibits high degree of contractility and irritability; it is extremely sensitive to any mechanical stimulus and also responds to external stimuli. When irritated, its all activities cease at once; the stalk is retracted and becomes coiled into closed spiral to reduce its size, then the disc is withdrawn and covered over by peristomial lip. Due to all these activities, its body becomes somewhat globular and remains motionless till normalcy is restored.

REPRODUCTION

Vorticella normally reproduces asexually by longitudinal binary fission, but at intervals conjugation also occurs which is sexual mode of reproduction. Encystment has also been reported to occur during unfavourable conditions.

Longitudinal Binary Fission

Binary fission of Peritrichia differs from that of other ciliates in being generally unequal and in a plane that is longitudinal running along the oral-aboral axis or nearly so. *Vorticella* closes its

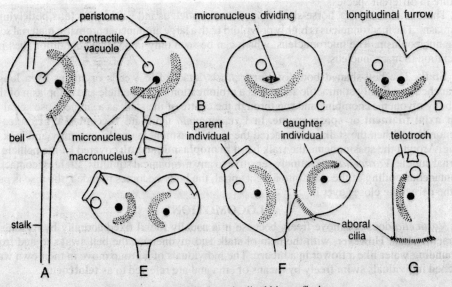

Fig. 21.4. *Vorticella.* Longitudinal binary fission.

peristome over the disc, the body becomes depressed and transversely elongated. Endoplasmic circulation continues and the contractile vacuole pulsates throughout division. The long macronucleus becomes condensed and short, it then becomes straight and lies transversely in the middle, then it divides into two amitotically. The micronucleus divides by an elongated mitosis. A constriction begins in the centre of the anterior end, and dividing the peristome, it passes down the length of the cell, just to one side of the stalk; this constriction divides the animal into two unequal parts, the slightly smaller part has no stalk, it has a ring of oral cilia and it develops a contractile vacuole and forms a ring of aboral cilia at its posterior end, it becomes cylindrical and gets detached, it is now called a telotroch. The telotroch swims away with its aboral pole foremost, it settles down by its aboral end which has a short scopula. The scopula is a circlet of stiff protoplasmic processes derived from cilia, it secretes a stalk by which the telotroch gets fixed, then it loses it scopula, its bell expands, a new disc is formed and it metamorphoses into an adult. Binary fission takes 20 to 30 minutes (Finlay, 1939). The larger product of division retains the old disc and stalk and it may be called the parent, while the smaller telotroch is the offspring. No such distinction is seen in other Protozoa. In unfavourable conditions the normal *Vorticella* also grows a posterior ring of cilia to become a telotroch which breaks from its stalk and swims away to some favourable spot and then grows a stalk. At times *Vorticella* encysts in a two-layered cyst while still fixed to its stalk, then the cyst falls from the stalk, on excystment it swims away as a telotroch.

Conjugation

Conjugation is a mode of sexual reproduction, which is very characteristic in *Vorticella*. The process of conjugation and syngamy was studied by Maupas (1888) in *Vorticella nebulifera* and by Finlay (1943) in *Vorticella microstoma*. However, the process of sexual reproduction in *Vorticella* described hereunder is a generalized description, it can be studied in the following two phases :

  (a) Formation of micro- and macrogametes, and

  (b) Conjugation of micro- and macroconjugants and their fusion.

  (a) Formation of micro- and macroconjugants. In sexual reproduction, *Vorticella* divides by binary fission into two very unequal parts, the larger cell is the ordinary individual, while the very small cell is called a microconjugant. In some species more than one microconjugant is produced by repeated fission. The microconjugants acquire a girdle of cilia at the posterior end of each. The microconjugants become detached and swim about; their swimming is an adaptation for conjugation in sessile species; microconjugants differ from telotrochs in being smaller and in the fact that they never metamorphose into adults nor do they form stalks. Microconjugants never feed or encyst, they live for about 24 hours, after which they die. A stalked *Vorticella* undergoes nuclear modifications, though it appears normal, it is then known as a macroconjugant. The macroconjugant is morphologically the same as a normal trophic individual, stationary and passive but it is specialized physiologically and it can attract microconjugants for about 2 hours.

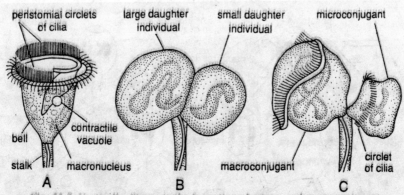

Fig. 21.5. *Vorticella.* Stages in the formation of micro- and macroconjugant.

  (b) Fusion of conjugants. While swimming, when a microconjugant approaches a macroconjugant then it gets attached to the lower end of macroconjugant near its stalk (Fig. 21.6). Thus, both the conjugants come together. Soon, cilia and pellicle of the microconjugant is thrown off and nuclear changes start taking place simultaneously in both the conjugants; the nuclear changes occur in the following way (Fig. 21.6).

(i) The macronuclei of both the conjugants degenerate and finally absorbed in the cytoplasm.

(ii) The micronucleus of macroconjugant divides two times to form four daughter micronuclei. But the micronucleus of microconjugant divides three times to form eight daughter micronuclei. In these divisions, the last being reduction division.

(iii) Three out of four daughter micronuclei of macroconjugant and seven out of eight daughter micronuclei of microconjoint degenerate. Thus, the left out one micronucleus in macroconjugant becomes female pronucleus, while the one micronucleus in microconjugant becomes the male pronucleus which are haploid.

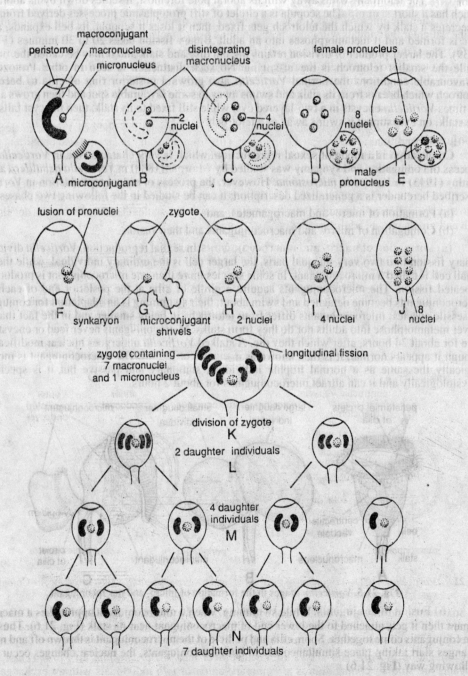

Fig. 21.6. *Vorticella.* Stages in conjugation.

(iv) The partition wall in between two conjugants disappears, thus, complete union occurs between the two conjugants.

(v) The male and female pronuclei fuse together to form zygote nucleus or synkaryon.

(vi) The synkaryon divides three times to form eight daughter nuclei, seven of these become macronuclei and one micronucleus.

(vii) This micronucleus divides into two and the zygote also divides, so that two daughter individuals are formed; one with four macronuclei and one micronucleus, and the other with three macronuclei and one micronucleus.

(viii) Then the micronucleus of each individual goes on dividing with the body of individual until the daughter individuals with one micro- and one macronucleus is formed.

(ix) Thus, the daughter individual with four macronuclei divides twice forming 4 offsprings (each with one macro- and one micronucleus) and the daughter individual with three macronuclei produces 3 offsprings (each with one macro- and one micronucleus). Therefore, total 7 individuals are formed which later develop stalk and metamorphose into adults.

Encystment

Von Brand (1923) has reported the formation of cyst around the body of *Vorticella* during unfavourable conditions. The encysted body breaks off from the stalk. In an encysted condition, the myonemes become indistinct, the pulsating rate of contractile vacuole is slowed down and finally it disappers, the peristome is also absorbed. In this condition, the *Vorticella* tides over the unfavourable conditions. After the return of favourable conditions, the cyst breaks and the individual emerges out (Fig. 21.7, E to G) develops contractile vacuole and becomes enlarged. It grows an aboral circlet of cilia to become a telotroch. It swims freely for some time and then settles at some substratum, develops a stalk and grows into an adult *Vorticella*.

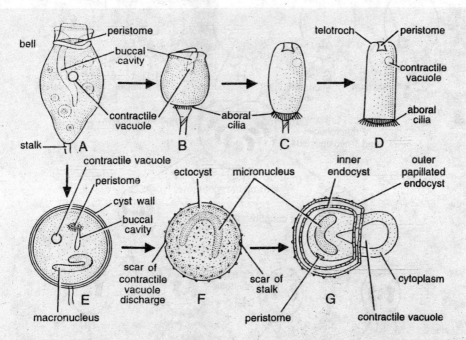

Fig. 21.7. *Vorticella*. A to D – Formation of telotroch; E and F – Encystment (E – Cyst in section, F– Complete cyst); G – Excystment.

Sometimes, during unfavourable conditions, *Vorticella* develops a posterior ring of cilia to become a telotroch. It separates away from the stalk and swims away to some favourable place where it develops stalk and starts leading normal life (Fig. 21.7, A to D). The telotroch helps in its dispersal.

Conjugation in *Vorticella* shows an advance over that in *Paramecium*. In *Paramecium* the conjugants are similar, conjugation is a temporary union of two individuals with an exchange of nuclear material, but there is no fusion of cytoplasm, both exconjugants reproduce by fission. In *Vorticella* conjugating gametes are dissimilar anisogametes, conjugation is permanent with a fusion of both cytoplasm and nuclei of gametes to form a zygote which reproduces by fission. *Vorticella* also shows a differentiation of sex in its dimorphic gametes, hence, the sexual process in *Vorticella* is somewhat intermediate between conjugation (in *Paramecium*) and syngamy (in *Plasmodium*).

REVISION QUESTIONS

1. Give an account of the structure and life-history of *Vorticella*.
2. Write an illustrated account of reproduction of *Vorticella*.
3. Give an account of habit, habitat and structure of *Vorticella*. Mention characters in which it resembles with *Paramecium*.
4. Give an account of conjugation in *Vorticella* and mention the way in which it differs from that of *Paramecium*.
5. Write notes on:
   (i) Bell of *Vorticella;* (ii) Peristome; (iii) Telotroch, (iv) Encystment in *Vorticella;* (v) Asexual reproduction of *Vorticella*.

22

Protozoa : Characters, Classification and Types

DEFINITION

The Protozoa may be defined as *'microscopic, acellular animalcules existing singly or in colonies, without tissues and organs, having one or more nuclei. When in colonies, they differ from Metazoa in having all the individuals alike except those engaged in reproductive activities'*.

GENERAL CHARACTERS

1. The protozoans are small, generally microscopic animalcules.

2. Simplest and primitive of all animals with very simple body organisation, *i.e.*, protoplasmic grade of organisation.

3. Acellular animals, without tissues and organs.

4. Body naked or covered by pellicle but in some forms body is covered with shells and often provided with internal skeleton.

5. Protozoans are solitary or colonial; in colonial forms the individuals are alike and independent.

6. Body shape variable; it may be spherical, oval, elongated or flattened.

7. Body protoplasm is differentiated into an outer ectoplasm and inner endoplasm.

8. Protozoans may have one or more nuclei; nuclei may be monomorphic or dimorphic, vesicular or massive. Vesicular nuclei are commonly spherical, oval or biconvex, consist of a central body, the endosome (nucleolus) encircled by a zone of nuclear sap.

9. Locomotory organelles are pseudopodia, flagella, cilia or none.

10. Nutrition may be holozoic (animal-like), holophytic (plant-like), saprozoic or parasitic. Digestion intracellular, takes place inside the food vacuoles.

11. Respiration occurs by diffusion through general body surface.

12. Excretion also occurs through general body surface but in some forms through a temporary opening in the ectoplasm or through a permanent pore, the cytopyge.

13. Contractile vacuoles perform osmoregulation in freshwater forms and also help in removing excretory products.

14. Reproduction asexual or sexual; asexual reproduction occurs by binary fission, multiple fission, budding or sporulation and sexual reproduction is performed by gamete formation or conjugation.

15. Life cycle often exhibits alternation of generation, *i.e.*, it includes asexual and sexual phases.

16. Encystment usually occurs to tide over the unfavourable conditions and it also helps in dispersal.

17. The single celled body of Protozoa performs all the vital activities of life and, therefore, no physiological division of labour is exhibited by them.

18. The protozoans exhibit mainly two modes of life, free-living inhabiting freshwater, salt-water and damp places, and parasitic living as ecto- and endoparasites. They are also commensal in habit.

CLASSIFICATION

The classification followed here is given by the Committee on Taxonomy and Taxonomic Problems of the Society of Protozoologists (Honigberg *et al.,* 1964). According to Honigberg *et al.,* (1964) Protozoa have been classified into four subphyla.

SUBPHYLUM I.
SARCOMASTIGOPHORA

1. Organelles of locomotion are pseudopodia or flagella,
2. Nucleus is of single type (monomorphic).
3. There is no spore formation.
4. Syngamy occurs in reproduction.

Superclass A. Mastigophora

1. They are commonly called flagellates.
2. Organelles of locomotion in adults are flagella.
3. Body is covered by pellicle.
4. Binary fission is longitudinal.
5. They are mostly free-living though some are parasitic.

Class 1. Phytomastigophorea

1. They generally possess chromatophores.
2. There are usually only one or two flagella.
3. The nucleus is vesicular.

Order 1. Chrysomonadina

1. Small flagellates with yellow or brown chromatophores.
2. One to three flagella.
3. Siliceous cysts.
4. Marine and freshwater.

   Examples : *Chromulina, Ochromonas, Chrysamoeba.*

Order 2. Coccolithophorida

1. Tiny marine flagellates covered by calcareous platelets coccoliths.
2. Two flagella.
3. Yellow to brown chromoplasts.
4. No endogenous siliceous cysts.

   Examples : *Coccolithus, Rhabdosphaera.*

Order 3. Heterochlorida

1. Two unequal flagella.
2. Yellow green chromoplasts.
3. Siliceous cysts.

   Examples : *Heterochloris, Myxochloris.*

Order 4. Cryptomonadida

1. They have green, yellow, brown or colourless chromatophores which form starch.
2. They have two flagella.
3. They have a gullet.

   Examples : *Chilomonas, Cryptomonas.*

Order 5. Dinoflagellida

1. There are two flagella, one lying transversely and the other pointing backwards.
2. Body is covered with thick cellulose which

may have an equatorial groove.
3. Chromatophores are green, yellow, or brown.
4. Reserve food is starch or oil.
5. There are complex vacuoles which are not contractile.

   Examples : *Noctiluca, Ceratium.*

Order 6. Euglenida

1. They have one or two flagella.
2. Pellicle is thick.
3. There is a mouth and a reservoir which contains the roots of flagella and receives the contents of the contractile vacuole.
4. They often have a stigma.
5. Reserve food is paramylum and oil.

   Examples : *Euglena, Peranema.*

Order 7. Volvocida (Phytomonadida)

1. Body is covered with cellulose.
2. There are two flagella.
3. There is a mouth or gullet.
4. Generally there is a stigma.
5. Chromatophores are green.
6. Reserve food is starch.
7. They undergo syngamy.

   Examples: *Volvox, Eudorina.*

Class 2. Zoomastigophorea
(Zoomastigina)

1. They have no chromatophores.
2. There are one to many flagella,
3. Often there is an undulating membrane.
4. Most of them are parasitic.

Order 1. Choanoflagellida

1. There is a single anterior flagellum surrounded at its base by a delicate collar.
2. They are solitary or colonial and are free-living in salt or freshwater.

   Example: *Proterospongia.*

Order 2. Rhizomastigida

1. They have pseudopodia and one to four flagella.
2. They are mostly free-living.

   Examples: *Mastigamoeba, Dimorpha.*

Order 3. Hypermastigida

1. They have numerous flagella.
2. Parabasal apparatus is multiple.
3. Nucleus is single.

   Examples: *Trichonympha, Leptomonas.*

Order 4. Diplomonadida

1. They are binucleate flagellates having bilateral symmetry.

2. Flagella are two or four.
3. There is a set of accessory organelles.
4. Parasitic or free-living in freshwater.
   Examples: *Giardia, Hepamita.*

Order 5. Kinetoplastida

1. There are one to four flagella.
2. Kinetoplast is present as a self-producing orgenelle.
3. They are mostly parasitic.

Suborder 1. Bodonina

1. They typically have two unequal flagella, one directed anteriorly and the other posteriorly.
2. There is no undulating membrane.
3. Kinetoplast may be absent secondarily in some.
4. They are both free-living and parasitic forms.
   Example : *Bodo.*

Suborder 2. Trypansomatina

1. There is a single flagellum which is either free or attached to the body by means of an undulating membrane.
2. All parasitic.
   Examples: *Trypanosoma, Leishmania.*

Order 6. Bicosoecida

1. Largely freshwater flagellates encased within a lorica.
2. Two flagella, one free the other attaching posterior end of the body to shell.
   Examples: *Salpingoeca, Poteriodendron.*

Order 7. Retortamonadina

1. Gut parasites of insects or vertebrates.
2. With one to four flagella.
3. One flagellum associated with ventrally located cytostome.
   Example: *Chilomonas.*

Order 8. Oxymonadina

1. Parastic multinucleate flagellates.
2. Each nucleus with four flagella, some of which are turned posteriorly and adhere to the body surface.
   Examples : *Oxymonas, Pyrsonympha.*

Order 9. Trichomonadina

1. Parasitic flagellates.
2. Four to six flagella one of which is trailing.
   Example: *Trichomonas.*

Superclass B. Opalinata

1. They have numerous cilia-like organelles in oblique rows over the entire body surface.
2. There is no cytostome.

3. Two or more monomorphic nuclei are present.
4. Binary fission is interkinetal.
5. There is syngamy with flagellated anisogametes.
6. All are parasitic.
   Example : *Opalina.*

Superclass C. Sarcodina

1. Their organelles of locomotion are pseu- podia.
2. The amoeboid form is predominant.
3. Some have a hard shell.
4. They generally do not form spores.
5. Formation of gametes and flagellated young ones are common.

Class 1. Rhizopodea

1. Their organelles of locomotion are lobo- podia or filopodia but never axopodia.
2. They are generally creeping forms.

Subclass (i) Lobosia

1. Pseudopodia are typically lobose rarely filiform or anastomosing.

Order (a) Amoebida

1. They are typically uninucleate.
2. Ectoplasm and endoplasm are clearly differentiated.
3. The ectoplasm is never vacuolar.
4. Majority are free-living but there are many parasitic forms.
   Examples : *Amoeba, Pelomyxa, Entamoeba.*

Order (b) Arcellinida

1. The body is encased in a test or rigid external membrane.
2. Pseudopodia are extruded through a definite aperture.
3. They are free-living mostly in freshwater.
   Examples: *Arcella, Difflugia.*

Subclass (ii) Filosia

1. They have tapering and branching filopodia rarely anastomosing.
   Examples: *Gromia, Allogromia.*

Subclass (iii) Granuloreticulosia

1. They have finely granular reticulose rhizopodia (reticulopodia).

Order (a) Foraminiferida

1. They have a test with one to many chambers.
2. Test is basically chitinoid.
3. Pseudopodia emerge from aperture or wall perforation or both.
4. Reproduction with alternation of sexual and asexual generations.
5. Gametes usually flagellate.

6. Nuclear dimorphism in developmental stages of some species.
   Examples : *Globigerina, Elphidium (Polystomella).*

Subclass (iv) Mycetozoia

1. The amoeboid trophic stage develops either into a multicellular aggregation or into a true multinucleate plasmodium.
2. Life cycle complex and has sexual reproduction.
3. Usually sporangia are formed which liberate spores.
4. Nutrition is phagocytic.
   Example: *Plasmodiophora.*

Class 2. Piroplasmea

1. Small, round, rod-shaped or amoeboid parasites in vertebrate red blood cells.
   Example: *Babesia.*

Class 3. Actinopodea

1. Their organelles of locomotion are delicate and radiose axopodia.
2. They are primarily sessile or floating forms.
3. Test is present or absent.
4. Gametes are usually flagellated.
5. Reproduction is both sexual and asexual.

Subclass 1. Radiolaria

1. Central capsule is perforated by one to many pores.
2. They have spicules or a siliceous skeleton.
3. Filopodia or axopodia are present.
4. The capsule separates the protoplasm into ectoplasm and endoplasm.
5. All are marine.
   Examples : *Thalassicola. Collozoum, Lithocircus.*

Subclass 2. Acantharia

1. Imperforate, non-chitinoid central capsule without pores.
2. Anisotropic skeleton of strontium sulphate.
3. Axopodia.
4. Marine.
   Example: *Acanthometra.*

Subclass 3. Heliozoia

1. There is no central capsule.
2. Rounded body with radiating axopodia.
3. Usually naked, if a skeleton is present it is made of siliceous scales and spines.
4. They have axopodia or filopodia.
5. There may be more than one nucleus, mostly in freshwater.
   Examples : *Actinophrys, Actinosphaerium, Clathrulina.*

Subclass 4. Proteomyxidia

1. Largely marine and freshwater parasites of algae and higher plants.

2. Filopodia and reticulopodia in some species.
   Example: *Vampyrella.*

SUBPHYLUM II. SPOROZOA

1. The adult has no external organelles of locomotion.
2. They are all parasitic and incapable of active life outside their hosts.
3. Cilia or flagella may be present in gametes.
4. Syngamy takes place after which many spores are formed.
5. The spores are simple and contain one to many sporozoites.
6. Sporozoites are the infective phase.
7. Nucleus is of the single type.

Class 1. Telosporea

1. Pseudopodia are generally absent and locomotion is by gliding or body flexion.
2. Spores are formed and there are flagellated microgametes in some.
3. Reproduction is both sexual and asexual.

Subclass 1. Gregarinia

1. Mature trophozoites are large and extracellular.
2. Reproduction is entirely sexual with sporogony.
3. The spores contain eight sporozoites.
4. They are parasites in the digestive tract and body cavity of invertebrates.
   Examples : *Gregarina, Monocystis, Nematocystis.*

Subclass 2. Coccidia

1. Mature trophozoite is small and typically intracellular.
2. Being parasitic in the digestive tract or blood.
3. Gametocytes are dimorphic.
4. Sporozoites multiply by schizogony in tissue cells.

Order (a) Eucoccida

1. Schizogony takes place.
2. There are both sexual and asexual phases in the life cycle.
3. They are parasitic in epithelial and blood cells of invertebrates and vertebrates.

Suborder 1. Eimeriina

1. Macrogamete and microgametocyte develop independently.
2. There is no syzygy.
3. Microgametocyte produces many microgametes.
4. Zygote is non-motile.
5. Oocyst does not increase in size during sporogony.
6. Sporozoites are encased in sporocyst.

Example: *Eimeria*.

Suborder 2. Haemosporina

1. Macrogamete and microgametocyte develop independently.
2. There is no syzygy.
3. Microgametocyte produces only a few microgametes.
4. Zygote is often motile.
5. Oocyst increases in size during sporogony.
6. Sporozoites are naked.
7. Schizogony in vertebrate and sporogony in invertebrate host.
8. Haemoglobin of host cells forms pigment.
   Example: *Plasmodium*.

Class 2. Toxoplasmea

1. Spores are absent.
2. There are no flagella or pseudopodia at any stage.
3. Reproduction by binary fission.
4. Cysts are formed which have many naked sporozoites.
   Examples: *Sarcocystis, Toxoplasma.*

Class 3. Haplosporea

1. Spores are present.
2. Pseudopodia may be present but flagella are absent.
3. Reproduction is only asexual and schizogony takes place.
   Examples : *Caelosporidium, Ichthyosporidium.*

SUBPHYLUM III. CNIDOSPORA

1. Spores have several cells having one or more polar filaments which are coiled threads and can be shot out, and one or more sarcoplasms or sporoplasms (analogous to sporozoites).
2. All are parasitic.
3. Zygote gives rise to one or more troph-ozoites without sporogony.

Class 1. Myxosporidea

1. Spores are of multicellular origin.
2. There are one or more sporoplasms, with two or three valves.
3. They are parasitic in fishes.
   Examples : *Myxobolus, Ceratomyxa.*

Class 2. Microsporidea

1. Spores are of unicellular origin.
2. There is one long tubular polar filament through which the sporoplasm emerges, one valve only.
3. They are cytozoic (intracellular parasites) in arthropods and vertebrates.
   Example: *Nosema.*

SUBPHYLUM IV. CILIOPHORA

1. All possess simple ciliary organelles for locomotion, infraciliature is subpeculiar.
2. They have two nuclei, a trophic macronucleus and a reproductive micronucleus.
3. Binary fission is perkinetal.
4. Conjugation takes place with fusion of nuclei, autogamy and cytogamy also occur.
5. There are never any free gametes.
6. Nutrition is mixotrophic or heterotrophic.
7. They usually have a cytostome.

Class 1. Ciliatea

1. All possess cilia or compound ciliary structure as locomotor or food acquiring organelles at some time in the life cycle.
2. Also present is an infraciliary system, composed of basal granules below the cell surface and interconnected by longitudinal fibrils.
3. Most ciliates possess a cell mouth or cytostome.
4. Two types of nuclei, one vegetative (macronucleus) and the other reproductive (micronucleus).
5. Fission is transverse.
6. Sexual reproduction never involves the formation of free gametes.

Subclass I. Holotrichia

1. With simple or uniform body cilia.
2. Buccal ciliature either absent or, if present, usually inconspicuous.

Order 1. Gymnostomatida

1. Chiefly large ciliates with no oral ciliature.
2. Cytostome opens directly to outside.
   Examples: *Coleps, Dileptus, Didinium, Nassula.*

Order 2. Trichostomatida

1. With vestibular but no buccal ciliature.
   Examples: *Colpoda, Balantidium.*

Order 3. Chonotrichida

1. Vase-shaped ciliates lacking body cilia.
2. A funnel at the free end of the body bears vestibular cilia.
3. Chiefly marine and ectocommensal on crustaceans.
   Examples : *Spirochona, Chilodochona.*

Order 4. Apostomatida

1. Body with spirally arranged ciliation.
2. Cytostome mid-ventral.
3. Marine parasites or commensals.
4. Complex life cycles usually involving two hosts, one of which is commonly a crustacean.
   Example: *Hyalophysa.*

Order 5. Astomatida
1. Commensals or endoparasites living chiefly in the gut and coelome of oligochaete worms.
2. Cytostome absent.
3. Body ciliation uniform.
   Examples: *Anoplophyra, Hoplitophyra.*

Order 6. Hymenostomatida
1. Small ciliates having a uniform body ciliation but possessing a buccal cavity.
2. Buccal ciliature consists of an undulating membrane and an adoral zone of membranelles.
   Examples: *Colpidium, Tetrahymena, Paramecium.*

Order 7. Thigmotrichida
1. A small group of marine and freshwater ciliates found in association with bivalve molluscs.
2. Anterior end of body bears a tuft of thigmotactic cilia.
   Examples: *Thigmophrya, Boveria.*

Subclass II. Peritrichia
Order 1. Peritrichida
1. Adult usually lacks body cilia, but the apical end of the body typically bears a conspicuous buccal ciliature.
2. Mostly attached stalked ciliates.
   Examples : *Vorticella, Trichodina.*

Subclass III. Suctoria
Order 1. Suctorida
1. Sessile, stalked ciliates with the distal end bearing few to many tentacles.
2. Adult stage completely devoid of any ciliature.
   Examples: *Acineta, Podophrya, Ephelota.*

Subclass IV. Spirotrichia
1. With generally reduced body cilia.

2. Well developed conspicuous buccal ciliature.

Order 1. Heterotrichida
1. With uniform body cilia or body encased in a lorica and body cilia absent.
   Examples: *Bursaria. Stentor, Spirostomum, Nyctotherus.*

Order 2. Oligotrichida
1. Small ciliates with body cilia reduced or absent.
2. Conspicuous buccal membranelles, commonly extending around apical end of body.
   Example : *Halteria.*

Order 3. Tintinnida
1. Loricate, mostly free swimming ciliates with inconspicuous oral membranelles when extended.
2. Chiefly marine.
   Examples: *Codonella, Favella.*

Order 4. Entodiniomorphida
1. Endocommensal ciliates in the digestive tract of herbivorous mammals.
2. Body cilia absent or reduced.
3. Prominent buccal ciliature often in separate anterior clumps.
4. Posterior end may be drawn out into spines.
   Examples: *Entodinium, Cycloposthium.*

Order 5. Odontostomatida
1. A small group of laterally compressed and wedge-shaped ciliates with carapace and reduced body and buccal cilia.
   Example: *Saprodinium*

Order 6. Hypotrichida
1. Dorsoventrally flattened ciliates in which the body cilia are restricted to fused tufts of cilia, or cirri, located on the ventral side of the body.
   Examples: *Euplotes, Stylonychia, Urostyla, Oxytricha.*

REPRESENTATIVE TYPES OF PROTOZOA

1. *Chrysamoeba.* Chrysamoeba (Fig. 22.1) is found in freshwater. Body egg-shaped while swimming but becomes amoeboid when on the substratum. Locomotory organ single flagellum. Protoplasm contains single nucleus, two or more contractile vacuoles and two yellow chromatophores. Gullet or cytopharynx and skeleton absent. Nutrition is holophytic or holozoic. Food ingestion takes place by means of pseudopodia.

2. *Cryptomonas.* Cryptomonas (Fig. 22.2) is found among algae containing chloroplasts in fresh and marine waters. The body is covered by a thin pellicle and provided with two flagella and a gullet. Protoplasm contains single nucleus and two usually green chromatophores. Locomotion by flagella. Nutrition is holophytic or saprophytic. Reserve food material is in the form of starch and oil.

3. *Volvox.* Volvox (Fig. 22.3) is a colonial flagellate. *V. globator* and *V. aureus* are cosmpolitan in freshwaters. The colony has a gelatinous matrix forming a round hollow ball filled with a fluid, it is known as a coenobium. In the matrix is a single layer of many biflagellate zooids (Fig. 22.4)

connected to each other by protoplasmic bridges. There are two kinds of zooids in the colony, somatic or vegetative zooids are numerous and small and reproductive zooids are few and larger in size. The zooids are independent but all contribute to coordinated locomotion by their flagella. A

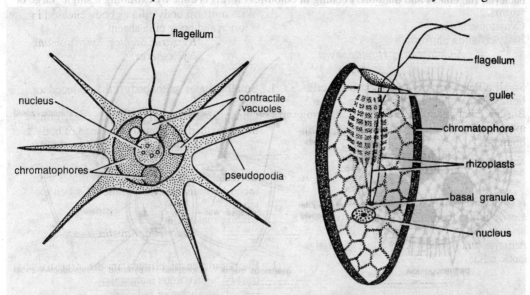

Fig. 22.1. *Chrysamoeba.*   **Fig. 22.2.** *Cryptomonas.*

zooid has a cellulose wall outside the cell membrane, it has a curved chloroplast with chlorophyll and pyrenoids, the product of photosynthesis is starch; there are two or more contractile vacuoles, a red stigma, and two projecting flagella. *Volvox* is of special significance because it shows a transition from a unicellular to a multicellular organism; it shows a differentiation into somatic cells which are trophic but unable to reproduce and into reproductive germ cells; the somatic cells die but germ cells live on as in Metazoa; it also illustrates a stage through which the ancestors of Metazoa must have passed in the course of evolution. Asexual reproduction: The reproductive zooids from the posterior side of the colony enlarge to form parthenogonidia which divide repeatedly by longitudinal binary fission to form a daughter colony. The cells of the daughter colony become arranged into a hollow ball called a plakea in which the flagellated ends of the cells point inwards, the plakea then turns inside out so that the flagellated ends of cells come to the exterior. These daughter colonies become motile but remain inside the parent coenobium, finally they escape by rupturing the wall of the parent or when the parent dissociates. Sexual reproduction: *V. globator* is monoecius but *V. aureus* is dioecious. Monoecious forms are protandrous hermaphrodites. True eggs or sperms are formed from reproductive zooids. The reproductive zooids drop into the hollow of the coenobium, they divide to form bundles of microgametes (sperms) in multiples of sixteen; a microgamete has two flagella. Later some other reproductive zooids enlarge to form macrogametes (ova) which remain in the colony. Microgametes escape from the colony and bring about cross fertilization to form zygotes; the zygote acquires a thick, brown, spiny shell. Next spring the zygote divides repeatedly to form a new colony. The old colony dies and new colonies escape. (This is an example of natural death in Protozoa). The gametes are haploid and the zygote diploid, meiosis occurs in the zygote. Thus, meiosis occurs after the formation of the zygote and is post-zygotic (in Metazoa it is pre-zygotic). In both sexual and asexual reproduction the zooids of the young colony have their flagella pointing inwards but inversion takes place before the new colony is completed. Some macrogametes develop parthenogenetically into colonies.

    4. Ceratium. The body of *Ceratium* (Fig. 22.5) is enclosed in a thick pellicle of cellulose called lorica which is made of closely fitting platelets. There are two to five but usually three armoured spines, one anterior and two posterior. From the body arise two flagella, one in a transverse groove or annulus which encircles the body and the other in a longitudinal groove or sulcus which goes backwards. The annulus is interrupted ventrally by a large membranous plate. There are rod-shaped chromatophores distributed in five distinct groups, they contain chlorophyll, nutrition is holophytic.

Chromatophores are green in freshwater forms but they are yellowish-brown in marine forms. There are reserves of starch, glycogen and fat droplets. The cytoplasm contains foreign bodies such as bacteria, flagellates and diatoms. Feeding in colourless forms is done by extruding a single large or

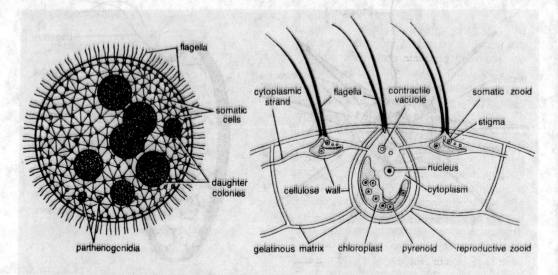

Fig. 22.3. *Volvox globator.*   **Fig. 22.4.** Zooids of *Volvox.*

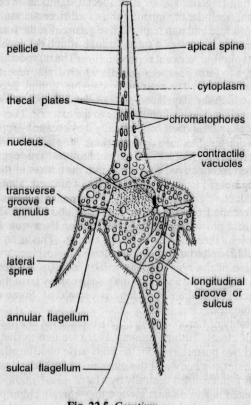

Fig. 22.5. *Ceratium.*

many small parts of the cytoplasm through pores, the latter form an anastomosing net on the body which entangles the prey for holozoic nutrition, partly digested food is withdrawn along with the cytoplasm into the body. Even coloured forms use this method and do not rely entirely on photosynthesis as a means of nutrition. *Ceratium hirudinella* is found in freshwater and the sea, other species occur all over the world in lakes and seas. Reproduction is by binary fission.

5. *Noctiluca.* The body of *Noctiluca* (Fig. 22.6) is spherical, about 1.5 mm in diameter, it is gelatinous and transparent, it is covered by thick pellicle, protoplasm is highly vacuolated and has delicate strands. There is a groove in the pellicle which is held uppermost in floating, but it marks the morphological ventral side. In the groove lies an elongate mouth and a soft flap inappropriately called a tooth which represents a transverse flagellum. Grouped close to the groove are a nucleus, flagella and mouth, all of them together are called a polar mass. From the polar mass branching and anastomosing threads of protoplasm pass into the interior. The central cortex is phosphorescent producing bluish-green light at night, hence, the name. Myriads or *Noctiluca* light up the sea.

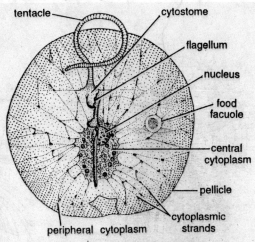

Fig. 22.6. *Noctiluca scintillans.*

Two flagella arise from the groove, a small flagellum and a large one modified into a stout, striated tentacle. It is marine, pelagic and holozoic, it reproduces by binary fission and by formation of spores after multiple fission. These spores are more like dinoflagellates than the adult.

6. *Proterospongia* *Proterospongia* (Fig. 22.7) is a free-living flagellate. It has a gelatinous matrix of irregular shape in which many zooids are embedded forming a colony. A zooid is an oval cell with a transparent collar at one end through which a flagellum comes out, these collared zooids are embedded on the outside. Inside the matrix are also some amoeboid zooids. *Proterospongia* colony resembles sponges closely.

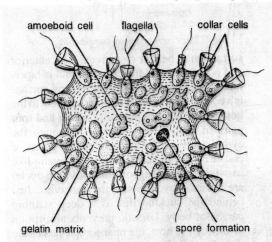

Fig. 22.7. *Proterospongia.*

7. *Mastigamoeba.* *Mastigamoeba* (Fig. 22.8) is a free-living flagellate found in freshwater ponds and lakes. It has a permanently amoeboid form. It possesses a single flagellum and numerous pseudopodia. Protoplasm contains single nucleus and contractile vacuole. Locomotion by pseudopodia. Nutrition is holozoic. It is considered to be a connecting link between Mastigophora and Rhizopoda.

8. *Trichonympha.* *Trichonympha* (Fig. 22.9) is one of the many genera of flagellates found in the gut of termites. Body has a complicated structure, and a large number of flagella are found in groups over the surface of the entire cell. In the ectoplasm are oblique fibres, an alveolar layer and transverse myonemes, in the endoplasm are longitudinal myonemes. There is a symbiotic relationship between *Trichonympha* and its host, it renders the cellulose of wood eaten by the termite digestible by the termite. Without the flagellates wood is not digested by termites. The flagellate lives in and obtains its food from the termite.

9. *Giardia.* *Giardia intestinalis* (Fig. 22.10) also called *G. lamblia* (old name *Lamblia*) is a parasite in the small intestine and colon of man, being attached in masses to the mucous membrane

from where it absorbs food consisting mainly of mucus. Occasionally the parasites invade the bile ducts and gall bladder. Other species of *Giardia* are parasitic in the intestine of vertebrates. *Giardia* has an elliptical body which is bilaterally symmetrical. The dorsal side is convex, but the ventral

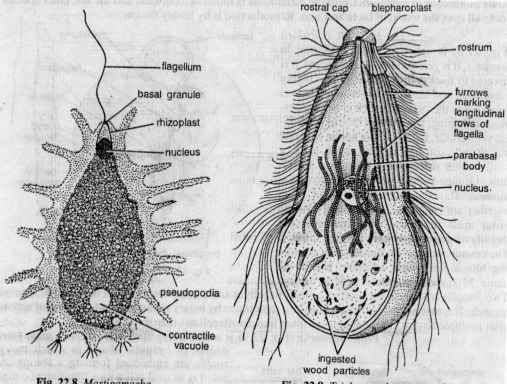

Fig. 22.8. *Mastigamoeba.*

Fig. 22.9. *Trichonympha campanula.*

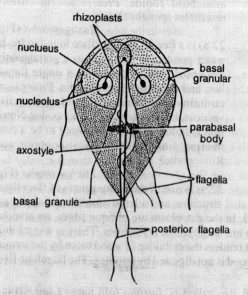

Fig. 22.10. *Giardia intestinalis.*

surface may be flat or convex. The anterior end is rounded and the posterior end is tapering. In the anterior half of the ventral surface is a concave **sucking disc** for attachment to the host. There are two vesicular nuclei and four pairs of long flagella. Passing through the cytoplasm from the anterior to the posterior end are two parallel, flexible, needle-like **axostyles** which support the body, the nuclei are attached by fibrils to the axostyles. Just behind the sucking disc is a deep staining parabasal body. *Giardia* prevents absorption of fats by the host, the unabsorbed fats cause **diarrhoea**. It forms oval, thick-walled cysts, division occurs in the cyst so that the cyst has four nuclei, the cysts pass out with the faeces and are infective for 10 days or more. Antimalarial drugs such as atebrin and chloroquin are effective in removing the parasites.

10. Leishmania. The genus *Leishmania* (Fig. 22.11) includes three species which are common parasites of man, *viz., (i) Leishmania donovoni, (ii) Leishmania tropica,* and *(iii) Leishmania brassiliensis.*

Leishmania donovoni has two phases in the life cycle, one flagellar Leishmania form in the reticulo-endothelial cells of man and other Leptomonas form in the gut of blood-sucking fly *Phlebotomus*. *Leishmania* form is intracellular and is found in the cells of liver, spleen, bone marrow, intestine and lymph glands in the reticulo-endothelial system. This form is oval or spherical 1–3 μ in diameter with a limiting membrane, the periplast or pellicle. The cytoplasm contains an oval nucleus, rod-shaped or dot-like kinetoplast and parabasal body. Reproduction by binary fission.

(i) *Leishmania donovoni* causes kala azar which is a chronic disease characterized by the enlargement of liver, spleen and by an irregular fever, anemaia and leucopenia.

(ii) *L. tropica* causes oriental sore or Delhi boils.

(iii) *L. brassiliensis* causes mucocutaneous American leishmaniasis.

11. *Trichomonas.* The body of *Trichomonas* (Fig. 22.12) is pear-shaped tapering posteriorly, provided with four flagella of which one is directed backwards united to the body by an undulating membrane. Cytostome is present antero-ventrally and

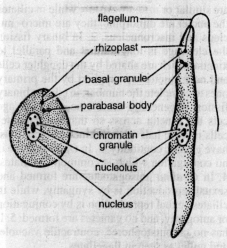

Fig. 22.11. *Leishmania.*

is used for the ingestion of food. An axostyle which is stout, rod-like extends from the posterior end medially through the body. Basal granule (blepharoplast) is minute structure situated at the anterior end, while parabasal body is club-shaped extends posteriorly from the basal granule. Single large nucleus situated anteriorly. Reproduction asexual by longitudinal binary fission. *Trichomonas* are parasites in many vertebrates and in few invertebrates. Three species are found in man which are as follows :

(i) *T. hominis* in the colon;

(ii) *T. buccalis* in the mouth;

(iii) *T. vaginalis* in the human vagina.

12. Opalina. *Opalina* (Fig. 22.13) is a parasite in the rectum of frogs and toads. Body is oval and flat with longitudinal rows of many equal-sized cilia-like organelles of locomotion. It is multinucleate, each nucleus has both trophochromatin and idiochromatin. There is no cytostome or contractile vacuole. The parasite absorbs digested food of the host. Reproduction is by longitudinal binary fission most of the year, in fission kinetia are not cut but shared equally between two daughter cells, this is an interkinetal division of kinetia. In spring reproduction is by binary plasmotomy in which cell division is repeated again and again without division of the nuclei, so that many daughter cells are produced, each having only a few nuclei, generally three to six.

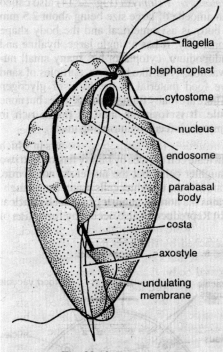

Fig. 22.12. *Trichomonas.*

The daughter cells become encysted and pass out of the host into water from where they are swallowed by tadpoles. The cysts dissolve in the intestine of tadpoles and the cells divide to form uninucleate microgametes or macrogametes, these gametes are anisogametes. The male and female anisogametes fuse to form a zygote. The zygote encysts, then by growth and nuclear division it becomes an adult which emerges from the cyst into the alimentary canal.

Previously *Opalina* was placed in Ciliophora, then it was placed in Flagellata, but, now it is placed in a separate superclass Opalinata since it is neither a ciliate nor a flagellate because of the following reasons : 1. Its many nuclei are similar or monomorphic, while in ciliates the nuclei are dimorphic, they are micro- nucleus and macronucleus. 2. In binary fission the cleavage is longitudinal and parallel to kinetia which are shared by the daughter cells and new kinetia are supplied by the primary ones to complete the number; in ciliates binary fission is generally transverse, the cleavage cuts the kinetia across so that the daughter cells receive half of each kinety which, thus, have genetic continuity. 3. In *Opalina* there is no conjugation which is common in ciliates. 4. In *Opalina* anisogametes are formed and sexual reproduction is by syngamy, while in ciliates sexual reproduction is by conjugation or autogamy, and no gametes are formed. 5. It has no chromatophores, contractile vacuole, and gullet as seen in flagellates.

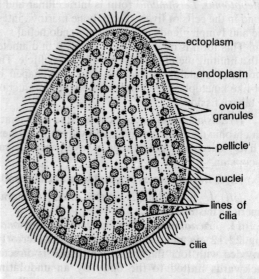

Fig. 22.13.*Opalina ranarum.*

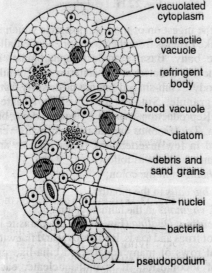

Fig. 22.14. *Pelomyxa palustris.*

13. *Pelomyxa.* *Pelomyxa* (Fig. 22.14) also called *Chaos* is an amoeba of large size being about 2.5 mm long. The body is asymmetrical and the body shape changes constantly. It has a single large, hyaline and blunt pseudopodium, cytoplasm has many small nuclei, food vacuoles, rod-like bacteria, particles of sand and reserve food material in the form of glycogen granules. There are many fluid-filled vacuoles but none is contractile. It is found in mud of ponds rich in vegetable matter, it feeds by ingesting mud.

Reproduction. (a) Plasmotomy occurs in which the multinucleate cell divides by binary fission into two or more daughter cells, but the nuclei do not divide, they are shared by the daughter cells. Later each daughter cell regains the normal number of nuclei by nuclear division. (b) Reproduction also occurs by formation of gametes.

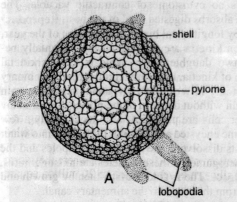
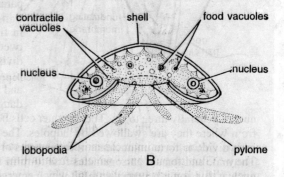

Fig. 22.15. *Arcella vulgaris.* A—Dorsal view; B—Side view.

14. *Arcella.* Arcella (Fig. 22.15) is a common freshwater amoeba found in freshwater ponds having weeds. The amoeboid body is symmetrical, it secretes a pseudochitinous shell of brown or yellow colour, the shell is single-chambered or unilocular, it is like a half globe and may be sculptured.

The shell is made of siliceous prisms embedded in a chitinoid substance known as tectin. The cytoplasm is joined to the shell by ectoplasmic strands. Ventrally the shell has an aperture called pylome from which 3 or 4 pseudopodia project. In the cytoplasm are two or more vesicular nuclei, and a ring of granules called chromidia, it has now been shown that chromidia are not made of chromatin as believed earlier, but are secretory granules. There are several contractile vacuoles, food vacuoles and some gas vacuoles filled with oxygen. Reproduction: Two nuclei divide into four nuclei, two of which along with some cytoplasm are extruded from the pylome, this extruded mass secretes a new shell, the double-shelled animal divides into two daughter cells, each of which receives a shell, then the daughter cells separate.

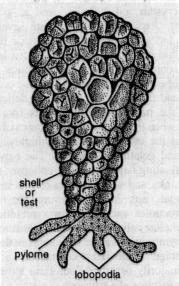

15. *Difflugia.* Difflugia (Fig. 22.16) is a shelled amoeba found in freshwater. It has an oval body to which particles adhere to form a spherical or oval shell. In locomotion pseudopodia are extended one after another through an opening in the shell, their tips are attached to the substratum, then the pseudopodia contract and the shell containing the body is pulled forward. Contraction of pseudopodia is much more than in *Amoeba*.

Fig. 22.16. *Difflugia.*

16. *Allogromia.* Allogromia (Fig. 22.17) is found both in fresh and marine waters. The body of the animal is covered by a shell which is one chambered (unilocular or monothalamous). The protoplasm flows out from the terminal opening of the shell and flows around the shell, in this way shell becomes internal. Protoplasm contains a single nucleus, a contractile vacuole and a food vacuole. Pseudopodia or reticulopodia are very long and delicate, unite to form a complicated network. They serve the animal in catching the prey. Reproduction by multiple fission.

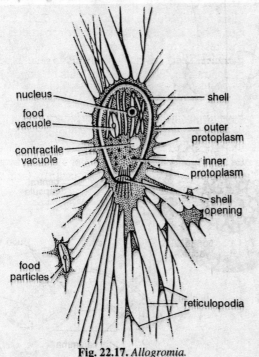

17. *Globigerina.* Globigerina (Fig. 22.18) is marine floating on the surface. The animal secretes a calcareous shell of a few round chambers lying in a rising spiral or helicoid arrangement, some species have long spines on the shell. When the living shell chamber becomes small for the animal, it secretes a new larger chamber, this many-chambered shell is known as a multilocular shell in which all the chambers communicate. The shell is made of calcium carbonate having some magnesium sulphate and silica. The shell has apertures through which fine, branching and anastomosing pseudopodia called rhizopodia or reticulopodia

Fig. 22.17. *Allogromia.*

emerge. When the animals die their shells sink to the bottom of the Atlantic Ocean where they form a gray "Globigerina ooze" which is rich in lime and silica, it covers an area of 20 million square miles. Chalk is made from the ooze.

18. *Thalassicola* and *Acanthometra*. *Thalassicola* (Fig. 22.19) is marine and pelagic; it has a perforated and membranous central capsule which divides the protoplasm into an intra-capsular endoplasm containing pigment granules, crystals, oil globules and a polyenergid nucleus in which there are several sets of chromosomes, and just outside the capsule into an extracapsular fluid ectoplasm which contains food vacuoles. A similar fluid layer of ectoplasm is spread over the outer surface and from this are given out delicate thread-like pseudopodia known as filopodia. Between the outer and inner zones of ectoplasm is the calymma, a thick, highly vacuolated and gelatinous material. The calymma is a floating device, when it collapses the animal sinks, and when bubbles reform in it the animal rises. In the calymma are many food vacuoles and numerous symbiotic *Zooxanthellae* called yellow cells. *Zooxanthellae* are symbiotic algae or flagellates in the palmella stage. There is no contractile vacuole. The majority of other Radiolaria have a central capsule and a siliceous skeleton which is absent in *Thalassicola*. The radiolarian skeleton may be made of long spines or needles which

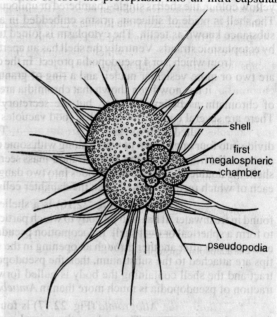

Fig. 22.18. *Globigerina.*

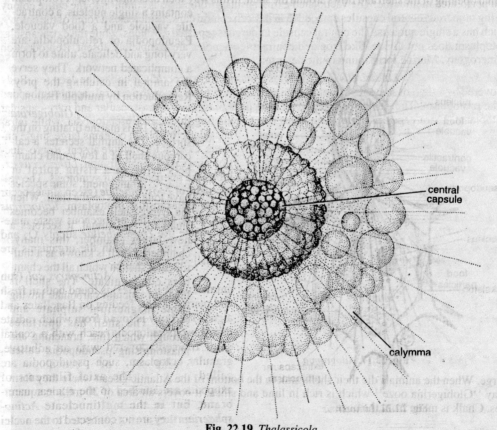

Fig. 22.19. *Thalassicola.*

radiate from the central capsule and extend outside the body as in *Acanthometra,* (Fig. 22.20) or the skeleton may be made of lattice-like spheres arranged concentrically. The siliceous skeletons of Radiolaria form a "Radiolarian ooze" covering three million square miles of the floor of the Indian and Pacific Oceans. Reproduction is by binary and multiple fission. In *Thalassicola* the central capsule separates from the animal and descends into the sea, its nucleus and cytoplasm divide to form many small cells called isopores which develop two unequal flagella in each, the isopores escape from the capsule and develop into adults.

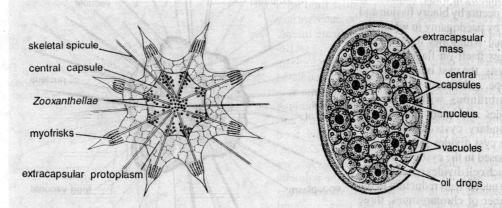

Fig. 22.20. *Acanthometra* (a radiolarian with skeleton).   **Fig. 22.21.** *Collozoum.*

19. Collozoum. *Collozoum* (Fig. 22.21) is a colonial form having a subspherical body measuring about 3–4 cm in length. Protoplasm is divided into an intracapsular and an extracapsular protoplasm by a perforated membrane. The vacuolated extracapsular protoplasm is common to the entire colony having numerous central capsules embedded in it. Each central capsule indicates a zooid of the colony, which has a single nucleus. The central capsule undergoes repeated divisions, while the extracapsular protoplasm does not divide. Skeleton and contractile vacuoles are completely absent. Reproduction by merogony. Marine form found in the deep sea.

20. Lithocircus. *Lithocircus* (Fig 22.22) is a marine form generally found in the deep sea. Body is covered by a shell of siliceous skeleton. The animalcule is provided with a central capsule embedded in the protoplasm. The central capsule divides the protoplasm into extra-capsular and intra-capsular protoplasm. Extra-capsular protoplasm gives rise to radiating thread-like pseudopodia, while intra-capsular protoplasm contains large single nucleus. Contractile vacuole absent. Repro- duction asexual by binary fission. *Lithocircus* exhibits the phenomenon of symbiosis. The yellow cells of *Zooxanthellae* (green algae) occur in the extracapsular protoplasm. *Lithocircus* supply the CO_2 and nitrogenous waste material, while the *Zooxanthellae* supply O_2 and starch. In this way both the organisms are mutually benefited.

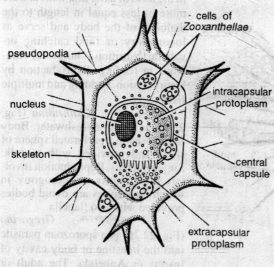

Fig. 22.22. *Lithocircus.*

21. Actinophrys. *Actinophrys sol* (sun animalcule (Fig. 22.23) is found both in fresh and marine waters feeding on flagellates and algae. The body is round from which radiate thin, long pseudopodia, each with a central axial filament covered with an adhesive, granular ectoplasm, such pseudopodia are called axopodia. The axial filaments of axopodia are attached to the nuclear membrane, but in the multinucleate *Actino-sphaerium* they are not connected to the nuclei but arise from the periphery of the medulla. The ectoplasm is frothy due to many vacuoles, there are one or two contractile vacuoles constant in position, they contract with violence. Marine forms have no contractile vacuole. Endo-

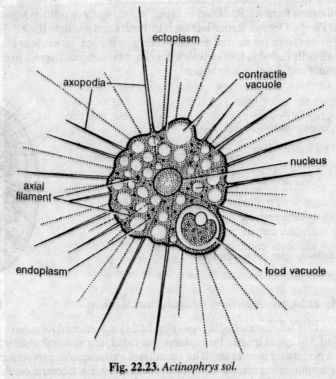

Fig. 22.23. *Actinophrys sol.*

plasm is granular having small vacuoles. It has a large nucleus and several food vacuoles. The animal has the power of rising and sinking in water. **Reproduction** occurs by binary fission and also by paedogamy in which the animal withdraws its axopodia gorges itself on flagellates and encysts, the cyst is a double envelope, gelatinous outside and membranous within, then it divides into many uninucleate secondary cysts. Each secondary cyst divides into two cells enclosed in the cyst, the nucleus of each cell divides twice to form four nuclei with reduction in the number of chromosomes, three of the four nuclei degenerate. The two cells of a cyst and their nuclei fuse to form a diploid zygote. The zygote produces by binary fission and the daughter cells escape from the cyst, they grow into adults.

22. *Actinospherium.* *Actinospherium* (Fig. 22.24) is found in freshwater floating among plants. The body is spherical measuring about 1 mm in diameter. The protoplasm is distinguishable into an outer layer, the ectoplasm or cortex and an inner central mass, the endoplasm or medulla. Ectoplasm contains large contractile vacuoles, while there are small vacuoles in the endoplasm. Numerous nuclei

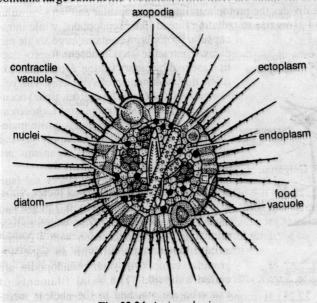

Fig. 22.24. *Actinospherium.*

(1–300) lie in the endoplasm. Pseudopodia or axopodia are numerous in the form of axial filaments and are more or less equal in length to the diameter of the body and serve as locomotory or food catching organelle. Nutrition is holozoic, voracious in feeding. Reproduction by binary fission, budding and multiple fission.

23. *Clathrulina.* *Clathrulina* (Fig. 22.25) is found in freshwater. Body is enclosed in a perforated sphere of silica and provided with a stalk. Single nucleus. Reproduction involves the process of merogony in which merozoites are ovoid bodies provided with two flagella.

24. *Gregarina.* *Gregarina* (Fig. 22.26) is a sporozoan parasite into the intestine or body cavity of insects or Annelida. The adult or trophozoite is extracellular, it has a thick cuticle, the ectoplasm has myonemes which grow in and divide the body into two parts, an anterior protomerite and a posterior deutomerite which contains a nucleus. When the trophozoite is attached to the gut it acquires an anterior epimerite having radiating spines, it gets attached by the epimerite, but the epimerite is lost when the trophozoite comes to the lumen of the gut.

Life cycle. Two trophozoites come together one behind the other, this is called syzygy, the anterior member in the chain is the primite or female, and the posterior member is the satellite or male. The trophozoites become rounded and are then called gametocytes which secrete a cyst. The gametocytes divide by multiple fission to form gametes which are isogamous in some species and anisogamous in others. Gametes of different gametocytes fuse to form zygotes. The zygote secretes a sporocyst to become a spore. The spore divides asexually to form eight sporozoites. The spore becomes complicated by forming several tubes called sporoducts. The sporozoites escape through the sporoducts and pass out with the faeces of the host to infect other insects in which they enter the cells of the intestinal epithelium and become intracellular. The sporozoites grow into trophozoites which remain attached, but project from the intestinal cells, later the trophozoites come into the lumen of the intestine.

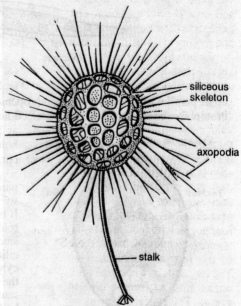

Fig. 22.25. *Clathrulina.*

siliceous skeleton

axopodia

stalk

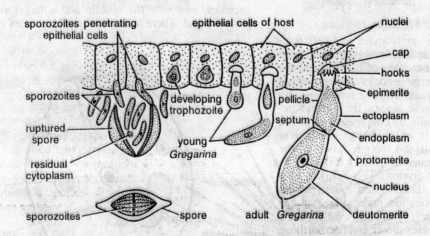

sporozoites penetrating epithelial cells

epithelial cells of host

nuclei

cap

hooks

sporozoites

developing trophozoite

pellicle

epimerite

septum

ectoplasm

ruptured spore

endoplasm

young *Gregarina*

protomerite

residual cytoplasm

nucleus

sporozoites

spore

adult *Gregarina*

deutomerite

Fig. 22.26. *Gregarina blattarum.* (Life history).

25. *Sarcocystis.* *Sarcocystis* (Fig. 22.27) is a parasite of vertebrates especially in sheep, rabbit, pig, rat, cattle, horses and also in reptiles and birds. It is occasionally found in man. The parasite forms a long spindle-shaped multinucleate cyst which is found embedded in the striped muscle fibres of the host. The masses of spindle-shaped parasites form long, slender, cylindrical bodies with pointed ends known as Miescher's or Rainey's tubes. Within each tube a large number of sickle-shaped spores are formed. These spores are known as Rainey's corpuscles. Very little is known regarding the mode of transmission of this parasite. *Sarcocystis* causes a disease known as sarcosporidiosis.

26. *Didinium.* *Didinium* (Fig. 22.28) is found in freshwater ponds and ditches in which *Paramecium* and other ciliates are in abundance. The body is barrel-shaped about 80–200 microns in length. Body is encircled by two hoops of cilia, one ring of cilia is close to the base of proboscis and the other on the posterior end. The anterior end of the body is prolonged into a tubular proboscis made

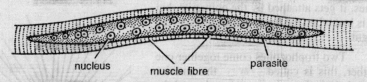

Fig. 22.27. *Sarcocystis.*

up of parallel trichocysts. The mouth opening or cytostome is situated at the tip of the proboscis. Protoplasm contains a horse-shoe-shaped nucleus in the centre, a contractile vacuole and cytopyge

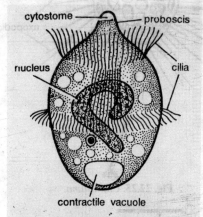

Fig. 22.28. *Didinium.*

at the extreme posterior end of the body. Nutrition is holozoic. Reproduction by transverse binary fission and conjugation.

    27. *Balantidium. Balantidium* (Fig. 22.29) is a ciliate parasitic in the large intestine of pigs, monkeys, and man, some species are parasitic in frog, fish, cockroach and horse. It is an egg-shaped animal pointed at the anterior end and rounded posteriorly. The body has longitudinal rows of small cilia. At the anterior end is a peristome with longer cilia, below the peristome is a mouth leading into short cytopharynx with no cilia (in *B. entozoon* parasitic in frog the peristome is a conical depression). There is a large sausage-shaped macronucleus obliquely in the middle of the body, and in its concavity near it is a small micronucleus. Unlike most parasitic Protozoa there are two contractile vacuoles, one near the middle and a larger one at the posterior end. There are several food vacuoles containing human erythrocytes and cell fragments, it also ingests starch and yeast from the colon of the host. At the posterior end is a permanent cytoproct. Reproduction is by transverse binary fission and occasionally by conjugation in which there is an exchange of nuclear material and reorganization of the macronucleus, this is followed by binary fission. The parasite also forms thick-walled cysts, but no multiplication takes place in the cyst. In human beings *Balantidium coli* causes ulcers and haemorrhage in the colon and caecum, which cause chronic dysentery. These parasites can be removed by administering small doses of aureomycin and terramycin for 10 to 15 days.

    Balantidium is now placed in subclass Holotrichia, order Tricho-

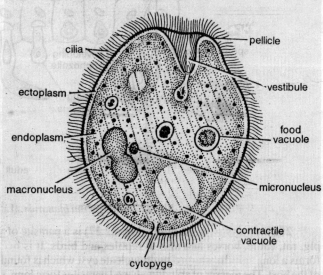

Fig. 22.29. *Balantidium coli.*

stomatida and not with Spirotrichia because : 1. Its peristomial ciliature develops from body kinetia which during binary fission form an incomplete band of stronger and longer cilia below the middle of the body, while in Spirotrichia the peristomial ciliature develops either from previous oral kinetosomes or from stomatogenetic kinetia. 2. It has no oral membranelle or buccal ciliature which are conspicuous in Spirotrichia.

28. Podophrya. *Podophrya* (Fig. 22.30) is found in ponds having rich vegetation under decomposition. The body of *Podophrya collini* is globular, measures about 40–50 microns in diameter, provided with a stalk having a basal disc for the attachment with the substratum. The body gives rise to 30–60 knobbed tentacles, giving a pin cushion-like appearance to the animal. Tentacles and the surface of the body are covered by gelatinous sheath. Endoplasm contains a large macro-

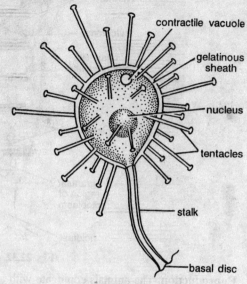

nucleus in centre with 3–12 small micronuclei and a contractile vacuole. Cytostome is absent. Nutrition is holozoic. The food consists chiefly of *Paramecia* and other ciliates. Reproduction by internal budding.

29. Ephelota. *Ephelota* (Fig 22.31) is a marine form, found in the sea water. The body is spherical and bearing a stalk. There are two types of tentacles on the body, *viz.*, long pointed tentacles used for piercing and short cylindrical for sucking. Protoplasm contains an oval nucleus and few contractile vacuoles. Reproduction by budding. The distal half of the animal may sprout a number of small elevations or buds. In budding process the nuclei behave as in the ordinary binary fission. The macronucleus extends into each bud and divides directly.

30. Stentor. *Stentor* (Fig. (22.32) is commonly found in freshwater ponds and ditches among aquatic plants and rich vegetation. Body of the organism is elongated funnel-shaped and highly contractile, measuring from

Fig. 22.30. *Podophrya.*

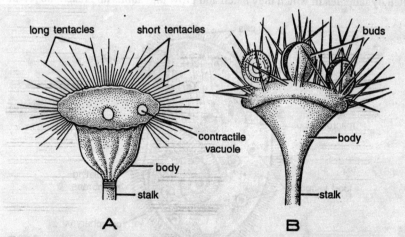

Fig. 22.31. *Ephelota.* A—Entire animal; B—Showing budding.

1–2 mm in length. The body is sometimes attached by the base but often free itself to swim. The body is covered with cilia. The anterior broad end bearing peristome is provided with large cilia which are arranged in clockwise manner. The posterior end is free of cilia but produces ramose pseudopodia for attachment. Protoplasm contains a beaded meganucleus or macronucleus, numerous micronuclei and anterior contractile vacuole. Reproduction by binary fission and conjugation.

31. Nyctotherus. *Nyctotherus* (Fig. 22.33) is a parasitic ciliate in the rectum of frogs and intestine of cockroaches. Its body is kidney-shaped with the longitudinal rows of equal-sized cilia, and a row of large adoral cilia on the peristome. The large peristome leads into a long, curved cytopharynx in which cilia are large and wind clockwise. In the anterior half of the body is a large kidney-shaped macronucleus and a small micronucleus, Near the posterior end is a single contractile vacuole and at the posterior end is a permanent cytoproct.

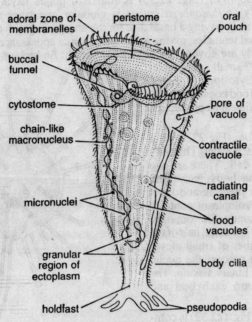

adoral zone of
membranelles

peristome

oral
pouch

buccal
funnel

cytostome

chain-like
macronucleus

micronuclei

granular
region of
ectoplasm

holdfast

pore of
vacuole

contractile
vacuole

radiating
canal

food
vacuoles

body cilia

pseudopodia

Fig. 22.32. *Stentor.*

Reproduction. The animals conjugate with an exchange of nuclear material. The conjugants separate and undergo binary fission. These daughter cells encyst and pass out with the faeces, these cysts are eaten by tadpoles in which they hatch and grow into adults and reach the rectum.

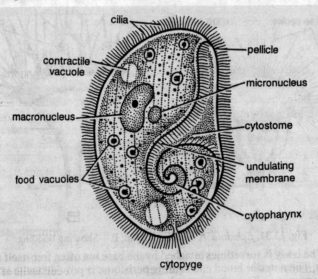

cilia

contractile
vacuole

macronucleus

food vacuoles

pellicle

micronucleus

cytostome

undulating
membrane

cytopharynx

cytopyge

Fig. 22.33. *Nyctotherus.*

REVISION QUESTIONS

1. Give an account of the characters of phylum Protozoa. Classify it up to classes giving characters and two examples of each class.
2. Give an outline classification of phylum Protozoa up to orders and mention examples of each order. What is the basis of classification of phylum Protozoa up to classes?
3. Write detailed notes on:
   (i) Reproduction in Volvox; (ii) Ceratium; (iii) Noctiluca; (iv) Giardia; (v) Leishmania; (vi) Opalina; (vii) Balantidium; (viii) Stentor; (ix) Nyctotherus; (x) Ephelota.

23

Protozoa in General

GENERAL ORGANISATION OF PROTOZOA

SIZE

The Protozoa are usually microscopic and not visible to the naked eyes. Their size varies from 2 microns to 250 microns (one micron (μ) is equal to 1/1000 mm or 0.001 mm). *Babesia, Leishmania* and *Plasmodium* are the smallest protozoans known so far. Some of the larger Protozoa, like *Amoeba* and *Paramecium*, can be seen with naked eyes. *Spirostomum*, a ciliate, grows to 3mm long. *Pelomyxa*, a giant amoeba, attains a diameter of about 1 to 5 mm. *Porospora gigantea*, a Sporozoa, grows to about 16 mm long. *Cycloclypeus*, a Foraminifera, exceeds a diameter of about 50 mm and some shelled marine protozoans have diameters of about 63 mm.

SHAPE OR FORM

Protozoa, the most primitive of all organisms, exhibit nearly all types of body shape. The body shape of a Protozoa is definite but it may usually vary within narrow limits. The body shape is usually determined by the consistancy of cytoplasm, limiting membranes of the body, shells and skeleton. *Amoeba* has an **irregular, asymmetrical** body shape because of the absence of rigid body enveiope. However, the floating forms usually possess **spherical** body shape like *Noctiluca*; the body shape is usually **elongated** in active swimmers like *Euglena* and *Paramecium*, the body shape may be **flattened** in creeping forms like *Oxytricha*. Shells and tests like those of *Difflugia* and *Arcella* determine the shape of these species. It may be funnel-shaped like *Stentor*, bell-shaped like *Vorticella* and so on. Some of the protozoans like Radiolarians exhibit **spherical symmetry** and attached species like *Vorticella* exhibit more or less **radial symmetry.**

BODY ENVELOPE AND SKELETON

In Protozoa, the body envelope and external skeletal layers mark the boundary line between the body protoplasm and external environment. These protect them from external environmental hazards. The body envelope, being selective in nature, allows exchange of substances across it and helps in perceiving various types of stimuli. However, the **body envelope,** in protozoans, may be either **plasmalemma** or **pellicle.** In some species like *Amoeba proteus,* the body envelope is a thin plasma membrane or plasmalemma which is mucopolysaccharide in nature. It helps in adhesion to the substratum and in the exchange of various materials. The **pellicle** is comparatively thicker, tough, elastic and proteinous in nature; it helps in maintaining the general shape of the protozoans and performs the usual functions as referred earlier.

The **skeletal layers** are secreted in still other protozoans in which their protoptasmic body remains protected. These include cyst, theca, lorica and test or shell. The **cyst** is an external temporary sheath formed both by free-living and parasitic individuals. It is primarily secreted during unfavourable conditions. The encysted individuals comfortably tide over the environmental hazards. The **theca** is another skeletal layer found in many dinoflagellates like *Ceratium* and *Glenodinium*. It is a coat of closely-fitted armour of **cellulose,** comparable to the thick cell walls of higher plants. The lorica, in majority of dinoflagellates, is differentiated into a number of plates arranged into a definite pattern; but in some forms, it may be formed of two valves. The **lorica** is still another skeletal layer found in certain protozoans like *Salpingoeca, Monosiga, Dinobryon, Synura splendida* and *Poteriodendron*, etc. In fact, it is a coat of less-closely fitted armour of protozoans than the theca. The lorica is usually vase-shaped or tubular having an opening for the emergence of the anterior part of the animal or its appendages. The base of the lorica is either attached directly to the substratum (in sessile individuals like *Salpingoeca)* or it may terminate in a stalk like *Monosiga.* In colonial loricated protozoans, one lorica may be attached to another lorica directly as in *Dinobryon* or one lorica may be attached to another lorica by a stalk as in *Poteriodendron* and *Synura splendida*. The shells or tests are still other skeletal layer of protozoans; these are of common occurrence. There are loose armour with one or more openings over the body of protozoans like *Arcella, Difflugia, Euglypha*, etc. In *Arcella* the shell is thin and composed of pseudochitin (proteins plus carbohydrates) and ventrally it has an aperture from which 3 or 4 pseudopodia project out. In *Difflugia* the shell is made of sand and other foreign substances like fragments of foraminiferan's shell and sponge spicules. These foreign substances get embedded in a secreted matrix by the animal, working like cement, to form the shell. The foraminiferan's shells are made of calcium carbonate, while shells found in some rhizopods like *Euglypha* are siliceous being made of silica.

The radiolarian's shells are internal skeletal layer lying between ectoplasm and endoplasm. It forms a central capsule, which is composed of pseudochitin or silica or strontium sulphate and secreted by the cytoplasm. The central capsule is perforated by one to many pores through which the extra-capsular cytoplasm extends out as fine pseudopodia.

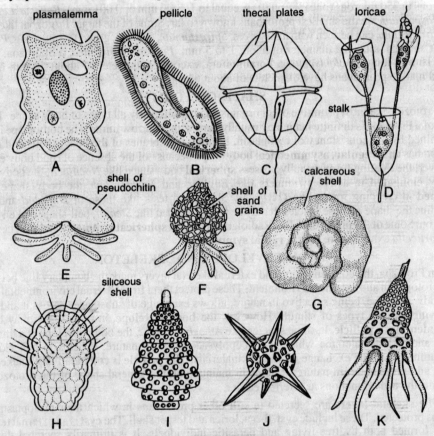

Fig. 23.1. Various types of skeletons in Protozoa. A—Plasmalemma of *Amoeba* ; B—Pellicle of *Paramecium* ; C—Thecal plates of *Glenodinium* ; D—Lorica of *Poteriodendron* ; E—Pseudo-chitinous shell of *Arcella* ; F—Sand grain shell of *Difflugia* ; G—Calcareous shell of *Discorbis* ; H—Siliceous shell of *Euglypha;* I to K—Radiolarian skeletons.

CYTOPLASM

The cytoplasm of Protozoa is generally colourless but certain coloured species are also found; *Blepharisma lateritia* is rose-red and *Stentor coeruleus* is blue. The cytoplasm is commonly divided into peripheral clear ectoplasm and inner granular endoplasm. These two may change from one to the other as is reported in *Amoeba proteus*. The cytoplasm contains various organelles like mitochondria, Golgi bodies, endoplasmic reticulum, ribosomes, lysosomes, centrioles, microtubules, plastids, etc. The organelles listed above are typically the same as found in a typical Metazoa cell. The other structures exclusively found in Protozoa are various types of vacuoles, stigma, trichocysts, etc.

NUCLEUS

The nuclei of Protozoa exhibit a greater variety of size, shape and structure than the nuclei of Metazoa. The nucleus of Protozoa has a nuclear membrane, nucleoplasm, oxychromatin, basichromatin, and there may be a nucleolus. The nuclear membrane remains intact even in cell division. There are various kinds of nuclei in Protozoa. 1. Vesicular nucleus has a large amount of nucleoplasm, the chromatin is small in quantity and it forms small granules, the achromatin (oxychromatin) is more fluid and its network, if present, is coarse, there is a round endosome of basichromatin or oxychromatin, or of both, *e.g., Euglena, Arcella, Entamoeba.* 2. Massive or compact nucleus has a small amount of nucleoplasm, there is a large amount of chromatin forming evenly scattered small granules, the achromatin is viscid forming a fine network, *e.g., Amoeba.* In the majority of Protozoa the nuclei show a structure intermediate between the vesicular and massive nuclei. 3. Polyenergid nucleus has several sets of chromosomes, instead of one set inside the nuclear membrane, this is due to mitosis occurring repeatedly inside the nuclear membrane. But the sets of chromosomes are finally liberated and each forms a new nucleus. The polyenergid condition is a provision for spore formation, *e.g.,* Radiolaria.

Usually Protozoa (Mastigophora, Sarcodina and Sporozoa) have a single nucleus, but some (Ciliophora and Opalinata) have more than one. When the nuclei are more than one, they may be alike or different. Some Sarcodina may have many similar nuclei, *e.g.,* two in *Arcella* and hundreds in *Pelomyxa.* In *Trypanosoma* (a flagellate) there are two dissimilar nuclei, the principal one is trophonucleus which regulates metabolism and trophic activities; the second one is a kinetonucleus which controls the locomotory organelles, the former is vesicular and the latter of massive type. 4. Chromosome nucleus, in this case the nucleus retains chromosomes in interphase, *e.g. Amoeba sphaeronucleus.* In *Opalina* many monomorphic nuclei are found. 5. Dimorphic nuclei are found in Ciliophora, the larger one is macronucleus containing trophochromatin, it controls vegetative functions, it divides amitotically, and in conjugation it disappears and is replaced by material from the synkaryon. The shape of the macronucleus is much varied. The second nucleus is a small round micronucleus, there may be one or more micronuclei; it contains idiochromatin and controls

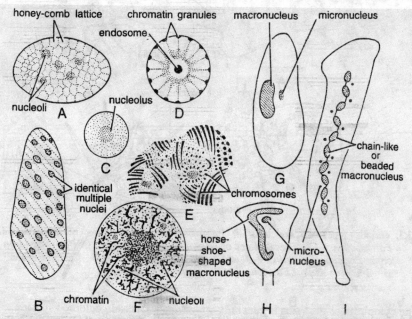

Fig. 23.2. Protozoan nuclei. A—Vesicular nucleus of *Amoeba proteus* ; B—Multiple nuclei of *Opalina*; C—Vesicular micronucleus of *Paramecium aurelia*; D—Vesicular nucleus of *Entamoeba*; E—Chromosome nucleus of *Amoeba sphaeronucleus* ; F—Polyploid nucleus of *Aulocantha scolymantha* ; G—Compact macronucleus and vesicular micronucleus of *Paramecium caudatum*; H—Horse-shoe-shaped micronucleus of *Vorticella*; I—Beaded macronucleus of *Stentor.*

reproduction. It divides mitotically in binary fission and conjugation; it gives rise to the macronucleus when the latter becomes effete and disintegrates. The shape of nuclei also varies; it may be sperical, *e.g., Entamoeba*, kidney-shapeed, *e.g.,* macronucleus of *Paramecium,* horse-shoe-shaped, *e.g.,* macronucleus of *Vorticella* and beaded , *e.g.,* macronucleus of *Stentor.*

LOCOMOTOR ORGANELLES

The Protozoa perform locomotion or movement by various organelles; **pseudopodia** characteristic of Sarcodina, **flagella**characteristic of Flagellata (Mastigophora), **cilia** characteristic of Ciliata and other **contractile structures of pellicle,** myonemes, characteristic of Sporozoa and few others. The seat of locomotion lies in the ectoplasm, since locomotor organelles either arise from it or are present in it.

1. Pseudopodia. Pseudopodia are generally temporary outgrowths of protoplasm from any part of the body, they are found in those Protozoa which are "naked" or have a very thin pellicle. Pseudopodia may be of ectoplasm or they may also have a core of endoplasm. Following kinds of pseudopodia are met with.

(a) **Lobopodia** are blunt, short or finger-like, they are made of ectoplasm with a core of fluid endoplasm, *e.g., Arcella* and *Amoeba.*

(b) **Filopodia** are fine, long threads, often with rounded ends, at times they may branch; they are made of only hyaline ectoplasm, *e.g., A. radiosa*–Radiolaria.

(c) **Rhizopodia** or **reticulopodia** are thin, long and branching, the branches of adjacent pseudopodia may anastomose to form a network which also serves as a trap for capturing food, *e.g., Elphidium.*

(d) **Axopodia** are long, stiff threads made of ectoplasm, with a hard central axial filament of endoplasm, unlike others they are semi-permanent, *e.g., Actinophrys.* Axopodia are not organelles of locomotion but are only for capturing food.

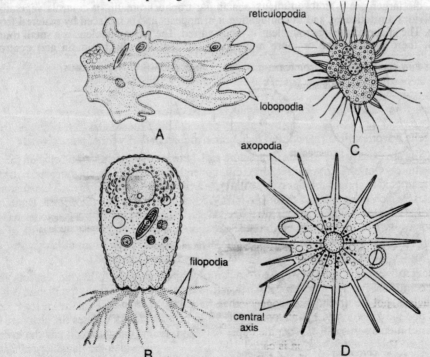

Fig. 23.3. Types of pseudopodia. A—Lobopodia of *Amoeba*; B—Filopodia of *Euglypha*; C—Reticulopodia of *Globigerina*; D—Axopodia of *Actinophrys sol.*

2. Flagella. Flagella are extremely fine fibres having a central axoneme made of two longitudinal fibrils, and an enveloping protoplasmic sheath having nine double longitudinal fibrils forming a ring. All 20 fibrils lie in a matrix of dense cytoplasm and they fuse at the base to join a basal granule or kinetosome. The kinetosome may be joined to the nucleus by a rhizoplast. The basal granule is often synonymous with a centriole because it initiates nuclear divisions, if it does not act as a centriole then it is connected by a rhizoplast to a centriole or to the nucleus. At the tip of the main flagellum may be a very fine end piece or mastigoneme, or the main axis of the flagellum may bear fine, flexible lateral processes or mastigonemes on one side or on both sides. Mastigonemes constitute the so-called flimmer or ciliary flagellum. Flagella are recognised to be of the following types depending upon the arrangement of mastigonemes in them :

(i) Stichonematic. When the mastigonemes are present on one side of the flagellum, it is called stichonematic flagellum, *e.g.,* flagellum of *Euglena.*

(ii) Pantonematic. When the mastigonemes are present in two or more rows arr- anged on both the sides of the flagellum, it is called pantonematic, *e.g.,* flagellum of *Paranema.*

(iii) Acronematic. When the mastigonemes are absent and the distal end of the flagellum ends in a terminal filament, *e.g.,* flagellum of *Chlamydomonas* and *Volvox.*

(iv) Pentachronematic. When the mastigonemes are present in two rows on the lateral sides of the flagellum but the flagellum ends in terminal filament, *e.g.,* flagellum of *Urcoelus.*

(v) In some cases, the flagellum is simple without mastigonemes and/or terminal filament, *Chilomonas, Cryptomonas.*

The number and arrangement of flagella varies greatly in Mastigophora. They may be one to eight in number. The free-living forms are usually with one to two flagella but the parasitic forms may have up to eight. Usually

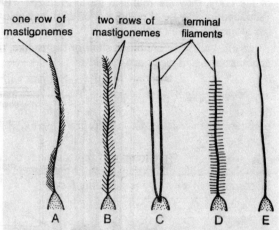

Fig. 23.4. Different types of flagella. A—Stichonematic; B—Pantonematic ; C—Acronematic; D—Pentachronematic; E—Simple.

flagella originate from the anterior end of body but in some cases like *Trypanosoma,* it originates from the posterior end and travels along the margin of undulating membrane and becomes free anteriorly. Flagella are primarily organelles of locomotion and secondarily for capturing food.

3. Cilia. Cilia are exactly like flagella in structure and there is no real distinction between them, except in the method of working. In primitive forms cilia cover the entire body, but in more specialized forms cilia are restricted to certain regions only. Cilia arise from kinetosomes, from each kinetosome arises a rhizoplast which does not join the nucleus, nor do cilia bear any mastigonemes. Running slightly to the right of a longitudinal row of kinetosomes is a delicate thread called kinetodesma. A row of kinetosomes with its kinetodesmata forms a longitudinal unit called kinety, all kinetia of an animal constitue its infraciliary system. Infraciliary system is characteristic of all ciliates, even in those forms in which cilia are lost in the adults the infraciliary system is retained.

The infraciliary system of ciliates differs from that of flagellates in the following respects. (*a*) The cilia are generally shorter and more numerous than flagella. (*b*) In ciliates the infraciliature is not joined to the nucleus, not are kinetia inter-connected; in flagellates rhizoplasts join the kinetosomes to the nucleus, and the kinetia may be interconnected (*c*) In cell division of ciliates the cleavage is perkinetal because it cuts across all kinetia, the upper halves go to one daughter cell and the lower halves to the other. This type of division is called homothetigenic in which the daughter cells are duplicates of each other. In cell division of flagellates the cleavage is interkinetal because it is longitudinal and parallel to kinetia, so that kinetia are not cut but are shared by dauughter cells. This type of division is called symmetrigenic in which the daughter cells are not duplicates but mirror images of each other. The normal number of kinetia of an animal is restored by division of kinetosomes. (*d*) Cilia have no mastigonemes as in flagella.

The cilia may form the following composite motile organelles : *(a)* **Membranelles** are membranes formed by fusion of two or more adjacent transverse rows of short cilia, they are found in the peristome making powerful sweeps. *(b)* **Undulating membranes** are made of one or more longitudinal rows of cilia fusing together, they are found in the peristome or cytopharynx and are used for food collection, *e.g., Vorticella.* The undulating membrane of *Trypanosoma* is only a web of ectoplasm, it is not made of cilia and it is locomotory. *(c)* **Cirri** are formed by fusion of two or three rows of cilia on the ventral side of some ciliates, they are locomotory and may also be tactile, *e.g., Stylonychia.*

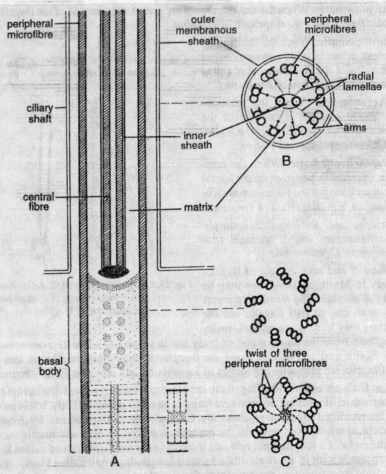

Fig. 23.5. Structure of cilium. A—L.S. ; B—T.S. ; C—Kinetostome in T.S.

4. Myonemes. Myonemes are contractile fibrils in the ectoplasm; they may be surrounded by a canal; they may be straight or may form a network. Myonemes have alternate rows of light and dark substance, *e.g., Stentor.* They are found in flagellates, ciliates and sporozoans. They are primarily organelles for metaboly, *e.g., Paramecium,* and secondarily for locomotion by muscle-like contraction in *Monocystis* and sporozoan like *Plasmodium.*

GENERAL PHYSIOLOGY
MODES OF LOCOMOTION

Different modes of locomotion are reported in Protozoa due to the presence of different types of locomotor organells in them. Thus, the various modes of locomotion found in Protozoa are as follows :

1. **Amoeboid** movement performed by **pseudopodia** and characteristic of *Amoeba.*

2. **Flagellar** locomotion performed by **flagella** and characteristic of flagellates like *Euglena*.

3. **Ciliary** locomotion performed by **cilia** and characteristic of ciliates like *Paramecium*.

4. **Gliding or metaboly** performed by **myoneme** fibrils and characteristic of Sporozoa like *Monocystis, Plasmodium.* Some ciliates and flagellates also exhibit this type of locomotion.

1. **Amoeboid movement.** *Amoeba* moves from one place to other by pseudopodia. The pseudopodia are finger-like temporary processes given out from any part of the body and withdrawn. The pseudopodium is formed by the projection of ectoplasm in which endoplasm flows. Thus, the cytoplasm which enters into pseudopodia is naturally drawn from the other parts of the body. *Amoeba* moves by the formation of pseudopodia, characteristic of this animal, is known as **amoeboid movement.** Various theories have been put forth to explain the way of formation of pseudopodia and amoeboid movement, already discussed in detail in Chapter 14.

However. **change of viscosity theory** or **sol-gel theory** proposed by **Hyman** (1917), later supported by **Pantin** (1923–26) and **Mast** (1925), explains well the way of the formation of pseudopodia and amoeboid movement. According to them the amoeboid movement is the result of changes within the colloidal protoplasm from fluid **plasmasol** to more solid **plasmagel** and vice-versa. Accordingly, the amoeboid movement is the net result of the following four steps occurring simultaneously in the body of *Amoeba* (Fig. 14.7) :

(i)   Attachment of the body of *Amoeba* to the substratum.

(ii) Conversion of plasmasol into plasmagel, *i.e.,* **gelation** at the anterior advancing tip.

(iii) Conversion of plasmagel into plasmasol, *i.e.,* **solation** at the posterior opposite end of the body.

(iv) Contraction of the plasmagel at the posterior end of the body to push the plasmasol forward.

These processes are repeated again and again and, thus, *Amoeba* moves ahead. The speed of amoeboid movement varies from 2 microns to 3 microns per second. This is supposed to be the most primitive type of animal movement.

Recently, a number of protozoologists have worked out the process of amoeboid movement variously. But nearly all of them conclude that the theory given by Hyman and supported by Pantin and Mast is essentially correct. For various theories, refer Chapter 14.

2. **Flagellar movement.** The free-living flagellates like *Euglena* moves by lashing the flagellum and by the movement of the whole body. Flagella performs lashing movements with a rowing action or undulating motion. In rowing the flagellum is held rigid but slightly concave in the direction of the stroke, in recovery it bends and is drawn back. In undulating motion it beats obliquely and undulations pass along the flagellum from the base to the tip causing the animal to rotate. However, flagellar locomotion has been described in detail in Chapter 12; the movement of flagellum results in a forward propulsion of the animal in a spiral fashion. The *Euglena* locomotes about 15 microns to 30 microns in a second.

3. **Ciliary movement.** The ciliates are characterised by the possession of numerous, small, fine, thread-like ectoplasmic processes, the **cilia.** The ciliary movement is like that of flagellar movement. The cilia are generally directed backward, whose constant beating pulls the animal forward. But if the cilia are directed forward, their constant beating pulls the animal backward. Ciliary movement has been discussed in detail in Chapter 20. However, the ciliary movements result in a forward propulsion of the animal in a spiral path. *Paramecium* is a typical example exhibiting ciliary locomotion. The speed of ciliary locomotion varies from 400 microns to 2,000 microns per second.

4. **Gliding movement.** The sporozoans usually exhibit a characteristic contractile movement due to the presence of **myoneme** fibrils. The myoneme fibrils are highly contractile and elastic in nature. They contract and expand bringing about a change in the shape of the body. Thus, the animal moves or glides from its original place. This type of movement is usually exhibited by parasitic forms like *Monocystis*.

The myoneme fibrils, found in certain free living forms like *Euglena*, cause waves of contraction to pass from anterior to the posterior end of the body. Thus, there occurs a series of changes in the shape of the body which help in crawling worm-like movement.

MODES OF NUTRITION

Nutrition is a process in which food is taken in, digested, absorbed and assimilated; in fact, it is the process by which the organisms derive their nutrients essential for the growth and maintenance of their life activities. The modes of nutrition vary greatly in Protozoa because of their various mode of living habits. However, in Protozoa, the nutrition is of the following types :

1. Holozoic or Zootrophic

Majority of Protozoa nutrite holozoically, *i.e.,* like animals on solid food. The food of Protozoa consists of micro-organisms like bacteria, diatoms, rotifers, crustacean larvae, other protozoans, algae, small fragments of large animals and plants, etc. This mode of nutrition essentially involves the processes like intake of food, *i.e.,* ingestion, digestion, absorption and egestion of undigested residues.

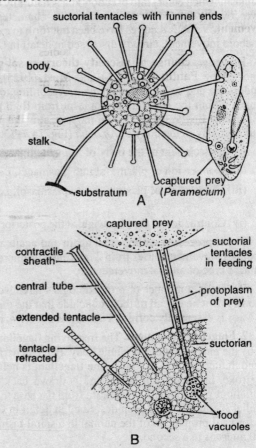

Ingestion. The mode of food ingestion in Protozoa is characteristically referred to as **phagocytosis** or **phagotrophy**. In fact, in **flagellates** which are colourless or who have lost their chromatophores capture food with the help of their **flagella**. The captured food is ingested either at definite sites on their naked bodies like *Budo* or through characteristic oral apparatus like *Euglena* where cytostome and cytopharynx help in ingestion. In some other flagellates like *Peranema*, special rod-like structures called **trichites** help in capturing the food. In **Sarcodina, pseudopodia** help in food capturing by forming food cups. **Rhumbler** (1930) has reported that the ingestion of food in *Amoeba* occurs by **circumvallation, circumfluence, import** and **invagination** as has already been discussed in Chapter 14 in detail. Different types of pseudopodia like **axopodia** in **heliozoans** and **radiolarians; reticulopodia** in **foraminiferans** also help in catching the prey.

In **ciliates** like *Paramecium*, the feeding apparatus is well developed with a definite cytostome. The cytostome is usually present at the base of the oral groove leading into the **cytopharynx**. The feeding apparatus is provided with some specialized cilia. The beating of the cilia of cytopharynx creates a whirl pool of water current. The food particles in the water current are directed into the cytopharynx through cytostome (Fig. 20.16).

Fig. 23.6. Mode of feeding in Suctoria A—*Podophrya* (a suctorian) sucking *Paramecium* (prey). B— Prey's cytoplasm flowing through tubular tentacle in suctorian's body.

The mode of feeding in **suctorians** is very characteristic; they feed with the help of their tentacles which are mostly knobbed at their tips (Fig. 23.6A). Each tentacle consists of a central tubular canal surrounded by a contractile sheath. The prey, as and when comes in contact with the tips of tentacles, soon gets adhered and paralysed by some toxin secreted by the suctorian. The prey's cytoplasm is then gradually sucked into the suctorian body through the central tubular canal of the tentacles (Fig. 23.6B).

Digestion. Digestion in Protozoa is **intracellular** within food vacuoles. The food vacuoles undergo changes in pH and in their size during digestion. At first the contents of the food vacuole are **acidic** and the vacuoles decrease in size, during this phase living prey dies. After the initial acid phase the cytoplasm of the protozoan produces enzymes in an alkaline medium, the enzymes pass into the food vacuoles and the vacuoles increase in size and become alkaline. Then the contents of the vacuoles are digested. In fact, proteolytic and carbohydrate digesting enzymes are reported in Protozoa; the proteins are converted into dipeptides in acidic medium and the dipeptides into amino-acids in alkaline medium. The carbohydrates are hydrolysed in alkaline medium. The fat digesting enzymes have also been reported in some Protozoa.

Absorption and assimilation. The digested food from the food vacuole is diffused out into the endoplasm and finally assimilated in the body to manufacture the protoplasm. The excess of food is stored in form of glycogen paramylon, paraglycogen bodies in the endoplasm.

Egestion. The undigestible remains of the food are egested out from the body at any body surface, *e.g.*, in *Amoeba*. But ciliates possess a definite opening for the egestion of undigested remains called cytoproct or cytopyge.

2. Pinocytosis

Pinocytois or **cell-drinking** has also been reported in some Protozoa like *Amoeba proteus,* and also in certain flagellates and ciliates. It is related to the ingestion of liquid food by invagination of the general body surface. It may occur at any part of the body;

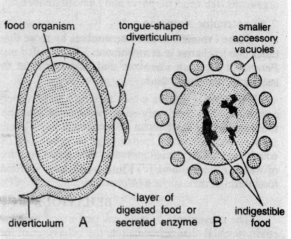

Fig. 23.7. Food vacuole. A—Recently formed food vacuole ; B—An older food vacuole.

during pinocytosis, some **pinocytic channels** are formed from the outer body surface deep into the body. The inner ends of these channels contain **pinocytic vesicles** or **pinosomes** which get separated after engulfing liquid food through the channels. The separated pinosomes become the food vacuoles. This process is induced in presence of certain salts and some proteins.

3. Autotrophic or Holophytic Nutrition

Protozoa with chlorophyll or some allied pigment can manufacture complex organic food, like those of green plants, from simple inorganic substances, *e.g.*, *Euglena, Noctiluca*. Often there may be protein bodies called pyrenoids which are the centres of **photosynthesis.** Some Protozoa have no chromatophores but they have chlorophyll-bearing algae *Zooxanthellae* or *Zoochlorellae* which manufacture organic food for the host by photosynthesis, *e.g.*, *Stentor, Thalassicola, Paramecium bursaria*. Nitrates or ammonium compounds are sufficient as the source of nitrogen for autotrophic forms.

4. Saprozoic Nutrition

Some Protozoa absorb complex organic substances in solution through the body surface by the process of **osmosis** called **osmotrophy.** These Protozoa are called **saprozoic.** Saprozoic forms need ammonium salts, amino acids, or peptones for their nutritional requirements. Decaying of animals and plants in water forms proteins and carbohydrates. The saprozoic Protozoa are usually parasites like *Monocystis.* But some parasites, like *Entamoeba histolytica* and *Balantidium coli* feeding holozoically also absorb dissolved organic substances through their general body surface. However, some colourless flagellates like *Chilomonas, Polytoma* and species of *Euglena* absorb nutrients from their surrounding environment through their general body sunface.

5. Parasitic Nutrition

The parasitic forms feed either **holozoically** or **saprozoically.** Thus, the parasites may be grouped into two categories on the nature of food and their mode of feeding :

(i) Food-robbers. The parasites feeding upon the undigested or digested foodstuffs of their hosts are known as food-robbers, such as some ciliate parasites like *Nyctotherus, Balantidium*. These parasites feed holozoically on solid food particles, while few others like *Opalina* feed upon the liquid food by the process of osmosis through their general body surfaces. The food-robbers are generally non-pathogenic to their hosts.

(ii) Pathogeinc. The protozoan parasites causing harm to their hosts, usually feed upon the living tissues of the host. They absorb liquid food through their general body surface, *e.g., Trypanosoma, Plasmodium,* etc.

6. Coprozoic Nutrition

Certain free-living protozoans are in habit of feeding upon the faecal matters of the other organisms like *Clamydophrys* and *Dimastigamoeba.*

7. Mixotrophic Nutrition

Some Protozoa nourish themselves by more than one method at the same time or at different times due to change in environment. This is called mixotrophic nutrition, *e.g., Euglena gracilis* and *Peranema* are both saprozoic and autotrophic in their nutrition, and some flagellates are both autorophic and zootrophic.

However, Protozoa which feed on a large variety of food organisms are called euryphagous, and those which feed only on a few kinds of food are stenophagous. On the basis of the nature of food and feeding mechanism in Protozoa, they are placed in the following groups : **(a)** Macrophagous feeders are those which feed on large pieces of food *(Amoeba),* **(b)** Microphagous feeders are those which feed on very small particles, they rarely stop feeding and their food is drawn in with a current of water *(Paramecium).* (c) Fluid feeders are saprozoic and parasitic Protozoa which absorb liquid food through their surface *(Monocystis).*

BEHAVIOUR IN PROTOZOA

The movements or reactions performed by an animal due to its sensitivity, in response to its environmental changes constitute the behaviour of the animal. The responses the animal makes for environmental changes follow a constant pattern for that animal, thus, each animal has its own characteristic behaviour. Any environmental change to which an animal responds is called a stimulus. Movements made by an animal in response to stimuli may be positive or negative. If the animal is attracted by a stimulus and turns towards it, then the response is positive; but if the animal is repelled by stimulus and moves away from it, then the response is negative. Reactions to stimuli are classified into kinesis and taxes. Kinesis is that reaction in which the stimulus leads to an increase in the movements of the animal. Taxes are those reactions which are directed to the stimulus, they depend on the possession of some sense organ. An animal may react to light, contact, temperature, gravity, chemicals or electric current. Positive reactions are rare exceptions in Protozoa, majority of their reactions are negative. The response of an animal to a stimulus depends not only on the nature of the stimulus, but also on the condition of the animal at the moment.

Amoeba. Amoeba has no structures for reception of stimuli but its responses to stimuli are due to the irritability of its protoplasm. To gentle contact an *Amoeba* reacts positively and forms a food cup, but to forceful contact it reacts negatively, it first stop then forms new pseudopodia and moves away either at right angle or in the reverse direction. If its surrounding water is changed to distilled water, or sugar or salt or weak acid is added to its surrounding water, then pseudopodia are withdrawn and body becomes rounded, this is followed by formation of a single pseudopodium by which the animal moves away. If a chemical is applied to a small area of the body, the stimulated region contracts away from the stimulus, and the animal moves away in the opposite direction. If the temperature of its environment is raised between 30° and 35° C, then all movements cease, death results at 40° C., but *Amoeba* becomes most active between 20° and 25° C. Strong light causes gelation of plasmasol in the illuminated side, but the opposite side forms pseudopodia and the animal moves away. *Amoeba* avoids darkness, medium light is most favourable which is called optimum. Sudden and intense increase of light causes stopping of all movement and rounding off of the body, but if the intense light is maintained then after some time movement is resumed, this shows that *Amoeba* can adapt itself to new conditions. The response of *Amoeba* to different stimuli varies with the strength of the stimulus.

Euglena. If a drop of water containing *Euglenas* is placed in direct sunlight and half of the drop is shaded, then it will be seen that animals avoid both the lighted and shaded parts and collect in the middle area of medium light which is the optimum. Like most organisms containing chlorophyll, *Euglena* reacts positively towards light, it orientates itself parallel to the light rays and moves towards the sources of the illumination. But very strong light makes *Euglena* stop, then move back and pivot on its posterior end, while the anterior end traces a wide circle; this behaviour is avoiding reaction. The anterior end of *Euglena* is sensitive to light and it rotates as it moves forwards but when the light falls upon it from one side only, it reacts by swerving violently, and it orientates itself parallel to the rays of light whenever its photoreceptor is shaded by the stigma. The stimuli other than light, *Euglena* behaves in much the same way as other Protozoa, giving a negative reaction to unpleasant changes of environment.

Paramecium. The behaviour of *Paramecium* is stereotyped, but it is well adapted to preserve it and to keep it within the bonds of a normally favourable environment. Special organelles for perception of stimuli are not seen, but the anterior end seems to be more sensitive than other parts of the body. When *Paramecium* comes in forceful contact with a solid object, it reacts negatively, the ciliary beat is reversed by which it moves backwards and pivots on its posterior end, while the anterior end revolves in a circle; this behaviour is an avoiding reaction by which different samples of surrounding medium are brought into its peristome, if a sample is favourable the animal moves forwards in the direction of the sample but if the sample is unfavourable it moves away at an angle. Detection of the external environment is probably by means of cilia, perhaps all the cilia are sensory receptors, but there are some long, stiff cilia which play no role in locomotion and are probably entirely sensory. Jarring of the surround-medium causes the animal to swim downwards. To all contact it gives the avoiding reaction, but when it is stimulated violently by contact or chemicals, it responds by discharging its trichocysts. If a small drop of 1/50% acetic acid is placed in a large drop of water containing Paramecia then they collect in the acid drop; but if the strength of acid is increased to 1/10%, then they move away from the acid drop. Thus, they swim into weak chemicals but give the avoiding reaction when they come in contact with boundary of the drop, this produces their aggregation. On the other hand, in a stronger chemical they give the avoiding reaction when they meet the outer boundary of the drop of acid so that they are unable to enter it. Light has no effect on *Paramecium,* but it gives an avoiding reaction to strong light and ultra-violet rays. The optimum temperature for *Paramecium* is between 24° and 28° C., and up to a point it becomes more active at higher temperature and less active at lower temperature, but to sudden temperature changes it gives an avoiding reaction. *Paramecium* is weakly negative to gravity in its reaction. If a weak electric current is passed in the medium containing Paramecia, it will be seen that the animals swim towards the cathode because the current causes a partial reversal of ciliary beat. With stronger current more cilia beat backward than forwards, so that the animal swims towards the anode.

The reactions of Protozoa show similarities in many details with those of higher animals, and their reactions are quite adequate to maintain them within their normal environment. The behaviour of Protozoa is explained by certain theories. 1. Tropism theory of Loeb says that Protozoa respond to stimuli in a forced compulsory way, not because of choice, but because they cannot behave in any other way; they act like automatons being driven entirely by external stimuli. 2. Trial and error theory of Jennings maintains that Protozoa escape unfavourable conditions and find more favourable ones by repeated avoiding reactions amounting to trial and error. The animals are not forced into or away from unfavourable regions like automatons, but they are in control of their activities and direct their own course. The expression klinokinesis is now substituted for trial and error behaviour and avoiding reaction.

CONTRACTILE VACUOLE AND OSMOREGULATION IN PROTOZOA

Shape, size and occurrence. The contractile vacuoles are usually large, colourless, pulsatile fluid-filled organelles found in majority of protozoans. These vacuoles are nearly always found in freshwater Flagellata, Sarcodina and Ciliata. The contractile vacuoles are also found in some marine ciliates but these are not at all found in parasitic protozoans.

The contractile vacuoles are found in their simplest form in Sarcodina like *Amoeba*. In this case, these are usually spherical vesicles or sometimes irregular and bounded by a limiting membrane. These vacuoles are found surrounded by a circlet of mitochondria which provide energy for their pulsating activity. In Flagellata like *Euglena,* the contractile vacuole is somewhat complicated and surrounded by a large number of accessory contractile vacuoles. In Ciliata like *Paramecium,* the contractile vacuoles are much complicated and found surrounded by 5 to 12 radiating canals or feeding canals which collect water from the various parts of the body. The number of radiating canals varies in different ciliates. The radiating canals discharge their contents in the main contractile vacuole, thus, serving as feeders.

Situation and number. The position of contractile vacuole is not definite in Sarcodina and, therefore, can be found anywhere in the endoplasm. In Flagellata, *e.g., Euglena* the contractile vacuole is found situated near the anterior end at the side of reservoir. In Ciliata like *Paramecium,* the contractile vacuoles are usually two in number, situated one at each end of the body. The number of contractile vacuoles varies in the different groups of Protozoa but its number remains constant in the same species. However, it is single in *Amoeba,* single in *Euglena,* two in *Paramecium* but these are many in **Radiolaria** and **Heliozoa.**

Structure. Contractile vacuole is an empty space filled with fluid. Electron microscopic studies have revealed that its limiting membrane is lipo-protein in nature, like that of the plasma membrane.

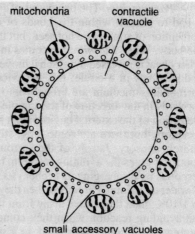

Fig. 23.8. Contractile vacuole of *Amoeba* surrounded by small accessory vacuoles and mitochondria.

Mode of working. The mode of working of contractile vacuole includes two steps, the **diastole** and the **systole.** The diastole is the phase of enlargement of the contractile vacuole to its maximum size and systole is the phase of its contraction to expel its contents. A contractile vacuole is usually formed by the fusion of a large number of very small droplets in the area where contractile vacuole is to be formed *(Amoeba)* or around the contractile vacuole *(Euglena).* The systole occurs by the sudden burst of the contractile vacuole in Sarcodina but in Flagellata like *Euglena,* it empties in reservoir and so is the case with other forms. As referred, the energy required for the working of contractile vacuole is furnished by the mitochondria surrounding the vacuole. However, the exact mechanism of working of contractile vacuole is not yet understood, even then the following theories have been put forth to explain its working :

1. Osmotic theory. This theory explains that the water from the surrounding cytoplasm enters into the contractile vacuole by **osmosis.**

2. Filtration theory. This theory explains that the water from the cytoplasm is forced into the contractile vacuole through its membrane due to internal hydrostatic pressure. **Kitching** has, however, contradicted this theory.

3. Secretion theory. This theory states that the water is actively secreted into the vacuole during diastole through the vacuole wall. This theory, too, is not widely accepted.

Function and significance. Contractile vacuole performs the function of **osmoregulation** by removing excess of water content from the body. In addition to its water regulatory function, the contractile vacuole is also believed to be **excretory** in function.

It has been observed that the water from the surrounding media continuously enters in the body of freshwater protozoans, therefore, water content of the protoplasm increases, *i.e.,* there is an increase in the internal hydrostatic pressure. This increased water content or hydrostatic pressure of the protoplasm inhibits the normal functioning of the body and if it continues to increase then a time may come when the body of the individual may burst. Thus, the contractile vacuole helps in removing the excess water content of the protoplasm, *i.e.,* it helps in maintaining the internal hydrostatic pressure. Actually, the body fluid is hypertonic to the surrounding medium in freshwater forms. In case of marine and parasitic protozoans the surrounding media is nearly is**a**tonic and, therefore, no excess water enters in the body. Hence, contractile vacuole is usually absent in these forms.

REPRODUCTION IN PROTOZOA

The process of reproduction is to continue one's kind in nature. The mode of reproduction in Protozoa is highly variable among different groups although it is primarily a cell division. Protozoa reproduce both **asexually** and **sexually.**

Asexual Reproduction

In asexual mode of reproduction no special sex cells are involved but there is always some form of fission present. An essential part of the process is the partition of some parent chromatin substance among daughter individuals. Hence, the fission of the cell body is preceded by the division of the nucleus. Asexual reproduction occurs by the following methods :

1. Equal or binary fission. Equal or binary fission takes place for reproducing and also for gamete formation. Usually there is a centriole within the nucleus, but unlike Metazoa no asters are formed, moreover the nuclear membrane persists intact during division in most Protozoa. The nucleus elongates and divides amitotically into two parts which travel apart, then the cell constricts in the middle to form two daughter cells. Macronuclei of ciliates divide amitotically. Binary fission is simple in Sarcodina like *Amoeba* where the plane of division is not definite and it is usually transverse in Ciliates like *Paramecium* but in most flagellates like *Euglena* it is longitudinal in which the nucleus elongates transversely, but the cell divides lengthwise, while binary fission is oblique in certain cases like *Ceratium.* In binary fission (in flagellates) a single flagellum is retained usually by one daughter cell, and the basal granule divided into two, the new basal granule forms a flagellum in the other daughter cell. When there are many flagella they are distributed among the daughter cells which grow new flagella to complete the number. Cilia are shared by daughter cells and new cilia are formed by kinetosomes to complete the number. Chromatophores usually divide but contractile vacuoles rarely divide, they are generally shared or are made anew. Complex organelles are destroyed and then re-made in the daughter cells.

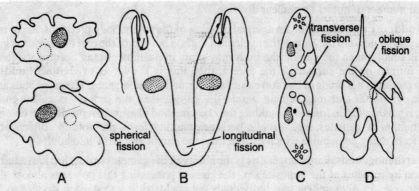

Fig. 23.9. Binary fission in Protozoa. A—*Amoeba* (irregular); B—*Euglena* (longitudinal) ; C—*Paramecium* (transverse); D—*Ceratium* (oblique).

2. Multiple fission. The nucleus divides repeatedly without division of the cytoplasm, later the cytoplasm separates into as many parts as there are nuclei, usually some residual cytoplasm is left unsegmented. If multiple fission produces four or more young ones by equal cell division, and the young ones do not separate till the process is completed, then such cell division is spoken of as repeated fission, *e.g., Vorticella.* Multiple fission produces small cells which may grow into adults or they may become gametes which require fertilization to form sporozoites *(Plasmodium).* The multiple fission may lead either to asexual or sexual reproduction.

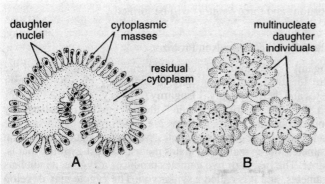

Fig. 23.10. A—Multiple fission ; B—Plasmotomy.

Products of multiple fission of a zygote generally form spores, sometimes the products of any multiple fission are called spores. A spore may be enclosed in a spore case *(Monocystis)* or they may be naked. The naked spores may be amoeboid *(Entamoeba)* or flagellated *(Chlamydomonas)* or ciliated (Suctoria). Spores may be gametes or serve for the distribution of the species. All types of fission occur within a cyst or without encystment. Cyst formation is common in freshwater and parasitic Protozoa, though all Protozoa do not form cysts. In cyst formation the animal becomes rounded, loses its organelles of locomotion, it ejects the food vacuoles and contractile vacuoles disappear. The animal then secretes a gelatinous covering which hardens into a chitinous epicyst, inside this a membranous endocyst is secreted; the cyst may have more than two layers. The function of the cyst is protection of the animal against unfavourable conditions of environment, or it may be reproduction. The cysts can be carried by wind or some other agent and are, thus, important in dispersal. Protozoa have the following kinds of cysts : (i) resting cysts enable an organism to proceed undisturbed in its normal activities *(Euglena)* ; *(ii)* resistance cysts are formed against unfavourable conditions of environment *(Amoeba)* ; (iii) gamocysts are those in which union of gametes takes place for reproduction *(Gregarina);* (iv) oocysts contain a zygote *(Plasmodium);* (v) sporocysts are those in which multiple fission occurs to form sporozoites *(Monocystis).* Finally excystment takes place on return of favourable conditions, but the individual leaving the cyst is never the same as the one that underwent encystment, it has a complement of new organelles and renewed vigour. The excystment may be through a minute pore in the cyst, but more usually it is due to the protozoan secreting some enzymes which rupture the cyst wall.

3. Plasmotomy. An asexual division of a multinucleate animal in which the cytoplasm divides but the nuclei do not is called plasmotomy *(Opalina, Pelomyxa).* Later each daughter cell regains the normal number of nuclei by nuclear division.

4. Budding or gemmation. An unequal division of the parent body produces one or more buds which may separate from the parent, the nucleus of the bud is a part of the parent nucleus, *e.g., Arcella.* The bud is smaller than the parent; the buds may grow into adults or may become gametes. When buds are formed on the surface of the parent, then this is known as exogenous budding, *e.g., Noctiluca* produces hundreds of buds on its surface as small protuberances. When the buds are formed inside the cytoplasm and may remain within the parent, then the process is called endogenous budding, *e.g., Arcella.* Endogenous budding may be a method of asexual reproduction or it may bring about formation of gametes, *e.g., Arcella* becomes multinucleate, protoplasm collects around the nuclei to form many amoebulae which escape from the parent and grow into adults.

5. Parthenogenesis. Parthenogenesis is the ability of the gametes to develop into adults without fertilization by gametes of the opposite sex, the gamete possessing this power is almost always the female one, *e.g.,* in *Actinophrys* two individuals get enclosed in a cyst, each divides to form two gametes, one gamete of an individual conjugates with a gamete of the other individual, the remaining gamete of each individual develops parthenogenetically into an adult. Thus, gametes which have been unable to undergo cross fertilization develop by parthenogenesis. Potential gametes of *Chlamydomonas* will grow and divide to become adults when they have missed syngamy. Endomixis of ciliates is also a parthenogenetic phenomenon. The chromosome condition in parthenogenesis may be expected to be haploid since no fertilization occurs, but it is generally diploid.

6. Regeneration. Regeneration is the capacity to form new tissues to replace a lost part, this capacity varies inversely with the complexity of an organism. In Protozoa any nucleated portion is capable of regeneration, while non-nucleated portions are not, *e.g., Stentor* has a long chain-like nucleus, if the animal is cut transversely into say three parts, then each piece having a portion of the nucleus will regenerate the missing portions and three *Stentors* will be formed.

Sexual Reproduction

Sexual reproduction occurs by the following methods in Protozoa :

1. Syngamy or copulation. Syngamy is the union and complete fusion of two gametes of the same species. If the two gametes are identical morphologically, though they may be different physiologically, then they are isogametes and their syngamy is isogamy *(Monocystis).* If the gametes differ in size and morphology, then they are anisogametes and their syngamy is anisogamy *(Plasmodium).* The smaller, usually numerous and motile gametes are male or microgametes; the larger, generally few and inactive gametes are female or macrogametes. Meiosis or reduction division occurs generally in the formation of gametes, but in many flagellates meiosis is post-zygotic, that is, it occurs after the formation of the zygote. The fusion of two gametes produces a zygote, its nucleus is formed by the fusion of nuclei of gametes, and it is called a synkaryon. The zygote may develop directly into an adult, or it may encyst and undergo multiple fission. Syngamy whether isogamous or anisogamous is always exogamous, that is, the fusing gametes come from different parents, hence, sex distinction may be said to exist in Protozoa, though sexes may not be distinguished.

2. Conjugation. Conjugation is a temporary union of two Protozoa of the same species for an exchange of nuclear material without the fusion of their cytoplasm, *e.g.,* in *Paramecium caudatum* (Fig. 20.21). In ciliates there is no formation of distinct gametes.

A sexual process somewhat intermediate between syngamy and conjugation occurs in *Vorticella* (Fig. 21.6) in which one individual forms one to four microgametes by repeated fission, and the other individual forms a macrogamete by nuclear modification, the macrogamete is a hologamete because it is not formed by fission. Thus, *Vorticella* shows sexual dimorphism in its gametes. a microgamete fuses with a macrogamete to form a zygote. The zygote by three divisions produces seven cells which grow into adults.

In both syngamy and conjugation there is a rejuvenation of the animal by replacement of the macronucleus with material from the synkaryon, both processes produce new types of individuals by combination of genes, hence, they give the race a better chance of survival.

3. Automixis. In some Protozoa the nucleus divides into two, the two nuclei fuse together, this is called automixis. If the two nuclei which fuse are present in a single cell, then the process is called autogamy, but if the two fusing nuclei are present in two different cells, then the process is known as paedogamy. Autogamy occurs in a single *Paramecium aurelia* which provides both the fusing nuclei to form a synkaryon (Fig. 20.23). Paedogamy occurs in *Actinosphaerium* and *Actinophrys* in which two cells of a secondary cyst and their two remaining nuclei fuse to form a zygote which reproduces by binary fission.

Sexual reproduction of Protozoa differs from the sexual reproduction of Metazoa in that the protozoan is both somatic and gametic. For many generations there is a somatic phase in which binary fission occurs, then one generation is gametic in which syngamy or conjugation takes place. The function of binary fission is reproduction or increasing the number of individuals; and the function of syngamy or conjugation is rejuvenation, but not reproduction although it is called "sexual reproduction". In the life cycle of some Protozoa binary fission alternates with syngamy, this alternation may have regular sexual and asexual generations (*Elphidium*), but more usually binary fission is repeated for many generations continuously, and it is broken only occasionally by syngamy or conjugation. Probably the occasional conjugation occurs only when the physiological condition of the animal becomes different from normal (*Paramecium*).

4. Endomixis. It is a type of nuclear reorganisation which usually occurs when conjugation is prevented. In this case fusion of pro-nuclei does not take place. But the macronucleus is reorganised from micronuclear material. The reorganised macronucleus accelerates the metabolic activities of the individual and helps in the renewal of the vigour as is reported in *Paramecium aurelia* (Fig. 20.22).

5. Hemixis. It has been reported in the various species of *Paramecium* like *P. caudatum, P. aurelia* and *P. multimicronucleatum.* In this case, the macronucleus throws away its many fragments of different sizes in the cytoplasm which are absorbed in it. The left out part of macronucleus, then starts behaving in a normal way and becomes the fresh macronucleus. The micronucleus, however, plays no part in hemixis and remains inactive and unchanged during this process.

PARASITISM IN PROTOZOA

The relationship between two organisms may be symbiosis, commensalism, or parasitism.

Symbiosis is a relationship in which there is reciprocal benefit between one animal called a symbiont and the other called a host, the symbiont lives in the body of the host, *e.g.,* *Trichonympha* lives in the gut of termites in symbiotic relationship, *Trichonympha* obtains food and lodging, and in return it digests the wood eaten by termites, the termites are incapable of digesting wood.

Commensalism is an association in which one organism called a commensal is benefited, and the other organism known as the host is neither benefited nor harmed, *e.g.,* *Nyctotherus* in cockroach gets food from the host, but the host is not injured in any way. The distinction between symbiosis and commensalism is not very sharp; *Entamoeba coli* in man is usually a commensal, but it may become symbiotic when it eats up bacteria which may be harmful to man.

Parasitism is an association in which one organism, the parasite lives on the body or inside the body and at the expense of another organism known as the host. Parasitic mode of life is a secondary state, the parasites having arisen frequently and independently from free-living ancestors. The relationship of a parasite to its host is of varying degrees of intimacy, the parasite may be **epizoic** or ectoparasitic which lives on the external surface of the host though it may wander into the buccal cavity or rectum, *e.g., Kerona,* a ciliate is an ectoparasite on hydras, another ectoparasite is *Oodinium,* a flagellate on the body of *Olikopleura,* but ectoparasites are rare in Protozoa. The parasite may be entozoic or endoparasitic which lives inside the body of the host. The endoparasites may be found in internal cavities *(Balantidium),* or they may be intracellular *(Plasmodium)* or they may be found in tissues of the hosts *(Entamoeba).* The endoparasites may feed on the food of the host *(Gregarina),* or on the body fluids of the host *(Trypanosoma)* or on the tissue cells of the host *(Plasmodium).*

Effects of parasitic life on parasites. In early parasitism there are no morphological changes in the parasite though physiological adaptations take place, later the following changes occur. (a) There is a reduction in the organelles of locomotions, since the parasites are transported by the host, so that the locomotor organelles are simplified and finally lost. In some intestinal Sporozoa *(Gregarina)* only metaboly occurs, but in intracellular parasites *(Plasmodium)* there is no locomotion. (b) The form and shape of the body become very simple with no complex organelles *(Plasmodium).* (c) Organelles of fixation appear in some intestinal parasites *(Gregarina).* (d) Organelles of nutrition are simplified *(Balantidium)* or even lost *(Plasmodium)* since food is absorbed by the body surface. (e) Parasites acquire an ability for rapid multiplication to form numerous young ones, this ensures that at least some of the offspring will find a suitable host and continue the species *(Plasmodium).* (f) Many have two hosts in their life cycle, and one of the hosts also acts as a vector to disseminate the parasite *(Trypannosoma* in man and tsetse fly).

Host specificity. Some parasites are restricted to a few hosts only, *e.g., Gregarina* in a few insects, or *Opalina* in Anura only, but some parasites have become adapted to a large variety of hosts, *e.g., Trypanosoma* is found in all classes of Vertebrates in which it parasitizes some five hundred species. Thus, in the development of host relationship the above two general trends are seen, this is due partly to the infective powers of the parasite, and partly to the degree of susceptibility of the host.

Effects of parasitism on the host. The following pathological conditions may be caused by parasites in their hosts. (i) Destruction of cells and tissues of the host may take place by movement or feeding activities of the parasite, *e.g., Entamoeba histolytica* eats the tissue cells of the colon and red blood corpuscles of the host; *Plasmodium* feeds on liver cells and erythrocytes. (ii) parasites may cause enlargement and disorders of lymph glands, spleen and liver, *e.g., Leishmania;* or parasites may cause ulcers in the intestine, liver and brain, *e.g., Entamoeba.* (iii) Parasites may secrete poisonous toxins which cause some disease in the host, *e.g., Plasmodium* causes malaria.

But in most cases of parasitism there is a mutual adaptation between the host and the parasite, the parasite is able to live and reproduce without any apparent injury, and the host offers a resistance or acquires an immunity against the parasite by producing antibodies which neutralize the effects of the parasite, or by becoming immune due to previous infection, or by increasing its powers of repairing and regenerating the injured tissue cells. At times the host destroys the parasite by phagocytosis with the aid of leucocytes or cells of the spleen, bone marrow and liver. The host may succeed in destroying the parasite or it may remain infected but become immune, so that it becomes a carrier of the parasite. Generally there is a delicate adjustment between the parasite and the host and they come to an elaborate compromise, if this mutual adjustment is lacking, then either the parasite is killed or the host is destroyed.

ECONOMIC IMPORTANCE OF PROTOZOA

Protozoa is a group of acellular microscopic animals which have occupied almost all possible ecological habitats on the earth. For instance, they live in water, in moist surface of soil, in air and even as commensals and parasites in animals and plants. Man being a biological species is invariably effected by these organisms. Some of them are beneficial in the sense that they are helpful in sanitation, provide food, make oceanic ooze and help in the study of various biological phenomena, while a large number of them are harmful to man because they cause serious diseases in man and domestic animals such as cattle, poultry and fishes.

A. Beneficial Protozoa

Some Protozoa are of great importance for mankind and other animals. According to their utility they can be classified into following categories :

1. Helpful in sanitation. Some protozoans play a vital role in the sanitary betterment and improvement of the modern civilization in keeping water safe for drinking purpose. The protozoans

living in polluted water feed upon waste organic substances and, thus, purify it. However, some protozoans feed on the bacteria holozoically and purify the water indirectly.

2. Protozoa as food. Although Protozoa have microscopic body but provide directly or indirectly the sources of food supplies to man, fish and other animals. The larvae of most aquatic insects feed on aquatic protozoans. The insect larvae are taken as food by clams, prawn and young fishes which are the ultimate source of food of man.

Pelagic protozoans such as Foraminifera and Radiolaria sink after death to the bottom of ocean and forming the fundamental source of food supply along with organic debris for the deep sea fauna. Few Protozoa have chlorophyll and are capable of synthesizing food by phtosynthetic activity.

3. Commensal Protozoa. The commensal protozoans are those which live on or in body of other animals (hosts) and derive some benefit from the relationship, however, the other partner is neither benefited nor injured. They may be of following two types :

(i) **Ectocommensal Protozoa.** The ectocommensal Protozoa live on the surface of the body of host. Various ciliates and suctorians lead an ectocommensal life on molluscs, arthropods, fishes and frogs, etc. The bodies of such hosts simply serve as substratum for these ectocommensals.

(ii) **Endocommensal Protozoa.** The endocommensal protozoans live inside the body of hosts. For example, *Trichomonas, Giardia,* etc., (Mastigophora), *Entamoeba coli* (Rhizopoda), and *Nyctotherus, Balantidium* and *Opalina* (Ciliata), live as endocommesals within the alimentary canal of man, frogs, cockroaches and others. They feed on bacteria and so have beneficial effect. In man, *Balantidium coli* (an endocommensal) feed upon harmful bacteria in the colon.

4. Symbiotic Protozoa. The symbiotic Protozoa are those protozoans which live in symbiotic relationship with other animals. In symbiotic association, the two partners become so dependent on each other that one cannot get along without the other and their separation results in the death of both. The most important symbiotic protozoans (symbionts) are some intestinal flagellates such as *Trichonympha, Colonympha,* etc., of termites and woodroaches. These symbionts help in the digestion of cellulose which is converted into glycogen. The glycogen is utilized by the symbionts and the hosts.

5. Commercial uses of protozoan skeletons. The skeletons of dead Foraminifera and Radiolaria sink to the sea bottom and form the oceanic ooze. This solidifies and convert into rock strata. Such sort of strata of oceanic ooze are white chalk cliffs of Dover and England, and stone beds of Paris, Cairo and North America. A large number of Paris buildings are built of the limestone which is exclusively composed of the shells of genus *Hiliolina.* Similarly pyramids of Egypt are constructed by lime-stone deposits of *Nummulite* shells. Sometimes, the skeletal deposits are used as filtering agents and as abrasives.

6. Zoological importance of Protozoa. The protozoans have been found as an ideal material for cytological, cytochemical, physiological, biochemical, and genetical studies, because of their small size, simple organization, quick reproduction and easy availability.

B. Harmful Protozoa

Almost all harmful protozoans lead a parasitic mode of life. They parasitize almost every species of plants and animals including the man and cause various fatal diseases.

1. Parasitic Protozoa. The parasitic protozoans live on or within the body of other organisms (known as host) for the sake of food, shelter and continuance of their races. The parasitic Protozoa belong to different groups of phylum Protozoa and members of class Sporozoa are exclusively parasitic. Such sort of taxonomic distribution of parasitic protozoans helps in drawing the conclusion that the parasitic mode of life is secondary state and the parasitic protozoans have evolved frequently and independently from different groups of free-living ancestors.

Kinds of parasitic Protozoa. The parasitic Protozoa can be classified into following two categories according to their occurrence on or within the body of host.

1. Ectoparasitic Protozoa. The Protozoa, which live on the external body surface of the host plant or animal, are known as ectoparasitic Protozoa. The ectoparasitic protozoans are less common and they occur in the epidermal layer of some animals. For example, 1. *Hydramoeba hydroxena* is the ectoparasite of *Hydra* and it feeds on the ectodermal cells. 2. *Ichthyophthirius multifiliis* is an

ectoparasite of freshwater fishes and it occurs in epidermal cells. It causes integumentary blisters.
3. *Leishmania tropica* is an ectoparasite of man which lives in skin and causes oriental sores.

    2. Endoparasitic Protozoa. The protozoans which occur inside the body of the host are known
as endoparasitic protozoans and because generally they cause diseases in their hosts, therefore, they
and also known as pathogenic Protozoa. In general, the pathogenic endoparasitic protozoans can be
classified in following groups according to their location inside the host body.

    (i) Coelozoic Protozoa. The endoparasitic protozoans living in the body cavity or coelom are
known as coelozoic protozoans, *e.g., Entamoeba, Trichomonas* and *Balantidium.*

    (ii) Histozoic Protozoa. The endoparasitic protozoans living in between the cells of tissues and
body organs are known as intercellular or histozoic protozoans, *e.g., Entamoeba, Giardia, Eimeria,
Balantidium, Trypanosoma* and many other endoparasitic protozoans.

    (iii) Cytozoic Protozoa. The endoparasitic protozoans living inside the host's body are termed
as intracellular or cytozoic protozoans, *e.g., Plasmodium, Leishmania, Babesia, Haemoproteus,
Sarcocystis,* etc.

    The endoparasitic pathogenic protozoans have also been classified into different groups accord-
ing to their exact location inside the body of host.

    1. Endoparasites of mouth. Some endoparasitic protozoans dwell in mouth or buccal cavity
and cause various diseases. A few most common endoparasites of mouth of man and other animals
are as follows :

    (i) Entamoeba gingivalis. E. gingivalis belongs to class Sarcodina and dwells in tartar of teeth
and abscesses of gums of man, dogs and cats. It causes pyorrhoea disease and its infection is caused
by kissing or feeding in the same bowl.

    (ii) Leishmania brassiliensis. L. brassiliensis is a member of class Mastigophora and lives in
the oro-nasal mucous membrane of man. It causes espundia or mucoutaneous leishmaniasis. The
man is infected by the biting of sandfly.

    (iii) Trichomonas tenax. T. tenax is a member of class Mastigophora which lives in mouth, in
tartar and unhealthy gums of man. It causes the disease pyorrhoea and its infection occurs by kissing.

    2. Endoparasites of digestive tract. Various species of pathogenic protozoans live in the
digestive tract of man and other animals and cause severe diseases. Some important pathogenic
endoparasites of digestive tract are as follows :

    (i) Entamoeba histolytica. E. histolytica inhabits the large intestine of man and causes several
diseases such as amoebic dysentery and ulceration of colon. In advanced stages of its infection it
invades the tissues of liver, spleen, heart, and lungs, etc., and causes amoebic abscesses in them. Its
infection occurs due to ingestion of its quadrinucleate cysts along with contaminated food or drinks.

    (ii) Giardia intestinalis. G. intestinalis belongs to class Mastigophora and dwells in large
intestine of man. It causes a disease, diarrhoea. Its transmission to man takes place by ingestion of
quadrinucleate cysts with contaminated food and drinks.

    (iii) Chilomonas. It is a member of class Mastigophora and lives in large intestine of man. It
causes various gastric disorders.

    (iv) Trichomonas hominis. T. hominis is a Mastigophora which dwells in the ileo-caecal region
of man, monkeys, cats and dogs and is supposed to cause diarrhoea and dysentery. Its infection
occurs due to ingestion of contaminated food and drinks which may contain its cysts.

    (v) Trichomonas gallinae. T. gallinae lives in the epithelial lining of the oesophagus and crop
of pigeons, turkeys, fowls, etc., and sometimes also lives in liver and lungs. It causes necrotic nodules
in these organs.

    (vi) Trichomonas gallinarum. T. gallinarum dwells in the epithelium of lower intestine and
liver of turkeys and fowls. It causes disease similar to black head disease.

    (vii) Histomonas meleagridis. H. meleagridis is a Mastigophora which lives in the caecum and
liver of turkeys and fowls and causes black head disease in them.

    (viii) Nosema apis. N. apis is a sporozoan which dwells in the intestinal epithelium and
Malpighian tubules of honey bees. It causes the noscular disease in them and its infection is caused
due to cytoplasmic inheritance.

(ix) Sarcocystis linedemanni. S. linedemanni is a sporozoan which lives in the striped muscle fibres of sheep's oesophagus. It causes the degeneration of muscles.

(x) Isospora hominis. I. hominis belongs to class Sporozoa and is a cytozoic parasite of epithelial cells of intestine of man. Its infection is caused due to ingestion of contaminated food which may carry its oocysts. It causes diarrhoea in man.

(xi) Eimeria sps. Eimeria belongs to class Sporozoa and its many species dewll in various animals such as sheep, birds and cattle. It causes dysentery and diarrhoea in them.

(xii) Balantidium coli. B. coli is a member of class Ciliata and it lives in the large intestine of man. It causes a chronic disease known as balantidiosis in man.

3. Endoparasiites of blood. Many species of endoparasitic protozoans dwell in the blood of vertebrates and cause various fatal diseases. Few important endoparasitic protozoans are described below.

(i) Trypanosoma sps. Trypanosoma belongs to the class Mastigophora and its various species cause disease in vertebrates. Few important pathogenic species of *Trypanosoma* and their diseases, etc., have been tabulated in the Chapter of *Trypanosoma.*

(ii) Leishmania sps. Leishmania is a member of class Mastigophora and parasitizes man and various domestic animals. Following species of *Leishmania* are common in man and other mammals.

(a) L. donovani. It is a cytozoic endoparasiitic pathogen which lives in the leucocytes and in the endothelial cells of lymph glands, blood capillaries, spleen, liver, bone marrow, etc. It causes the disease visceral leishmaniasis or kala azar in which the man is affected by fever, anemia and enlargement of liver and spleen. Its infection occurs through the blood-sucking fly, *Phlebotomus.*

(b) L. infantum. It is a cytozoic parasite of cells of liver and spleen of children. It causes the enlargement of spleen.

(c) L. brassiliensis. It is a endoparasite of man, dogs, cats, etc.

(iii) Plasmodium. It is a sporozoan and its many species lead a cytozoic mode of life and live in red blood cells of various vertebrates. Few important species are as follows :

P. vivax. It is intracellular endoparasite of red blood cells and liver cells of man. It causes the malaria disease in man and its infection is caused by biting of blood-sucking female mosquito, *Anopheles.*

P. falciparum, P. malariae, and *P. ovale* also cause malaria and have similar nature to *P. vivax.*

(iv) Babesia. Babesia belongs to class Sporozoa and its various species are cytozoic of red blood cells of many mammals. Few important cytozoic endoparasitic species of *Babesia* are follows :

(a) B. bigemina. It is cytozoic of red blood corpuscles of cattle and causes the diseases known as Texas fever or Red water fever with anaemia and diarrhoea. Its infection takes place through bite of vector female tick, *Boophilus annulatus.*

(b) B. canis. It is cytozoic pathogen of red blood corpuscles of dog and causes anaemia, malignant jaundice, fever in dogs. It is transmitted to the dogs by biting of ticks.

(c) B. equi. It is cytozoic pathogen of red blood corpuscles of horses and causes anaemia, jaundice and paralysis of hind limbs. Its transmission to host takes place by biting of ticks.

(v) Haemoproteus. It belongs to class Sporozoa and is an intracellular endoparasite of red blood corpuscles and endothelial cells of blood vessels of birds.

4. Endoparasites of urinogenital tract. Various endoparasitic Protozoa dwell in urinogenital organs and cause various pathogenic diseases. Some important endoparasitic protozoans of urinogenital tract are as follows :

(i) Trichomonas vaginalis. It occurs in the urinogenital system of women and men. It causes annoying itch, abnormal discharges and various ailments. Infection occurs directly in coitus.

(ii) Trichomonas foetus. It occurs in the urinogenital system of cattle, horses and sheep. It causes abortions, delayed conceptions and inflammation of perputial sacs. Transmission takes place by direct method in coitus.

2. Other harmful Protozoa. Some protozoans affect the mankind indirectly. For example, several species of Protozoa live in soil. They devour the nitrifying bacteria (which produce nitrogen and increase the fertility of soil) and make the soil unfertile, due to which the yield of crop is invariably effected.

Moreover, various species of Protozoa make drinking water polluted and unpalatable. For example, the protozoan *Bursaria* gives salt marshy smell to water, *Ceratium* imparts foul smell to water and *Eudorina, Pandorina* and *Volvox*, etc., give odour like the ripe cucumber to the drinking water.

PROTOZOA AND DISEASE

Protozoa cause many diseases in man and animals. Most of these diseases are more prevalent in the tropical and subtropical regions. These diseases by their prevalence render large areas of the earth uninhabitable by man. All classes of Protozoa have disease-producing members, but they are more so in Flagellata and Sporozoa. Human beings alone have over fifteen species of parasitic Protozoa. They are various amoeba, flagellates, ciliates and sporozoans. Some of these are harmless but others are responsible for some fatal diseases. The human parasitic Protozoa spend all or at least part of their life cycles in the body tissues, alimentary canal or blood of the host.

Protozoa and disease has been discussed in detail under the following two headings :

Protozoa and Human Diseases

The diseases occur as a result of the interaction between the protozoans and the human beings under specific environmental conditions. This interaction is referred to as **infection**, the manifestation of which is always the **infectious disease.** The infectious disease is caused by the development of an infection in which pathogenic parasites, which are the pathogenic agents of diseases, enter the human body's normal vital activities as a result of morphological and physiological damage. The pathogenic parasites belonging to various groups of Animal Kingdom, share the following common characteristic features :

1. All are **obligatory parasites,** *i.e.,* they depend for their existence upon their hosts.

2. All exhibit **host specificity,** *i.e.,* they harbour selective hosts.

3. They complete their life cycle in one or more than one host.

4. They secrete toxic substances which cause the particular disease.

Parasitic species are found in all classes of Protozoa. Approximately 15 different genera of Protozoa have been found living as parasites within the human body. The majority of these have relatively little effect upon their hosts, while certain parasites cause some of the worst human diseases. Most significant of these protozoan diseases are as follows :

1. Amoebiasis. Amoebiasis, also known as amoebic dysentery, is caused by *Entamoeba histolytica.* Infection generally occurs through drinking water. The trophozoite of *E. histolytica* penetrates the wall of the colon, secretes histolytic enzymes and feeds upon its cells causing ulcers. These ulcers rupture and discharge mucus and blood into the intestine that pass along with stools and results in amoebic dysentery. If the infection is allowed to continue the parasite may reach the liver, lungs and brain where it causes abscesses which prove fatal.

There is no intermediate host in the life cycle of *E. histolytica.* Transmission of the parasite from man to man takes place through the tetranucleate cysts. Before the cyst-formation the trophozoite changes into a smaller **minuta form,** which then encysts to form a tetranucleate cyst. These tetranucleate cysts are voided with the faecal and contaminated water and food and are then transmitted into new hosts. Faecal contamination of drinking water, vegetables and food are the primary causes. Eating of uncooked vegetables and fruits which have been fertilized with infected human faeces has often led to the occurrence of disease. Occasionally drinking water supply contaminated with infected faeces gives rise to epidemics. Houseflies may transmit cysts while passing from faeces to unprotected foodstuffs. The cysts of *E. histolytica* have been found in the droppings of cockroaches which also serve as a source of infection.

Amoebiasis is endemic in tropical countries. It can be treated with Emetine, Fumagillin, Metronidazole, Tinidazole, Terramycin, Erythromycin, Aureomycin and Chloroquine, etc.

2. Diarrhoea. Diarrhoea, which is characterized by loose bowels, is caused by a flagellete parasite *Giardia* (=*Lamblia*) *intestinalis* and a sporozoan *Isopora hominis*.

Giardia intestinalis is a parasite in the small intestine and colon of man. It has an elliptical or pear-shaped body which is bilateraly symmetrical with dorsal side convex and ventral side flattened and deepened anteriorly to form a concave sucking disc. It bears two nuclei and four pairs of long flagella arranged symmetrically. With the help of sucking disc the parasite attaches itself on to the convex surface of the epithelial cells in the intestine and may cause a disturbance of intestinal function leading to malabsorption of fat which causes diarrhoea. Consequently the patient may complain of persistent looseness of bowels. The parasite is also capable of producing epigastric pain, abdominal discomfort, loss of appetite, headache and toxic effect (allergy).

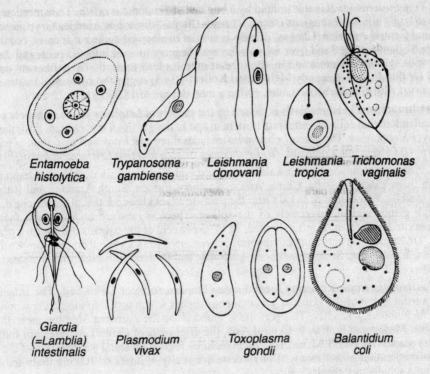

Fig. 23.11. Some pathogenic protozoan parasites of man.

Infection in man is brought about by ingestion of cysts. Transmission of the parasite takes place through cysts which are voided with faeces and are transmitted to new hosts with contaminated water and food. The infection of *Giardia* is more common in children than in adults. Atebrin, Chloroquine and Acranil are effective drugs in the treatment of *Giardia*. Metronidazole has also been reported to be quite effective in its treatment.

Isopora hominis is a rare infectious parasite amongst human beings inhabiting the small intestine of man and may cause intestinal symptoms like colic and diarrhoea. Dogs are supposed to be reservoir hosts of *I. hominis*.

3. Trypanosomiasis. Trypanosomiasis is caused by the species of *Trypanosoma* which are flagellate parasites of blood plasma (in vertebrate hosts) and gut (in invertebrate hosts). *Trypanosoma* is generally transmitted by blood-sucking insects. It is the most dreadful of all pathogenic protozoans. Sleeping sickness is a dangerous disease of man in Africa. Three species cause sleeping sickness in man which are as follows :

    (i) *Trypanosoma gambiense* is transmitted by tsetse flies, *Glossina palpalis* and *G. tachinoides*. It causes Gambian or Central African sleeping sickness.

    (ii) *Trypanosoma rhodesiense* is transmitted by tsetse fly *Glossina morsitans*. It causes Rhodesian or East African sleeping sickness.

Both the above species of *Trypanosoma* are confined to those parts of Africa where tsetse flies, their vectors, are found. On infection by the parasite trypanosome fever is caused during which the parasite lives freely in the blood, then the parasites collect in the lymph glands, spleen and liver causing their enlargement, finally they enter the cerebrospinal fluid causing sleeping sickness which results in coma and eventually in death.

Suramin and Pentamidine are considered to be the drugs of choice for early and acute infection. As they cannot pass the blood-brain barrier, they are not of any value when the central nervous system is involved in which case an arsenical is needed. The arsenicals include Tryparsamide, Melarsen, Melarsoprol (Mel B) and Trimelarsen. Nitrofurazone, an oral trypanoside may be used in cases resistant to arsenic.

(iii) *Trypanosoma cruzi* is transmitted by a bug called *Triatoma megista.* Transmission to man is not due to bug's bite but through its faeces. It causes Chagas' disease or American trypanosomiasis in South and Central America. Chagas' disease is similar to sleeping sickness. It causes continuous fever, lymph glands, spleen and liver are swollen with degeneration of infected cells, and disorders of the nervous system. Anaemia and injury to heart muscles lead to death. No permanent cure was suggested for this disease. Recently Melzer and Kollert (1963) suggested successful treatment of a case of *T. cruzi* with Nitrofurazone tablet, giving a total dosage of 18.375 gm in 27 days.

4. Leishmaniasis. Leishmaniasis is caused by the species of *Leishmania,* the flagellate parasite in the reticulendothelial cells of vertebrate host, man and in the gut of an invertebrate host, the blood sucking fly, *Phlebotomus.* The genus *Leishmania* includes three species which are common parasites of man, *viz., (i) Leishmania donovani; (ii) Leishmania tropica* and *(iii) Leishmania brasiliensis.*

(i) *Leishmania donovani* causes kala-azar or visceral leishmaniasis which is widespread and endemic in many places in India, China, Africa, Southern Europe, South America and Russia. Its vector is a sand fly, *Phlebotomus.* In kala-azar the parasite attacks the endothelial cells, bone marrow, liver, lymph glands and blood vessels of the spleen. These organs are enlarged and there is a bloodlessness and high fever. If left untreated, 75 to 95 per cent of the patients die within a period of two years. Treatment with antimony compounds proves successful. Urea stibamine, Aminostiburea, Neostibosan, Solistibosan, Sodium-antimony-gluconate and Pentamidine isoethionate are mst effective drugs.

(ii) *Leishmania tropica* causes Oriental sore (Tropical sore) or Delhi boil. The infection is limited to a local lesion of the skin and subcutaneous tissues which turn into ulcerating wounds. Its vector is *Phlebotomus,* a sandfly. This parasite is found along the shores of Mediterranean through Syria, Arabia, Mesopotamia, Iran to Central Asia, the drier parts of Central and Western India and also in many places of Central Africa. Treatment includes regular cleaning and dressing of the boils, Pentavalent preparation of antimony. Dehydroemetine orally in doses of 100 mg daily for 10–21 days has given satisfactory result.

(iii) *Leishmania brasiliensis* causes a disease called Espundia or American leishmaniasis producing multiple sores over large areas of the skin and oro-nasal mucosa. Ulceration in nasal cavities, mouth and pharynx is quite frequent. The vectors are anthropophilic sandflies. The parasite is confined to Central and South America. Treatment includes Pentavalent preparation of antimony. In resistant cases Pyrimethamine or Amphotericin B may be useful.

5. Trichomoniasis. Trichomoniasis is caused by the species of flagellate parasite, *Trichomonas.* Its body is pear-shaped provided with one nucleus, an axostyle, a parabasal body, 3–5 anterior free flagella, and one backwardly directed flagellum along the side of the body. *Trichomonas* are parasites in vertebrates and many invertebrates. Three species are found in man which are : (i) *Trichomonas hominis, (ii) Trichomonas lenax* and (iii) *Trichomonas vaginalis.*The most common pathogenic species is *Trichomonas vaginalis*. It inhabits the vagina of women and causes vaginitis. The disease is characterized by inflammation of vaginal mucosa, burning sensation, annoying itch and abnormal discharges. Transmission of parasite is always during sexual intercourse by male members who act as intermediaries. *T. vaginalis* is also found in urinary tract of men infecting the urethra and prostate. Arsenic and iodine drugs and antibiotics such as Terramycin and Aureomycin have proved useful in the treatment of the disease.

6. Malaria. Malaria is caused by the species of a sporozoan parasite, *Plasmodium.* It is transmitted through the bite of female anopheles mosquito. In man the parasite attacks the liver cells and red blood cells. A toxic substance, the haemozoin, released by the parasite causes malaria. There are following four species of *Plasmodium* which cause human malaria : (i) *Plasmodium vivax* causes benign malaria in which fever comes on every 48 hours; (ii) *Plasmodium malariae* causes quartan malaria in which fever comes every 72 hours; (iii) *Plasmodium falciparum* causes malignant sub-tertian malaria in which the fever is more or less continuous; (iv) *Plasmodium ovale* causes mild tertian malaria in which fever comes on every 48 hours. All the four species multiply asexually in cells of the liver and erythrocytes of man. In malaria the spleen is enlarged, erythrocytes decrease in number, the blood becomes watery, pigment granules collect in the spleen and there is high temperature accompanied by chills and shivering. Malaria not only causes millions of deaths annually in the tropics but it also prevents the cultivation of the most fertile regions of the earth. Various drugs which are now used for the treatment of malaria include Quinine, Camoquine, Chloroquine, Plasmoquine, Resochin, Pentaquine, Pamaquine, Paludrine, etc.

7.Toxoplasmosis. Toxoplasmosis is caused by a sporozoan parasite, *Toxoplasma gondii*. Human infection of *Toxoplama gondii* has been reported from European countries, Middle East, Sri Lanka, U.S.A, Australia, Hawaii and many other places. The infection appears to be cosmopolitan. The dissemination of the parasite occurs through the blood stream ultimately localizing in various organs such as brain, spinal cord, eyes, lungs, liver, spleen, bone marrow, lymph nodes, heart muscles and skeletal muscles. The parasites multiply by endodyogeny but under certain conditions large cysts are also formed. Symptoms of the disease are hydrocephalus and chorioretinitis. Infection occurring in early months of pregnancy results either in abortion or still birth of the foetus. Pyrimethamine (Daraprim) combined with Sulphadiazine have been found to be an effective remedy.

8. Balantidial dysentery. Balantidial dysentery is caused by a ciliate parasite, *Balantidium coli*. It inhabits the large intestine of man. It may bore into the tissues of the intestine causing ulcers which results in dysentery and diarrhoea. This may prove fatal. The transmission of the parasite to a new host takes place through cysts in contaminated water and food. Drugs used for the treatment are Carbarsone, Diodoquin and Oxytetracycline have been found to be effective.

Protozoa and Animal Diseases

Protozoa cause many diseases in domestic and wild animals. Some of the parasitic Protozoa causing diseases in animals are as follows :

1. *Trichomonas hominis* is a Mastigophra inhabiting the ileo-caecal region of monkeys, cats and dogs and is supposed to cause diarrhoea and dysentery. Its infection occurs due to ingestion of contaminated food and water which may contain cysts.

2. *Trichomonas gallinae* lives in the epithelial lining of the oesophagus and crop of pigeons, turkeys, fowls, etc. and sometimes also lives in liver and lungs. It causes necrotic nodules in these organs.

3. *Trichomonas gallinarum* dwells in the epithelium of lower intestine and liver of turkeys and fowls. It causes disease similar to black head disease.

4. *Trichomonas foetus* inhabiting the urinogenital system of cattle, horses and sheep. It causes abortions, delayed conception and inflammation of perputial sacs. Transmission takes place directly during coitus.

5. *Histomonas maleagridis* is a Mastigophora inhabiting the caecum and liver of turkeys and fowls and causes black head disease in them.

6. *Trypanosoma* species also causes diseases in domestic animals. The species of *Trypanosoma* causing diseases in various animals are as follows :

(i) *Trypanosoma brucei* causes nagana disease in domestic animals in Africa. Nagana is similar to sleeping sickness. Its vector is *Glossina morsitans*.

(ii) *Trypanosoma evansi* causes surra disease in horses, camels, dogs, mules and cattles. Its vectors are flies *Tabanus* and *Stomoxys*. Surra occurs in India and various other regions and it is especially deadly in horses.

(iii) *Trypanosoma equiperdum* causes dourine, a disease of sex organs in horses. It is transmitted by contact during copulation. It has no vector.

(iv) *Trypanosoma equinum* causes Mal de Caderas in horses in South America. Its vector is a tabanid fly.

(v) *Trypanosoma hippicum* causes Murina or Deren gadera in horses and mules in Panama. Its vectors are flies.

7. *Sarcocystis linedamanni* is a sporozoan inhabiting the striped muscle fibres of sheep's oesophagus. It causes degeneration of muscles.

8. *Eimeria* species is also a sporozoan and its many species dwell in various animals such as sheep, cattle, and birds. It causes dysentery and diarrhoea in them.

9. *Babesia bigemina* is a sporozoan parasite in erythrocytes (RBCs) of cattle. The parasite causes Texas fever or Red water fever destroying red blood cells. Texas fever is widespread in America and Australia where it kills many cattle. Its infection takes place through bite of vector female tick, *Boophilus annulatus*.

10. *Babesia canis* parasitic in the red blood corpuscles of dog. It causes anaemia, malignant jaundice, fever in dogs. It is transmitted to dogs by biting of ticks.

11. *Babesia equi* is a parasitic in the red blood corpuscles of horses and causes anaemia, jaundice and paralysis of hindlimbs. Its transmission to host takes place by biting of ticks.

12. *Nosema apis* is a sporozoan which dwells in the intestinal epithelium and Malpighian tubules of honey bees. It causes muscular disease in them and its infection is caused due to cytoplasmic inheritance.

REVISION QUESTIONS

1. Give an account of the general shape, size and skeleton in Protozoa.
2. Write a brief essay on nucleus in Protozoa.
3. What are different locomotor organelles in Protozoa ?
4. What do you know about various modes of locomotion in Protozoa ?
5. Write an essay on modes of nutrition in Protozoa.
6. What do you know about various behavioural responses in Protozoa ?
7. Write an essay on contractile vacuole in Protozoa.
8. Give a brief account of the modes of reproduction in Protozoa.
9. Write an essay on parasitism in Protozoa.
10. Write an essay on the economic importance of Protozoa.
11. Write an essay on Protozoa and disease.
12. Write short notes on :
    (i) Vesicular nucleus; (ii) Pseudopodia; (iii) Amoeboid movement; (iv) Pinocytosis; (v) Parasitic nutrition; (vi) Avoiding reactions in Protozoa; (vii) Osmoregulation; (viii) Binary fission in Protozoa; (ix)Budding in Protozoa; (x) Syngamy in Protozoa; (xi) Automixis; (xii) Conjugation ; (xiii) Symbiosis; (xiv) Protozoan parasites of digestive tract; (xv) Commercial uses of protozoan skeleton.

24

Phylum Porifera

The name Porifera (L., *porus*=pore; *ferro*=to bear) comes from Grant (1836). The nature of sponges was debated until well into the nineteenth century, although evidence of their animal nature was given in 1765 by Ellis,who saw the water currents and movements of the oscula. As a result, Linnaeus, Lamarck, and Cuvier classified the sponges under zoophytes or polyps and regarded them as allied to anthozoan coelenterates. Although de Blainville (1816) separated the sponges in a group Spongiaria allied to Protozoa. The morphology and physiology of sponges were first adequately understood by Grant who created in 1836 the name Porifera for the group by which it is now generally known. Huxley (1875) and Sollas (1884) proposed the complete separation of sponges from other Metazoa on the grounds of many peculiarities. Sponges are now recognized as constituting a separate isolated branch of the Metazoa named Parazoa, after Sollas.

Porifera include the sponges which are most primitive of multicellular animals, they are sessile, plant-like animals, they are fixed to some submerged solid rock or shell and are incapable of any movement. The Porifera are exclusively marine except for a single family of freshwater species. Their shape may be cylindrical, branching,vase-like or globular,some are dull in colour but most are brightly coloured, they have red, orange, purple, green or yellow colour. The body is perforated by pores and canals but there are no organs, such as mouth or nervous system. Though sponges are multicellular animals their cells do not form organized tissues. They usually have an endoskeleton of separate spicules. Digestion takes place within the cells. Because of their endoskeleton and obnoxious ferments they are generally not eaten by animals. Sponges are cultivated for commercial purposes. Approximately 10,000 species of sponges are known at present, and the phylum is divided into three classes,*viz.,* Calcarea or Calcispongiae,Hexactinellida or Hyalospongiae, and Demospongiae and about twelve orders chiefly on the type of skeleton.

25

Leucosolenia

The biology of sponges can best be understood by the study of a simple type. One of the simplest sponges is *Leucosolenia* (*Gr., leukos* = white; solen=pipe) a genus of marine sponges represented by many species in shallow waters along the shore.

LEUCOSOLENIA
SYSTEMATIC POSITION

Phylum	...	**Porifera**
Class	...	**Calcarea**
Order	...	**Homocoela**
Genus	...	*Leucosolenia*

HABIT, HABITAT AND DISTRIBUTION

Leucosolenia is a small, delicate branching,colonial marine sponge. It grows in shallow water below low tide mark on sea shore rocks where wave action is intense and is not found in calm water. *Leucosolenia* is found abundantly along the northern Atlantic coast and is supposed to be very sensitive to external conditions. About 100 species of *Leucosolenia* have been reported from different seas all over the world . However, *L. botryoides*, *L.complicata* and *L. variabilis* are common species.

STRUCTURE

The colony of *Leucosolenia* is whitish yellow in colour. In the simplest species of *Leucoso-lenia*,the colony consists of few simple vase-like,cylindrical individuals each terminating in an osculum and united at their bases by irregular horizontal tubes. Most species are more complicated, consisting of a confused network of branching tubes from which stand out a few larger erect cylinders bearing an osculum at their summit. Finally, in the most complicated species, the outermost tubes fuse together forming a false surface or pseudoderm leaving a few large openings or pseudopores so that the sponge appears solid and simulates a higher type of sponge; but sections show the network of ascon tubes in the interior.

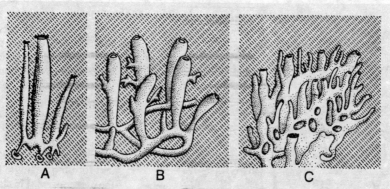

Fig. 25.1. Types of *Leucosolenia*.A—Simple ; B—Branching ;.C—Reticulate.

Each tube of the colony may reach up to 25 mm in height and also produces a number of buds. Each main tube opens to the exterior by an aperture called osculum at the summit. The cavity of the tube is known as spongocoel or paragastric cavity.

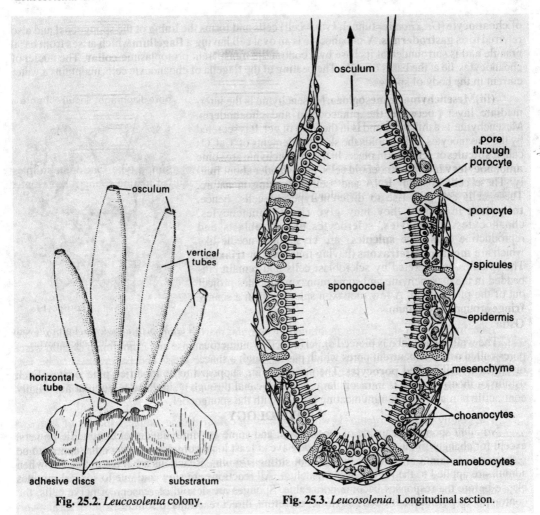

Fig. 25.2. *Leucosolenia* colony.

Fig. 25.3. *Leucosolenia*. Longitudinal section.

Body Wall

The body wall is thin and consists of an outer epidermis, the pinacoderm and an inner endodermis, the choanoderm separated by a jelly-like non-cellular layer of **mesenchyme** or mesogloea, enclosing a central cavity, the spongocoel. The wall of each tube is perforated by numerous pores through which water enters the spongocoel and passes out by osculum.

(i) Pinacoderm. The outer epidermis consists of thin, scale-like, flattened cells, called pinacocytes (*Gr., pinako* = plank; *kytes* = cell) which lie with the edges touching and forming a single layer of cells, the pinacoderm. This layer forms the outer protective covering of the tube. A pinacocyte has thin highly contractile margins and contains a central bulging having nucleus.

(ii) Choanoderm. The inner epithelium consists of a single layer

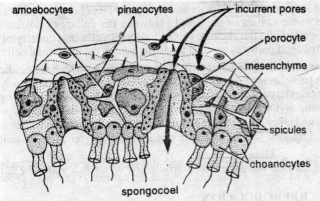

Fig. 25.4. *Leucosolenia*. Diagrammatic cross section of a portion of body wall highly magnified to show the cellular structure.

of **choanocyte** (*Gr., choane*=funnel; *kytos*=cell) cells and forms the lining of the spongocoel and also referred to as **gastrodermis**. A choanocyte is an oval cell having a **flagellum** which arises from basal granule and is surrounded at its base by a contractile transparent protoplasmic **collar**. The nuclei of choanocytes lie at the bases of cells. The beating of the flagella of choanocyte cells maintains a water current in the body of sponge.

(iii)**Mesenchyme or mesogloea.** Mesenchyme is the intermediate layer between the pinacoderm and choanoderm.
Mesenchyme is a thin layer and is in the form of gel. It is secreted
by the choanocytes and it holds the skeletal elements of $CaCO_3$
called **spicules** or **sclerites** in place. In the mesenchyme are some
amoebocytes which are amoeboid cells, they wander about freely. These cells contain RNA and self-replicating in nature.
These cells can give rise to different types of cells, hence,
totipotent in action; they may give rise to pinacocytes,
choanocytes, collencytes, sclerocytes or scleroblasts and
reproductine cells. The **spicules** are crystalline, needle-like
which are **monaxons, tetraxons** (having four rays) or **triaxons**.
The spicules are secreted by scleroblast cells and remain embedded in the mesenchyme and some monaxon spicules project
out of the pinacoderm. A few monaxon spicules form a scanty
fringe around the osculum.

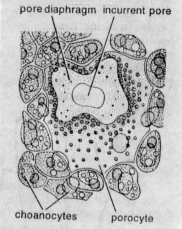

Fig. 25.5. *Leucosolenia*. Porocyte with surrounding choanocytes.

Ostia

The wall of each tube is pierced or perforated by numerous pores called **ostia** or incurrent pores which pass through a space or lumen of cells called **porocytes**. The porocytes are supposed to be modified pinacocytes. Each ostium or incurrent pore is intracellular, *i.e.,* it is a canal through a single, large, tubular and highly contractile porocyte cell communicating outside with the spongocoel.

PHYSIOLOGY

No adult sponge is capable of locomotion, and some are quite devoid of contractile powers, except for changes in the porocytes. Most do have at least local contractile powers that appear to be restricted to within 3 or 4 mm of the point of strong stimulus. Reactions are most noticeable when stimuli are applied to the region of the osculum. All reactions are slow and one to several minutes elapse before the responses become noticeable. Sponges are devoid of sensory or nerve cells, the contractile responses mentioned above are, therefore, direct reactions to stimuli.

Under normal conditions all the apertures (ostia and oscula) of a sponge are widely open and a current of water flows in through the incurrent openings or ostia and out through the osculum. The water currents are caused by the beating of the flagella of the choanocytes. This flow brings food and provides opportunity for gaseous exchange and the elimination of metabolic wastes. The structure of sponge is such that the flow of water passes the choanocyte areas quite slowly.

The **food** comprises the plankton–microscopical animals and plants and bits of organic matter. It appears that food particles adhere to the collars or are caught between the collars of adjacent choanocytes. The food particles are ingested into the choanocytes or passed directly into underlying amoebocytes. Some observers think that food particles are also taken in through the epidermal cells.

Digestion is always **intracellular,** as in Protozoa, occurring in food vacuoles which are acidic at first and alkaline later. Undigestible particles are ejected from the amoebocytes and find their way into the outgoing currents. Several enzymes have been identified in sponge extracts: protein-digesting enzymes similar to trypsin, pepsin, rennin and erepsin; lipase; invertase; and amylase in some cases. Since sponges usually contain bacteria and other organisms, it is not clear that the enzymes in question really come from the cells of sponge. Digested food is stored in certain amoebocytes as glycogen, glycoproteins and lipoproteins.

Respiration and elimination of metabolic wastes are accompanied by osmosis without the aid of special structures.

REPRODUCTION

Leucosolenia reproduces both **asexually** and **sexually.**

Asexual Reproduction

Leucosolenia reproduces asexually by budding. In budding, *Leucosolenia* sprouts new horizontal branches which grow over rocks and other substrata and give rise to erect vase-shaped individuals. When the upright branches attain sufficient size their tops break through as oscula. *Leucosolenia* has also remarkable power of regeneration. Any piece of broken *Leucosolenia* is capable of growing into a complete individual. This process is slow, and months or even years may be required before size is attained.

Sexual Reproduction

Sexual reproduction takes place by the formation of gametes, *i.e.,* ova and sperms. *Leucosolenia* is hermaphrodite, because both the gametes are formed in the body of same individual, though gonads are altogether absent. The gametes are, however, formed by the differentiation (say, gametogenesis) of amoebocyte cells.

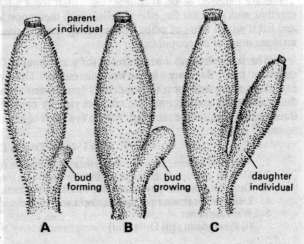

Fig. 25.6. *Leucosolenia*. Diagram showing stages in budding.

Cross-fertilization occurs, which is internal. The sperms are drawn in the body of *Leucosolenia* with the water current which fertilize the ova. The development of *Leucosolenia* have been described by Metschnikoff (1879) and Minchin (1896).

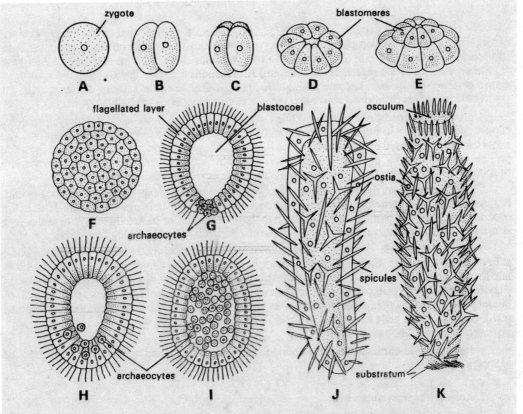

Fig. 25.7. *Leucosolenia*. Stages in development. A—Zygote; B to E—Cleaving stages ; F—Early blastula ; G and H—Coeloblastula ; I—Parenchymula ; J—Young sponge ; K—Adult sponge.

Development (Fig. 25.7). The fertilized egg undergoes equal and holoblastic cleavage to form an oval hollow blastula, called coeloblastula. The coeloblastula is composed entirely of a narrow flagellated cells except at the posterior pole, where there is a group of rounded non-flagellated cells. These are believed to be archaeocytes which form all future archaeocytes of the sponge. These together with adjacent flagellated cells (which thereupon lose their flagella) wander into the interior and fill it with a mass of cells. The resulting larva is, thus, a stereogastrula or parenchymula and an inner mass of amoeboid cells.

The parenchymula swims freely for some hours. Then it attaches by the anterior pole and develops into a flat plate with an irregular outline. The amoeboid cells (interior cells) migrate to the external surface and form the epidermis (pinacoderm) and mesenchyme. The flagellated cells are, thus, enclosed and become the choanocytes. A central spongocoel appears, an osculum breaks through, and spicules are secreted. After a few days of attachment, the larva is converted into the adult asconoid sponge.

REVISION QUESTIONS

1. What is a sponge? Describe the cellular organisation of *Leucosolenia*.
2. Give an account of the structure and life-cycle of a simple sponge you have studied.
3. Describe structure, physiology and asexual reproduction of *Leucosolenia*.
4. Describe the structure of *Leucosolenia* with the help of its longitudinal section.
5. Write notes on:
   (i) Pinacoderm ; (ii) Ostia ; (iii) Parenchymula ; (iv) Osculum.

Scypha (Gr., *skyphos* = cup) was formerly called *Sycon.* According to de Laubenfels (1936) the name *Sycon* must be replaced by *Scypha. Scypha* is somewhat more complex type in comparison to *Leucosolenia* because *Leucosolenia* is primitive asconoid type without any folding in its body wall; the body wall of *Scypha* is somewhat folded and, therefore, its spongocoel is comparatively reduced. In fact, due to various degrees of folding in the body wall, the organisation of such sponges varies much. *Scypha,*however, represents first stage of folding in its body wall having finger-like horizontal folds, referred to as typical syconoid type. *Grantia,* an European genus, is another syconoid sponge.

SCYPHA (=SYCON)
SYSTEMATIC POSITION

Phylum	....	Porifera
Class	....	Calcarea
Order	....	Heterocoela
Genus	...	*Scypha (Sycon)*

HABIT, HABITAT AND DISTRIBUTION

Scypha, also known as crown sponge, is a small, marine sponge found attached by a sticky secretion to some submerged solid object like rocks, shells of molluscs and corals. It is found in shallow water up to a depth of 50 fathoms(1 fathom = 6 feet) where waves provide the animal with plenty of food and well oxygenated water. It is a branching colonial sponge,though solitary individuals are also found. *Scypha* is widely distributed and found in abundance near North Atlantic shores. The different species of *Scypha* are *S. ciliatum, S. elegans, S. coronata, S. lingua, S. gelatinosum* and *S. raphanus.*

EXTERNAL FEATURES

Scypha is vase-shaped and is 2.5 to 7.5 cm in length. It has several cylinders, all the cylinders are connected at the base by which it is attached by a sticky secretion to some submerged solid object in the sea. It is grey or light brown in colour. The distal or free end of each cylinder has a single large opening, the osculum or exhalent or excurrent pore. The osculum is encircled by an upstanding collar of long monaxon spicules termed the oscular fringe looking like a crown, hence, the name crown sponge is given to it. It prevents the entry of other animals into the sponge, Below the osculum is a short, narrow collar region. The body of the sponge is covered externally by a thin dermal epithelium or ectoderm. The surface of a cylinder has polygonal elevations, and between the elevations are depressed lines, in the depressions are groups of ostia which are inhalent or incurrent pores. These are intercellular apertures and not intracellular as in *Leucosolenia.* Inside each cylinder is a spongocoel (Gr., *spongos* = sponge; *koilos* = hollow) or paragastric cavity which is not digestive cavity. The wall of the cylinder is thick due to increase in the amount of mesogloea, the wall has folded in such a way as to form two types of canals, the incurrent canals and radial canals, they lie alternately and radially around the spongocoel,but ostia and canals are absent from the collar and basal regions,

CANAL SYSTEM

Scypha, like all other sponges, possesses the characteristic peculiarity–the canal system. The sponge body is traversed by numerous canals of several types which together form the canal system. It plays a very important role in the life of *Scypha* like those of other sponges. The particular type of canal system found in *Scypha* is known as syconoid type which is more advanced than the asconoid type. It consists of the following :

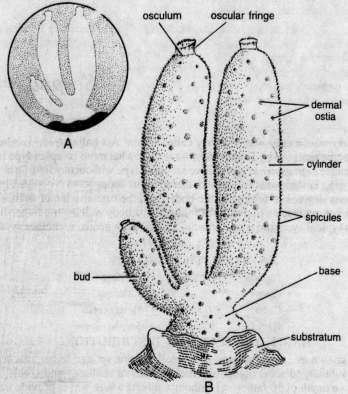

Fig. 26.1. *Scypha.* A—Colony in natural size; B—Colony magnified.

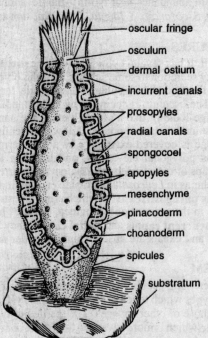

Fig. 26.2. *Scypha.* A diagrammatic L.S. of a cylinder showing gross internal structure.

(i) Spongocoel. If the cylindrical body of *Scypha* is cut open longitudinally, it shows that osculum leads into a narrow tubular cavity called the paragastric cavity or spongocoel. The spongocoel is lined with thin, gastral ectodermal cells called, **pinacocytes.**

(ii) Radial or flagellated canals. The thick body wall lining the spongocoel contains many finger-like, straight outpushings at regular intervals called radial or flagellated canals. The radial canals are lined with flagellated collar cells or **choanocytes.** Each radial canal appears octagonal in cross section. The radial canals are closed at their outer ends towards the surface of cylinder but at their inner ends each communicates with a small wide excurrent canal by an aperture called **apopyle** (Gr., *apo* = away from; *pyle* = gate) or internal ostia which joins the spongocoel.

(iii) Excurrent canal. The excurrent canal is a short and wide passage between the radial canal and spongocoel. It leads radial canal into the spongocoel. The excurrent canals are lined with flat ectodermal cells like the spongocoel. The broad connection between the excurrent canal and the spongocoel is called the **gastric ostium.** Between the radial canal and excurrent canal is a thin diaphragm perforated by large hole called **apopyle.** The apopyle is surrounded by contractile **myocytes** (Gr., *myos*=muscle; *kytos* =cell) due to which it can contract or dilate.

(iv) Incurrent canals. In between the two successive radial canals, a tubular space called incurrent canal is present. Thus, radial canals and incurrent canals are arranged alternately. The incurrent canals are narrow passages some-what square in section. The incurrent canals open to the exterior between the blind outer ends of the radial canals by apertures termed dermal **ostia** (L., *ostium*=door) or **dermal pores.** Incurrent canals are lined by flat ec-todermal cells called pinacocytes like the spongocoel. Externally an incurrent canal is covered by a **pore membrane** pierced by 3 or 4 ostia which are intercellular (in *Leucosolenia* the ostia are intracellular). The incurrent canals end blindly, at their inner ends, not reaching the spongocoel. Between the incurrent canal and spongocoel, the mesogloea is specially thickened to form the **gastral cortex**.

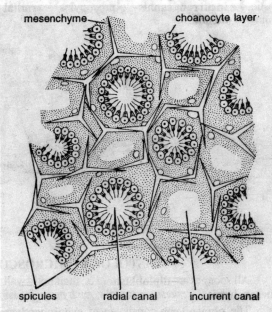

The incurrent and radial canals run side by side. The wall between the incurrent and radial canals is pierced by numerous minute pores called **prosopyles** (Gr., *pros* = near, *pyle* = gate). The prosopyles are perforations in **porocytes.** The porocytes are tubular contrac-tile cells formed from modified pinacocytes.

Fig. 26.3. *Scypha* cylinder. Diagrammatic V.S. through the wall.

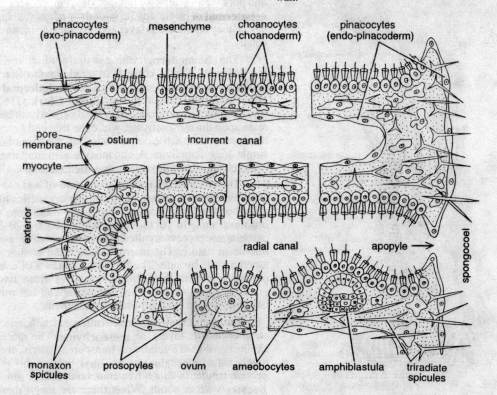

Fig. 26.4. *Scypha.* A diagrammatic sectional view of the body wall showing one incurrent and one radial canal.

The circulation of water in *Scypha* takes place in the following way. The water enters into the incurrent canals through the ostia, passes into the radial canals through prosopyles and from radial canals into the spongocoel by apopyles and leaves the spongocoel by terminal osculum. In other way, the course of water into the canal system can be represented as : **water from outside** → dermal ostia→ **incurrent canals**→ prosopyles →**radial canals**→ apopyles →**spongocoel** →osculum →**outside**.

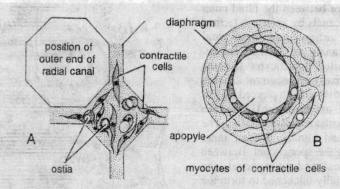

Fig. 26.5. *Scypha* A—Magnified surface view of pore membrane showing ostia; B—An apopyle surrounded by its diaphragm.

HISTOLOGY (MICROSCOPIC STRUCTURE)

All sponges are **diploblastic**, *i.e.,* their body wall is composed of two layers with an intermediate **mesenchyme** (Gr.,*mesos* = middle; *enchyme* = infusion) or **mesohyl.**

The **pinacoderm** consisting of **exopinacoderm** covering the body surface except ostia and osculum and **endopinacoderm** lining the incurrent canals and spongocoel. It is made of thin, large and polygonal, scale-like pinacocytes. Pinacocytes are **ectodermal** in origin and lie with their edges touching so that they form a loose layer and also line the incurrent canals.

The **choanoderm** forming gastral epithelium, lining the radial canals, consists of single layer of large choanocytes or collar cells which are **endodermal** in origin and were discovered by **James Clark** (1867). The choanocytes are rounded or oval cells whose base rests upon the mesenchyme, while the free end bears a transparent contractile collar encircling the base of the single long flagellum. A choanocyte also contains a nucleus, a contractile vacuole and food vacuoles.

The electron microscopic structure of a choanocyte reveals the presence of all cellular organelles like mitochondria, Golgi body, endoplasmic reticulum, ribosomes, etc., in it. Its collar is formed by 20–30 cytoplasmic processes called **microvilli** which are contractile in nature. The microvilli are often connected together side by side. The flagellum consists of usual pattern of fibrils in 9+2 and originates from basal granule or kinetosome. The choanocyte cell has root-like processes embedded in the mesenchyme.

Between the dermal epidermis and endoderm is an intermediate layer, the **mesenchyme.** The mesenchyme consists of a gelatinous transparent matrix, commonly called **mesogloea** or **mesohyl**, presumably of a protein nature, in which free amoeboid cells or **amoebocytes** wander about. When there are much meso-

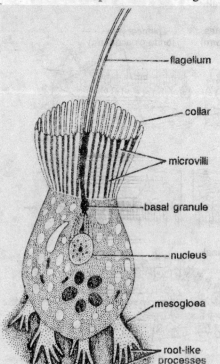

Fig. 26.6. A choanocyte cell as seen under electron microscope.

gloea and relatively few cells, the mesenchyme is termed collenchyma ; when the cells are numerous, the name parenchyma is applied. The mesenchyme is like a gel and holds the spicules in place.

Sponge Cells or Cellular Elements of *Scypha's* Body

There are several types of cells found in sponges which are not organized into well defined tissues, the cells form loose collections and they act more or less independently of each other. The sponge cells are as follows :

1. Pinacocytes are thin polygonal scale-like cells, they are large and flat with a central nucleus, they lie with their edges touching, they are highly contractile. Contractions or expansions of the edges of pinacocytes can slightly decrease or increase the size of the entire sponge. Pinacocytes form the external dermal layer, they line the incurrent canals, and in some they also line the spongocoel. The external pinacocytes are spoken of as "ectoderm" and those lining the spongocoel as "endoderm".

2. Porocytes or pore cells are modified pinacocytes, they are large-size contractile cells; through the porocyte runs a large perforation called prosopyle which connects an incurrent canal to a radial canal or to a flagellated chamber.

3. Choanocytes or flagellate endoderm cells are large, oval, nucleated cells, each with a contractile vacuole and some food vacuoles; at one end is a long flagellum arising from a basal granule, the basal granule is joined to centriole and the two together are called a centroblepharoplast which controls the movements of the flagellum. Below this is a parabasal body joined by a fibril to the centroblepharoplast and the nucleus. The flagellum has two central fibrils and nine double peripheral fibrils, it is surrounded at its base by a transparent contractile collar made of a ring of erect and closely set microvilli which project from the cell. Choanocytes form a layer of adjacent cells in radial canals or flagellated chambers of sponges, the movement of their flagella causes a current of water. Choanocytes are endodermal in origin.

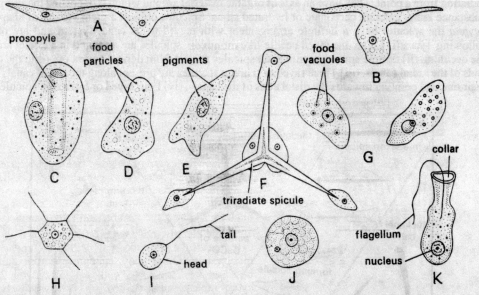

Fig. 26.7. *Scypha.* Cellular elements. A—Pinacocytes ; B—Myocyte; C—Porocyte; D—Thesocyte; E—Chromocyte ; F—Scleroblast ; G—Archeocytes; H—Collencyte; I—Sperm; J—Ovum; K—Choanocyte.

4. Amoebocytes are amoeboid cells with pseudopodia, they wander about freely in the mesogloea, they are modified to form the following types of cells :

(i) Collencytes have several slender, long, branching pseudopodia, the branches are like connective tissue cells in the mesogloea.

(ii) Archeocytes are large amoebocytes, they have a few blunt pseudopodia, the nucleus is large, they are generalized cells and they transport food and waste substances. They can give rise to other types of amoebocytes, and they form sperms, eggs and asexual reproductive bodies called gemmules, such cells which can change into almost any kind of cell within an animal are said to be totipotent.

(iii) Chromocytes are pigmented amoebocytes having lobose pseudopodia. They probably impart colouration to the body of sponge.

(iv) Thesocytes are amoebocytes having lobose pseudopodia like chromocytes but filled with food reserves. Thus, these cells work as storage cells.

(v) Trophocytes are found loaded partly or completely with digested food and serve to transfer it from one place to other.

(vi) Phagocytes collect food from choanocytes through their pseudopodia and also engulf excreta and damaged tissues.

(vii) Myocytes are fusiform contractile cells, they form a sphincter around apertures, such as oscula and apopyles where they act like muscles to open or close these apertures, they show some similarity to involuntary muscles in shape and contractility.

(viii) Scleroblasts are amoebocytes in the act of secreting the skeleton of a sponge. They are called **calcoblasts** if they secrete calcareous spicules, or **silicoblasts** if they secrete siliceous spicules, or **spongioblasts** if they secrete spongin fibres.

(ix) Gland cells are amoeboid with a long strand at one end, they are found attached by their strands to the surface of a sponge, they secrete slime.

(x) Germ cells are male and female gametes (sperm and ova)differentitate from archeocytes cells. In some cases,the germ cells are said to be differentiated from choanocytes.

SKELETON

In *Scypha* the skeleton consists of calcareous spicules. The spicules or sclerites are definite bodies, having a crystalline appearance and consisting in general of simple spines or of spines radiating from a point. They have an axis of organic material around which is deposited the inorganic substance either calcium carbonate or hydrated silica. Spicules present a great variety of shape. In *Scypha* the spicules have a definite arrangement with regard to its canal system and are of the following types:(i) Large one rayed needle-like **monaxon** spicules are arranged in a circlet around the osculum. (ii) Simple spear-like monaxon spicules project from dermal cortex opposite the outer ends of the radial canals. (iii) Three rayed or **triaxon** spicules are present along the radial canals with their one end pointing towards the distal ends of the canals. (iv) Four rayed or **tetraxon** spicules are

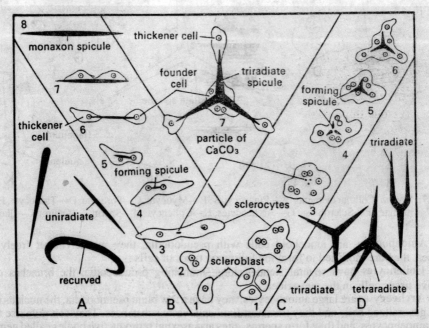

Fig. 26.8. *Scypha*. Structure and development of spicules. A—Kinds of monaxon spicules'; B—Development of monaxon spicules; C—Development of triaxon spicules; D—Kinds of triradiate spicules.

present, along with triaxon spicules in the thick gastral cortex surrounding the spongocoel. In the body of *Scypha*, the monaxon spicules project from the body surface and may be needle-like or spear-like, while the triradiate spicules lie embedded inside forming a network. On the outer surface the monaxon spicules project in masses from the polygonal elevations where they partly conceal and protect the ostia, each group of these spicules is collectively called oxeote spicules.

WATER CURRENT

Water current plays a very important role in the physiology of the sponges. The current of water brings in food and oxygen and it takes away waste products. Under normal conditions all the apertures of a sponge are widely open and a current of water flows through the animal and out at the oscula. The water current is caused by the beating of the flagella of the choanocytes, but as the flagella do not beat in coordination, the way in which a current of water is produced is not clearly understood. The most plausible explanation is that of Van Tright based on observations of thin expansion of freshwater sponges. The flagellar movement consists of a spiral undulation passing from base to tip and creating a water current in the same direction. As the choanocytes in each flagellated chamber are grouped near the prosopyle with their collars more or less pointed towards the apopyle, the water currents tend to flow from the flagellar tips towards the apopyle. The mechanism will obviously be more effective when the apopyles are larger than prosopyles, as is usually the case in sponges, since the water will tend to seek the larger outlet.

The water current enters the body of *Scypha* through its ostia into the incurrent canals, then through the prosopyles it goes to the radial canals lined by choanocytes. From the radial canals the water enters the excurrent canals through the apopyles from where it enters the spongocoel, then the water goes out through the large osculum.

NUTRITION

Scypha feeds on particles of organic matter and small living organisms, such as bacteria, diatoms and Protozoa, they are drawn in with the water current. Food is ingested partly by porocytes but mainly by choanocytes either through the side of the cell or through its collar. In the cell a food vacuole is formed in which digestion occurs. Digestion is entirely intracellular, as in Protozoa. The contents of the food vacuoles are first acidic, then they become alkaline. Several enzymes have been identified in sponge extracts. Partly digested food is taken up by amoebocytes in which digestion is completed, the amoebocytes transport and supply the digested food to all parts of the body. Digested food is stored as reserves, chiefly glycogen, fat and glycoproteins, and lipoproteins in amoebocytes which are termed as thesocytes. Undigested remains of food are cast out through the collars of choanocytes from where they pass out with the current of water. But in non-calcareous sponges the food is transferred from choanocytes to amoebocytes,or amoebocytes engulf the food directly, digestion occurs only in amoebocytes which also egest the undigested particles.

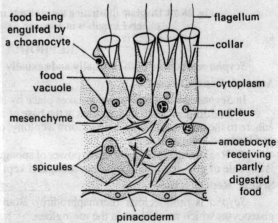

Fig. 26.9. *Scypha*. Ingestion of food by choanocyes and its diagestion.

RESPIRATION

Special respiratory organs are wanting in sponges. Gaseous exchange occurs by simple diffusion, between the cells of sponge and the current of water. Oxytgen dissolved in water is taken in by diffusion through the general body surface by the pinacocytes and internally by the choanocytes. Amoebocytes distribute the oxygen throughout the mesenchyme and take away the carbon dioxide. The process of respiration is entirely intracellular as in Protozoa. Sponges prefer places where water contains plenty of oxygen. If kept in foul water or water deficient in oxygen contents or if their dermal pores become clogged with silt,the sponges die or undergo reduction. The rate of consumption of *Scypha* was found to range from 0.16 ml. of oxygen per gram of fresh weight per hour in the smaller specimens to 0.04 in the larger ones. The upper half just above the osculum consumes 10 to 50 per cent more oxygen per gram per hour than the basal half.

EXCRETION

Egested wastes and excretory matter (largely ammonia) leave the body with the current of water. Some observers claim that amoebocytes containing excretory granules and inclusions are discharged by sponges.

NERVOUS SYSTEM AND BEHAVIOUR

Sponges are devoid of sensory or nerve cells. The sponge body displays only very slight powers of conductivity. Strong stimuli such as cuts or sharp blows are transmitted not at all or only 3 or 4 mm at the most. Conductivity is the best developed at the osculum where transmission occurs more readily away from than toward opening. The oscular rim appears to be the most sensitive part of the sponge. However, Tuzet (1953) and Pavans de Ceccatty (1955) believe that the collencytes are nervous in function; some of them behave like neurons and constitute a diffused nerve net connecting the pinacoderm, choanoderm and myocytes. Thus, these cells acting as neurons are believed to receive and conduct the various types of stimuli.

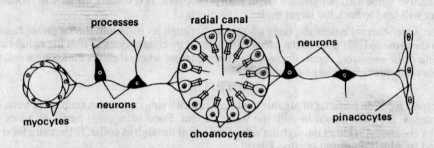

Fig. 26.10. Diagram illustrating the probable mechanism of reception and conduction of nerve impulses in a sponge.

REPRODUCTION

Scypha reproduces both asexually and sexually.

Asexual Reproduction

In *Scypha* asexual reproduction takes place by budding and regeneration.

(i) Budding. A small bud appears at the base of an adult *Scypha* and grows into full size. It may adhere to the parent and, thus, help to form a colony, or it may break free and forms a new individual and leads an independent life.

(ii) Regeneration. Regenerative power of sponges is very high. Any piece of the body of *Scypha* is capable of growing into a complete sponge, if kept in a suitable environment.

Sexual Reproduction

Scypha is monoecious (hermaphrodite). Both sperms and ova are produced from the archaeocytes which are present in the mesogloea.

Oogenesis. The egg mother cell or ovocyte is first derived from an enlarged amoebocyte with a large nucleus and conspicuous nucleolus. It grows and aquires food stores by engulfing or fusing with other similar amoebocytes or may receive supplies from special trophocytes. Upon attaining full size it undergoes the usual maturation divisions to form the ovum which lies in the wall of the radial canal, ready to be fertilized by a sperm from another sponge.

Spermatogenesis. The sperm mother cell or spermatogonium is described as an enlarged amoebocyte that soon becomes enveloped by one or more flattened cover cells derived by the division of the mother cell or consisting of other amoebocytes. The whole is called spermatocyst. The spermatogonium divides two or three times into the spermatocytes which give rise to sperm. The sperm comprises a rounded nucleated head and vibratile long tail. Other authors state that spermatogonia are transformed choanocytes, and Gatenby has described the transformation of an entire flagellated chamber into spermatozoa.

Fertilization. Due to protogynous condition cross fertilization occurs which is internal and the eggs are fertilized in situ. The sperm does not enter directly in the ovum but reaches a radial canal and is dispersed by the water currents. The sperm enters a choanocyte adjacent to ripe ovocyte. The choanocyte loses its collar and flagellum, becomes amoeboid,and plasters itself to the surface of the ovocyte, which forms a conical depression to receive it. The sperm in the meantime has lost its tail,and its swollen head becomes surrounded by a capsule. The capsule carrying the sperm head penetrates into the ovocyte. According to Gatenby and others the sperm enters a choanocyte, which acts as a nurse cell and then fuses with the egg but according to Duboscq and Tuzet(1937) the sperm carrying choanocyte departs after the transfer of the sperm into the ovocyte.

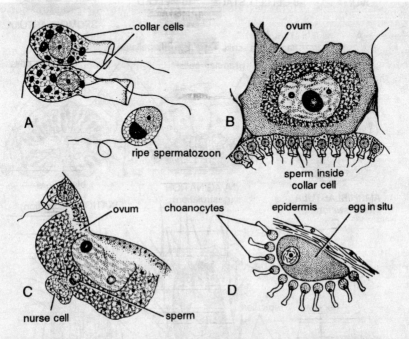

Fig. 26.11. Fertilization in *Grantia*. A—A ripe spermatozoon near two choanocytes; B—Sperm enters a collar cell adjacent to an ovum; C—Nurse cell giving up sperm into ovum; D—Fertilized egg in situ.

Early embryonic development. The fertilized egg undergoes maturation and holoblastic cleavage and develops in situ into a blastula. The first-three cleavages are vertical and produce a disc of eight pyramidal cells or blastomeres. A horizontal cleavage then divides the blastomeres unequally, yielding eight large cells macromeres produce the future epidermis and eight small cells micromeres give rise to future choanocytes. At the 16 cell stage the embryo lies just beneath the maternal choanocyte layer as a flattened disc-shaped body. The micromeres (small cells) increase rapidly, elongate and each acquires a flagellum on its inner end facing the blastocoel. The large cells remain undivided for some time, become rounded and granular and in their middle an opening forms that functions as a mouth to ingest adjacent maternal cells. This stage is called stomoblastula by Duboscq and Tuzet.

The stomoblastula,thus, is the blastula stage of *Scypha* consisting of many small, elongated and flagellated micromeres and 8 spherical granular macromeres. It bears a blastocoel which opens out by an aperture, the mouth which is formed in the macromeres. The mouth is used for engulfing the surrounding maternal cells for nutrition. The stomoblastula undergoes a process of inversion in which the embryo turns out through its mouth, so that the flagella become directed towards the outside. Now, the embryo is called amphiblastula larva.

Amphiblastula larva. The amphiblastula larva occurs in the development of most of the Calcarea. It is more or less oval in shape and consists of one-half of small, narrow flagellated cells and the other half large rounded granular cells. The amphiblastula larva forces its way into the adjacent radial canal and escapes through the osculum of the parent to swim for some hours with the flagellated cells directed forward. After swimming for a few hours gastrulation takes place by the **invagination** of the flagellated cells. Now the larva becomes a typical gastrula with a blastopore at the invaginated side.

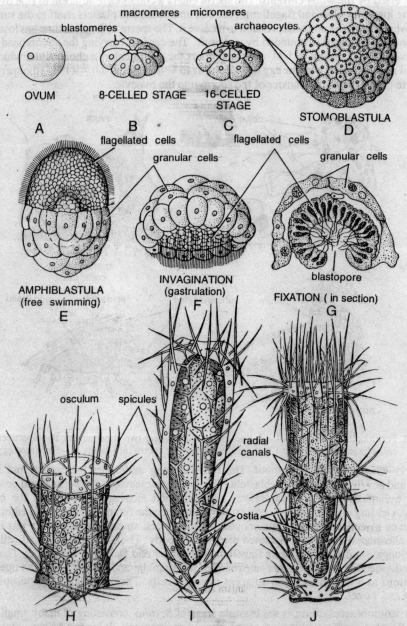

Fig. 26.12. *Scypha.* Development. A—Ovum; B—8-celled stage; C—16-celled stage; D—Blastula; E—Amphiblastula; F—Beginning of invgination; G—Gastrula showing fixation (in section); H—Young sponge; I—Asconoid (olynthus) stage; J—Syconoid stage.

Post-embryonic development (metamorphosis). The gastrula soon gets attached to some substratum like rock, sea weed, etc., by its blastoporal end and develops into a cylinder. At the free end of the cylinder an opening, the **osculum** is formed. A large number of small perforations are formed on the cylinder which are the **ostia**. The non-flagellated granular cells give rise to the dermal epithelium, scleroblasts and porocytes. The flagellated cells give rise to the choanocytes, archaecocytes and amoebocytes. The mesenchyme arises from both the layers. The young *Scypha* now reaches the olynthus stage (Fig. 26.13) resembling the asconoid type of sponge. The adult or

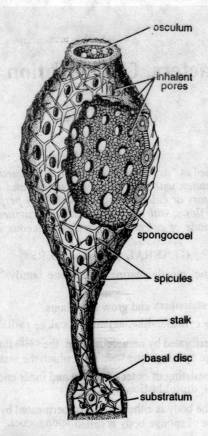

Fig. 26.13. Olynthus stage of *Clathrina* (a calcareus sponge) with a portion of the wall cut to show the spongocoel.

syconoid stage develops from the olynthus stage by pushing out of the wall, first at the middle, into radial canals. The choanocytes are shifted in these radial canals and the body wall increases in thickness. Thus, the adult *Scypha* is formed and its colony develops later on by further branching.

REVISION QUESTIONS

1. Give an illustrated account of the general anatomy of a syconoid sponge.
2. Describe the habit, habitat and structure of *Scypha*.
3. What is canal system? Describe the canal system of *Scypha*.
4. Give an account of microscopic structure or the cell elements of *Scypha* and mention the role of these cells.
5. Give an account of feeding mechanism and process of digestion in a sponge you have studied.
6. Describe different types of spicules found in *Scypha* and discuss its asexual mode of reproduction.
7. Describe the process of sexual reproduction in *Scypha*.
8. Draw labelled diagrams:
   (i) Sectional view of the body wall of *Scypha* showing incurrent and radial canals;
   (ii) Choanocyte cell.
9. Write short notes on:
   (i) Spongocoel;(ii) Ostium; (iii) Collar cell; (iv) Archaeocyte; (v) Scleroblasts; (vi) Spicules;
   (vii) Pinacocytes; (viii) Stomoblastula; (ix) Amphiblastula;(x) Olynthus stage.

27

Porifera : Characters, Classification and Types

DEFINITION

The Porifera may be defined as *"asymmetrical or radially symmetrical multicellular organisms with cellular grade of organisation without well-defined tissues and organs; exclusively aquatic; mostly marine, sedentary, solitary or colonial animals with body perforated by pores, canals and chambers through which water flows; with one or more internal cavities lined with choanocytes;and with characteristic skeleton made of calcareous spicules, siliceous spicules or horny fibres of spongin"*.

GENERAL CHARACTERS

1. Porifera are all aquatic, mostly marine except one family Spongillidae which lives in freshwater.

2. They are **sessile** and sedentary and grow like plants.

3. Body shape is vase or cylinder-like, asymmetrical or radially symmetrical.

4. The body surface is perforated by numerous pores, the ostia through which the water enters the body and one or more large openings, the oscula by which the water passes out.

5. Multicellular body consisting of outer ectoderm and inner endoderm with an intermediate layer of mesenchyme, therefore, diploblastic animals.

6. The interior space of the body is either hollow or permeated by numerous canals lined with choanocytes. The interior space of sponge body is called spongocoel.

7. Characteristic skeleton consisting of either fine flexible spongin fibres, siliceous spicules or calcareous spicules.

8. Mouth absent,digestion intracellular; excretory and respiratory organs absent.

9. The nervous and sensory cells are probably not differentiated.

10. The sponges are monoecious ; reproduction both by asexual and sexual methods.

11. Asexual reproduction occurs by buds and gemmules.

12. The sponges possess high power of regeneration.

13. Sexual reproduction occurs by ova and sperms; fertilization is internal but cross-fertilization occurs as a rule.

14. Cleavage holoblastic, development indirect through a free-swimming ciliated larva called amphiblastula or parenchymula.

15. The organisation of sponges has been grouped into three main types ,*viz.,* ascon type, sycon type and leuconoid type due to simplicity in some forms and complexity in others.

CLASSIFICATION

The classification of Porifera is based chiefly on types of skeleton found in them. This phylum has been classified variously but the classification suggested by Hyman (1940) and Burton (1967) are of considerable importance. However, classification of Porifera followed here is based on Storer and Usinger (1971) which appears to be a modified form of Hyman's classification.

CLASS I. CALCAREA (L., *calx*=lime) OR CALCISPONGIAE
(L., *calx*=lime,Gr., *spongos*=sponge)

1. They have a skeleton of separate calcareous spicules which are monaxon or tetraxon; tetraxon spicules lose one ray to become triadiate.
2. They are solitary or colonial ; body shape vase-like or cylindrical.
3. They may show asconoid, syconoid, or leuconoid structure.
4. They are dull-coloured sponges less than 15 cm in size.
5. They occur in shallow waters in all oceans.

Order 1. Homocoela

1. Asconoid sponges with radially symmetrical cylindrical body.
2. Body wall is thin and not folded, spongocoel is lined by choanocytes.

   Examples: *Leucosolenia, Clathrina.*

Order 2. Heterocoela

1. Syconoid or leuconoid sponges having vase-shaped body.
2. The body wall is thick and folded, choanocytes line only radial canals.
3. Spongocoel is lined by flattened endoderm cells.

   Examples : *Sycon or Scypha, Grantia.*

Class. II. HEXACTINELLIDA OR HYALOSPONGIAE
(Gr., *hyalos* = glassy; *spongos* = sponge)

1. They are called glass sponges; skeleton is of siliceous spicules which are triaxon with six rays. In some the spicules are fused to form a lattice-like skeleton.
2. There is no epidermal epithelium.
3. Choanocytes line finger-shaped chambers.
4. They are cylindrical or funnel-shaped and are found in deep tropical seas, they grow up to one metre.

Order 1. Hexasterophora

1. Spicules are hexasters, *i.e.,*star-like in shape.
2. Radial canals or flagellated chambers are simple.
3. They are not attached by root tufts but commonly attached to a hard object.

   Examples: *Euplectella, Farnera.*

Order 2. Amphidiscophora

1. Spicules are **amphidiscs.** No hexasters.
2. They are attached to the substratum by root tufts.

   Examples : *Hyalonema, Pheronema.*

CLASS III. DEMOSPONGIAE
(Gr., *dermos* =frame; *spongos*=sponge)

1. It contains the largest number of sponge species. Large-sized, solitary or colonial.
2. The skeleton may be of spongin fibres or of spongin fibres with siliceous spicules or there may be no skeleton.
3. Spicules are never six-rayed, they are monaxon or tetraxon and are differentiated into large megascleres and small microscleres.
4. Body shape is irregular and the canal system is of leucon type.
5. Generally marine, few freshwater forms.

Subclass I. Tetractinellida

1. Sponges are mostly solid and simple rounded cushion-like flattened in shape usually without branches.
2. Skeleton comprised mainly of tetraxon siliceous spicules but absent in order Myxospongida.
3. Canal system is leuconoid type. Shallow water form.

Order 1. Myxospongida

1. Simple structure.
2. Skeleton absent.

   Examples: *Oscarella, Halisarca.*

Order 2. Carnosa

1. Simple structure.
2. Spicules are not differentiated into megascleres and microscleres.
3. Asters may be present.

   Example : *Plakina.*

Order 3. Choristida

1. Spicules are differentiated into megascleres and microscleres.

   Examples : *Geodia, Thenea.*

Subclass II. Monaxonida

1. Monaxonids occur in variety of shapes from rounded mass to branching type or elongated or stalked with funnel or fan-shaped.
2. Skeleton consists of monaxon spicules with or without spongin.
3. Spicules are distinguished into megascleres and microscleres.
4. They are found in abundance throughout the world.
5. Shallow and deep water forms.

Order 1. Hadromerida

1. Monaxon megascleres in the form of tylostyles.
2. Microscleres when present in the form of asters.

3. Spongin fibres are absent.

Examples : *Cliona, Tethya.*

Order 2. Halichondrida

1. Monaxon megascleres are often of two types, *viz.,* monactines and diactines.

2. Microscleres are absent. Spongin fibres present but scanty.

Example : *Halichondria.*

Order 3. Poecilosclerida

1. Monaxon megascleres are of two types, one type in the ectoderm and another type in the choanocyte layer.

2. Microscleres are typically chelas, sigmas and toxas.

Example : *Cladorhiza.*

Order 4. Haplosclerida

1. Monaxon megascleres are of only one type, *viz.,* diactinal.

2. Microscleres are absent.

3. Spongin fibers are generally present.

Examples: *Chalina, Pachychalina, Spongilla.*

Subclass III. Keratosa

1. Body is rounded and massive with a number of conspicuous oscula.

2. Skeleton composed of network of **spongin** fibres only.

3. Siliceous spicules are absent.

4. They are also known as horny sponges found in shallow and warm waters of tropical and subtropical regions.

Examples : *Euspongia, Hippospongia.*

REPRESENTATIVE TYPES OF PORIFERA

1. *Euplectella.* *Euplectella aspergillum* (Fig. 27.1) is commonly known as Venus' flower basket. It is a glass sponge. The body is cylindrical and curved with thin walls, the upper end is closed by an oscular sieve formed of fused spicules, and the lower end has anchoring siliceous root spicules, inside is a spongocoel. There is no epidermis of pinacocytes. Encircling the cylinder are projecting ledges of spicules, with many openings or parietal gaps in the meshwork of spicules, they connect with the spongocoel but are not a part of the canal system. Flagellated chambers lie radially in the

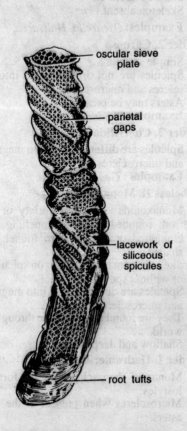

Fig. 27.1. *Euplectella aspergillum.*

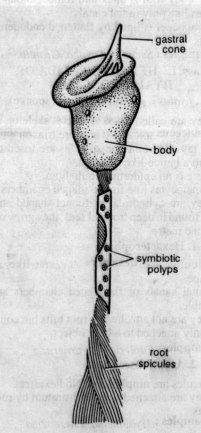

Fig. 27.2. *Hyalonema.*

sponge wall. Skeleton is made of four and six-rayed siliceous spicules bound together by siliceous cement so that they form a network of great complexity, but the canal system is of the simple sycon type.

In the spongocoel very often a pair of Crustacea called *Spongicola venusta* live in commensal relationship feeding on plankton brought in with the water current.

Euplectella is found attached by its siliceous roots to the bottom of deep sea near the Philippine Is., its curved structure is an adaptation to the slow, constant water current at great depth of the sea.

2. *Hyalonema*. Hyalonema (Fig.27.2) is commonly known as glass-rope sponge, is marine and is about 38 cm long. The body is rounded or oval, below which a bundle of long spicules projects as a root tuft which is often spirally twisted, the root tuft looks like a stalk. The bundle of spicules also forms an axis as columella which passes through the body, the spicules are bound together by siliceous cement. Regularly growing in symbiotic relationship with *Hyalonema* are several polyps of a Zoanthid *Palythoa* or of *Epizoanthus*, an anemone.

3. *Pheronema*. Pheronema (Fig. 27.3) has a cup or bowl-shaped thick-walled body with lateral pleural prostals and long twisted root tufts. The spongocoel opens to the exterior at the summit by an osculum which is surrounded by spicules known as marginal prostals. Skeleton consists of siliceous glassy spicules and amphidiscs. They are attached to the muddy bottom of the sea by spirally twisted long root tufts of spicules. *Pheronema* is found in deep sea in the muddy bottom.

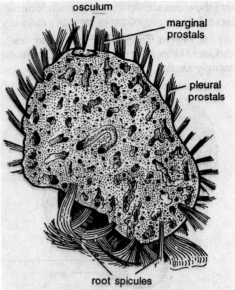

Fig. 27.3. *Pheronema.*

4. *Oscarella*. Oscarella (Fig. 27.4) is a brightly coloured, small low encrusting sponge with the lobulated upper surface. The basal part of the sponge is filled with eggs and embryos and the peripheral part encloses the canal system. Each lobe or fold encloses an excurrent canal surrounded by flagellated chambers. The incurrent canals are situated in depressions between the lobes of the body. Canal system leuconoid type. Skeleton entirely absent.

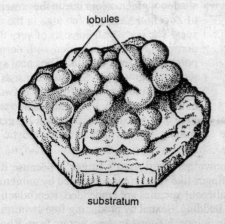

Fig. 27.4. *Oscarella.*

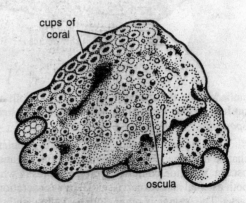

Fig. 27.5. *Cliona.*

5. *Cliona*. Cliona (Fig. 27.5), the boring sponge is found inhabiting the interior of coral skeletons, mollusc shells and other calcareous objects. It is a sulphur-yellow or green coloured sponge with small elevations on the surface, the skeleton is made of spongin fibres and siliceous spicules; it has the leucon type of canal system. It secretes droplets of an acid which dissolves and bores channels into rocks or shells of living or dead molluscs, honeycombing and destroying them, then it grows into the channels and also over them forming a mass 15 to 20 cm in diameter. Boring is begun by the larva. It is cosmopolitan in all seas especially along the Atlantic coast.

6. *Tethya. Tethya* (Fig. 27.6) is somewhat spherical in shape having a characteristic tuberculate surface. Skeleton consists of radiating bundles of monaxon spicules and asters. Spongin fibres are entirely absent.

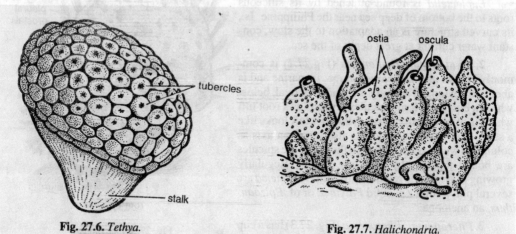

Fig. 27.6. *Tethya.*   Fig. 27.7. *Halichondria.*

7. *Halichondria. Halichondria* (Fig. 27.7) has flattened elongated tubular growths opening by high delicate oscula. The sponge is soft and brownish yellow in colour. Skeleton consists of oxeas of various sizes. *Halichondria* is popularly known as Crumb of bread sponge. It occurs in shallow and deep waters of sea and worldwide in distribution.

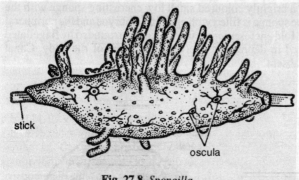

Fig. 27.8. *Spongilla.*

8. *Spongilla. Spongilla* (Fig. 27.8) is probably the best known of freshwater sponges. It is found in ponds, lakes and slow streams growing on submerged sticks and plants. The colony of *Spongilla* is profusely branched exhibiting various shades of green colour due to the presence of *Zoochlorellae,* a green alga in the tissues. The body wall consists of very thin dermal membrane provided with dermal pores and several oscula. The canal system is rhagon type. Skeleton consists of siliceous spicules in the form of network of smooth or spiny large and small oxeas embedded in the spongin. Reproduction both asexual and sexual. Asexual reproduction by gemmules. Sexual reproduction by way of unusual free swimming larva which is characteristic of *Spongilla.*

9. *Chalina. Chalina* (Fig. 27.9) is popularly known as "dead man's finger", because it is shaped like a hand with many fingers. Each branch or finger-like structure is perforated by numerous oscula. Skeleton comprises spongin fibres in which siliceous spicules are embedded. Reproduction both asexual and sexual. Asexual by regeneration and budding. Sexual by producing free swimming larva. The sponge is orange or red, yellowish brown in colour, is found in deep waters from Rhode Island to Labrador. It is not found in shallow waters except when it is broken from its stalk and washed ashore.

10. *Euspongia. Euspongia* (Fig. 27.10) is the common bath sponge. Body is rounded and large, it is of light brown colour. There are many large and small oscula.

The body has a large number of small projections called conuli, which are due to strands of spongin fibres. Inside the sponge are numerous inhalant canals, flagellated chambers and exhalant canals and spaces. The skeleton is made of spongin fibres only which form a network, the thickest fibres run radially and each ends in a conulus. *Euspongia* is regarded as a colony, but the individuals of the colony are unrecognisable. Sexes are separate but male colonies are rare.

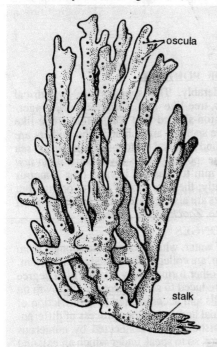

Fig. 27.9. *Chalina.*

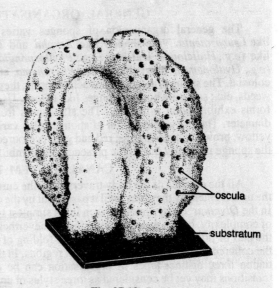

Fig. 27.10. *Euspongia.*

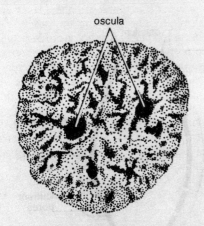

Fig. 27.11. *Hippospongia.*

The cleaned spongin skeleton of *Euspongia* is used as commercial bath sponge. *E. officinalis* is found in the Mediterranean, West Indies and Australia up to a depth of 180 metres. *E. mollisima* is the most valuable bathe sponge, it is cup-shaped, light yellow, and found near Asia Minor.

11. *Hippospongia.* *Hippospongia* (Fig.27.11), the commercial horse sponge is a typical horny sponge, occurs in Florida on rocky bottoms at depths up to 10–15 metres. A single sponge is made up of few to many individuals provided with few to large number of oscula. The body of the sponge is covered by a dark thin membrane provided with numerous flagellated chambers internally. Skeleton consists of spongin fibres without spicules forming an irregular network. Canal system is leuconoid type with aphodal chambers. *Hippospongia* carries small crustaceans and worms in its large cavities. The sponge may live up to 50 years and grows extremely large and massive.

REVISION QUESTIONS

1. Give an account of the characters of phylum Porifera. Classify it up to orders giving examples.
2. Give an outline classification of phylum Porifera up to orders, mention examples of each order. How can you say that the classification of Porifera is based on their skeleton ?
3. Write short notes on:
   (i) *Euplectella;* (ii) *Hyalonema;* (iii) *Spongilla ;* (iv) *Chalina ;* (v) *Euspongia ;* (vi) *Cliona.*

28
Porifera in General

GENERAL ORGANISATION OF PORIFERA

The general organisation of sponges varies considerably. The sponges are cylindrical like *Leucosolenia*, vase-shaped like *Scypha* and *Grantia*, tree-like (*e.g., Microciona*), finger-like (*e.g., Haliclona*), leaf-like (*e.g., Phyllospongia*), cushion-shaped like *Euspongia*, rope-like (*e.g., Hyalonema*), bowl-shaped like *Pheronema*, etc. Some sponges are solitary, while others are colonial. The sponges are mostly attached forms; they are found attached to stones, shells, sticks, sea weeds, etc.; some are boring sponges like *Cliona*. Usually, the sponge body is asymmetrical but few forms exhibit radial symmetry. The size varies from few mm to massive having 1 or 2 metres diameter. The body colouration of sponges also varies greatly; they are mostly white or grey but yellow, brown, purple, orange, red and green coloured species are also reported. The green colour of the sponge is usually due to the presence of a symbiotic algae, *Zoochlorella* , in them.

CANAL SYSTEM IN SPONGES

All the cavities of the body traversed by the currents of water, which nourish the sponge from the time it enters by the pores until it passes out by the osculum, are collectively termed **canal system.** In the *Olynthus* canal system is seen in its simplest type. In other forms it may attain a high degree of complexity, but its general evolution can nevertheless be reduced to simple process of growth on the part of primitive *Olynthus* resulting in folding of the walls and accompanied by a restriction of the collared (choanocyte) cells to certain regions. In the gradual and continuous process of differentiation three distinct types of organisation can be distinguished which connected by numerous transitions may yet be considered as three styles of architecture, so to speak under which all existing forms may be classified. There are usually three types of canal system met within sponges, *viz.*, **asconoid type, syconoid type** and **leuconoid type.**

Asconoid Type

Asconoid type of canal system is the simplest of all the types. In this there is a radially symmetrical vase-like body consisting of a thin wall enclosing a large central cavity the **spongocoel** opening at the summit by the narrowed osculum. The wall is composed of an outer and inner epithelium with a mesenchyme between. The outer or dermal epithelium here termed **epidermis** consists of a single layer of flat cells. The inner epithelium, lining the spongocoel, is composed of **choanocytes.** The mesenchyme contains skeletal spicules and several types of amoebo-cytes, all embedded in a gelatinous matrix. The wall of the asconoid sponge is perforated by numerous microscopic apertures termed **incurrent pores** or **ostia** which extend from the external surface to the spongocoel. Each pore is intracellular, *i.e.*, it is a canal through a tubular cell called a **porocyte.** The water current impelled by the flagella of the choanocytes passes through the incurrent pores into the spongocoel and out through the osculum (water from exterior → incurrent pores → spongocoel → osculum → water out) furnishing in its passage food and

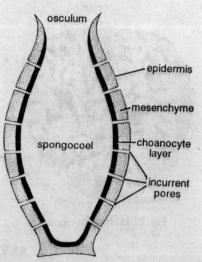

Fig. 28.1. Asconoid type of canal system.

oxygen and carrying away metabolic wastes. Asconoid type of canal system is found only in few sponges, *e.g., Olynthus, Leucosolenia.*

According to Hyman the important features of the asconoid structure are the simple wall and the complete continuous lining epithelium of choanocytes, interrupted only by the inner ends of the porocytes. The asconoid type of sponge superficially resembles a typical gastrula.

Syconoid Type

Syconoid type of canal system is the first stage above the asconoid type. It is formed by the outpushing of the wall of an asconoid sponge at regular intervals into finger-like projections, called radial canals. At first these radial canals are free projections and the outside water surrounds their whole length,for there are no definite incurrent channels. But in most syconoid sponges, the walls of the radial canals fuse in such a manner as to leave between them tubular spaces, the incurrent canals, which open to the exterior between the blind outer ends of the radial canals by apertures termed dermal ostia or dermal pores. Since these incurrent canals represent the original outer surface of the asconoid sponge, they are necessarily lined by epidermis. Radial canals being the outpushings of the original spongocoel are necessarily lined by choanocytes and are, therefore, better called flagellated canals. The interior of the syconoid sponge is hollow and forms a large spongocoel which is lined by the flat epithelium derived from epidermis. The openings of the radial canals into the

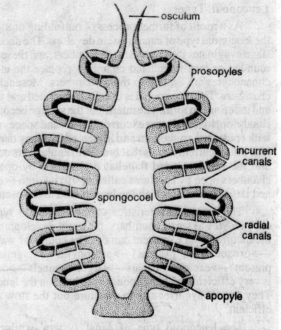

Fig. 28.2. Syconoid type of canal system. (Early stage without cortex).

spongocoel are termed internal ostia. The syconoid sponges retain the radial vase form of the asconoids and the spongocoel opens to the exterior by the single terminal osculum. The wall between the incurrent and the radial canals, is pierced by numerous minute pores called prosopyles. The water current in syconoid sponges takes the following route : dermal pores→incurrent canals→prosopyles→radial canals→ internal ostia (apopyles)→spongocoel→ osculum→out.

The syconoid sponges differ from the asconoid type in two important particulars : (i) in the thick folded walls containing alternating incurrent and radial canals and (ii) in the breaking of the choanocyte layer, which no longer lines the whole interior but is limited to certain definite chambers (radial canals).

The syconoid structure occurs in two main stages. The first type

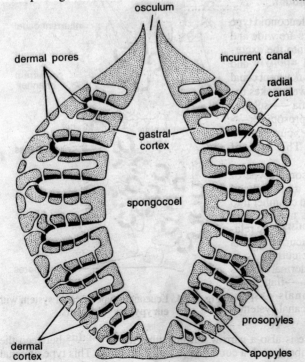

Fig. 28.3. Final syconoid canal system (with cortex).

illustrated in a few of the heterocoelous calcareous sponges, especially members of the genus *Sycon*. In the second stage, the epidermis and mesenchyme spread over the outer surface forming a thin or thick cortex often containing special cortical spicules. The epidermis becomes pierced by more definite pores than lead into narrowed incurrent canals.

Leuconoid Type

As a result of further process of outfolding of the choanocyte layer and thickening of body wall the leuconoid type of canal system develops. The choanocyte layer of the radial canal of the syconoid stage evaginates into many small chambers, and these may repeat the process, so that clusters of small rounded or oval flagellated chambers replace the elongated chambers of the syconoid stage. The choanocytes are limited to these chambers. Mesenchyme fills in the spaces around the flagellated chambers. The spongocoel is usually obliterated and the whole sponge becomes irregular in structure and indefinite in form. The interior of the sponge becomes permeated by many incurrent and excurrent canals join to form larger excurrent canals and spaces which lead to the oscula. The surface is covered with epidermal epithelium and is pierced by many dermal pores (ostia) and oscula. The dermal pores lead into incurrent canals that branch irregularly through the mesenchyme. The incurrent canals lead into the small rounded flagellated chambers by opening still termed prosopyles. The flagellated chambers open by apertures called apopylés into excurrent channels, and these unite to form larger and larger tubes, of which the largest lead to the oscula.

The main characteristics of the leuconoid type of canal system are the limitation of the choanocytes to small chambers, the great development of the mesenchyme, and the complexity of the incurrent and excurrent canals. The course of water current is dermal ostia—> incurrent canals —>prosodus (if present)—>prosopyles—>flagellated chambers—>apopyles—> aphodus (if present)—>excurrent canals—>larger channels—>oscula—>out. The leucon type of canal system is very efficient and most sponges are built on the leuconoid plan and they attain a considerable size. They are always irregular in structure but the flow of the current of the water is fairly rapid and efficient.

The leuconoid type of canal system exhibits numerous variations but presents three stages of evolution,*viz.,* eurypylous, aphodal, and diplodal.

(i) Eurypylous. In the eurypylous leuconoid type of canal system,the flagellated chambers are wide and thimble-shaped,each opening directly into the excurrent canal by a wide aperture called apopyle and receive the water supply direct from the incurrent canal through the prosopyle. The current of water takes the following route —>dermal pores or ostia —>subdermal spaces—>incurrent canals—>prosopyles—> flagellated chambers—>apopyles—>excurrent canals —>spongocoel—>oscula—>out. This type of canal system is found in *Leucilla*.

(ii) Aphodal. In the aphodal leuconoid type of canal system, the flagellated chambers are small and rounded. The opening of each flagellated chamber into the excurrent canal is drawn out into a narrow tube, usually not of great length, termed aphodus. The relation of the flagellated chambers to the incurrent canals remain as before. The route of water current is as follows : dermal pores or ostia—>subdermal spaces —>incurrent canals—>prosopyles—>flagellated chambers—>aphodus—>excurrent canals—>spongocoel —>oscula—>out. This type of canal system is found in *Geodia* and *Stelleta*.

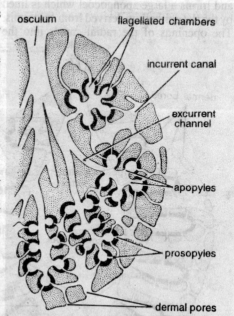

Fig. 28.4. Leuconoid type of canal system with **eurypylous** chambers.

(iii) Diplodal. In some cases there is also a narrow current tube, the prosodus between the incurrent canal and the flagellated chambers, such a condition is called diplodal. This type of canal system is found in *Oscarella, Spongilla,* etc. The current of water takes the following route:dermal pores or ostia—>subdermal spaces—>incurrent canals —>prosodus —>flagellated chambers —>aphodus —>excurrent canals —>spongocoel—> oscula—>out.

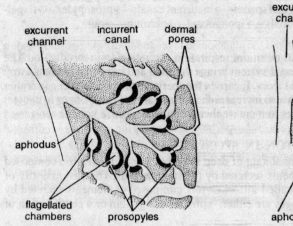

Fig. 28.5. Leuconoid type of canal system with **aphodal** chambers.

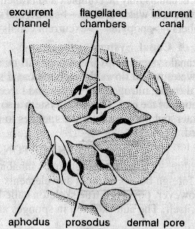

Fig. 28.6. Leuconoid type of canal system with **diplodal** chambers.

Rhagon Type

In calcareous sponges, the leuconoid structure may be attained by way of asconoid and syconoid stages. But in Demospongiae it is derived from a stage termed a rhagon which in turn arises by direct rearrangement of the inner cell mass.

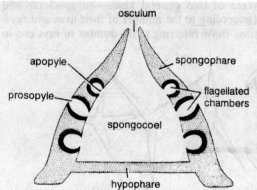

Fig. 28.7. *Rhagon* larva V. S. showing rhagon type of canal system.

The rhagon type of sponge has a broad base and it is conical in shape with a single osculum at the summit. The basal wall is termed the hypophare which is devoid of flagellated chambers. The upper wall bearing a row of small, oval flagellated chambers is called spongophare. Spongocoel is bordered by oval flagellated chambers opening into it by wide apopyles. Between the chambers and the epidermis lies a considerable thickness of mesenchyme traversed by incurrent canals and subdermal spaces. Dermal pores or ostia open into subdermal spaces which extend below the entire surface of the body. Branching incurrent canals lead from the subdermal spaces into small flagellated chambers which

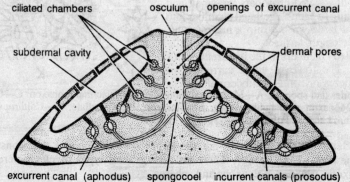

Fig. 28.8. *Spongilla*. Diagrammatic vertical section showing rhagon type of canal system.

have been formed by breaking down of radial canal, the flagellated chambers alone are lined by choanocytes. From the flagellated chambers excurrent canals lead into a spongocoel. The incurrent and excurrent canals may be complex and branched. The spongocoel opens by a single osculum. The course of current of water is ostia—>subdermal spaces—>incurrent canals—>prosopyles—>flagellated chambers—>apopyles—>excurrent canals—>spongocoel—>osculum—>out.

Functions of Canal System

The canal system helps the sponges in nutrition, respiration, excretion and reproduction The current of water which flows through the canal system brings the food and oxygen and takes away the carbon dioxide, nitrogenous wastes and faeces. It carries the sperms from one sponge to another for fertilization of the ova. The canal system also increases the surface area of the sponges in contact with the water and, thus, enables the sponges to increase their volume as surface volume ratio must remain fixed.

SKELETON IN SPONGES

According to Haeckel few sponges inhabitant of deep sea have a pseudoskeleton composed entirely of foreign bodies without any elements secreted by the sponge itself. The vast majority of sponges, however, possess a true skeleton called autoskeleton composed of elements secreted by the sponge itself. The autoskeleton in sponges are either spicules or spongin or a combination of both.

Spicules

The spicules or sclerites are definite bodies, having a crystalline appearance and consisting in general of simple spines or of spines radiating from a point. They have an axis of organic material around which is deposited the inorganic substance, either calcium carbonate or hydrated silica. They present a great variety of shape and as reference to the shape is essential in the description of sponges, a large terminology exists.

Classification of spicules. First, spicules are of two general kinds— megascleres and microscleres. The spicules are further classified according to the number of their axes and rays. Words designating the number of axes end in axons, those referring to the number of rays end in actine or actinal.

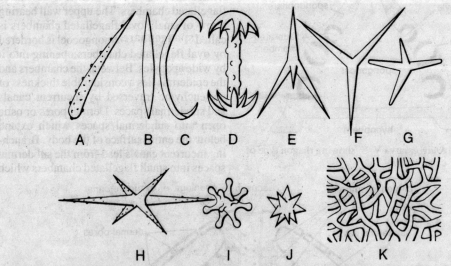

Fig. 28.9. Spicules and spongin. A—Monactinal monaxon; B—Diactinal monaxon; C—Curved monaxon; D—Monaxon with hooked ends; E—Tetraxon; F—Triradiate; G—Calthrops; H—Hexactinal triaxon; I and J—Polyaxon; K—Spongin fibres.

1. Megascleres. The megascleres are the larger skeletal spicules that constitute the chief supporting framework of the sponge. There are five general types of megasclere spicules, *viz.,* monaxons, tetraxons, triaxons, polyaxons and spheres.

(i) Monaxons . These are formed by growth in one or both directions along a single axis, which may be straight or curved. When growth has occurred in one direction only, the spicule is called monactinal monaxon or style. Styles are typically rounded (strongylote) at one end and pointed **(oxeote)** at the other. Styles in which the broad end is knobbed are called tylostyles ; those curved with thorny processes are acanthostyles. Usually the pointed end of styles projects to the exterior. Monaxons that develop by growth in both directions from a central point are named diactinal monaxons, diactines or briefly rhabds. Rhabds pointed at each end are oxeas, lance-headed at each end tornotes; rounded at the ends, strongyles and knobbed at each end, like a pin head, tylotes.

(ii) Tetraxons. Tetraxon spicules are also called tetractines and quadriradiates. They consist typically of four rays, not in the same plane, radiating from a common point. The four rays of the tetraxon spicule may be more or less equal, in which case the spicule is called a calthrops. Generally one ray, rhabdome, is elongated bearing a crown of three smaller rays; such spicules are termed triaenes. By loss of one smaller ray results into a diaene. If the elongated ray bears a disc at both ends, it is called amphidisc. Loss of elongated ray results into a triradiate or triactinal spicule, called a triod characteristic of calcareous sponges.

(iii) Triaxons . The triaxon or hexactinal spicule consists fundamentally of three axes crossing at right angles, producing six rays extending at right angles from a central point. From this basic type all possible modifications arise by reduction or loss of rays, branching and curving of the rays, and the development of spines, knobs, etc., upon them. The triaxon spicules are characteristic of class Hexactinellida.

(iv) Polyaxons. These spicules in which several equal rays radiate from a central point.

(v) Spheres. These are rounded bodies in which growth is concentric around a centre.

(vi) Desma. A special type of megasclere known as desma occur in a number of sponges. A desma consists of an ordinary minute monaxon, triadiate,or tetraxon spicule, termed the crepis, on which layers of silica have been deposited irregularly. Desmas are named from the shape of the crepis, as monocrepid, tricrepid and tetracrepid. They are usually united into a network and such a reticulated skeleton is called **lithistid.**

2. Microscleres. The microscleres are the smaller flesh spicules that occur strewn throughout the mesenchyme. However, they do not form the supporting framework. The microspheres are of two types,*viz.,* spires and asters.

(i) Spires. Spires are curved in one plane or spirally twisted and exhibits many shapes. The most common types are the C-shaped forms, called sigmas; the bow-shaped ones, or toxas and the chelas with recurved hooks, plates or flukes at each end. When two ends are alike,chelas are called isochelas, when unlike, anisochelas. Spirally twisted sigmas are termed sigmaspires.

(ii) Asters . Asters include types with small centres and long rays and large centres and small rays. Among the small centred forms are oxyasters with pointed rays, strongylaster with rounded ends and tylasters with knobbed rays. Large-centred forms include spherasters with definite rays and sterrasters with rays reduced to small projections from the spherical surface. Short spiny microscleric monaxons are known as streptasters, of which the principal sorts are the spirally twisted spirasters, rod shapes as sanaidasters, plesioasters with a few spines from a very short axis, and amphiasters with spines at each end. Microscleric forms of diactines are **microrhabds, microxeas,** and **microstrongyles.**

Development of Spicules

Spicules are secreted by mesenchyme cells, called scleroblasts. Very little is known about the formation of various kinds of spicules. The process is best known for calcareous spicules. On the basis of development, the spicules may be **primary** which owe their first origin from a single mother cell or scleroblast, or **secondary** which arise from more than one scleroblast.

(i) Development of monaxon spicules. In calcareous sponges a monaxon spicule is secreted

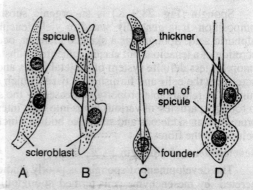

Fig. 28.10. Secretion of a monaxon spicule.

within a binucleate sclerobast, probably arising by the incomplete division of an ordinary scleroblast. The calcium carbonate is deposited around an organic axial thread in the cytoplasm between the two nuclei. As the spicule lengthens, the two nuclei draw apart until the scleroblast divides into two. One cell, the founder is situated at the inner end, the other the thickner at the outer end of the spicule, since monaxon spicules usually project from the body wall. The spicule is laid down chiefly by the founder which moves slowly inward, establishing the shape and length. The thickner deposits additional layers of calcium carbonate, also moving inward during this process. When the spicule is completed, both cells wander from its inner end into mesogloea, the founder first and the thickner later.

The development of siliceous spicules is poorly known and requires further exploration. It appears that in most cases they are formed completely with one scleroblast called silicoblast.

(ii) Development of triaxon spicules. Triaxon or triradiate calcareous spicules are secreted by three scleroblasts which come together in triangle and divide in two, each into an inner founder and an outer thickner. Each pair secretes a minute spicule and these three rays are early united into a small triradiate spicule. Each ray is then completed in the same manner as a monaxon spicule. Later on, three rays or spicules unite together forming a triaxon or triradiate spicule.

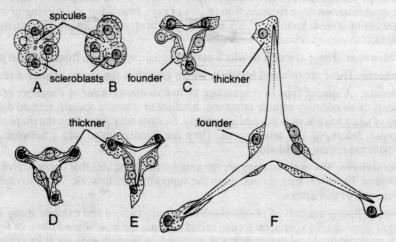

Fig. 28.11. Secretion of a triaxon spicule.

(iii) Development of other spicules. In the formation of quadriradiate or tetraxon spicules, the fourth ray is added to forming triradiate spicule by an additional scleroblast. The hexactinal spicules of Hexactinellida arise in the centre of a multinucleate syncytial mass which is probably formed by repeated nuclear division of an original silicoblast.

Spongin

Spongin (Fig. 28.9 K) is an organic substance allied to silk but apparently of variable composition. It is generally stated to yield leucin and glycin, but not tyrosin when heated with sulphuric acid. Spongin, as a skeletal element, occurs into two distinct forms. First as a cuticular secretion of a tenacious but elastic cementing substance which glues siliceous spicules together into a more or less definite system of skeletal fibres and secondly in the form of minute elastic fibrillae secreted in the cells and furnishing a tissue which may be compared to the elastic tissue of higher animals. A remarkable property possessed by the spongin fibres of many sponges is that of taking up foreign particles of various kinds into their interior. Sand grains, sponge spicules, radiolarian or foraminiferan skeletons and such like bodies which fall on the surface of the sponge body become included in the fibres.

Development of Spongin

The development of spongin is poorly studied and it needs further study. Spongin fibres are secreted by mesenchyme cells termed spongioblasts. These arrange themselves in rows and the spongin rod secreted by each fuses with those of adjacent spongioblasts to form a long fibre. The spongioblasts become vacuolated and degenerate after having secreted a certain amount of spongin.

Taxonomic Importance of Spicules

As referred earlier, the main basis of the classification of phylum Porifera is the skeletal structures found in them. We have seen that phylum Porifera has been divided into three classes :

1. **Class Calcarea.** Having calcareous spicules.

2. **Class Hexactinellida.** Having six-rayed (hexasters) siliceous spicules.

3. **Class Demospongiae.** Having siliceous spicules and spongin fibres.

REPRODUCTION IN SPONGES

The sponges reproduce both asexually and sexually.

1. Asexual Reproduction

Asexual reproduction occurs throughout the Porifera. It takes place by regenerataion, formation of reduction bodies, budding and gemmule formation.

(i) Regeneration. The power of regeneration is very great in sponges, any cut part will regenerate the whole sponge. If the sponge is macerated and squeezed through fine silk cloth, its cells and clusters of cells will pass through, these can regenerate new sponges. The regeneration power is used for cultivation of bath sponge industrially.

(ii) Formation of reduction bodies. Another very unusual method of asexual reproduction is the formation of reduction bodies. Many freshwater and marine sponges disintegrate in adverse circumstances. The disintegrating sponge will usually collapse leaving small rounded balls, called reduction bodies. Each reduction body consists of an internal mass of amoebocytes, covered externally by a pinacoderm. When the favourable conditions return, these reduction bodies grow into complete new sponges.

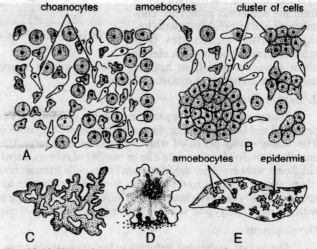

Fig. 28.12. Wilson's experiment on regenerataion in sponges. A—Cells of *Microciona* separated by squeezing living sponge through bolting cloth; B—Cells aggregating into small masses; C—A reticulate reunion mass; D—Later stage forming a young sponge or spongelet; E—Section through a stage like D.

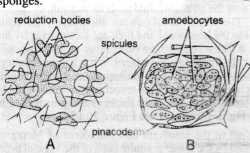

Fig. 28.13. Formation of reduction bodies. A—Reduction bodies of a calcareous sponge ; B—Reduction body in section.

(iii) Budding. In sponges budding takes place in various ways.

(a) Exogenous budding. A sponge forms external buds vegetatively at the bases of branches, thus, forming a group of individuals. Eventually the buds constrict from the parent and each forms a new sponge.

(b) Endogenous budding. Asexual reproductive bodies called gemmules are formed internally in all freshwater sponges and some marine sponges. Archeocytes collect in groups in the mesogloea, they then become multinucleate, they also get filled with proteins as reserve food material which is supplied to archeocytes by special nurse cells trophocytes. Some amoebocytes encircle this mass of food-laden archeocytes and secrete a hard double-layered shell, the shell has a small outlet or micropyle. Then some scleroblasts secrete spicules which are placed radially between two layers of the shell, some spicules project outside the shell, the spicules in *Spongilla* are monaxon spicules but in others they are amphidiscs. Amphidiscs are straight rods with thorny sides and a ring of hooks at each end. Thus, a gemmule is formed after which the surrounding amoebocytes, scleroblasts and trophocytes depart. Gemmules are formed in large numbers in autumn after which the sponge disintegrates, they remain in the sponge remnants or become free, in any case they fall to the bottom. Gemmules can withstand unfavourable conditions, but they hatch when spring comes. In hatching the archeocytes streamout of the micropyle, then these multinucleate archeocytes divide to form uninucleate archeocytes and small cells called histoblasts. The histoblasts by differentiation and rearrangement form the epidermis porocytes, choanocytes and internal endoderm lining; modified archeocytes from scleroblast which secrete spicules. In

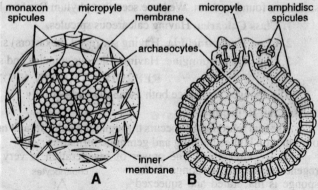

Fig. 28.14. A—Gemmule of *Spongilla* ; B—Gemmule of *Ephydatia* (section).

about a week's time from hatching a young sponge surrounds the empty gemmule shell. The uninucleate archeocytes remain embryonic.

2. Sexual Reproduction

Sponges have no sex organs but amoebocytes form sex cells in the mesenchyme ; first eggs are produced and later the sperms, hence, sponge is protogynous in which cross fertilization takes place. The amoebocytes get filled with food and become large, they become round to form eggs. Other amoebocytes divide to produce a large number of sperms, a sperm has an oval head and a long tapering tail. Some workers claim the formation of sex cells from archeocytes or even from choanocytes. Eggs of one sponge are fertilized by sperms from another sponge to form zygotes. In cross fertilizaion the sperm probably enters a choanocyte which fuses with the egg setting free the sperm which then fuses with the egg. The zygote secretes a covering called brood capsule which encloses the zygote.

Development

The zygote undergoes holoblastic but unequal cleavage ; in holoblastic division the zygote is completely segmented. The first three divisions are vertical which form eight pyramidal cells, then a horizontal division forms eight small upper cells at the animal pole, and eight large lower cells at the vegetal pole. The upper small cells divide rapidly, become clear and acquire flagella, the lower cells divide slowly and become granular. This forms a blastula which has a blastocoel cavity internally. The blastula is called an amphiblastula after the formation of flagella. So far the development takes place in the body of the sponge, now the amphiblastula finds its way into excurrent canals and leaves the parent through the osculum. The amphiblastula swims about freely for some hours, then the upper flagellated cells invaginate into the blastocoel and they are grown over by the lower granular cells; this forms a gastrula which is like a cup with an outer layer of granular cells called ectoderm, and an inner layer of flagellated cells known as endoderm, it has a large opening, the blastopore. This embryo attaches itself to some solid object by its blastoporal end and it begins to grow. Both ectoderm and endoderm layers secrete mesogloea and its amoebocytes. According to some mesogloea is secreted only by choanocytes (endoderm). The wall thickens and gets folded to form canals, perforations form ostia and osculum. For development see Figure 26.12 .

The germ layers of sponges are not equivalent to the ectoderm and endoderm of Metazoa, because the outer ectoderm of sponge has been formed by the lower granular cells of the vegetal pole, and endoderm is formed by the upper flagellated cells of the animal pole. In Metazoa the cells of the animal pole become the ectoderm, and those of the vegetal pole form the endoderm.

ANIMAL NATURE OF SPONGES

For a long time sponges were not regarded to be animals, exactly because of their non-animal-like appearance; they are sessile and do not possess the ability to catch the food or getting rid of their wastes and exhibit more or less no response to stimuli. However, it was Robert Grant (1836) who recognized the animal nature of sponges by suggesting that the water current flows through a definite path in the body of sponges; entering the sponge body through minute pores called ostia, scattered all over the body surface and pass out through larger holes called oscula. In fact, the **holozoic** mode of nutrition in sponges; they feed on solid food particles coming along the water current, devoid of cellulose cell wall, and presence of free-swimming ciliated larva in the life cycle resembling to those of other marine animals clearly suggested that the sponges are animals and nothing else.

AFFINITIES OF PORIFERA

There has been a great controversy over the nature and affinities of sponges ever since they were discovered. Aristotle (384–322 B.C.)was the first to recognise them as animals. But the biologists after Aristotle believed them as plants for centuries on account of their sessile habit and insensitive nature. Ellis (1765) pointed out that continuous water current enters in and expelled out from the body of sponges; it was further confirmed by Robert Grant (1836). However, Linnaeus, Lamarck and Cuvier placed them along coelenterates in Zoophyta. Robert Grant (1836) finally established a separate group Porifera for the sponges. Thus, they show affinities with Protozoa as well as with Metazoa.

Affinities with Protozoa

Resemblances. Sponges exhibit resemblances with colonial Protozoa in having the following features :

1. Absence of digestive cavity and presence of intracellular digestion.

2. Presence of collar cells and amoeboid cells like those of colonial flagellates.

3. The production of skeleton by single cell or a group of cells.

4. The cells of sponge body are interdependent in their function.

5. A process known as inversion occurs in amphiblastula larva like those of *Volvox*. The flagellated sponge larva are considered as the remnant of some flagellated colonial protozoan ancestor.

Differences. Sponges differ from Protozoa in having the following features :

1. The canal system.

2. The characteristic skeleton.

3. The development of a multicellular body from a fertilized egg by cleavage; and in this feature the sponges become more complex than a colonial protozoan and resemble with the Metazoa. Therefore, its protozoan affinity stands no longer.

Affinities with Metazoa

Resemblances. Among Metazoa, coelenterates exhibit certain similarities with sponges in the following features :

1. Both are sedentary in habit.

2. Both are diploblastic and acoelomate. A non-cellular mesogloea layer is found in between the ectoderm and endoderm. Mesoderm is absent in both the cases.

3. The spongocoel of sponges opening out through terminal osculum can be compared with the gastrovascular cavity, opening to the exterior by terminal hypostome of coelenterates.

4. Asexual reproduction occurs in both the cases and the colonies are formed by budding.

5. The parenchymula larva of sponges are comparable with the planula of coelenterates.

Differences. The sponges differ from Metazoa in having the following features :

1. In sponges, the cells are comparatively less specialized and inter-dependent than the cells of Metazoa.

2. Sponges possess choanocytes which are not found in any Metazoa.

3. Sponges are at the cellular grade of construction but the Metazoa are at the tissue and organ grade of construction.

4. The sponges are diploblastic, while Metazoa (except Coelenterata) are triploblastic.

5. The sponges do not possess an anterior end or head like those of Metazoa. The osculum acts only as exhalent aperture.

6. The body of sponges is perforated by numerous minute pores and they possess a unique system of canals in their body ; all these are never found in Metazoa.

7. Sponges have no nervous tissues to co-ordinate the body activities.

8. There is complete absence of digestive cavity in sponges, unlike those of Metazoa.

9. Sponges have greater number of fats and fatty acids which are of a higher molecular weight than those found in the Metazoa.

10. In the development of sponges, the flagellated upper cells of the embryo, situated at the animal pole, become the endoderm and the granular cells of vegetal pole become the ectoderm; in no Metazoa does such an inversion occur during development.

Due to these differences, the sponges cannot be grouped with Metazoa and, therefore, a separate phylum has been created for the sponges. Thus, in spite of its resemblances with Protozoa and Metazoa, it is believed that sponges have diverged from the main line of Metazoa evolution and they are a dead-end phylum. Considering this, a separate subkingdom Parazoa has been created to include the sponges and, therefore, they have an isolated phylogenetic position.

ORIGIN OF PORIFERA

There is a great controversy regarding the origin of Porifera. However, they look more nearer to Protozoa though they differ from them in being multicellular. Porifera probably originated from flagellated protozoan like *Proterospongia,* a colonial flagellate. The colony of *Proterospongia* has collared and flagellated cells embedded in a gelatinous matrix having amoeboid cells. These cells are the choanocytes and amoebocytes of sponges. Even then, the origin of sponges is believed to be uncertain. Conclusively it can be said that, sponges diverged from metazoan evolutionary line in the very early stage and, therefore, occupy a separate status.

ECONOMIC IMPORTANCE OF PORIFERA

The sponges are of great economic importance, both beneficial and harmful, to mankind.

A . Beneficial Sponges

Sponges are beneficial to mankind and other animals in the following way :

1. As food. Sponges are rarely taken as food by other animals because of their bad taste, odour and sharp spicules. However, crustaceans are found leading parasitic life on them and some molluscs like **nudibranchs** depend upon them for their diet.

2. As commensals. Sponges serve as protective houses for several animals like crustaceans, worms, molluscs, small fishes, etc., because their enemies cannot feed the sponges. In addition to the protection, the animals living inside the sponge body get a rich food supply from the water circulating through them. These animals do not cause any apparent harm to sponges, they are regarded as commensals.

3. Other uses. The dried, fibrous skeleton of many sponges like *Spongia, Hippospongia* and *Euspongia* are used for the purpose of bathing, polishing, washing oars, walls, furnitures, and scrubbing floor etc. The skeleton of some sponges like *Euplectella* are of great commercial value and used as decorative pieces.

B. Harmful Sponges

Only a few sponges are harmful. They may cause the death of some sessile animals by growing over them and cutting off their food and oxygen supply. The boring sponges, like *Cliona* attach themselves to the shells of oysters, clams, and barnacles, etc. It bores into the shells of these animals and completely destroy them. The boring sponges also cause great harm to oyster beds. The boring sponges also destroy rocks by penetrating into them and breaking them into pieces.

SPONGE INDUSTRY AND SPONGE FISHING

Sponge fishing and its industry is of great economic value to the present synthetic world. The sponge bed is present almost all over the world but the Western Altantic coast and the countries producing bulk of sponge are U.S.A., U.K., Cuba, Japan, Bahama Is., Syria, Turkey, Egypt and Lebanon. Millions of sponges are sold every year, making sponge fishing a source of income. The best commercial sponges are those from Turkey. Tarpon Springs and Florida are the best sponge fishing centres in United States, where the sponges collected per year cost more than one million dollars.

Sponge culture is considerably new venture for getting sponges because of their great commercial use. Among the countries engaged in sponge culture, Japan stands at the top. The species of sponge commonly used for culture processes is *Euspongia*. Sponge fishing involves collection of sponges from the sea beds by divers.

REVISION QUESTIONS

1. What is canal system? Write an essay on canal system in sponges.
2. What are skeletal elements of sponges? Describe the structure, function and mode of development of various skeletal elements found in sponges.
3. Give an account of reproduction in sponges.
4. Give an account of the economic importance of sponges.
6. Write short notes on:
    (i) Spongin fibres; (ii) Spicules; (iii) Gemmules; (iv) Justify that the sponges are animals and not plants; (v) Sponge industry and its fishing .

29

Metazoa

Protozoa are acellular animals of small size, they have a permeable limiting membrane which prevents the animals from growing beyond a certain size, and it precludes the formation of structures which will give strength and rigidity necessary for large size. But more important than strength is the factor that the activities of Protozoa involve an exchange of substances between their protoplasm and their surrounding liquid medium, these processes are governed by the ratio of their surface area to their volume; the smaller the animal, the relatively larger is its surface area, this ratio limits their size. In Protozoa the small acellular body performs all vital functions, and no single function predominates over the others.

The attainment of multicellular structure is foreshadowed by colonial Protozoa, they have groups of many individuals either attached to each other, or connected to each other by protoplasmic strands, or embedded in a common matrix of noncellular material. But colonies are different from multicellular animals because their cells are functionally independent of each other.

The larger multicellular animals in which limitations of size are removed are called Metazoa, their cells are potentially capable of performing all essential vital activities, but these cells are dependent on each other, and all of them are not similar because specialization has taken place, this has opened up vast possibilities for an increased complexity of body form and structure. Cell specialization in turn has led to the development of tissues in which groups of similar cells are organized into sheets or layers. In lower metazoans the tissues are primitive and cells arranged in layers, but in higher forms the tissues become organized to form organs and organ systems. Metazoa are multicellular animals which are distinguished not only by their larger size, but by a high degree of differentiation and specialization of their parts,this is called morphological differentiation. With this morphological differentiation of structure there is a physiological division of labour among the permanently associated and mutually dependent parts of an animal; this implies that parts of the body are specialized to perform definite functions for the entire animals. Differentiation of structure is also seen in many Protozoa, but it attains a much higher degree of complexity in Metazoa.

In Metazoa special regions of the body are set aside for dealing with different functions. The Metazoa produce gametes of two types,the male gametes are spermatozoa and female gametes are ova. A spermatozoan fertilizes an ovum to form a zygote which undergoes a series of mitotic cell divisions to form a hollow ball of cells called blastula, it has a cavity known as blastocoele. Further increase of the cells of the blastula causes an invagination of the wall on one side, and by different processes the cells eventually come to lie in two layers, an outer layer of ectoderm and an inner layer of endoderm, the blastocoele is obliterated; the mouth of the invagination is a blastopore which leads into a new cavity, the archenteron; this two-layered bag is a gastrula.

The development of some Metazoa stops at the gastrula stage,these two-layered Metazoa are diploblastica, such as Cnidaria and Ctenophora. In all other metazoan phyla a third layer of cells called mesoderm arises between the ectoderm and endoderm. The phyla which possess three layers are triploblastica, and their mesoderm opens up further possibilities of increase in size and complexity. In triploblastic phyla the ectoderm and endoderm retain most of the functions which they perform in diploblastic animals. The ectoderm forms the outer protective epidermis, external sense organs, nephridia and the nervous system, but in Echinodermata part of the nervous system is mesodermal in origin. The endoderm gives rise to the lining of the alimentary canal, and organs associated with digestion and respiration. The mesoderm is not single entity but has parts which originate in two ways; the cells which migrate from the ectoderm or endoderm form a loose cellular tissue called mesenchyme which fills the spaces between the other layers, and it is comparable to the cells which are found in the mesogloea of Cnidaria. The second type of cells which form the wall of the body cavity are known as mesothelium or real mesoderm which gives rise to connective tissue, muscles, skeleton, blood,circulatory system, excretory system and reproductive system. In lower triploblastic phyla (Platyhelminthes and Aschelminthes) there is no mesothelium, in Chaetognatha there is no mesenchyme, but the other phyla possess both kinds of mesoderm. The triploblastic acoelomate animals may attain a degree of complexity not seen in diploblastic animals,though the gut of some triploblastic acoelomate animals has only a single opening, the mouth which serves both for ingestion and egestion. The diploblastic animals are no doubt simpler, but the higher diploblastic animals approach a condition found in the lower triploblastic animals in having what amounts to third layer of cells, *i.e.,* cells in the mesogloea; thus, the distinction between diploblastic and triploblastic animals is by no means very sharp.

In Metazoa the cells are closely associated to form tissues which are specialized for performing some functions. Cnidaria have no organised tissues, but in triploblastic animals the tissues unite to form organs, the organs are then associated together to form systems, each of which carries on some important general function, though there may be some overlapping. The epidermis along with underlying mesodermal tissue called dermis forms the skin ; in invertebrates it is either columnar or syncytial; in vertebrates it is stratified. In lower invertebrates the cells of the "skin" are ciliated, when cilia are absent then a protective cuticle is formed.

A special region of the body is set aside for dealing with food, it may be a simple sac or a complicated alimentary canal for enclosing the food and secreting digestive enzymes. Digestion is originally entirely intracellular in endoderm cells, this may be preceded by an extracellular digestion, but in higher phyla (Annelida, Arthropoda, some Mollusca and Chordata) it is entirely extracellular. The enzymes secreted by the animal render the major part of the food soluble and capable of absorption and assimilation. Such a digestive system is essential for larger animals, for they require such large quantities of food for their vital activities that it cannot be taken into food vacuoles. In large Metazoa parts of the body lie at some distance from the digestive system, so they cannot receive nourishment by mere diffusion, as is done in lower Metazoa, hence, they require a transporting system of tubes (as in jelly fish) or a blood vascular system (as in most higher animals) which can transport the digested food.

In early stages stimuli are transmitted from sensory cells or receptors to muscles or other cells called the effectors which are set in action. But in larger Metazoa where the effectors may lie at some distance from the receptors, it became essential to have a system for concluding and co-ordinating, thus, a neuro-sensory system is developed. This is done by formation of nerve cells or neurons which have several branching cytoplasmic processes called nerve fibres. In its simplest form the neuro-sensory system would have a series of receptors on the body surface from which nerve fibres pass to the effectors. But such a simple system does not exist, there is no direct connection between receptors and effectors, but conduction takes place through a chain of neurons; the neurons are not joined but there are minute terminal buttons at the end of an axon which lie in contact with the dendrites of the next neuron, these junctions are called synapses. In lower Metazoa the nerve fibres intermesh to form a network which is superficial in position and is called a nerve net. In higher Metezoa the nerve fibres of a neuron are not equally formed on all sides, one or more of them are long, and the fibres are bound together to form nerves, and the cell-bodies of neurons become collected together to form a central nervous system. The nerves which connect the central nervous system to receptors and effectors constitute a peripheral nervous system. Thus, impulses are conducted from receptors along definite paths and not in any direction, as in a nerve net.

Most of the smallar Metazoa are aquatic, their relatively large surface provides an adequate area for interchange of gases necessary for respiration, and allows nitrogenous waste substances to diffuse out quickly. The larger Metazoa have a relatively smaller surface area, and they may have an external covering, hence, they form respiratory organs. These organs of respiration may be covered or lined by ectoderm (gills of crustaceans and annelids, external gills of tadpole and lungs of snails); or they may be covered by endoderm (gills of fish and lungs of vertebrates). The skin in many small and large animals is respiratory. Aquatic respiration is affected by pressure changes of oxygen in water, aerial respiration is affected by pressure changes of carbon dioxide, in foul water the amount of free carbon dioxide is so large as to be an important factor.

The organs of excretion are very varied, they are needed for removal of carbon dioxide, water and solid nitrogenous waste substances. The excretion may occur through the body surface through the ectoderm and perhaps also endoderm (Cnidaria), or in triploblastic animals by a large excreting surface inside a complicated system of fine, branching tubules which form ectodermal nephridia or mesodermal uriniferous kidney tubules, both of which open directly or indirectly to the exterior.

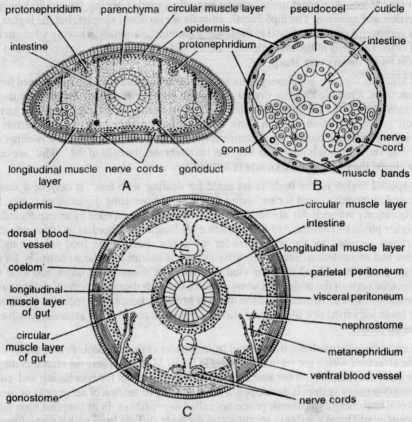

Fig. 29.1. Diagrammatic cross sections of grades of structure; A—Acoelomate grade; B—Pseudocoelomate grade; C—Eucoelomate grade.

The triploblastic animals have a rigid **skeleton** for support and attachment of body muscles. In Arthropoda there is an exoskeleton of cuticle secreted by the ectoderm, though ingorwths from it may form a kind of internal skeleton for attachment of muscles. But Echinodermata and Vertebrata have an endoskeleton of mesoderm which is of great importance.

In simpler triploblastic animals the mesenchyme forms a peculiar cellular tissue called parenchyma which forms a packing around all organs, and through which nourishment is conveyed to all parts from the alimentary canal,and gases and waste nitrogneous substances are conveyed to the excretory organs. These relatively simple triploblastic animals have no body cavity or coelom, they are known as acoelomate animals (Platyhelminthes, Aschelminthes, Acanthocephala and Entoprocta). In some higher triploblastic animals either the mesoderm becomes split into two layers, an outer parietal or somatic mesoderm and an inner visceral or splanchinic mesoderm, the space between the two layers of mesoderm is an extensive, fluid-filled, perivisceral **coelom** which is called a schizoc. elous coelom. In other triploblastic animals pouches arise from the archenteron, they fuse together to form a coelom which. is known as an enterocoelous coelom. A coelom is found in all higher triploblastic animals which are grouped together as coelomate phyla (Chaetognatha,

Pogonophora, Phoronida, Ectoprocta, Brachiopoda, Sipunculida, Annelida, Arthropoda, Mollusca, Echinodermata, Hemichordata, and Chordata). The coelom constitutes one or more perivisceral spaces around the heart, alimentary canal and other organs, it contains a coelomic fluid. The internal organs of the coelom of triploblastic animals become large and are not affected by movements of the body wall, and they are able to freely perform movements of their own. In coelomate animals the gonads arise from the walls of the coelom, and germ cells are shed either into the perivisceral coelom, or the gonad itself contains a separated portion of the coelom. The coelom communicates with the exterior by either dorsal pores (earthworms) or by two sets of ducts called nephridia and coelomoducts. Nephridia are intracellular ectodermal tubes which remove water and excretory matter. Coelomoducts are mesodermal tubes which open usually at one end into the coelom and at the other end to the exterior, they may be only excretory or only for taking out germ cells or they may combine both the functions.

In some coelomates is a space containing blood and lymph, it is usually in the form of a branching system of tubes through which the fluid is made to circulate by a muscular heart, this space is a haemocoele. In some coelomates (Arthropoda and Mollusca) the haemocoele forms large perivisceral sinuses around the internal organs, but it never contains germ cells nor does it communicate with the exterior. The enlarged haemocoele reduces the coelom to small cavities in the excretory and reproductive organs. In such animals the haemocoele is spoken of as a primary body cavity,while the coelom is called a secondary body cavity.

The body of the embryo or the adult of a triploblastic coelomate animal consists of a longitudinal series of more or less similar segments, such an animal is said to be metamerically segmented or to show metamerism. In metamerism there is a serial repetition of homologous parts which work in co-operation with the others for the benefit of the body as a whole, the segments are integrated and interdependent. In many coelomates most of the organs are arranged mathematically throughout the length of the body which itself is divided into segments (Annelida), the muscles, glands, nephridia, ganglia, nerves, blood vessels and coelomic chambers are repeated in the segments. The embryos of vertebrates show conspicuous metamerism, which is hidden in the adults by structural advances, so that metamerism is never uniform throughout the adult. One of the factors which obscures metamerism is the specialization of the anterior end to form a head, this is called cephalization and it is due to a concentration of sense organs at the anterior end along with the formation of a brain. Formation of limbs and restriction of internal organs to certain segments also obscures metamerism.

On the basis of embryological development the Metazoa are divided into two main evolutionary lines. One line contains the flatworms, annelids, molluscs, arthropods, and several smaller phyla, they constitute the division known as Protostomia (protostomes). From the other line have evolved the echinoderms, chordates and several smaller phyla, they are known as Deuterostomia (deuterostomes). Each line displays a plan of development distinct from the other, though all members of each group do not have an identical pattern of development and there are many modifications in every phylum mainly due to the distribution and the amount of yolk present in the egg.

In protostomes the mouth is formed usually from the blastopore, coelom is schizocoelic, and the fate of the blastomeres is fixed at a very early stage of development. If the egg of a marine annelid undergoes two cleavages to form four blastomeres, and these blastomeres are separated, then each will develop only into a fixed quarter of the gastrula and the larva. Thus, each blastomere has a fixed and predetermined fate which cannot be changed even if the cell is moved from its original position. This formation of blastomeres with fixed fates is known as determinate cleavage. Moreover, in protostomes cleavage is total and the axes of cleavage planes are oblique to the polar axis (the axis passing from the animal to the vegetal pole). Such cleavage results in blastomeres having a spiral arrangement so that any single blastomere lies between two cells above or below it, and each tier of cells alternates with the next tier. Such a cleavage pattern is known as spiral cleavage. Thus, determinate and spiral cleavage are characteristic of protostomes.

In deuterostomes the blastopore forms the anus, coelom is enterocoelic, and the fate of blastomeres is not fixed. If the egg of a starfish divides twice to form four blastomeres which are then separated, then each blastomere is capable of forming a complete gastrula and then a larva. In the embryo of a frog the ectoderm cells of the mid-dorsal side give rise to the central nervous system. If, however, the ectoderm cells from the sides of the early gastrula are transplanted dorsally above the notochord, then these cells will form the central nervous system. Thus, in deuterostomes the ultimate fate of blastomeres is not fully fixed and they can follow different lines of development, such formation of blastomeres with unfixed fates is known as indeterminate cleavage. Moreover, the pattern of cleavage is also different. The areas of early cleavage planes are either parallel or at right angles to the polar axis, and the resulting blastomeres are situated directly above or below one another, such a cleavage pattern is called radial cleavage. Thus, indeterminate and radial cleavage are characteristic of deuterostomes.

REVISION QUESTIONS

1. Give a detailed account of Metazoa.
2. What do you mean by tissue grade of organisation? Explain different conditions of coelom.
3. Diffrentiate between :
   (i) Diploblastic and triploblastic conditions;
   (ii) Pseudocoelomate, acoelomate and coelomate conditions;
   (iii) Determinate and indeterminate cleavage;
   (iv) Radial cleavage and spiral cleavage.

30

Phylum Coelenterata (Cnidaria)

As in the case of sponges, the nature of coelenterates was long debated. Aristotle knew the stinging qualities of coelenterates and considered these organisms as intermediate between plants and animals and termed them Acalephae or Cnidae (Gr., *akalephe*=nettle; *cnidos*=thread). They were long included in the Zoophyta (Gr., *zoon*=animal; *phyton*=plant) together with various forms from sponges to ascidians. The animal nature of coelenterates was established by Peyssonel (1723) and Trembly (1744). Linnaeus, Lamarck and Cuvier grouped the coelenterates under Radiata which included the echinoderms also because of their symmetry. Finally, Leuckart (1847) separated the coelenterates from echinoderms and created a separate phylum Coelenterata (Gr., *koilos*=cavity; *enteron*=intestine). However, the Coelenterata of Leuckart also included the sponges and ctenophores. Hatschek(1888) splitted Leuckart's Coelenterata into three distinct phyla: Spongiaria (Porifera), Cnidaria (Coelenterata) and Ctenophora. The coelenterates or cnidaria are distinguished from sponges in being "tissue animals"(Metazoa) that have distinct digestive cavity. The coelenterates differ from ctenophores in being primarily radial in symmetry, in possessing nematocysts, in having a polyp stage, and in reproducing both asexually and sexually.

Coelenterata or Cnidaria are radially symmetrical diploblastic animals with only epidermis and gastrodermis, between these two layers is a jelly-like mesogloea which is originally structureless but in higher forms it becomes fibrous and has wandering amoebocytes. Epidermis and gastrodermis are in two layers, each made of a variety of cells showing a division of labour,the cells form poorly organized body tissues. All functions of the body are performed by tissues and never by organs. The radially symmetrical body has an oral-aboral axis, there is a single coelenteron or gastrovascular cavity which has only one aperture, the mouth. The mouth is used both for ingestion and egestion. There is no coelom. They bear tentacles and nematocysts. The nervous system is a primitive nerve net. They may have an exoskeleton, and in some there is an endoskeleton. There is an oval ciliated planula larva during development. Coelenterata include some 9,000 living species and there are many known fossil forms dating back to the Ordovician period. Except for a few species of freshwater forms almost all Coelenterata are marine. They include hydras, jelly-fishes, sea anemones, and corals. The phylum is divided into three classes, namely, Hydrozoa, Scyphozoa and Anthozoa.

31
Hydra

Hydra, a small freshwater commonest polyp, is readily obtainable coelenterate. It serves a good example from the coelenterates to illustrate the fundamental characteristics of Metazoa. Leeuwenhoek (1702), first described it to the Royal Society of London but Trembley (1744) recognised its animal nature. Reaumur called it a *polyp,* while Linnaeus gave the name *Hydra* because of its special power of regeneration. Actually Hydre was a nine-headed dragon serpentine of the Greek mythology. When one of its head was cut off, two new ones immediately appeared in its place. Thus, the name *Hydra* was given to this animal because of its special power to regenerate its lost part like Hydre.

Hydra is represented by several species in the different parts of the world. Some of the common species are *H. vulgaris,* which is orange-red coloured found in the freshwaters of America and Europe. *H. fusca* or *H. oligactis* which is now known as *Pelmatohydra* is the brown hydra reported chiefly from Punjab in India,North America and Europe. *H. viridis* now known as *Chlorohydra viridissima* is the green hydra of America and Europe. Its green colour is due to the presence of a symbiotic green algae, *Zoochlorellae* in its endodermal cells. *H. gangetica* is found in the pond and other water reservoirs along the river Ganges.

HYDRA
SYSTEMATIC POSITION

Phylum	....	**Coelenterata**
Class	....	**Hydrozoa**
Order	....	**Hydroida**
Suborder	....	**Anthomedusae**
Genus	....	*Hydra*

HABIT AND HABITAT

Hydra is found in freshwater ponds, pools, lakes, streams and ditches. It usually remains attached to submerged vegetation or with any solid object. When it is undisturbed its body remains extended with tentacles spread out and shows expansions and contractions without any apparent reason. It is carnivorous in habit and feeds on small insects, insect larvae and small crustaceans. It lives singly, *i.e.,* solitary in habit. It reproduces sexually as well as asexually.

COLLECTION AND CULTURE OF HYDRA

Hydra can be collected from freshwater lakes, ponds, etc., usually during winter months. If we collect a jar of water with *Hydrilla* plants and put it undisturbed for a day or two; we may notice a number of *Hydra* attached either with the wall of glass jar or with the leaves of *Hydrilla* plant. These may be examined under microscope by putting them on a glass slide with the help of dropper. For making its culture in laboratory, the same may be transferred in aquarium and a sufficient amount of food must be supplied daily. Its food generally consists of *Daphnia* readily available in stagnant water. By budding,their number increases very soon in the aquarium.

EXTERNAL STRUCTURE

Shape and size. *Hydra* is a polypoid coelenterate with a cylindrical body. It is easily visible to the naked eyes and when fully extended, it becomes elongated and slender. It measures from 2 to 20 mm in length. This variation in the length is due to its remarkable power of contraction and expansion.

Body form. *Hydra* appears tubular. It is sessile but its proximal or aboral end is drawn out into a slender stalk at the end of which is the basal disc or pedal disc for attachment to the substratum. The pedal disc region of the body is provided with gland cells which secrete adhesive substance for attachment to the substratum and also a gas bubble for floating. The free distal end or oral end of the body bears a conical elevation called hypostome. The hypostome bears an aperture at its apex called mouth which opens into the gastrovascular cavity or enteron. The hypostome is encircled by a circlet of 6–10 tentacles (L., *tentare*=to feel). The tentacles are hollow; their cavity is communicated to the gastrovascular cavity, slender, thread-like processes having nematocysts. The tentacles can be greatly extended at the time of feeding or locomotion. At the proximal end of the body it may bear lateral projections called buds in various stages of development. A well developed bud bears its own mouth, hypostome and tentacles. When the fully formed buds are detached from the parent body, they give rise to new individuals. Gonads may also be present on its body. The testes occur near the oral end which are conical projections, while ovaries are situated towards the proximal end and these are oval projections.

INTERNAL STRUCTURE

The internal structure of *Hydra* can be well explained with its longitudinal and

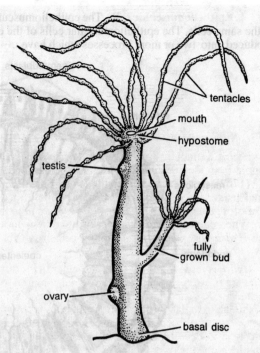

Fig. 31.1. *Hydra.*

transverse sections. However, the internal structure reveals the presence of body wall and a central cavity extended into the tentacles also called the coelenteron (Gr., *koilos*=hollow; *enteron*=gut) or gastrovascular cavity or enteron.

Histology of body wall. The body wall consists of two cellular layers, an outer epidermis derived from ectoderm and an inner gastrodermis derived from endoderm. In between the outer epidermis and inner gastrodermis a thin non-cellular layer of jelly-like substance called mesogloea is present. Both the epidermis and gastrodermis are composed of different kinds of cells, hence, they are described separately.

Epidermis. The epidermis is made up of small cubical cells and is covered with a delicate cuticle. It forms a thin layer, about one-third of the thickness of body wall. This layer contains several types of cells–epitheliomuscular, interstitial, gland, cnidoblast, sensory, nerve, and germ cells. The epidermis is protective, muscular and sensory in function.

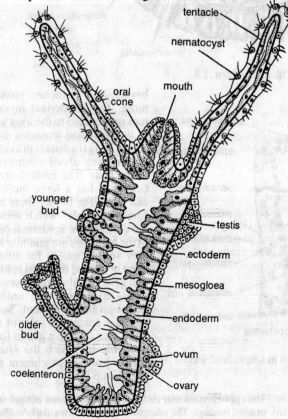

Fig. 31.2. *Hydra.* L.S.

1. Epitheliomuscular cells. The epitheliomuscular cells have both epithelial and muscular parts in the same cells. The epitheliomuscular cells of the epidermis are cylindrical with their inner ends produced into two or more processes which have myonemes or unstriped muscle fibres, these fibres

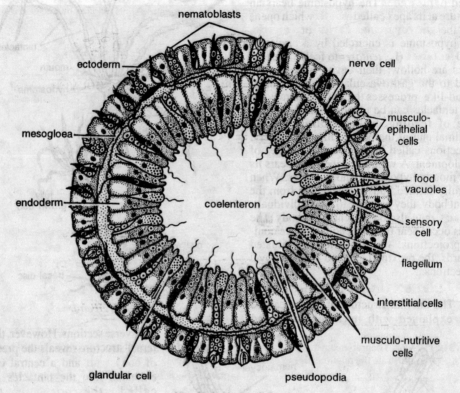

Fig. 31.3. *Hydra.* T.S.

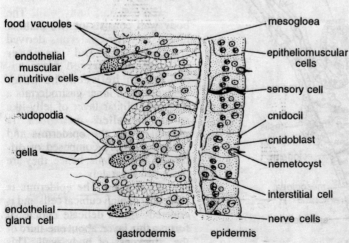

Fig. 31.4. *Hydra.* A portion of body wall in longitudinal section (magnified).

branch and branches anastomose. The ectodermal myonemes run parallel to the long axis of the body and tentacles, they form longitudinal muscles which bring about contraction of the body. The epitheliomuscular cell has a large nucleus, and along the border there is a row of granules which secrete the cuticle. The epidermal cells of the basal disc are granular and they secrete mucus for attachment of *Hydra;* the basal epidermal cells can also form pseudopodia by which the animal glides on its attachment. Some granular epidermal cells of the basal disc secrete a gas to form a bubble by which the *Hydra* breaks from its attachment and is lifted up.

Ultrastructure of epitheliomuscular cell. The epitheliomuscular cells are large possessing columnar or cuboidal shape and contain a centrally or basally situated nucleus. The nucleus is large and irregularly outlined and contains coarsely granular material and a large dense central nucleolus. In the cytoplasm is present both rough and smooth surfaced endoplasmic reticulum. Many free ribosomes and numerous typical mitochondria are present in the ground substance of the cytoplasm. One to few Golgi complex lie oriented parallel to the long axis of the cell. Golgi complex is composed of parallel lamellae, vesicles and vacuoles. Some vesicles of Golgi

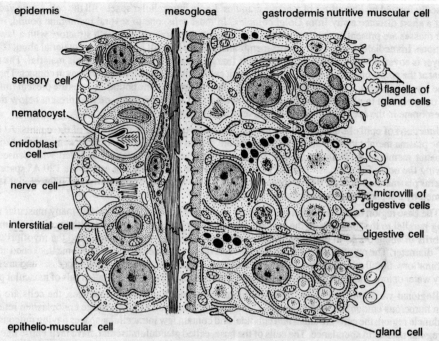

Fig. 31.5. *Hydra.* Diagrammatic representation of an electron micrograph of a section of a portion of body wall to illustrate the relationships of cell layers and cell types.

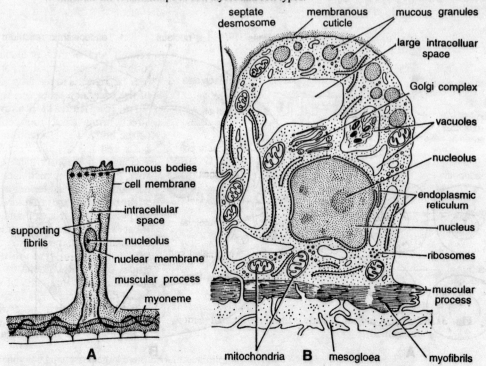

Fig. 31.6. *Hydra.* Epitheliomuscular cell. A—Under light microscope ; B—Under electron microscope.

complex are filled with dense material. In the apex regions of the cells, elaborated from Golgi apparatus, are present large numbers of membrane bound mucous granules. The mucous granules are spherical about 0.5 to 1.0 μ in diameter and contain finely granular material. The surface of the cell is covered by a membranous cuticle supposedly formed by liberations of mucous granules. Large intracellular spaces fill the cell. Large vacuoles are present a short distance away from Golgi complex. In most cells, one to several membrane bound, irregularly shaped masses are present in the apex region. The plasma membrane is a smooth structure with a few outward projections. Immediately above the plasma membrane is a thin layer of homogeneous material about 0.1μ thick; this layer is covered by a thick feltwork (0.5 μ) of fine granular, fibrillar or filamentous material. The thin layer is absent at the points of contact between two adjacent cells,only the thick feltwork comes in contact. The function of these layers appears to be primarily protective. A few small membrane bound vesicles are present immediately below or connected to plasma membrane. Microtubules, 200 A° in diameter, are also present below the plasma in a membrane in the apex of the cell showing selective uptake of materials.

Junctions of epitheliomuscular cells have a characteristic complex consisting of three parts. At the upper part, the plasma membranes are straight and a constant distant apart (120 A°). Below is an occluded zone where the plasma membranes are indistinct and the space between them narrows and filled with dense material. Following the occluded zone, are regularly spaced transverse bars extending across the 120 A° space between the lateral plasma membranes. Below these bars, also called septate desmosomes, an intercellular space may be formed by a separation of adjacent cell membranes.

The base region of the epitheliomuscular cell lies above the mesogloea and has many muscular processes running parallel to the long axis of the animal. The muscular processes are filled with two types of myofibrils. Myofibrils of about 50 A° in diameter are more numerous, within which are scattered the myofibrils of about 200 A° diameter. The myofibrils terminate obliquely on the plasma membrane and become thickened at the point of terminations. Small microtubules (200 A° in diameter) lie parallel to the muscular processes and are supposed to carry water or ions and may, therefore, be involved in changes in the electrical potentials of muscular processes.

Regional variations have been observed in epitheliomuscular cells. In tentacles, the cells are large and contain numerous cnidoblasts and more apical mucous granules and more elaborate endoplasmic reticulum. In the peduncle region, the cells are small and cuboidal and contain few intracellular spaces having mucous granules and irregular masses in abundance. The cells of the base, called glandulomuscular, have their entire interior filled with mucous granules which are elaborated by Golgi complex. The endoplasmic reticulum is well developed. The basal regions of the cells contain smaller mucous granules, while the apex has larger ones.

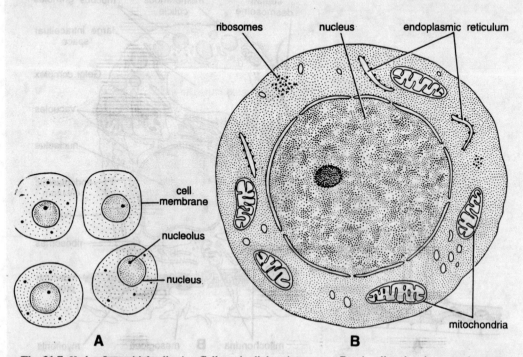

Fig. 31.7. *Hydra.* Interstitial cells. A—Cells under light microscope ; B—A cell under electron microscope.

Functions. The epitheliomuscular cells perform the following functions : 1. They form a protective covering of the body; 2.They help in contraction, shortening and bending of body; 3. They help in locomotion; 4. They help in attachment with the solid object, and 5. They help in respiration through mucous layer at the cell surface.

2.Interstitial cells. Lying in the spaces between the inner ends of cells of epidermis and between outer ends of cells of gastrodermis are interstitial cells (Fig. 31.6) lying in groups. These are small, oval or round cells with a large nucleus. Interstitial cells form a growth zone just below the tentacles, from this zone all kinds of new cells arise which push out the old worn out cells, which are shed at the proximal and distal ends. Interstitial cells form nematocysts and germ cells, they can also form epitheliomuscular cells, they renew all cells of the animal once every 45 days (Brein, 1955), thus, they are totipotent.

Ultrastructure of interstitial cell. Each interstitial cell is small, round or oval, about 5 μ in diameter. The cytoplasm is filled with free ribosomes and contains few smooth membrane bounded vesicles and mitochondria. The central nucleus contains scattered granules; the nucleolus is smaller or absent.

Functions. The interstitial cells perform the following functions : 1. These cells are the main · agent in rebuilding tissues during growth, budding and regeneration; 2. They form gonads during breeding season to give rise germ cells; 3. They reform the worn out cells of gastrodermis and also differentiate to form new nematocysts to replace to older and worn out ones.

3. Gland cells. These are tall cells found chiefly on the pedal disc and around the mouth region. They produce a secretion by which the animal can attach itself and sometimes a gas bubble by which the animals can rise and fasten on to the surface of the water to float.

4. Cnidoblasts. Cnidoblasts (Gr., *knide*=nettle; *blastos*=germ) are found throughout the epidermis but specially on the tentacles. Some interstitial cells of the epidermis give rise to highly specialized cells called cnidoblasts. These are somewhat oval-shaped cells, contain the cell organoid, the nematocyst (Gr., *nema*=thread; *kystis*= bladder) or stinging cell. The nematocyst is made up of rounded capsule which encloses a coiled tube or thread that is continuous with the capsular wall to which it is attached.

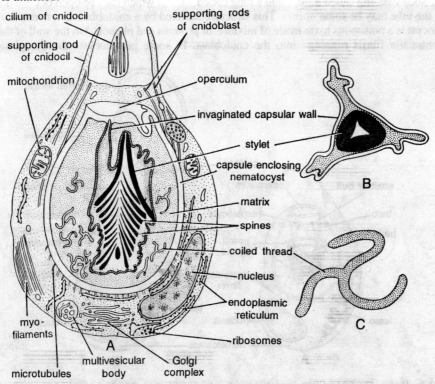

Fig. 31.8. *Hydra.* Diagrammatic representation of an electron micrograph of a cnidoblast containing a nematocyst.

Ultrastructure of cnidoblast. The cnidoblasts possess a thin cytoplasmic rim which surrounds the large centrally located nematocyst. The nucleus of cnidoblast is situated between the nematocyst and plasma membrane. The nucleus contains a small inconspicuous nucleolus. A few rough surfaced lamellae and isolated smooth surfaced vesicles of endoplasmic reticulum are present in the cytoplasm. Free ribosomes are scattered throughout cytoplasm. Golgi complex is small and lies in the basal region. Mitochondria, lipid droplets, and mulitivesicular bodies are also present in the cytoplasm. A bundle of small myofilaments is present in the basal region of the cnidoblast extending from the capsule of the nematocyst. The nemataocyt lies in the cnidoblast enclosed by a thick capsule and consists of a thread or tube containing spine and stylets. The capsule is composed of collagen-like protein. At the apex of nematocyst the capsular material narrows and invaginates towards the centre of the nematocyst. In the space left by the invagination of the capsule the nematocyst membrane is extended. The space is filled with fine granular material and is called the operculum of the nematocyst. The invaginated capsular wall encloses the stylets and spines of the nematocyst.

The apices of the three stylets lie close to each other but their bases are turned outwardly. Each stylet is a large rod overlying the spines. The spines are small and more than 50 in number. These are stacked in a pyramidal manner with the apex pointing upward. The invaginating capsule wall exhibits a trifoliate outward extension from the stylets towards the apex. At the base of stylets and spines, the invaginated wall forms the outer wall of the thread. The thread lies coiled in the basal region of the nematocyst.

All the intracapsular spaces are filled by a fine granular matrix. Situated at the apical surface of the cnidoblast and projecting above the surface is a pointed spike-like structure called cnidocil (Gr., *knide*=nettle; *cilium*=hair). The cnidocil is composed of a central core surrounded by large rods. The core contains smaller fibrils. From the capsule 20–21 hollow rods extend upward converging around the core. The core appears to be a modified cilium. At the tip of the cnidoblast, rods terminate in close proximity to the plasma membrane. Numerous dense granules are present at the periphery both intra-and extracellularly. At the terminal regions of the rods, 20–21 projections of plasma membrane extend outward to form the external portion of the cnidocil. The external flagellar material of the epidermis overlies the membranes of the external rods. Microtubules extend from the region of the cnidocil to surround the underlying nematocyst capsule.

Nematocyst . A nematocyst is not a cell because it is chitinous and non-living. A clear space arises in the cnidoblast, the space grows and the cell secretes a double-walled chitinous capsule which has a lid or operculum. One end of the capsule forms a tube lying coiled in the capsule, the tube may have a basal swelling called a butt, and a long coiled thread which may be open or closed at the tip, inside the tube may be some spines. This structure secreted by a cnidoblast is a nematocyst. In the nematocyst is a poisonous toxin made of mixture of proteins and phenols. On the wall of the capsule are contractile fibrils running into the cnidoblast. In some nematocysts the cytoplasm of the

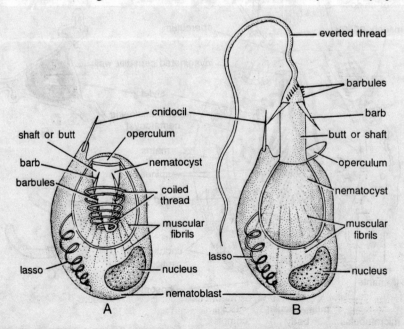

Fig. 31.9. *Hydra.* Cnidoblast with nematocyst. A—A cnidoblast at rest; B—A cnidoblast with nematocyst discharged.

cnidoblast forms contractile muscle fibrils. Some nematocysts have a lasso or restraining thread attached to the base of the cnidoblast, the lasso prevents certain nematocyst from being thrown out of the body of an animal.

Nematocysts are produced only on the stomach, cnidoblasts containing developing nematocysts migrate through the body wall or into the enteron from where they are taken up by pseudopodia of endoderm cells and transferred to mesogloea through which they travel and penetrate outwards again through the body wall to reach their ultimate positions where development is completed; the cnidoblast gets fixed in the ectoderm with its base reaching the mesogloea, the cnidocil bores through the cuticle and projects outside. *Hydra* has four kinds of nematocysts confined to the ectoderm.

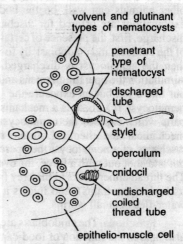

1. Penetrants or stenoteles have a large capsule, the butt is stout with their spiral rows of spines on its distal half, the lowest spine of each row is a large stylet; the thread had spirals of small spines and it is open at the tip. Stenoteles are weapons of defence and offence, their thread penetrates the body of the prey, they are also used for obtaining food.

2. Desmonemes or volvents have a small oval capsule, there is no butt, the thread is thick with no spines and it is closed at the tip, it lies in a single loop inside the capsule. On being discharged the volvents are thrown out of the body and the thread coils around the bristles of the prey; they are used for obtaining food.

3. Small glutinants or atrichous isorhizas have an elongate capsule, butt is absent, thread is open at the tip, and it has no spines, they fix the tentacles to an object when the animal walks on its tentacles.

4. Large glutinants or holotrichous isorhizas have an oval capsule, the butt is narrow and the thread is open at the tip, there are small spines on the butt and thread. Their function is doubtful but they stick to the surface of the prey.

Fig. 31.10. A portion of tentacle showing epidermal cells with batteries of nematocysts.

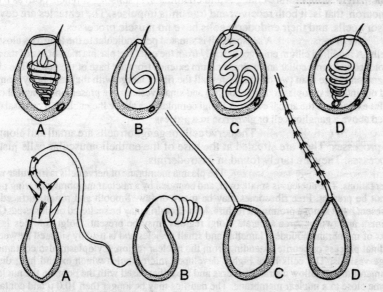

Fig. 31.11. *Hydra.* Types of nematocysts (upper figures undischarged; lower figure discharged). A—Penetrant; B—Volvent; C—Small glutinant; D—Large glutinant.

Distribution of nematocysts. Nematocysts are plentiful on the tentacles and body, but they are absent from the basal disc. All four kinds of nematocysts are found on the tentacles in abundance, hypostome has only holotrichous isorhizas, the body has mostly stenoteles and some holotrichous isorhizas.

Discharge of nematocysts. Nematocysts are discharged but once, after discharge they are cast off, though volvents are thrown out being discharged, new nematocysts are found all the time. The method of discharge of nematocysts is not clear, but they are not under the control of the nervous system, hence, they are independent effectors, they are functional even in the bodies of some other animals. An anaesthetised *Hydra* will discharge its nematocysts in the usual way when stimulated; even nematocysts removed from the body will shoot out their thread if an adequate stimulus is applied to them. Some animals swimming near a *Hydra* will cause the nematocysts to discharge, yet some other animals can walk on the body of *Hydra* without discharging the nematocysts. Following explanations are offered for discharge of nematocysts. (a) There are two factors responsible for discharge, first the presence of certain liquid-like chemicals in the water, second a mechanical contact of the cnidocil and cnidoblast by food animal or prey, if both chemical and tactile sitmuli are present then the nematocyst is discharged. (b) The thread within the capsule is gelatinous, on suitable stimulation the operculum opens and water enters the capsule, then the thread is liquefied and forced out like a jet, but on exposure the jet of liquid solidifies and becomes the external thread of the nematocyst. (c) There is a mechanism in the cnidoblast which possesses both receptor and effector parts which explode the nematocyst on stimulation of cnidoblast under the combined influence of mechanical and chemical stimuli received by the cnidocil and conducted to the cnidoblast. In discharge of a nematocyst the operculum opens, water enters the capsule, the tube is turned inside out and shot out with a force, the eversion causes the spines to come to the outer surface of the tube. The thread either sticks to the prey (glutinants), or coils around its bristles (volvents),or it penetrates its body (penetrants), and injects a powerful toxin which paralyses even such large animals as a water-flea or small worms.

Functions. The cnidoblasts are supposed to be the organ of offence and defence of *Hydra*. They also help in the function of food-capture, locomotion and anchoring with the substratum.

5. Sensory cells. They are long narrow cells with a large nucleus and one projecting flagellum or sensory hair, their base may be produced into nodulated processes which join the nervous system. Sensory cells are found in both germinal layers. but they are more abundant in the ectoderm, they are sensory to touch, light, temperature changes and chemicals. A sensory cell acts both as a receptor and as a sensory neuron, that is, it both receives and transmits impulses. The tentacles are devoid of gland cells and sensory cells, and their endoderm cells have no muscle processes.

Ultrastructure of sensory cell. A sensory cell is situated perpendicular to the long axis close to the apices of epithelial cells. A modified cilium emerges apically from the cell. The plasma membrane of the apical surface of the cell is notched to form a collar and a single cilium extends from the base of the notch. The cilium consists of nine peripheral and more than two central fibres; all the fibres merge with the basal body from which small rootlets spread out into the cytoplasm. Mitochondria and small vesicles are present in the apical cytoplasm and the microtubules extend into the apical collar. A Golgi complex lies above the nucleus. The basal end of the cell is either situated above a ganglion cell or gives rise to a process.

6. Nerve cells or ganglion cells. The nerve cells or ganglion cells are small and elongated having one or more processes. They are situated at the base of the epitheliomuscular cells just above their muscular processes. They are rarely found in gastrodermis.

Ultrastructure of nerve or ganglion cell. The plasma membrane of nerve cells is irregular with numerous crests and indentations. The nucleus is small, oval, and bounded by a nuclear membrane bearing pores. Nucleoli may or may not be present. Free ribosomes may be many or few. Smooth and rough surfaced endoplasmic reticulum is present but it is not a prominent feature. Mitochondria may be scattered or clustered. Golgi complex is most prominent and two or three separate Golgi regions may be present. Golgi complex is composed of flattened stacks of membrane bounded lamellae and small vesicles and is usually situated between the nucleus and a longitudinal process or neurite extending from the nuclear region. Cytoplasm also contains a number of small and large vesicles. The cells have highly developed microtubules which extend long distances in the neurites. The microtubules follow a straight course and are either fused with the pores in the nuclear membrane or curve to come close to a nuclear membrane. The neurites may be longer then 10.0 µ and contain ribosomes, small and large vesicles, mitochondria and microtubules. The neurite is lined by plasma membrane of the neuron.

7. Neurosecretory cells. The neurosecretory cells are named on the basis of their membrane bound dense granules. They are deeply situated and contain a cilium that extends towards the surface. The cilium arises from the base of an indentation of the plasma membrane. Finger-like projections extend into the space produced by the indentation but the projections do not reach the base of the indentation. The projections surround the cilium. Below the cilium striated rootlets extend for a

considerable distance into the cytoplasm. The neurosecretory cells are identical to nerve cells except for numerous membrane bound granules. These granules are 1000 to 1200 A° in diameter and present in the cytoplasm in close approximation to be within the dilated ends of Golgi complex lamellae. Neurites of these cells also contain dense granules which at the end of neurites are enclosed within smooth surfaced vesicles.

Nerve cells of the base region of *Hydra* differ in structure. They contain less ribosomes and lack the microtubules. Golgi complex is usually present and the granules are small (200–300 A° in diameter) lie in the lamellae and vesicles of the Golgi complex. It is presumed that these cells arise from one or the other types of neurons because interstitial cells from which neurons differentiate are absent at the base.

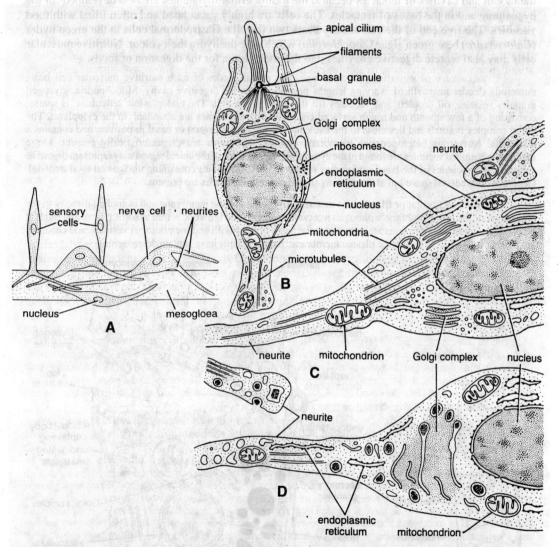

Fig. 31.12. *Hydra.* Sensory and nerve cells. A—Under light microscope ; B—Sensory cell under electron microscope ; C—Nerve or ganglion cell under electron microscopoe ; D—Neurosecretory cell under electron microscope.

8. Germ cells. Germ cells originate by the repeated divisions of the interstitial cells in certain restricted regions of the body of *Hydra* during the summer. These form the gonads which later differentiate either into testes or ovaries.

Gastrodermis. The inner gastrodermis, a layer of cells lining the coelenteron has a plan similar to the epidermis. It is made up chiefly of large columnar epithelial cells with irregular flat bases. The free ends of the cells give a jagged and uneven contour to the coelenteron in cross section. The gastrodermis forms about two-thirds of the body wall and is secretory, digestive, muscular and sensory. The cells of gastrodermis include nutritive muscular, interstitial and gland cells.

1.Nutritive muscular or digestive cells. The epitheliomuscular cells of gastrodermis are long and club-shaped, their outer ends have two processes containing a myoneme which does not branch; these myonemes lie at right angles to the long axis of the body, they form circular muscle layer by which the animal contracts and slowly expands the body. Some of them serve as sphincters to close the mouth and cavities of tentacles because the gastrodermal myonemes are best developed in the hypostome and in the bases of tentacles. The cells are highly vacuolated and often filled with food vacuoles. The free end of the cell usually bears two flagella. Gastrodermal cells in the green hydra (*Chlorohydra*) bear green algae (*Zoochlorella*) which give the hydra their colour. Nutritive muscular cells may also secrete digestive enzymes into the coelenteron for the digestion of foods.

Ultrastructure of nutritive muscular cell. The apical border of each nutritive muscular cell bears numerous slender microvili of varying lengths projecting into the digestive cavity. Mitochondria, glycogen granules,vesicles, oil droplets and vacuoles fill the apex of the cell. The endoplasmic reticulum is sparse, consisting of a few smooth and rough surfaced cisternae. Free ribosomes are abundant in the cytoplasm. The Golgi complex is small and lies close to the nucleus. The nucleus is central or basal in position and contains a nucleolus. Numerous heterogeneous membrane bounded structures are characteristically present. Large membrane bounded vacuoles are found in the cytoplasm, the vacuoles of the apical region may represent digestive vacuoles, the vacuoles of the basal region may represent residual bodies containing undigested food material. Generally, one central space but at times many small intracellular spaces are present.

A feltwork of fibrillar or filamentous material covers the plasma membrane and is applied directly to the outer layer of the unit membrane without an intervening space. The feltwork is thin at some places and thick at others. Pinocytotic invaginations are common at the bases of microvilli and membranous vesicles, and channels are present immediately below the plasma membrane. Adjacent cells have septate desmosomes.

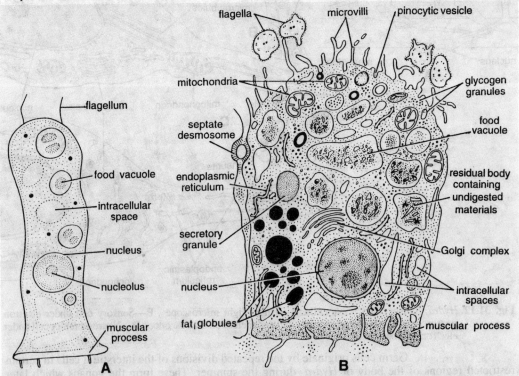

Fig. 31.13. *Hydra*. Nutritive muscle cell. A—Under light microscope ; B—Under electron microscope.

Circularly oriented muscular processes containing myofilaments lie above mesogloea. Each cell bears a pair of flagella which are typical in structure, that is, each flagellum consists of nine peripheral and two central fibres enclosed in a sheath.

Digestive cells of tentacles are pyramidal in shape and contain a large intracellular space surrounded by a thin rim of cytoplasm in which lipid droplets and food vacuoles are found. Free microvilli and pinocytotic vesicles are present. The digestive cells of hypostome are irregular in shape, between the bases of these are found numerous gland cells. The cells of peduncle are small and cuboidal containing a large intracellular space. They are like the digestive cells of the tentacles but do not possess as many lipid droplets. The digestive cells of the base are large, cuboidal and contain large intracellular spaces. They have few microvilli and pinocytotic vesicles, but small lipid droplets are numerous. Towards the base, within the coelenteron, are present many cell fragments containing various cytoplasmic inclusions. According to one view the aged cells are extruded through the basal pore, while the other view holds that by endogenous fragmentation digestive cells cast out fragments which are carried to different regions by flagellar currents.

The ultrastructure of the digestive cells of different regions suggests that the digestive cells of stomach, budding and hypostome regions perform ingestion and digestion, those of peduncle and tentacles of storage; and those of base provide energy for mucous secretion since they contain large amounts of lipid droplets.

2. Interstitial cells. There are a few of these small cells scattered among the bases of nutritive cells. They may transform into other types of cells when the need arises, *i.e.*, totipotent in nature.

3. Gland cells. Gland cells are often club-shaped, with the larger end facing the coelenteron. They are interspersed singly between the digestive cells. Most are club-shaped tapering to a narrow base which extends towards the mesogloea but do not reach it. Gland cells are of two kinds,*viz.*, (i) mucous gland cells are found in the mouth and hypostome, they secrete mucus which helps in swallowing solid food, (ii) enzymatic gland cells are found in the stomach where they secrete digestive enzymes. The gastrodermis of the stalk and tentacles is devoid of gland cells. Gland cells pour their secretions into the coelenteron for extracellular digestion. Gland cells are not under the control of the nervous system, they are independent effectors.

Ultrastructure of gland cell. In the gland cell, the nucleus is basal containing a large nucleolus in the differentiating cell but none in a mature cell, which contains full complement of the secretory granules. The mitochondria contain closely packed cristae. The endoplasmic reticulum is composed of stacks of rough-surfaced

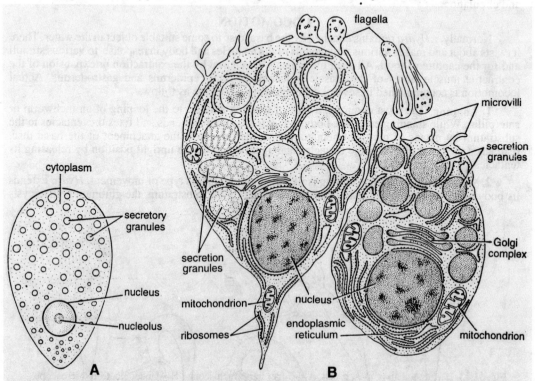

Fig. 31.14. *Hydra.* Gland cells. A—Under light microscope ; B—Under electron microscope showing different types of secretory granules.

lamellae and fill the basal region of the cell and occupy the narrow spaces between secretory granules. The plasma membrane possesses few microvilli and flagella and is covered by a feltwork of fibrillar nature. One or more Golgi complex is found near the nucleus and is surrounded by the rough-surfaced endoplasmic reticulum. The lamellae of Golgi complex are sometimes dilated and filled with material similar to secretory granules. The larger secretory granules are apparently formed by fusion of smaller Golgi vesicles and vacuoles and are more numerous in the apical part of the cell. When more than one type of granule is present within a single cell, each type is associated with a separate Golgi complex. Although several types of membrane-bounded granules can be distinguishable and histochemically divided into mucus and enzyme secreting types, yet it appears that there may be one basic type of gland cell which is capable of secreting any type of granules. Gland cells are most abundant in the hypostome, numerous in stomach and budding zone, rare in peduncle and virtually absent in tentacles and base. The cells develop from interstitial cells most frequently in growth region but very little is known about the replacement of all gland cells exhausted during secretion.

Mesogloea. The mesogloea (Gr., *meso* = middle; *glea*=glue) lies between the epidermis and gastrodermis and is attached to both layers. It is gelatinous or jelly-like and has no fibres or cellular elements. It is a continuous layer which extends over both body and tentacles, thickest in the stalk portion and thinnest on the tentacles. This arrangement allows the pedal region to withstand great mechanical strain and gives the tentacles more flexibility. The mesogloea supports and gives rigidity to the body, acting as a sort of elastic skeleton.

Ultrastructure of mesogloea. The mesogloea is an acellular layer, about 0.1 μ thick within which are embedded small filaments, about 100 A° thick. The small filaments show transverse striations and are either randomly dispersed or lie parallel or obliquely to the longitudinal axis. The filaments are not inserted on the plasma membrane. Small dense granules of glycogen are present in the mesogloea. The mesogloea is continuous with the intercellular spaces between the epitheliomuscular and digestive cells. Except the small differentiating interstitial cells near the regenerative area, no other cells or neurites of nerve cells cross the mesogloea. Processes of both epitheliomuscular and digestive cells extend for various distances into the mesogloea, sometimes interlocking with one another.

Gastrovascular cavity. The L.S. (Fig.31.2) and T.S. (Fig.31.3) of *Hydra* shows a central cavity in its body called coelenteron (=hollow gut) functionally referred to as gastrovascular cavity. Mouth opens in this cavity and there is no other exit in it. However, this cavity remains continuous in the tentacles and, therefore, the tentacles are hollow. The gastrovascular cavity is the site of digestion and circulation.

LOCOMOTION

Normally, a *Hydra* remains attached by the basal disc to some suitable object in the water. There it twists about and makes various movements of the tentacles and body in response to various stimuli and for the capture of food. All such movements are caused by the contraction or expansion of the contractile muscle fibres of the muscle processes of both epidermis and gastrodermis. Actual locomotion is accomplished in several different ways which are as follows :

1. Looping. The most common, a type of walking similar to the looping of an inchworm or caterpillar. While standing erect, the body first extends and then bends and fixes the tentacles to the substratum by means of glutinant nematocysts. It then releases the attachment of the basal disc, reattaches the basal disc near the tentacles and again assuming an upright position by releasing its tentacles.

2. Somersaulting. Somersaulting is like the looping. In this type of movement, *Hydra* extends its body and is bent to one side to place the tentacles on the substratum, the glutinant nematocysts

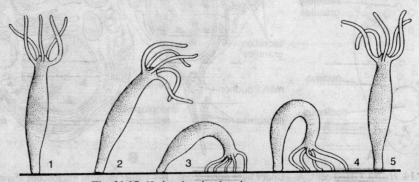

Fig. 31.15. *Hydra* showing looping movements.

help to fix the tentacles. The basal disc is freed from its attachment, and the animal stands on its tentacles, the body then contracts strongly till it appears like a small knob. The body is then extended and bent to place the basal disc on the substratum, the tentacles loosen their hold and the animal regains an upright position. These movements are repeated and the *Hydra* moves from place to place. This is the normal method of locomotion.

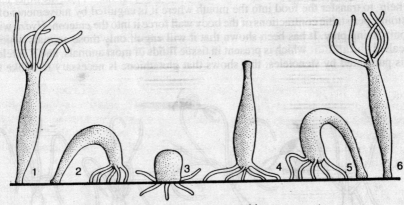

Fig. 31.16. *Hydra* showing somersaulting movements.

3. **Gliding.** *Hydra* can glide slowly along its attachment by alternate contraction and expansion of basal disc.

4. **Cuttle-fish-like movement.** The tentacles are fixed to the substratum and with the pedal disc up, *Hydra* moves over the substratum by pulling its tentacles along .

5. **Floating.** Sometimes, *Hydra* can produce a bubble of gas secreted by some ectodermal cells of the basal disc which helps the animal to float on the surface of the water and is passively carried from one place to another by water current or wind below.

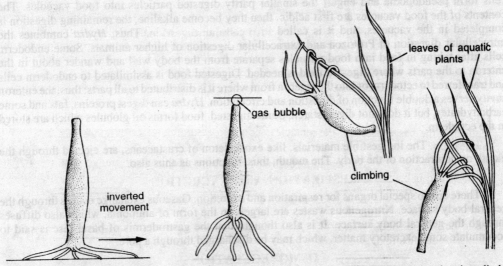

Fig. 31.17. *Hydra* showing cuttle-   **Fig. 31.18.** *Hydra* showing floating. **Fig. 31.19.** *Hydra* showing climb-
fish-like movements.   ing.

6. **Climbing.** *Hydra* can climb by attaching its tentacles to some distant objects and then releasing the basal disc and by contracting the tentacles the body is drawn up to a new position.

7. **Swimming.** By freeing itself from the substratum and with the help of wave-like movements of the tentacles, *Hydra* swims in water.

NUTRITION

Food and its ingestion. The food consists of small crustaceans like *Cyclops*, small annelids and insect larvae, thus, it is carnivorous. On touching a tentacle by the prey the stenoteles penetrate it and inject a poisonous toxin to paralyse it, the volvents coil around the bristles to hold the food. The tentacle holding the captured animal contracts and bends over the mouth, the other tentacles also bend and help to transfer the food into the mouth where it is engulfed by movements of the mouth and hypostome; peristaltic contractions of the body wall force it into the enteron. *Hydra* will normally swallow only living prey. It has been shown that it will engulf only those animals which contain a chemical called glutathione which is present in tissue fluids of most animals, and it is released when the body is punctured by stenoteles; this shows that glutathione is necessary to evoke the feeding reaction.

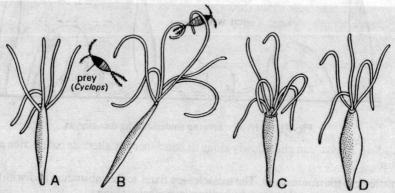

Fig. 31.20. *Hydra.* Capturing and ingesting the prey.

Digestion. The mucous gland cells of the hypostome cover the engulfed food with mucus, then enzymatic gland cells produce a proteolytic enzyme like trypsin which partly digests the proteins into polypeptides in an alkaline medium in the enteron, this digestion is extracellular. Some endoderm cells form pseudopodia and engulf the smaller partly digested particles into food vacuoles. The contents of the food vacuoles are first acidic, then they become alkaline, the remaining digestion is completed in the vacuoles, and it is called intracellular digestion. Thus, *Hydra* combines the intracellular digestion of Protozoa and extracellular digestion of higher animals. Some endoderm cells after taking in food into food vacuoles separate from the body wall and wander about in the enteron to the parts where digested food is needed. Digested food is assimilated to endoderm cells and transferred to ectoderm or into the enteron from where it is distributed to all parts; thus, the enteron cavity serves a double function of digestion and circulation. *Hydra* can digest proteins, fats and some carbohydrates, but it does not digest starch. Some digested food forms oil globules which are stored in the ectoderm.

Egestion. The indigestible materials, like exoskeleton of crustaceans, are ejected through the mouth on contraction of the body. The mouth, thus, functions as anus also.

RESPIRATION AND EXCRETION

There are no special organs for respiration and excretion. Gaseous exchange occurs through the general body surface. Nitrogenous wastes are largely in the form of ammonia, which also diffuses through the general body surface. It is also thought that the gastrodermis of basal disc is said to accumulate some excretory matter, which may be discharged through a pore.

OSMOREGULATION

The water that continuously enters into the body cells by endosmosis is finally collected into the gastrovascular cavity and from here expelled out through mouth due to a wave of muscle contraction passing from the basal disc region to the hypostomal region.

NERVOUS SYSTEM

There are many nerve cells, each with two to four branching nerve fibres, the nerve fibres are primitive because they do not form axons or dendrites, moreover the nerve fibres form actual contacts with fibres of other nerve cells, recent studies have shown that there are no synapses, thus, they form a continuous nerve net . In *Hydra* there are two nerve nets, one in connection with the ectoderm which is more highly developed, and the other near the endoderm, the two nerve nets lie in and on either side of the mesogloea. But the ectodermal nerve net is more strongly developed and is particularly concentrated around the mouth and basal disc regions. The two nerve nets are joined to each other and to the sensory cells of both ectoderm and endoderm, they are also joined to the epitheliomuscular cell. The fibres of both nerve nets are continuous and there are no synapses. Sensory cells are receptors for touch, light and chemicals, and stimuli pass from them through the nerve nets to muscle processes which act as effectors. This is a diffused nervous system which works as a receptor —> conductor—> effector system. The nerve cells form conducting chains between receptors and effectors. The messages radiate in all directions from the point of stimulation but there is no co-ordination because the messages do not evoke responses equally in all the effectors.

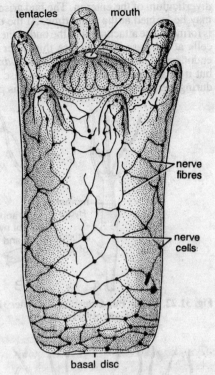

Fig.31.21. *Hydra.* Nerve net.

BEHAVIOUR

The movements of *Hydra* connected with feeding are automatic, they are governed by the external environment. It responds to contact, if a tentacle is touched then the other tentacles and even the body may contract; this shows that there is a transmission of the stimulus, the stimulation is conducted in all directions by the nerve nets. The response is greatest near the point of stimulation and it gets progressively less in more distant regions because each nerve net offers some resistance to the passage of impulses, this resistance occurs at the numerous nerve cells. Hydras are found more towards the top of a pond than at great depth, thus, they can obtain more oxygen. If *Hydra* is attached near the bottom, then the body is held upright, but at average depth it is horizontal with the hypostome lower than the foot. It also hangs with the head down by its foot from the surface of water with the aid of a gas bubble. It can alter the shape of the body becoming long and slender or small and contracted like a barrel.

Behaviour of *Hydra* depends on its physiological state, the response of a well-fed *Hydra* to stimuli is slow and sluggish, but a hungry *Hydra* will respond vigorously to the same stimuli. However, *Hydra* responds to various stimuli in the following way :

Light . *Hydra* shows positive response to mild light but avoids or shows negative response to both strong light or very less light. Actually, it becomes restless and moves in a number of directions in darkness.

Temperature. *Hydra* prefers mild temperature which suits best for its life activities, say from 20 to 25° C. Any increase or decrease from these levels in temperature is avoided by *Hydra*.

Electricity. *Hydra* reacts to weak constant electric currents by bending towards the anode and then contracting the entire body. If attached by the basal disc, the oral end bends towards the anode but if fixed by tentacles, the basal disc bends towards the anode side.

Chemicals. *Hydra* always shows negative response to injurious chemicals but exhibits positive response to food.

REPRODUCTION

Hydra reproduces asexually as well as sexually.

Asexual Reproduction

Hydra reproduces asexually by budding. In fact this is the usual means of reproduction during the warmer months of the year.

Asexual budding. A bud develops as a simple evagination of the bodywall. The ectoderm cells increase in number at one point to form a protuberance below which the endoderm cells acquire reserve food, then both ectoderm and endoderm are pushed out to form a bud which contains a diverticulum of the enteron. The bud arises at the junction of the stalk and stomach, and several buds may be formed at the same time. At the distal end the bud grows tentacles one by one and a mouth is formed. The attachment of the bud to the mother *Hydra* constricts to separate the bud, but endoderm cells at the base unite before this, after constriction ectoderm grows over the foot to cover the endoderm. The bud grows into a new *Hydra* which migrates towards the surface of water for dispersal, but it finally gets fixed by its basal disc so that it becomes a solitary individual. Budding occurs during the warmer months when food is plentiful.

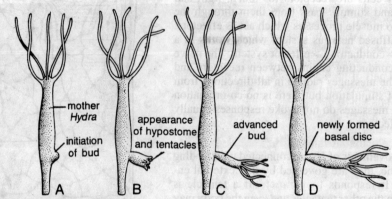

Fig. 31.22. *Hydra.* Bud formation. A—After 3 hours; B—After 24 hours; C—After 48 hours; D—After 72 hours; (After **Ganguly**, *et al.*).

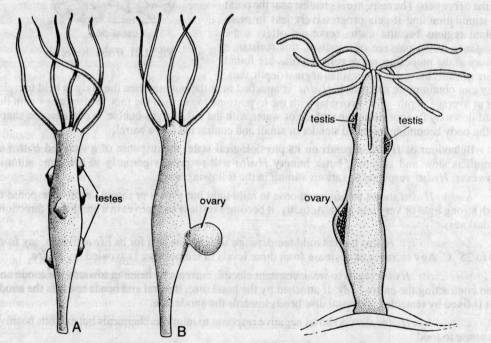

Fig. 31.23. *Hydra.* A—Male ; B—Female. **Fig. 31.24.** *Hydra viridissima.* A monoecious form showing male and female reproductive organs.

Sexual Reproduction

In *Hydra,* it starts with the development of temporary structures called gonads during autumn months. Actually, sexual reproduction occurs during the unfavourable conditions like excessive high and low temperatures of the water in which *Hydra* lives or also due to an increase in the amount of free carbon dioxide in the surrounding water.

Generally, the gonads develop due to the repeated proliferation of the interstitial cells of the epidermis which form bulgings on the body wall. The bulgings of gonads differ from the bulgings of buds as the mesogloea and gastrodermis do not enter into the gonads. Mostly, the species of *Hydra* are dioecious, *i.e.*, sexes separate; the individuals bear either male or female gonad, *e.g.*, *H.oligactis*. But some species are monoecious or hermaphrodite also, *i.e.*, both male and female gonads are found on the body of same individual, *e.g.*, *H. viridissima*. Usually, the testes develop towards the distal part of the body, while ovaries develop towards the proximal part of the body. In *H. oligactis*, where sexes are separate, male and female can be marked easily. The males are smaller and bear 1–8 conical testes having a teat-like structure over them. The females are comparatively longer and bear 1–2 oval ovaries.

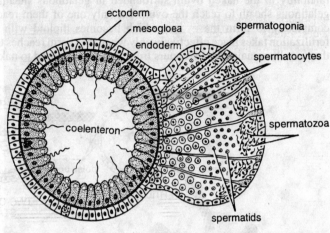

Fig. 31.25. *Hydra*. T.S. through testis showing stages of spermatogenesis.

Testes and spermatogenesis. The interstitial cells of epidermis multiply rapidly to increase in number and finally push out the other cells of epidermis to form swellings on the outer body surface of *Hydra*. Thus, the structure formed is called testis. The testes are rounded spherical structures in dioecious forms, while they are blunt conical structures in monoecious forms. Now, the interstitial cells start behaving like sperm mother cell or spermatogonia. These divide to form secondary spermatogonia which develop into spermatocytes. The spermatocytes undergo two maturation divisions, one being reduction division to form spermatids. The spermatids then differentiate to form spermatozoa. Each spermatozoa being haploid carries 15 chromosomes in *H. oligactis* and possesses a cylindrical head containing nucleus, a middle piece and a vibrating long tail. Due to the pressure of spermatozoa in testis, its wall ruptures to release spermatozoa in the surrounding water.

Ovary and oogenesis. The ovary also develops in the same way as testis from the interstitial cells of the epidermis. The interstitial cells behave like oogonia. Now, one of the oogonia, usually that which is centrally located, becomes larger and amoeboid called oocyte. The other oogonia are used up as nourishment and for forming yolk. The oocyte undergoes two maturation divisions, one of them being reduction division to form a large yolk-laden ovum and two polar bodies. The ovum being haploid contains 15 chromosomes in *H. oligactis*. The ovum is a large yolk-laden mass occupying most of the space inside the ovary. The ovum remains surrounded by epidermal cells in the beginning but when it matures the epidermal cells break up and withdraw. Thus, the ova becomes naked on all sides except where it is attached to the body of *Hydra* by an epidermal cup. Each ovary produces a succession of ova but usually one at each time,

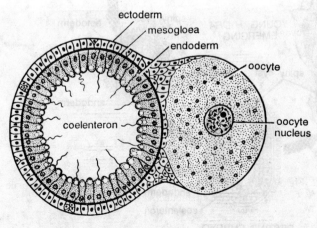

Fig. 31.26. *Hydra*. T.S. through ovary showing mature ovum.

sometimes there are found two in *H.viridissima* or more in *H. dioecia*. The ovum remains attached with the parent body and secretes a protective gelatinous sheath around it.

Fertilization. Cross-fertilization occurs as a rule in the different species of *Hydra*. To avoid self-fertilization, even in monoecious species, the testes mature first, *i.e.*, protandrous condition exists. However, fertilization takes place when mature spermatozoa released from testes approach randomly to the naked ovum surrounded in gelatinous sheath. Many sperms may penetrate the gelatinous sheath to reach the ovum but only one of them reaches to the ovum and fuses with it completely to form the zygote which becomes diploid with 30 chromosomes. The process of fertilization takes place effectively only when the sperm reaches the ovum within its viable condition; that usually remains for two hours from its being exposed to naked otherwise it perishes.

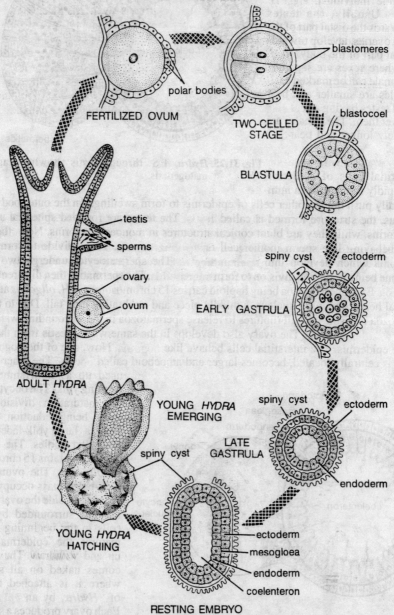

Fig. 31.27. *Hydra.* Stages in the development and hatching.

Development

The development of zygote starts soon after fertilization when it still remains attached to the parent body. The zygote undergoes total equal cleavage, *i.e.*, holoblastic to form a hollow ball of cells. The cells are called blastomeres which soon get arranged to form a single layered embryo with a central cavity called blastocoel. The embryo is now known as blastula. The cells of blastula divide rapidly and some of them delaminate into the blastocoel to completely obliterate it. Now the embryo is called gastrula which has an outer layer of cells, forming ectoderm and an inner core of cells, forming endoderm. The solid gastrula is neither ciliated nor free swimming because it is still attached to the parent body. This type of gastrula is characteristically called stereogastrula which represents the planula stage of *Hydra*. The outer ectodermal layer of the embryo soon secretes some secretion which hardens to form a protective covering round it called theca. The theca is two-layered being formed of an inner thin membrane and outer thick and chitinous layer. The theca may be smooth as in *H. oligactis* or spiny, it may be oval or round. At this stage, the embryo gets detached from the parent body, settles at the bottom and remains dormant till the advent of favourable environmental conditions. After the approach of favourable conditions the embryo again becomes active and development starts. The endodermal cells get arranged into a layer beneath the ectodermal layer and, thus, a new cavity called coelenteron or gastrovascular cavity appears. A layer of mesogloea develops between ectoderm and endoderm. These two germ layers, *i.e.*, ectoderm and endoderm give rise to their different derivatives, a circlet of tentacles develop, hypostome and mouth is formed. Thus, a young *Hydra* is formed.

Hatching. With the above developments the embryo increases in size and the theca ruptures to release young *Hydra* resembling a   It soon elongates and gets fixed by its aboral end and grows into an adult.

REGENERATION

Regeneration may be defined as the ability of certain animals to restore the lost or worn out parts of their bodies. *Hydra* has the considerable power of regeneration. Trembley (1744 or 1745) first of all demonstrated that an individual *Hydra* can be cut into several pieces, and each will regenerate the lost parts, developing a whole new individual. The parts usually retain their original polarity, with oral ends developing tentacles and aboral ends, basal discs.

Parts of two different individuals, often of different species, may be brought together and grafted together in various arrangements. The germ layers, however, will not mix. The epidermis will only fuse with epidermis and gastrodermis with gastrodermis.

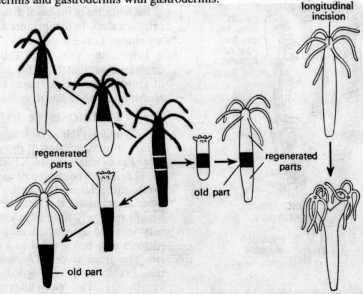

Fig. 31.2 . *Hydra*. Diagrams to show the process of regeneration.

Trembley (1744 or 1745) also demonstrated that if the head end of *Hydra* is split into two and the parts are slightly separated it results into a Y-shaped *Hydra* or two-headed individual having two mouths and two sets of tentacles. Each head may be again split in a similar manner. In this way Trembley succeeded in producing a seven headed *Hydra*.

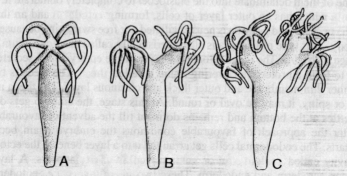

Fig. 31.29. *Hydra* showing the formation of multiheaded specimen by regernaation. A—Single head *Hydra* ; B—Two-headed *Hydra;* C—Four headed *Hydra*.

Occasionally, even in nature, a *Hydra* becomes turned inside out. In the laboratory this can be accomplished mechanically or by overdoses of glutathione. Trembley (1744) thought that under these conditions the epidermis becomes gastrodermis and gastrodermis becomes epidermis. More modern studies, however, demonstrate conclusively that this does not occur. Rather, the *Hydra* usually turns itself right side again, but if it does not, the layers switch location by migration of cells through the mesogloea.

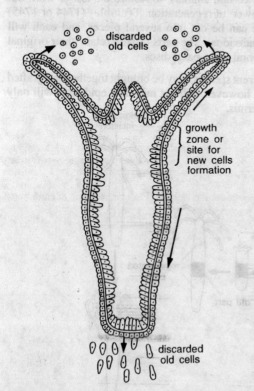

Fig. 31.30. *Hydra*. Diagram to show cell replacement.

IMMORTALITY OF *HYDRA*

Brien (1955) and others have found that a *Hydra* is at least potentially immortal. There is a growth zone just below the base of tentacles in which interstitial cells give rise to new body cells of all types. As these new cells are formed, other cells are pushed toward the end of the tentacles or the basal disc where the old cells are shed. In this manner all of the cells are renewed once in about 45 days. So far as is known, this process of cell replacement continues indefinitely. If the interstitial cells of growth zone are destroyed by X-rays, the *Hydra* lives only a few days.

SYMBIOSIS IN *HYDRA*

Symbiosis (Gr., *sym* = together+ *bios* = living) is an association of two different species of individuals in which both the partners are benefited. The degree of association in a symbiotic relationship varies from rather loose associations in which the two partners benefit relatively little from each other, to a very intimate association in which the two partners may be regarded as a single organism. The green Hydra, *Chlorohydra viridissima* exhibits a very good example of symbiosis. The gastrodermal cells of *C.viridissima* are harboured by a large number of unicellular green alga *Chlorella* referred as *Zoochlorella* in this case (or *Zooxanthella).* The algae are passed from one generation of *Hydra* to the next through the eggs. It seems impossible to deprive a *Chlorohydra* of its *Zoochlorella* and, thus, it is evident that they are mutually benefited; the alga gets shelter and protection and also at the same time obtains carbon dioxide from hydra's respiration and nitrogenous compounds from its excretory wastes, in return the *Hydra* obtains oxygen and carbohydrates from alga due to its photosynthetic activity. In this association, one individual in which other harbours are called host and symbiont respectively.

PHYSIOLOGICAL DIVISION OF LABOUR

H.M. Edward, a French scientist advocated that even the primitive multicellular animals exhibit physiological division of labour like those of higher Metazoa and human society. We know that in human society different set of people like washerman, cobbler, blacksmith, carpenter, potter, farmer, teacher, doctor, engineer, etc., perform different functions for the society; they are specialized to do their jobs efficiently. Likewise, for proper functioning of a multicellular body the different life activities are performed by different cells present in its body. Certain cells become specialized for one function, others for different function unlike to that of a unicellular body in which all life activities are performed by the single cell. In lower Metazoa similar cells performing similar functions form tissue, while in higher Metazoa similar tissues together constitute an organ and similar organs performing similar functions form systems. All these are specialized to do their jobs efficiently. This is called physiological division of labour where different cell types are specialized structurally and physiologically to perform different functions.

This phenomenon is well illustrated by coelenterates. *Hydra,* however, exhibits it but still at a primitive level. We have noted that the ectoderm of *Hydra* is protective, muscular and sensory,its nematocysts are used for defence and for obtaining food. The ectoderm of basal disc is glandular which helps in fixing the *Hydra* with the substratum; its central part can produce gas bubble which helps in floating. The endoderm is digestive, vascular, muscular and also secretory. The interstitial cells form gonads and replace both ectodermal and endodermal cells. The enteron carries on digestion and circulation. The mouth serves for ingestion of food and egestion of wastes. The tentacles are used for obtaining food and for locomotion. All this division of labour is possible because *Hydra* is beginning to show a differentiation of its parts. Thus, it can be said that the physiological division of labour is correlated with a morphological differentiation of structure.

REVISION QUESTIONS

1. Give an account of the histological structure of the body wall of *Hydra*.
2. Give an account of locomotion and nutrition of *Hydra* .
3. Describe the structure of cnidoblast of *Hydra* and write a detailed account of nematocyst.
4. Give an account of reproduction in *Hydra*.
5. What do you mean by physiological division of labour? Explain it with reference to *Hydra* .
6. Write short notes on :
   (i) Collection and culture of *Hydra* ; (ii) Interstitial cells; (iii) Discharge of nematocyst; (iv) Gastrovascular cavity ; (v) Behaviour of *Hydra* ; (vi) Regeneration in *Hydra;* (vii) Immortality of *Hydra* ; (viii) Mesogloea.
7. Draw labelled diagrams only :
   (i) T.S. of *Hydra*; (ii) Electron structure of epitheliomuscular cell; (iii) Electron structure of cnidoblast; (iv) L.S. of *Hydra*.

32
Obelia

Contrary to *Hydra*, which is a solitary hydrozoan, most of the hydrozoans are colonial forms. *Obelia*, commonly referred to as the 'sea-fur', is a colonial form. The individuals of the colony are called zooids. The colonial hydrozoans, like *Obelia*, exhibit complexity in their life-histories due to the presence of alternation of generations between their asexual and sexual generations, and they also exhibit the phenomenon of polymorphism (Gr., *poly*=many; *morphe* = form), *i.e.,* occurrence of more than one type of individuals or zooids in their colonies performing different functions. *Obelia*, however, represents a typical example of colonial hydrozoans. Various species of *Obelia* are reported to have wide distribution throughout the world but the most common and greatly studied species is *Obelia geniculata*.

OBELIA (THE SEA-FUR)
SYSTEMATIC POSITION

Phylum	....	**Coelenterata**
Class	....	**Hydrozoa**
Order	....	**Hydroida**
Suborder	....	**Leptomedusae**
Genus	....	*Obelia*

HABIT AND HABITAT

Obelia is sedentary, marine colonial form found attached on the surface of sea weeds,molluscan shells, rocks and wooden piles in shallow water up to 80 metres in depth. *Obelia* is cosmopolitan in distribution, forming a whitish or light-brown plant-like fur in the sea, hence, the common name sea-fur is assigned to it.

OBELIA COLONY – A GROSS STRUCTURE

Each colony of *Obelia* consists of a horizontal thread-like root called hydrorhiza which is attached to a weed or any substratum. From hydrorhiza arises a vertical branching stem about 2.5 cm long which is known as a hydrocaulus. The hydrorhiza and hydrocaulus are hollow tubes. The hydrocaulus bears zooids or polyps on either side in a cymose formation. At the growing ends of the main branches are immature club-shaped polyps. Each polyp has a stem and a terminal head called a hydranth. The hydranths are feeding polyps, they feed by capturing minute animals and larvae. Towards the base of the hydrocaulus in the axils of the polyps are reproductive polyps called blastostyles. The polyps, their tubular connections and blastostyles are made of ectoderm, mesogloea and endoderm, these layers are together called coenosarc and its cavity is an enteron which is continuous and common to all the members, through the enteron digested food is distributed in solution. The entire colony is covered by a tough, yellow chitin secreted by the ectoderm, this covering is known as perisarc. The perisarc constitutes the exoskeleton and it covers the hydrorhiza, hydrocauli and their branches, and at the base of each polyp it forms a clear, wine glass-shaped hydrotheca. The hydrotheca has a shelf across the base which supports the hydranth, and the hydranth can contract and withdraw into the hydrotheca. The perisarc around a blastostyle is a gonotheca, the blastostyle and gonotheca are together called a gonangium. The perisarc is an exoskeleton, at first it is continuous with the coenosarc but on growing thick, it separates and is joined to the coenosarc only at intervals by minute projections, at these places it gets ringed which allows bending.

The *Obelia* is a trimorphic colony, that is, having three kinds of zooids which are as follows :

1. Polyps or hydranths (nutritive zooids);
2. Gonangia or blastostyles (budding zooids);
3. Medusae. (sexual zooids).

In fact, to start with *Obelia* is a monomorphic form having polyp only but later due to the development of blastostyle it becomes a dimorphic colony and finally medusae bud over the blastostyle in a mature colony, then it becomes a trimorphic colony.

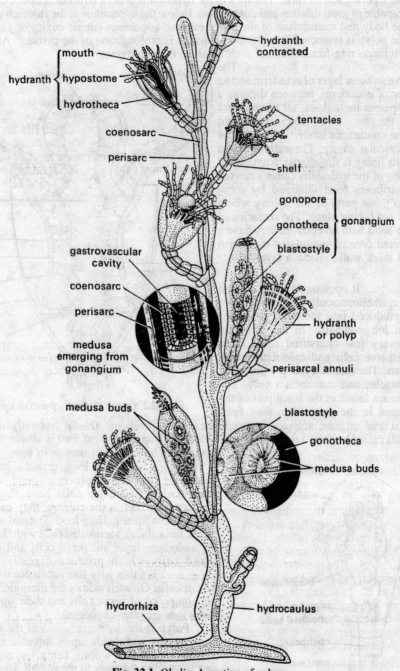

hydranth { mouth
hydranth { hypostome
hydranth { hydrotheca

hydranth contracted

coenosarc

perisarc

tentacles

shelf

gonopore

gonotheca } gonangium

blastostyle

gastrovascular cavity

coenosarc

perisarc

medusa emerging from gonangium

medusa buds

hydranth or polyp

perisarcal annuli

blastostyle

gonotheca

medusa buds

hydrorhiza

hydrocaulus

Fig. 32.1. *Obelia.* A portion of colony.

POLYP OR HYDRANTH

The colony of *Obelia* has many polyps (Gr., *polypus* =many-footed) or hydranths (Gr.,*hydra* =water serpent; *anthos* =flower) or gastrozooids. Each polyp is very much like a miniature *Hydra*. It has a cylindrical body attached to the axis of the hydrocaulus by its proximal end and free at its distal end. It is covered by a cup-shaped hydrotheca. The free distal end is produced into a conical elevation, the hypostome or manubrium which is about one-third of the length of the hydranth. The hypostome is surrounded by a circle of numerous (about 24)tentacles. The tentacles are longer than hypostome, tapering and filiform. The apex of the hypostome bears a terminal aperture called mouth which is capable of great dilation and contraction. Below the hypostome is the stomach region of the polyp. The body and manubrium of the polyp enclose a spacious enteric cavity or gastrovascular cavity. The polyp is protected in hydrotheca, which is prolongation of the perisarc. At the base of the polyp it forms ring-like horizontal shelf at which the polyp rests.

Histology of polyp or hydranth. The polyps have an outer layer of ectoderm and an inner layer of endoderm, between them is a thin, transparent mesogloea; all these layers constitute the coenosarc which is soft and tubular, the continuous cavity is the enteron or gastrovascular cavity. The enteron has a fluid and its lining is flagellated. Rhythmical contractions of the hydranths cause a current which distributes food obtained by some polyps to those parts of the colony where feeding is not taking place. The tentacles of polyps are solid with no enteron, they have a single-layered core of vacuolated endoderm cells with thick walls inside a layer of ectoderm.

Ectoderm. It consists of long, conical columnar epitheliomuscular cells, their inner ends are produced into muscular processes which run longitudinally. In the ectoderm layer are very few interstitial cells, some branching nerve cells and cnidoblasts with nematocysts. The nematocysts are abundant on the tentacles and manubrium only. The cnidoblasts are found in the basal part of the hydranth and in the coenosarc, they form

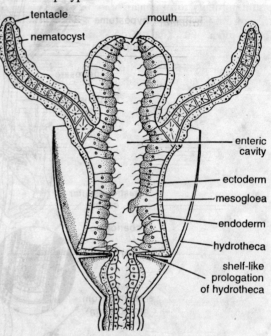

Fig. 32.2. *Obelia.* V.S. of a polyp or hydranth.

nematocyst and migrate actively to reach their final positions. *Obelia* has only one kind of nematocysts called basitrichous isorhizas in which the capsule is oval, butt is absent, the thread is open at the tip and has spines on its base.

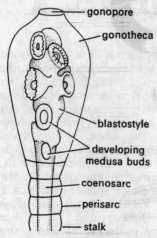

Fig. 32.3. *Obelia.* A gonangium.

Endoderm. It has long, granular epitheliomuscular cells, their muscle processes point outwards and are circular. Endoderm cells have flagella which produce a current in the enteron, they can also form pseudopodia for engulfing food. The endoderm of tentacles has cubical, vacuolated cells with thick walls. In the endoderm layer are nerve cells and club-shaped gland cells which produce digestive enzymes. Mesogloea is a thin jelly-like substance with no structure or cells. On each side of the mesogloea is a nerve net composed of nerve cells and their fibres, the two nerve nets are inter-connected.

Polyp is the nutritive zooid of the colony. It is carnivorous and feeds upon aquatic crustaceans, nematodes and other worms. Tentacles help in catching and conveying the prey to the mouth, Digestive juice is secreted in the gland cells of gastrodermis and the process of digestion in extracellular as well as intracellular.

GONANGIUM

The gonangium (Gr., *gonos*=seed; *angeion*=vessel) (Fig. 32.3) is club-shaped, cylindrical form. It is covered by a transparent gonotheca and contains an axis or blastostyle on which lateral buds form that develop into medusae or gonophores. The blastostyle has no mouth and no tentacles, but ends distally into a flattened disc. The gonotheca opens at its distal end by a gonopore, through which the medusae escape. Gonotheca, blastostyle and the gonophores together form a gonangium.

Asexual reproduction. When the temperature of the water exceeds 20°C, the buds which would normally form gonangia in the colony break free from the colony and settle down; a stolon arises from the lower end of the bud which produces a new colony of *Obelia* asexually. This is a special mode of asexual reproduction.

MEDUSA

The medusa is a modified zooid produced as a hollow bud from the coenosarc of the blastostyle in spring and summer. Medusa swims freely on the surface water.

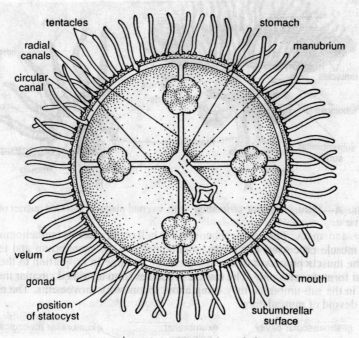

Fig. 32.4. *Obelia.* Medusa in oral view.

Structure of medusa. It is saucer-shaped, it is attached by the middle of the convex surface to the blastostyle, when fully formed it breaks free and emerges from the mouth of the gonotheca. The medusa is circular and tiny umbrella-like in shape. The convex outer surface is known as the ex-umbrella and the concave inner surface is the sub-umbrella. From the centre of the sub-umbrella arises a short projecting manubrium (L., *manus*=handle), at its apex is a square mouth surrounded by four oral lobes. The mouth leads into an enteric cavity or gastric cavity in the manubrium. From the enteric cavity arise four radial canals which are delicate ciliated tubes, they run to the margin of the bell to join a ciliated circular canal running near the margin. The enteric cavity and the canals represent the enteron which distributes food. Projecting from the middle of the radial canals are four gonads, since sexes are separate they are either four testes or four ovaries, they are patches of modified sub-umbrellar ectoderm. The gonads mature after the medusae escape from the gonotheca. The edge of the bell is produced inwards as a thin fold called velum. Velum is characteristic of hydrozoan medusae but it is insignificant in *Obelia*. The medusae with a velum are called craspedote, and those with no velum are acraspedote (Scyphozoa). From the edge of the bell numerous small solid tentacles hang downwards. The tentacles have swollen bases due to the accumulation of interstitial cells which are practically absent from other regions. The basal swellings of tentacles are called vesicles or bulbs, nematocysts are formed continuously in the bulbs from where they migrate to the tentacles. Digestive enzymes are secreted from the endoderm of bulbs. Near the bulbs the ectoderm has pigment granules and nerve cells, they are often called ocelli and it is claimed that the ocelli are sensory to light, but more probably there are no ocelli, the pigment granules are accumulated excretory matter. Above the bulb of every tentacle is a tiny fluid-filled vesicle. Nematocysts are confined to the manubrium and tentacles, there may be some on the bell margin. There are eight marginal sense organs called statocysts or lithocysts lying at regular intervals, being attached on the sub-umbrella side to the bulbs of eight tentacles, they are developed in response to a locomotory habit. A statocyst is a tiny, circular closed vesicle lined with ectoderm and filled with a fluid containing calcareous granules called otoliths which lie in a special cell called lithocyte. The lining has some sensory cells with thin sensory processes on which the otoliths produce a stimulus which is transmitted by nerves to muscles; the muscles coordinate the snake-like swimming movements of the medusa, and should the medusa become tilted, the muscles contract to right the position of medusa bell, thus, statocysts are balancing organs.

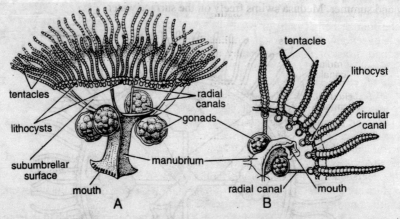

Fig. 32.5. *Obelia*. A—Mature medusa swimming with everted medusa; B—One quarter of the same in oral view.

   Histology of medusa. The ectoderm covers the bell on all sides, its epitheliomuscular cells are produced into muscle processes which run longitudinally in the manubrium and tentacles. In the sub-umbrella the muscle processes of the ectoderm are so large in proportion to the epithelial part that they almost form muscles only. The muscle processes form a striated circular muscle and some radial muscles in the sub-umbrella, they bring about locomotory movements. The ectoderm of the ex-umbrella is devoid of musculature.

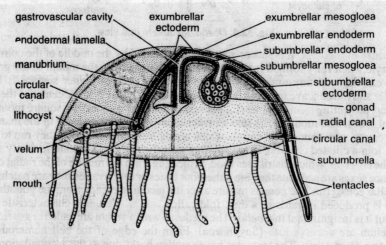

Fig. 32.6. *Obelia*. Diagrammatic structure of medusa with more than one-quarter of the umbrella and manubrium cut away.

The endoderm lines the enteric cavity and the radial and circular canals. The endoderm cells have no muscle processes, they are ciliated epithelial cells, they are digestive. Between the two ectoderm layers of the bell is a thin sheet of endoderm lamella except where the enteron lies. The endoderm lamella is formed by the fusion of upper and lower layers of endoderm, the fusion having occurred at all places except in the region of the enteron. Between the ectoderm and endoderm is thick mesogloea forming the bulk of the bell of the medusa, manubrium and tentacles. The velum has a double layer of ectoderm and the thick mesogloea in the middle, it has no endoderm.

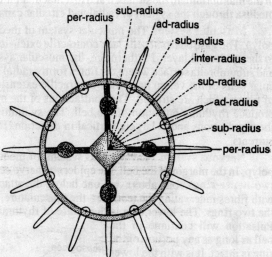

Fig. 32.7. *Obelia*. Medusa showing radial symmetry and various orders of radii.

Radial symmetry of medusa. Like polyp, the medusa is radially symmetrical. The presence of the four radial canals distinguishes the four principal radii or per-radii. Halfway between any two per-radii a radius of the second order or inter-radius may be taken. Halfway between any per-radius and inter-radius on either side a radius of third order, or ad-radious, and halfway between any ad-radius and the adjacent per- or inter-radius, a radius of fourth order or sub-radius. Thus, there are four per-radii, four inter-radii, eight ad-radii and sixteen sub-radii. In *Obelia* the radial canals, the angles of the mouth and four of the tentacles are the per-radial, four more tentacles are inter-radial, and the remaining eight tentacles, bearing the lithocysts are ad-radial. Sub-radii are of no importance in this particular form.

Development of medusa. The blastostyle produces medusae by budding in large numbers. The cavity of the blastostyle pushes the coenosarc out to form a small protuberance or bud. The bud grows larger and its coenosarc becomes like a vesicle which is attached to the blastostyle by a narrow stalk. The cavity of the vesicle is continuous with the enteron of blastostyle. The distal ectoderm of the vesicle separates into two layers, then the inner layer of ectoderm splits to acquire a cavity called a bell rudiment. There are now two layers of ectoderm outside the bell rudiment and one layer on the inner side. The cavity of the bell rudiment assumes the shape of the sub-umbrella, and a manubrium is formed in the centre. The two layers of ectoderm which enclose the bell rudiment from outside now break leaving a marginal and circular shelf called velum. In most hydrozoan medusae the velum grows and becomes prominent, but in *Obelia* it decreases and becomes insignificant. The manubrium acquires a mouth, marginal tentacles are formed, the stalk breaks and its aperture closes up, thus, a medusa is formed which is set free, it escapes from the gonotheca, later its gonads mature.

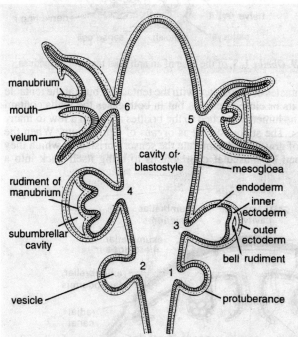

Fig. 32.8. *Obelia*. Stages of the development of medusa from a blastostyle.

Nutrition . Medusae are carnivorous and the processes of their nutrition are essentially the same as in the polyp. The food consists of living animals or bodies of animals. Digestion is both extracellular and intracellular. Extracellular digestion occurs in the main part of the gastrovascular cavity and is purely proteolytic. Hyman (1940) has shown that although food particles are distributed throughout the gastrovascular cavity, most intracellular digestion takes place in the manubrium, in the stomach and in tentacular bulbs. The digested food is distributed to the entire medusa through the system of radial and circular canals.

Muscular system. The muscular system of medusa is somewhat more specialized than in the polyp. The gastrodermal cells lack contractile extensions, and the muscular system is, thus, restricted to the epidermal layer. Furthermore, the muscular system is best developed around the bell margin and subumbrella surface where the fibres form a radial and circular system. Some of the epitheliomuscular cells of the velum have their contractile extensions oriented to form a powerful circular band of fibres which are striated. The contractions of the muscular system, particularly of circular fibres produce rhythmic pulsation of the bell. The swimming movement of the medusa is dependent on these pulsations and is largely vertical in direction. Horizontal movement is dependent upon water currents.

Nervous system. The nervous system of medusa is more highly specialized than that of the polyp. In the margin of the bell, the epidermal nerve cells are usually organized and concentrated into two nerve rings, one above and one below the attachment of the velum. The nerve rings connect with fibres innervating the tentacles, the musculature, and the sense organs. Fibres also interconnect the two rings. The lower ring is the centre of rhythmic pulsations, *i.e.*, it contains the pacemakers. Pulsation will continue in the bell as long as any portion of the ring is intact. It is with the lower ring that the statocysts are connected.

Sense organs. The bell margin is richly supplied with sensory cells and also contains two types of true sense organs, *viz.*, light sensitive ocelli and statocysts. The ocelli consist of patches of pigment and photoreceptor cells organized either within a flat disc or a pit. The ocelli are typically located on the side of the tentacular bulbs.

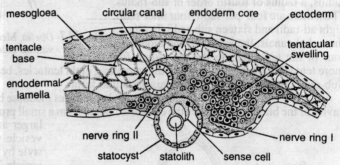

Fig. 32.9. *Obelia*. L.S. of the base of an ardradial tentacle of medusa.

Statocysts are located between the tentacles or associated with the tentacular bulb at the tentacle base. They may be either in the form of pits or closed vesicles but in both cases the walls contain sensory cells with bristles projecting into the lumen. Attached to the bristles are from a few to many calcareous concretions known as statoliths. The statocysts act as organs of equilibrium. When the bell tilts, the statoliths respond to the pull of gravity and stimulate the sensory bristles to which they are attached. The animal may then respond by muscular contractions to bring itself back into a horizontal position.

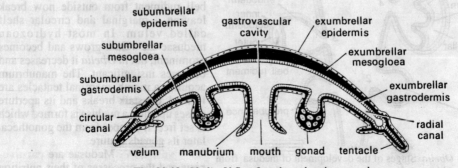

Fig. 32.10. *Obelia*. V.S. of medusa showing gonads.

Reproductive organs. The medusae are sexual or reproductive zooids possessing gonads. The medusae are **dioecious,** they have either four **testes** or four **ovaries** in the sub-umbrella just below the radial canals. A gonad has an outer ectoderm and inner endoderm with mesogloea between the two layers, the gonad has a small diverticulum of the radial canal. The germ cells of *Obelia* do not arise in the gonads, they arise from interstitial cells of the ectoderm of the blastostyle where they may be seen in various stages of maturation, then they migrate into the medusa, then through the radial canals they take up their position in the ectoderm of the gonads. When germ cells mature, the gonads rupture and spermatozoa and ova are discharged externally into water.

LIFE HISTORY

Fertilization. Fertilization usually takes place in open sea water where the gametes are set free. Sometimes, the sperms are carried into the female medusae with water currents and there they fertilize the eggs in situ. However, the parent medusae die soon after liberating their respective gametes.

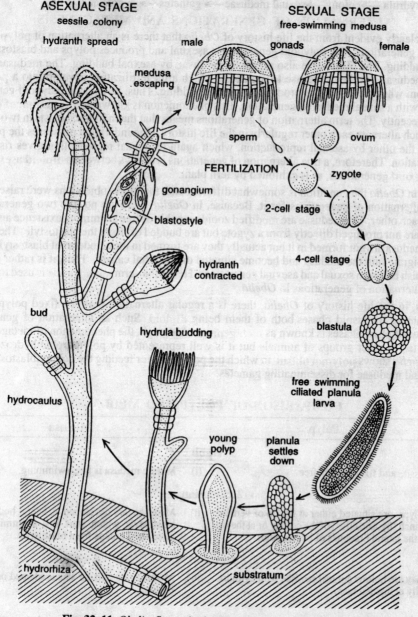

ASEXUAL STAGE
sessile colony

hydranth spread

male

SEXUAL STAGE
free-swimming medusa

gonads

female

medusa
escaping

sperm

ovum

FERTILIZATION

gonangium

zygote

blastostyle

2-cell stage

hydranth
contracted

4-cell stage

bud

hydrula budding

blastula

hydrocaulus

free swimming
ciliated planula
larva

young
polyp

planula
settles
down

hydrorhiza

substratum

Fig. 32. 11. *Obelia.* Stages in the development and life history.

Development. The zygote undergoes complete or holoblastic and equal cleavage to form a single-layered blastula with a blastocoele. Some cells migrate into blastocoele, eventually filling it completely to form a solid gastrula known as stereogastrula. Its outer cell layer becomes the ectoderm and inner cell mass the endoderm. The gastrula elongates and its outer layer of ectoderm cells becomes ciliated,and now it is called planula. Soon, a cavity called enteron develops in the solid endodermal cell mass by the process of delamination and the planula becomes a two-layered larva having an outer ciliated ecodermal cells and an inner layer of endodermal cells. The planula after a short free-swimming existence settles on some solid object by its broader end. The free end forms a manubrium with a mouth and a circlet of tentacles. Thus, a simple polyp or hydrula is formed which grows a hydrorhiza from its base, from which an *Obelia* colony is formed by budding.

The free swimming planula stage in the life history of *Obelia*, helps in the dispersal of the species. The life history may be represented as : male and female gametes —→zygote—→ planula larva —→hydrula —→colony—→sexual medusae—→ gametes—→ zygote and so on.

ALTERNATION OF GENERATIONS AND METAGENESIS

It is clearly evident from the life history of *Obelia* that there is an alternation of polypoid and medusoid generations. The polypoid generation is asexual and produces polyps and blastostyles by asexual budding. The blastostyle also produces medusae by asexual budding. The medusae do not produce medusae but they give rise to gametes, which after fertilization develop into a polypoid colony from which medusae are produced again by budding. Thus, an asexual polypoid generation alternates with a sexual medusoid generation. This phenomenon is known as alternation of generations, till recently. The term alternation of generations means that the individual exists in two distinct forms, which alternate each other regularly in the life history. One individual possesses the power to reproduce the other by asexual reproduction, which again by sexual reproduction gives rise to the next generation. Therefore, a true alternation of generations is always between a diploid asexual and haploid sexual generations, as is exhibited by fern plant.

But, in *Obelia* the condition is somewhat different and, therefore, objections were raised to use the term alternation of generations for it. Because, in *Obelia*, there are no true two generations to alternate each other. The medusae are modified zooids capable of free swimming existence and moreover they are not produced directly from a zygote but are budded off from the blastostyle. The gonads found in medusa are not formed in it but actually they are formed in the ectoderm of blastostyle which later on migrate into the medusa and become situated on its radial canals. Thus, it is rather difficult to distinguish between sexual and asexual generations. Hence the term metagenesis is used to replace the term alternation of generations in *Obelia*.

Thus, in the life history of *Obelia*, there is a regular alternation between fixed polypoid and free-swimming medusoid phases,both of them being diploid. Such an alternation of generations between two diploid phases is known as metagenesis. Although, the phenomenon of metagenesis is also reported in other groups of animals but it is well represented by polymorphic hydrozoan like *Obelia*. *Obelia* shows polymorphism in which the polyps are for feeding the colony,blastostyles for budding and medusae for disseminating gametes.

COMPARISON OF POLYP AND MEDUSA

Polyp	Medusa
1. Habit	
(i) Sessile and fixed, rarely free.	(i) Mature medusa is free-swimming.
2. Situation	
(ii) Polyps are situated either at the tip of vertical branch (hydrocaulus) of the colony or at the tip of the lateral branches of hydrocaulus.	(ii) Medusae are developed as lateral buds on the blastostyle which start free-swimming life after their escape from blastostyle.
3. Shape and Size	
(iii) They are hollow conical sac-like with cylindrically elongated body.	(iii) Medusae are circular saucer-shaped or umbrella-like.

	Polyp		Medusa
(iv)	Small measuring about only few mm in length.	(iv)	Medusa measures about 6–7 mm in diameter.

4. Structure

	Polyp		Medusa
(v)	The polyps are covered in protective cup-shaped covering called hydrotheca.	(v)	Adult medusa is not covered in hydrotheca or in any other protective covering.
(vi)	The manubrium is conical and directed upwards. It constitutes nearly one-third of the whole body of the polyp.	(vi)	The manubrium is elongated, tubular comparatively smaller and hangs downwards freely.
(vii)	Mouth is circular situated at the tip of the manubrium.	(vii)	Mouth is rectangular situated at the tip of manubrium surrounded by 4 oral lobes.
(viii)	The tentacles are usually 24 situated in a circlet around the mouth.	(viii)	The tentacles are 16 in young condition but many in adult stage. The tentacles are situated around the margin of the bell.
(ix)	Polyps are simple in structure.	(ix)	Medusae are complicated in structure.
(x)	The bases of tentacles are not swollen.	(x)	The bases of tentacles are swollen.
(xi)	The velum is absent.	(xi)	The velum is present around the margin of umbrella which is poorly developed.
(xii)	The sense organs are absent.	(xii)	The marginal sense organs, statocysts are present at the bases of 8 adradial tentacles.
(xiii)	The enteron or coelenteron is simple but spacious and without radial and circular canals.	(xiii)	The enteron or coelenteron is represented by the stomach, having 4 radial canals and a circular canal.
(xiv)	Nervous system is poorly developed; represented by few nerve cells.	(xiv)	Nervous system is well developed with a double ring of irregular nerve cells.
(xv)	The musculature is not developed.	(xv)	The muscle processes of epitheliomuscular cells are well developed and constitute a well developed musculature.
(xvi)	The mesogloea is poorly developed and is in the form of a thin sheet.	(xvi)	The mesogloea is well developed.

5. Reproduction

	Polyp		Medusa
(xvii)	The gonads are absent.	(xvii)	The gonads are present on the radial canals in 4 groups.
(xviii)	Polyp is a nutritive zooid and represents the asexual generation.	(xviii)	The medusa is a reproductive zooid which represents the sexual generation.
(xix)	Polyp reproduces asexually by budding	(xviv)	Medusa reproduces sexually by the formation of gametes.

Advancement of Medusa over Polyp

Medusa exhibits many features of advancement over polyp, few of them are as follows :

1. The epidermis resembles the epithelium of higher Metazoa forming a thin, protective and sensitive layer of small cells.

2. The enormous development of mesogloea reduces the gastrovascular cavity or enteron to a system of canals and also provides lightness which helps in buoyancy.

3. The nervous system shows differentiation into two nerve rings constituting the central nervous system and nerve nets forming the peripheral nervous system.

4. The marginal sense organs present at the bases of 8 tentacles are of special advantage to the free swimming habit of the medusa.

5. The mode of sexual reproduction provides wide dispersal of the species due to its free swimming habit.

Similarities between Polyp and Medusa

Striking as is the difference between polyp and medusa, they are strictly homologous or typically similar structures. Both of them are formed on the same pattern. However, the features of similarity between them are listed below :

1. Both are **radially** symmetrical.

2. Both are **diploblastic** with outer epidermis (ectodermal)and inner gastrodermis(endodermal).

3. The **mouth** is homologous in both the cases; the mouth situated on the hypostome in polyp is homologous with the mouth situated on the manubrium of the medusa. **Anus** is absent in both the cases.

4. The stomach, radial canals and circular canal of medusa are homologous with the gastrovascular cavity of the polyp. All these are lined by gastrodermis and serve the purpose of digestion and distribution of digested food.

5. Both are **carnivorous** ; the food is captured and ingested with the help of tentacles.

6. Digestion is **extracellular** as well as **intracellular** in both the cases.

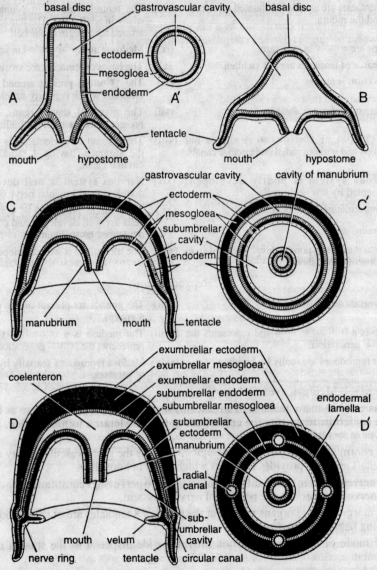

Fig. 32.12. Diagram illustrating the derivation of the medusa from the polyp. A—Polyp in L.S.; A—Polyp in T.S.; B—Polyp form with extended tentacular region; C—Vertical and C—Transverse section of form with tentacular region extended into the form of a bell ; D—Vertical and D—Transverse section of medusa.

7. The outer, exumbrellar surface of the medusa is homologous with the base of the polyp providing attachement with the parental colony.

DERIVATION OF MEDUSA FROM POLYP

Striking as is the difference between polyp and a medusa, they are strictly homologous structures, and the more complex medusa is readily derived from the simpler polyp-form. The apex of the umbrella of medusa corresponds with the base of a hydranth. The mouth and manubrium are also homologous structures. Suppose the tentacular region of a polyp to be pulled out, as it were, into a disc-like form and afterwards to be bent into the form of saucer with the concavity distal, that is towards the manubrium. The result of this to be a medusa-like body with a double wall to the entire bell, the narrow space between the two layers containing a prolongation of coelenteron and being lined with gastrodermis. From such a form the actual condition of things found in the medusa would be produced by the continuous cavity in the bell being for most part obliterated by the growing together of its walls so as to form the endodermal lamella. The cavity would remain only along four meridional areas, the radial canals and as a circular area the circular canal close to the edge of the bell. In this way a medusa is derived completely from a polyp (Fig. 32.12).

COMPARISON OF *HYDRA* AND *OBELIA*

	Hydra		*Obelia*
1.	Simple, solitary and freshwater form.	1.	Colonial, trimorphic and marine form.
2.	Body form cylindrical and tubular.	2.	The colony looks plant-like with many lateral branches .
3.	Body is covered by soft cuticle.	3.	Body is covered by an exoskeleton of stiff chitinous perisarc.
4.	Tentacles are few and hollow.	4.	Tentacles are many and solid.
5.	Nematocysts occur all over the body of *Hydra*.	5.	Nematocysts are confined all over to the manubrium and tentacles both in the polyp and medusa.
6.	Polyp remains naked.	6.	Polyp remains covered by a cup of perisarc called hydrotheca.
7.	Polyp reproduces asexually by budding to form new polyps.	7.	Polyp reproduces asexually by budding to form medusa.
8.	*Hydra* bears temporary gonads.	8.	*Obelia* has permanent gonads on the medusa.
9.	There is no free-swimming stage in the life history of *Hydra*. Even the larval development is passed in an embryonic theca.	9.	Medusae are free-swimming and the planula larvae are also free-swimming.

REVISION QUESTIONS

1. Describe the structure and development of any hydrozoan medusa, you have studied.
2. Describe in detail the structure of an *Obelia* colony and give an account of its life-history.
3. Give an account of the various types of zooids found on the *Obelia* colony.
4. Describe fully the nutritive and asexually budding zooids of *Obelia* .
5. Describe in detail the structure of polyp of *Obelia* and compare it with its medusa.
6. What is polymorphism? Explain it with the example of *Obelia* colony.
7. Describe the life history of *Obelia* and comment upon alternation of generations.
8. What do you mean by metagenesis and alternation of generations? Explain by taking the example of *Obelia*.
9. "Striking as is the difference between polyp and medusa but they are homologous structures". Discuss.
10. How can you say that medusae are more advanced than polyps? How can you derive a medusa from a polyp?
11. Write short notes on:
    (i) Blastostyle; (ii) Metagenesis; (iii) Symmetry of medusa; (iv) Statocyst of medusa; (v) Planula.
12. Give an account of the structure of *Obelia* and compare it with that of *Hydra* .
13. Draw labelled diagrams only:
    (i) Life history of *Obelia*; (ii) *Obelia* colony; (iii) V.S. of hydranth of *Obelia;* (iv) Medusa of *Obelia*; (v) Gonangium of *Obelia*.

33
Aurelia

Aurelia commonly referred to as jelly-fish because of its jelly-like appearance. In this case, medusa is the dominant phase in life history having a free-swimming planula larva, reduced fixed polypoid phase and a free-swimming disc-like ephyra larva. Different types of jelly-fishes are known but here *Aurelia aurita* (commonly referred to as moon-jelly) has been chosen for detailed study which represents typical features of jelly-fishes.

AURELIA AURITA (A JELLY-FISH)
SYSTEMATIC POSITION

Phylum	....	**Colenterata**
Class	....	**Scyphozoa**
Order	....	**Semaeostomeae**
Genus	....	*Aurelia*
Species	....	*aurita*

HABIT AND HABITAT

Aurelia is a commonest jelly-fish or moon-jelly, occurs in coastal waters of tropical and temperate oceans of the world close to the surface of water. It is cosmopolitan in distribution. It lives either singly or in large groups found floating or swimming freely. It is carnivorous and reproduces both by asexual and sexual methods.

STRUCTURE

Shape, size and colour. The medusa of *Aurelia* is flattened, bowl or saucer-shaped gelatinous structure called the bell or umbrella. It exhibits tetramerous radial symmetry. It usually measures about 7.5–10 cm in diameter, though much larger forms (up to 30 cm in diameter) have also been recorded from Atlantic coast. It is almost transparent having bluish-white body with pinkish gonads.

External structures. The bell or umbrella is distinctly divided into a slightly convex upper surface and a concave lower surface; the convex surface is known as exumbrellar surface and the concave surface is known as subumbrellar surface. The margin of umbrella is circular which is broken by eight notches. Each notch is provided with a pair of marginal lappets enclosing sense organ called tentaculocyst or rhopalium. The margin of umbrella, in between notches, is provided with numerous, small, closely arranged hollow marginal tentacles. The margin of umbrella, bearing marginal lappets and marginal tentacles, is thin ridge-like called velarium or pseudovelum. A true velum like those of hydrozoan medusae is absent in *Aurelia* because it lacks muscles and nerve ring.

The subumbrellar surface bears the following :

Manubrium. In the centre of subumbrellar surface, there is a well developed but short and inconspicuous manubrium bearing a large squarish mouth.

Oral arms. All the four corners of the mouth are drawn out into four long, mobile, delicate, frilled and tapering processes called the oral-arms. The oral arms are provided with a ciliated groove on its inner side and they are also provided with numerous nematocysts.

Gonads and subgenital pits. Four horse-shoe-shaped pinkish gonads, which later become circular, are situated between oral arms in the centre of the subumbrellar surface. Gonads are, in fact, internal lying into the gastric pouches but they are visible externally. Just below each gonad in the subumbrellar surface is a circular aperture called subgenital pit of unknown function. The gonads, however, have no connection with subgenital pits. The gonads are provided with delicate fine thread-like gastric filaments bearing nematocysts in the gastric pouches.

A system of fine branched or unbranched radiating canals are clearly visible on the surface of umbrella; these are per-radial, inter-radial and ad-radial in positions. The corners of mouth and oral arms are per-radial in position, while gonads and subgenital pits are inter-radial in position. Out of eight marginal notches, four are per-radial and four are inter-radial in positions.

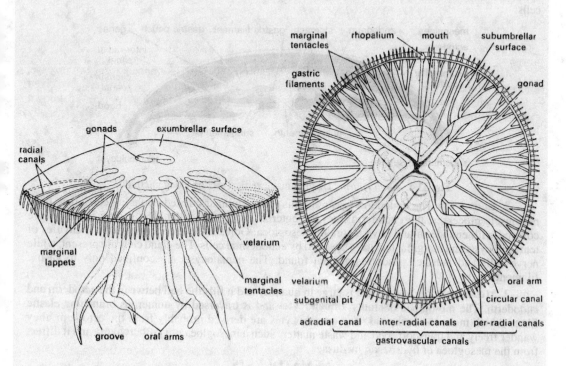

Fig. 33.1. *Aurelia aurita.* Lateral view.   **Fig. 33.2.** *Aurelia aurita.* Ventral view (Subumbrellar surface).

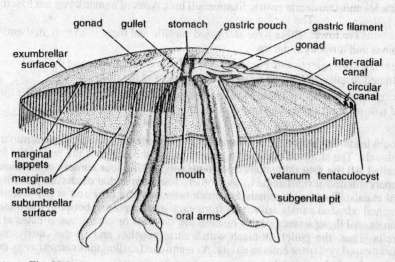

Fig. 33.3. *Aurelia aurita.* Side view with one-fourth of umbrella cut away.

HISTOLOGY

Histologically, the general plan of the structure of *Aurelia* resembles to that of the medusa of *Obelia*. However, its body consists of the following layers :

1. Ectoderm. The ectoderm (epidermis) covers the bell all around, it has the columnar epithliomuscular cells, sensory cells, nerve cells which produce mucus. In the epitheliomuscular cells the epithelial part is much reduced, and on the subumbrella side it is entirely absent, the muscular part is converted into contractile striated muscle fibres. The sensory cells constitute a sensory epithelium between the epithelial cells. The manubrium and oral arms are also lined by epidermal cells.

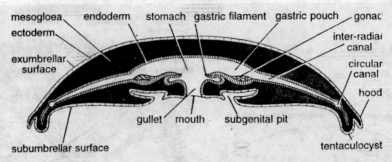

Fig. 33.4. *Aurelia aurita.* Diagrammatic vertical section along interradii.

2. Endoderm. The endoderm (gastrodermis) has columnar ciliated epithelial cells, they have no muscle processes; the endoderm lines the enteron except the gullet. The gastric filaments are covered with endoderm and have a core of mesogloea. Gonads are endodermal and the cavities of tentaculocysts and marginal tentacles are lined by endodermal cells. The gland cells are present, while nerve cells and muscle processes are not found. The nematocysts are confined only to gastric filaments.

3. Mesogloea. The mesogloea is large in quantity and it fills the bell between the ectoderm and endoderm. The mesogloea contains amoebocytes and is traversed by numerous branching elastic fibres which make the bell rigid. The amoebocytes are derived probably from the ectoderm, they wander freely and transport food and waste matter. Such a mesogloea is a collenchyma and it differs from the mesogloea of hydrozoan medusae.

NEMATOCYSTS

The nematocysts are found distributed on the oral arms, ex- and subumbrellar surfaces, on the marginal tentacles and also on the gastric filaments. Three types of nematocysts are found in *Aurelia*. These are as follows :

1. Atrichous isorhizas. These have elongated capsule and there is no butt in them. The thread is without spines and it opens at the tip.

2. Heterotrichous microbasic euryteles. These have small capsule and the butt is short in them. The butt is dilated distally and has unequal spines; it opens at the tip.

3. Holotrichous isorhizas. These have oval capsule and their butt is narrow. The thread is long having spiral row of small spines and opens at the tip.

GASTROVASCULAR CANAL SYSTEM

The mouth leads into a short gullet within the manubrium which finally opens into a four-lobed spacious stomach. The stomach occupies a greater part of the centre of the bell in the form of four extensions called gastric pouches situated inter-radially. At the four corners of the mouth are four per-radial canals situated at right angle to each other, four inter-radial canals are present in between the per-radial canals. These eight canals are much branched and they end at the marginal lappets. Eight unbranched adradial canals arise, two from each gastric pouch, between the inter-radial and per-radial canals. All these sixteen canals open in the circular or ring canal situated at the margin of the umbrella. Thus, the gullet, stomach with gastric pouches and all the canals constitute the gastrovascular canal system or enteron cavity. As mentioned earlier, the enteron cavity except gullet is lined by ciliated endodermal cells.

MUSCULATURE

The musculature of the body of *Aurelia* is well developed and confined to its subumbrellar surface only. It consists of the striated and non-striated muscle processes of the epitheliomuscular cells of epidermis only. The muscle processes are arranged longitudinally in tentacles, manubrium and oral arms. The muscle processes constitute a strong, broad circular band called coronal muscle. Radial muscles extend from the manubrium to the coronal muscles. The rapid and rhythmic contraction of these muscle processes brings about swimming movements in *Aurelia*.

CIRCULATION

Beating of cilia of endodermal lining of the enteron causes a circulation of fluids; water is drawn into the mouth→gullet→ stomach → gastric pouches→ eight adradial canals→ circular canal→ inter-radial and per-radial canals→gullet→ exhalant grooves of oral arms; water takes in food, removes waste substances and helps in respiration.

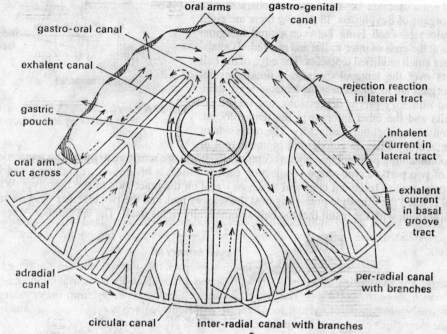

Fig. 33.5. *Aurelia aurita.* Circulation of water (Only one quadrant of the body and two arms are shown).

NUTRITION

Aurelia is carnivorous, its food consists of eggs, fish, small larvae and pieces of animals. The food is caught by oral arms and tentacles and transferred to the mouth. But ciliary feeding also takes place, as the animal moves downwards, plankton is trapped in mucus covering the sub-umbrella surface, flagella moves the food-laden mucus to the bell margin from where it is taken up by oral arms and transferred to the mouth, The gastric filaments kill or paralyse living food. The endoderm of gastric filaments and enteron produces digestive enzymes. Food undergoes preparatory digestion in the stomach and its pouches, this is, extracellular digestion. Partly digested food which has been broken into small filaments is swept by the cilia into the canals. Food particles are ingested into food vacuoles by endoderm cells of gastric filaments and the canals where intracellular digestion occurs. Enzymes digest proteins, carbohydrates, fats and even chitin. The digested food is taken up by amoebocytes and distributed by them. The endoderm of gastric pouches stores reserve food as fat droplets and glycogen. The gastrovascular system fulfils the functions of digestion and circulation.

RESPIRATION AND EXCRETION

There are no specialized organs for respiration and excretion. These processes are presumably performed by the whole body surface. The gastrovascular system brings about respiration since the current of water carries oxygen in its circulation and removes carbon dioxide. The oxygen requirement of the medusa is very small compared to its weight, because the jelly-fish contains about 96% of water. The gastrovascular system also removes excretory matter.

NERVOUS SYSTEM

The nerve cells and their fibres form two nerve nets joined to the sensory cells and muscle fibres. The nerve net in the sub-umbrella lies in the ectoderm, it is concentrated near the ten-

cysts and it extends into the oral arms and tentacles, this is the main nerve net, it causes pulsations of the bell by controlling the ectodermal coronal and radial muscles. The second nerve net is more diffuse with smaller nerve cells in the endoderm of both sub-umbrella and ex-umbrella, it controls local reactions, such as feeding, but it can also inhibit bell pulsations because the two nerve nets are joined through the tentaculocysts.

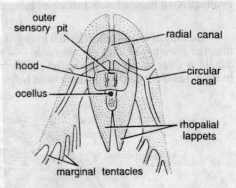

SENSE ORGANS

Tentaculocysts or rhopalia are characteristic sense organs of Scyphozoa. In *Aurelia* there are eight tentaculocysts, each lying between paired marginal lappets at the ends of inter-radial and per-radial canals. They are small modified tentacles. The edge of the bell projects over the tentaculocysts as a hood. Several sense organs are localized near the tentaculocyst, there are two **olfactory pits** as depressions, one on the ex-umbrella and the other internal to the tentaculocyst, their sensory epithelium is olfactory. The outer side of the tentaculocyst has an ectodermal pigment spot or

Fig. 33.6. *Aurelia aurita.* A portion of umbrella edge showing tentaculocyst or rhopalium.

ocellus containing pigment and photoreceptor cells, ocelli are sensitive to light. The tentaculocyst is made of two parts, a club-shaped projection called **lithostyle** or **statocyst** containing endodermal calcareous **otolith** (pigment cup) and a **sensory pad** on the inner side of the lithostyle. When the animal is tilted the lithostyle presses against the sensory pad, and the two together work as an organ of equilibrium, with the result that the bell automatically rights itself. The appearance of tentaculo-

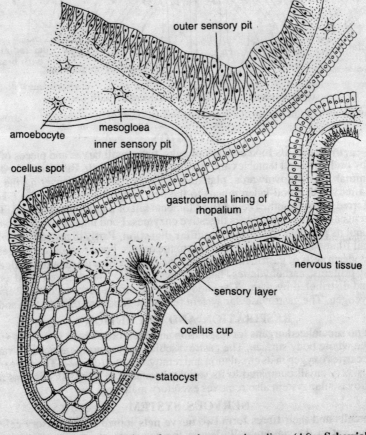

Fig. 33.7. *Aurelia* . Sectional view of tentaculocyst or rhopalium. (After **Schewiakoff**).

cysts marks the formation of an organ in Coelenterata which have in general reached only a tissue grade of organisation.

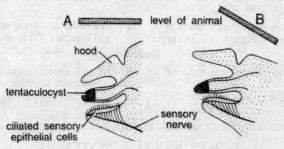

Fig. 33.8. *Aurelia.* Diagram showing the working of tentaculocyst.

COMPARISON OF STRUCTURE OF *AURELIA* AND *OBELIA* MEDUSA

Aurelia	*Obelia* medusa
Adult *Aurelia* represents large medusoid phase of life history; it is the dominant stage.	*Obelia* medusa represents one of the zooids in the life history of polymorphic colony of *Obelia* .

External Morphology

Aurelia	*Obelia* medusa
1. It is large-sized, umbrella-shaped commonly known as jelly-fish or moon-jelly.	1 It is small-sized, inverted bell-like commonly known as swimming bell.
2. Manubrium is not well developed. Mouth is situated in the centre of sub-umbrellar surface.	2. Manubrium is well developed and long. Mouth is situated at the tip of the manubrium.
3. Mouth is surrounded by oral arms.	3. Oral arms are not found.
4. The margin of umbrella is very thin and flexible called velarium which contains endodermal canals. True velum is , however, absent.	4. A true velum is present but without endodermal canals.
5. The margin of umbrella is broken at eight places to form marginal lappets.	5. The margin of bell is complete with no marginal lappets.
6. The marginal tentacles are numerous, hollow and short.	6. The marginal tentacles are sixteen in young stage but become numerous in mature stage. The tentacles are solid and long.

Anatomy

Aurelia	*Obelia* medusa
7. Stomach is four-lobed and extends into four gastric pouches.	7. Stomach is not lobed and gastric pouches are absent.
8. Gastric filaments present.	8. Gastric filaments absent.
9. Gastrovascular canal system is complicated and consists of 4 per-radial, 4 inter-radial, 8 ad-radial canals and a circular canal.	9. The canal system is poorly developed and consists of 4 radial canals and a circular canal.
10. A current of water is circulated in the gastrovascular canal system.	10. No current of water circulates in the canal system.
11. Mesogloea is very thick gelatinous having elastic fibres and wandering cells.	11. Mesogloea is comparatively thinner without fibres and cells.
12. The striated and non-striated muscle fibres are ectodermal in origin.	12. The muscle strands are both ecto- and endodermal in orgin.
13. The marginal nerve ring is not well developed or even absent.	13. There is a double nerve ring around the margin of umbrella.
14. The sense organs are situated per-radially and inter-radially; and are protected by marginal lappets.	14. These are situated ad-radially at the base of the tentacles without any protective lappets.

Aurelia		Obelia medusa	
15.	The sensory organs are 8 tentaculocysts at the margin of umbrella in notches.	15.	The sensory organs are 8 statocysts situated at the bases of adradial tentacles.
16.	The ocelli and olfactory pits are other sensory structures.	16.	The ocelli and olfactory pits are not found.
17.	The nematocysts are situated all over umbrella, tentacles and oral arms. These are of three types.	17.	The nematocysts are only found on manubrium and tentacles. These are of only one type.
	Gonads		
18.	Gonads situated on stomach and endodermal in origin.	18.	Gonads situated on radial canals and ectodermal in origin.
19.	Gonads are horse-shoe-shaped.	19.	These are oval, knob-like.
20.	It is dioecious.	20.	It is also dioecious.

REPRODUCTIVE SYSTEM

Aurelia is dioecious, *i.e.,* the sexes are separate. The four gonads (testes or ovaries) lie inter-radially on the floor of the gastric pouches. The gonads are horse-shoe-shaped and reddish in colour. Gonads of *Aurelia* are endodermal in origin unlike those of *Obelia* medusae which are ectodermal in origin. Sex cells originate in the endoderm of gonads. The ripe gametes are shed into the stomach and passed out through the mouth.

DEVELOPMENT AND LIFE HISTORY

Fertilization. The male and female gametes are formed separately in different medusae of *Aurelia* . The male gametes or spermatozoa from a male medusa are discharged internally and finally they leave the body through mouth with outgoing water current in the sea water. These are, then, drawn into the body of female medusa through its mouth along with the water current. The ova are fertilized inside the gastric pouches of female medusa as soon as they are discharged from the ovaries. The zygotes, thus formed, are passed out of the mouth of female medusa along with outgoing water current and finally they get attached in the grooves of the oral arms. At this place each zygote gets enclosed in a pouch where it undergoes development.

Development and formation of planula larva. Inside the pouch, the zygote undergoes holoblastic cleavage but unequal and results in the formation of a solid ball of cells called morula. Soon a cavity appears in the centre of the morula called blastocoel which is filled with a fluid and the cells of morula get arranged in a single layer. This single layered hollow morula is now called blastula. The cells of blastula, from one pole, invaginate to form a double layered gastrula. The outer cell layer of gastrula represents ectoderm and inner cell layer represents endoderm which encloses a cavity, the coelenteron opening to the exterior by a wide aperture called blastopore. Then the gastrula elongates, its blastopore closes and ectoderm becomes ciliated to form the planula larva. The planula differs from that of Hydrozoa in its method of formation and in having a coelenteron and blastopore. Planula larva may be seen in masses on the oral arms of female medusae. The planula is set free after a time from the oral arms, after a brief free-swimming existence it sinks, loses its cilia, the blastopore closes, and it gets fixed to some object by its aboral end.

Development and formation of scyphistoma from planula larva. The planula will metamorphose into a small polyp or hydratuba which has no perisarc. In this metamorphosis an oral cone or manubrium is formed, the blastopore opens to become the mouth. Four hollow buds arise per-radially to become tentacles. Subsequently four inter-radial and eight ad-radial tentacles are formed. The endoderm of coelenteron forms four inter-radial longitudinal ridges called gastric ridges or mesenteries. The mouth becomes square and the manubrium sinks down to form funnel-like depressions called septal funnels or infundibula. These changes metamorphose a planula into a hydratuba. A root-like stolon arises at the base of the hydratuba, which feeds and buds off new hydratubae from its stolon throughout summer. These hydratubae may separate from the stolon of the parent, as in *Hydra*. After summer the hydratuba ceases to bud, it continues feeding and storing food. The hydratuba generally winters over the first year and may bud other hydratubae, but next winter it undergoes a process of transverse fission and called strobilation, the dividing hydratuba is called a scyphistoma or strobila. The transverse discs of the scyphistoma which have been produced by strobilation look like a serial pile of saucers, and each disc is an ephyra larva. One scyphistoma may strobilate a dozen or more ephyra in which growth begins at once in the margin. Ephyra larvae lie on each other, they are joined by muscular strands in the mesenteries which are continuous through all the ephyrae. The muscular strands contract and break, so that the ephyrae are constricted off one by one and they swim away. The ephyrae break away one by one from the upper surface of the scyphistoma, and then they get inverted. Before the first ephyra is released from the top its 16 tentacles are absorbed and 8 notched lobes are formed with a tentaculocyst in each lobe. The successive ephyrae released from the strobila are devoid of tentacles.

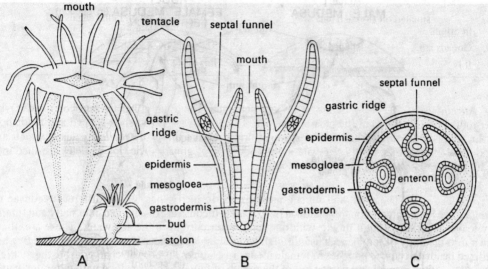

Fig. 33.9. *Aurelia.* Young scyphistoma. A—Outer view ; B—V.S. through inter-radius ; C—T.S. through septal funnels.

The basal part of the scyphistoma which was not segmented grows new tentacles, after a period of rest it resumes its existence as a hydratuba, it starts strobilating again in the next winter, it may live for years feeding and budding in summer and producing ephyra in winter.

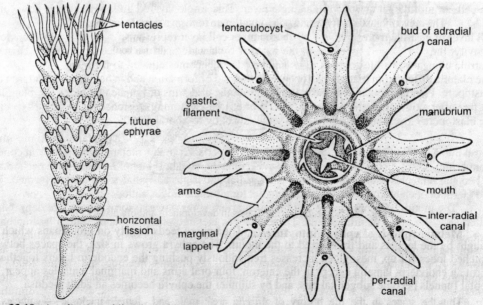

Fig. 33.10. *Aurelia.* A strobilated scyphistoma.

Fig. 33.11. *Aurelia.* An ephyra larva.

Ephyra larva. The ephyra (Fig. 33.11) is a young medusoid form. It has eight notched lobes or **arms** which are per-radial and inter-radial, each lobe has two exaggerated marginal lappets with a deep groove between them having a short tentacle which becomes a tentaculocyst. An ephyra bears a short stomach or gastric cavity with a short manubrium and four-sided mouth on its subumbrellar surface. The gastric cavity grows into the lobes to form branched per-radial and inter-radial canals, later the ad-radial canals also appear. Four pairs of gastric filaments form in the inter-radial mesenteries.

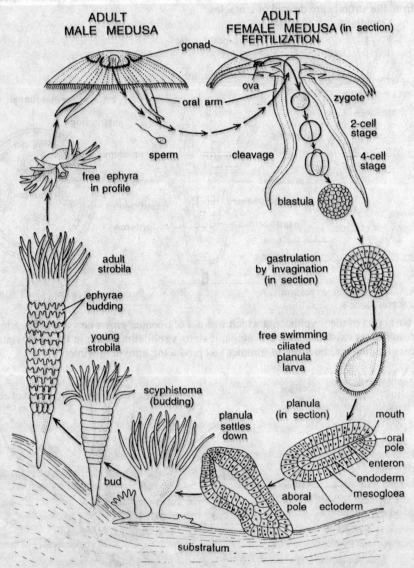

Fig. 33.12. *Aurelia aurita.* Stages in development and life history.

Metamorphosis of ephyra into *Aurelia.* The ephyra feeds largely on protozoans which are caught by the lappets and transferred to the mouth. The ephyra grows in size, the spaces between notched lobes fill up, mesogloea increases tremendously pushing the endoderm layers together to form an endoderm lamella except in the enteron, four oral arms and marginal tentacles appear, the septal funnels become subgenital pits, and by summer the ephyra becomes an adult medusa.

Thus,the stages in the life history of *Aurelia* are : male and female medusae→gametes→ zygotes→ ciliated planula larvae→ hydratubae →scyphistomae→ephyra→medusae→ ♂ and ♀ .

In *Aurelia* there are several phases that show variations which are found in the life-cycle of other Scyphozoa. Very large eggs of *Aurelia* become actinula larvae (an advanced type of planula which is like a polyp and has a short stem) which directly form ephyrae larvae. Smaller eggs form planula larvae which become hydratubae and then scyphistomae which strobilate ephyrae. Strobilation is brought about by intensive feeding followed by a drop in the temperature. In *Aurelia* if the food is plentiful and the temperature is low, then many ephyrae are produced at one time (polydisc strobilation). If there is less food and the temperature is high then ephyrae are produced one at a time (monodisc strobilation).

ALTERNATION OF GENERATIONS

In the life history of *Aurelia*, the sexual medusoid form always alternates with the asexual polypoid (scyphistoma) form. Thus, in a sense, *Aurelia* exhibits the phenomenon of alternation of generations in its life history . The free swimming adult *Aurelia*, representing the medusoid form, is the sexual generation which reproduces by the formation of gametes. The zygote develops into fixed polypoid form called scyphistoma through a free swimming planula stage. The polypoid form scyphistoma represents asexual generation,which reproduces asexually by budding or fission.

Some workers do not agree with this plan and deny the existence of alternation of generations or metagenesis in *Aurelia*. However, alternation of generations shown by *Aurelia* does not truly correspond with that found in *Obelia*,because; (i) The medusoid phase, in *Aurelia*, is formed by the metamorphosis of ephyra and not as a bud from the polypoid (scyphistoma) form, and (ii) The polypoid phase–scyphistoma is greatly reduced in size and multiplies by fission in addition to budding.

Therefore, it will be better to regard the life history of *Aurelia* as a case of prolonged metamorphosis, which becomes complicated by the multiplication (budding or fission) in the larval (scyphistoma) condition, instead of alternation of generations or metagenesis.

SIMILARITIES AND DISSIMILARITIES IN THE LIFE HISTORY OF *AURELIA* AND *OBELIA*

	Aurelia		*Obelia*
1.	Medusoid phase is dominant. The polypoid phase is reduced but prolonged.	1.	Polypoid phase is dominant . The medusoid phase is reduced.
2.	Gonads are horse-shoe-shaped and develop in adult medusoid form.	2.	Gonads are sac-like and develop in medusae budding from blastostyle.
3.	Dioecious, *i.e.* sexes separate and gonads are alike.	3.	Dioecious.
4.	Gonads are situated on the roof of gastric pouches internally and they also discharge their contents internally.	4.	Gonads are situated on the radial canals externally and they also discharge their contents externally.
5.	The reproductive cells are derived from endoderm.	5.	The reproductire cells are derived from ectoderm.
6.	Subgenital pits below gonads present.	6.	These are absent.
7.	Fertilization internal, usually takes place inside gastric pouches of female medusae.	7.	Fertilization external, it takes place out side the body of female medusa in open sea.
8.	Zygote undergoes holoblastic but unequal cleavage.	8.	Zygote undergoes holoblastic but equal cleavage.
9.	Gastrula is formed by invagination of outer ectoderm in the blastocoel.	9.	Gastrula is formed by delamination and immigration of ectodermal cells in blastocoel.
10.	Planula with blastopore and coelenteron.	10.	Planula without blastopore and coelenteron.
11.	Planula grows into polypoid hydratuba and scyphistoma representing asexual generations.	11.	Planula grows into hydra-like hydrula larva which produces directly by asexual budding, a new *Obelia* colony; it is a dominant polymorphic colony.
12.	Scyphistoma undergoes strobilation producing saucer-shaped ephyra.	12.	Scyphistoma and ephyra not found .
13.	Blastostyles not found.	13.	The colony buds off blastostyles.

Aurelia	*Obelia*
14. The ephyrae undergo metamorphosis to form the medusae.	14. The blastostyles directly bud off medusae.
15. Life history can be represented as: ♂ and ♀ medusae⟶gametes⟶zygotes⟶ planulae ⟶ hydratubae ⟶ scyphistomae (polypoid phase) ⟶ephyrae⟶ ♂ and ♀ *Aurelia* medusae.	15. Life history may be represented as: *Obelia* colony⟶blastostyles⟶ ♂ and ♀ medusae ⟶ gametes ⟶ zygotes ⟶ planulae ⟶ hydrula ⟶*Obelia* colony.
16. Alternation of generations or metagenesis controversial.	16. Alternation of generations or metagenesis found.

COMPARISON OF SCYPHOZOAN POLYP AND SEA-ANEMONE

Scyphozoan polyp	Sea-anemone
1. Body trumpet-shaped.	1. Body stumpy and cylindrical having flower-like appearance.
2. Solitary form but may form colony by budding.	2. Solitary forms, resembling polyps in general appearance and organisation.
3. Its body may be divided superficially into manubrium, column and basal disc.	3. Its body is divided into three distinct parts: oral disc, column and pedal disc. Manubrium is absent in it. Clear cut grooves demarcate these parts.
4. Mouth is squarish situated on a raised manubrium.	4. Mouth is elongated, slit-like, centrally placed opening on the expanded oral disc.
5. Mouth is surrounded by 16 long slender tentacles arranged in a single circlet.	5. Tentacles are many arranged in several rows around the mouth.
6. The tentacles are never branched.	6. Tentacles may be branched.
7. The manubrium is lined internally by endoderm.	7. The stomodaeum is lined internally by ectoderm.
8. The siphonoglyphs are not found.	8. The ciliated grooves called siphonoglyphs are found in the stomodaeum.
9. Only four longitudinal septa or gastric ridges are placed inter-radially extending from the body wall into the enteric cavity.	9. A large number of septa or mesenteries extend from the body wall into the enteric cavity.
10. All septa are of the same size and are not distinguished into primary, secondary and tertiary sets.	10. The mesenteries are of different sizes which are distinguished into primary, secondary and tertiary sets.

REVISION QUESTIONS

1. Give an account of general morphology of *Aurelia*.
2. Give an account of the structure of *Aurelia*. How does *Aurelia* differ from the medusa of *Obelia* ?
3. Describe the sense organs and mode of nutrition in *Aurelia* .
4. Describe the life history of *Aurelia*.
5. Give a comparative account of the life histories of *Aurelia* and *Obelia* .
6. Describe the scyphozoan polyp and compare it with that of sea-anemone.
7. Draw labelled diagrams only :

   (i) Medusa of *Aurelia*; (ii) Life history of *Aurelia*.
8. Write short notes on :

   (i) Gastrovascular canal system of *Aurelia;* (ii) Tentaculocyst; (iii) Scyphistoma; (iv) Ephyra.

34

Metridium (Sea Anemone)

The representatives of class Anthozoa (Gr., *anthos*=flower; *zoios*=animal) are commonly referred to as sea anemones because of their flower-like appearance. The sea anemones are either solitary or colonial polyps which are much larger and do not resemble in many aspects with the hydrozoan polyps studied so far. *Metridium* (L., *metricus*=rhythm) has been described in the following pages which represents a typical anthozoan polyp.

METRIDIUM (SEA ANEMONE)
SYSTEMATIC POSITION

Phylum	...	**Coelenterata**
Class	...	**Anthozoa**
Subclass	...	**Hexacorallia (Zoantharia)**
Order	....	**Actiniaria**
Genus	....	*Metridium*

HABIT AND HABITAT

Sea anemones, such as *Metridium* and *Tealia* are common in all seas being specially abundant in warmer climates in shallow and coastral waters. The sea anemone is so called because its upper free end looks like the flower anemone, they exhibit beautiful colour patterns. Sea anemones are solitary, sessile animals found attached to rocks where many individuals are fixed close together, but they are never fixed immovably. Anemones form remarkable symbiotic relationship with other animals,particularly with hermit crabs. Generally *Adamsia* or *Sagartia* are fixed to the shell of a snail inhabited by particular species of hermit crabs.

Metridium is one of the commonest sea anemones found attached to the rocks, piles of wharves and solid objects from tide pool to a depth of 90 fathoms.

STRUCTURE

External Features

Metridium has a short, cylindrical body about 8 cm in length. The body is radially symmetrical and divisible into three distinct regions, *viz.*, oral disc, column and pedal or basal disc.

1. **Oral disc.** The upper free end is the flat, circular oral disc or peristome having a large oval mouth on a slight elevation. Around the mouth are numerous short, conical and hollow tentacles in five circles or cycles, generally each cycle has tentacles in multiples of six, the number of tentacles increases with age. Tentacles are very sensitive to chemical stimulation by food juices; tentacles bear numerous nematocysts.

2. **Column.** The column may be cylindrical throughout, but in some genera, including *Metridium,* it is differentiated into an upper short, thin-walled capitulum and a lower main thick-walled scapus. On the column are wart-like tubercles. In some anemones, such as *Metridium* and *Tealia,* the upper edge of the scapus forms a prominent

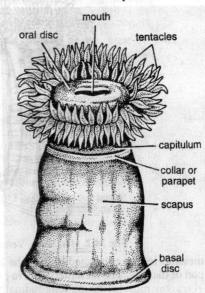

Fig. 34.1. *Metridium.*

fold called collar or parapet which forms a groove or fossae below the capitulum. In the upper part of the scapus is a circular muscle layer called sphincter which can close the margin of the scapus over the capitulum and retracted oral disc. The animal is capable of extreme contraction and the oral disc can be drawn inwards.

3. Pedal disc. The pedal or basal disc is expanded and is used for fixing the animal to rocks or shells, it adheres by mucus secretion and by muscles of the basal disc, but the animal is not sedentary because it can creep by gliding motion of the basal disc which puts out a turgid lobe in the direction of movement, while the opposite end contracts, then waves of muscular contractions pass over the basal disc from behind forward so that the rear end advances first, or the muscular contractions may pass from before backward so that the front lobe is pushed out . The rate of locomotion is about 8 cm per hour. Anemones never have a skeleton of any kind.

Internal Anatomy

The internal anatomy of *Metridium* can be studied with the help of its longitudinal and transverse sections (Fig. 34.2 and 34.3 respectively) in the following headings :

1. Stomodaeum. The mouth leads downwards into a long stout tube called pharynx or stomodaeum which extends about two-thirds of the length of the column, it is lined with invaginated ectoderm and it hangs in the coelenteron. In the stomodaeum are two longitudinal ciliated grooves called siphonoglyphs (Gr., *glyphe*=carving), in some genera there is a single siphonoglyph. The cilia of siphonoglyphs cause a respiratory current of water to pass downwards. The external surface is not sufficient to meet the respiratory need of the animal, and the current of water passing through the siphonoglyphs aids in respiration. The cilia of the stomodaeum causes a current which removes water and waste through the mouth.

2. Gastrovascular cavity . The stomodaeum extends up to about two-third of the gastrovascular cavity The gastrovascular cavity of *Metridium* is partitioned by vertical septa called mesenteries into radial chambers.

3. Mesenteries. From the body wall thick longitudinal septa or mesenteries run radially inwards, they divide the coelenteron into compartments. The mesenteries are of two types, the complete mesenteries run from the body wall to the wall of the stomodaeum, the incomplete

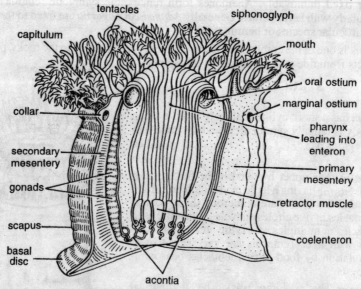

Fig. 34.2. *Metridium.* Vertical longitudinal section to show internal structure.

mesenteries are connected only to the body wall, they extend into the gastrovascular cavity only a part of the way. The mesenteries lie in pairs, and on one surface each mesentery bears an endodermal retractor muscle running longitudinally, they can cause intense contraction of the animal by which water is ejected through the mouth. Six pairs of mesenteries are complete, they run from the body wall to the stomodaeum, these six pairs are called primary mesenteries, two pairs of primaries are joined to the two siphonoglyphs, they are called directives in which the retractor muscles face away from each other, whereas in all the other mesenteries the muscles face each other. Between the adjacent primary mesentery pairs are six pairs of incomplete secondaries which do not reach the

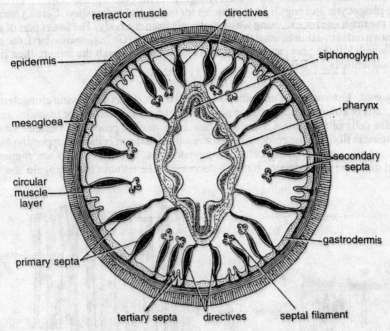

Fig. 34.3. *Metridium*. Cross section through the pharynx.

stomodaeum. Between the primary and secondary mesentery pairs are 12 pairs of smaller tertiaries, similarly there may be 24 pairs of still smaller quarternaries. Below the oral disc the primary and secondary mesenteries are pierced by holes called oral stoma or ostia, they may also be pierced near the body wall by marginal stoma or ostia, these ostia permit water to flow between the inter-mesenteric chambers. The lower edges of mesenteries are fixed to the basal disc, but their free inner

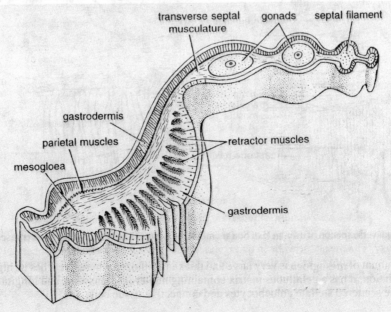

Fig. 34.4. *Metridium*. Diagrammatic representation of a septum.

edges in the coelenteron bear thick convoluted gastric filaments or septal filaments which are trilobed in section in the upper part. The upper part of each gastric filament performs the functions of digestion and water-circulation, they have digestive gland cells, ciliated cells, and nematocyst. The lower part of each gastric filament is exclusively digestive, they have gland cells but no ciliated cells, their cells are phagocytic and engulf food particles for intracellular digestion. Certain areas of gastric filaments are the main site for excreting waste materials from the body. The lower part of each gastric filament is drawn out into a thin twisted thread called acontium (Gr., *akontion*=dart), the acontia bear nematocysts which kill the prey, acontia can also be shot out through the mouth, then they help to overcome small animals for food.

HISTOLOGY

1. Body wall. Externally the anemone is covered by an epidermis having elongated epidermis or ectoderm cells of columnar shape, these ectoderm cells are ciliated on the tentacles and oral disc, a few ectoderm cells of the tentacles and oral disc have muscle processes, besides these there are independent muscle fibres in the epidermis. Between the ectoderm cells are supporting cells, slender sensory nerve cells, mucous gland cells and nematocysts. The nerve cells are numerous in the tentacles, oral disc, and stomodaeum, but they decrease in the column and are again abundant in the basal disc.

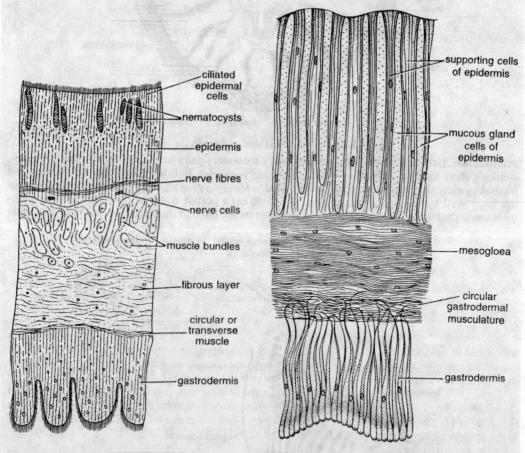

Fig, 34.5. Transverse section of a tentacle of Sea anemone.   **Fig. 34.6.** *Metridium.* Transverse section through the body wall.

The amount of mesogloea is very large and thick in Anthozoa where it reaches its highest degree of differentiation, it has a gelatinous matrix containing numerous transverse and longitudinal fibres, and there are scattered stellate amoebocytes and connective tissue cells.

The innermost layer of gastrodermis or endodermis is made of columnar epitheliomuscular cells in which the bases of cells are drawn out into muscle fibres, these muscle fibres are circular in the tentacles, oral disc, column and basal disc, but on the mesenteries they form strong retractor muscles which run longitudinally, main contraction of the anemone is brought about by these retractors. Between the epitheliomuscular cells are granular gland cells which secrete enzymes, the endoderm also has sensory cells, and nematocyst on mesenteries and acontia.

2. Tentacles. Histologically tentacles consist of epidermis, mesogloea and gastrodermis. Both epidermis and gastrodermis are made up of tall columnar ciliated cells. Mesogloeal layer is extremely thick and contains delicate fibres and scattered cells.

3. Mesenteries. The mesenteries are composed of two layers of gastrodermis enclosing a central layer of mesogloea. The mesenteric filaments show a characteristic structure in their upper portion. Each mesenteric filament has a trilobed shape in section. The central ridge known as the cnidoglandular band consists of nematocysts and gland cells. The two lateral ridges consist of all flagellated (ciliated) cells and are known as flagellated band.

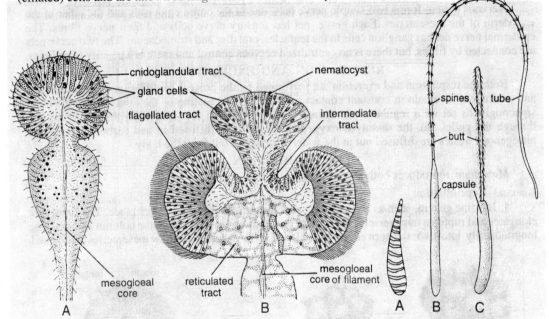

Fig. 34.7. *Metridium*. A—T.S. of a septal filament at level below the pharynx; B—T.S. of septal filament at level through the pharynx.

Fig. 34.8. *Metridium*. Nematocysts. A—Spirocyst; B—Basitrichous isorhiza; C—Microbasic amastigophore.

4. Nematocysts. *Metridium* has four kinds of nematocysts, but these nematocysts of Anthozoa are devoid of cnidocil. 1. Spirocyst has a thin capsule containing a long spirally-coiled tube of the even diameter, they are found only on tentacles and oral disc. 2. Basitrichous isorhiza has an oval capsule, there is no butt, the thread has spines only on the base and is open at the tip. 3. Microbasic mastigophore has a rounded capsule, butt is long and bears spines in a spiral, the thread is long and closed at the tip. 4. Microbasic amastigophore has an oval capsule, butt is short with spines in a spiral, thread is absent. Nematocysts are found in wart-like batteries on the tentacles, they also occur in the epidermis, endoderm, gastric filaments and acontia.

FEEDING AND DIGESTION

Food consists of animals or pieces of animals of suitable size, the food may be living or dead; it is carnivorous. Food is stunned by nematocysts of tentacles, then the tentacles push the food into the mouth, cilia of the mouth sweep the food into the stomodaeum and coelenteron. The food is held by mesenteries and broken into smaller pieces. A proteose of the nature of trypsin is secreted by the gland cells of the endoderm cells of gastric filaments and acontia, this breaks up the food in an alkaline medium and emulsifies fats. After this preliminary extracellular digestion the food broth is ingested by phagocytic endoderm cells and intracellular digestion takes place in these cells by proteoses of the type of pepsin, erepsin, and lipase secreted by gland cells. Many small sea anemones are ciliary feeders, body cilia beat towards the oral disc sweeping up the food, from the oral disc ciliary currents sweep the food particles to the tips of the tentacles, the tentacles bend and transfer the food into the mouth.

MUSCULAR SYSTEM

Muscular system is highly developed, the ectodermal muscles form longitudinal fibres in the tentacles and radial fibres in the oral disc, but the main musculature is endodermal. Endodermal muscles form a circular layer in the mesogloea of tentacles, oral disc, column, stomodaeum, and the basal disc. The endodermal muscles form highly developed retractor muscles running longitudinally through the mesogloea of the mesenteries, these retractor muscles are the chief means of contraction of the animal. At the junction of the oral disc and column the endodermal circular muscles form a sphincter by which the body is retracted and it covers the oral disc.

NERVOUS SYSTEM

Nervous system forms two simple nerve nets, one in the entire epidermis and the other in the endoderm of the mesenteries. Each nerve net has sensory nerve cells and their nerve fibres. The epidermal nerve net has ganglion cells in the tentacles, oral disc and stomodaeum. The two nerve nets are connected by fibres, but there is no centralized nervous control and there is a paucity of reflexes.

RESPIRATION AND EXCRETION

Both the respiration and excretion are performed by the process of diffusion as the epidermis and gastrodermis remain in constant contact with water. The beating of the cilia of the gullet and siphonoglyphs set up a regular water current entering through the siphonoglyphs and going out through the gullet. So, the dissolved oxygen in the water is diffused in and carbon dioxide and nitrogenous wastes are diffused out in the water which goes out from the body.

REPRODUCTION

Metridium reproduces both asexually and sexually.

Asexual Reproduction

1. In some genera, such as *Sagartia,* asexual **longitudinal fission** takes place. The basal disc elongates and ruptures transversely, the rupture proceeds upwards dividing the column and oral disc longitudinally into two, the torn edges of each half grow together and new mesenteries are formed.

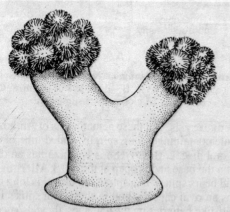

Fig. 34.9. *Metridium.*Longitudinal binary fission.

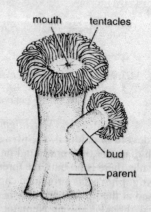

Fig. 34.10. *Metridium.* Budding.

2. **Pedal laceration** or **fragmentation** occurs in several genera, lobes are constricted off from the basal disc, each lobe grows tentacles and mesenteries to form a new anemone. At times the anemone moves away from its attachment leaving behind lobes of its basal disc and some mesenteries, these regenerate a new anemone at the old site, while the parent develops its lost portions, In anemones formed by pedal laceration there are many irregularities as to the arrangement and number of mesenteries and siphonoglyphs. 3. If an anemone is cut across the column into two, then the lower

part regenerates a new oral disc with tentacles, but the upper part usually fails to form a new basal disc, instead it may form a second set of tentacles on its lower aboral surface, thus, showing heteromorphosis. 4. A few instances of budding from column or pedal disc have been reported.

Sexual Reproduction

Sexes are separate, endodermal gonads form thick longitudinal bands on the larger mesenteries lying parallel to gastric filaments. But some anemones are hermaphrodite. Gametes are produced by interstitial cells of the endodermal gonads, but they mature in the mesogloea. In dioecious forms only sperms are expelled from the male into sea water, the females retain their eggs. Sperms enter the gastrovascular cavity of the female through the mouth and fertilize the eggs. The fertilized egg forms an oval ciliated planula larva which is free-swimming. The planula undergoes metamorphosis to acquire a mouth, stomodaeum, siphonoglyphs, and 6 to 24 mesenteries. The embryo sinks and gets fixed by its aboral end and tentacles are formed on the oral disc.

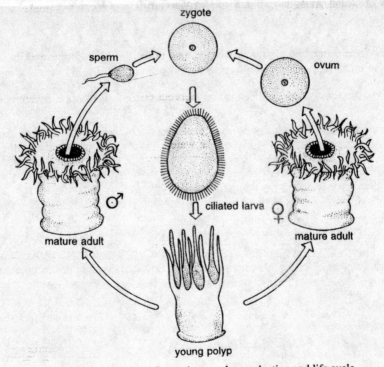

Fig. 34.11. *Metridium.* Stages in sexual reproduction and life cycle.

COMPARISON OF POLYP OF *METRIDIUM* AND *OBELIA*.

Metridium polyp	*Obelia* polyp
1. Mouth does not directly opens into gastrovascular cavity but leads into the stomodaeum .	1. Mouth leads directly into the gastrovascular cavity because stomodaeum is not found.
2. Tentacles arranged in five circlets around the mouth which are short and conical.	2. Tentacles arranged in a single circlet around the hypostome which are filiform.
3. Mesenteries present between the body wall and stomodaeum divide the gastrovascular cavity into radial chambers.	3. Mesenteries are not found .
4. Mesogloea possesses fibrous elements and amoeboid cells.	4. Neither fibrous elements nor any type of cells are found in mesogloea.
5. Muscular system, mainly endodermal but ectodermal also, well developed.	5. Muscular system is poorly developed.

Metridium polyp	*Obelia* polyp
6. Sex cells are endodermal.	6. Sex cells are not found in it.
7. Feeding as well as reproductive individual.	7. Exclusively feeding individual.
8. Blastostyles and medusae not found.	8. It buds off blastostyles which in turn give rise to medusae.

REVISION QUESTIONS

1. Give an account of the external and internal structure of *Metridium*.
2. Describe the histology of a sea-anemone with the help of suitable diagrams.
3. Compare the polyps of *Metridium* and *Obelia*.
4. Write short notes on :(i) Siphonoglyph ; (ii) Mesenteries ; (iii) Asexual reproduction of *Metridium*.
5. Draw labelled diagrams only : (i) L.S. of *Metridium* ; (ii) T.S. of *Metridium*.

35

Coelenterata : Characters, Classification and Types

DEFINITION

The Coelenterata may be defined as *"diploblastic Metazoa with tissue grade of construction having nematocysts and a single gastrovascular cavity or the coelenteron."*

GENERAL CHARACTERS

1. Coelenterates are Metazoa or multicellular animals with tissue grade of organization.

2. They are aquatic, mostly marine except few freshwater forms like *Hydras*.

3. They are sedentary or free-swimming and solitary or colonial.

4. Individuals are radially or biradially symmetrical with a central gastrovascular cavity communicating to the exterior by the mouth.

5. They are diploblastic animals ; body wall consists of an outer layer of cells called ectoderm and inner layer of cells the endoderm cemented together by an intermediate layer of non-cellular gelatinous mesogloea.

6. Acoelomate animals because they do not possess a second body cavity, the coelom.

7. Short and slender tentacles encircle the mouth in one or more whorls.

8. The tentacles are provided with nematocysts ; tentacles serve for food capture, its ingestion and for defence. These are also present on body layers, these are adhesive organs.

9. They exhibit the phenomenon of polymorphism with very few exceptions ; the main types of zooids in polymorphic forms are polyps and medusa. Polyp is sessile and asexual zooid, while medusa is free-swimming and sexual zooid.

10. Skeleton, either exoskeleton or endoskeleton is of common occurrence.

11. They are usually carnivorous ; digestion is extracellular as well as intracellular. Anus is not found.

12. Nervous system consists of one or more networks or nerve-cells and neurites located in the ectoderm and endoderm.

13. Respiratory, circulatory and excretory systems are wanting .

14. Reproduction is both by asexual and sexual methods.

15. Asexual reproduction occurs by budding and sexual reproduction by the formation of gametes.

16. A ciliated planula larva usually present in the life history.

17. The life history exhibits the phenomena of alternation of generations or metagenesis in which the asexual polypoid, sessile generation alternates with sexual medusoid, free-swimming generations.

CLASSIFICATION

The classification followed here is given by Hyman, L.H. , (1940). According to Hyman, Phylum Coelenterata has been divided into three classes, *viz.*, Hydrozoa, Scyphozoa and Anthozoa.

CLASS I. HYDROZOA
(Gr., *hydra*= water; *zoios* =animal)

1. Hydrozoa are solitary and freshwater or mostly colonial and marine, sessile and free swimming forms.
2. They exhibit tetramerous or polymerous radial symmetry.
3. Body wall consists of an outer ectoderm and an inner endoderm separated by non-cellular mesogloea.
4. Gastrovascular cavity without stomodaeum, septa or nematocysts bearing gastric filament.
5. Skeleton or horny structure is horny perisarc in some forms, while coenosarc secretes a skeleton of calcium carbonate forming massive stony structure or coral in other forms.
6. They exhibit polymorphism. There are two main types of zooids, the polyp and medusa.
7. Medusa is provided with true muscular velum.
8. Many Hydrozoa exhibit alternation of generations.
9. Reproductive products or sex cells are usually ectodermal in origin and discharged externally.
10. Cleavage is holoblastic, embryo ciliated planula.

Order 1. Hydroida

1. Solitary or colonial forms.
2. Polypoid generation well developed gives rise to free or abortive medusae by budding.
3. Sense organs of medusae are ocelli and statocysts and exclusively ectodermal in origin.

Suborder 1. Anthomedusae or Athecata

1. Solitary or colonial.
2. Polyps are not enclosed in hydrothecae and the medusae are also naked without gonothecae.
3. Medusae are tall, bell-like, bearing gonads on the manubrium having strongly arched umbrella.
4. Medusae bear eye spots or ocelli at the bases of tentacles .
5. Statocysts are absent.
   Examples : *Hydra, Tubularia, Bougainvillea, Hydractinia, Eudendrium, Pennaria.*

Suborder 2. Leptomedusae or Thecata

1. Colonial Hydrozoa.

2. Polyps are enclosed in hydrotheca and medusae are covered with gonothecae.
3. Free medusae are flattened, bowl or saucer-shaped, bearing gonads on the radial canals.
4. Medusae usually bear statocysts.
5. Eye spots or ocelli are absent.
   Examples : *Obelia Sertularia, Plumularia, Campanularia.*

Order 2. Milleporina

1. Colonial coral-like Hydrozoa without perisarc.
2. Massive calcareous skeleton is secreted by ectoderm provided with pores through which polyps protrude out.
3. Colony have two kinds of zooids, the gastrozooid and the dactylozooid.
4. Gastrozooids(nutritive zooids) are short provided with mouth and tentacles.
5. Dactylozooids are elongate, hollow, slender with tentacles but without mouth.
6. Medusae develop in small chambers, becoming free, devoid of mouth, radial canals and tentacles.
   Example : *Millepora.*

Order 3. Stylasterina

1. Colonial coral-like Hydrozoa colony have two kinds of zooids, the dactylozooids and gastrozooids.
2. Dactylozooids are small, solid without tentacles.
3. Gastrozooids have a cup with pointed spine.
4. Medusae develop in special cavities reduced to sporosacs.
5. Larva is liberated as planula.
   Example : *Stylaster.*

Order 4. Trachylina

1. Polypoid stage reduced or absent.
2. Medusae are large, provided with tentaculocysts, statocysts and lithocysts encl- osed in the endoderm.

Suborder 1. Trachymedusae

1. Margin of the umbrella is smooth.
2. Manubrium is long.
3. Gonads borne on the radial canals.
   Example : *Geryonia.*

Suborder 2. Narcomedusae

1. Margin of the umbrella is scalloped or clefted by tentacle bases.
2. Manubrium is short.
3. Gonads borne in the floor of the stomach.
   Examples : *Cunina, Solmaris.*

Order 5. Siphonophora

1. Siphonophora are polymorphic, free swimming or floating colonial Hydrozoa.
2. Colony consists of several types of polypoid and medusoid individuals attached to stem or disc.
3. Polyps without tentacles.
4. Medusae always incomplete and rarely freed.

Suborder 1. Calycophora

1. The upper end of the colony is provided with one or more swimming bells.
2. Apical float or pneumatophore absent.
   Example : *Diphyes.*

Suborder 2. Physophorida

1. Upper end of the colony bears a float or pneumatophore.
   Examples : *Physalia, Velella, Porpita, Halistemma.*

CLASS II. SCYPHOZOA
(Gr., *skyphos* = cup; *zoios* = animal)

1. Scyphozoa include large jelly-fishes or true medusae are exclusively marine.
2. Medusae are large, bell or umbrella-shaped, without true velum, free swimming or attached by an aboral stalk.
3. Marginal sense organs are tentaculocysts having endodermal statoliths.
4. Polypoid generation absent or represented by small polyp, the scyphistoma which gives rise to medusae by strobilization or transverse fission.
5. Gastrovascular system without stomodaeum with gastric filaments and may or may not be divided into four inter-radial pockets by septa.
6. Mesogloea is usually cellular.
7. Gonads are endodermal and the sex cells are discharged.

Order 1. Stauromedusae or Lucernaridae

1. Sessile, sedentary Scyphozoa attached by an aboral stalk.
2. Body globet or trumpet shaped.
3. Mouth cruciform (four cornered) with small oral lobes and a short quadrangular manubrium.
4. Gastrovascular system is divided into central stomach and four per-radial pouches by the four inter-radial septa.
5. Gonads are elongated band-like borne on the faces of septa.

6. Marginal sense organs absent.
7. Fertilization is external.
8. Larva is planula without cilia.
   Examples : *Lucernaria, Haliclystus.*

Order 2. Cubomedusae or Carybdeida

1. Free-swimming Scyphozoa found in warm and shallow waters of tropical and subtropical regions.
2. Body cubical with four flat sides.
3. Four hollow inter-radial tentacles borne on the margin of the subumbrella.
4. Four per-radial tentaculocysts or rhopalia are present.
5. Each tentaculocyst is provided with a lithocyst and one or more ocelli.
6. Mouth is cruciform and gastric pouches are present.
7. Gonads are leaf-like .
   Examples : *Charybdaea, Tamoya.*

Order 3. Coronate

1. Free-swimming scyphomedusae found inhabiting the deep waters of ocean.
2. Body conical, dome-shaped or flattened, grooved.
3. The umbrella is divided by a coronal groove (horizontal furrow) into an upper cone and a lower crown.
4. The crown consists of pedal lobes, pedalia.
5. The pedalia bear solid tentacles.
6. The bell margin is scalloped into lappets alternate with pedalia.
7. Mouth is cruciform.
8. Tentaculocysts are four to sixteen.
   Examples : *Pericolpa, Periphylla.*

Order 4. Semaeostomeae

1. Most common free-swimming medusae found inhabiting the coastal waters of all oceans.
2. The umbrella is flat, saucer or bowl-shaped.
3. Mouth is square.
4. The corners of the mouth produce four oral arms which are grooved with frilled edges.
5. The margin of the umbrella is fringed with hollow tentacles.
6. Eight or more tentaculocysts are present .
7. Gastric pouches and filaments are are absent.
   Examples : *Aurelia, Cynaea.*

Order 5. Rhizostomae

1. Free-swimming Scyphozoa found in shallow waters of tropical and subtropical oceans.

2. The umbrella is saucer or bowl-shaped or flattened or even concave on the top.
3. Mouth is surrounded by eight oral arms. bearing numerous funnel-shaped mouth on their edges.
4. Marginal tentacles are absent but 8 or more tentaculocysts are present.
5. Four subgenital pits are generally present.

Examples : *Rhizostoma or Pilema, Cassiopeia.*

CLASS III. ANTHOZOA
(Gr., *anthos*=flower; *zoios* =animal)

1. Solitary or colonial exclusively marine forms.
2. They are exclusively polypoid.
3. Medusoid stage is altogether absent.
4. Body usually cylindrical with hexamerous, octomerous or polymerous biradial or radio-bilateral symmetry.
5. The oral end of the body is expanded radially into an oral disc bearing hollow tentacles surrounding the mouth in the centre.
6. The stomodaeum is present, often provided with one or more ciliated grooves the siphonoglyphs.
7. Gastrovascular cavity is divided into compartments by complete or incomplete septa or mesenteries.
8. Mesenteries bear nematocysts at their inner free edges.
9. Mesogloea contains fibrous connective tissue and amoeboid cells.
10. Skeleton either external or internal.
11. Exoskeleton is formed from calcium carbonate which often form massive corals.
12. Nervous system is in the form of typical nerve net without a concentrated central nervous system.
13. Gonads are endodermal, develop in the mesenteries.
14. The ripe sexual products are discharged into coelenteron.
15. Fertilization is external.
16. The fertilized egg develops into a planula larva, which after a short free life settles down and develops into an adult.

Subclass 1. Alcyonaria or Octocorallia
1. Colonial marine forms.
2. Polyps are long or short cylinder terminating orally into a flat circular oral disc having the oval or elongated mouth in the centre.

3. Polyps always bear eight pinnate, hollow tentacles.
4. Eight complete mesenteries are present.
5. Single ventral siphonoglyph is present.
6. Endoskeleton is the product of mesogleal cells comprised calcareous spicules either calcareous or horny in nature.
7. Polyps are dimorphic in some forms.

Order 1. Stolonifera
1. The stolonifera are inhabitants of shallow waters in the tropical and temperate regions.
2. Polyps arise singly from a creeping base and are connected by one or more solenial tubes.
3. Skeleton consists of loose spicules or of compact tubes and platforms.

Examples : *Tubipora, Clavularia.*

Order 2. Telestacea
1. Colony consists of simple or branched stems arising from a creeping base.
2. Each stem is very elongated polyp bearing lateral polyps.
3. Skeleton consists of spicules fused by calcareous or horny secretions.

Example: *Telesto.*

Order 3. Alcyonacea
1. Colony mushroom-shaped or branched into stout blunt processes.
2. Lower part of the polyp fused into a fleshy mass with only oral ends protruding.
3. Polyps are dimorphic in some forms bearing autozooids and siphonozooids.
4. Skeleton consists of separate calcareous spicules, not axial.

Examples : *Alcyonium, Xenia.*

Order 4. Coenothecalia
1. Skeleton is massive, composed of crystalline calcareous fibres of calcium carbonate, not of fused spicules.
2. Skeleton is perforated by numerous larger and smaller erect cavities. The larger ones contain the lower ends of the polyps, while the smaller ones the erect terminal tubes.
3. Commonly known as blue corals found on the coral reefs in the Indo-Pacific.

Example : *Heliopora.*

Order 5. Gorgonacea
1. The colony is usually plant-like, consists of a main stem arising from basal plate or tuft of stolons and number of branches bearing polyps.

2. The axial skeleton composed of calcareous spicules or horn-like material, gorgonin is present.

3. Commonly known as sea fans, sea feathers and sea whips are found in tropical and subtropical shores.

   Examples : *Gorgonia, Corallium.*

Order 6. Pennatulacea

1. The colony is elongated and divided into a proximal stalk or peduncle and a distal rachis.

2. Peduncle is embedded in the mud and sand.

3. Rachis is the axial polyp bears numerous dimorphic polyps on its lateral branches.

4. The main stem is supported by calcareous or horny skeleton.

   Examples : *Pennatula, Renilla, Cavernularia, Pteroides.*

Subclass II. Zoantharia or Hexacorallia

1. Solitary or colonial marine forms.

2. Tentacles simple, rarely branched hollow cone-shaped, numerous arranged in the multiple of five and six but never eight.

3. Mesenteries are numerous arranged in the multiple of five or six, may be complete or incomplete.

4. Two siphonoglyphs are commonly present.

5. Endoskeleton when present is calcareous, derived from ectoderm.

6. Polyps are usuallly monomorphic.

Order 1. Actiniaria

1. Solitary or colonial.

2. Body cylindrical divided into oral disc, column and base.

3. The aboral end is also provided with a pedal disc.

4. Tentacles and mesenteries are numerous and often arranged in the multiple of six.

5. Siphonoglyph is one or more.

6. Skeleton absent.

   Examples: *Actinia, Metridium, Adamsia, Edwardsia.*

Order 2. Madreporaria

1. Mostly colonial rarely solitary form.

2. Exoskeleton is hard and calcareous secreted by the ectoderm.

3. Polyps are small enclosed in the cup-like cavities of the exoskeleton.

4. Siphonoglyph is usually absent.

   Examples : *Astraea, Fungia, Favia, Madrepora, Meandrina.*

Order 3. Zoanthidea

1. Mostly colonial sometimes solitary forms.

2. Skeleton and pedal disc absent, but the body wall may contain calcareous bodies.

3. Polyps are generally small.

4. Mesenteries are paired. A pair composed of one complete and one incomplete mesentary.

5. Only one ventral siphonoglyph present.

   Example : *Zoanthus.*

Order 4. Antipatharia

1. Plant-like colonial forms found in the deep waters in the oceans.

2. The lower end of the colony usually consists of a basal plate for the attachment with some objects.

3. Skeleton in the form of a branched chitinoid axis derived from the ectoderm.

4. The axial skeleton bears the polyps which are dioecious but the colony may be hermaphrodite.

5. Mesenteries and tentacles are 6–24 in number.

6. Two siphonoglyphs present.

   Example : *Antipathes.*

Order 5. Ceriantharia

1. Long solitary anemone-like forms living in the vertical cylindrical cavities in the sea bottom.

2. Body smooth cylindrical and elongated with an oral disc.

3. Pedal disc and skeleton absent.

4. Tentacles are simple numerous and of two types, marginal and oral.

5. Mesenteries are numerous, single and complete.

6. Only single dorsal siphonoglyph present.

   Example: *Cerianthus.*

REPRESENTATIVE TYPES OF COELENTERATA

1. *Bougainvillea. Bougainvillea* (Fig. 35.1) is a dimorphic colony; a creeping hydrorhiza gives off branches which produce numerous polyps and medusae. The polyp has a long stalk and a hydranth. The hydranth has a mouth on a manubrium. Just below the manubrium is a ring of tentacles, there is a second ring of larger aboral tentacles around the lower part of the hydranth. Both kinds of tentacles are solid with an axis of vacuolated endoderm cells. A stiff perisarc covers the hydrorhiza, branches and stalks, but it stops short at the base of the hydranth, and it does not form a hydrotheca. From the

coenosarc of the stalk arise several buds, within each bud a single medusa develops. The medusa is like a deep bell, it breaks from the stalk and swims away ; there is no blastostyle.

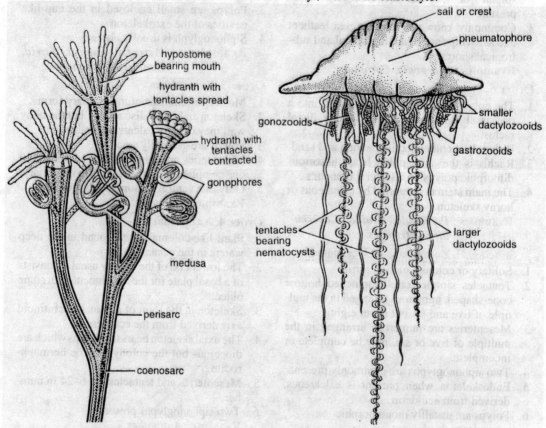

Fig. 35.1. *Bougainvillea.*   **Fig. 35.2.** *Physalia.*

2. *Physalia* **(Portuguese man-of-war).** *Physalia* (Fig. 35.2) is a polymorphic colony of bright blue colour. It is found floating in tropical and sub-tropical oceans. The members of the colony arise from the coenosarc. There is a large gas-filled **pneumatophore**, formed by several medusoids, it floats above the surface, it contains gas glands which produce a gas having 90% nitrogen, 9% oxygen and 1% argon. In some species, but not in *Physalia,* the pneumatophore has a pore through which gas can be let out to sink the colony. Below the pneumatophore hangs a colony of several non-linear **cormidia;** a cormidium is a group of polymorphic individuals which are modified polyps, they are dactylozooids, gonozooids, and gastrozooids. **Dactylozooids** are of various sizes, each is a tubular, mouthless individual with a long tentacle having strong muscles and a twisting ribbon of nematocysts. Dactylozooids may be up to 12 metres long, they form a drift net for capturing fish for food, the tentacles pull them up. **Gastrozooids** are tubular with a mouth and a long tentacle may be present. The lips of gastrozooids are applied to the fish and partly digested food is sucked up in liquid form. **Gonozooids** or gonodendra are branching blastostyles having leaf-like **gonopalpons** and male and female medusae or **gonophores.** The female gonophores are degenerate, they are set free for a short time, the male gonophores are degenerate but are permanently attached. The germ cells form a planula larva which gives rise to a new colony. The pneumatophore and gonophores are modified medusoids. A small fish *Nomeus* lives near the deadly tentacles in a commensal relationship with *Physalia.* The members of the colony of *Physalia* show a division of labour and, thus, simulate the organs of Metazoa.

3. *Halistemma.* *Halistemma* (Fig. 35.3) is a polymorphic colony consisting of a long, slender, floating stem to which polymorphic zooids are attached along its length. The upper end of the stem has a small **pneumatophore** which is like an invaginated cup, it is gas-filled. Below the pneumatophore are several closely set nectocalyces or swimming bells, they are transparent and look like medusae without manubria, but they have a velum, muscles and canals. Nectocalyces contract rhythmically to take in water and pump it-out at once by which they propel the colony in sea water. Below the nectocalyces on the stem are several cormidia in groups one after another in a linear series. A cormidium has a gastrozooid, dactylozooid, hydrophyllium and gonozooids. Gastrozooid is tubular with a mouth and a tentacle which is long and branched and bears numerous nematocysts. Dactylozooid is tubular with no mouth, but an unbranched tentacle which is sensory. Gonozooids or sporosacs lie in groups, they bear male and female medusae or gono- phores. Hydrophyllium is a shield-shaped leaf which covers and protects the rest of the cormidium. The upper end is the proximal end, it corresponds to the attached end of *Obelia*. Coelenterata are radially symmetrical, but *Halistemma* shows bilateral symmetry. Germ cells form a zygote which develops into a planula, one end of the planula invaginates to form the pneumatophore, while the lower end forms a polyp, this first polyp by elongation and budding forms the colony.

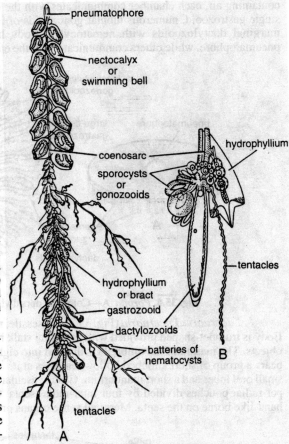

4. *Velella. Velella* (Fig. 35.4) is a polymorphic colony which looks like a single medusa. It has a rhomboidal body on whose upper surface is an oblique sail. Dorsally there is a pneumatophore like a chitinous chambered disc which contains air, the chambers communicate with the exterior. From the middle of the body hangs a single large gastrozooid having a mouth. All around the gastrozooid are numerous gonozooids or blasto-

Fig. 35.3. *Halistemma.* A—Entire colony; B—cormidium.

styles, each having a mouth, they produce free-swimming medusae. On the margin of the body is a circle of long tentacle-like dactylozooids having nematocysts. In the body are numerous ramifying canals of ectodermal and endodermal origin, the endodermal canals communicate with the enteron of gonozooids and gastrozooid, while the ectodermal canals open into the chambers of the pneumatophore. The pneumatophore and its sail are a modified medusoid, but the gastrozooid, gonozooids, and dactylozooids are modified polyps, *Velella* is found along the Southern Atlantic coast where the colony is carried about by the wind.

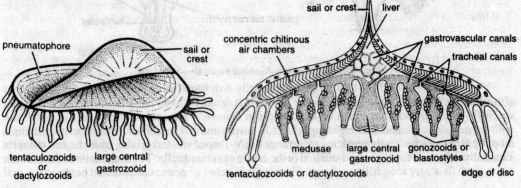

Fig. 35.4. *Velella.*

Fig. 35.5. V.S. of *Valella.*

5. *Porpita.* *Porpita* (Fig 35.6) is a polymorphic colony allied closely to *Velella*. The colony resembles a medusa. It has a large disc-like body with a chitinous, chambered pneumatophore containing air, each chamber communicates with the exterior by two pores. From the body hang a single gastrozooid, numerous tubular gonozooids or blastostyles bearing medusae, and many long marginal dactylozooids with nematocysts. Body has ramifying canals, some open into the pneumatophore, while others communicate with the enteron of zooids.

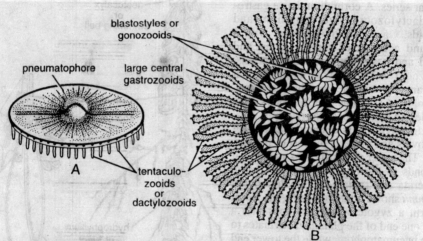

Fig. 35.6. *Porpita*. A—Colony in dorsal view; B—Colony in ventral view.

6. *Lucernaria.* *Lucernaria* (Fig. 35.7) is a sessile, marine Scyphozoa found in the British coasts. Body is trumpet-shaped provided with an aboral stalk by which it is attached to sea weeds and other objects. The margin of the umbrella is divided into eight short and hollow adradial lobes. Each lobe bears a group of short knobbed hollow tentacles at its end. Mouth is cruciform (four-cornered) with small oral lobes and a short manubrium. Gastrovascular system consists of a central stomach and four per-radial pouches divided by four inter-radial septa. Gastric filaments are numerous. Gonads are band-like borne on the septa. Marginal sense organs or tentaculocysts and velum are absent.

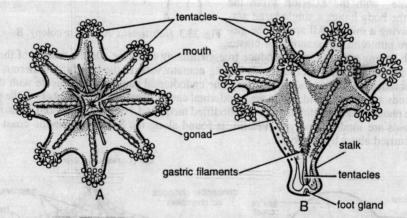

Fig. 35.7. *Lucernaria*. A—Oral view; B—Side view.

7. *Cyanea.* *Cyanea* (Fig. 35.8) is a common jelly-fish found in coastal waters of America and also extend in the polar regions. The disc or umbrella is usually 5 to 40 cm in diameter but the largest species *Cyanea arctica* may reach up to 2 meters in diameter. The umbrella is saucer or bowl-like with its margin scalloped into eight lappets. It is purple and red in colour. Each lappet contains a rhopalium in its niche . Eight tentacles are arranged in V-shaped clusters arising from the subumbrella adradially. Mouth is four cornered situated in the centre of subumbrella. The four corners of the mouth extend into four very long frilly oral arms. Four large bunches of gonads are situated between the oral arms and tentacles. Numerous radial canals branch into the rhopalia and tentacles near the margin. Ring canal is absent. *Cyanea arctica* is commonly known as sea blubber.

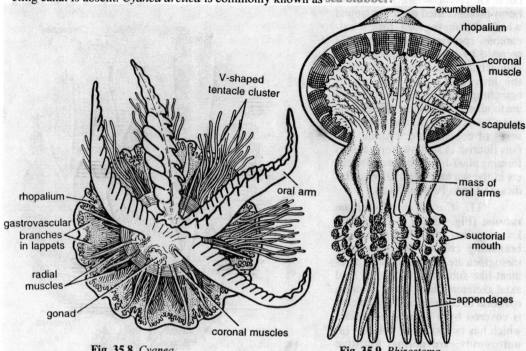

Fig. 35.8. *Cyanea.*   **Fig. 35.9.** *Rhizostoma.*

8. *Rhizostoma*. *Rhizostoma* (Fig. 35.9) is a large jelly-fish found in the shallow waters of Indo-Pacific region. It has a saucer-shaped umbrella with a scalloped margin having eight or sixteen tentaculocysts in different species, there are no marginal tentacles. In a young *Rhizostoma* there is a central mouth, but in the adult the mouth is closed by the overgrowth and folding of four oral arms, and it is replaced by thousands of pore-like suctorial mouths which lie along the closed grooves of oral arms,they are connected to the canals. The oral arms become organs of external digestion,they digest the food and the fluid is absorbed by sucking mouths. This polystomatous (many-mouthed) condition is unique in animals. Oral arms are bifurcated distally to form eight long, club-shaped terminal appendages. Tentacles lie only on oral arms in two groups, they look like filamentous roots and bear nematocysts. Additional mouth-bearing outgrowths called scapulets occur on the oral arms just below the bell.

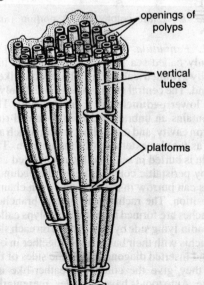

Fig. 35.10. *Tubipora musica.*

9. *Tubipora*. *Tubipora* (Fig. 35.10) is commonly known as organ pipe coral. Elongated polyps lie parallel to each other, their internal skeleton made of fused spicules, from mesogloea forms erect parallel tubes which arise from a basal plate and are joined by calcareous platforms. Polyps lie in the tubes partly projecting above. Polyps are green and the skeleton is dark red due to iron salts. *Tubipora* is widely distributed on coral reefs.

10. *Gorgonia*. *Gorgonia* (Fig. 35.11) is commonly known as sea fan. It forms large, upright lattice-like branching colonies of yellow and red colour, they are up to 50 cm in height. The colony is fixed by a basal plate from which branches arise in one plane only. The branches anastomose in some species. Branches bear

slender polyps with eight pinnate tentacles. Branches are joined by cross connections in *G. flabellum*, but in *G. verrucosa* there are no cross connections. The skeleton is not calcareous but is made of a

horny protein called gorgonin around which the mesogloea forms calcareous spicules. The skeleton is secreted by the outer surface of the animal but it appears internal. Within the mesogloea is a network of branching tubes called solenia which are tubular extensions of enteron carrying water, oxygen, and food. The sexes of colonies are separate. Sea fans flourish in shallow tropical seas forming plant-like grooves and thickets in the sea near Malaya, West Indies, and Indo-Pacific Ocean.

11. *Corallium. Corallium rubrum* (Fig. 35.12) is commonly known as red coral. It is an upright branching colony. Spicules from mesogloea are compacted with a cement-like substance to form a hard axial skeleton which is the precious red coral of commerce. The skeleton is covered by a delicate coenosarc which has two kinds of polyps : (a) autozooids are normal nutritive polyps with eight pinnate tentacles and mesenteries, they bear gonads, (b) siphonozooids have no tentacles, mesenteries are reduced,they are small and pump water into the canals of the colony; thus, *Corallium* is a dimorphic colony. It is found near Japan and in deep Mediterranean, it is highly valued as it is used for making jewellery.

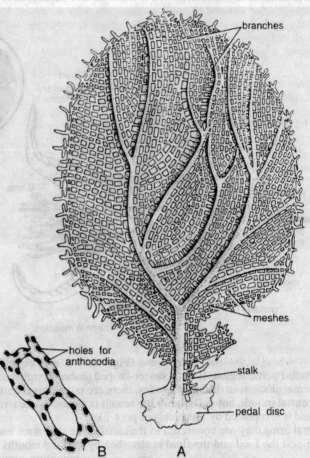

Fig. 35.11. *Gorgonia*. A—Entire colony; B—A portion (magnified).

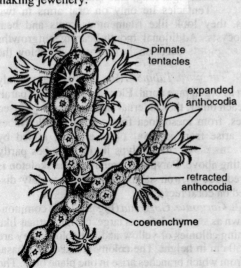

Fig. 35.12. *Corallium rubrum.*

12. *Pennatula. Pennatula* (Fig.35.13) is commonly called sea pen. It forms a quill-like bilaterally symmetrical colony which looks like a fern frond. The central stem is a huge axial polyp. It has a lower peduncle and a distal rachis. The stem contains an unbranched horny skeletal rod, an enteron cavity, and mesogloea within which are solenia as tubular extensions of the enteron. The peduncle is buried in sea mud by an enlarged end bulb, by peristaltic contractions of the peduncle sea pens can burrow in the mud and even change their position. The rachis bears lateral branches, the branches are formed by nutritive polyps called anthocodia lying side by side in rows on each side of the rachis with their bases fused together in one plane and inserted diagonally into the sides of the rachis, they give the colony a feather-like appearance. Autozooids have tentacles, mesenteries and gonads. On the back of the rachis, lying in two

zones are reduced polyps called siphonozooids, they have no tentacles,their mesenteries are reduced, but their siphonoglyphs are enlarged, they cause circulation of water in the canals of the colony. The skeleton has a horny axis in the stem, and calcareous spicules in the mesogloea, there is no axis in the branches. *Pennatula sulcata* has a bright orange-red colour, some species may be 3 metres long, it is found in the warm coast of the Atlantic and Pacific Oceans.

13. *Renilla.* Renilla (Fig. 35.14) is commonly called sea pansy Colony consists of a short peduncle which is embedded in the mud and a circular kidney-shaped (reniform)leaf-like rachis. Rachis is broad on the ventral surface and devoid of polyps. The dorsal surface is pink or violet in colour and covered with white zooids or polyps. The colony is dimorphic, bears two kinds of zooids : (i) Autozooids or antho-codia are scattered irregularly on the dorsal surface and nutritive in function. (ii) Siphonozooids are arranged in clusters and maintain the circulation of water within the colony. A median bare track devoid of polyps extends from the peduncle to about the middle of the rachis where it terminates at a special exhalent siphono-zooid. An axial skeleton is entirely absent. *Renilla* is a colonial form and occurs in shallow waters of coasts of North and South Carolina and West Indies.

14. *Adamsia.* Adamsia (Fig. 35.15) is found at-tached to the empty shells of gastropods inhabited by hermit crab, *Eupagurus,* Body is large cylindrical and divisible into three distinct regions, the pedal disc, column and oral disc. Pedal disc is flat, sucker-like and bilobed by which it is attached to the molluscan shell.

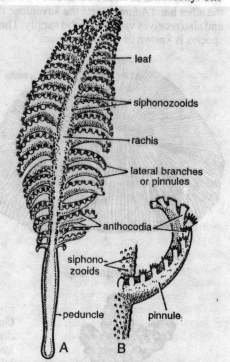

Fig. 35.13. *Pennatula.* A—Entire colony; B—A portion magnified.

Column is cylindrical bears a band of cinclidal tubercles at its base. Two siphonoglyphs and six pairs of mesenteries are present. Oral disc bears a central mouth surrounded by large number of tentacles.

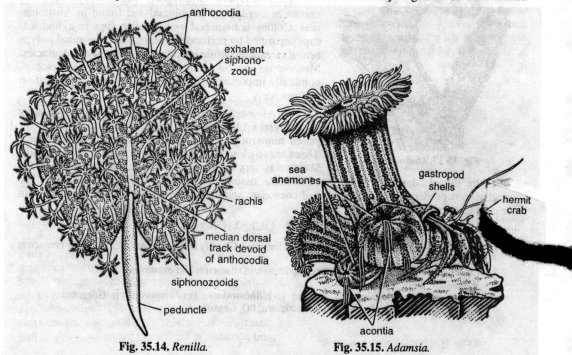

Fig. 35.14. *Renilla.*

Fig. 35.15. *Adamsia.*

Adamsia furnishes a good example of commensalism (mutual benefit). *Adamsia* protects the hermit crab from the attacks of its enemies by covering the body and stinging by means of nematocysts. On the other hand *Adamsia* gets the advantage of transportation from one place to another by hermit crab and also receives variety of food supply. This kind of partnership between individuals of two different species is known as commensalism.

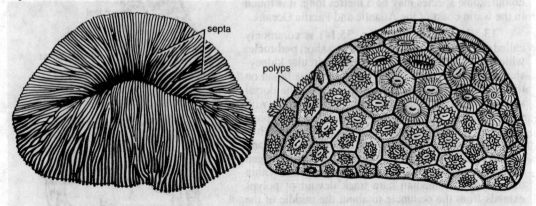

Fig. 35.16. *Fungia*.   Fig. 35.18. *Astraea*.

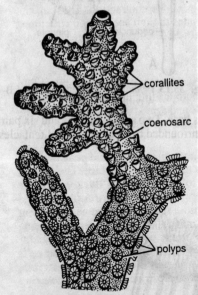

Fig. 35.17. *Madrepora*.

15. *Fungia*. *Fungia* (Fig. 35.16) commonly known as mushroom coral, is solitary found in warm seas usually in Gulf of California. The mushroom coral is of large size, with discoidal corallite, convex on the upper and concave on the lower surface, Septa are numerous and connected together by small synaptacula. Theca is present only on the lower surface. Adult animal bears a single large polyp with many tentacles. Siphonoglyph absent. Reproduction resembling more or less transverse fission.

16. *Madrepora*. *Madrepora* (Fig. 35.17) commonly known as horn coral is colonial and found in Australian seas. Colony is branched with small polyps in cylindrical cups separated by perforated coenosteum. Terminal polyps bear six tentacles, while lateral polyps bear twelve tentacles. Mesenteries are bilaterally arranged. *Madrepora* is economically important because it takes part in the formation of coral reefs.

17. *Astraea*. *Astraea* (Fig. 35.18) is a massive stony coral found on the coasts of warm seas. The colony comprises numerous closely fitted polygonal cups or theca. Theca are so closed to each other as to have common walls. Skeleton is very hard made up of calcium carbonate and is secreted by the ectoderm for support of delicate tissues. The colony is formed by buds. The coenochyme is produced by calcification of coenosarc and also gives rise to corallites which lie in close contact to each other.

REVISION QUESTIONS

1. Give in detail the characters of Phylum Coelenterata. Classify it up to classes and give their characters and examples.
2. Classify Coelenterata up to orders giving important characters and examples.
3. Write short notes on :
   (i) *Physalia* ; (ii) *Porpita*; (iii) *Velella* ; (iv) *Rhizostoma* ; (v) *Tubipora* ; (vi) *Gorgonia* ; (vii) *Pennatula* ; (viii) *Renilla* ; (ix) *Madrepora*; (x) *Corallium*.

36

Coelenterata in General

TISSUES

The tissues of Coelenterata consist of ectoderm and endoderm, each forming a single layer of a variety of cells, and Coelenterata are regarded as animals at the tissue level of organization. Together the cells form a thin body wall surrounding an enteron cavity. Increase in thickness and complexity of the body wall is made possible by the development of an intermediate gelatinous layer called mesogloea. The polyps of lower Coelenterata have a very thin mesogloea, but in polyps of Anthozoa the mesogloea contains fibres and cells and it has become much thicker ; in the larger medusae it is very thick and firm, it has become like an internal skeleton and it also stores food. The chief type of cell found in lower Coelenterata is a columnar epitheliomuscular cell produced into muscle fibres which are embedded in the mesogloea. Such a cell is like a protozoan because its parts carry on different functions. The endodermal cells can form flagella for churning up the fluid in the enteron, or the flagella can be withdrawn and pseudopodia formed by the same cells for engulfing food into food vacuoles, the same cells also form muscle processes for contraction. Thus, all the functions of the body are carried out by tissues and never by organs though specialized structures, such as tentaculocysts, may be regarded as organs, but in general the Coelenterata have reached only a tissue-grade of organization.

POLYP AND MEDUSA

The polyp leads an easy sedentary life, it has a fixed cylindrical body with a comparatively thin body wall, the free distal end has a hypostome with an apical mouth leading into an enteron, below the hypostome is a circle of extensible tentacles directed upwards and armed with nematocysts , the tentacles may be hollow containing an extension of the enteron, the proximal end of the polyp is closed.

The medusa leads a freely drifting life which requires an elaborate structure and physiological development. Great widening of the body has occurred, especially along the oral surface. The enteron is restricted to a central gastric cavity and canals, this is due to an increase in thickness of the mesogloea on the aboral side which pushes the two endoderm layers together to form a double layered endoderm lamella. The hypostome has become the manubrium whose rim has become wide and bent downward to form a bell, this has pushed the tentacles to the margin of the bell, tentacles hang downwards, and at times a second set of tentacles may develop on the manubrium. The muscular system of the medusa is highly developed because the muscular portion of epitheliomuscular cells increases to form elongated striated muscle fibres and the epithelial part diminishes. The nervous system is diffuse, as in the polyp, but in some medusae it becomes concentrated to form a nerve ring and in connection with this well defined sense organs are formed.

POLYMORPHISM

Polymorphism (Gr., poly= many ; morphe=form) is the occurrence of several different types of individuals or zooids in a single species during its life cycle or as members of the colony, the members perform different functions so that there is a division of labour amongst the members. Coelenterata are noted for their polymorphism, but the various types are reducible to either a polypoid or medusoid type. The polyp and medusa occur in a number of morphological variations. However, polymorphism may be defined as *the representation of a single organism by more than one kind of individuals or zooids which differ in their form and function.*

Patterns of Polymorphism

Most Hydrozoa exhibit dimorphism, there is a nutritive polyp or gastrozooid which is sessile, it has a mouth, tentacles and an enteron cavity for food. The second individual is a medusa which is jelly-like, saucer-shaped, with tentacles on the margin, it is free-swimming and bears gonads. Alcyonaria have only polyps, but they are dimorphic, a nutritive and reproductive polyp called autozooid which has tentacles, gonads and mesenteries; the other polyp is a siphonozooid with no tentacles or gonads, it only maintains a circulation of water in the canals of the colony.

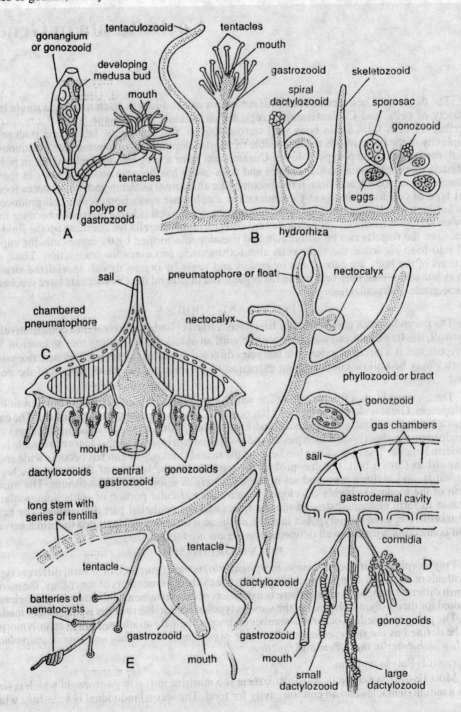

Fig. 36.1. Polymorphic colonies of Hydrozoa. A—*Obelia* ; B—*Hydractinia* ; C—*Velella*; D—*Physalia* showing a single cormidium; E—Generalized calycophoran Siphonophora showing a single cormidium.

Some hydrozoan colonies are **trimorphic,** besides the nutritive polyps and reproductive medusae, they also have modified polyps called gonozooids or blastostyles, often enclosed in a chitinous gonotheca, they have no mouth or tentacles, and they produce medusae or their morphological equivalents by budding.

Siphonophora show the highest degree of polymorphism which is not found anywhere else in the animal kingdom. They may have three kinds of polypoid zooids and four kinds of medusoid zooids.

The **polypoid zooids** are as follows :

1. Gastrozooids are tubular or saccular with a mouth, and there may be one tentacle bearing nematocysts, they are used for digestion and ingestion of liquid food. Usually a single long and contractile hollow tentacle arises from the base of gastrozooid which bears numerous fine lateral contractile branches called **tentilla.** The tentilla has knob or coil of nematocysts .

2. Dactylozooids are for defence and obtaining food, they are tubular with no mouth, with a long tentacle armed with batteries of nematocysts. Modified dactylozooids associated with gonophores on gonozooids are termed gonopalpons. The dactylozooids are also called **palpons** or **feelers.**

3. Gonozooids may be like gastrozooids or they may be branching blastostyles bearing clusters of degenerate male and female medusae which produce germ cells for reproduction. Mostly, the gonozooids take the form of a branched stalk called **gonodendron** having tufts of **gonophores** with **gonopalpons.**

The **medusoid zooids** are as follows :

1. Pneumatophore is a gas-filled vesicle or bladder which functions as a float and helps in swimming, the pneumatophore is an inverted medusoid devoid of mesogloea, but its walls are muscular and it has gas glands. It shows great variation in its structure and size in different siphonophores.

2. Phyllozooids are leaf-like **bracts** or thick and gelatinous medusoids having a canal of the enteron. They are protective and shield some zooids of a colony.

3. Nectocalyces or **nectophores** are bell-shaped medusoids with a velum, radial canals and circular canal, they have no mouth, manubrium, tentacles or sense organs, A nectocalyx is muscular and brings about locomotion of the colony by swimming. It is also referred to as **nectophore** or **nectozooid.**

4. Gonophores occur singly or in clusters on blastostyles, they are degenerate medusae with no mouth, tentacles or sense organs, but they have a velum, canals and a manubrium which bears gonads. Gonophores are dioecious and produce germ cells for reproduction.

Origin of Polymorphism

A number of theories are given to illustrate the origin of polymorphism in Coelenterata ; some of these theories are as follows :

1. Poly-organ theory. This theory was proposed by **Huxley, Eschscholtz** and **Metschnikoff.** According to this theory, a polymorphic colony is supposed to be a single medusoid zooid; its various components are regarded to be the modified organs of this medusoid zooid. The various parts of the zooid, *i.e.,* manubrium, tentacles, umbrella, etc., multiply independently from one another and they have assumed different forms to perform different functions.

2. Poly-person theory. This theory was proposed by **Leuckart, Vogt** and **Gegenbaur.** According to this theory a polymorphic coelenterate is supposed to be a colonial form in which various types of zooids have been aggregated to perform different functions. All the zooids of the colony are either polyps or medusae or both but the primitive zooid of the colony is of polyp type.

3. Haeckel, Balfour and **Sedgwick** have agreed that poly-person theory is more correct but they are of the view that the primitive zooid of the colony is probably medusoid which have produced other medusae by asexual budding. Thus, the zooids of the colony are nothing more than the organs of medusiform zooid which have shifted their attachment.

4. Recently, **Moser** has revived the poly-organ theory. According to him, the various zooids of the colony are organs which have not yet attained the grade of polymorphic form. Thus, the siphonophores are the most primitive existing coelenterates. This theory has not been recognised in general because it altogether denies the colonial nature of siphonopohores.

Polymorphism and Alternation of Generations

Polymorphism is, no doubt, a phenomenon of division of labour, *i.e.,* different functions are attributed to different individuals of the polymorphic form, rather than to the parts or organs of one individual or zooid.

All the members of the colony whether polypoids or medusoids, are formed from the coenosarc. Polymorphism is associated with the life cycles of Coelenterata. In monomorphic forms, like *Hydra,* the polyp reproduces both asexually and sexually, this condition also applies to Anthozoa. The life cycle remains very simple ; it may be represented as : polyp–egg–polyp. With the origin of polymorphism, the reproductive powers of the organisms are divided among the different zooids of the colony. In these cases the polyps reproduce asexually to give rise to medusoid forms (*i.e.,* gonophores) which reproduce sexually to form polyp. The life cycle, thus, becomes complicated and may be represented as polyp–medusa–egg–planula–polyp. Therefore , the so called alternation of generations or metagenesis comes into existence where, in fact, asexual polypoid generation alternates sexual medusoid generation.

Significance of Polymorphism

The polymorphism is essentially a phenomenon of division of labour in which different functions are performed by the different members or zooids of the colony, *viz.,* polyps are related to feeding and asexual reproduction, while medusae are related to sexual reproduction and so on.

CORALS AND CORAL REEFS

Corals

Corals are animals belonging to the phylum Coelenterata. These are solitary or colonial polypoid forms and live in a skeleton of calcium carbonate secreted by themselves. Some of them grow into huge mounds, while others are large and branched colonies. However, most of the corals belong to the class Anthozoa and few others to the class Hydrozoa.

The hydrozoan corals belong to order Milleporina, *e.g., Millepora* and order Stylasterina, *e.g., Stylaster.* These are colonial forms and secrete massive exoskeletons. Within the exoskeletons, two types of polypoid forms, the gastrozooids and branched dactylozooids are found . In fact the epidermis of these polypoid forms is modified and referred to as the calicoblast layer which secretes the calcareous exoskeleton. These corals are found with other corals forming huge mounds.

The anthozoan corals belong to subclasses Octocorallia and Hexacorallia both. The octocorallia corals belong to order Stolonifera, *eg., Tubipora ;* order Alcyonacea, *e.g., Alcyonium ;* order Coenothecalia, *e.g., Heliopora* and order Gorgonacea including sea fans like *Gorgonia* and *Corallium.* The Hexacorallia corals belong to the order Madreporaria, *eg., Astraea, Fungia, Madrepora* and *Meandrina* , etc.; and to the order Antipatharia, *eg., Antipathes.*

Among Octocorallia, Stolonifera includes colonial corals like *Tubipora* or organ pipe coral. In it the skeleton is made of fused calcareous spicules which form vertical parallel tubes connected together by plateforms. The skeleton is tinged red by iron salts and the polyps lie in the tubes partly projecting above. It is widely distributed on coral reefs. The Alcyonacea includes soft corals like *Alcyonium.* In it the coral is a colony of polyps having an endoskeleton of separate caleareous spicules embedded in its massive mesogloea. The Coenothecalia includes a single genus of blue coral, the *Heliopora.* In it the coral is a colony of polyps which secrete calcareous spicules to form a massive skeleton called corallium. The Gorgonacea includes horny corals, the sea fans like *Gorgonia.* In it the coral is a branched colony of polyps which secrete a horny proteinaceous material with calcareous spicules around the polyps.

Among Hexacorallia, Antipatharia includes black corals like *Antipathes.* In it the colony is tree-like and its skeleton consists of branched chitinoid axis. The Madreporaria includes stony corals or true corals like mushroom coral (*Fungia*), star coral (*Astraea*) and brain coral (*Meandrina* or *Meandra*). Among these some are solitary, while most of them are colonial forms and the principal builders of the coral reefs.

The stony corals, in general, have polyps which are very similar in structure to sea anemones with tentacles and mesenteries in multiples of six, but they are different in having no siphonoglyphs and in being usually colonial. They have an ectodermal external skeleton of calcium carbonate. The exoskeleton of a polyp is called a corallite. and the exoskeleton of the colony is a corallum. The epidermis of polyp secretes a basal disc of calcium carbonate, then walls of a cup called theca which immovably ensloses the polyp, in the theca are radiating septa like mesenteries of an anemone, the septa bear nematocyst. In the centre of the theca is a vertical rod called columella to which the primary septa are fused. All these form the exoskeleton of a polyp , the polyp fills the corallite and partly projects above. In a colony thousands of polyp form their corallites which are fused together to form a corallum, but all the polyps in a corallum are joined together by lateral connections. A coral colony increases in size by budding new polyps along the margin of the colony. Feeding in corals occurs only at night.

As mentioned, the corals, in general, have diverse shapes and sizes, some are solitary and have large polyps, but the majority are colonial with very small polyps. Some corals are used as ornaments and jewellery. Coral colonies are most abundant in tropical seas though some occur in arctic and temperate seas, but most of them flourish at a temperature above $22^{\circ}C$.

Coral Reefs

Definition. Vaughan (1917) has defined coral reef as *"a ridge or mound of lime stone, the upper surface of which is near the surface of the sea and which is formed of calcium carbonate by the actions of organisms, chiefly corals. "*

The coral reefs are, in fact, produced by corals belonging to Anthozoa, particularly by stony corals, the Madreporaria. Hence, these are supposed to be the principal builders of coral reefs though there are certain other contributors also. A coral reef, in fact, is a ridge of lime stone whose upper surface is just below the sea surface and it is exposed at low tides.

Distribution and conditions of reef formation. Corals have built a thick stratum of the earth's crust, they have coral reefs in the Caribbean seas and in the Indo-Pacific region from east coast of Africa to the northeastern coast of Australia which is known as the Great Barrier Reef. However, Fiji islands of Pacific Ocean and those situated in Bahama islands region are the best known coral islands of the world. Bermuda is a coral island where houses are built of coral blocks. Around India, coral reefs are found off Port Okha and Dwarka in the gulf of Kutch and also off Rameshwaram in the gulf of Mannar between India and Sri Lanka. The coral reefs are also located at Andaman and Nicobar islands and at Lakshadeep Islands.

The coral reefs grow best at a depth of about 30 metres or less and normally in warm water up to about $20^{\circ}C$. Light and amount of sediment also limit the reef forming corals. They also fail to grow in dark shaded areas and they completely die in total darkness. Below 50 metres no reef building corals are found though some solitary corals exist up to 8000 metres.

Components of coral reefs. In addition to stony corals, other components in the formation of coral reefs are Millepora, Tubipora, Heliopora, Alcyonaria, Gorgonians, Foraminifera, Coralline algae and branching algae, etc. The coral reefs are also inhabited by a number of sponges, anaemones, sea-urchins, starfishes, crabs, snails, bivalves, etc.

Types of coral reefs. The various types of coral reefs are grouped into three major types :

1. Fringing reefs. The fringing reefs also referred to as the shore reefs are built from the sea bottom and extend from the shore up to 1/4 miles having no navigable channel between the shore and reef. This zone of the sea is called edge or front . However, sometimes reef beds are broken to result into irregular channels called lagoon. Such reefs are composed largely of coral sand having living and dead corals building reefs, mud and other animals. Fringing reef is very common in East Indies.

2. Barrier reef. The barrier reefs are like fringing reefs but they are situated in the sea nearly 1 km to 15 km away from the shore. Therefore, navigable channel called lagoon separates these reefs from the shore. The lagoon may be 20 to 40 fathoms deep, hence, it becomes navigable. The Great Barrier Reef on the north-east coast of Australia is 1,200 miles long, about 20–70 miles wide and situated nearly 90 miles away from the shore.

3. Atoll reef. The atoll reef, also referred to as coral island or lagoon island, is a circular or horse-shoe-shaped reef enclosing a lagoon of water which may be small or large up to 50 miles across. Atoll reef may be broken to form channels; some suitable for navigation and other may not be suitable for it. An interesting atoll reef example is Aldabra in the Indian Ocean about 260 miles northeast of the Malagasy Republic and 400 miles from the coast of Africa.

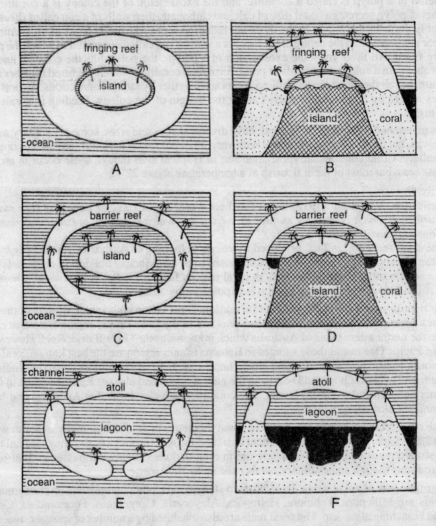

Fig. 36.2. Coral reefs. A—Fringing reef ; B—Fringing reef in section; C—Barrier reef ; D—Barrier reef in section ; E—Atoll reef; F—Atoll reef in section.

Formation of coral reefs. The coral reefs have great vertical thickness though reef-building corals live only up to depth of 50 metres, and those of past geological ages also lived in shallow littoral waters. How the great thickness of coral reefs has been made is explained by several theories of which two may be considered.

1. Darwin's subsidence theory. This theory states that coral reefs were first formed as fringing reefs on sloping shores, they became barrier reefs when the shores sank with water channel between them and the land. If the land is an island which sinks completely, then an atoll is formed. Thus, sinking or subsidence has caused the thickness of the reefs.

2. Daly's glacial-control theory. This theory states that during the last glacial period the formation of ice caps lowered the ocean level by 60 to 70 metres below the present surface. Waves cut the shores to make flat platforms suitable for growth of corals. As the ice caps melted and temperature rose, corals began to grow on these platforms and rose upwards with rising ocean level, and all types of reefs were formed on the pre-existing platforms. There is evidence that coral reefs are growing today on submerged land and the foundations of reefs are now at a much greater depth than they were when corals first began to grow.

Observation of living corals shows that their rate of growth is from 5 mm to 20 cm per year, thus, a 50 metre deep reef could be formed in less than 8,000 years, and all the known reefs could have been built in under 30,000 years. Some borings made in coral reefs showed that the reef rested on level platforms, but some other borings showed that reefs had no underlying platforms but had only sand and shell below them. It appears from these facts that some reefs were laid down on pre-existing platforms, but many reefs were formed according to Darwin's subsidence theory.

REVISION QUESTIONS

1. Give a detailed account on polymorphism in coelenterates.
2. Write an essay on corals and coral reefs.
3. Write notes on :
   (i) Justify that coelenterates are at tissue level of body organization;
   (ii) Generalized polyp and medusa;
   (iii) Corallite;
   (iv) Types of coral reefs.

37

Phylum Ctenophora

The Ctenophora (Gr., *kestos*=comb ; *phors*=bearing) are marine, pelagic or free, solitary and biradially symmetrical organisms, with transparent gelatinous bodies, lacking nematocysts, possessing ciliary plates in eight rows and possessing a gelatinous ectomesoderm containing mesenchymal muscle fibres. All the ctenophores have transparent gelatinous bodies and are commonly known as "comb-jellies". *Pleurobrachia*, a typical example of Ctenophora, has been described in the following pages.

PLEUROBRACHIA
SYSTEMATIC POSITION

Phylum	....	**Ctenophora**
Class	....	**Tentaculata**
Order	....	**Cydippida**
Genus	....	*Pleurobrachia*

HABIT AND HABITAT

Ctenophores are very common marine animals found in diverse habitat. They are widely distributed being specially abundant in the warmer seas, though some occur in temperate or arctic regions. They are of planktonic habit floating in the surface waters, mostly near shores but a few live to depth of even 3000 metres. Ctenophores feed on small marine animals including the eggs and larvae of molluscs, crustaceans and fish.

EXTERNAL FEATURES

Pleurobrachia has a pear-shaped body about 5–20 mm in diameter, and of glass transparency. The mouth is situated at the centre of the oral pole and the opposite or aboral pole is occupied by a complicated and characteristic sense organ. This sense organ is a modified statocyst and acts as an organ of equilibrium. From the opposite sides of the broad end hang two long tentacles provided with numerous little tag-like processes. Each tentacle springs from a deep cavity of sheath into which it can be retracted completely. The surface bears eight equidistant meridional bands or swimming plates or costae starting from near the aboral pole and extending about two-thirds of the distance towards the oral pole. Each band is constituted by a row of transversely arranged comb-like structures, consisting of narrow plates frayed at their outer ends. During life the frayed ends are in constant movement lashing to and fro, and so propelling the animal through the water.

HISTOLOGY

The body is covered externally by a delicate ectodermal epithelium. The epithelium of stomodaeum is ectodermal, that of infundibulum and its canals en-

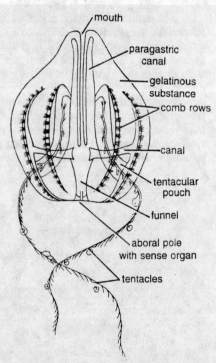

Fig. 37.1. *Pleurobrachia.* (From the side).

dodermal. Both ectodermal and endodermal epithelia are ciliated. The space between the external epithelium and canal system is filled by a soft, jelly-like mesogloea. The tentacle sheath is an invagination of the ectoderm, and the tentacle itself is covered by a layer of ectoderm. Delicate muscle

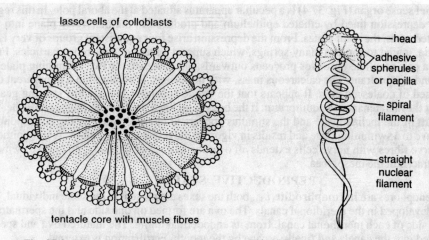

Fig. 37.2. Cross section of branch or pinna.   **Fig. 37.3.** A colloblast. (Highly magnified).

fibres lie beneath the external epithelium and beneath the epithelium of the canal system, and also traverse the mesogloea in various directions. Ectodermal cells are cuboidal or columnar in shape and are ciliated in certain regions. These cells are interspersed with numerous gland cells and sometimes certain pigment granules or branched pigment cells. The sensory cells are of two types : (i) one type is having several stiff bristles and (ii) the other type is with a single stout bristle.

DIGESTIVE SYSTEM

The mouth, lying in the centre of the lower end, is an elongated slit leading into a deep flattened tube called the stomodaeum. Towards its upper or aboral end the stomodaeum gradually narrows and opens into a cavity called the infundibulum, which is probably equivalent to the stomach of an anthozoan or a medusa, and is flattened in a direction at right angles to the stomodaeum, *i.e.*, in the transverse plane. From the infundibulum three tubes are given off: one, the infundibular canal, passes directly upwards; and immediately beneath the aboral pole divided into four short branches, two of which open on the exterior by minute apertures, the excretory pores. The two other canals given off from the infundibulum are the per-radial canals. The per-radial canals pass directly outwards, in the transverse plane, and each divided into two inter-radial canals. which in their turn divide each into two adradial canals. Each per-radial canal gives off a stomodael canal which passes downwards parallel to and in close contact with the stomodaeum and a tentacular canal which extends outwards

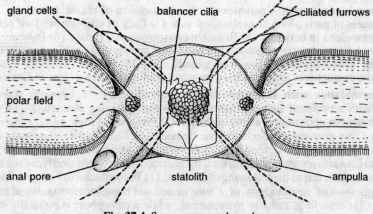

Fig. 37.4. Sense-organs enlarged.

and downwards into the base of the corresponding tentacle. Most of the digestion is completed extracellularly in the stomodaeum. Undigested food passes out through either the mouth or anal pores.

SENSE ORGANS

The chief sense organ (Fig. 37.4) is a peculiar apparatus situated at the aboral pole. In this region is a shallow depression lined by ciliated epithelium and produced in the transverse plane into two narrow ciliated areas, the polar plates. From the depression arise four equidistant groups of very large S-shaped cilia, united to form as many springs, which support a mass of calcareous particles. From each spring a pair of ciliated grooves proceeds outwards,and passes to the two swimming plates of the corresponding quadrant. The calcareous mass, with its springs, is enclosed in a transparent case or bell, formed of coalesced cilia. It appears that the whole apparatus is a kind of steering gear or apparatus for the maintenance of equilibrium. If the body is inclined the statolith presses more heavily the ciliary tuft of the inclined side and the stimulus appears to be transmitted by the corresponding ciliated groove to a swimming plate and results in vigorous movement of the combs. A sub-epithelial plexus of nerve fibres with nerve cells extends all over the surface of the body, and nerve elements can also be traced in the mesogloea.

REPRODUCTIVE SYSTEM

The ctenophores are hermaphrodite, *i.e.,* both the sexes are present in the same individual. The gonads are developed in the meridional canals. The ova are formed on one side and the spermatozoa on the other side of each meridional canal, from its endodermal lining. The matured ova and sperms are discharged into the canals and finally escape by the mouth. Fertilization is external.

DEVELOPMENT

Development of *Pleurobrachia* is not well-known but the following description of development in other forms of Ctenophora will give an idea of the development in Ctenophora.

After fertilization, the zygote undergoes cleavage and gives rise to four blastomeres by two meridional cleavages. The third cleavage is nearly vertical resulting in a curved plate of eight cells arranged in two rows. The eight blastomeres divide twice along the horizontal plane and give rise in each time eight small cells, the micromeres and eight large cells, the macromeres. The micromeres are the source of ectoderm and the macromeres give rise to endoderm in due course. Micromeres undergo rapid division and proliferate as a wreath of small cells over the macromeres which ultimately grow down as a one-layered sheet. Invagination starts and gastrulation goes on by combined processes of emboly and epiboly. Micromeres cover the embryo to become the ectoderm. Four inter-radial bands of small rapidly dividing cells become noticeable which differentiate extensively to form stomodaeum from which coelenteron arises by endodermal outgrowth. Biradial symmetry persists throughout the development.

AFFINITIES AND SYSTEMATIC POSITION OF CTENOPHORA

The ctenophores possess many characters of Coelenterata, but they differ considerably from the other members of the phylum Coelenterata. This group has also some similar features with different animals of diverse phyla, which will be discussed here to judge its systematic position.

1. Resemblance with Coelenterata. (1) Possession of radial symmetry and tentacles. (2) Arrangement of parts along an oral-aboral axis. (3) Lack of coelom. (4) Two cell-layers with a gelatinous mesogloea in between. (5) Branching gastrovascular canals. (6) Presence of mesogloea. (7) Presence of diffused nerve network. (8) Presence of statocyst as sense organ. (9) General lack of organ system. (10) Endodermal origin of gonads. (11) Absence of nephridia. Due to the above similarities the ctenophores are considered by many zoologists to be a class of Coelenterata.

2. Resemblance with Hydrozoa. An anthomedusan form *Ctenaria* shows remarkable similarities with a cydippid such as *Hormiphora* in the following characters: (1)Presence of two tentacles, situated at opposite per-radii, in sheath. (2) Presence of eight radial canals formed by the bifurcation of four inter-radial pouches of the stomach. (3) The subumbrellar cavity of the *Ctenaria* can be homologised with the stomodaeum of *Hormiphora*. But these similarities are superficial and the claim that *Ctenaria* represents a form directly intermediate between the Hydrozoa and Ctenophora seems to be untenable due to the following objections : (1) The tentacles of *Ctenaria* have no muscular base. (2) Eight rows of nematocysts of *Ctenaria* are not homologous to rows of comb-plates of a ctenophore. (3) *Ctenaria* is radially symmetrical, while a ctenophore is biradially symmetrical. (4) The development of gonad is different. In *Ctenaria*, the gonads develop from manubrium but in

Ctenophora gonads develop from meridional canals. (5) Absence of characteristic aboral sense organs in *Ctenaria*.

Hydractinia, a narcomedusan, shows some closer resemblances with Ctenophora. These resemblances are : (1) Possession of two tentacles with sheath situated between the margin and the apex of the bell. (2) Possession of aboral sense organ. But the presence of swimming-plates in Ctenophora and the presence of velum in *Hydractinia* remain as important differences to visualise a close relation among them.

3. Resemblance with Anthozoa. The ctenophores also possess certain anthozoan features which are as follows : (1) Ciliated ectoderm of Anthozoa is probably a forerunner of the ciliated band of Ctenophora. (2) Presence of well-developed stomodaeum. (3) The gut in embryos of both is four-lobed, thus, presenting a biradial symmetry. (4) Mesogloea is cellular. (5) The gonads develop in connection with the endoderm and the sexual elements passed out through the mouth.

Both the aboral sense organ and rows of comb-plates of a ctenophore have no parallel parts in an anthozoan. Lasso cells differ structurally from the nematocysts and tentacles are hollow in Anthozoa, while solid in Ctenophora.

4. Differences from Coelenterata. The ctenophores differ greatly from coelenterates in the following points : (1) Possession of oppositely placed tentacles suggesting a biradial symmetry. (2) Presence of an aboral sensory region. (3) Absence of nematocysts except in one or two cases. (4) Presence of eight locomotory meridional ciliated bands of comb-plates over the body. (5) Presence of colloblasts (special adhesive cells) over the tentacles. (6) Presence of mesenchymal muscles. (7) Presence of definite organisation of digestive system with anal pores. (8) Presence of determinate type of development.

5. Affinities with Platyhelminthes. The *Platyctenea* has been considered to be a connecting link between Ctenophora and the Bilateria. Besides, Ctenophora, in general, exhibits many structural similarities with the Platyhelminthes and particularly with the turbellarians. The similarities are as follows : (1) Ciliation of the body. (2) Dorso-ventrally flattened body. (3) Crawling mode of life. (4)Origin of the so-called mesoderm is more or less similar. (5) The dorsal polar nerve of Turbellaria can be compared with the statocyst of Ctenophora. (6) Ctenophora exhibits both radial as well as biradial symmetries. (7) Similar earlier stages of segmentation and gastrulation. (8) Gelatinous mesenchyme with muscle fibres and cells. The view that the primitive Bilateria have evolved through *Platyctenea* has not been accepted. A careful thorough examination of the *Platyctenea* reveals that it is a ctenophore which has become extensively modified for sessile habits. It can further be suggested that *Platyctenea* is a tissue-grade diploplastic animal whereas Polyclad is an organ-grade triploblastic form. Further it can be stated that amongst the Platyhelminthes,the Acoela is the most primitive group and not the polyclads. The Ctenophora, on the other hand, exhibits no close similarity with the Acoela.

Ctenophora exhibit many striking characteristics of their own so that it appears more justified to treat them a separate phylum rather than a class of the phylum Coelenterata. They present certain advanced structural features that appear to look forward to the Bilateria. These are (1) Prominence of an apical organ. (2)Mode of origin of musculature from mesoderm. (3) Presence of gonoducts. (4) Determinate type of cleavage.

It appears that Ctenophora are intermediate between Radiata and Bilateria. They appear to have diverged very early from trachyline stem which also gave off the other three branches of Coelenterata. The Ctenophora themselves represent a blind offshoot. Not in the direct line of ancestry, the Ctenophora appear to indicate the structural advances along which the Bilateria have evolved from the ancestral stock.

CHARACTERS AND CLASSIFICATION OF CTENOPHORA

Definition

Ctenophores are free-swimming, transparent, jelly-like, soft-bodied, marine animals having biradial symmetry, comb-like ciliary plates for locomotion, the lasso cells but nematocysts are wanting.

General Characters

1. Free-swimming, marine, pelagic and solitary animals.

2. Body gelatinous, transparent, pear-shaped,cylindrical or flat or ribbon-shaped.

3. Biradially symmetrical body along an oral-aboral axis.

4. Comb-like eight ciliary plates on the body for locomotion.

5. Nematocysts absent; mesogloea cellular with muscular elements.

6. Digestive system with mouth, pharynx and stomach ; the stomach is highly branched to form a complex system of gastrovascular canals.

7. The digestive system terminates out at anal pore.

8. Colloblasts, also referred to as lasso cells, are special adhesive cells present on the tentacles which help in food capture.

9. Skeletal,circulatory, respiratory and excretory systems are absent.

10. Nervous system is diffused type and the aboral end bears a sense organ, called statocyst.

11. Monoecious (hermaphrodite) ; gonads endodermal situated on the walls of gastric canals.

12. Development direct with a characteristic larva called cydippid.

13. Regeneration and paedogenesis are of common occurrence. Alternation of generations not found.

14. Body organization cell-tissue grade.

CLASSIFICATION

CLASS 1. TENTACULATA

1. Adults nearly always with two long aboral tentacles.
2. In some only the larva has tentacles, while adults possess oral lobes.
3. Mouth narrow and pharynx small.

Order 1. Cydippida

1. Simple, rounded or oval body.
2. Digestive canals terminate blindly; no anal pore.
3. Tentacles two long and branched.
4. Tentacles are retractile into sheath.

   Examples: *Mertensia, Pleurobrachia.*

Order 2. Lobata

1. Laterally compressed oval body.
2. Adults with two large oral lobes.
3. Tentacles reduced and without sheath.
4. The gastrovascular canals are connected by a ring canal at the oral end.

   Examples : *Mnemiopsis, Bolinopsis.*

Order 3. Cestida

1. Body elongated and compressed, ribbon-like.

2. Comb plates in four rows but rudimentary.
3. Tentacles and tentacular sheaths along the oral margin reduced.

   Examples : *Cestum, Velamen.*

Order 4. Platyctenea

1. Greatly compressed body in oral-aboral axis.
2. Two well developed tentacles with sheaths.
3. Adults often without comb plates.
4. Flattened creeping forms.

   Examples: *Ctenoplana,, Coeloplana.*

CLASS 2. NUDA

1. Body large, conical and compressed laterally.
2. Tentacles and oral lobes absent.
3. Wide mouth and large pharynx.
4. Voracious feeders.

Order 1. Beroida

1. Since class Nuda has only one order Beroida, hence, class characters are the characters of the order.

   Example : *Beroe.*

REPRESENTATIVE TYPES OF CTENOPHORA

1. *Cestum.* *Cestum* (Fig. 37.5) is commonly known as Venus's girdle. It inhabits warmer seas specially the Mediterranean. The body is greatly elongated horizontally in the sagittal, and compressed in the lateral plane so that it appears ribbon-like in form. It is usually green, blue or violet coloured. Out of eight comb-plates, four are very small and the other four are continued all along the aboral edge of the body. The base of two principal tentacles are large and are enclosed in sheaths and numerous small tentacles spring from grooves and are continued the whole length of oral edge; the small lateral tentacles line the oral ridge. Mouth lies in the mid-oral edge. The only sense organ, statocyst, is found on the aboral edge. *Cestum* swims mainly by graceful serpentine movements by the muscular undulations of the body as well as by the beating of comb plates.

2. *Ctenoplana.* *Ctenoplana* (Fig. 37.6) is a small marine, solitary planktonic ctenophore reported once off the west-coast of Sumatra and once among the islands to the east of Papua. Its body is nearly circular in outline, flattened dorso-ventrally. It measures about 6 mm in diameter. Its dorsal

surface is mostly olive green, brown or reddish in colour. In the centre of aboral or dorsal surface of its body is a sense organ with a statolith surrounded by a ring of small ciliated tentacles. The mouth

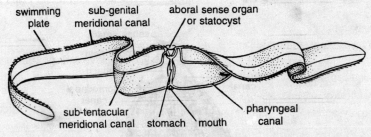

Fig. 37.5. *Cestum.*

lies in the centre of ventral or oral surface. Tentacles two, pinnate and retractile. The gastrovascular canal system is devoid of meridional canals but comprises a set of branching and anastomosing peripheral canals. The organs of locomotion are eight small deeply sunk swimming plates. While swimming it draws downwards the edges of the disc so that it becomes somewhat halmet-shaped when viewed laterally.

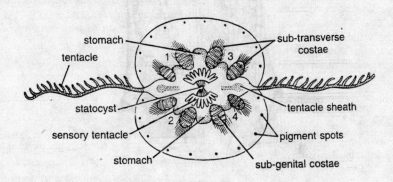

Fig. 37.6. *Ctenoplana* (Dorsal view).

3. *Coeloplana. Coeloplana* (Fig. 37.7) is a marine solitary ctenophore found in the Red Sea and on the coast of Japan. It resembles in most of the features to *Ctenoplana*. However, its body is oval and dorso-ventrally flattened but elongated in the tentacular plane. It measures about 60 mm in length.

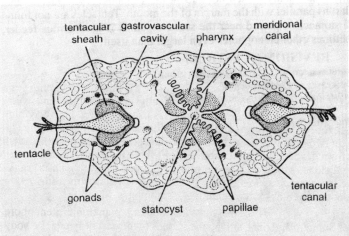

Fig. 37.7. *Coeloplana.*

Mouth is ventral in position. Tentacles paired and retractile. Anastomosing gastrovascular canal system. Sense organ (statocyst) is dorsally placed. Swimming plates are not found. It moves by creeping. Gonads are found in the walls of meridional gastrovascular canals. The fertilized eggs are attached to the oral surface of the mother by the sticky secretion and each developing into a typical cydippid larva with comb-plates. The cydippid larva after free-swimming for some time metamorphoses into adult *Coeloplana.*

4. Beroe. *Beroe* (Fig. 37.8) is commonly known as sea mitres or mitre jelly-fish. It is found in great swarms and cosmopolitan in distribution. Its body is thimble-shaped and measures about 10–20 cm in height. It is usually pinkish in colour. The rounded aboral end bears the sense organ

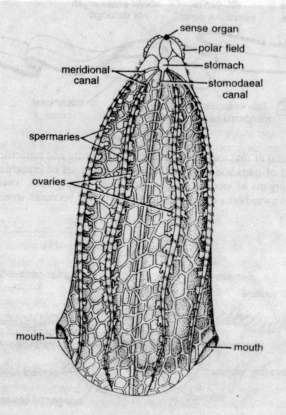

Fig. 37.8. *Beroe.*

surrounded by polar fields. The oral end is truncated and is occupied entirely by a wide mouth. The greater part of the body is occupied by the huge stomodaeum, infundibulum, per-radial and infundibular gastrovascular canals, etc., all these being crowded into a small space at the aboral pole. The meridional canals send off branches which unite with one another, forming a complex network of tubes. At the oral end the four meridional canals of each side and the corresponding stomodaeal canal unite into a horizontal tube which runs parallel with the margin of the mouth. Tentacles are not found in any stage of the life. A small stomach is placed near the sense organ. It is a voracious feeder, swallowing crustaceans and sometimes other ctenophores even larger than itself.

REVISION QUESTIONS

1. Classify Ctenophora giving characters and examples of each group.
2. Describe the various life processes of *Pleurobrachia*.
3. Discuss the affinities and systematic position of Ctenophora.
4. Write notes on:
   (i) *Cestum* ; (ii) *Ctenoplana* ; (iii) *Beroe.*

38

Phylum Platyhelminthes

The term Platyhelminthes "flatworms" was first proposed by Gaugenbaur (1859) and applied to the animals now included under that heading. The name Platyhelminthes has been derived from the Greek *platys*=flat+*helmins* =worms. At first nemertines and others were also included but later were removed to other groups. The phylum is now restricted to three classes, Turbellaria, Trematoda, and Cestoda. Although these classes have many structural differences, they all show enough similarity in the body pattern to indicate a common origin.

Platyhelminthes include the flatworms, their bodies are compressed dorsoventrally and show bilateral symmetry. They are the lowest triploblastic acoelomate Metazoa, but they are more advanced than Coelenterata because their tissues are organized into organs. The mesoderm forms a type of connective tissue called parenchyma which fills the body spaces between the ectoderm and endoderm so that there is no coelom or haemocoele, hence, they are called acoelomate animals, mesoderm also forms organs, such as the excretory and reproductive organs. The excretory system has one or two canals with branches, the finer branches end in flame cells, the canal has no internal opening but it opens to the exterior only. Blood vascular system and respiratory system are absent. There is no anus and in some even the mouth and alimentary canal are absent. The nervous system consists of a network, but it has ganglia at the anterior end which serves as a brain. Reproductive organs are very highly developed, most Platyhelminthes are hermaphrodite. The phylum includes some 15,000 species, and it is divided into three classes. Class Turbellaria includes ciliated flatworms which are generally free-living, Trematoda are non-ciliated parasitic flatworms or flukes, while Cestoda are all endoparasitic flatworms or tapeworms. The typical structure of Platyhelminthes is seen only in Turbellaria, because the Trematoda and Cestoda, due to parasitic habit, have become different from their free-living ancestors, they have lost their ciliated epidermis and have acquired a cuticle and organs of attachment. The trematodes have retained the body form and alimentary canal of Turbellaria, but the tapeworms have become elongated into a chain and the alimentary canal is lost.

39

Dugesia (= *Euplanaria*)

Dugesia, a planarian, is a common free-living, freshwater flatworm representing fundamental characteristics of the phylum Platyhelminthes. Other planarians belong to the genus *Procotyla*, *Phagocota*, *Polycelis*, etc. *Dugesia*, also referred to as *Euplanaria*, has many species in India found in the mud at the bottom of freshwater ponds, lakes and springs. However, the account on *Dugesia* discussed below relates to its species *tigrina*.

DUGESIA TIGRINA
SYSTEMATIC POSITION

Phylum	....	**Platyhelminthes**
Class	....	**Turbellaria**
Order	....	**Tricladida**
Suborder	....	**Paludicola**
Genus	....	*Dugesia (Euplanaria)*
Species	....	*tigrina*

HABIT AND HABITAT

Dugesia is gregareous (lives in groups) found on the underside of leaves, logs, debris and rocks submerged in cool, clear and running water of streams, ponds and lakes. They are not easy to see unless they are moving, for they are small and flat and their dark mottled colour blends perfectly with the rocks or plants to which they cling. They live in damp surroundings as their bodies are not protected against desiccation. *Dugesia* is world-wide in distribution.

STRUCTURE

Shape, size and colour. *Dugesia* is about 12 mm long and is dark brownish or blackish in colour. It is a thin flattened worm with definite sides, there is an anterior end directed forwards in moving, one surface of the body is always uppermost, this is the dorsal surface, while the surface towards the substratum is ventral. The dorsal surface is darker in colour than the ventral surface. It has bilateral symmetry which is in direct correlation with progression towards the anterior end.

External morphology. The anterior end forms an obvious head which is triangular with two laterally projecting head lobes or auricles. On the head are two cup-shaped black eyes. The head is separated from the body by a neck-like constriction. The body is elongated with the dorsal

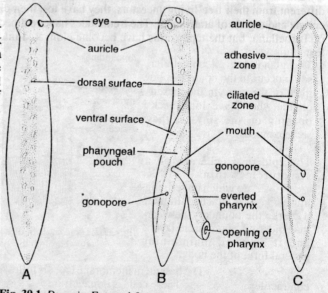

Fig. 39.1. *Dugesia*. External features. A—Dorsal surface ; B—Body twisted to show a part of ventral surface ; C—Ventral surface.

surface slightly arched and the ventral surface flat. Behind the middle of the body on the ventral side is a mouth which leads into a pharyngeal sheath containing a cylindrical pharynx which can be seen through the body wall, the pharynx can be everted through the mouth as a proboscis. On the ventral surface encircling the margin is an adhesive zone through which an adhesive substance comes out from glands. The animal clamps itself to the substratum by the adhesive zone. The animal when moving leaves behind a mucus trail, mucus is secreted by mucous glands opening on the ventral surface. Just a little behind the mouth aperture on the ventral surface, there is a genital aperture in sexually mature forms.

BODY WALL

The body wall is made of an outer epidermis and inner muscle layers. Both these layers are separated by a basement membrane. The space between muscle layer and the alimentary canal is filled with a special type of tissue called mesenchyme or parenchyma therefore, no coelom or body cavity is found in it. However, a detailed study of the body wall represents the following structures :

Epidermis. It is single cell-layered thick and made of cuboidal epithelial cells. The epidermis is ciliated all over in most planarians, but in *Dugesia* cilia are found only on the ventral surface where they are absent from the adhesive zone. Between the epidermal cells are sensory cells and mucous gland cells in certain areas. The gland cells provide a mucus coating for the animal and they lay down a slime trail for its locomotion. In the epidermal cells are characteristic erect hyaline rods called rhabdites, they are more abundant on the dorsal than the ventral side. Rhabdites are secreted by rhabdite gland cells usually located in mesenchyme. After the rhabdites are secreted in the rhabdite gland cells, they migrate to the epidermal cells where they lie. Rhabdites are absent in the adhesive zone. The function of rhabdites is not known, but they form a slimy substance on discharge to the exterior which may be protective, and help in obtaining living food. Below the epidermis are granules and rods of pigment. The glands are all unicellular, some occur in the epidermis but most of them are in the mesenchyme, they have long necks opening on the surface, they secrete mucus.

Basement membrane. The epidermal cells rest on a structureless thin basement membrane to which underlying muscle layer is attached. In fact, it marks the boundary between the epidermis and muscle layers and it helps in maintaining general form of the body.

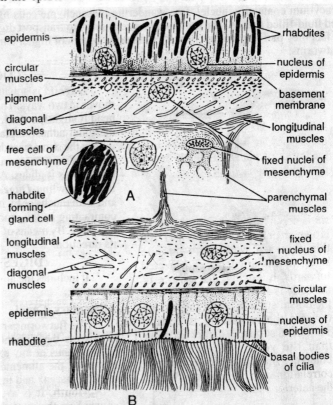

Fig. 39.2. *Dugesia*. L.S. of body wall. A—Through the dorsal body wall; B—Through the ventral body wall.

Muscle layer. The basement membrane layer is followed by muscle layer. It contains elongated contractile muscle cells. These cells originate from myoblasts which are mesodermal in origin. The muscle layer is differentiated into an outer layer of circular muscles, middle layer of diagonal muscles and inner layer of longitudinal muscles. The longitudinal muscle layer is more developed on the ventral side. The dorso-ventral muscles extend across the body between dorsal and ventral surfaces.

Parenchyma or mesenchyme. It is a special type of connective tissue of mesodermal origin. It is filled in the spaces between various internal organs and body wall. It is, in fact, a net-like

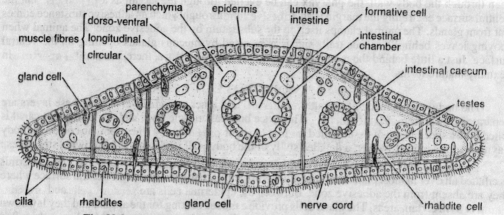

Fig. 39.3. *Dugesia*. Diagrammatic transverse section through the body.

syncytium containing nuclei, free wandering mesenchyme cells like **neoblasts** or **formative cells** and fluid-filled spaces. The mesenchyme cells serve to transport digested food and excretory wastes; in fact they perform the function of circulatory system of higher animals as this system is wanting in flatworms.

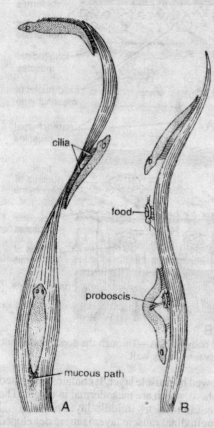

Fig. 39.4. *Dugesia*. A—Locomotion; B—Feeding.

LOCOMOTION

Dugesia is aquatic but it does not swim. *Dugesia* moves in two ways. The usual way is **gliding.** In gliding, head is slightly raised, over a slime tract secreted by its marginal adhesive glands. The beating of the ventral cilia in the slime tract drives the animal along. Rhythmic waves of movement can be seen passing backward from the head as it glides. A less common method is **crawling.** In crawling, *Dugesia* lengthens, anchors its anterior end with mucus or by its special adhesive organ, and by contracting its longitudinal muscles pulls up the rest of the body. By means of its oblique muscles it can change its direction.

DIGESTIVE SYSTEM

It includes the alimentary canal, food, feeding and digestion.

Alimentary Canal

The flatworms are the first in the animal kingdom to possess the alimentary canal which is **incomplete** because anus or any exit for defaecation is not found. However, the alimentary canal of *Dugesia* consists of mouth, pharynx and intestine.

Mouth. It is a small oval or rounded aperture situated on the ventral side behind the middle of the body. It serves both for ingestion and egestion. It leads into a short mouth cavity which joins a cylindrical thick-walled **pharynx.**

Pharynx. The pharynx lies in a **pharyngeal cavity** or **pouch** bounded by a muscular sheath called the **pharyngeal sheath.** The thick-walled, muscular and cylindrical pharynx in the pharyngeal pouch is attached to the anterior end of the pharyngeal sheath.

The pharynx can be everted or protruded through the mouth opening as a proboscis which can be extended greatly. The eversible proboscis of *Dugesia* helps in feeding.

The pharynx in section is circular enclosed in a circular pharyngeal cavity, it consists of following layers from the surface to the lumen, epitheilal cells, longitudinal muscle layer, circular muscle layer, outer gland cells, nerve plexus, inner gland cells, longitudinal muscle layer, circular muscle layer and an endodermal epithelial lining.

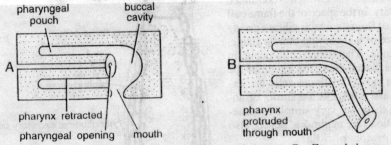

Fig. 39.5. *Dugesia*. Diagram to show : A—Retracted pharynx; B—Everted pharynx.

Intestine. The attached end of the pharynx leads into an intestine which divides at once into three branches characteristic of order **Tricladida** to which *Dugesia* belongs, one extending forward in the middle line up to the head, and the other two going backwards to the posterior end, one on either side of the pharyngeal cavity. All the three branches of intestine give off numerous branching diverticula, all ending blindly, there being no anus. The much-branched intestine is a means of increasing the surface area for digestion, absorption and distribution of food. The intestine is made of a single layer of vacuolated columnar cells containing granules, between the columnar cells are some gland cells of triangular shape containing reserve proteins.

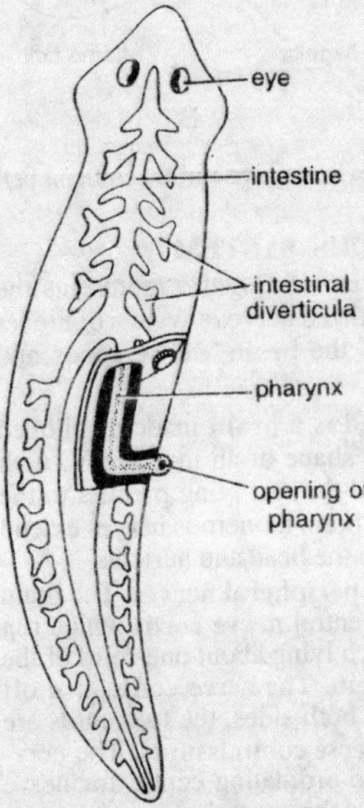

Food, Feeding and Digestion

The animal is **carnivorous**. The food consists of small living worms, crustaceans and snails, and pieces of larger dead animals. In feeding the animal perceives the presence of food at a distance and moves towards it, living food is often entangled in the slimy secretions of mucous glands and rhabdites, then it encloses the food in the everted pharynx and digestive juices are poured into the food, the food is broken up by a pumping action of the pharynx and acted upon by extruded digestive juices for **extracellular digestion**, after which the food is swallowed. Digestion is both **extracellular** and **intracellular**; the mesenchyme helps to distribute digested food. Undigested food is egested through the mouth. Planarians can live without food for long periods, they obtain nourishment by dissolving their reproductive organs, parenchyma, and muscles, they get smaller in size. The missing parts are regenerated when they feed again.

RESPIRATORY SYSTEM

There are no respiratory organs. Exchange of gases takes through the body surface, *i.e.*, respiratory exchange is by **diffusion**.

Fig. 39.6. *Dugesia*. Digestive system.

EXCRETORY SYSTEM

The excretory system of *Dugesia* consists of a system of **excretory tubules** having a large number of excretory cells called **flame cells** or **protonephridia**.

Excretory tubules. There is one pair of **longitudinal excretory trunks** running on each side of the body which open to the dorsal surface by several minute pores called **nephridiopores**, each pair of trunks is considerably coiled together, and the two pairs are connected together in the head by a transverse vessel. Each longitudinal trunk divides into a number of branches, the branches divide into extremely fine cappillaries which end in flame cells. The capillary is actually a part of the flame cell.

Flame cell. The flame cell is nucleated and has a number of protoplasmic processes reaching into the mesenchyme. The flame cell has an intracellular space which is continued into the capillary. In the space of the flame cell are a number of flagella which vibrate giving the appearance of a flickering candle flame, hence, the name. The flame cells occur in large numbers placed along the length of the body on each side. The flame cells are excretory units and work like nephridia of annelids. Since, these are very simple in structure and function like nephridia, hence, also referred to as protonephridia.

Physiology. Excretory substance is collected from the mesenchyme and is transferred into the cavities of flame cells. The beating of flagella of flame cells causes hydrostatic pressure by which fluid waste passes into longitudinal trunks and goes out of nephridiopores. The excretory system is spoken of as a protonephridial system. But more important than removal of excretory matter, the system brings about elimination of excess water from the animal, it functions as an osmoregulatory system.

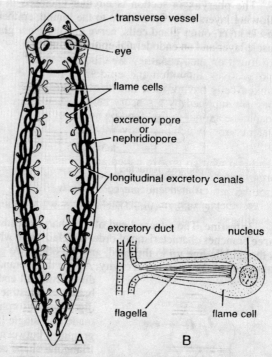

Fig. 39.7. *Dugesia.* A—Excretory system ; B—A flame cell.

NERVOUS SYSTEM

The nervous system of *Dugesia* represents the primitive type of centralized nervous system of higher animals. It consists of the brain, nerve cords and peripheral nerves.

Brain. In the head is a brain made of bilobed cerebral ganglia in the shape of an inverted V, with limbs near the eyes and the rest lying parallel to the head margin. From the brain numerous nerves extend forward and laterally to the head and auricles.

Nerve cords and peripheral nerves. The brain is continued into two ventral nerve cords which run to the posterior end, each lying about one-third of the distance from the margin. The nerve cords give off transverse branches on both sides, the two cords are joined by some transverse commissures. The nervous system acts as a co-ordinating centre for nerve impulses. In addition to the central nervous system there is a sub-epidermal plexus or nerve net just below the epidermis, and a deeper sub-muscular plexus in the mesenchyme below the muscle layers of the body wall, both are joined to the nerve cords.

In fact, the brain and nerve cords constitute the central nervous system, while the various nerves originating from central nervous system constitute the peripheral nerves.

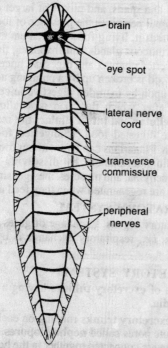

Fig. 39.8. *Dugesia.* Nervous system.

SENSE ORGANS

In *Dugesia*, sense organs consist of chemoreceptors, auricular organ, tangoreceptors, rheoreceptors and eyes or ocelli.

1. Chemoreceptors. Chemoreceptors are found on the head, they are ciliated pits and grooves in which the epidermis has sunken cells having cilia but no rhabdites, they are supplied by a sensory nerve. They enable the animal to find food by means of a water current which passes over them.

2. Auricular organ. On each side of the head is a whitish groove called an auricular organ lying near the base of the auricle. The grooves are ciliated and are provided with nerves, they are organs of chemical sense for smelling and tasting.

3. Tangoreceptors. These are sensory cells for **touch** stimuli and found distributed at the anterior end most abundantly on the ventral surface around the mouth opening.

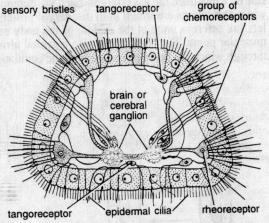

Fig. 39.9. *Dugesia.* Diagrammatic T.S. of anterior end to show various receptors.

4. Rheoreceptors. These are sensitive to water currents ; their sensory processes project much beyond the level of body cilia.

5. Eyes or ocelli. Eyes are two round dark spots on the dorsal surface of the head. The eye has a pigment cup with its open mouth facing laterally forward. Projecting into the pigment cup are several retinal cells, they are bipolar nerve cells with expanded inner ends which are striated, and outer ends joined to the brain. Eyes are capable of a crude discrimination of the direction of light. The pigment cup serves as a shield and light can enter only through its opening to stimulate the photosensitive expanded ends of retinal cells, thus, the animal can detect the direction of light. The animal is negatively phototactic and is most active at night.

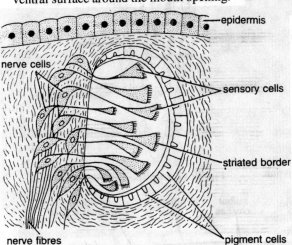

Fig. 39.10. *Dugesia.* V.S. of eye.

REPRODUCTION

Dugesia reproduces both asexually and sexually.

Asexual Reproduction

Dugesia exists in asexual and sexual strains. The asexual form has no reproductive organs, it reproduces by fission. Fission occurs when the animal has attained maximum size, the posterior end adheres firmly, while the anterior region advances forward so that the animal ruptures into two behind the pharynx. Each new animal regenerates its missing parts. The separated anterior part regenerates the posterior region and the rear end grows into a complete worm. Locomotion and adhesion are essential for fission.

Sexual Reproduction

Reproductive organs are temporary in *Dugesia*, they are formed during the breeding season, after which the reproductive organs degenerate and the animal becomes an asexual strain which will reproduce by fission till early summer of the following year. The sexual strain develops hermaphrodite organs and it reproduces sexually every year in early summer.

(i) **Male reproductive organs.** Male reproductive organs consist of two rows of testes, vasa efferentia, a pair of vas deferens and a penis. The testes are numerous, small and round. They are situated on the right and left borders of the body. Each testis is connected to the vas deferens of its side by a tiny duct, the vas efferens. Each vas deferens enlarges posteriorly to form a seminal vesicle where the sperms are stored until discharged posteriorly through the muscular penis. The right and left vas deferens unite at the middle of the body and form a median duct which passes through a muscular penis. The penis opens into a genital atrium, a cavity that terminates in the genital pore through which the penis extends during the copulation.

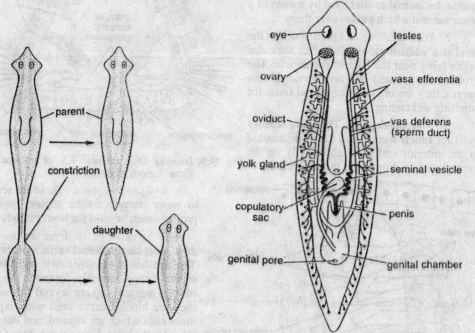

Fig. 39.11. *Dugesia.* Asexual reproduction by fission.

Fig. 39.12. *Dugesia.* Reproductive system.

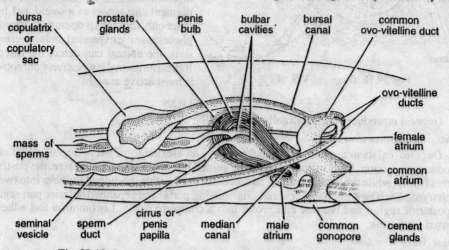

Fig. 39.13. *Dugesia.* A part of the reproductive system in lateral view.

(ii) **Female reproductive organs.** There is one pair of small ovaries lying laterally behind the head. From each ovary arises a long oviduct which runs laterally. At the commencement of each oviduct where it arises from the ovary, is a small dilated seminal receptacle. On each side of body there are numerous small yolk glands which join the oviducts, yolk cells from yolk glands pass into oviducts, hence, called **ovo-vitelline duct**. Opening into the genital atrium is large club-shaped **copulatory sac**. Numerous small **cement glands** open into the genital atrium and oviduct. The genital atrium opens externally by a genital pore situated on the ventral side behind the mouth.

Copulation, Fertilization and Development

During **copulation** the two worms come together by their ventral surfaces facing in the same direction. The penis papilla of each emerges by elongation through the genital pore and is inserted into the copulatory sac of the other worm by which mutual insemination occurs. The sperms are discharged into the copulatory sac where they stay only a short while, they travel up the oviducts to reach the seminal receptacles. As the eggs come out of the ovary they are **fertilized**, and they pass down the oviducts becoming mingled with yolk cells from yolk glands. The eggs and yolk cells collect in the genital atrium where a **capsule** or **cocoon** is formed around them from yolk cells. The capsule contains several fertilized eggs, and it is laid through the genital pore under stones. While passing out the capsule receives the secretion of cement glands, this adhesive secretion forms a stalk on the capsule. The capsules get attached to stones by their stalk. One animal copulates several times during the breeding season and lays a cocoon every few days.

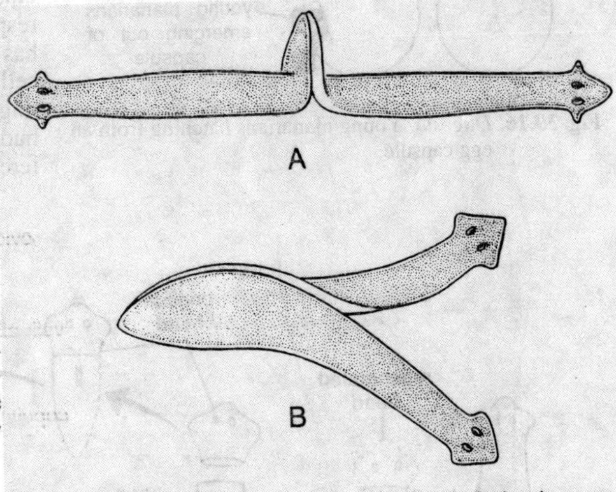

The **development** is **direct**, *i.e.*, without any larval form. Each zygote in capsule develops into a young worm in

Fig. 39.14. *Dugesia.* Copulation. A—Head ends facing in opposite directions; B—Head ends facing in the same direction.

about two weeks, finally the capsule ruptures and the young worms hatch out (Fig. 39.16). These resemble their parents except that they are smaller in size and without reproductive organs which has not yet developed . They feed, grow and develop sex organs to reproduce again.

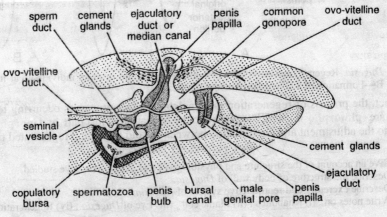

Fig. 39.15. *Dugesia.* A copulating pair in section.

REGENERATION

Dugesia has great powers of **regeneration**. Regeneration is a process of restitution and involves the development of lost part of the body automatically. If it is cut into two, each part will form the lost portion. A cut piece of moderate size from any part of the body will form a new worm. Some pieces taken from posterior side form animals with reduced heads or no head at all. The ability of a piece to regenerate into a complete worm depends upon the regeneration of head at the anterior cut surface, because the head controls the morphological pattern. If a sexually mature planarian is cut into two between the pharynx and the copulatory apparatus, then the reproductive organs degenerate, and each piece will regenerate into an asexual worm. Longitudinal cuts can be made to produce double heads or tails. It was thought that interstitial cells are responsible for regeneration. But recently it has been shown that on cutting a planarian free cells from the mesenchyme called **neoblasts** migrate to the cut surface and give rise to a bud-like structure called **blastema** which differentiate into the lost part.

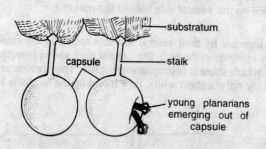

Fig. 39.16. *Dugesia.* Young planarians hatching from an egg capsule.

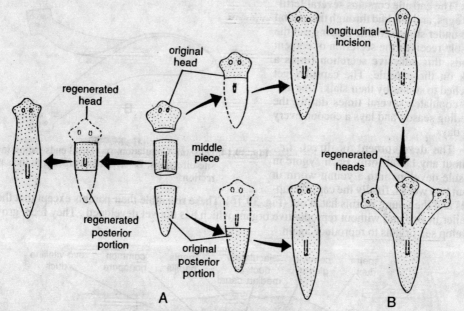

Fig. 39.17. *Dugesia.* Regeneration A—Three individuals regenerate from an individual cut into three parts ; B—Formation of a heteromorph with three heads.

In fact, the process of regeneration is completed by two processes occurring together. These processes are **epimorphosis** , which is related to the formation of lost part, and **morphollaxis**, which is related to the adjustment and coordination between the old tissue and regenerated tissues.

REVISION QUESTIONS

1. Give an account of the structure and physiology of a planarian you have studied.
2. Describe the structure of body wall of *Dugesia*.
3. Describe excretory and reproductive system of *Dugesia*.
4. Write notes on : (i) Rhabdites ; (ii) Flame cell ; (iii) Eye of *Dugesia* ; (iv) Regeneration.

The monogenetic trematodes are a group of flukes that as a rule are ectoparasites in nature, infesting poikilothermic vertebrates. A few species, however, have been reported to be attached to aquatic mammals, crustaceans and cephalopods. At least three species are known to be true endoparasites : *Dictyocotyle* species in the coelom of the ray *Raja lintea, Acolpenteron ureterocetes* in the ureters of freshwater fishes, and *Polystoma integerrimum* in the bladder of amphibians. The affinity of *P. integerrimum* for the urinary bladder represents one of the unsolved problems of parasitism, that of host and tissue specificity. *Polystoma integerrimum* is described here in detail.

POLYSTOMA INTEGERRIMUM
SYSTEMATIC POSITION

Phylum	...	**Platyhelminthes**
Class	...	**Trematoda**
Order	...	**Monogenia**
Genus	...	*Polystoma*
Species	...	*integerrimum*

HABIT AND HABITAT

Polystoma integerrimum is an endoparasite in the urinary bladder of frogs and toads. Heavy infection is, however, not known in the adult host. Young forms may be found attached to the gills of tadpoles.

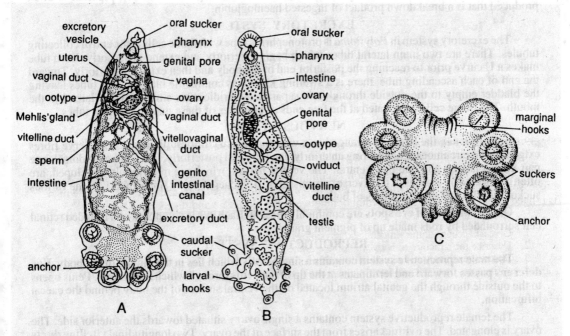

Fig. 40.1. *Polystoma integerrimum.* A—Bladder generation from urinary bladder of frog; B—Gill generation; C—Opisthaptor.

STRUCTURE

The body of *Polystoma integerrimum* is leaf-like and dorso-ventrally flattened and measure not more than 3 cm in length. It is attached to its host by opisthaptor. The opisthaptor contains three pairs of suckers, two anchors and six marginal chitinous hooks. At the anterior end is the mouth and shortly behind on the ventral side is the gonopore.

Head glands and head organs are commonly present. The secretions of these glands and the adhesive nature of the organs suggest that these functions primarily as auxiliary attachment organs. Near the suckers, certain gland cells are frequently present in the body wall and these cells secrete into prohaptors and opisthaptors.

BODY WALL

The body surface of *Polystoma* is covered by a thin layer of non-cellular cuticle. Immediately beneath the protective cuticle is a thin layer of circular muscles. Below the circular muscles is found a thin layer of diagonal muscles and below the diagonal muscles is a thick layer of well-developed longitudinal muscles. The region between the body wall and the internal organs is packed with a loose parenchyma consisting of cells, fibrils and spaces. If the inner and outer parenchyma is separated, the medial zone is termed the medullary parenchyma and the outer zone the cortical parenchyma. The parenchyma serves as a site of glycogen storage.

ALIMENTARY CANAL

The mouth is located at the anterior end of the body, flanked on each side by a prophator. The mouth leads into the muscular pharynx which in turn leads into the oesophagus. The oesophagus opens into the intestine. The intestinal tract is in the form of an inverted Y with the caeca bifurcating from the posterior extremity of the oesophagus which represents the stem of Y. The caeca not only give rise to numerous diverticula, but some of these actually extend into the disc-shaped opisthaptor. The intestinal caeca are lined with epithelial cells that are either closely packed or sparsely arranged.

Polystoma feeds primarily on blood, sloughed epithelial cells and mucus. But it can also derive oxygen and other chemicals from the aquatic environment in which it is bathed. Hence, the body wall is important as an absorptive layer.

Although nothing is known about the digestive enzymes present, a black pigment is often produced that is a breakdown product of ingested haemoglobin.

EXCRETORY SYSTEM

The excretory system in *Polystoma* is protonephritic type with flame cells at the end of collecting tubules. There are two main lateral tubes which begin anteriorly and extend posteriorly. Each tube makes a U curve prior to reaching the posterior end of the body and then extends anteriorly. Toward the end of each ascending tube, there is a swelling known as contractile bladder. The tubes leaving the bladder empty to the outside through two separate nephridiopores situated dorso-lateral to the mouth. The flame cells are located at the free ends of branches of these main collecting tubes.

NERVOUS SYSTEM

In *Polystoma*, the brain is arranged in a well formed circumoesophageal ring. Nerve fibres extgend from circumoesophageal ring anteriorly, laterally and posteriorly, one pair being dorsal, one pair ventro-lateral, and one pair ventral. The ventral nerves, which are most highly developed, are often connected by a series of transverse commissures. Branches of nerve fibres innervate the various sucker muscles and other portions of body.

One or two pairs of eye spots are commonly present. Each eye is composed of a rounded retinal cell surrounded by rods made up of pigment granules.

REPRODUCTIVE SYSTEM

The male reproductive system contains a single testis which lies in the middle of the body. Vas deferens passes forward and terminates at the tip of the penis through which it traverses. Penis opens to the outside through the genital atrium located on the ventral surface of the body behind the caecal bifurcation.

The female reproductive system contains a single ovary situated towards the anterior side. The ovary is elongated. The oviduct arises from the surface of the ovary. Two longitudinal vitelline ducts are connected by a transverse duct ; a median vitelline duct connects with the oviduct and another genito-intestinal canal opens in to the vitelline ducts, one on each side, are a pair of vaginae. Oviduct after receiving the vitelline duct continues as ovo-vitelline duct and opens into a small chamber called ootype where eggs are assembled. Numerous unicellular glands collectively known as Mehlis' gland, surround and secrete into the ootype. The secretions of these glands apparently serve as a lubricant that facilitates the passage of completely formed eggs from the ootype up the uterus. A uterus containing fertilized eggs comes out of the ootype to open into the genital atrium.

Functionally, the common vitelline duct is the tube through which the shell-forming materials and some yolk are carried into the oviduct. The seminal receptacle serves as a storage for spermatozoa received by the female during copulation.

The male cirrus is inserted in the vagina of the female during copulation and spermatozoa are introduced down this tubular canal.

LIFE CYCLE

The monoecious adult of *Polystoma integerrimum* inhabits the urinary bladder of frogs and toads. During the winter months the gonads are non-functional, but activity commences with the coming of spring, producing large eggs. The number of eggs produced ranges from 4 to 122 per day for one week. These eggs are expelled to the exterior.

Embryonic development within the egg-capsule (shell) is affected by temperature. At suitable temperature above 50° F., development of the onchomiracidium normally takes less than three weeks. If, however, the temperature drops below 50° F., development may take six to thirteen weeks.

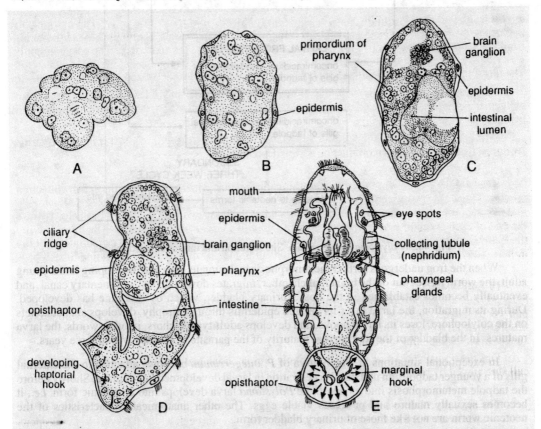

Fig. 40.2. *Polystoma integerrimum.* Stages during development. A—Early stage showing epiboly; B—Later stage, epidermis seperating from cell mass; C—Formation of organs from cell masses, cavity differentiating into digestive lumen; D—Later stage; E—Larva with areas of ciliated epidermis.

The correlation between the hatching of *P. integerrimum* eggs and the development and metamorphosis of the frog is one of astounding natural synchronization and suggests a hormonal influence. The barrel-shaped onchomiracidium, which bears 16 arrow-shaped hooklets on its opisthaptor, emerges from the egg and becomes free-swimming at the time that the tadpoles lose their external gills and acquire internal ones. The larva actively seeks out such a tadpole and enters the gill-chamber, in which it becomes attached to the gill-filaments by its armed opisthaptor. In this attached position, development continues for about eight weeks while the larva subsists on mucus and sloughed host cells.

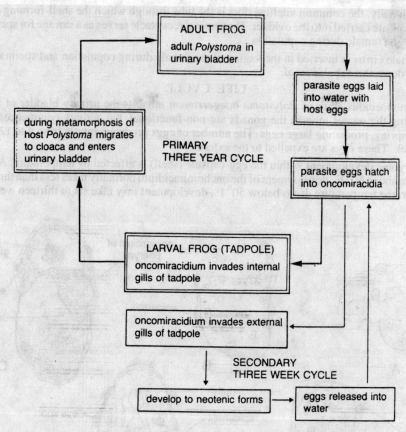

Fig. 40.3. *Polystoma integerrimum*. Site selection and migration in Amphibia.

When the frog undergoes further metamorphosis by losing its gills and developing into a young adult, the worm passes out of the branchial chamber, migrates down the host's alimentary canal, and eventually becomes established in the host's urinary bladder, which by this time has developed. During its migration, the larva loses its ciliated epidermis through atrophy, develops six suckerlets on the cotylophore, loses its larval hooks, and develops adult-type anchors, in other words, the larva matures. In the bladder of the frog, sexual maturity of the parasite is attained within three years.

In exceptional situations in which larva of *P. integerrimum* becomes attached to the external gills of a younger tadpole, an unnatural acceleration in larval development takes place. Shortly before the tadpole metamorphosis into an adult, the *Polystoma* larva develops into a neotenic form, *i.e.*, it becomes sexually mature and produces viable eggs. The other anatomical characteristics of the neotenic worm are not like those of urinary bladder form.

The correlation between the maturation process of the host and the developmental pattern of the parasite again strongly suggests that the parasite is controlled by the hormonal influence of the host. Hyman (1951) suggested that the neotenic form may be an alternating one with the urinary bladder form, whereby the larvae produced from eggs laid by the branchial form directly invade the urinary bladder of the frog through the anus. Gallien (1935), however, proposed that the larvae of branchial forms leave the host and seek out other tadpoles at the internal gill stage and follow the normal pattern after that.

Recent experiments by Miretski (1951) have revealed that maturation of *Polystoma* is controlled directly or indirectly by the hormonal activity of the frog. This investigator reported that when hypophysis extract is injected into an infected immature frog, the polystomes within the frog mature within 4 to 8 days and produce a small number of eggs for approximately one week. This period of time corresponds approximately to the time frogs spend in spawning. This synchronized mechanism results in the release of the parasite's eggs only when the frogs enter water to breed. In addition, it also assures that by the time the onchomiracidia hatch, there are abundant tadpoles available for reinfection.

How the hypophysis extract affects the maturation of polystomes is still uncertain. It is possible that either the increased level of gonadotrophins or sex hormones, brought about by the hypophysis extract, could be responsible.

REVISION QUESTIONS

1. Describe the structure and life cycle of *Polystoma*.
2. Describe the reproductive system of *Polystoma*.

41
Fasciola (A Liver Fluke)

Fasciola, a common fluke, is a parasitic flatworm, It inhabits the liver and bile passage of vertebrates, *viz.,* cattle, sheep, goat, rabbit, dog, pig and man. The various species of *Fasciola* like *F. hepatica* (the liver fluke of sheep) and *F. gigantica=F. indica* (the liver fluke of cattle)cause great damage to liver tissues and bile passages, a condition called fascioliasis or liver rot. The other related species are *Fasciolepsis buski, Fascioloides magna, Opisthorchis sinensis,* etc. However, the account on *Fasciola* discussed below relates to its species *hepatica.*

FASCIOLA HEPATICA (SHEEP LIVER FLUKE)
SYSTEMATIC POSITION

Phylum	....	**Platyhelminthes**
Class	....	**Trematoda**
Order	....	**Digenia**
Genus	....	*Fasciola*
Species	....	*hepatica*

HABIT AND HABITAT

Fasciola hepatica (L., *fasciola* = small bandage; Gr., *hepar*=liver),the sheep liver fluke,lives as an endoparasite in the bile passages of sheep. Its life cycle is digenetic, *i.e.,* completed in two hosts (a primary vertebrate host, the sheep and a secondary or intermediate invertebrate host, the gastropod mollusc). The adult parasite is found in the primary host, while a part of its life cycle as larval stages are found in the invertebrate host. *Fasciola hepatica*, in addition to sheep, also infects other vertebrates like goat, deer, horse, dog, ass, ox and occasionally man. Its secondary hosts are either *Planorbis* sps, *Bulinus* sps., or *Limnaea truncatula,* all being freshwater gastropod molluscs. *Fasciola hepatica* is worldwide in distribution, particularly sheep and cattle raising areas are the primary zones where human beings are also infected. Its other Indian species *F. gigantica* (= *indica*) is found in the bile passages of buffaloes, cow, goats and pigs.

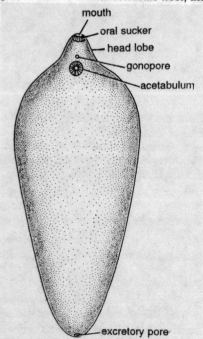

Fig. 41.1. *Fasciola hepatica.* Adult in ventral view.

STRUCTURE

Shape, size and colour. *F. hepatica* has a thin, dorsoventrally flattened, leaf-shaped, elongated and oval body. It measures about 25 to 30 mm in length and 4 to 12 mm in breadth. The maximum width is at about anterior third of the body from where the body tapers anteriorly as well as posteriorly, however, the anterior end is somewhat rounded, while it is bluntly pointed posteriorly. *F. indica* has its greatest width at about the middle of the body, and the posterior end is rounded. It is usually pinkish in colour but it appears brownish due to ingested bile of the host.

External morphology. The anterior end of the body is distinguished into a triangular **oral cone** or head lobe giving it a shouldered appearance. The head lobe, at its tip, bears a somewhat triangular aperture called mouth. There are two muscular suckers : an oral sucker at the anterior end encircling the mouth, and a large ventral sucker or acetabulum situated mid-ventrally 'about 3 to 4 mm behind the oral sucker. The suckers are cup-like muscular organs meant for attachment to the host by vacuum. In addition to mouth aperture, there are two permanent apertures on the body ; one situated mid-ventrally in front of the ventral sucker is the common genital aperture or gonopore, and the other is situated at the posterior end of the body called the excretory pore. In addition to these apertures, a temporary opening of Laurer's canal appears during the breeding season on the dorsal surface just anterior to the middle of the body. Anus is wanting because alimentary canal is incomplete.

BODY WALL

The body wall of *F. hepatica* lacks a cellular layer of epidermis, unlike those of the turbellarians. However, it consists of a thick layer of cuticle followed by a thin basement membrane and underlying muscle layers surrounding the mesenchyma.

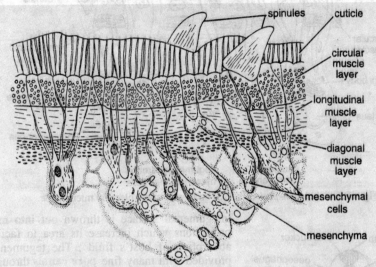

Fig. 41.2. *Fasciola hepatica.* T.S. through body wall.

Cuticle. A tough resistant cuticle, made of a homogeneous layer of scleroprotein, covers the fluke and protects it from the juices of the host. It bears small spines, spinules or scales. The spinules anchor the fluke to the bile duct of the host, provide protection and facilitate locomotion. The cuticle of *F. indica* has broad, stout, and blunt scales. The epidermis has been lost during development of the cercaria stage. However, the cuticle is secreted by special mesenchymal cells situated below muscle layers. These cuticle secreting cells were believed to be sunken epidermal cells (Hein, 1904 and Roewer, 1906).

Basement membrane. The lowest layer of the cuticle is a thin, delicate basement membrane. It demarcates the boundary between cuticle and muscle layers.

Muscle layer. The basement membrane is followed by a sub-cuticular musculature. It consists of an outer layer of circular muscle fibres, middle layer of longitudinal muscle fibres and an inner layer of diagonal muscle fibres which are more developed in the anterior half of the body. All muscles are smooth. The muscles form stout bundles of radial fibres in the suckers.

Mesenchyme. Below the muscles is parenchyma (mesenchyme) having numerous loosely arranged uninucleate and binucleate cells with syncytial network of fibres having fluid-filled spaces. Some of these cells are large and provided with large processes extending up to the base of the cuticle to which they are said to secrete. In fact, the mesenchyme forms a packing material between the muscle layer and internal organs. It helps in the transport of nutrients and waste substances.

The body wall plays a significant role in the physiology of fluke. It provides protection, it is the site of gaseous exchange, various nitrogenous wastes are diffused out through it and it also helps in the absorption of amino acids to some extent.

Structure of body wall under electron microscope. The electron microscopic studies of the body wall of *F. hepatica* by Threadgold (1963), Bils and Martin (1966) have clearly revealed that cuticle is a syncytial layer of protoplasm having mitochondria, endoplasmic canals, vacuoles and pinocytic vesicles. Hence, cuticle is now referred to as the integument because it is metabolically active. The tegument is continuous with tegument secreting cells lying in the mesenchyme. The outer

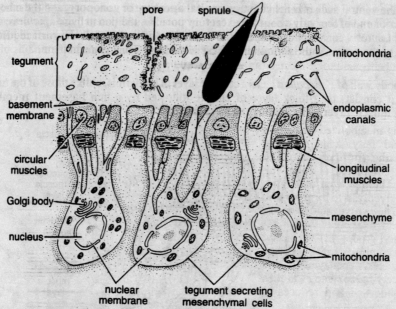

Fig. 41.3. *Fasciola hepatica.* V.L.S. body wall under electron microscope.

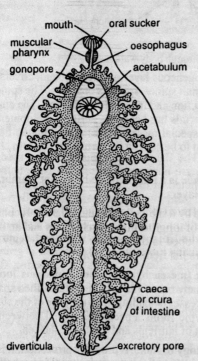

Fig.41.4. *Fasciola hepatica.* Digestive system.

integumental surface is thrown out into many fine projections which increase its area to facilitate the absorption of host's fluid . The tegument is also provided with many fine pore canals through which dissolved substances in the form of solution are absorbed into the mesenchyme.

DIGESTIVE SYSTEM

Alimentary canal. The oral sucker encloses a ventral mouth which leads into a funnel-shaped mouth cavity, followed by a round muscular pharynx with thick walls, and a small lumen. The pharynx has pharyngeal glands. *F. indica* has a short muscular pharynx from which arises an oral pouch which is about half the size of the pharynx. There is a short narrow oesophagus leading into an intestine which divides into two branches or intestinal caeca or crura each running on one side to the posterior end, and ending blindly. The intestinal caeca give out a number of branching diverticula in order to carry food to all parts of the body since there is no circulatory system. The median diverticula are short and lateral ones are long and branching. There is no anus.

The interior part of the alimentary canal up to the oesophagus is lined with cuticle and serves as a suctorial fore gut ; the intestine is lined with endodermal columnar epithelial cells. The caceal epithelium has secretory gland cells.

Food, feeding and digestion. It feeds on bile, blood, lymph and cell debris. The oral sucker and pharynx together constitute an effective suctorial apparatus. Digestion is extracellular, occurs in intestine. The digested food material is distributed by branching diverticula of intestine to all parts of the body as the circulatory system is not found in this animal. Thus, the digestive system functions as a gastrovascular system. In fact, the digested nutrients are passed into the parenchyma through intestinal diverticula; from parenchyma they are diffused into the various organs of the body. Reserve food, mostly in the form of glycogen and fats is stored in the parenchyma. However, monosaccharide sugars like glucose, fructose, etc., are directly diffused into the body of the fluke through general body surface from the surrounding fluid of the host. The indigestible remains of the food, if any, are probably said to be ejected through the mouth.

RESPIRATION

Mode of respiration is anaerobic or anoxybiotic. In fact, glycogen is metabolized to carbon dioxide and fatty acids releasing energy in the form of heat. The process is completed in following steps : (i) The glycogen undergoes anaerobic glycolysis to form pyruvic acid , (ii) The pyruvic acid is decarboxylated to form carbon dioxide and an acetyl group, (iii) The acetyl group then combines with coenzyme A to form acetyl coenzyme A, and (v) The acetyl coenzyme A is then finally condensed and reduces to form fatty acids.

The carbon dioxide, thus, produced is diffused out through general body surface and the fatty acids are excreted through the excretory system.

EXCRETORY SYSTEM

The excretory system of *Fasciola* is concerned with excretion as well as osmoregulation. It consists of a large number of flame cells or

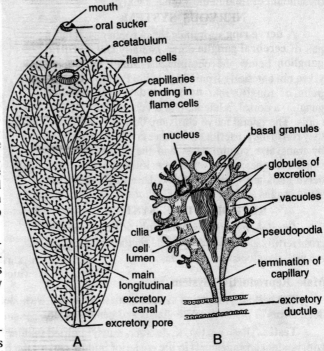

Fig. 41.5. *Fasciola hepatica.* A—Excretory system ; B—A flame cell.

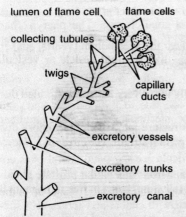

Fig. 41.6. *Fasciola.* Arrangement of flame cells and excretory ducts.

flame bulbs or protonephridia connected with a system of excretory ducts.

Flame cells. The flame cells, supposed to be modified mesenchymal cells, are numerous, irrgular in shape bulb-like bodies found distributed in the mesenchyma through out the body of *Fasciola*. The distribution pattern of flame cells follows a specific pattern referred to as 'the flame cell pattern' (Faust, 1919). The flame cells are characteristic, each has a thin elastic wall with pseudopodia-like processes, a nucleus and an intracellular cavity having many long cilia arising from basal granules. In living condition the cilia vibrate like a flickering flame, hence, the name flame cell.

Excretory ducts. There is an excretory pore at the posterior end from which arises a longitudinal excretory canal, from this arise four main branches, two dorsal and two ventral, which subdivide into numerous small capillaries which anastomose; the capillaries are continued into the intracellular cavity of flame cells. The longitudinal excretory canal is non-ciliated but the capillaries are lined with cilia.

Process of excretion. The excretory wastes, generally fatty acids and ammonia, are diffused from surrounding mesenchyma into the flame cells and finally collected into their intracellular cavities. The vibrating movement of the cilia causes the flow of wastes from the intracellular cavities of flame cells into the excretory ducts and then into the main excretory canal and finally to the exterior through excretory pore by hydrostatic pressure.

Such an excretory system of flame cells and canals or ducts of various orders with no internal opening and leading to an excretory pore which opens to the exterior is spoken of as a **protonephridial system** which is excretory but its main function is to regulate the amount of fluid in the animal's body.

NERVOUS SYSTEM

A **nerve ring** surrounds the oesophagus, it has a pair of **cerebral ganglia** dorso-laterally, and a **ventral ganglion** below the oesophagus. Small **nerves** are given out anteriorly from the ganglia. Posteriorly three pairs of longitudinal **nerve cords** arise from the ganglia, a dorsal, a lateral, and a ventral pair of nerve cords. The lateral nerve cords are best developed and they run to the posterior end. Nerve cords are connected by transverse commissures and they give out many small branches, some of which form plexuses. The nerve cells are mostly **bipolar**. Due to parasitic life sense organs are lost in adult *Fasciola*.

REPRODUCTIVE SYSTEM

Fasciola hepatica is **hermaphrodite** but usually cross fertilization takes place. The reproductive organs are well developed and complex.

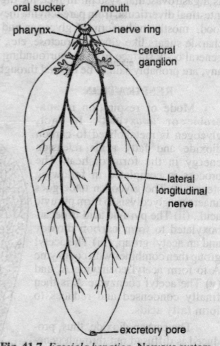

Fig. 41.7. *Fasciola hepatica*. Nervous system.

Male Reproductive System

The male reproductive system consists of testes, vasa deferentia, seminal vesicle, ejaculatory duct, cirrus or penis, prostate glands and genital atrium.

Testes. These are two in number, much ramified tubular and placed one behind the other (*i.e.,* with tendem arrangement) in the posterior middle part of the body. In fact, they occupy major space from behind the middle part of the body of *Fasciola*. The cells lining the wall of testes give rise to spermatozoa.

Vasa deferentia. A narrow and slender **vas deferens** or **sperm duct** arises from each testis and runs forwards.

Seminal vesicle. The two vasa deferentia unite together near the acetabulum (ventral sucker) and become dilated to form a muscular, elongated, broad, bag-like **seminal vesicle** or **vesicula seminalis.** It serves the purpose of storing sperms.

Ejaculatory duct. The seminal vesicle continues anteriorly into a very narrow and coiled duct called **ejaculatory duct.**

Cirrus. The cirrus (penis) is a muscular and elongated structure into which ejaculatory duct opens. The cirrus opens by **male genital aperture** in a common genital atrium. The cirrus of *F. indica* is covered with small spines.

Prostate glands. The ejaculatory duct is surrounded by numerous unicellular prostate glands. These glands open into the ejaculatory duct and their secretion (alkaline) helps in free movement of sperms during copulation.

Genital atrium. The genital atrium is a common chamber for male and female genital apertures, it opens externally by a **gonopore** lying ventrally in front of the acetabulum. The cirrus can be everted through the gonopore during copulation.

The cirrus or penis, seminal vesicle and prostatic glands are surrounded in a common cirrus sheath or cirrus sac.

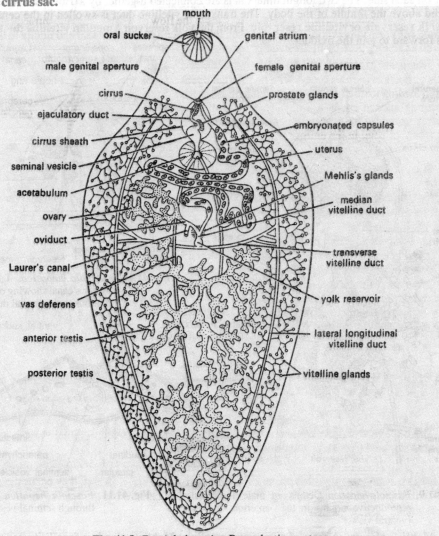

Fig. 41.8. *Fasciola hepatica.* Reproductive system.

Female Reproductive System

The female reproductive system consists of ovary, oviduct, uterus, vitelline glands, Mehlis's glands and Laurer's canal.

Ovary. The ovary is single, tubular, highly branched and situated to the anterior of testes at the right side in anterior one-third of the body.

Oviduct. All the branches of ovary open into a short and narrow tube called oviduct. The oviduct travels down obliquely and opens into the median vitelline duct.

Uterus. From the junction of oviduct and median vitelline duct arises a wide convoluted uterus having fertilized shelled eggs or capsules. The uterus opens by female genital aperture into the common genital atrium on the left side of male genital aperture. The uterus is comparatively small and it lies in front of the gonads. The terminal part of uterus has muscular walls, referred to as metraterm which ejects the eggs and also sometimes receives the cirrus during copulation.

Vitelline glands. On both lateral sides and also behind the testes are numerous follicles constituting the vilellaria, yolk glands or vitelline glands which produce albuminous yolk and shell material for the eggs. The vitelline glands open by means of minute ducts into a longitudinal vitelline duct on each side. The two longitudinal ducts are connected together by a transverse vitelline duct placed above the middle of the body. The transverse vitelline duct is swollen in the centre to form the yolk reservoir or vitelline reservoir. From the yolk reservoir a median vitelline duct starts and runs forward to join the oviduct.

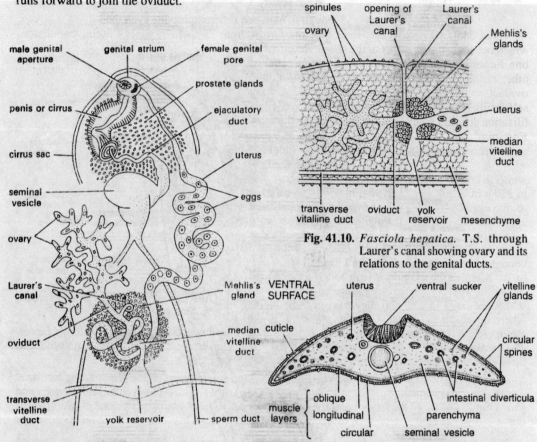

Fig. 41.9. *Fasciola hepatica.* Details of male and female reproductive organs in the anterior region (ventral view.)

Fig. 41.10. *Fasciola hepatica.* T.S. through Laurer's canal showing ovary and its relations to the genital ducts.

Fig. 41.11. *Fasciola hepatica.* T.S. body through seminal vesicles.

Mehlis's glands. A mass of numerous unicellular Mehlis's glands is found situated around the junction of median vitelline duct, oviduct and uterus. The secretion of Mehlis's glands lubricates the passage of eggs in the uterus and probably hardens the egg shells, it probably also activates spermatozoa. The junction of oviduct and median vitelline duct is swollen to form ootype in certian flukes like *F. indica*, in which the parts of an egg are assembled and the eggs are shaped, but an ootype is lacking in *F. hepatica* (according to some authorities).

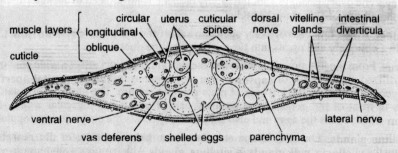

Fig. 41.12. *Fasciola hepatica.* T.S. of body through uterus.

Laurer's canal. From the oviduct arises a narrow Laurer's canal, it runs vertically upwards. This canal opens on the dorsal side temporarily during breeding season and acts as vestigial vagina to serve as copulation canal.

LIFE HISTORY

Copulation and fertilization. Though *F. hepatica* is hermaphrodite even then cross-fertilization is of common occurrence. Hence, before fertilization copulation occurs ; during copulation, which occurs in the bile duct of the sheep, the cirrus of one *Fasciola* is inserted into the Laurer's canal of other *Fasciola* and the sperms are deposited into the oviduct, so that cross-fertilization takes place. During self-fertilization, which occurs only when cross-fertilization does not take place, the sperms from the same *Fasciola* enter the female genital aperture and pass down the uterus to fertilize the eggs in the oviduct.

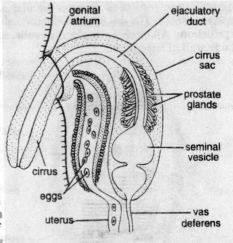

Fig. 41.13. *Fasciola hepatica.* Cirrus protruded through gonopore.

Formation of egg capsules. The eggs are brownish in colour, oval in shape and measure about 130 to 150 μ in length and 63 to 90 μ in width. As referred to, the eggs are fertilized in the oviduct, the fertilized eggs receive yolk cells from vitelline glands and they get enclosed in a chitinous shell formed by granules in the yolk cells giving out droplets, the shell hardens and becomes brownish yellow; the shell has an operculum or lid. Mehlis's glands play no role in the formation of the shell. The completed 'eggs' are called capsules which are large in size and they pass into the uterus where development starts. Capsules come out of the gonopore into the bile duct of the sheep, they reach the intestine and are passed out with the faeces. The capsules which fall in water or damp places will develop at about 75°F. Capsules are produced throughout the year, and one fluke may produce 500,000 capsules.

Development. Development starts in the uterus and is continued on the ground. The fertilized egg divides into a small propagatory cell and a larger somatic cell. The somatic cell divides and forms the ectoderm of the larva. Later the propagatory cell divides into two cells, one of which forms the endoderm and mesoderm of the larva, and the other forms a mass of germ cells at the posterior

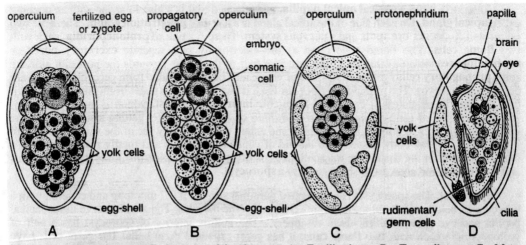

Fig. 41.14. *Fasciola hepatica.* Early stages of development. A—Fertilized egg ; B—Two cell stage ; C—Many cell stage ; D—Miracidium in capsules.

end of the larva. This method of development takes place in the formation of all larval stages during the life history. In two weeks time a small ciliated miracidium larva is formed and it comes out of the shell by forcing the operculum. The miracidium produces a proteolytic enzyme which erodes the lower surface of the operculum.

Miracidium larva. Miracidium larva is a minute, oval and elongated, free-swimming stage, it is covered with 18 to 21 flat ciliated epidermal cells lying in five rings. The **first ring** is made of six plates (two dorsal, two lateral and two ventral), **second ring** has again six plates (three dorsal and three ventral), **third ring** has three plates (one dorsal and two ventro-lateral), **fourth ring** has four plates(two right and two left) and **fifth ring** has two plates (one left and one right). A **sub-epidermal musculature**, consisting of outer circular and inner longitudinal fibres, is situated beneath the epidermal cells. The sub-epidermal musculature is followed by a layer of cells constituting the **sub-epithelium**. All these, *i.e.*, epidermal cells, sub-musculature and sub-epithelium, together form the **body wall** of miracidium.

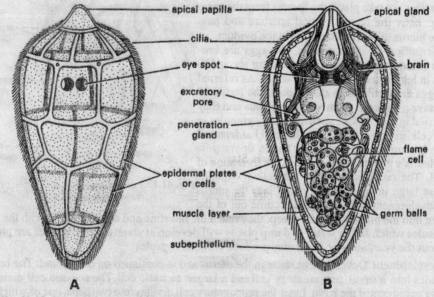

Fig. 41.15. *Fasciola hepatica*. Miracidum larva. A—External structure; B—Internal structure.

Anteriorly it has a conical **apical papilla**, and attached to it is a glandular sac with an opening called **apical gland.** On each side of the apical gland is a bag-like **penetration gland.** There are two pigmented X-shaped **eye spots** and a **nervous system.** There is a pair of **protonephridia,** each with two **flame cells.** The flame cells open to the exterior by two separate **excretory pores** or **nephridiopores** situated laterally in the posterior half of the body. Towards the posterior side are some **propagatory cells** (germ cells), some of which may have divided to form germ balls which are developing embryos. The miracidium does not feed, it swims about in water or moisture film, but it dies in eight hours unless it can reach a suitable **intermediate host,** which is some species of amphibious snail of genus *Limnaea* or even *Bulinus* or *Planorbis.* After getting a suitable host the miracidium adheres to it by its apical papilla and enters the pulmonary sac of the snail, from where it penetrates into the body tissues with the aid of penetration glands and finally reaches to snail's digestive gland. In the tissues the miracidium casts off its ciliated epidermis,loses its sense organs and it swells up and changes in shape to form a **sporocyst.**

Sporocyst. The sporocyst is an elongated germinal sac about 0.7 mm long and covered with a thin cuticle, below which are mesenchyme cells and some muscles. The glands, nerve tissue, apical papilla and eye spots of miracidium disappear. The hollow interior of sporocyst has a pair of protonephridia each with two flame cells, it has germ cells and germ balls. The germ cells have descended in a direct line from the original ovum from the miracidium developed. The sporocyst moves about in the host tissues and its germ cells develop into a third type of larva called **redia larva.** A sporocyst forms 5 to 8 rediae. The rediae larvae pass out of the sporocyst by rupture of its body wall into the snail tissues with the aid of the muscular collar and ventral processes, then the rediae migrate to the liver of the snail.

Redia. The redia is elongated about 1.3 mm to 1.6 mm in length with two ventral processes called **lappets** or **procruscula** near the posterior end and a **birth pore** near the anterior end. Body

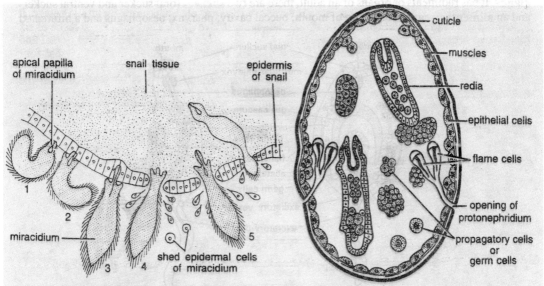

apical papilla of miracidium **snail tissue** **epidermis of snail**

cuticle

muscles

redia

epithelial cells

flame cells

opening of protonephridium

propagatory cells or germ cells

1

2

miracidium

3 4 5

shed epidermal cells of miracidium

Fig.41.16. Miracidium of *Fasciolopsis buski.* Stage of penetration through snail epidermis.

Fig. 41.17. *Fasciola hepatica.* Sporocyst.

wall has cuticle, mesenchyme and muscles, and near the anterior end, just in front of the birth pore, the muscles form a circular ridge, the **collar** used for locomotion. Redia has an anterior **mouth**, **pharynx** in which numerous **pharyngeal glands** open, sac-like **intestine** and there is a pair of

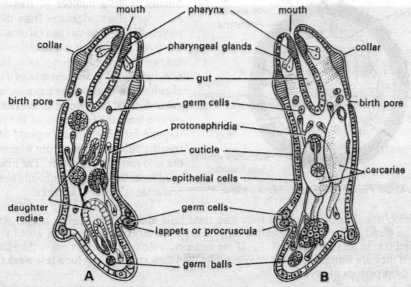

mouth **pharynx** **mouth**

collar **collar**

pharyngeal glands

gut

birth pore **germ cells** **birth pore**

protonephridia

cuticle

cercariae

epithelial cells

daughter rediae **germ cells**

lappets or procruscula

germ balls

A B

Fig. 41.18. *Fasciola hepatica.* A—Redia with daughter rediae ; B—Redia with cercariae.

protonephridia with two pairs of **flame cells.** Its cavity has germ cells and germ balls. The germ cells of redia give rise during **summer** months to a second generation of **daughter rediae,** but in **winter** they produce the fourth larval stage, the **cercaria larva.** Thus, either the primary redia or daughter redia produce cercaria larvae which escape from the birth pore of the redia into the snail tissues. Each redia forms about 14 to 20 cercariae.

Cercaria. The cercaria has an oval body about 0.25 mm to 0.35 mm long and a simple long tail. Its epidermis is soon shed and replaced by cuticle ; below the cuticle are muscles and cystogenous glands. It has rudiments of organs of an adult, there are two suckers (oral sucker and ventral sucker) and an alimentary canal consisting of mouth, buccal cavity, pharynx, oesophagus and a bifurcated

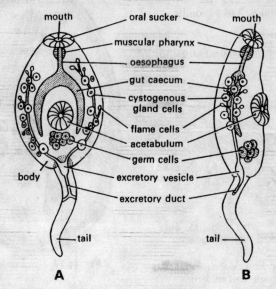

Fig. 41.19. *Fasciola hepatica*. A—Cercaria in ventral view ; B—Cercaria in lateral view.

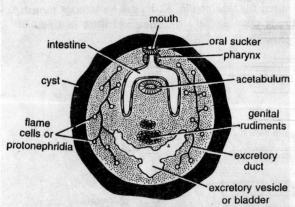

Fig. 41.20. *Fasciola hepatica*. Metacercaria.

intestine. There is an excretory bladder with a pair of protonephridial canals (excretory tubules) with a number of flame cells. An excretory duct originates from the bladder, travels through the tail and bifurcates to open out through a pair of nephridiopores. There are two large penetration glands, but they are non-functional in the cercaria of *Fasciola*. It also has the rudiments of reproductive organs formed from germ cells. The cercariae escape from the birth pore of the redia, then migrate from the digestive gland of the snail into the pulmonary sac from where they pass out into surrounding water. The time taken in snail from the entry of miracidia to the exit of cercariae is five to six weeks.

Metacercaria. The cercariae swim about in water for 2 to 3 days, they then lose their tails and get enclosed in a cyst secreted by cystogenous glands. The encysted cercaria is called a metacercaria which is about 0.2 mm in diameter and it is in fact a juvenile fluke. If the metacercariae are formed in water they can live for a year, but if they are formed on grass or vegetation then they survive only for a few weeks, they can withstand short periods of drying.

The various larval stages (the miracidium, sporocyst, redia, and cercaria) are all formed in the same way from germ cells which are set aside at the first division. There is, thus, a distinction between germ cells and somatic cells, and germ cells alone form the various larval stages.

Infection of the primary host (Sheep). Further development of the metacercaria takes place only if it is swallowed by the final host, the sheep. Metacercariae can also infect man if they are swallowed by eating water cress on which cercariae encyst, but such cases are rare. But the metacercarie are not infective until 12 hours after encystment. In the alimentary canal of a sheep the cyst wall is digested and a young fluke emerges and bores through the wall of the intestine to enter the body of the host. After about two to six days they enter the liver and their movements in the liver may cause serious injuries. The young flukes stay in the liver for seven or eight weeks feeding mainly on blood and then they enter the bile duct and bile passages. The young flukes have been growing in the liver and after several weeks in the bile duct they become sexually mature adults. The period of incubation in the sheep takes 3 to 4 months.

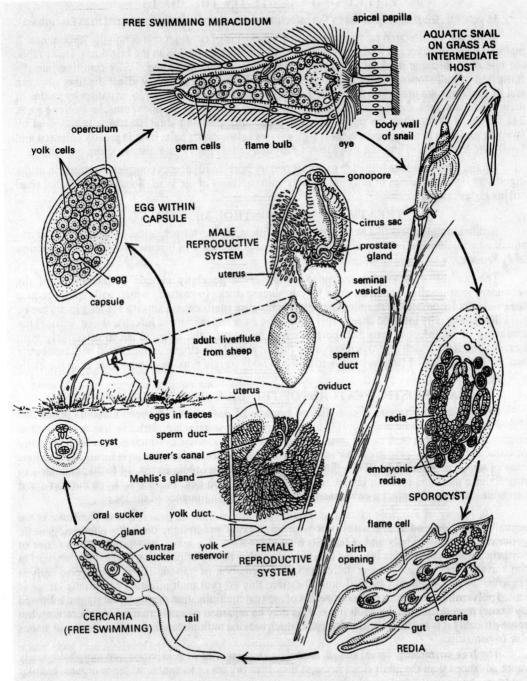

Fig. 41.21. *Fasciola heptica.* Life history.

However, the life history of *F.hepatica* can be summarized as under :

Adult flukes in liver →copulation and fertilization →laying of capsules in the bile ducts →capsules in the intestine (stages in sheep's body) →capsules out in faeces→miracidia escape from capsules (stages in open) →miracidia →sporocysts →Rediae →cercariae→(stages in snail's body) →cercariae→metacercariae (stages in open)→metacercariae →young flukes →adult flukes (stages in a fresh sheep's body).

EFFECT OF PARASITE ON THE HOSTS

In general , the disease caused by the infection of *Fasciola hepatica* is referred to as fascioliasis.

However, its infection on the primary host (sheep) is of considerable economic importance. It mainly affects the liver but it also causes hepatitis and inflammation in the bile ducts. Due to this, the bile ducts become thickened which is followed by calcification and finally resulting into the formation of gall stones. During heavy infection the liver flukes seriously affect the liver of sheep and its functions are upset, the sheep get a disease called "liver rot" due to irritation by means of their cuticular spines, the sheep acquire large quantities of water in the body, muscles become weak and functions of the liver are upset. The sheep becomes dull and sluggish which is followed by swelling and pain in abdomen, weight is lost, eye-sockets become pale, liver is greatly enlarged and finally the sheep dies. Thus, the infection of *Fasciola* causes heavy mortality in sheep population.

On the other hand, its infection to the secondary host (snail) causes complete destruction of the digestive glands or the site of infection, finally causing death of the snail. Sometimes infected snail attains gigantic size.

TREATMENT AND CONTROL MEASURES

Antihelminthic drugs like hexachloroethane, filicin, carbon tetrachloride, tetrachloroethane and emetine hydrochloride, etc., are effectively used for the treatment of disease caused by the infection of *F. hepatica.*

The control or preventive measures (prophylaxis) generally include (i) the killing of the secondary host (snail) ; it can be done by introducing ducks to pastures which will rapidly reduce the snail population, and by draining the pastures because snails cannot survive for long in dry areas, (ii) killing of heavily infected sheep , (iii) destroying eggs and manure of infected sheep, and (iv) the spreading of its infection can also be prevented by treating the infected sheep effectively with hexachloroethane which destroys most of the flukes; hexachloroethane administered with bentomite and water at the rate of 10 gms of drug to 50 kg of body weight removes the parasite from the cattle and sheep.

CHARACTERISTIC FEATURES OF THE LIFE HISTORY OF *F.HEPATICA*

Life history of *Fasciola* is complicated because of parasitism. A sheep harbours about 200 flukes which will produce about 100 million eggs. The miracidium larva is free living and is structurally adapted to seek out an intermediate host, a snail *Limnaea,* which is found conveniently in water and damp places in grass in wide areas where sheep graze. The sporocyst forms 5 to 8 rediae, each of which produces 8 to 12 daughter rediae, each daughter redia forms 14 to 20 cercariae ; so that about a thousand cercaria larvae are produced from each egg. From this large number some cercariae are bound to infect a new sheep, thus, ensuring a continuance of the race.

Life history of *Fasciola* affords an example of alternation of generations. The fluke is the sexual generation and it alternates, not with an asexual generation, but with parthenogenetic generations of sporocysts and rediae. Such an alternation of a sexual generation with a series of parthenogenetic generations is called heterogamy. This theory of parthenogenetic development in the various larval stages is now discounted, and formation of various larvae from germ cells is regarded as simple mitotic asexual multiplication; this asexual multiplication of various larvae is called polyembryony. Thus, there is a period of asexual multiplication during larval stages, followed by sexual reproduction in the adult fluke. This may be regarded as an alternation of generations, but more probably it is continuous life history in which asexual multiplication occurs in the larval stages due to parasitism.

The free swimming larval stages, miracidia and cercariae of *F.hepatica*, are morphologically more advanced than the adult fluke because they bear organs of locomotion, sense organs, cellular epidermis and a well developed body cavity.

PARASITIC ADAPTATIONS OF *FASCIOLA*

As adult *Fasciola* lives in the liver and bile ducts of sheep as an endoparasite, it is very well adapted for its parasitic mode of life. In fact, on one hand adult fluke exhibits certain adaptive features and on the other a number of adaptive features may also be accounted from the various stages of its life history. So, the adaptive features of *Fasciola* can be discussed in the following two headings :

A. Adaptations of the adult fluke. These can be accounted as under :

1. Its body is dorsoventrally flattened, leaf-shaped which increases surface area of the body for increased diffusion of substances through fluid of the body.

2. Its body is covered with a thick cuticle which protects it from host's antitoxins.

3. Cilia are absent in adult flukes.

4. Adhesive organs like suckers (anterior sucker and ventral sucker) well developed which provide it firm attachment with the host tissue. Many cuticular spines over its body erode the host tissue forming its food and also serve in saving the fluke from being pushed away in the ducts with bile.

5. Its mouth is situated anteriorly and the muscular pharynx serves for sucking the nutrinets from the host body. Since it feeds on predigested and digested substances of the host body, hence, its alimentary canal is not well developed and digestive glands are not found.

6. Since process of digestion does not occur, anus is absent and, hence, circulatory system is wanting because the various organs of alimentary canal (intestine and its various branches) distribute the already digested food substances to the different parts of its body.

7. Since it lives in an environment which is devoid of oxygen, hence, anaerobic mode of respiration occurs ; respiratory organs are completely wanting.

8. Its nervous system is very simple and the sense organs are completely wanting , as the flukes are endoparasites.

9. Locomotory organs are not found as the flukes lead a well protected life.

10. The excretory system consists of a complicated arrangement of branched tubules so as to facilitate the collection of various metabolic excretory wastes of the body.

11. The reproductive system is well developed and best suited for its parasitic mode of life.

12. Since adult fluke lives in the body of the sheep, hence, it may die with the death of the sheep. Therefore, there is a need of secondary host for the transference of the parasite from one host to the other, so that its race may be continued. Hence, snail is the secondary host.

B. Adaptations in life history. The various parasitic adaptive features in the life history of *Fasciola* can be accounted as under :

1. Production of enormous number of eggs to overcome their wastage during transference.

2. The eggs are to pass down the bile duct, into the intestine of sheep and then to the outside with its faeces, hence, the fertilized eggs are enclosed in a chitinous covering, theshell, which protects the zygote from the enzymes of the host. The shelled eggs are called capsules.

3. Miracidia are the first larvae to come out of the capsules ; miracidia are well adapted to lead free swimming life (it has ciliated body to help in swimming, eye spots are developed) and also for entering into the body of the secondary host, *Limnaea, Planorbis* , etc. (penetration glands help them to enter into snail's body).

4. The sporocyst leads parasitic life; its body is covered in a cyst-like structure to protect it from digestive enzymes of the snail. The germ balls in sporocyst give rise to rediae which may further produce either large number of daughter rediae or cercariae.

5. The locomotory organs of rediae (lappets or procruscula) and cercariae (tail) enable them to move and find their way into the fresh tissues of the snail.

6. Cercariae find their way out of the body of snail and lead a very short free life and then get enclosed in a cyst secreted by them itself on vegetations.

7. The cysted cercariae called metacercariae on vegetation make sure of their entry into the sheep's body due to herbivorous habit of the sheep.

8. Metacercariae can live for a longer period waiting for entry into sheep's body as they are well protected in cyst to overcome climatic hazards.

9. Mode of parthenogenetic reproduction of larvae further ensures the continuity of their race.

However, the high rate of reproduction, adaptations of the larvae, sexual and asexual mode of reproduction and adaptations in the morphology and physiology of the fluke are to ensure the survival and continuity of the race.

REVISION QUESTIONS

1. Describe the structure of *Fasciola hepatica* and explain how it is adapted to the parasitic mode of life.
2. Describe the structure of the body wall of *Fasciola hepatica* and mention its functions.
3. Describe the reproductive system of *Fasciola hepatica*.
4. Give an account of the life history of *Fasciola hepatica*.
5. What is digenetic life cycle? Explain it with reference to the life history of *Fasciola hepatica*.
6. Give a detailed account of the parasitic adaptations of *Fasciola hepatica*.
7. Draw labelled diagrams only :
   (i) V.S. body wall of *Fasciola hepatica;*
   (ii) T.S. *Fasciola hepatica* through uterus;
   (iii) Larval forms of *Fasciola hepatica*.
8. Explain the life history of *Fasciola hepatica* with the help of diagrams only.
9. Write short notes on :
   (a) Liver rot ; (b) Flame cell ; (c) Miracidium ; (d) Redia ; (e) Sporocyst ; (f) Cercaria ; (h) Characteristic features in the life history of *Fasciola hepatica*.

42

Taenia (A Tapeworm)

Taenia, commonly called tapeworm because of its long, flat, ribbon-like body-form, is exclusively endoparasitic flatworm. Various species of *Taenia* parasitize man and other animals. The common species of *Taenia* parasitizing man are *T. solium* (the pork tapeworm), *T. saginata* (the beef tapeworm), *T. acanthotrias* and *T. nana*. *T. pisiformis*, *T. caninum*, *T. cucumarina* and *T. madagascariensis* are commonly found parasitizing dogs and cats. *T. flavopunctata* parasitizes mouse and rat. Other tapeworms like *Moniezia* parasitizes sheep, *Hymenolepis* (the dwarf tapeworm) parasitizes children, mice and rat and *Echinococcus* (probably the smallest tapeworm) parasitizes dogs, cats and wolves. However, *Taenia solium* has been described in detail in the following pages.

TAENIA SOLIUM (THE PORK TAPEWORM OF MAN)
SYSTEMATIC POSITION

Phylum	....	**Platyhelminthes**
Class	....	**Cestoda**
Subclass	....	**Eucestoda**
Order	....	**Taenioidea**
Genus	....	*Taenia*
Species	....	*solium*

HABIT AND HABITAT

Taenia solium, the pork tapeworm of man, as adult lives in the intestine of man leading an endoparasitic life. Its life history is completed in two hosts, *i.e.,* digenetic ; man being the primary host and pig as secondary host. Except the adult, various stages of its life history are passed in the body of secondary host. Other animals like goat, cattle, horse and monkey may also serve as secondary host. *T. solium* is, however, reported from those parts of the world where pork is eaten, either raw or improperly cooked, especially in European countries. Since, it lives in adult stage in the intestine of man, it causes injuries to mucous membrane lining the alimentary canal where it adheres by its scolex ; it may even cause mechanical injury by obstructing the passage of alimentary canal ; it causes abdominal pains, weakness, loss of weight and excessive appetite. However, disease caused by this worm is called taeniasis.

STRUCTURE

The body of *Taenia solium* is long, dorsoventrally flattened, narrow, ribbon-like, reaching a length of two to three metres. The colour of the body is opaque-white. Body consists of scolex, neck and strobila or body segments.

(i) Scolex. The anterior end of the body of *Taenia* has a knob-like scolex. The scolex is smaller than the

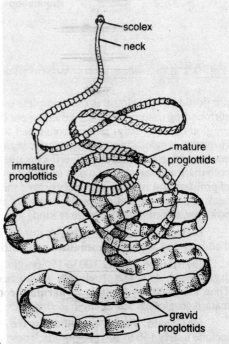

Fig. 42.1. *Taenia solium.*

scolex
neck
immature proglottids
mature proglottids
gravid proglottids

head of a pin about 1 mm in diameter with 4 cup-like muscular suckers having radial muscles, and an anterior round prominence, the rostellum having about 22 to 32 curved, chitinous hooks in two circles, the inner circle with larger hooks and outer circle with smaller ones. The long and short hooks alternate with each other. Each hook is made of a base by which it fixes, a handle directed towards the apex and a conical blade directed outwardly. The rostellum can be protruded slightly. The scolex with its suckers and hooks is an organ of attachment to the intestinal wall of the host, thus, working as an organ of adhesion or the holdfast.

The scolex is, sometimes, wrongly referred to as 'head' but it cannot be the head because it is neither related to food-perception nor an organ of catching the food.

(ii) Neck. Behind the scolex is a thin, small, narrow, unsegmented neck which grows continuously and proliferates proglottids by transverse fission or asexual budding. Therefore, this region is variously called like growth zone, area of proliferation or budding zone, etc.

(iii) Strobila. The neck is followed by the flattened, ribbon-like body called strobila. The strobila forms the main bulk of the body and consists of a series of proglottids arranged in a linear fashion. The strobila of a mature tapeworm measures about three metres in length having 800 to 900

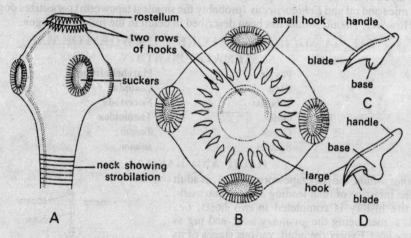

Fig. 42.2. *Taenia solium.* Scolex. A—Scolex mangified; B—Frontal view of scolex; C—Small hook; D—Large hook.

proglottids. A proglottid is one complete unit of the body having a complete set of genitalium and surrounding tissue. The linear arrangement or repetition of these units is called proglottization. The proglottids, internally, remain connected together by muscles,excretory vessels and nerve cords. However, proglottids are not metameric segments like those of annelids, arthropods and other animals because these are independent, self-contained units, each with a complete set of reproductive organs both male and female and a part of excretory and nervous systems ; and they are formed at the zone of proliferation situated anteriroly behind the scolex. Therefore, the youngest proglottid is next to the neck and the oldest at the posterior end of the strobila. The proglottids in a mature tapeworm are, however, differentiated into three kinds :

(a) Immature. The proglottids just behind the neck, devoid of reproductive organs, are broader than long and are called immature proglottids. These include nearly 200 anterior proglottids.

(b) Mature. Nearly 100 to 150 proglottids, after immature proglottids, bear male reproductive organs only. As these proglottids are pushed back they develop female reproductive organs also. Thus, the mature proglottids are hermaphrodite and they number about 300 to 400 proglottids. The mature proglottids are squarish in shape (Fig. 42.8).

(c) Gravid. These proglottids are the oldest and towards the posterior side of the strobila and include nearly 150 to 200 proglottids. These segments are longer than their breadth and no reproductive organs are found in them. They contain only branched uterus packed with fertilized eggs (Fig.42.12).

In fact, the proglottids of strobila widen gradually along their length from anterior to posterior side. The proglottids bear genital papilla and pore, alternating once to right and then to left. In *T. solium* like other tapeworms, the gravid proglottids are regularly cut off either singly or in group of two to five proglottids from the posterior end of strobila ; this is called apolysis. These detached proglottids are passed out from the body of the host during defaecation along with the faeces. The phenomenon of apolysis is significant because it helps in transferring the developing embryos to the outside from the body of primary host so that they can find a secondary host, and it also keeps the size of strobila restricted within a limit due to continuous proliferation of new proglottids from the neck region.

BODY WALL

The body wall consists of cuticle, subcuticular muscles, subcuticular cells and parenchyma or mesenchyma.

1. Cuticle. The cuticle forms the outermost, thick, waxy and enzyme resistant covering of the body. It is composed of protein impregnated with calcium carbonate, and it is traversed by many fine canals. However, it consists of three layers, an outer comidial layer having fine thread-like spines called microtriches, a thick middle homogeneous layer, and the innermost thin basement membrane. As referred to, some of the fine canals in cuticle layer are connected by gland cells and some receive free nerve endings.

2. Subcuticular muscles. Just below the basement membrane of cuticular layer, subcuticular musculature is situated. It consists of outer circular muscle layer and inner longitudinal muscle layer.

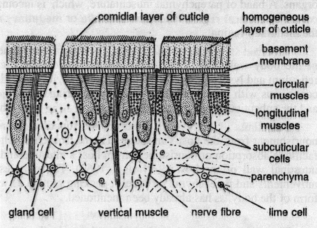

Fig. 42.3. *Taenia solium.* T.S. of body wall.

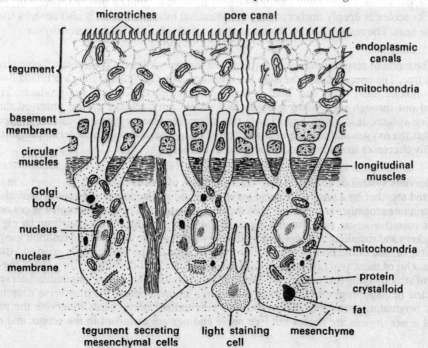

Fig. 42.4. *Taenia solium.* T.S. of body wall as seen under electron microscope.

Some longitudinal and circular or transverse muscle fibres are also found in the mesenchyme which constitute mesenchymal or parenchymal musculature.

3. Subcuticular cells. A large number of long necked subcuticular cells are also found in the mesenchyma which open just below the basement membrane. These cells are said to secrete cuticle. The **epidermis** is absent; in fact, both ectoderm and endoderm are absent in the adult, only mesoderm is present which forms the various organs of the body.

4. Parenchyma or mesenchyma. It is a fluid-filled spongy network of branching mesenchyme cells forming a packing substance around the internal organs and subcuticular muscle layer. Therefore, there is no body cavity in it. The turgidity of fluid in the mesenchyme cells helps in maintaining the form of the body. It contains some calcareous lime cells whose secretion probably neutralizes the acid of the digestive juice of the host. The parenchyma in the neck and young proglottids is thicker and contains some free cells which later differentiate to form the reproductive organs. A band of parenchymal musculature, which is incomplete at the edges, divides it into outer cortex or cortical region and inner medulla or medullary region; the reproductive organs lie in the medullary region.

Electron structure of body wall. Threadgold and others have studied the electron structure of the body wall (Fig. 42.4); their studies suggest the presence of mitochondria, endoplasmic reticulum and lysosomes in the cuticle. Therefore, it is considered to be living syncytial layer being continuous with the subcuticular cells. Considering this Meglitsch (1972) has called it tegument and the subcuticular cells as the tegument secreting cells which continuously renew the tegument.

Functions of body wall. It serves the function of protecting internal organs and absorbs nourishment from the host's intestine. The microtriches help in increasing its surface area which facilitate absorption or nourishment from host's intestine and also perform anchoring role with the intestinal wall of the host (Rothman, 1963). The muscles of body wall enable it to perform movements and parenchyma provides a packing ground as well as it also helps in maintaining the form of the body, as has already been mentioned.

NUTRITION

The alimentary canal is altogether absent in *T. solium,* therefore, its mode of nutrition is saprozoic, *i.e.,* it absorbs digested liquid food from the intestine of the host through its general body surface. In fact, the digested nutrients like glucose, amino acids, glycerol, etc., from the host's intestine, particularly form ileum, diffuse directly through its general body surface. It is also thought that as its scolex is deeply anchored into the intestinal mucosa, hence, it also absorbs tissue fluids from the host. The reserve food is stored as glycogen and lipoids in the parenchyma.

RESPIRATION

The mode of respiration is anaerobic, as the tapeworm lives in the intestinal contents which is oxygen free. The energy is derived from the breakdown of glycogen. During the breakdown process carbon dioxide, fatty acids and other organic acids are produced as waste products. The CO_2 is diffused out through its general body surface, while fatty acids, etc., are removed through the excretory system. It is interesting to note that whenever free oxygen is available to tapeworm, it consumes the oxygen and the rate of consumption being maximum in the anterior proglottids which gradually decreases towards the posterior side of the body.

NERVOUS SYSTEM

Nervous system of *T. solium* (Fig. 42.5) consists of two small cerebral ganglia in the scolex connected together by a thick transverse nerve band and by the dorsal and ventral commissures. All these structures together are referred to as the brain complex. The brain complex is connected with another rostellar nerve ring having a pair of rostellar ganglia in the rostellum by eight nerves. The suckers and rostellum are supplied by the nerve fibres from cerebral and rostellar ganglia. From the posterior side of the brain complex, five pairs of longitudinal nerve cords arise and travel in the strobila. Out of these two lateral longitudinal nerves are best developed, they run along the entire length of strobila lying just outside the longitudinal excretory canal. The longitudinal nerve cords are connected in each proglottid by a ring connective situated below the transverse excretory canal. Nerves originating from ring connective and longitudinal nerve cords innervate the proglottids. Special sense organs are absent but free nerve endings are abundant in the scolex and rest of the body.

EXCRETORY SYSTEM

There are four longitudinal excretory vessels, two on each side, along the margins. Two of these are dorsal in position and they exist only in the anterior part of the strobila ; but the other two are ventral and run along the whole length. The four excretory vessels are joined in the scolex by the nephridial plexus. The dorsal excretory vessels carry fluid towards the scolex and the ventral vessels away from it. The ventral excretory vessels are of unequal diameter and are joined by a transverse excretory canal in the posterior margin of each proglottid. The excretory canals are lined by cuticle and are non-ciliated, but they are fed by small ciliated branches which ramify into fine capillaries terminating in characteristic flame cells found all over in the paren- chyma. The long cilia of flame cells flicker and maintain a hydrostatic pressure by which waste is driven into the excretory canals. The last proglottid has a pulsatile bladder or caudal vesicle opening out by an excretory pore, but when this proglottid is shed, the caudal vesicle is lost and the ventral excretory canals open independently to exterior. The metabolic waste products like fatty acids, organic acids, etc., are removed by the excretory system. This system is said to regulate the fluid contents of the body of *Taenia*, hence, also regarded to be osmoregulatory in function.

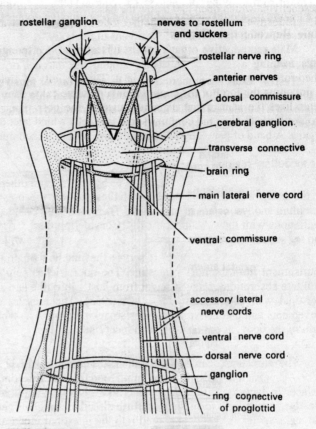

Fig. 42.5. *Taenia solium.* Nervous system.

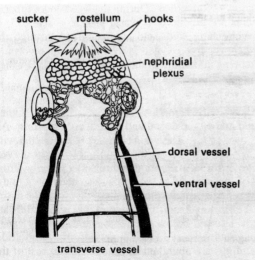

Fig. 42.6. *T. solium.* Excretory system showing excretory vessels and nephridial plexus in the anterior end.

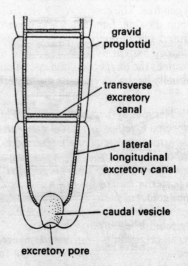

Fig. 42.7. *T. solium.* Excretory vessels with caudal vesicle in last proglottid.

REPRODUCTIVE SYSTEM

It has already been referred to, that nearly 300 to 400 proglottids of mature proglottids are hermaphrodite having complete sets of male and female reproductive organs. However, the structure of a mature proglottid clearly exhibits the reproductive organs in the following way.

Male Reproductive Organs

Male reproductive organs consist of testes, vasa efferentia, vas deferens, cirrus or penis and cirrus sac.

Testes. There are numerous small spherical bodies found scattered throughout the parenchyma in the greater part of the proglottid towards the dorsal side. Few workers are of the view that testis is single but it is branched so that numerous small rounded follicles are formed ; however, in the present text the follicles have been referred to as testes.

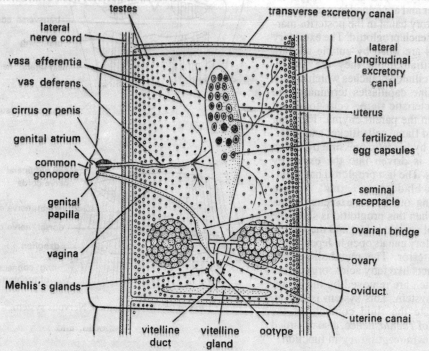

Fig. 42.8. *T. solium.* A mature proglottid to show the reproductive organs.

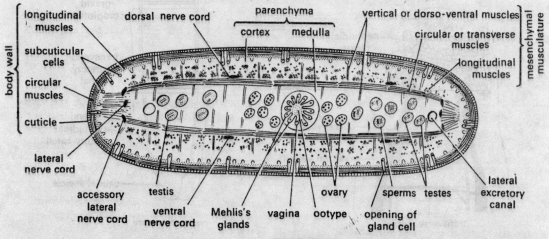

Fig. 42.9. *T. solium.* T.S. mature proglottid passing through ootype.

Vasa efferentia From each testis minute capillary originates, called vas efferens. The vasa efferentia from surrounding testes unite to form a common sperm duct approximately in the middle of the proglottid.

Vas deferens. The common sperm duct or vas deferens runs as a convoluted duct transversely to open in the cirrus.

Cirrus and cirrus sac. The cirrus or penis is a muscular intromittent organ in which vas deferens continues. The cirrus is protrusible and is surrounded by the cirrus sac. The cirrus opens by male gonopore into a cup-shaped genital atrium, situated more or less in the middle of the proglottid and at its lateral margin. The genital atrium opens by the common gonopore on a swollen genital papilla. The genital papilla lie alternately, more or less regularly, in the successive proglottids on the right and left sides.

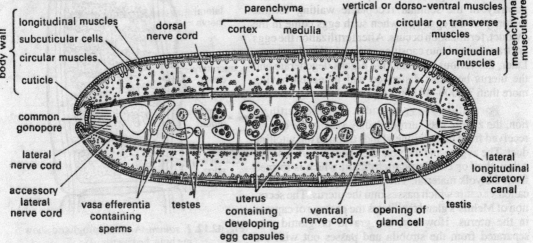

Fig. 42.10. *T. solium*. T.S. mature proglottid passing through uterus and genital atrium.

Female Reproductive Organs

Female reproductive organs consist of a bilobed ovary, oviduct, ootype, vagina, uterus, Mehlis's glands and vitelline gland.

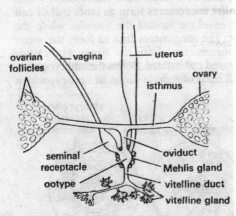

Fig. 42.11. *T. solium*. Details of the arrangement of ducts of female reproductive organs.

Ovary. It is bilobed situated ventrally in the posterior part of the proglottid, and also called germarium. Both the lobes are connected by a transverse ovarian bridge or isthmus. Each lobe of ovary is formed of a number of radially arranged follicles.

Oviduct. Nearly from the middle of ovarian bridge a median short but wide oviduct arises which opens into the ootype.

Ootype. It is a small, spherical bulb-like structure situated at the junction of oviduct, uterus and vitelline duct.

Vagina. It is a narrow tubular structure that runs slightly obliquely inwards from the female gonopore in the genital atrium and dilates to form seminal receptacle. The seminal receptacle stores the sperms temporarily and continues as a narrow short fertilizing duct to join the oviduct.

Uterus. It is a blind club-shaped, sac-like structure; it originates from the ootype and extends towards the anterior side of the proglottid. The fertilized eggs are packed in it and in gravid proglottids (Fig. 42.12), it becomes highly branched having 7 to 10 branches.

Vitelline gland. It is a large lobulated glandular mass situated at the posterior margin of the proglottid. A median **vitelline duct** originates from it which joins the ootype.

Mehlis's glands. The ootype is surrounded by a large number of unicellular glands called Mehlis's glands.

LIFE HISTORY

Copulation and fertilization. Self-fertilization occurs by the insertion of the cirrus of one proglottid into the vagina of the same proglottid and sperms are deposited there. From the vagina the sperms come to lie in the seminal receptacle from where they fertilize the eggs in oviduct. But cross-fertilization between different proglottids of the same tapeworm is very common. Actually, *T. solium* is **protandrous**, *i.e.*, the testes mature first. Hence, after copulation the sperms are stored temporarily in the seminal receptacle waiting for the maturity of the eggs and when such eggs come in the oviduct, fertilization occurs. After fertilization the eggs are transformed into capsules and packed in the uterus. Later, the various reproductive organs degenerate and the uterus becomes distended and branched having more than 30,000–40,000 **egg capsules.**

Formation of egg capsules. Just after fertilization, the zygote gets surrounded by yolk in the ootype received from the vitelline glands through the vitelline duct. The zygote and the yolk then become enclosed in a thin **shell** or **chorionic membrane** which is formed from the yolk material. The structure, thus, formed, is called **capsule** which passes into the uterus. The secretion of Mehils's gland facilitates the passage of capsule in the uterus. However, the gravid proglottid gets separated from the strobila and passes out with the faeces of the host.

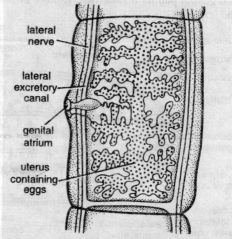

lateral nerve

lateral excretory canal

genital atrium

uterus containing eggs

Fig. 42.12. *T. solium.* A gravid proglottid showing branched uterus.

Development. It starts when the eggs enter the uterus. The zygote first divides unequally to give rise a larger **megamere** and a smaller **embryonic cell.** The megamere divides a number of times to give rise several similar megameres. Similarly, the embryonic cell divides repeatedly to give rise two types of cells, larger **mesomeres** and smaller **micromeres.** Hence, from zygote, three types of cells are resulted. These are larger megameres, medium-sized mesomeres and smaller micromeres which are arranged in a characteristic sequence. In fact, the smaller micromeres form an inner ball of cell mass called **morula;** the mesomeres are placed as an envelope around the morula, while the megameres as an outer envelope around the mesomeres. The megameres fuse to form the **outer embryonic membrane** which finally disappears; the mesomeres form the **inner embryonic membrane** or **embryophore** which is thick, hard, cuticularized and striated. Below the embryophore, a thin **basement membrane** is also formed. The inner cell mass of morula forms an **embryo** which

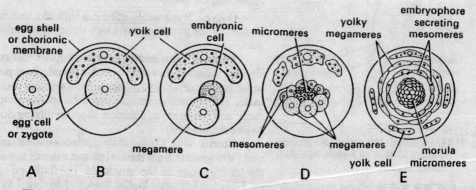

egg shell or chorionic membrane

yolk cell

embryonic cell

micromeres

yolky megameres

embryophore secreting mesomeres

egg cell or zygote

megamere

mesomeres

megameres yolk cell

morula micromeres

A   B   C   D   E

Fig. 42.13. *T. solium.* A—Zygote; B to E—Stages illustrating the formation of onchosphere.

develops six chitinous hooks at its posterior side. The hooks are secreted by some differentiated cells of morula called onchoblasts. This six-hooked embryo is called hexacanth which possesses a pair of penetration glands and is surrounded by two hexacanth membranes. The hexacanth embryo, hexacanth membranes, basement membrane, embryophore and the egg shell or chorionic membrane together is known as onchosphere. The gravid proglottids which pass out from the host body contain embryos in onchosphere stage.

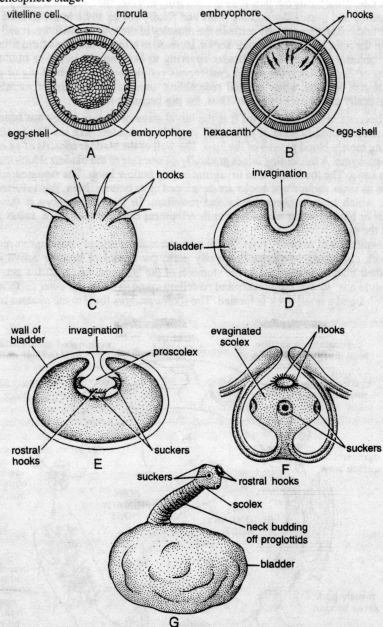

Fig. 42.14. *T. solium.* Stages in the life cycle. A—Young onchosphere ; B—Mature onchosphere; C—Free hexacanth ; D—Bladderworm with invagination ; E—Bladderworm with proscolex; F—Bladderworm with evaginated scolex and G—Cysticerus with neck budding off proglottids.

Transmission to secondary host. The gravid proglottids or sometimes when they disintegrate, the onchospheres ar eaten up by the pigs with human faeces due to their coprophagous habit. After reaching in the stomach of a pig the capsule shell and other membranes around the hexacanths are dissolved resulting into the liberation of hexacanths. Sometimes dogs, camels and monkeys may also become infected by these onchospheres.

However, the hexacanth now starts boring through the intestinal wall with the help of a pair of unicellular penetration glands found in it between the hooks. The hooks do not play any role in boring the interstinal tissue but they help in anchoring it. Thus, the hexacanth enters the blood vessels of the intestine and passes through the heart and finally comes to lie in the striated muscles in any part of the body. But, they usually settle in the muscles of the tongue, neck, heart and shoulder. After reaching in the muscles, they lose their hooks, increase in size and acquire a fluid filled central cavity then they become encysted in a cuticular covering to become cysticerci or bladderworms. The cysticercus of *Taenia solium* is called cysticercus cellulosae. The flesh of pig or pork containing these cysticerci appears white spotted resembling something like that of measles, hence, it is characteristically called measly pork. Thus, the pig becomes infected.

Cysticercus or bladderworm. It is the larval stage of *Taenia* which has been formed by the transformation or modification of hexacanth stage. It is a bladder-like sac filled with a clear watery fluid having mostly blood plasma of the host. The wall of the bladder consists of an outer cuticle and inner mesenchyme. A thickening arises gradually on one side of the bladder which marks the anterior end of the larva. The thickened area invaginates as a hollow knob. The invaginated knob develops suckers on its inner surface and hooks are developed at its bottom. Now, this inverted knob is called proscolex which bears suckers, hooks and rostellum. In fact, the embryo at this stage is called cysticercus or bladderworm whose further development does not take place unless it reaches to the main host the man.

Transmission to primary host. When man, the main or primary host ingests raw or improperly cooked pork containing cysticerci or measly pork, the cysticerci become active in the intestine. Actually their bladder is digested in the stomach of the host and the proscolex gets evaginated or turned inside out, so that the suckers and rostellum come to lie on the outer surface as in the adult. Thus, a scolex and a small neck is formed. The scolex anchors itself to the mucous membrane of the

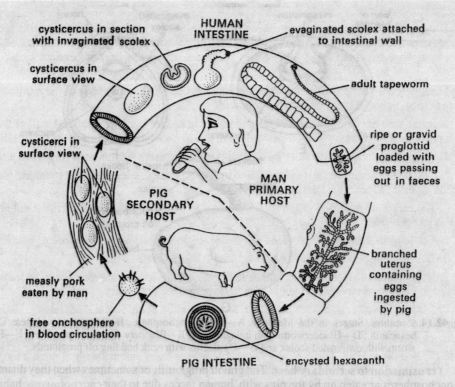

Fig. 42.15. *Taenia solium.* Diagrammatic life cycle.

intestine and the neck proliferates a series of proglottids to form the strobila. It takes nearly ten to twelve weeks to a proscolex to be converted into an adult *Taenia* and the adult *Taenia*, thus, formed, starts producing gravid proglottids with onchospheres within eight to ten weeks.

The life history of *Taenia solium* is not so complicated because it does not involve any asexual generations. However, the complete life history of *Taenia solium* may be represented with the help of the following flow-chart :

Adult tapeworm in human gut—→Fertilized eggs in mature proglottids—→Egg capsules in gravid proglottids—→Onchospheres in gravid proglottids—→Gravid proglottids or onchospheres in human faeces—→Out from the human body with faeces—→Onchosphere in the gut of pig due to coprophagy—→Hexacanths in the gut —→Hexacanth in the intestinal blood vessels—→Hexacanth in the heart—→Hexacanth in the muscles—→Cysticercus in the striped muscles—→Measly pork—→Cysticercus in the gut of human beings—→Adult tapeworm in human gut.

Effect of parasite on the host. The infection of *Taenia* causes a disease called taeniasis in human beings. The taeniasis is characterised by abdominal discomforts like pain, indigestion, vomiting, constipation, loss of appetite, diarrhoea and nervous disorder like nervousness, insomnia, nausea and epileptic fits, etc. Its infection may cause eosinophilia up to 13 per cent and obstruction in the passage of alimentary canal.

Taeniasis is comparatively lesser dangerous than cysticercosis caused by the infection of bladderworm or cysticercus larva. Sometimes, it has been seen that if somehow man ingests onchospheres with contaminated food and drink or due to antiperistaltic movements of the intestine, then bladderworm enters through the intestinal circulation in different parts of the body. After reaching in the vital organs like liver, eyes and brain, the cysticerci get encysted and cause serious even fatal diseases. Encystment in eyes may cause blindness and in brain develops epilepsy.

Treatment and control measures. Antihelminthic drugs like carbon tetrachloride, oil of chenopodium and oil of male fern *Dryopteris* may be used to remove the adult tapeworm from the human intestine. These drugs usually remove the strobila only, while scolices can only be removed by surgical operations.

The mode of infection can be checked by the destruction of developmental stages like onchospheres and cysticerci. The onchospheres may be destroyed through proper disposal of human faeces by sewage system or else by preventing the pigs from visiting human faeces.

PARASITIC ADAPTATIONS OF *TAENIA*

The tapeworm exhibits a number of adaptive features to live comfortably in the intestine of the human beings. Some of these include the following :

1. It has well developed four suckers and hooks to anchor with the intestinal wall of the host, which prevents it from being pushed out with food due to peristaltic movements of the intestine.

2. Its body is covered externally by tegument which protects it form hosts' digestive juice.

3. Loss of alimentary canal is compensated by freely permeable tegument for water and nutrients from the digested food of the host intestine.

4. The power of anaerobic respiration enables it to live in an enviroment of intestinal contents which is oxygen-free.

5. The long flattened body provides larger surface area for its saprozoic mode of nutrition.

6. The sense organs are altogether absent due to its sheltered habit.

7. Huge power of reproduction makes it able to ensure for the transference of at least a few embryos to pig and of larvae from pig to man, to maintain the continuity of the race.

8. A tapeworm can survive for more than thirty years and every year it sheds nearly 2500 gravid proglottids containing nearly 30,000–40,000 onchospheres in each of them.

9. The simplicity of its life cycle lowers the chances of hazards it has to face in transfer from man to pig and pig to man. The pigs being coprophagous in habit automatically approach the human faeces containing onchospheres and ingest them to become infective. Man also feeds on pork and, hence, by ingesting measly pork it becomes infected.

TABLE 42.1. COMPARISON OF *FASCIOLA* AND *TAENIA*

Fasciola hepatica (Sheep liver-fluke)	*Taenia solium* (Pork tapeworm)

A. Habit, Habitat and Distribution

1. Endoparasitic.	1. Endoparasitc.
2. Adults live in bile passages of sheep or goat (primary host).	2. Adult lives in the intestine of man (primary host).
3. Larval stages are passed in a freshwater snail, either *Limnaea* or *Planorbis* sp. (secondary host).	3. Larval stages are found in pig (secondary host).
4. Usually cosmopolitan.	4. Mostly cosmopolitan.

B. Structure

5. Body dorsoventrally flattened, oval, leaf-like.	5. Body dorsoventrally flattened, long tape or ribbon-like.
6. Measuring about 1.2 to 5 cm in length and about 1.2 cm in width.	6. It measures up to two to three metres in length.
7. Pinkish or dark brown coloured .	7. Opaque white in colour.
8. Anteriorly body is produced into a conical head lobe ; body unsegmented.	8. Body divisible into anterior scolex, neck and a long strobila consisting of about 800–900 proglottids (segments).
9. Adhesive organs are an oral or anterior sucker and a ventral or posterior sucker; suckers are devoid of hooks.	9. Scolex acts as adhesive organ ; it bears four cup-shaped suckers and two rows of hooks for the purpose.
10. Body apertures comprise mouth, a common genital aperture and an excretory pore. Opening of Laurer's canal appears temporarily only during the breeding season.	10. Body apertures comprise a common gonopore on each proglottid and one or two excretory pores.

C. Body wall

11. It is covered with cuticle having thrown out into minute spicules or scales.	11. It is covered with cuticle having thrown out into minute microvilli referred to as microtriches.
12. Musculature consists of circular, longitudinal and diagonal muscles.	12. Musculature consists of circular and longitudinal muscles only ; diagonal muscles absent.
13. Mesenchymal musculature wanting.	13. Mesenchymal musculature consists of longitudinal, circular and dorsoventral muscle fibres.

D. Digestive System

14. Present but incomplete; it consists of mouth, pharynx, oesophagus and bifurcated intestine with diverticulae; mode of nutrition holozoic.	14. Absent ; mode of nutrition saprozoic.

E. Respiratory System

15. Mostly anaerobic but aerobic may also occur if oxygen is available.	15. Mostly anaerobic but aerobic may also occur in presence of oxygen.

F. Nervous System

16. A nerve ring bearing a pair of cerebral ganglia and a ventral ganglion surrounds the oesophagus. From the nerve ring three pairs of longitudinal nerve cords run posteriorly.	16. A pair of cerebral ganglia connected by a transverse nerve band and a ganglionated ring commisure in the scolex. Five pairs of longitudinal nerves travel into the strobila.

Fasciola hepatica (Sheep liver-fluke)	*Taenia solium* (Pork tapeworm)

G. Excretory System

17. It consists of a system of ramifying excretory ducts which finally terminate as flame bulbs or flame cells; found distributed throughout in the body parenchyma. The excretory ducts open into a median longitudinal excretory canal ; it opens at the posterior end of the body by an excretory pore.

17. It consists of flame cells and four main excretory ducts, only two of these extend up to the last proglottid and open through a common excretory pore. When the last proglottid is lost by apolysis, the two excretory ducts open separately.

H. Reproductive System

18. Monoecious; one set of complete male and female reproductive organs are found in each adult.

18. Monoecious ; one set of complete male and female reproductive organs are found in each mature proglottid.

(i) Male Reproductive Organs

19. There is a pair of large and highly branched testes situated in the middle of the body one behind the other.

19. There are numerous, small follicular (rounded) testes found scattered throughout in the proglottid.

20. Vasa deferentia two ; one arising from each testis .

20. Single vas deferens formed by the union of numerous vasa efferentia, one vas efferens arises from each testis.

21. Both vasa deferentia run forwards and join to form a pear-shaped seminal vescle from which ejaculatory duct arises and enters into the muscular penis or cirrus.

21. The vas deferens is convoluted duct, runs transversly outwards and opens into the muscular penis ; seminal vesicle and ejaculatory duct absent.

22. Ejaculatory duct is surrounded by many unicellular prostate glands.

22. Prostate glands are absent.

23. Cirrus sheath is present.

23. Cirrus sheath is absent.

(ii) Female Reproductive Organs

24. Ovary is single and highly branched situated on the right side in front of the testes.

24. Ovary is single but bilobed ; both the lobes connected together by a transverse ovarian bridge or isthmus. It is situated in the posterior part of the proglottid.

25. An oviduct extends from the ovary downwards to meet the median vitelline duct.

25. An oviduct extends from the middle of isthmus and opens into ootype which receives vitelline duct.

26. Ootype is not found.

26. Ootype is present.

27. Vagina and seminal receptacle is not found.

27. A slender and tubular vagina extends from the genital atrium which expands near the oviduct to form seminal receptacle.

28. A blind Laurer's canal extends from the oviduct to the dorsal side ; it opens temporarily at the time of copulation and acts as vagina.

28. Laurer's canal is not found.

29. Vitelline glands are numerous, rounded vesicular glands scattered on the lateral sides of the body.

29. Vitelline gland is single, large, lobulated situated in the posterior part of each proglottid below the ovary.

30. The secretion of vitelline glands is collected by a system of ducts to the yolk reservoir from which median vitelline duct originates to meet the oviduct.

30. Yolk reservoir absént ; a vitelline duct starts from the middle of the vitelline gland to open into ootype.

31. Uterus is a long, convoluted and tubular structure ; it starts from the junction of oviduct and median vitelline duct, extends anteriorly to open into genital atrium by female gonopore.

31. Uterus is straight, blind, club-shaped sac that extends to the anterior part of the proglottid from the ootype.

Fasciola hepatica (Sheep liver-fluke)	*Taenia solium* (Pork tapeworm)
32. Uterus enlarges to store the capsules but does not branch.	32. Uterus enlarges and develops lateral branches to store the capsules.
33. Mehlis's glands are numerous, found around the junction of oviduct, uterus and median vitelline duct.	33. Mehlis's glands are found around the ootype.
34. Reproductive organs persist even after capsule formation.	34. Reproductive organs except uterus degenerate after capsule formation ; such proglottids are called gravid.

I. Life History

35. Life history digenetic.	35. Its lif history is also digenetic.
36. Usually two different flukes copulate so that cross-fertization occurs but sometimes self-fertilization is also reported.	36. Usually self-fertization occurs but inter proglottid cross-fertilization is of common occurrence.
37. After fertilization egg capsules are laid into the bile passage of the sheep from where they finally reach to the outside with host's faeces.	37. Gravid proglottids packed with egg capsules are detached from the body of the tapeworm (apolysis) and reach to the exterior with the host's (man) faeces. Outside the proglottids break to release capsules.
38. Capsules with operculum.	38. Capsules without operculum.
39. Development starts after capsules are laid (*i.e.*, outside the worm's body) and continue to develop if dropped at suitable places of temperature, moisture, etc.	39. Development starts after capsule formation n the gravid proglottids.
40. A free-swimming miracidium comes out from a capsule which is conical and ciliated. It swims freely for sometime then penetrates into the body of the snail.	40. A six-hooked hexacanth larva develops in a capsule ; this larva with its protective covering is called onchosphere. The onchospheres are ingested by the pig due to its coprophagous habit.
41. In snail's body the miracidium changes into sporocyst which gives rise the first generation of rediae, the radiae produce second generation of rediae which in turn produce cercariae.	41. In the intestine of pig from the onchospheres hexacanths are released ; they bore through the gut wall to reach into the intestinal blood vessels and reach to the voluntary muscles where they become encysted to form cysticercus or bladderworm.
42. Cercariae find their way from the body of the snail and finally encyst on vegetation as metacercariae.	42. Cysticercus does not leave the body of the pig.
43. Sheep gets infection by ingesting metacercariae with vegetation.	43. Man gets infection by eating improperly cooked pork infected·with cysticerci (*i.e.*, measly pork).
44. Several flukes can live in single host.	44. Only one tapeworm can live in one host.

J. Pathogenicity

45. Highly pathogenic, causing fascioliasis or to say liver rot.	45. It is also highly pathogenic causing taeniasis; cysticercosis is also caused by the infection of its larvae cysticerci.

TABLE 42.2. COMPARISON OF BODY WALL OF *PLANARIA*, *FASCIOLA* AND *TAENIA*

Planaria	*Fasciola*	*Taenia*
1. Body wall consists of an outer epidermal layer and inner muscle layers.	1. Its body wall consists of a thick layer of cuticle followed by underlying muscle layers.	1. Its body wall consists of thick cuticle layer followed by sub-cuticular muscle layers.

Planaria	*Fasciola*	*Taenia*
2. Epidermis is a distinct cellular layer being made of cuboidal epithelial cells.	2. A distinct epidermal layer is absent; however, the cuticle secreting cells are believed to be sunken epidermal cells.	2. Epidermis is absent.
3. Epidermis is followed by a thin basement membrane.	3. The lowermost layer of cuticle forms a delicate basement membrane.	3. The innermost cuticular layer forms a thin basement membrane.
4. The muscle layer is made of three types of muscle fibres arranged in a characteristic sequence : circular, diagonal and longitudinal muscles fibres.	4. Subcuticular musculature consists of circular, longitudinal and then diagonal muscle fibres.	4. Subcuticular musculature consists of only circular and longitudinal muscle fibres. Diagonal muscle fibres are absent.
5. Epidermal cells characteristically bear rod-shaped bodies called rhabdites.	5. Rhabdites are not found.	5. Rhabdites are absent.
6. The epidermal layer, on the ventral surface of the body wall, is ciliated.	6. Cilia are not found.	6. Cilia are absent.

REVISION QUESTIONS

1. Give an account of the structure of *Taenia solium*.
2. Describe mode of nutrition, excretion and nervous system of *Taenia solium*.
3. Give an account of the structure of body wall of *Taenia solium*.
4. Describe the reproductive organs of *Taenia solium*.
5. Describe the life history of *Taenia solium*.
6. Give an account of parasitic adaptive features of *Taenia solium*.
7. Draw labelled diagrams only :
   (a) Mature progllotid of *Taenia*; (b) T.S. of mature proglottid of *Taenia*.
8. Write short notes on :
   (a) Scolex ; (b) Gravid proglottid ; (c) Hexacanth ;(d) Cysticercus.
9. Compare the structures of *Fasciola* and *Taenia*.
10. Give a comparative account of the reproductive organs of *Fasciola* and *Taenia*.
11. Compare the body wall of flatworms studied by you.

43

Platyhelminthes :Characters,Classification and Types

DEFINITION

Platyhelminthes are triploblastic, bilaterally symmetrical, dorsoventrally flattened, acoelomate flatworms with organ grade of construction without definite anus, circulatory, skeletal or respiratory systems but with protonephridial excretory system and mesenchyme filling the space between the various organs of the body.

GENERAL CHARACTERS

1. Platyhelminthes are bilaterally symmetrical and dorsoventrally flattened, triploblastic worms.

2. Body shape generally worm-like but varies from moderately elongated flattened shape to long flat ribbons and leaf-like.

3. The flatworms are small to moderate in size varying from microscopic to extremely elongated forms measuring up to the 10–15 metres.

4. Majority of flatworms are white, colourless, some derive colour from the ingested food, while the free-living forms are brown, grey, black or brilliantly coloured.

5. Anterior end of the body is differentiated into the so called head.

6. Ventral surface bearing mouth and genital pores is well marked in turbellarians but is less marked in trematodes and cestodes.

7. Presence of great variety of adhesive secretions, organs of attachment and adhesion (*e.g.,* hooks and suckers).

8. Body is covered with a cellular syncytial one layered partly ciliated epidermis ; while in parasitic trematodes and cestodes epidermis is lacking and the body is covered with cuticle.

9. Exo- and endoskeloton are completely absent, hence, the body is generally soft. Hard parts consist of cuticle, spines, thorns, hooks, teeth, etc.

10. Acoelomate, *i.e.,* true coelom is absent.

11. Body space between the various organs is filled with a mesenchyme usually called parenchyma.

12. Digestive system is totally absent in Acoela and tapeworms but in other flatworms it consists of mouth, pharynx and blind intestine (anus absent),

13. Respiratory and circulatory systems are absent.

14. Excretory system consists of single or paired protonephridia with flame cells or bulbs. In Acoela the protonephridia are absent.

15. Nervous system is primitive. The main nervous system consists of a pair of cerebral ganglia or brain and one to three pairs of longitudinal nerve cords connected to each other by transverse commissures. This type of nervous system is called ladder type of nervous system.

16. Sense organs are of common occurrence in Tubellaria but these are greatly reduced in parasitic forms. Chemo-and tangoreceptors commonly occur in the form of ciliated pits and grooves.

17. Sexes are united, *i.e.*, hermaphrodite with very few exceptions.

18. Reproductive system is highly evolved or complex in most of the forms.

19. Asexual reproduction by fission occurs in many freshwater Turbellaria.

20. In majority of forms eggs are devoid of yolk but provided with special yolk cells and are covered by egg shell.

21. Cross-fertilization in trematodes and self-fertilization in cestodes is very common. Fertilization is internal.

22. Life cycle complicated involves one or more hosts.

23. Parthenogenesis and polyembryony commonly occur in trematodes and tapeworms. Some tapeworms propagate by endogenous or exogenous budding.

24. The flatworms are either free-living or ecto- or endocommensals or parasites.

CLASSIFICATION

The classification adopted here is from Hyman, L.H., (1951) up to suborders only with certain modifications.

CLASS 1. TURBELLARIA
(L., *turbella* = a little string)

1. Mostly free-living flatworms but some ectocommensals and endocommensals or parasitic.
2. Body unsegmented.
3. Body covered with a cellular or syncytial epidermis usually with mucous cells and which is usually partly ciliated.
4. Adhesive organs abundantly present.
5. Digestive system usually consists of mouth, pharynx and intestine, anus not found.
6. Excretory system consists of protonephridia, the flame cells.
7. Sense organs consist of tangoreceptors and chemoreceptors.
8. Mostly hermaphrodite.
9. Reproduction sexual, asexual and by regeneration.
10. Life cycle simple.

Order 1. Acoela

1. Small turbellarians exclusively marine.
2. Digestive system consists of ventral mouth and simple pharynx.
3. Intestine absent.
4. Excretory system totally absent.
5. Definite gonads, gonoducts and yolk glands absent.
6. Usually free-living found under stones or on bottom mud ; some live in the intestine of sea-urchins and sea-cucumbers.
7. Some coloured or brown by symbiotic algae.

Examples : *Convoluta, Ectocotyle, Afronta.*

Order 2. Rhabdocoela

1. Small freshwater, marine, and terrestial forms.
2. Digestive tract complete with simple pharynx and intestine sac-like without diverticula.
3. Nervous system with two main longitudinal trunks.
4. Eye usually present.
5. Excretory system consists of protonephridia.
6. Reproductive system comprises few compact gonads, gonoducts and a cuticularized structure instead of penis papilla present.
7. Free-living, commensal or parasitic forms.

Suborder 1. Notandropora

1. Exclusively freshwater forms.
2. Pharynx simple.
3. Excretory system consists of single median protonephridia.
4. Testis single compact mass, penis unarmed.

5. Protonephridial excretory system present as lateral network with many nephridiopores.

6. Male reproductive organs consist of two to numerous testes; a penis papilla present.

7. Female reproductive organs consist of a pair of ovaries with yolk glands and a copulatory bursa.

8. Gonopore single.

1. Exclusively marine forms.

2. A pair of eyes and auricular grooves present.

3. Typical penis papilla sometimes armed with stylet.

4. Rounded copulatory bursa is generally present.

5. Only sexual reproduction takes place
   Bdelloura, Syncoelidium

1. Mostly freshwater, rarely brackishwater forms.

2. Eyes two to many or completely absent.

3. Bursa usually present anterior to penis.

4. Reproduction mainly asexual.
   Planaria, Dugesia

1. Terrestrial, tropical and subtropical forms.

2. Body usually elongated.

3. Eyes two to many.

4. Bursa mainly absent.

5. Male and female pores usually separate.

6. Asexual reproduction may also occur.
   Bipalium, Rhynchodemus

1. Moderate sized turbellarians, exclusively marine.

2. Body usually broad and flattened, some are elongated.

3. Pharynx plicate opens into main intestine.

4. Intestine with numerous branches and highly diverticulated.

5. Nervous system consists of numerous radially arranged nerve cords.

6. Eyes numerous.

7. Testes and ovaries are numerous and scattered.

8. Yolk glands absent.

9. Gonopores separate.

1. Pharynx usually vertical curtain-like.

2. Sucker absent behind the gonopore.

3. Tentacles nuchal type.

4. Eyes never occur as a pair of clusters on the anterior margin.
   Notoplana

1. Pharynx tubular.

2. Sucker present behind the female pore.

3. A pair of marginal tentacles bearing eyes or a cluster of eyes at the anterior margin.
   Thysanozoon, Yungia

(Or *Trematodes* = having pores)

   Order *Proseriata*

1. _____ forms, commonly called _____

2. Body shape usually _____ dorsoventrally flattened.

3. Body wall without epidermis and cilia.

4. Body subdivided and covered with a _____

5. Well developed suckers usually present.

6. Digestive tract incomplete consisting of mouth, pharynx and two forked or many branched intestine; anus absent.

7. Protonephridial excretory system consisting of _____

8. Mostly hermaphrodite.

9. Ovary single, testes two to many.

10. Life history simple or complicated.

1. Ecto or ectoparasitic forms of vertebrates.

2. Oral sucker either weak or absent.

3. Anterior end provided with a pair of glandular adhesive structures.

4. Posterior end provided with an adhesive disc usually with hooks.

5. Excretory pores paired, situated anteriorly on the dorsal side.

6. Male and female gonopores usually separate.

7. Free-swimming ciliated larva called onchomiracidium.

8. Only one host in life cycle.

   Examples : *Diplozoon, Polystoma, Gryodactylus.*

Order 2. Aspidobothria

1. Endoparasites in the gut of fishes and reptiles.

2. Oral sucker absent.

3. Anterior end without paired adhesive structures.

4. The entire ventral surface acts as adhesive organ but subdivided into compartments without hooks.

5. Nephridiopore single.

6. Only one testis in male reproductive system.

7. Life cycle simple, no alternation of hosts.

   Examples: *Cotylapsis, Aspidogaster.*

Order 3. Digenia

1. Endoparasites of vertebrates and invertebrates.

2. Mostly with two suckers without hooks ; an oral sucker around the mouth and the ventral sucker or acetabulum.

3. Excretory pore single at the posterior side.

4. Vagina absent; uterus usually long with many shelled eggs.

5. Life cycle complicated involving many larval stages.

6. One to more intermediate hosts in life cycle.

   Examples : *Fasciola, Schistosoma, Bucephalus, Opisthorchis (=Clanorchis).*

CLASS 3. CESTODA
(Gr., *kestos* = girdle+*eidos*=form)

1. Endoparasites in the intestine of vertebrates.

2. Commonly called tapeworms.

3. Body without epidermis and cilia but covered with cuticle.

4. Body usually divided into few to many segments (proglollids), rarely undivided.

5. Anterior end (scolex) is provided with adhesive structures (hooks, suckers) except in Cestodaria.

6. Mouth and digestive tract totally absent.

7. Excretory system consists of protonephridia with typical terminal flame bulbs.

8. Nervous system usually comprises a pair of ganglia and two lateral longitudinal nerve cords.

9. Each segment (proglottis) contains one or two sets of complete hermaphroditic reproductive system.

10. Life cycle complicated usually involving two or more hosts.

11. Embryos possess hooks.

Subclass 1. Cestodaria

1. Endoparasitic in coelom or intestine of vertebrates.

2. Body undivided (monozoic).

3. Scolex absent.

4. Alimentary canal absent.

5. Only one set of monoecious reproductive organs.

6. Larva lycophore with ten hooks

Order 1. Amphilinidea

1. Endoparasitic forms in the coelom of fishes.

2. Body flattened, oval or elongated.

3. Scolex absent.

4. Suckers absent.

5. Anterior end bears protrusible proboscis and frontal glands.

6. Male and vaginal pores situated posteriorly.

7. Uterus is very much coiled opening near the anterior end.

   Example : *Amphilina.*

Order 2. Gyrocotylidea

1. Endoparasitic forms in the intestine of fishes.

2. Body elongated and flattened.

3. An anterior sucker and a posterior rosette-shaped adhesive organ present.

4. Anterior end bears eversible proboscis.

5. Uterine, male and vaginal pores are together situated in the anterior half of the body.

6. Uterus short, straight runs directly to pore.

   Example : *Gyrocotyle.*

Subclass 2. Eucestoda

1. Endoparasitic forms in the intestine of fishes.

2. Body usually very elongated ribbon-like.

3. Body divisible into anterior scolex, neck and strobila consisting of few to many proglottids (polyzoic).

4. Scolex expanded bearing adhesive structures.

5. Each proglottis with more than one set of monoecious reproductive organs.

6. Larva with six hooks.

Order 1. Tetraphyllidea

1. Endoparasitic forms; exclusively in the intestine of elasmobranch fishes.

2. Scolex bears four bothridia (sessile suckers) often provided with hooks.

3. Testes lie in front of ovaries.

4. Vitelline glands scattered in two lateral bands.

5. Cirrus armed with spines or hooks.

6. Common genital atrium marginal.

  Examples : *Phyllobothrium, Myzophyllobothrium.*

Order 2. Diphyllidea

1. Parasitic in the intestine of elasmobranch fishes.

2. Anterior scolex with two bothria and a spiny head stalk.

3. Strobila consists of not more than 20 proglottids.

  Example : *Echinobothrium.*

Order 3. Trypanorhyncha

1. Parasitic in the spiral valve of digestive tract of elasmobranch fishes.

2. Body size moderate.

3. Scolex provided with four bothria and four protrusible spiny proboscides.

4. Vitellaria in cortical parenchyma placed in continuous layer.

5. Testes extend behind the ovary posteriorly.

6. Gonopores lateral; uterus opens ventrally.

  Examples: *Haplobothrium, Tetrarhynchus.*

Order 4. Pseudophyllidea

1. Parasitic in the intestine of teleost fishes and terrestrial vertebrates.

2. Body segmented into strobila or unsegmented.

3. Scolex with two to six shallow bothria (suckers) rarely without adhesive organs.

4. Ovary bilobed, testes numerous, follicular and scattered in the mesenchyma of proglottids.

5. Vitellaria follicular, numerous.

6. Gonopores midventral.

  Examples: *Bothriocephalus, Dibothriocephalus.*

Order 5. Taenioidea or Cyclophyllidea

1. Parasitic in the intestine of reptiles, birds and mammals.

2. Large-sized tapeworms.

3. Scolex bears four large incupped suckers (acetabula) often with an apical rostellum armed with hooks.

4. Ovary two to many lobed; uterine opening absent.

5. Gonopores on one or both margins.

6. Excretory system consists of four longitudinal vessels.

7. Vitellaria (yolk gland) single and compact.

  Examples : *Taenia, Echinococcus, Hymenolepis, Moniezia.*

REPRESENTATIVE TYPES OF PLATYHELMINTHES

1. *Convoluta.* Convoluta (Fig. 43.1) is exclusively marine form living under stones among algae. It is a small worm with sides of body curved ventrally. Anterior end has a cluster of frontal glands, a pair of eyes and a statocyst. Mouth situated ventrally near the anterior end. Intestine is absent. Excretory system is completely absent. Hermaphroditic with protandrous condition. *Convoluta* exhibits symbiotic phenomena by having algal cells in symbiotic association in its body.

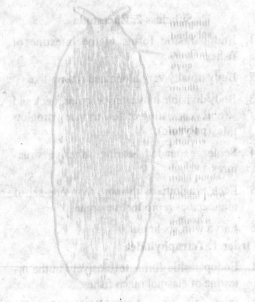

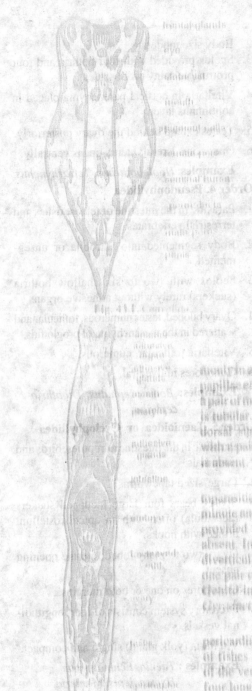

Thysanozoon (Fig. 41.2) is found commonly in less cold water of sea. Body is covered with numerous papillae each containing an intestinal branch. Anterior end bears a pair of marginal tentacles and numerous cerebral eyes. Pharynx is tubular. Glandulo-muscular adhesive organ is present on the dorsal surface behind the female gonopore. Hermaphrodite with a pair of male pore and single female pore. Genital bursa is absent.

Gyrodactylus (Fig. 41.3) is an ectoparasite on the gills and skin of freshwater fishes. Body is minute and elongated. Anterior sucker absent but anterior end is provided with adhesive organs and adhesive glands. Eyes are absent. Intestine is sac-like forked into two branches without diverticula. The opisthaptor is disc shaped and provided with one pair of anchors (hooks) and 16 marginal hooks (hooklets). Genito-intestinal canal is absent. Genital pore is median. Gyrodactylus is viviparous.

Aspidogaster (Fig. 41.4) live in the pericardial and renal cavities of freshwater mussel and in the gut of fishes and turtles. A large sucker occupying the greater portion of the ventral surface is present. The sucker is subdivided into four longitudinal rows of sucking cups or alveoli. The narrow anterior end has a subterminal mouth which is devoid of an oral sucker. The gut is simple, straight and sac-like. Excretory system consists of ... Wide tubular excretory bladders. Hermaphrodite. Single testis and folded ... ovary. Life cycle simple without alternation of host ...

Opisthorchis sinensis (Fig. 41.5) (formerly called Clonorchis). It is called a Chinese liver fluke. It is present in the bile ducts of man in China, India, Japan, and

into China, it is also found in fish-eating mammals. The size ranges from 10 to 25 mm. The two suckers are small, the alimentary canal is well-formed, excretory bladder is Y-shaped.

Two branched testes lie one behind the other in the posterior region, a vas efferens arises from each testis, the two vasa efferentia unite in the middle of the body to form a vas deferens which joins a seminal vesicle. A narrow ejaculatory duct arises from the seminal vesicle to open into a genital atrium which opens by a gonopore on the ventral surface just in front of the acetabulum. A penis, prostate glands and cirrus are lacking. —A small lobed ovary lies in front of the testes. From the ovary arises a short oviduct. In the middle one third of the body on each side are small follicles of vitelline glands. Small ducts arise from vitelline glands to form two transverse vitelline ducts which unite to form a small common vitelline duct. The

common vitelline duct joins the oviduct, after which the oviduct joins an ootype which is surrounded by shell cells of Mehlis's gland. In the ootype the egg and yolk get enclosed in a shell to form a capsule which has an operculum, and comma-shaped appendage. From the ootype arises a long, coiled uterus containing capsules, it opens into the genital atrium. Behind the a very little a sac-like seminal receptacle from which a small duct joins the oviduct, but before it joins the oviduct it receives a Laurer's canal. The Laurer's canal curves behind the seminal receptacle and opens dorsally by a small pore in the middle.

Fertilized eggs pass out of the gonopore into bile ducts from where they reach the human intestine and go out with the faeces. The capsules do not hatch unless eaten by snails *Parafossalurus* or *Bythinia*. In the snail's intestine miracidium larvae hatch from capsules, they bore into tissues of the snail. The miracidium gives rise to a rounded sporocyst. Sporocyst produces rediae which have no birth pore. The rediae produce cercaria larvae.

A cercaria has a long tail with fluted lateral fins. The cercariae escape from the snail to enter a second intermediate host which is a fish belonging to the carp or minnow family. The cercariae encyst in the muscles of the fish. When raw or insufficiently-cooked fish is eaten, young flukes emerge from the cysts in the human small intestine from where they reach the bile ducts within a few hours; in three weeks the flukes mature.

6. *Schistosoma*. *Schistosoma* (Fig. 43.6) (old name *Bilharzia*). It is a dioecious digenetic trematode, being parasitic in the human hepatic portal or pelvic veins ; some species are parasitic in veins of birds and mammals. It is peculiar in having separate males and females, but the two are found together in pairs. A thick male permanently carries a slender but longer female in a gynaecophoric canal formed by folding of the ventral body wall. Body surface is rough and spiny, and both have an oral sucker and an acetabulum. There is no pharynx, and the two branches of the

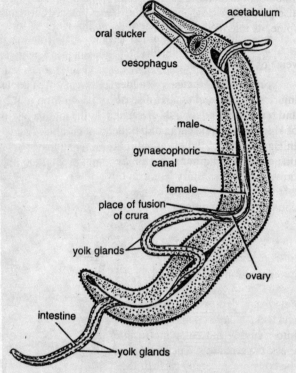

Fig. 43.6. *Schistosoma* (male and female).

intestine reunite in the middle of the body, this character and being dioecious distinguish these blood flukes from other trematodes. Male organs—The male has four testes ; a short vas deferens arises from the testes and joins a seminal vesicle which enters a penis, the penis opens by a gonopore below the acetabulum. Female organs—The female has an elongate ovary above the point where the intestinal caeca rejoin, from the ovary an oviduct passes in front. In the posterior third of the female are vitelline glands from which a vitelline duct joins the oviduct. The oviduct meets an ootype surrounded by Mehlis's gland. From the ootype arises a straight uterus containing a few capsules, it opens by a female gonopore below the acetabulum. After fertilization the female leaves the male to lay eggs one at a time in the smaller blood vessel. The capsules lacerate the capillaries and reach the urinary bladder and are voided with urine. Immediately the urine is diluted with water, the capsules hatch into miracidium larvae which enter a freshwater snail and reach its liver. The miracidium forms a sporocyst. The first generation of sporocyst may again produce miracidium larvae, which then form a second generation of sporocysts. Either the first generation or the second generation of sporocysts can give rise to cercaria larvae which have forked tails. There is no redia stage. The cercariae come out of the snails and swim freely in water, and without encysting they penetrate the human skin with great rapidity during bathing or washing or they may be swallowed by drinking infected water. Cercariae enter the blood vessels, go to the heart, then lungs, and then to the liver where they grow ; after that they enter the hepatic portal or pelvic veins and become sexually mature. The cercariae developing from one egg will produce flukes of only one sex, and females do not mature in a host where no males are present. When a male finds a female, it encloses her in the gynaecophoric canal.

There are three species of *Schistosoma* parasitic in human beings. 1. *S. haematobium* is found in Africa, Palestine, Iraq and Portugal in human pelvic veins, its capsule has a sharp terminal spine, its intermediate host is *Bulinus*. 2. *S. mansoni* is found in Africa and tropical America in the veins near the ileocaecal junction, its capsule has a lateral spine, the intermediate host is *Planorbis*. 3. *S. japonicum* is found in Japan, China and Philippines in the hepatic portal and mesenteric veins, it is also parasitic in dogs, cats, cattle, horses and pigs, its capsule is small and has a rudimentary lateral spine, its intermediate host is *Oncomelania*.

S. indicum is found in portal veins of Indian cattle.

Schistosoma causes bladder injuries, bladder stones, skin disease and haematuria which is a disorder of kidneys with discharge of blood. In Egypt 60% of the population is infected. The diseases can be prevented by sanitary control of water, and they can be cured by compounds of antimony.

7. *Gyrocotyle.* Gyrocotyle (Fig. 43.7) is found in the intestine of chimaeroid fishes. Body is elongated flattened with a ruff, the rosette, at one end surrounding funnel-shaped depression. The anterior end bears a large opening that leads into a highly muscular protrusible mass, the proboscis. The margins of the body are generally ruffled. Hermaphroditic. Male system consists of scattered testes, sperm duct and penis papilla, while female system comprises ovary, oviduct and uterus, Yolk glands consist of follicles scattered throughout most of the body.

8. *Tetrarhynchus.* Tetrarhynchus (Fig. 43.8) is an endoparasite in the intestine of elasmobranch fishes. Body is long, divisible into scolex and proglottids and broader at the posterior end. Scolex is elon-

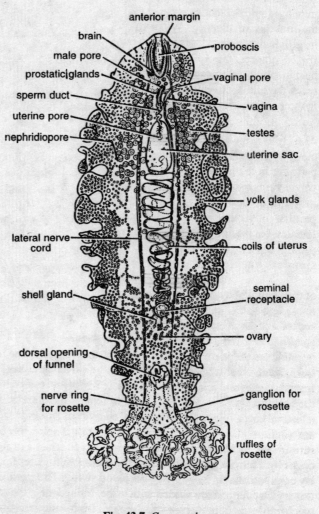

Fig. 43.7. *Gyrocotyle.*

gated and divisible into a long proximal part containing the proboscis apparatus and a distal part bearing the bothria. Scolex bears four bothria (suckers) each with a eversible proboscides armed with spines. Proboscides or rostella are enclosed in muscular sheaths which end below in muscular bulbs. Reproductive system single in each proglottid.

9. *Diphyllobothrium.* Diphyllobothrium latum (Fig. 43.9), the broad fish tapeworm, is the largest and most injurious parasite in the intestine of man. Body length reaches up to 18 metres and have 3,000 to 4,000 proglottides. Scolex is fusiform, bears two slit-like bothria, followed by the long slender neck. Mature proglottid is broader than long. Excretory system protonephridial type. Hermaphroditic. Male system consists of numerous testes, vas deferens, seminal vesicle and cirrus. Female system consists of a bilobed ovary, oviduct and a coiled uterus. Each segment has a single

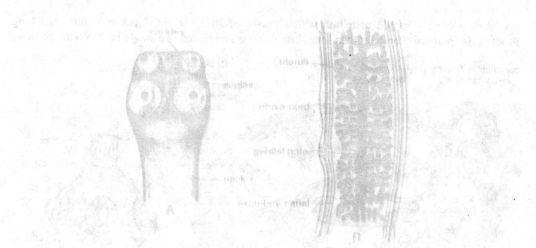

Fig. 43.10 *Taenia* ... ... A, Scolex; B ... A mature proglottid

stalks or fall free into the fluid-filled cavity of the cyst. With age more brood capsules are formed and older brood capsules form from 3 to 30 scolices on their inner walls. Sometimes due to pressure ferula-like buds arise from the mother cyst, these are ...

... the daughter cysts have a fibrous cyst wall and a bladder wall, they may arise inside the mother cyst by ... or externally by exogenous budding. The exogenous daughter cysts may detach themselves and migrate, they could ... it develop ment in some other part of the body. The daughter cysts also give rise to several scolices from their inner bladder wall ...

The hydatid cyst has a ... fluid which may be from 2 to 50 quarts but older cysts have a granular deposit consisting of brood capsules and free scolices. The scolices are finally evaginated in brood capsules and in endogenous and exogenous daughter cysts, and should they reach the final host, a dog, cat or wolf, they develop into adult *Echinococcus*.

Hydatid cysts are often enormous and the liver is enlarged by them. In the brain or eye they prove fatal. The hydatid fluid contains toxins and should it leak from the cyst, eosinophilia results. If the hydatid cyst is ruptured by pressure, not only is the toxic fluid liberated, but the scolices, brood capsules and daughter cysts become scattered in the body and each may develop into a new cyst.

Hymenolepis nana (Fig. 43.11) commonly known as ... is an endoparasite in the intestine of man. It is the smallest tapeworm measuring 7 to 100 mm in length. Body consists of a scolex, neck and proglottids. Scolex bears a well developed retractile rostellum with a crown of 20–30 hooks. Neck is slender and long. Proglottids are usually broader than long. Life cycle is completed in a single host. No intermediate

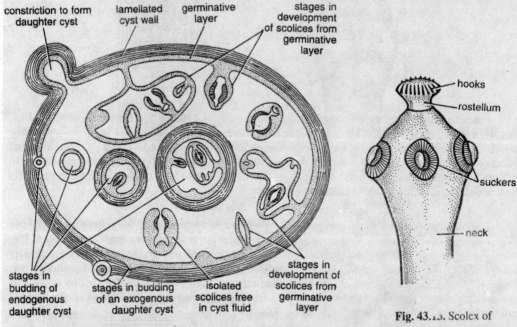

Fig. 43.12. *Echinococcus granulosus.* Hydatid cyst.

Fig. 43.13. Scolex of *Hymenolepis nana.*

host is required. *Hymenolepis nana* causes severe toxic symptoms including abdominal pain and diarrhoea, etc. It is worldwide in distribution. It is the commonest tapeworm in Southern United States.

REVISION QUESTIONS

1. Classify Platyhelminthes up to classes giving characters of the phylum and the classes. Give two examples of each class.
2. Classify Platyhelminthes giving characteristic features and at least two examples of each group.
3. Write short notes on :
   (i) *Thysanozoon* ; (ii) *Polystoma* ; (iii) *Opisthorchis* ; (iv) *Schistosoma* ; (v) *Diphyllobothrium* ; (vi)*Taenia saginata* ; (vii) *Echinococcus* ; (viii) *Hymenolepis*.

44

Platyhelminthes in General

PARASITISM

Parasitism is defined as the association of two organisms of same or different species, in which one lives at the cost of other. A parasite is that which lives on other organism called a host, receiving nourishment and shelter without any compensation for the host. According to Elton, the union of parasite and host is usually an elaborate compromise between extracting sufficient nourishment to maintain and propagate itself and not impairing too much the vitality or reducing the number of its host which is providing it with a home and free ride.

Origin and Evolution of Parasitism

Parasitism dates back to ancient geological time and arose soon after the differentiation of life began in the world. Parasitism is a secondary mode of life. It has arisen from free living way of life. This get together of different individuals started with comparatively smaller animals occasionally taking shelter temporarily on the body of some larger forms. When this temporary shelter was repeatedly used, the association of two organisms became more intimate and the smaller organisms got not only shelter, but also free transport and a bit of nourishment from the host, of course without doing any harm to the host body.

Still later, the weak organism started living within the body of the host without doing any harm to the host. Finally they started to feed on the body tissues of the host so that the latter has to suffer with some harm. This association has been called parasitism.

It may be presumed that the parasite first confines itself to the external surface of the body and is called ectoparasite. The ectoparasites may gradually change to endoparasites when they get their entire nourishment from the host.

Kinds of Parasitism

The parasitism can be classified into following categories :

1. Accidental. Some free-living animals are capable of leading a parasitic life for a certain period in a host, if swallowed accidentally.

2. Facultative. When the animals can live both as parasitic or free living, they are known as facultative parasites.

3. Obligatory. These include forms which have lost the power of living a completely free life, and must live on or in some other suitable organism during all or part of their lives, otherwise they die.

(i) Ectoparasitism. In ectoparasitism the animals live on the external surface of the body of host and totally depend for food on the host.

(ii) Endoparasitism. In endoparasitism, the animals live inside the body of host and depend entirely for the food on the host.

PARASITIC ADAPTATIONS

The helminthes are modified morphologically as well as physiologically to live in their particular environment.

Morphological Adaptations

The Trematoda and Cestoda due to their parasitic mode of life show a departure in their anatomy and physiology from their free-living ancestor, the differences are pronounced especially in their locomotor, trophic and sensory organs; and more so in Cestoda than Trematoda.

1. The shape of the body becomes flattened like a leaf of a ribbon so that they can fit in the spaces where they have their habitat.

2. Cilia have disappeared entirely from the outer surface as they are no longer necessary.

3. There are no epidermal cells in the adult, instead of which the body is covered by a several layered thick cuticle which protects the parasite from the juices of the host.

4. Organs of attachment such as suckers and hooks are formed by which the parasite is not dislodged from the host.

5. There are no organs of locomotion since they are not needed, the hosts transporting the parasites.

6. There is a reduction in trophic organs, and in cestodes the mouth and alimentary canal have disappeared, since they absorb digested food from the gut of the host.

7. The nervous system is of a lower character than in the free living forms and there is a complete absence of sense organs.

8. The reproductive organs are well developed and the production of eggs is prolific to ensure the continuance of the species, in cestodes the reproductive organs are repeated in each proglottis, and in some each proglottis has two sets of reproductive organs.

9. Some parasites have an additional multiplicative phase at some stage of the life cycle, in trematodes the rediae may produce daughter rediae, or the sporocyst may either divide by transverse fission or it may produce miracidium larvae, in cestodes there may be several generations of bladder worms as in a hydatid cyst.

10. Parasites find means of passing out fertilised eggs from the host into suitable places, the eggs have thick shells which are protective and prevent desiccation.

11. Most parasites have one or more intermediate hosts which act as transmitting agents to new final hosts.

A few physiological adaptations are also brought about in the body of the parasite, these are as follows.

1. The osmotic pressure of the body fluids of a parasite becomes the same as that of the host to prevent a disturbing exchange of water.

2. Parasites living in blood or tissues find an abundance of oxygen, but those found in alimentary canal or bile duct have a considerable tolerance to an absence of oxygen, they become modified to obtain oxygen by anaerobic respiration since in most internal habitats the oxygen content is very low, they obtain their energy by an oxybiotic process in which glycogen is utilized as the source of energy, and the end products are carbon dioxide and fatty acids which are given off.

3. Cestodes stimulate the gut of the host to secrete mucus which forms a protective envelope around the tapeworms.

4. Gut parasites secrete anti-enzymes to neutralise the digestive juices of the host.

| (i) | *Ascaris* *lumbricoides* | 20-35 cm. | Small intestine | Eats coarsely on water plants | *Ascaris suum* (male) | Intestinal inflamation and haemorrhage, ulcers, anaemia toxaemia | India, China, Thailand, Formosa, Sumatra |

45

Phylum Aschelminthes

Gegenbaur (1859) created a group Nemathelminthes to place some pseudocoelomate animals, however, Grobben (1910) introduced the term Aschelminthes in place of Nemathelminthes to avoid certain confusions. The Aschelminthes (Gr., *askes*=cavity+*helmins*=worm) is a heterogeneous assemblage of common marine and freshwater animals, They include several classes such as Nematoda, Nematomorpha, Rotifera, Gastrotricha and Kinorhyncha. The Aschelminthes are pseudocoelomate (presence of a cavity, the pseudocoel, between the gut and body wall), mostly vermiform Bilateria with an unsegmented or superficially segmented body covered with a cuticle and with a straight or sometimes curved digestive tube lacking a definite muscular wall and terminating in an anus located at or near the posterior end or at least well posterior to the mouth. They are mostly of minute to small size although some reach considerable to great lengths. The body is usually vermiform without definitely delimited head, and is covered in a tough, resistant cuticle. Beneath the cuticle is found a syncytial or cellular epidermis underlain by muscle fibres not arranged in regular circular and longitudinal layers. Between the body wall and digestive tract lies a cavity, pseudocoel. The digestive tract is straight, sometimes curved, epithelial tube that may be covered with a net of muscle fibres, its two ends are of stomodaeal and proctodaeal nature. Pharynx is highly differentiated. Respiratory and circulatory systems are absent. The typical protonephridia occur in rotifers, gastrotrichs, kinorhynchs. Excretory canals and also gonoducts may open into the rear part of the digestive tube that then constitutes a cloaca. The nervous system consists of an anterior brain mass or of a circumenteric nerve ring and from these nerves extend, including main ventral or lateral ones. The sexes are nearly always separate, and the reproductive system is relatively simple. The cleavage is generally of the determinate type and the life cycle may be simple or complicated. Numerical constancy of the cells or the nuclei that compose the various organs, a condition known as eutely, prevails throughout the phylum. The numbers are characteristic for each species but vary from one species to another. The condition is perhaps associated with the extremely small size characteristic of many members of the group. The Aschelminthes are predominantly aquatic animals, inhabiting both fresh and salt waters, but many nematodes become terrestrial. The phylum includes free-living, epizoic and parasitic members. More than 12,000 species of Aschelminthes are known.

46

Ascaris (A Common Roundworm)

Ascaris is the most common roundworm ; its species are found as intestinal parasites in vertebrates like man, pig, cattle, house chicken, etc. The species of *Ascaris* are quite large in size. *Ascaris lumbricoides* is one of the most common human roundworms in the intestine amongst nematodes. *A. megalocephala* is found in horse, *A. suum* is found in pig but supposed to be a variety of *lumbricoides* as both of these are morphologically identical and *A. galli* is found in the chicken. *Taxascaris* is another related genus reported from the intestine of carnivores ; *T. canis* from dog and *T. mystax* from cat. However, the basic structural body plan of nematodes is so constant that a good knowledge of nematode anatomy can be obtained by studying the typical and common roundworm *Ascaris lumbricoides.*

ASCARIS LUMBRICOIDES

SYSTEMATIC POSITION

Phylum	....	**Aschelminthes**
Class	....	**Nematoda**
Order	....	**Ascaroidea**
Genus	....	*Ascaris*
Species	....	*lumbricoides*

HABIT AND HABITAT

Ascaris lumbricoides is an endoparasite in the small intestine of man lying freely in the lumen. It has been living in man from time immemorial. It is cosmopolitan in distribution. It is found more commonly in children than in adults. Sometimes it migrates from intestine to stomach and comes out through the mouth or nostrils of the host. As many as 1000 to 5000 adult worms may inhabit a single host. Mode of nutrition is holozoic, as it feeds on host's partly digested food by sucking action of its pharynx. It produces anti-enzymes to protect itself from the action of the host enzyme. Sexual dimorphism is well distinct ; only sexual reproduction takes place, asexual reproduction does not occur. Life cycle is simple and monogenetic ; no secondary host.

EXTERNAL FEATURES

Shape and size. *Ascaris lumbricoides* is elongated, cylindrical, and tapering at both ends. It is a large sized nematode showing sexual dimorphism, *i.e.,* sexes are separate. The female is 20–41 cm (8–16 inches) long and 4–6 mm in diameter, but the male is smaller, being 15–31 cm (6–12 inches) and 2–4 mm in diameter; its posterior end (tail) is curved ventrally.

Colouration. Generally nematodes have no colour, the external cuticle is whitish or yellowish but some, like *Ascaris* have a definite reddish tint caused by the presence of haemoglobin.

Morphology. The anterior end of both the sexes exhibits the same structure. The body is covered with a smooth, tough and elastic cuticle which is striated transversely and gives the pseudosegmented appearance to the worm. The cylindrical body has four longitudinal epidermal chords visible externally, the narrow one mid-dorsal, one mid-ventral and two thick ones are lateral. The dorsal and ventral chords appear white, while the laterals appear brown. In nematodes the anterior mouth is bounded by six lips or labia but they are reduced by fusion to three in *Ascaris*, one elliptical mid-dorsal and two oval latero-ventral in position. Therefore, the mouth of Ascaris is a triradiate aperture. The dorsal lip has 2 double sensory papillae, and each latero-ventral lip has 1 double sensory papilla ; these four papillae form an outer labial circle though most nematodes have 6 papillae in the outer labial

The body wall of *Ascaris* consists of outer _____ middle _____ of _____ of a _____ and inner _____

_____ It is a thick, tough, wrinkled and transparent outermost layer of the body wall, and it is continuous with the cuticular lining of the pharynx and rectum. It is non-cellular and made of albuminous protein which is resistant to the digestive juices of the host but it is _____ to salts and water. The cuticle is not chitin and it is soluble in KOH, but true chitin is present in egg shells. However, under light microscope, cuticle can be identified into four distinct layers being made of different chemical composition and different structural arrangements, these are _____ _____ being made of keratin and resistant to the action of host's digestive enzymes

_____ It is of a spongy consistency having a protein _____ rich in sulphur; it is an elastic layer and contains several fine fibres

_____ It is in fact the inner layer but not the last layer of cuticle ; it has dense connective tissue with interlacing collagen fibres, and _____

_____ it constitutes the innermost layer of cuticle

But the recent electron microscopic studies of the cuticle of *Ascaris* revealed the presence of one more layer in addition to the above four layers. However, cuticle under electron microscope appears to be made of following layers (i) _____ it is about 1000°A' thick thin layer of an osmophilic membrane (ii) _____ (iii) _____ it is composed of an outer _____ and a _____ (iv) _____ it is composed of collagen fibres arranged in three strata, and (v) _____ it is a thin layer surrounding the epidermis or hypodermis.

The cuticle moults four times in the lifetime and the moultings occur only during the period of growth.

Below the cuticle lies a _____ with many nuclei but no cell walls; the nuclei lie in the longitudinal epidermal chords only; the number of epidermal cells is small. The epidermis secretes the cuticle and forms four longitudinal thickenings, the _____ two of these are thicker lateral lines or chords and two thinner are dorsal and ventral lines. The lateral

388

Invertebrate Zoology

lines contain excretory canals, and the dorsal and ventral lines contain nerves. Epidermis of free-living nematodes contains unicellular epidermal glands. Fat and glycogen reserves are abundantly found in the epidermis.

Muscle layer. Internal to epidermis and lying between the epidermal chords is the body wall musculature consisting exclusively of a single layer of longitudinal fibres running along the length of the body. Each muscle cell or fibre has two zones, an outer fibrillar zone of longitudinally striated, spindle-shaped muscular part which is contractile and lies towards the epidermis ; and a second protoplasmic zone which is club-shaped, bladder-like mass of protoplasm with a nucleus and a network of supporting fibrils form a fibrous process or muscle tail. Muscle tails of the upper half are inserted into the dorsal line and joined to the dorsal nerve, and in the lower half the muscle tails are inserted into the ventral line and joined to ventral nerve. Dobell (1965) has emphasized that muscle tails are cellular extensions which form synapses on the motor nerves of the dorsal and ventral nerve cords. The muscles lie in four quadrants being separated by the longitudinal chords. Each

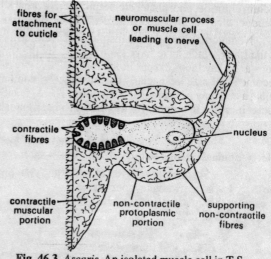

Fig. 46.3. *Ascaris*. An isolated muscle cell in T.S.

quadrant has about 150 muscle cells. Contractions of these elongated muscles cause a twisting and bending of the body ; it results into undulating movement of *Ascaris* to counteract the peristaltic activity of host's intestine. When the muscle cells are many in each quadrant and extend well into the body cavity, then this condition is called polymyarian, as in *Ascaris* . When muscles are flattened and only 2 or 3 occur in each quadrant, the condition is termed meromyarian, as in *Oxyuris*. But when the muscles are small and closely packed together forming a complete layer then this type is holomyarian as in *Trichuris*. In a transverse section the longitudinal muscles show a peripheral U-shaped fibrillar zone enclosing a club-shaped protoplasmic zone from which muscle tails project. Special muscles occur in the pharynx, vagina of female, and in connection with the spicules of the male.

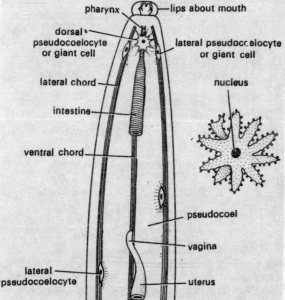

Fig. 46.4. *Ascaris lumbricoides*. A—Position of giant cells (pseudocoelomocytes) in pseudocoel ; B—Single pseudocoelomocyte enlarged.

BODY CAVITY OR PSEUDOCOEL

The space between the body wall and alimentary canal is not a coelom but a pseudocoel because it is bounded by muscles outside and the cuticle of the intestine inside. It is formed by the breakdown of connective tissue cells. In the young animal the organs are packed in parenchyma, but almost all of it disappears in the adult so that the organs hang loosely. Pseudocoel has fibrous tissue and fixed cells called coelomocytes or pseudocoelocytes or giant cells, there are four such cells occupying fixed positions along the lateral chords, they are branched and giant-sized, so that they fill the body cavity, the confluent vacuoles of these giant cells represent the pseudocoel, hence, the pseudocoel is an intracellular space. Pseudocoel is filled with a clear, protein-rich fluid, the pseudocoelomic fluid or perienteric fluid which distributes digested food and transports various metabolites. It is composed of 93 per cent water and remaining solids like protein, glucose, non-protein, nitrogenous substances, sodium chloride, phosphate, etc. Reproductive organs lie free in the pseudocoel. In free-living forms pseudocoelocytes are small in size and more numerous.

Nematodes show certain histological peculiarities, they have a constancy in the number of cells in the body which have have been formed by the time hatching takes place, because cell division stops after hatching (except in the reproductive organs); hence, with growth the cells elongate and become giant-sized, especially the muscle cells, coelomocytes in the pseudocoel, and excretory canal cells ; a cell may be more than 1 cm long. There is tendency towards formation of syncytia, probably nuclei increase in number by fragmentation or amitosis and the cell walls break down.

DIGESTIVE SYSTEM

Alimentary canal. It consists of the mouth, a short pharynx or oesophagus forming the foregut; a long tubular intestine or the midgut and a short rectum or hindgut.

Mouth. As already referred to, the mouth is a triradiate aperture situated at the anterior tip surrounded by three lips or labia.

Pharynx. The terminal mouth leads into a cylindrical thick-walled pharynx or oesophagus which has a posterior swelling called end bulb which is provided with valves, The pharynx has muscular walls having radial muscle fibres which dilate the lumen. Internally it is lined by cuticle which, at the margin of mouth, is continued with the cuticle of the body wall. The pharynx has 3 large branching gland cells which open by cuticular ducts into the lumen; these are in fact, pharyngeal or oeso-phageal glands. The cavity of the pharynx has three deep longitudinal grooves lined by cuticle, and in a transverse section the lumen appears triradiate, connective tissue fibres arise from each of the three internal grooves and go to the cuticle cover-ing the pharynx, they maintain the triradiate shape of the lumen. This much constitutes the stomodaeum or foregut.

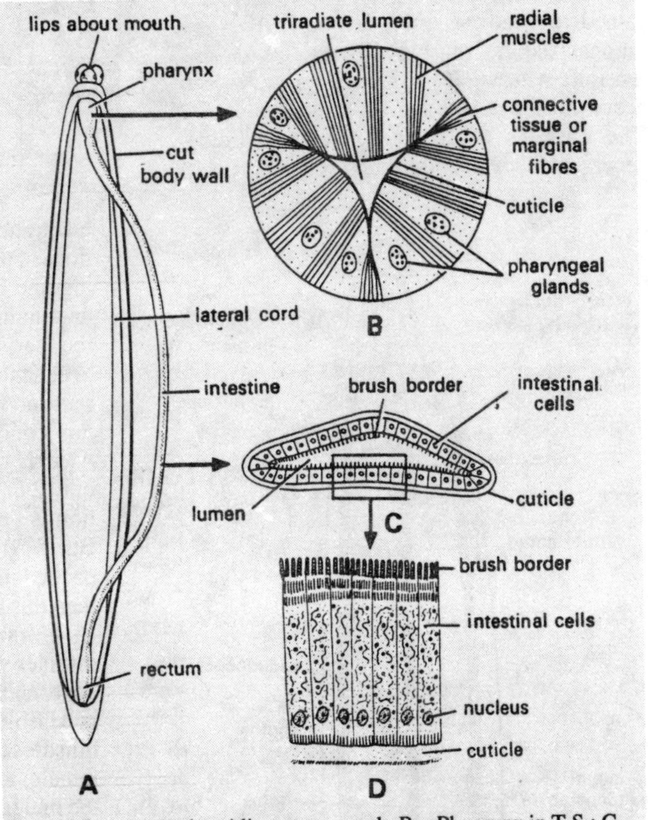

Intestine. The pharynx opens posteriorly into a thin-walled dor-soventrally flattened intestine or

Fig. 46.5. *Ascaris.* A—Alimentary canal ; B—Phyarynx in T.S.; C—Intestine in T.S. ; D—A portion of intestinal wall showing brush border,

midgut which extends almost the entire length of the body. It is formed of a single layer of columnar epithelial cells lined externally by a thin layer of cuticle. The free inner margin of each cell is produced into several finger-like projections, the microvilli (Kessel *et al.,* 1961). They form a sort of tightly packed brush border which increases the surface area. The intestine has no muscle layer.

Rectum. The intestine is followed by the hindgut or rectum which is also flattened dor-soventrally. Its wall consists of tall columnar cells and lined internally by cuticle and externally by

few muscle fibres. In male the rectum opens out by ... because it receives the ejaculatory duct but in female the rectum opens out by a transverse slit-like aperture, the ...

guarded by anterior and posterior lips and is provided with a few special dilator muscles running from that rectum to the body wall, called ... Their contraction from time to time causes the faecal matters to be discharged out. The rectum also has large unicellular ... 3 in the female and 6 in the male

Food of *Ascaris* comprises blood, tissue exudes and partly or fully digested food of the host. Food is sucked in by the sucking action of the pharynx. Digestion is ... which occurs in the intestinal lumen, the process of digestion is facilitated by the enzymes like ... and ... secreted by the gland cells of the pharynx. The digested nutrients are absorbed in the intestinal wall and finally distributed by the pseudocoelomic fluid. Excess food is generally stored as reserve glycogen and fat in the intestinal wall, mostly in its medial epidermis ... digestion has also been reported to occur in the cells of intestinal wall which engulf solid particles to digest intracellularly. The undigested wastes, if any, are defaecated out by the ...

canal to open by a minute ventral excretory pore just behind the lips. The canals are more developed on the left side than on the right. The canals are lined by a firm membrane and covered with a layer of cytoplasm ; they are intracellular excavations in the single giant cell whose nucleus lies on the transverse canal. The excretory system has no internal openings, cilia, flame cells, or nephridia.

Physiology. Excretory physiology of *Ascaris* is very poorly understood. However, the nitrogenous waste chiefly comprises **urea** which diffuses into the pseudocoelomic fluid. The excretory canals are said to secrete this urea which is eliminated through the excretory pore; some ammonia and urea are also passed out along with the faecal matters. Observations are also there to suggest that *Ascaris* excretes more urea when water is scarce.

NERVOUS SYSTEM

The nervous system of *Ascaris* (Fig.46.8 and 46.9) is well developed and complicated and like the excretory system it is also situated in the body wall, *i.e.,* it is hypodermic. However, it consists of circumpharyngeal ring or nerve ring and nerves originating from it.

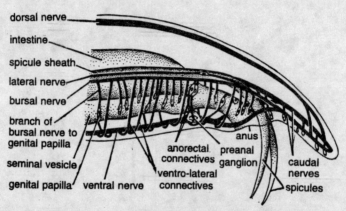

Fig. 46.9. *Ascaris lumbricoides*. Lateral view of posterior end showing nervous system.

There is a circumpharyngeal ring around the pharynx, it is made of nerve fibres and some diffusely arranged nerve cells. Associated with this ring are many ganglia; there is an unpaired **dorsal ganglion,** and close to it is a pair of subdorsal ganglia. On each side of the ring is a lateral ganglion which is divided into six ganglia. On the lower side of the ring is a pair of large-sized ventral ganglia. Each ganglion has a fixed number of nerve cells. From the circumpharyngeal ring arise six small nerves anteriorly, each having a ganglion, they are arranged radially and go to the sense organs of the anterior end (papillae and amphids). Posteriorly six long nerves arise from the ring and run to the posterior end ; of these six nerves one is a mid-dorsal nerve and one is a mid-ventral nerve, the former lies in the dorsal line and the latter in the ventral line. The mid-ventral nerve is the main nerve and it is ganglionated along the anterior length, it may be called the nerve cord. Near the anus it has an anal ganglion which sends nerves to the tail. The other four posterior nerves are thinner, they are one pair of dorsolateral nerves and a pair of ventrolateral nerves, they lie on the sides close to the excretory canals. The dorsal and ventral nerves are connected by a number of transverse commissures, and the ventral nerve and lateral nerves are joined together by many ventrolateral commissures. Posteriorly the innervation is more complicated in males than in females.

SENSE ORGANS

Due to parasitic mode of life, *Ascaris* has developed sense organs (Fig. 46.10) which are very simple. They are either as minute elevations or pits in the cuticle of the body. However, they are as follows :

Labial papillae. The labial papillae are four, two on the dorsal lip and one each on the ventro-lateral lips, each is a double sense organ. Each labial papilla consists of a fine fibre of sensory nerve surrounded by many supporting cells (Fig. 46. 10 B). These are gustatory or taste organs.

Amphids. The amphids are two, situated one each, on the ventro-lateral lips. These are small pits containing glandular and nerve cells supplied by amphidial nerve from the lateral or amphidial ganglia (Fig. 46.10 A). These are olfactory chemoreceptors.

Phasmids. The phasmids are unicelludar glands situated one on each side of the tail behind the anus. These are pit-like and chemoreceptors (Fig. 46.10 E).

Cervical papillae. The cervical papillae are a pair of small pits situated just a little behind the oral lips in the lateral sides of the body. These are bulb-like nerve endings with supporting cells (Fig. 46.10 F). These are probably tactile in function.

Cephalic papillae. The cephalic papillae are also pit-like being formed of nerve fibres surrounded by supporting cells but the nerve fibre has a lens-like expansion just beneath the cuticle and then narrows to form canal which widens before opening at the surface (Fig. 46.10 C).

Genital papillae. The genital papillae are found in males. These consist of nearly 50 pairs of preanal and 5 pairs of postanal papillae . These are also formed of 1–3 nerve fibres embedded in supporting cell (Fig. 46.10 D). These are also tactile in function and help during copulation.

The various receptor organs of nematodes are of taxonomic importance.

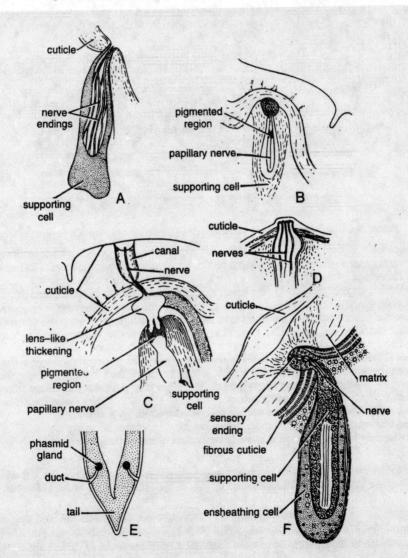

Fig. 46.10. *Ascaris lumbricoides.* Receptors. A—Amphid; B—Labial papilla ; C—Cephalic ; D—Genital ; E—Phasmid ; F—Cervical papilla.

The gonads are tubular glands, situated one on each side of the body behind the [illegible].

In *Ascaris*, like other nematodes, sexes are separate (i.e., sexes are) and readily distinguishable externally and are [illegible] the male is smaller in size than the female. Its tail is curved, while female's tail is straight. It is closed with a pair of spicules in case of male but female possesses anus and spicules absent, male possesses pre- and post anal papillae which are absent in female. The male system is reduced to a single tube but the female system is double.

The gonads are confined to the posterior two of the body and consist of testis, vas deferens, seminal vesicle, ejaculatory duct and penial setae.

(i) **Testis** — [illegible] single in *Ascaris* but it may be [illegible] two testes in [illegible] nematodes. However, the testis of *Ascaris* is a long, thread-like, coiled tube. Its wall is composed of a single layer of cuboidal cells being surrounded by the basement membrane. Its central axis is solid [illegible] the rachis is surrounded by clusters of germ-cell cells in various stages of their development. In fact, these are developing [illegible].

(ii) [illegible] The testis continues distally into a short and thick coiled tube of the same diameter, the [illegible]. However, it is distinguished from the testis in possessing a central lumen in place of the solid rachis.

(iii) [illegible] The vas deferens joins posteriorly with a much thicker, wider somewhat muscular and straight tube called [illegible] it lies below the intestine in the posterior one third of the pseudocoel.

(iv) [illegible] The seminal vesicle narrows at its posterior end to form a short, but muscular [illegible] with [illegible] into the rectum to form the [illegible]. This duct bears a number of [illegible] whose secretions help in copulation. The cloaca opens out by cloacal aperture.

(v) **Penial setae.** Dorsal to the cloaca is a pair of muscular sacs, the **penial sacs** or **spicule pouches,** the two spicule pouches unite and join the cloaca. The pouches contain a pair of **spicules** or **penial setae** which are cuticular with a cytoplasmic core. The spicules can be protruded and retracted through the cloacal aperture by the action of special sets of **protractor** and **retractor** muscles. They serve in copulation to open the female genital pore, and, thus, help to transfer sperms, their function is aided by a chitinous plate, the **gubernaculum** lying in the wall of the cloaca.

Female reproductive organs. These are confined in the posterior two-third of the body and consist of ovaries, oviducts, uteri and vagina.

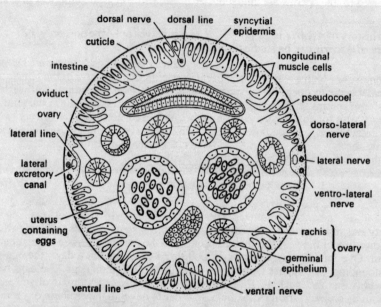

Fig. 46.14. *Ascaris lumbricoides.* T.S. of a mature female.

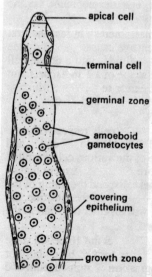

Fig. 46.15. *Ascaris lumbricoides.* Telogonic origin of sex cells in the proximal end of gonad. Maturation zone of the gonad not shown.

In fact in *Ascaris,* like most of the nematodes, there is a set of two parallel tracts of female reproductive organs, *i.e.,* an ovary, oviduct and a uterus in one tract; this condition is called **didelphic**, although **monodelphic** (one tract) and **polydelphic** (many tracts)conditions are also found.

(i) Ovaries. The paired **ovaries** of *Ascaris* are long, thread-like and highly twisted tube-like and terminate blindly in the pseudocoel. Internally it has a single layer of cuboidal epithelial cells, a cytoplasmic **central rachis** and externally a basement membrane surrounding the epithelial cells. The rachis is encircled round by group of developing ova.

(ii) Oviducts. The ovaries are continued posteriorly into somewhat broader **oviducts** having similar structure to ovaries but in place of solid rachis there is a lumen in the oviducts.

(iii) Uteri. Each oviduct is further continued into still broader, thicker and muscular **uterus** ; it has a thick inner layer of circular muscles and a thin outer layer of oblique muscles. The first part of uterus serves as **seminal receptacle** where sperms, after copulation, are stored and where fertilization occurs, the remaining uterus stores fertilized eggs, and its cells produce yolk and material for egg shells.

(iv) Vagina. The two uteri unite and open into a short median, muscular **vagina** lined with cuticle. The vagina opens by a transverse **gonopore** or **vulva** which lies mid-ventrally about 1/3 of the length from the anterior end. In some nematodes the end part of the uterus or the end part of the vagina, when present, forms muscular **ovejectors** which by peristaltic movement force the eggs one by one through gonopore.

Formation of gametes in *Ascaris*. Gonads may be hologonic or telogonic. In hologonic gonads germ cells arise along their entire length. In *Ascaris* the gonads are telogonic in which germ cells arise at the proximal end only which is called germinal zone or the zone of proliferation. Next part of the gonad is a growth zone where gametogonia enlarge. In the ovary the elongated developing eggs are arranged radially around a central cytoplasmic rachis. In the testis the developing amoeboid sperms are packed around the central rachis. In the last of part the gonads gametocytes are formed and become free from the rachis, here they undergo maturation division to form eggs or sperms. The last part of gonads where developing gametes undergo maturation are referred to as the maturation zone. As referred to, the sperms are amoeboid in shape, while eggs are elliptical in shape.

LIFE HISTORY

The life history of *Ascaris* is monogenetic as it involves only one host only, *i.e.*, man. However, the life history of *Ascaris* can be studied as under :

1. Copulation and fertilization. Copulation takes place in host's intestine. During copulation male *Ascaris* moves in such a way that its cloacal aperture faces the vulva of the female and then male thrusts its penial setae to open the vulva of female. Then, soon the cloacal wall of male contracts causing transfer of sperms into the vagina of the female and they come to lie in the seminal receptacle part of the uteri, wait for eggs to come through the oviduct for fertilization. During fertilization the entire sperm enters the egg. Soon, after fertilization the glycogen globules of the egg migrate to the surface to form the fertilization membrane which soon hardens into a thick, clear inner chitinous shell. Soon, thereafter, the fat globules of the egg form a lipoid layer below the chitinous shell. Now, as the fertilized egg passes down, the uterine wall secretes an outer thick, yellow or brown albuminous (proteinous) coat or outer shell having a characteristic wavy surface or ripplings. These eggs are now known as mammiliated eggs ; such eggs are elliptical in shape measuring 60–70 μ by 40–50 μ.

2. Zygote . So, to say the zygote has a thick, clear inner shell, a lipoidal layer and an outer shell which is warty and yellow or brown in colour. The fertilized eggs (zygotes) are laid by female *Ascaris* in the small intestine of the host and they pass out with the faeces ; they are unsegmented when they leave the host. One female may lay from 15,000 to 200,000 eggs in a day ; the egg production of *Ascaris* is astounding, one mature female may have up to 27 million eggs. The eggs become stained yellowish or brown in the intestine. Eggs fall on the ground and can remain alive for months in the moist soil though complete drying kills them. In order to develop they require oxygen, moisture and a temperature lower than that of the human body, the most favourable temperature is 85°F. They require a period of incubation outside the human body.

3. Early development (Outside the host). The stages of early embryonic development, say the cleavage or segmentation, etc., start in the soil. The pattern of cleavage is spiral and determinate.

The fertilized egg undergoes two cleavages to form four cells or blastomeres ; in fact the first cleavage results in a dorsal cell AB and a ventral cell P_1, the second cleavage causes AB to divide into an anterior cell A and a posterior cell. B, while the ventral cell P_1 divides into a dorsal cell EMST and a ventral cell P_2. These four cells are at first arranged in the shape of a T in *Ascaris*, but later they become arranged in a rhomboid shape, as P_2 comes to lie posterior to EMST , which is characteristic of nematodes. However, these four cells are now called A, B, P_2 and S_2 or EMST. These cells undergo further cleavage to form smaller blastomeres.

However, in the next cleavage A and B divide into A_1, A_2 and B_1, B_2 cells respectively, P_2 divides into P_3 and C, while EMST into MST and E. Thereafter, P_3 and E divide into P_4 and D and E_1 and E_2 respectively. The P_4 further divides into G_1 and G_2. The fate of the various cells resulted so far is fixed, *i.e.*, the descendants of A and B will give rise to the entire ectoderm, except that of the posterior end, MST form the mesoderm of the body wall, pseudocoel cells, and the lining of the stomodaeum, the descendants of E (E_1 and E_2) give rise to the entire endoderm of the intestine, the descendants of P_4 (G_1 and G_2) will give rise the germ cells and C and D will together take part in the formation of ectoderm and mesoderm.

Thus, the cleavage of embryonic cells continues giving rise to a blastula at the 16-celled stage which is characterised by having a cavity, the balstocoel. Then gastrula is formed by epiboly or overgrowth of ectodermal cells over the endodermal cells, and by invagination of stomodaeum and endodermal cells. Finally a juvenile is resulted in about 10–14 days from the begining of segmentation. Structurally, a juvenile possesses an alimentary canal, a nerve ring and a lateral excretory system. This juvenile resembles very much with *Rhabditis* (a soil nematode), hence, it is also referred to as rhabditiform larva or rhabditoid. This larva moults within the egg shell in about seven days and becomes the second stage juvenile or second stage rhabditoid ; this stage of the life history of

through the aorta and enters arteries that go to the heart, brain. When they enter circulation again through the body along with the blood stream, then they go through pulmonary artery into the lungs. In the lungs juveniles rupture the capillaries and enter the alveoli where they live for some days, here they grow and moult to become _____ which moult again to become _____.

From the alveoli of the lungs, the 4th stage juveniles make their way through the bronchioles and bronchus into the trachea, then up to the throat from where they are swallowed into the oesophagus and reach the _____ for the second time. During this 10 day tour the juveniles have grown about ten times and are 1.5 mm long. In the intestine the fourth and final moulting takes place, and in 60 to 75 days they grow into adult males and females and attain sexual maturity. The length of life of the parasite in the host averages only 9 months to a year.

However, the life history of *Ascaris lumbricoides* can be represented as Adults ➝ fertilized eggs passed out ➝ embryos develop in egg shell and moult twice ➝ swallowed by man ➝ juveniles hatch ➝ intestine ➝ mesenteric veins ➝ hepatic portal vein ➝ liver ➝ hepatic vein ➝ postcava vein ➝ right side of heart ➝ pulmonary artery ➝ lungs ➝ alveoli ➝ third moulting occurs ➝ bronchioles ➝ bronchus ➝ trachea ➝ glottis ➝ oesophagus ➝ intestine where fourth moulting occurs ➝ grow into adults.

As many as 500 to 5,000 adult Ascaris may be present in a single host and they may cause abdominal discomfort and colic pains accompanied with diarrhoea, vomiting, and a slight temperature. They may block the intestine and appendix. Because of their habit of wandering in the gut they may enter the bile or pancreatic ducts and interfere with digestion, or they may injure the intestine and cause _____. At times they wander into the nose. They produce toxins which irritate the mucous membrane of the gut, or prevent digestion of proteins by the host by destroying trypsin, or they may cause general nervousness, delirium or convulsions. In children where infection is more common they dull the mental capacity and stunt growth. Their juveniles cause inflammation and haemorrhage in the lungs which results in pneumonia which may prove fatal. The disease caused by Ascaris is generally referred to as _____.

Because sanitary conditions are the only sure means of prevention, a drug treatment is the best method of treatment. A mixture of oil of chenopodium and tetrachlorethylene is good, but one gm of hexylresorcinol in gelatine capsule with fasting for 12 hours before treatment and 4 hours afterwards, followed by _____.

a purgative removes about 95% of *Ascaris* infection. Other anti-helminth drugs like hetrazan, piperazine hydrate or citrate, tetramezole and dithiazanine are used successfully for the treatment of ascariasis these days.

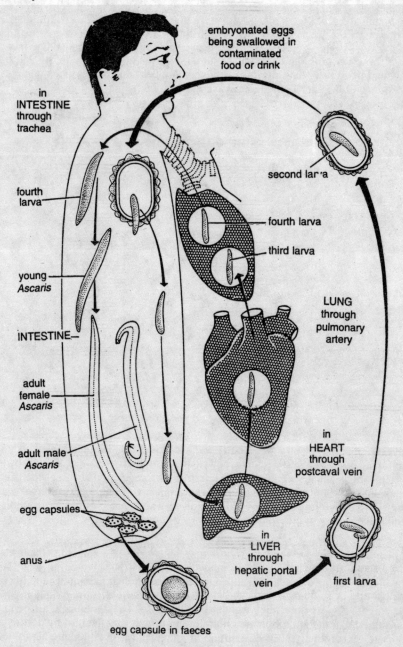

Fig. 46.18. *Ascaris lumbricoides*. Life cycle.

PROPHYLAXIS (PREVENTION)

Keeping good sanitary conditions is the only way to prevent the infection of *Ascaris*. However, pollution of soil with human faeces should be avoided, vegetables should be thoroughly washed (preferably in a mild solution of KMnO₄) and properly cooked before use, raw vegetables and nuts should not be used, finger nails should be regularly cut to avoid the collection of dirt and eggs below them, hands should be properly washed with some antiseptic soap before touching edibles or eating.

PARASITIC ADAPTATIONS OF *ASCARIS*

Ascaris, like those of other helminth intestinal parasites, exhibits a number of adaptive features to live comfortably and lead a successful life. However, some of them are as under :

1. Body is long and cylindrical in shape with both the ends pointed.

2. Body is covered externally with resistant cuticle and it also secretes antienzymes ; both these protect the worm from the digestive enzymes of the host.

3. Adhesive organs are not found in *Ascaris* ; lack of such organs is compensated by a very poor power of locomotion as by slight movement it maintains its position in the intestine of the host and also counteracts the intestinal peristalsis.

4. Cilia are completely wanting.

5. As the parasite feeds on digested and predigested food of the host, its alimentary canal is simple and poorly developed but pharynx being muscular facilitates ingestion by suctorial action.

6. Since circulatory system is absent, hence, its function of distributing the digested food to the body tissues and transfer of waste substances from the tissues to the excretory canals are performed by pseudocoelomic fluid.

7. Mode of respiration is anaerobic because it lives in an environment which is nearly fully deficient of oxygen.

8. Sense organs are very poorly developed because it leads a sheltered life.

9. Production of huge number of eggs compensates the wastage that takes place during their transfer from one host to new host.

10. The hard shelled covering of the eggs protects the developing juveniles from environmental hazards.

11. The eggs, being very small in size, are easily dispersed.

12. Mode of **direct** infection due to absence of secondary host from the life history has increased the chances for juveniles to reach a fresh human host.

REVISION QUESTIONS

1. Give an account of the habit, habitat and external features of *Ascaris* .
2. Describe in detail the structure of the body wall of *Ascaris.*
3. Give an account of the nervous system and sense organs of *Ascaris.*
4. What is sexual dimorphism ? With the help of labelled diagrams differentiate a male *Ascaris* from a female.
5. Describe the reproductive system of *Ascaris.*
6. Give an account of the life history of *Ascaris.*
7. Describe the pathogenic effects of *Ascaris* and also its parasitic adaptations.
8. Write notes on : Pseudocoel; Muscle cell.
9. Draw labelled diagrams only :
   (a) T.S. Male *Ascaris* ; (b) T.S. Female *Ascaris.*

47

Ancylostoma (A Common Hookworm)

Ancylostoma, the common hookworm of man, was first discovered in 1838 by an Italian physician Angelo Dubini. The pathogenesis and mode of entrance of the larvae into man was worked out by Looss in 1898. However, *Ancylostoma doudenale* or the Old World hookworm parasitizes the intestine of man, while *Ancylostoma caninum* is parasitic in dogs, cats and jackals. Another related genus *Necator americanus,* the American hookworm or the New World hookworm is most common in Sri Lanka and India (except Punjab and Uttar Pradesh). Although first discovered in America, it is more likely of African origin. From its original focus (Tropical and South Africa) it has spread to India, Far East, Australia and America. In the present chapter, however, *Ancylostoma duodenale*, the hookworm of man or the Old World hookworm is described in detail.

ANCYLOSTOMA DUODENALE
SYSTEMATIC POSITION

Phylum	....	**Aschelminthes**
Class	....	**Nematoda**
Order	....	**Strongyloidea**
Genus	....	*Ancylostoma*
Species	....	*duodenale*

HABIT AND HABITAT

The adult worms of *Ancylostoma duodenale* are endoparasites and live in the intestine of man particularly in the jejunum, less often in the duodenum and rarely in the ileum. The infective juveniles find their way in the human host percutaneously from the soil contaminated by the faeces in which they live. Hookworms flourish under primitive conditions where people move barefoot, modern sanitary conditions do not exist and human faeces are deposited in the ground.

GEOGRAPHICAL DISTRIBUTION

Ancylostoma duodenale is widely distributed in all tropical and sub-tropical countries, occurring in places wherever humidity and temperature are favourable for the development of larvae in the soil. It is found in Europe, North Africa (specially prevalent in Egypt), India (Punjab and Uttar Pradesh), Sri Lanka, Central and North China, Pacific Islands and Southern States of America. About one-half billion people or nearly 25 per cent of the world population are infected by the hookworm.

STRUCTURE

Shape, size and colour. Adults *Ancylostoma duodenale* are small and cylindrical in shape. Sexes are separate ; the male is about 8 mm in length and 0.4 mm in diameter, while female is generally longer about 12.5 mm in length and 0.6 mm in diameter. When freshly passed, it has a reddish brown colour due to ingested blood in its intestinal tract.

External and internal structures. The anterior end of the worms of both sexes is slightly bent dorsally (hence, the name hookworm) and has a large buccal capsule. The large and conspicuous buccal capsule is lined with a hard substance and is provided with 6 cutting plates or teeth, 4 hook-like on the ventral surface and 2 knob-like (triangular plates) or sharp lancets on the dorsal surface. The buccal capsule helps in attachment with the intestinal wall of the host. The posterior end of female worm tapers bluntly in a short post-anal tail, while that of the male is expanded and umbrella-like. This expanded structure is called copulatory bursa which surrounds the cloaca. The copulatory bursa has two lateral lobes with six muscular rays in each, and a small median dorsal lobe with one main dorsal ray which is divided only at the tip. The arrangement of rays is remarkably constant and each ray is given a name, the main ray in the dorsal lobe is called a dorsal ray, in each lateral lobe beginning from the dorsal side the six rays are called externo-dorsal, postero-lateral, medio-lateral, externo-lateral, latero-ventral, ventro-ventral. The teeth in the buccal capsule and bursal rays are of taxonomic importance.

The body of *Ancylostoma* is covered externally by **cuticle**, it is followed internally by the **epidermis** and **musculature** which is directed longitudinally. Its body cavity is the **pseudocoel** surrounding the various organ systems.

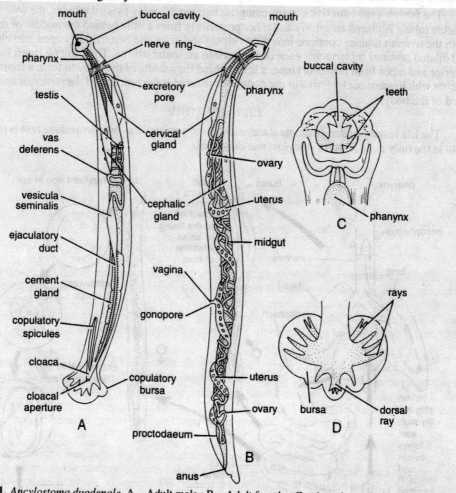

Fig. 47.1. *Ancylostoma duodenale.* A—Adult male ; B—Adult female ; C—Anterior end ; D—Posterior end of male.

Digestive system. It is tubular and very simple. It consists of the mouth, buccal capsule, muscular pharynx having a triradiate lumen lined by cuticle, oesophageal bulb, intestine, rectum and cloaca in male but an anus in female. There are five glands connected with the digestive system ; one of them, called the **oesophageal gland**, secretes a ferment which prevents the clotting of blood so that the worm can suck blood from the host. In fact, its food consists of intestinal mucous membrane and blood. In the process the tiny teeth and cutting plates of the buccal capsule make small wounds in the intestinal mucosa through which the food and body fluid is sucked by the suctorial action of the pharynx. After feeding it leaves a bleeding wound and moves to another location. An adult worm is said to suck nearly 0.8 ml of blood in a day from the host causing severe anaemia. Digestion is, however, completed in the intestine.

The mode of respiration, excretory system, nervous system and receptors are like those of *Ascaris lumbricoides*.

Reproductive organs. As mentioned earlier, sexes are separate and sexual dimorphism is well distinct. However, male reproductive organs comprise a single, tubular, thread-like testis twisted around the intestine in the middle of the body. Testis continues posteriorly in a vas deferens which finally opens into an elongated, swollen, sac-like seminal vesicle. The seminal vesicle soon tapers to form a narrow passage called the ejaculatory duct which opens into the cloaca.

The female reproductive organs comprise two much highly twisted tubules, the ovaries. One ovarian tubule is placed anteriorly and other posteriorly from a little behind the middle of the body. Both the ovarian tubules continue into the oviducts and, thus, the two oviducts open into elongated and dilated seminal receptacles each continues into muscular uterus. Thus, the two uteri (one from anterior and other from posterior) meet a little behind the middle of the body to form a short tubular vagina which opens out by vulva or the gonopore situated at the junction of the posterior and middle third of the body.

LIFE HISTORY

The life history of *Ancylostoma duodenale* is monogenetic as no intermediate host is required ; man is the only main host for *Ancylostoma duodenale*.

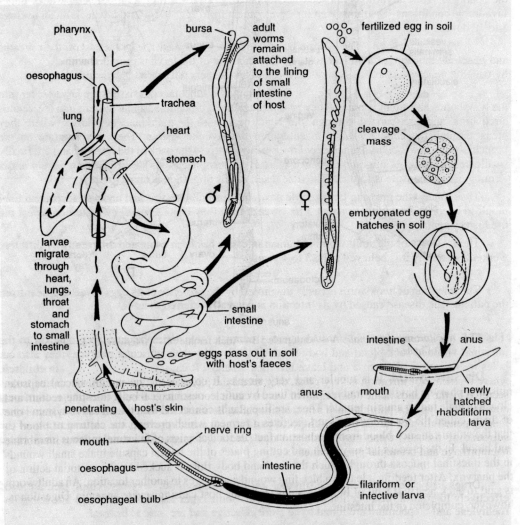

Fig. 47.2. *Ancylostoma duodenale.* Life cycle.

Copulation and fertilization. Copulation occurs in the intestine of the host, during the process the copulatory bursa of male is applied on the vulva of female and sperms are transferred. In fact, during copulation the worms (a male and a female) assume a Y-shaped figure owing to the position of the genital openings. The sperms, thus, transferred come to lie in the seminal receptacles where fertilization takes places. The fertilized eggs are then pushed into the uteri for laying through vagina and gonopore.

Egg laying. The female worm lays eggs in the intestine of the host which pass out with faeces. On an average nearly 9,000 eggs are laid per day by a female.

Eggs. The eggs are oval or elliptical in shape measuring 65 μm in length by 40 μm in breadth, colourless and protected by a transparent hyaline shell-membrane. An egg that comes out of the host body possesses an embryo up to 4-celled or 8-celled stage. The eggs, which passed out with the faeces, are not infective to man.

Development in soil. Under favourable conditions of environment like moisture, oxygen and temperature (about 68–85°F), the embryo develops into a rhabditiform larva or first stage juvenile; it is about 250 μm in length. This larva hatches out of the egg in the soil in about 48 hours. This larva possesses the mouth, buccal capsule, elongated pharynx, bulb-like oesophagus and intestine. It feeds on bacteria and other debris of the soil and moults twice on the third day and the fifth day. It then develops into a filiform larva measuring about 500 to 600 μm in length. It is the infective stage of the parasite. This larva does not feed but remains infective and alive for several weeks under favourable conditions. The time taken for development from eggs to filiform larvae, is on an overage 8 to 10 days.

Infection to new host. The filiform larvae are infective to man. The larvae cast off their sheaths and penetrate the skin of a human host. The anterior end of the larva is provided with oral spears by which it penetrates the soft skin of the feet and hands, generally through hair follicles.

Migration and later development. On reaching the subcutaneous tissues the larvae enter into the lymphatics and small venules. They pass through the lymphatic-vascular system into the venous circulation and are carried through the right heart into the pulmonary capillaries, where they break through the capillary walls to enter into the alveolar spaces. They then migrate on the bronchi—>trachea —>larynx, and crawl over the epiglottis to the back of the pharynx and are finally swallowed. During its migration, when it reaches to oesophagus, its third moulting occurs and a terminal buccal capsule is formed. The time taken in this migration is about 10 days.

Thus, finally the growing larvae settle down in the small intestine and undergo fourth and final moult to become the adults. In about 3 to 4 weeks time they become sexually mature to repeat the life history again.

The life span of the adult worm in human intestine has been estimated differently by different workers; generally it is believed to be 3 to 4 years.

DIAGNOSIS AND DISEASE

The infection of hookworm is easily diagnosed by the presence of its eggs in faecal smear from the patient. The disease caused by its infection is generally referred to as ancylostomiasis.

PATHOGENICITY

The hookworms are the most dangerous parasitic nematodes because they hold on to the intestinal villi and suck blood and body fluids of the host by their muscular pharynx, they also cut holes in the intestinal mucosa and leave bleeding wounds. It causes severe anaemia. In children, where incidence of infection is very great, they retard the physical and mental growth. Some toxins secreted by the glands in the head region of worms cause stomachache, food fermentation, diarrhoea, constipation, dyspnea, palpitation of heart, eosinophilia, ill health and the patient may finally collapse. During penetration of larvae in the skin local irritation is caused resulting into inflammation of the surrounding tissues ; these may result into tiny sores. The migratory larvae in lungs may cause haemorrhage and bronchial pneumonites.

TREATMENT

Drugs like carbon tetrachloride, thymol, oil of chenopodium, hexylresorcinol, etc., are used effectively to control the infection of *Ancylostoma*. Some other anti-helminth drugs like tetrachloroethylene and blephenium are found to be more effective and are safe to be used.

PREVENTION

The infection of *Ancylostoma duodenale* can be checked effectively by improving the sanitary conditions to avoid the contamination of faeces with the soil and other edibles, by protecting feet and hands from being touched with the soil. Children should be directed to keep their hands and nails clean.

REVISION QUESTIONS

1. Give an account of the habit , habitat, distribution and structure of *Ancylostoma duodenale*.
2. Describe the life history of *Ancylostoma duodenale* and comment upon its pathogenic effects.
3. Write short notes on :
   (a) Rhabditiform larva ; (b) Economic importance of hookworm.

48

Wuchereria (A Filarial Worm)

The larval forms of the filarial worm, *Wuchereria*, were first discovered by Demarquay in the hydrocele fluid of man in 1863. Later, Wucherer (1866) reported them in the chylous urine and Lewis (1872) found them in the human blood. Bancroft, however, discovered the adult females in 1876. The filarial worm, *Wuchereria (=Filaria) bancrofti* of man is a very dangerous nematode parasite causing wuchereriasis or filariasis in human beings. Another related genera is *Brugia malayi*, the common Malayan filarial worm. The present chapter, however, deals in detail about *Wuchereria bancrofti*.

WUCHERERIA BANCROFTI
SYSTEMATIC POSITION

Phylum	....	**Aschelminthes**
Class	....	**Nematoda**
Order	....	**Filarioidea**
Genus	....	*Wuchereria*
Species	....	*bancrofti*

HABIT AND HABITAT

Wuchereria bancrofti is a dreadful endoparasite of man ; adults harbouring the lymphatic vessels and lymph nodes. Its life history is digenetic, as it involves a secondary host, the blood-sucking insects, *i.e.*, the female mosquitoes of the genus *Culex, Aedes* or *Anopheles* ; the secondary host for *W. bancrofti* in India and China is *Culex pipiens* , in Pacific Islands (except Fiji and New Caledonia) is *Anopheles punctatus* and in Polynesian Islands is *Ades polynesiensis*. *Wuchereria bancrofti* is viviparous or to say ovo-viviparous ; its larvae are referred to as microfilariae which harbour the blood of human beings.

GEOGRAPHIC DISTRIBUTION

Wuchereria bancrofti is largely confined to the tropical and sub-tropical countries of the world. However, it occurs in India, West Indies, Puerto Rico, Southern China, Japan, Pacific Islands, West and Central Africa and South America. In India, the parasite is chiefly distributed along the sea coast and along the banks of big rivers (except Indus); it has also been reported from Rajasthan. Punjab, Delhi and from various vicinities of Uttar Pradesh.

STRUCTURE

The adult worms are long, hair-like, transparent and often creamy-white in colour. They are filiform in shape having tapering ends ; the head end terminating in a slightly rounded swelling. Sexes are separate and sexual dimorphism is distinct. The male worm measures 2.5 to 4 cm in length and 0.1 mm in diameter having a ventrally curved tail-end containing a number of genital papillae and two spicules of unequal copulatory spicules. The female worm measures 8 to 10 cm in length and 0.2 to 0.3 mm in diameter having a narrow and abruptly pointed tail. The female genital pore or vulva is located ventrally in the pharyngeal region and is characteristically provided with a pyriform ovijector. The male and female worms remain coiled together ; females are usually more in number than the males. Its mouth is simple without lips, pharynx is divisible into an anterior muscular and a posterior glandular parts, the oesophageal bulb is not found and the intestine is like those of other nematodes.

The microfilariae are very active and can move both with and against the blood stream. They have colourless and transparent bodies with blunt anterior ends and rather pointed tails. A microfilaria measures about 290 μm in length and 6 to 7 μm in diameter. The body of a microfilaria is covered in a hyaline sheath followed by cuticula being lined by flattened subcuticular cells or epidermis and an inner column of cytoplasm containing nuclei. However, various structures from anterior end downwards are : future mouth or oral stylet, nerve ring band, nephridiopore, renette cells and a dark coloured inner mass and four cells of future anus.

The microfilariae do not undergo further development in the human body unless they are taken up by their suitable secondary host (mosquito). If these microfilariae are not sucked up by the mosquito, they die in course of time. Their life span in human body is probably 70 days.

PERIODICITY OF MICROFILARIAE

The microfilariae of oriental countries like India and China exhibit nocturnal periodicity, as they appear in peripheral circulation periodically at night only generally between 10 pm and 4 am, but disappear inside during the rest of the day. It is believed that during daytime they retire inside the deeper blood vessels. In fact, the nocturnal periodicity of microfilariae is said to be related with the nocturnal feeding habit of their secondary host, *Culex pipiens.*

LIFE HISTORY

It has already been mentioned earlier that *W. bancrofti* is digenetic, *i.e.,* its life history is completed in two hosts ; man is the main host, while female mosquito, usually *Culex pipiens,* is the secondary host.

Mature male and female worms copulate in the lymph glands of man where they usually live. Since female worm is viviparous or ovoviviparous, it delivers numerous larvae called microfilariae.

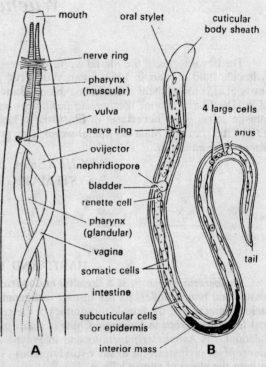

Fig. 48.1. *Wuchereria bancrofti.* A—Anterior part of female ; B—Microfilaria.

The microfilariae are born in very immature stage. However, microfilariae find their way into the blood stream where they can live for a considerable time without undergoing any developmental changes. As referred to, due to their nocturnal periodicity they are sucked up by the secondary host when it comes to take its blood-meal from the human body.

The microfilariae, after reaching in the body of the secondary host, undergo further development to become infective to man. In fact, immediately after their entry in the stomach of mosquito, the sheaths around their bodies are shed off and then they penetrate the gut wall within an hour or two and migrate to the thoracic muscles. Here they become short and thick like sausages within 2 days having short spiky tails and measure 124 to 250 µm in length and 10 to 17 µm in diameter, they also possess rudimentary digestive tract. These are first stage larvae. Within next 3 to 7 days they grow rapidly and moult once or twice to become the second stage larvae ; they measure 225 to 330 µm in length and 15 to 30 µm in diameter. Finally, by 10th or 11th day they become fully grown and are referred to as third stage larvae ; they measure about 1500 to 2000 µm in length and 18 to 23 µm in diameter. This stage is infective to man. These larvae are inactive and come to lie in the labium of the mosquito. When the mosquito bites the warm and moist skin of man, the larvae creep out of the labium to the human skin, then they penetrate into the skin and finally come to settle down in the lymphatics. Here, they grow and become fully adult and sexually mature within a period of 5 to 18 months. These sexually mature worms start reproduction to repeat the life history again. The life span of adult worms is very long, probably ranging from 5 to 10 years.

DIAGNOSIS AND DISEASE

The infection of *Wuchereria bancrofti* is diagnosed by the presence of microfilariae in stained blood smear and by the biopsy of lymph nodes. The disease caused by the infection of *W. bancrofti* is, in general, referred to as wuchereriasis or filariasis.

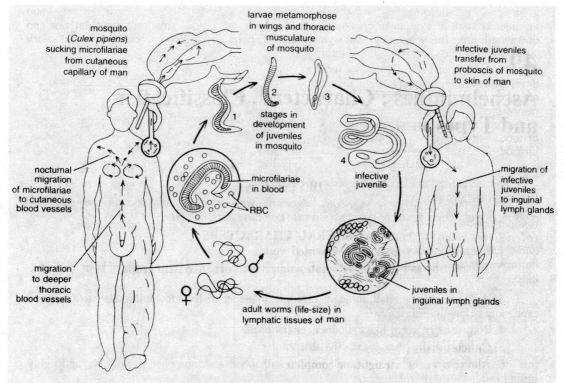

Fig. 48.2. *Wuchereria bancrofti.* Life cycle.

PATHOGENICITY

In fact, the pathogenic effects seen during filariasis are caused by living or dead adult worms. A light infection does not produce serious effects ; it causes filarial fever, headache and mental depression, etc. But, during heavy infection a large number of pathological effects are observed; in this condition they block the lymphatic vessels and glands causing **lymphatic obstruction** so that lymph cannot get back to the circulatory system. Hence, there occurs accumulation of lymph in the affected organs due to which they swell fantastically, a condition called **lymphoedema**. When they infect lymph nodes then they cause **lymphadenitis**, in lymph vessels they cause **lymphangitis** and after infecting epididymis and related areas they cause **hydrocele**. However, the affected organs sometimes become enormously enlarged, producing a tumor-like ugly look, this condition is called **elephantiasis** ; the elephantiasis of feet, hands, scrotum, etc., are of common occurrence in the areas where *W. bancrofti* is prevalent.

TREATMENT AND PREVENTION

So far, no satisfactory treatment has been reported. However, heterazan and compounds of antimony and arsenic are used to reduce or eradicate microfilariae from the circulatory system. The only way of prevention is to protect our bodies from mosquito bite.

REVISION QUESTIONS

1. Describe habit, habitat, geographic distribution and structure of *Wuchereria bancrofti*.
2. Give an account of the life history of a filarial worm and discuss its pathogenic effects.
3. Write notes on microfilaria larva.

49

Aschelminthes : Characters , Classification and Types

DEFINITION

Aschelminthes are pseudocoelomate, bilaterally symmetrical, triploblastic, unsegmented, vermiform, organ-system grade of construction with complete digestive tube.

GENERAL CHARACTERS

1. Bilaterally symmetrical, unsegmented worms.

2. Triploblastic and pseudocoelomate animals with organ-system grade of body organization.

3. Body size mostly small, some microscopic, while others from few millimetres to a metre or even more in length.

4. Body usually worm-like cylindrical or flattened.

5. Cuticle usually present and cilia absent.

6. Alimentary canal straight and complete with mouth and anus, pharynx muscular and highly specialized.

7. Respiratory and circulatory systems absent.

8. Excretory system includes a system of canals, protonephridia present in some forms for osmoregulation.

9. Nervous system simple and consists of a circumenteric nerve ring having anterior and posterior longitudinal nerves.

10. Sense organs are in the form of pits, papillae, bristles and eye spots.

11. Sexes separate, *i.e.*, dioecious and reproductive organs relatively simple.

12. Asexual reproduction does not occur.

13. Eggs shelled, cleavage determinate and spiral ; life cycle simple or complicated usually with no special larval stages.

14. Heterogeneous group inhabiting aquatic and terrestrial environment ; many are well known parasites.

CLASSIFICATION OF ASCHELMINTHES

This phylum is, in fact, a heterogeneous assemblage of different animals, hence, has been classified differently by different zoologists. Classification of Aschelminthes followed here is based and modified from L. H. Hyman (1951) but Storer and Usinger (1971) have regarded different classes of Aschelminthes as separate phyla and rank Aschelminthes as superphylum. Thus, the classification of Aschelminthes is as under :

CLASS 1. NEMATODA
(Gr., *nema*=thread+*eidos*=form)

1. Aquatic or terrestrial, free-living or parasitic, elongated roundworms.
2. Body wall with cuticle, cellular or syncytial epidermis and longitudinal muscles in four bands.
3. No cilia, no circulatory and respiratory systems.
4. Digestive system complete with muscular pharynx and glands.
5. Excretory system of glandular organs or canals or both.
6. Dioecious; male smaller than female.
7. Fertilization internal.

Order 1. Enploidea

1. Cuticle not ringed, often with cuticular bristles.
2. Anterior end with six labial papillae.
3. 10 to 12 bristles in one or two circlets.
4. Oesophagus into two parts, anterior muscular and posterior glandular.
5. A pair of cephalic slits and cyathiform amphids.
   Examples : *Enoplus, Anticoma, Synonchus.*

Order 2. Dorylaimoidea

1. Cuticle smooth without bristles.
2. Anterior end with two circlets of papillae of 6 and 10 each.
3. Buccal cavity armed with a protrusible spear.
4. Rear part of pharynx enlarged.
5. Amphids cyathiform.
   Examples: *Dorylamius,, Tylencholaimus, Actinolaimus.*

Order 3. Mermithoidea

1. Smooth, filiform nematodes, parasitic in invertebrates (mainly insects) in juvenile stages or free-living as adults in soil or water.
2. Head sense organs reduced to papillae, usually six.
3. Pharynx long, blind; intestine also blind, altered into a food storing organ.
4. Amphids cyathiform or reduced.
   Examples: *Mermis, Paramermis, Aproctonema.*

Order 4. Chromadoroidea

1. Aquatic nematodes with smooth or ringed cuticle.
2. Usually cuticle heavily ornamented with bristles, knobs, punctations, etc.
3. Pharynx with a posterior bulb.
4. Amphids spiral or derivable from a spiral.
   Examples : *Paracytholaimus, Paracanthonchus.*

Order 5. Araeolaimoidea

1. Cuticle smooth, sometimes with bristles.
2. Labial papillae present.
3. Anterior end usually with four cephalic bristles.
4. Amphids spiral or loop-like.
   Examples: *Plectus, Wilsonema, Odontophora.*

Order 6. Monhysteroidea

1. Cuticle smooth or slightly ringed, often provided with bristles.

2. Anterior end with four, six or eight bristles, or multiples thereof.
3. Amphids circular.
   Examples :*Cylindrolaimus,Siphonolaimus.*

Order 7. Desmoscalecoidea

1. Cuticle heavily ringed, with prominent bristles throughout or in restricted areas.
2. Anterior end with 4 bristles.
3. Amphids crescentic.
4. Marine nematodes.
   Examples : *Desmoscolex, Tricoma, Greeffiella.*

Order 8. Rhabditoidea or Anguilluloidea

1. Free-living or parasitic nematodes with ringed or smooth cuticle.
2. Pharynx with posterior bulb and also usually with swelling anterior to the nerve ring.
3. Caudal glands absent.
4. Amphids small pockets.
   Examples : *Rhabditis, Diploscapter, Diplogaster.*

Order 9. Rhabdiasoidea

1. Smooth nematodes without definite pharyngeal bulb.
2. Hermaphrodite; parthenogenesis also occurs.
3. Parasitic stages in animals.
4. Free-living stages may develop into males and females.
   Examples : *Rhabdias, Entomelas.*

Order 10. Oxyuroidea

1. Pharynx with a posterior bulb, usually valvulated.
2. Females with a long pointed tail ; terminal parts of female system often heavily muscularized.
3. Males with one spicule or two equal spicules.
4. Usually caudal alae forming a cuticular bursa.
   Examples: *Oxyuris* or *Enterobius.*

Order 11. Ascaroidea

1. Mouth surrounded by three prominent lips.
2. Pharynx without posterior bulb or if present it is not valvulated.
3. Pharynx or intestine or both often with caeca.
4. Buccal capsule absent.
5. Tail of female blunt ; male without caudal alae and possesses two equal or nearly equal spicules.
   Example ; *Ascaris.*

Order 12. Strongyloidea

1. Mouth without conspicuous lips but often with leaf crowns.
2. Pharynx without bulb.
3. Females usually with ovijectors.
4. Males with copulatory bursa supported by muscular rays ; typically 13 in number.
   Examples : *Ancylostoma, Strongylus, Necator.*

Order 13. Spiruroidea

1. Mouth usually with two lateral lips ; sometimes 4 or 6 small ones.
2. Pharynx without bulb, anteriorly muscular and posteriorly glandular.
3. Males without bursa; spicules unequal and dissimilar.
   Examples : *Thelazia, Rictularia, Oxyspirura.*

Order 14. Dracunculoidea

1. Without definite lips or cuticularized buccal capsule.
2. Pharynx as in Spiruroidea.
3. Vulva near or behind the middle of body ; usually not functional.
4. Males with equal filiform spicules ; bursa wanting.
   Examples : *Dracunculus, Philometra, Micropleura.*

Order 15. Filarioidea

1. Filiform worms without lips.
2. Buccal capsule small or rudimentary.
3. Pharynx as in Spiruroidea, pharyngeal bulb wanting.
4. Vulva anterior in female.
5. Bursa wanting, spicules as in Spiruroidea.
   Examples : *Wuchereria, Loa loa.*

Order 16. Trichuroidea or Trichinelloidea

1. Body filiform anteriorly.
2. Mouth without lips.
3. Pharynx slender.
4. Provided with a cirrus, spicule if present one only.
   Examples : *Trichinella, Trichuris.*

Order 17. Dioctophymoidea

1. Moderate to very long-sized nematodes.
2. Mouth without lips surrounded by 6, 12 or 18 papillae.

3. Pharynx elongated without bulb.
4. Males with muscular bursa but without rays.
   Examples : *Dictyophyme, Hystrichis, Eustronglides.*

CLASS 2. NEMATOMORPHA
(Gr., *nema*=thread+*morphe*=shape)

1. Hair worms, found in springs.
2. Body very long, thin, slender and worm-like.
3. Body wall with thick cuticle.
4. Digestive system complete.
5. Pseudocoel mostly filled with parenchyma.
6. No circulatory, respiratory and excretory systems.
7. Dioecious, gonads and reproductive ducts paired.
8. Freshwater or terrestrial forms ; only *Nectonema* is marine.

Order 1. Cordioidea

1. Swimming bristles are wanting.
2. Pseudocoel is filled with parenchyma.
3. Gonads paired.
   Examples: *Paragordius, Gordius.*

Order 2 . Nectonematoidea

1. Swimming bristles arranged in two rows.
2. Pseudocoel unfilled.
3. Gonad only one.
4. Marine form.
   Example : *Nectonema.*

CLASS 3. ROTIFERA
(L., *rota* = wheel + *ferre*=to bear)

1. Microscopic animals in ponds, lakes and streams ; commonly called wheel bearers.
2. Body wall thickened into plates or lorica.
3. Anterior end with ciliated corona.
4. Post-anal foot with toes.
5. Digestive system with a feeding organ.
6. Excretory system with two protonephridia.
7. Sensory organs antennae and eye spots.
8. Sexes separate, males very minute or degenerate.
9. Female oviparous, no larval stage.

Order 1. Seisonacea

1. Body elongated with long neck.
2. Corona small.
3. Gonads paired.
4. Found as commensals on crustaceans.
   Example: *Seison.*

Order 2. Bdelloidea

1. Corona usually with two trochal discs.
2. Pedal glands more than two.
3. Males degenerate; females with paired germovitellaria.
4. Swimming or creeping forms.

    Examples : *Rotaria* or *Rotifera, Philodina, Mniobia.*

Order 3. Monogonontea

1. Swimming or sessile forms.
2. Males small or degenerate.
3. Males usually with one testis.
4. Females possess single germovitellaria.

    Examples : *Mytilina, Limnias.*

CLASS 4. GASTROTRICHA
(L., *gaster*=stomach + *trichos*=hair)

1. Microscopic, marine and freshwater forms.
2. Body wall with cuticle bearing short spines.
3. Posterior end forked.
4. Pharynx triradiate and muscular.
5. Excretory system with two protonephridia.
6. Dioecious or monoecious ; parthenogenetic females occur.
7. Development direct.

Order 1. Macrodasyoidea

1. Marine worm-like forms.
2. Adhesive tubes many.
3. Protonephridia not found.

    Example: *Macrodasys.*

Order 2. Chaetonotoidea

1. Mostly freshwater forms found on vegetation.
2. Adhesive tubes on tail.
3. Protonephridia one pair.
4. Reproduction by parthenogenesis.

    Examples : *Chaetonotus, Neodesys.*

CLASS 5. KINORHYNCHA
(Gr., *kineo*=more + *rhynchos*=beak)

1. Marine, microscopic worm-like forms.
2. Superficial segmentation of the body.
3. Body surface with spiny cuticle but no cilia.
4. Head protrusible.
5. A pair of adhesive tubes in front part of the ventral surface.
6. Digestive system complete with salivary glands.
7. Nervous system epidermal.
8. Dioecious ; gonads in the form of paired tubular sacs.
9. Development includes a series of juvenile stages.

Order 1. Homalorhagida

1. Head and neck both protrusible.

    Example : *Trachydemus.*

Order 2. Cyclorhagida

1. Only head ring is protrusible.

    Example : *Echinoderes.*

REPRESENTATIVE TYPES OF NEMATODA

1. *Rhabditis.* The genus *Rhabditis* (Fig. 49.1) contains numerous species of nematodes normally found in soil, organic matter or water, and frequently in faeces of man or animals. They closely resemble with free-living generation of *Strongyloides* but have no alternation of generations.

Rhabditis pellia is a species which has on few occasions been found living in the human vagina, the larvae escaping in the urine. *R. hominis* and other species have been recorded from stools of man and animals. In most of these cases there was a suspicion of their being true parasites, but the worms have not been found on re-examination and in some cases clear evidence of contamination with soil or water was obtained. There is yet no conclusive evidence that any of these species are more than coprophagous. Their only importance is then possible confusion with *Strongyloides.*

Adult male and female of *Rhabditis maupasi* measure 2.0 and 1.7 mm in length respectively. Excretory system is H-shaped and reproductive system is J-shaped. Male possesses single tubular testis and female has two ovaries. Oviducts and seminal receptacle are present and uteri are short. Vulva is situated posterior to the middle part of the body. Life cycle is simple and direct. Adults breed as protandric hermaphrodites.

2. *Enterobius vermicularis* or *Oxyuris. Enterobius vermicularis* (Fig. 49.2) is commonly known as pinworm, which is cosmopolitan, but more common in Europe and America. In some communities 40–100% of the population may be infected. Pinworms are parasites in the human caecum, colon and appendix. It has 3 small lips and a pair of cephalic expansions at the anterior end. Female is 10 mm long with a long pointed tail, the male is 3.5 mm with blunt, curved tail with a bursa-like expansion and a single spicule ; males are few and rare. Fertilized females make nightly trips to the anus to lay eggs, or they may creep out of the anus and lay eggs. Egg-laying is stimulated

by contact with air, at times the female bursts and releases showers of eggs. Eggs are well advanced when laid, each contains a tadpole-like juvenile. Persons reinfect themselves by scratching with hands from where eggs may get into the mouth. Eggs may infect the entire family through clothes, furniture, air and dust in the room. Eggs hatch in small intestine, the juveniles descend slowly, moult 4 times and become adults. *Enterobius* causes pinworm disease, their movements cause intense itching of the anus, inflammation of mucous membrane of colon and appendix, and often insomnia and loss of appetite. Each generation lasts from 3 to 4 weeks, and the infection will die out if re-infection does not occur.

Enteric-coated capsules of gentian violet of one grain given for 8 days remove most of the worms.

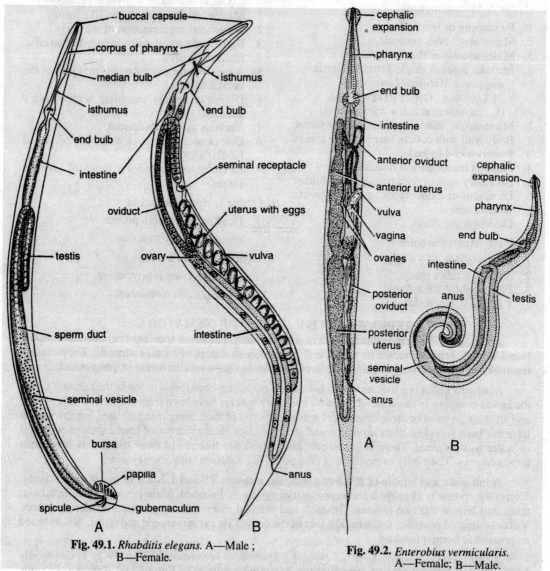

Fig. 49.1. *Rhabditis elegans.* A—Male ; B—Female.

Fig. 49.2. *Enterobius vermicularis.* A—Female; B—Male.

3. *Dracunculus medinensis.* *Dracunculus medinensis* (Fig. 49.3) is commonly called **guinea worm.** It is parasitic in the deeper subcutaneous tissues of human beings where the long female lies in a loose coil under the skin. They are a scourge in Western Asia from Arabia to India, and also in East Indies and Africa ; they have been known from ancient times as "fiery serpents." The female is 75 cm to 1.30 metre long and 1.5 mm in diameter, the head is blunt and tail has sharp hooks. The males are few, they are 20 to 30 mm long with a spirally coiled tail having 10 pairs of papillae and two large equal spicules. The anterior end in both sexes has a cuticular ring encircling the mouth and bearing 6 labial papillae and 4 double papillae. In mature females the alimentary canal and vulva atrophy and the body gets occupied by an embryo-filled uterus.

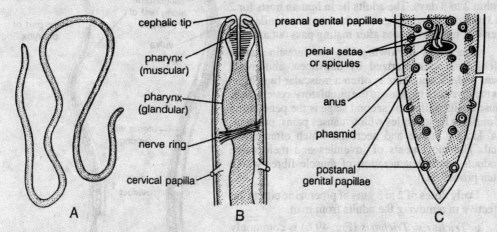

Fig. 49.3. *Dracunculus medinensis.* A—Entire ; B—Anterior end of male ; C—Posterior end of male in ventral view.

The mature female pierces the skin of its host by its anterior end and produces a toxin which causes a blister, the blister enlarges into an ulcer from which the anterior end of the roundworm protrudes. When the ulcer comes in contact with water, the uterus of the female projects from the ulcer and releases hordes of tiny, coiled juveniles, this is repeated every time the ulcer touches water. When juveniles are all passed out the parent worm shrivels up and dies. The juveniles may be swallowed by *Cyclops*, a freshwater crustacean which is the intermediate host. In the *Cyclops* the juveniles moult twice and become infective in 3 weeks. If an infected *Cyclops* is swallowed by man the juveniles come into his alimentary canal from where they bore into the subcutaneous tissue, moult twice again, and become adults in about a year.

The infected person after formation of an ulcer may get urticaria, diarrhoea, asthma, giddiness, and eosinophilia, bacterial infection of the ulcer also sets in. Extraction of the nematode by slowly winding its end projecting from the ulcer on a stick by making one turn each day has been successfully practised in India. If worms are not removed, they eventually die by becoming calcified. Injections of phenothiazine emulsified in olive oil given for a week prove effective and worms can be extracted.

4. Loa loa. *Loa loa* is parasitic in the subcutaneous tissues of man in Africa. The female is 2 to 7 cm long, the male is 2 to 3.5 cm long. The worm has cuticular warts on its body. It creeps about below the skin at the rate of 2.5 cm in two minutes causing intense itching and swellings known as "Calabar swellings," these swellings in the eyes are painful.

The mature female produces ensheathed juveniles which swarm in the peripheral circulation in the day-time but disappearing at night. Intermediate hosts are flies of genus *Chrysops*, larvae moult and develop in the fly and invade the proboscis, they enter the human skin when the infected *Chrysops* bites.

5. Trichinella spiralis. *Trichinella spiralis* (Fig. 49.4) is commonly known as **trichina worm.** It is a small intestinal parasite of man in Europe and America, but it is absent from the tropics, it is also parasitic in pigs, domestic animals and rodents. Man becomes infected by eating insufficiently cooked pork. They are slender worms with the body tapering from the middle to the anterior end, the long pharynx has an anterior muscular part and posterior glandular part. Females are 3 to 4 mm long, males are 1.5 mm long with a pair of conical appendages at the posterior end, they have no spicules. The fertilized female bores through the intestine into a spiral lymph space and gives birth to juveniles. The juveniles travel through the lymph and blood vessels into every organ, but eventually come to lie in voluntary muscles especially in the diaphragm, tongue, eyes and limbs where they roll themselves into a spiral and a lemon-shaped **cyst** is formed around them ; each cyst may have 1 to 7 embryos. No further development occurs in the cyst, after years the cyst becomes calcified and the embryos die. If partly cooked pork or meat containing cysts is eaten by man, the embryos come out in the intestine and undergo several moults to become mature within 2 to 3 days. The adults lie in human hosts for 2 to 3 months only, they give birth to many juveniles and then die, but most males after mating pass out and die.

The adults burrowing into the intestine cause trichiniasis characterized by diarrhoea, abdominal pains and nausea, there is often a muscular twitching. As the juveniles increase in the circulatory system, they cause eosinophilia, the second stage is the penetration of muscles by juveniles which causes pains, pneumonia, kidney failure and necrosis, which often prove fatal. The movements of juveniles and their waste products cause degeneration of muscle fibres which often proves fatal.

Daily doses of 2 to 3 gms of piperazine citrate are effective in removing the adults from man.

6. *Trichuris.* Trichuris (Fig. 49.6) is commonly known as whipworm because of its whip-like body shape. It is a parasite of the intestine of man and other mammals. The human species *T. trichiura* also occurring in other primates and in pigs, is a cosmopolitan inhabitant of the caecum appendix and colon of man especially in warm moist climates. The anterior part of the body containing the pharynx is generally more slender than the posterior part. The slender anterior region is usually buried in the host's mucosa. The mouth is simple, without lips ; the arrangement of papillae is not well known. One or more bacillary bands are present anteriorly, these are longitudinal tracts of minute projections that constitute the outlets of sub-cuticular glands. The female reproductive system is single, long and tubular with a variously placed vulva. Males either lack a copulatory apparatus altogether or are provided with an eversible spicule sheath, hence, a cirrus, armed or not with one spicule.

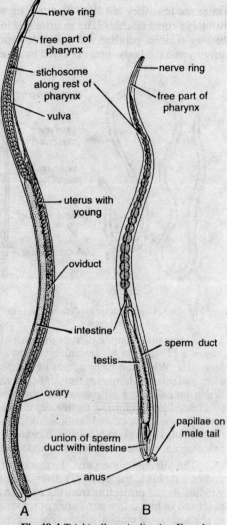

Fig.49.4. *Trichinella spiralis.* A—Female; B—Male.

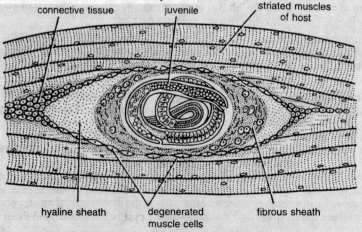

Fig. 49.5. *Trichinella spiralis* ensheathed in host muscle.

The eggs are laid uncleaved and develop outside, best in moist, heavy soils to the infective stage but do not hatch until ingested by the appropriate definitive host. The life cycle is typically simple without the intervention of an intermediate host ; the juveniles are provided with a buccal stylet.

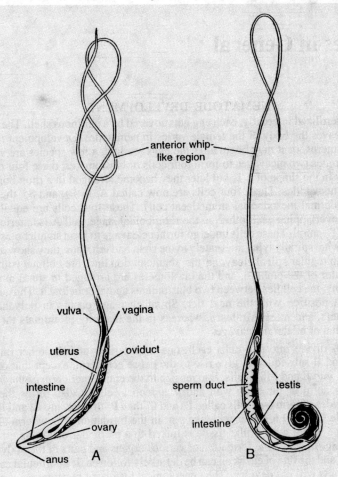

Fig. 49.6. *Trichurus ovis*. A—Female; B—Male.

REVISION QUESTIONS
1. Give an account of the characters of Aschelminthes. Classify it up to orders giving examples.
2. Classify nematoda up to orders giving characters and examples.
3. Write short notes on :
   (a) *Enterobius* ; (b) Guinea worm ; (c) *Loa loa* ; (d) *Trichinella* spiralis.

50

Nematodes in General

NEMATODE DEVELOPMENT

The eggs are fertilized internally, each egg gets covered by a chitinous shell. The stage at which the fertilized egg leaves the body of the female varies in nematodes. Development may start while the eggs are in the uterus, or it may begin after the eggs are laid, a few species are viviparous. The fertilized egg undergoes two cleavages to form four cells or blastomeres, these four cells are at first arranged in *Ascaris* in the shape of a T, but later they become arranged in a rhomboid shape which is characteristic of nematodes. These four cells are now called A, B, P_2, and S_2, the S_2 cell is also called EMST (ectodermal-mesodermal-stomodaeal cell). These four cells are equal and lie in the same plan slightly overlapping each other, in the rhomboidal stage, cell A is anterior, B dorsal, P_2 posterior, and EMST ventral. These cells undergo further cleavage to form smaller blastomeres which are displaced somewhat spirally lying alternately to the right and left, thus, they show a modified type of spiral cleavage. In regular spiral cleavage the segmentation lines are oblique with respect to the polar axis and equator of the embryo, and the blastomeres are arranged in spiral alternately to the right and left, and any one cell lies between two blastomeres above or below it. Thus, one set of cells or tier alternates in position with the next tier. Spiral cleavage occurs in polyclad Turbellaria, Nematoda, Polychaeta, and most Mollusca, whereas in the majority of animals the round zygote undergoes other radial or bilateral cleavage.

Cells A and B divide into two cells each, one on the right and the other on the left, these descendants of A and B subsequently give rise to the entire ectoderm, except that of the posterior end. EMST divides into E and MST cells, E gives rise to the entire endoderm of the intestine, while MST form the mesoderm of the body wall and pseudocoel cells, it also forms the lining of the stomodaeum. P_2 divides to form two cells called P_3 and C, then P_3 divides into P_4 and D. P_4 will form the germ cells, while C and D together will take part in the formation of ectoderm and mesoderm. Cleavage of this type where a particular tissue is linked to a particular cell in an embryo is called determinate cleavage in which the formation of various organs and parts of the body is determined at a very early stage, and the fate of each cell can be definitely followed. If a particular cell is destroyed the corresponding parts will not develop. The geneological history of blastomeres is also called cell lineage, the cells of the developing embryo occupy definite areas having different qualities, each area contributes to the formation of a particular tissue or organ, thus, the fate of different cells of the embryo can be observed as followed.

Cleavage of the embryonic cells continues giving rise to a blastula at the 16-cell stage, it has a blastocoele cavity. Then a gastrula is formed by epiboly or overgrowth of ectoderm cells over the endoderm cells, and by invagination of stomodeum and endoderm cells. The blastocoele will become the perivisceral cavity in which large vacuolated cells develop. Thus, an embryo is formed which has a digestive tract, after more cell divisions the embryo becomes a juvenile. The juveniles on hatching have all the structure of the adult except some parts of the reproductive system. The juvenile undergoes 2,4 or 6 moultings to become an adult.

In this nematode development the future germ cells become differentiated very early from somatic cells. The germ cells remain their full number of chromosomes, but in the somatic cells some of the chromatin of chromosomes is broken and given up into the cytoplasm, this is called chromatin diminution. After the formation of the juvenile all cell division ceases in the somatic cells, and cell division takes place only in the germ cells. Thus, the number of cells in a nematode is small and constant for each species. Further growth occurs only by differentiation, vacuolation, and increase in the size of cells which have already been formed by the time hatching takes place. In *Rhabditis* there are 120 epidermal cells, 172 cells in the digestive tract, 200 nerve cells, and 68 muscle cells.

TABLE 50.1. SOME COMMON NEMATODE PARASITES OF MAN

S.No.	Name	Site of infection	Mode of infection	Disease and pathogenic effect	Distribution
1.	*Ascaris lumbricoides* (Roundworm)	Small intestine	Direct, by ingesting eggs with food and drink.	Ascariasis ; anaemia, diarrhoea, bronchitis, pneumonia	Worldwide.
2.	*Ancylostoma doudenale* (Hookworm)	Intestine	Larvae penetrate dirctly through the skin.	Ancylostomiasis; itching and inflammation of skin, anaemia, mental and physical retrardation.	Tropical and subtropical countries.
3.	*Wuchereria bancrofti* (Filarialworm)	Lymphatic vessels, lymph nodes	By the bite of infected female mosquito (secondary host) while taking blood-meal; liberates microfilariae.	Wuchereriasis or Filariasis ; lymphatic obstruction (lymphedema, hydrocele, elephantiasis.	Tropical and subtropical countries.
4.	*Enterobius (= Oxyuris) vermicularis* (Pinworm)	Large intestine, caecum and appendix	Direct by ingesting eggs.	Oxyuriasis , anal itching, appendicitis, etc.	Cosmopolitan ; common in Europe, America, India.
5.	*Dracunculus medinensis* (Guineaworm or The fiery serpent)	Subcutaneous tissue	By ingesting infected *Cyclops* with water.	Guinea worm disease; ulcers, diarrhoea, asthma, giddiness, eosinophilia.	Western Asia, Arabia to India, East Indies and Africa.
6.	*Loa loa* (Eyeworm)	Subcutaneous conective tissue of eyes.	By ingesting infected *Cyclops*.	Conjunctivitis ; calabar swellings.	Africa.
7.	*Trichuris trichiura* (Whipworm)	Caecum, appendix and colon	By ingesting eggs with food.	Trichuriasis; abdominal pain, anaemia , bloody stool.	Worldwide.
8.	*Trichinella spiralis* (Trichinaworm)	Small intstine and muscles	By eating infected ill cooked pork.	Trichinosis ; muscular pain, pneumonia.	Europe, America.

REVISION QUESTIONS

1. Give a generalized account of the development of nematodes.
2. Describe five nematode parasites of man giving their zoological and common names, site of infection, mode of infection, pathogenic effects and geographical distribution.

51
Helminths and Human Diseases

Helminths include the animals belonging to the Phylum Platyhelminthes and Class Nematoda of Phylum Aschelminthes. Many of the parasitic forms of this group are popularly known as parasitic worms. These are the endoparasites of the gut and blood in the human body and cause various diseases collectively called helminthiasis. The following three types of helminthiasis are most common and widespread : 1. Nematodiasis ; 2. Trematodiasis ; and 3. Cestodiasis.

NEMATODIASIS

The diseases caused by the nematode worms constitute nematodiasis. The most common widespread human diseases caused due to infestation with the nematodes are as follows :

1. Ascariasis

Ascariasis is a highly prevalent disease caused by the largest nematode (roundworm) *Ascaris lumbricoides*. It resembles an ordinary earthworm. When fresh from the intestine, it is light brown or pink in colour but it gradually changes to white. It is most frequently seen in the stool of children. The male of *A. lumbricoides* measures about 15 to 25 cm in length, while the female is longer and stouter measuring 25 to 40 cm in length. The egg-laying capacity of mature female *Ascaris* has been found to be enormous, liberating about 200,000 eggs daily. The eggs liberated by a fertilized female pass out of the human host with the faeces and may remain alive for several days. Infection is effected by swallowing ripe eggs (embryonated eggs) with raw vegetables cultivated on a soil fertilized by infected human excreta. Infection also occurs by drinking contaminated water. Among children playing in the contaminated soil, there is also hand to mouth transfer of eggs by dirty fingers. Infection may also occur by inhalation of desiccated eggs in the dust reaching the pharynx and swallowed. A rhabditiform larva is developed from unsegmented ovum within the egg-shell in 10 to 40 days in the soil. The ripe egg containing the coiled-up embryo is infective to man. When ingested with food, drink or raw vegetables, the embryonated eggs pass down to the duodenum where the digestive juices weaken the egg-shell. Splitting of the egg-shell occurs and the rhabditiform larvae are liberated in the upper part of the small intestine. The newly hatched larvae burrow their way through the mucous membrane of the small intestine and are carried by the portal circulation to the liver. Finally they pass out of the liver and *via* right heart enter the pulmonary circulation. Breaking through the capillary wall they reach the lung alveoli. From the lung alveoli the larvae crawl up the bronchi and trachea, they are propelled into larynx and pharynx and are once more swallowed. The larvae pass down the oesophagus to the stomach and localize in the upper part of the intestine, their normal abode. The larvae on reaching habitat grow into adult worms and become sexually mature in about 6 to 10 weeks' time. Four moultings of the larva occur—one outside while within the egg-shell, two in the lungs and one in the intestine.

The symptoms attributed to *Ascaris* infection may be divided into two groups : (i) those produced by migrating larvae, and (ii) those produced by the adult worms.

(i) Symptoms due to the migrating larvae. In heavy infections typical symptoms of pneumonia such as fever, cough and dyspnoea may appear. Urticarial rash and eosinophilia are seen in such cases. Disturbances have been reported due to their presence in the brain, spinal cord, heart and kidneys.

(ii) Symptoms due to the adult worms. With the adult worms inhabiting the intestine the patient complains of abdominal pains, vomiting, headache, irritability, dizziness and night terrors. Sometimes there is a diarrhoea and salivation. Often the patient grits his teeth in the sleep. When the adult worms migrate through the intestinal wall they cause severe peritonitis. Wandering *Ascaris* may enter the lumen of the appendix, causing appendicitis. Obstructive jaundice and acute haemorrhagic pancreatitis have been known to occur when the worm has entered into the biliary passage. At times it penetrates high up in the liver causing one or more abscesses.

The treatment of human ascariasis has been fairly successful through the oral administration of piperazine citrate syrup (two spoonful twice a day for one week, followed by another course after a gap of one week) and hexyl-resorcinol tablets (10 mg taken at bed time with water). Other drugs which are known to have specific action on *Ascaris* include the following : tetramisole, pyrantel pamoate, bephanium hydroxynaphthoate, diethylcarbamazine(Hetrazan), thiobendazole and mebendazole.

2. Ancylostomiasis

Ancylostomiasis is caused by two hookworms *Ancylostoma duodenale* and *Necator americanus*. Both the hookworms are parasites within the intestine. The adult worms live in the small intestine of man particularly in jejunum, less often in duodenum and rarely in ileum. They are most frequent in rural areas. Female hookworms produce 5000 to 10,000 eggs per day which pass out in the stools. Man acquires infection when the eggs hatch and the larvae penetrate through the skin of the hands and feet. Infection occurs when man walks bare-foot on the faecally contaminated soil. The filariform larvae penetrate directly through the skin with which they come in contact. The most common sites of the entry are : (i) the thin skin between the toes ; (ii) the dorsum of the feet, and (iii) the inner side of the soles. Infection may also occur by accidental drinking of water contaminated with filariform larvae. The filariform larvae enter the blood vessels and are carried to the lungs. Now they make their way to one of the bronchi,trachea and larynx, crawl over the epiglottis to the back of the pharynx and are ultimately swallowed. The growing larvae settle down in the small intestine, undergo moulting and develop into adult worms.

The characteristic symptoms of ancylostomiasis are ancylostome dermatitis or ground itch, and creeping eruption by ancylostome larvae, and gastro-intestinal disorders, and severe anaemia by adult worms. Gastro-intestinal manifestations produce dyspeptic troubles associated with epigastric tenderness stimulating duodenal ulcer. Due to severe anaemia the skin becomes pale yellow in colour and the mucous membrane of the eyes, lips and tongue becomes extremely pale. The face appears puffy with swelling of lower eyelids and there is oedema of the feet and ankle. The general appearance of the patient is a pale plumpy individual with protruded abdomen and dry lustreless hair.

For the treatment of hookworm infection the following steps are to be taken : (i) expulsion of worms by antihelminthic drugs and (ii) treatment of anaemia.

3. Enterobiasis

Enterobiasis is caused by *Enterobius vermicularis* commonly called pinworm, threadworm or seatworm. These worms are small and white in colour. Male worm measures 2 to 4 mm and female worm measures 8 to 12 mm in length. Adult worms (gravid females) live in the caecum, colon and vermiform appendix of man. The females migrate out through the colon and rectum and enormous number of eggs in the skin folds about the anus, where they cause intense itching . Each of the egg, newly laid in perianal skin, containing a tadpole-like larva completes its development in 24 to 36 hours time, in the presence of oxygen. Infection occurs by the ingestion of these eggs. When the skin about the anus is scratched, eggs are easily picked upon the fingers and under the nails from where they find their way to food and are swallowed. The egg-shells are dissolved by digestive juices and the larvae escape in the small intestine where they develop into adult worms.

The pinworm infection is more frequent in children than in adults. The symptoms of enterobiasis include severe itching around the anus, loss of appetite, sleeplessness and sometimes inflammation of the vermiform appendix.

Enterobiasis is treated with antihelminthics such as piperazine citrate, pyrevinium pamoate (Povan), pyrental pamoate, stibazium iodide, thiobendazole and mebendazole.

4. Trichuriasis

Trichuriasis is caused by *Trichuris trichura*, commonly known as whipworm. The adult worms live in the large intestine of man, particularly in the caecum ; also in vermiform appendix. The worm resembles a whip in shape and general appearance. Male measures 3 to 4 cm and female measures 4 to 5 cm in length. The females lay enormous number of eggs daily that pass in the stool. Development proceeds slowly in water and damp soil. A rhabditiform larva develops within the egg in the course of 3 to 4 weeks in tropical countries. The embryonated eggs are infective to man. Man is infected when the embryonated eggs are swallowed with food or water. The egg-shell is dissolved by the digestive juices and the larva emerges. The liberated larvae pass down into the caecum, their site of localization. They grow directly into adult worms and embed their anterior parts in the mucosa of the intestine. The worms become sexually mature within a month from the time of ingestion of the eggs and gravid females begin to lay eggs. The cycle is then repeated.

The patient suffering from trichuriasis (whipworm disease) shows the symptoms of acute appendicitis. In heavy infections the patient often complains of abdominal pain, mucous diarrhoea often with blood streaked stool and loss of weight. Prolapse of rectum has occasionally been observed in massive trichuriasis.

The drugs at present most commonly used for the treatment of trichuriasis are stibazium iodide, deftarsone, thiobendazole and mebendazole.

5. Trichinosis

Trichinosis is caused by *Trichinella spiralis*, the trichinia worm. It is one of the smallest nematodes infecting man. The male measures 1.4 to 1.6 mm and female measures 3.0 to 4.0 mm in length. This disease is common and widespread in Europe and America. Although it prevails in areas where pork is eaten. Humans become infected by eating undercooked or raw meat containing encysted larvae mainly pork. The cysts, located in striated muscles, are digested liberating larvae that mature to adult worms that attach to the wall of small intestine. Female worms there liberate larvae that invade the intestinal wall, enter the circulation and penetrate the striated muscles, where they encyst and remain viable for years. Usually one larva is present in a single cyst.

The early symptoms of trichinosis is eosinophilia. The invasion of muscle by larvae is associated with muscle pain, swelling of the eyelids and facial oedema, eosinophilia and pronounced fever. Respiratory and neurologic manifestations may appear. On invasion of the muscle layer the larvae cause inflammation and destruction of muscle fibres. The most frequently involved muscles are those of limbs, diaphragm, tongue, jaw, larynx, ribs and eyes. Larvae in other organs, including the heart and brain cause oedema and necrosis. The diagnosis is made by identifying larvae in muscle biopsies or by serological tests.

Antihelminthic drugs remove adult worms from the intestine. Promising results have been obtained in the treatment of trichinosis by thiobendazole (Botero, 1965). Corticosteroids have been found to be useful in alleviating clinical symptoms.

6. Strongyloidiasis

Strongyloidiasis is an infection caused by the nematode *Strongyloides stercoralis*, commonly called threadworm. It is found worldwide but is most common in tropical countries. *S. stercoralis* is a complex organism that has three life cycles which are as follows : (i) Parasitic pathogenic females live in the human small intestine and lay eggs that hatch in the mucosal epithelium, releasing rhabditiform larvae. These larvae become infective filariform larvae in the intestine or on the perianal skin and invade human host directly (the autoinfection cycle). (ii) The rhabditiform larvae pass in the faeces, become infective filariform larvae in the soil and later penetrate human skin(direct development cycle). (iii) The rhabditiform larvae passed in the faeces become free-living adults in the soil and eventually produce infective filariform larvae. These infective larvae penetrate the skin, enter blood vessels and pass to the lungs, where they invade alveoli. They ascend the trachea, descend the oesophagus and mature to become parthenogenic females in the small intestine.

Invading larvae cause dermatitis. Larvae migrating through lungs may provoke cough, haemoptysis and dyspnoea, Severe infection of the intestine causes vomiting, diarrhoea, and constipation. Female worms and rhabditiform larvae living in jejunum crypts cause mild eosinophilia and chronic inflammation. By contrast patients with hyperinfection may have ulceration, oedema, congestion fibrosis and severe inflammation of the intestine. The diagnosis is made by identifying larvae in the stool.

The most specific antihelminthic drug for treatment of strongyloidiasis is thiobendazole.

7. Filariasis or Elephantiasis

Filariasis is caused by *Wuchereria bancrofti* commonly called the filaria worm. The adult worms inhabit lymphatic vessels, most frequently those in the lymph nodes, testes and epididymis. The female worm discharges microfilariae that circulate in the blood. Humans are the only definitive host of these worms. Insect vectors which serve also as intermediate hosts, include 80 species of mosquitoes of the genera *Culex, Aedes, Anopheles* and *Mansonia*. Filariasis is endemic in large regions of Africa, coastal areas of Asia,Western Pacific islands and coastal areas and islands of the Caribbean basis. In India, it is distributed chiefly along the sea coast and along the banks of big rivers (except Indus); it has also been reported from Rajasthan, Punjab, Uttar Pradesh and Delhi. Following copulation the female worm delivers larvae called microfilariae. These, at night, get in the blood capillaies of the skin to be sucked up by the mosquito with blood meal. When the infected mosquito bites a human being, the microfilariae are not directly injected into the blood but are deposited on the skin near the site of puncture. Later, attracted by the warmth of the skin, the microfilariae either enter through the puncture wound or penetrate through the skin on their own. After penetrating the skin, microfilariae reach the lymphatic channels, settle down at some spot (inguinal, scrotal,or abdominal lymphatics) and begin to grow into adult forms.

Features of acute infection include fever, lymphangitis, lymphadenitis, orchitis, epididymitis, urticaria, eosinophilia and microfilaremia. Chronic infection is characterized by enlarged lymph nodes, lymphoedema, hydrocele and elephantiasis. Filariasis also causes tropical eosinophilia which is characterized by cough, wheezing, eosinophilia and diffuse pulmonary infiltrates. The infection of the filaria worms also causes enlargement of the limbs, scrotum and mammae. The swelling takes place due to blockage of the lymph circulation by the parasitic worms resulting into the inflammation of lymph vessels and lymph glands. The diagnosis is usually made by identifying the microfilariae in the blood.

There is no effective drug for the eradication of the filaria worm. The drug of choice is diethylcarbamazine (Hetrazan) which kills microfilariae and possibly adult worms.

8. Loiasis

Loiasis is an infection caused by the filarial nematode *Loa loa*, the African eyeworm or loa-worm. It inhabits the rain forests of Central and West Africa. Humans and baboons are definitive hosts and infection is transmitted by mango flies (*Chrysops* species). The adult *L.loa* migrates in the skin and occasionally crosses the eye beneath the conjunctiva, making the patient actually aware of his infection. Gravid worms discharge microfilariae that circulate in the blood stream during the day but reside in capillaries of the skin, lungs and other sense organs at night.

Most infections are symptomless but persist for years. Ocular symptoms include swelling of lids, congestion, itching and pain. Female worms, and rarely male worms may be extracted during their migration beneath the conjunctiva. Systemic reactions include fever, pain, itching, urticaria and eosinophilia. The diagnosis is made by identifying microfilariae in the blood films taken during the day, by removal of adult worm from conjunctiva, or by identifying microfilariae or adult worms in biopsy specimen.

Diethylcarbamazine (Hetrazan)is an effective remedy for loiasis, causing a quick disappearance of microfilariae from the peripheral blood and even death of adult worms in some cases.

9. Onchocerciasis

Onchocerciasis is the infection caused by the filarial nematode *Onchocerca volvulus*. It is one of the world's major endemic diseases, afflicting an estimated 40 million people, of whom about 2 million are blind. Man is the only known definitive host. Onchocerciasis is transmitted by several species of black flies of the genus *Simulium*, which breeds in fast flowing streams. There are endemic regions throughout the tropical Africa and in focal areas of Central and South America. The adult worms live singly and as coiled entangled masses in the subcutaneous tissues of man. The gravid female worms produce millions of microfilariae which migrate from the nodule into the skin, eyes, lymph nodes and deep organs causing the onchocercal lesions. The diagnosis is made by identifying the microfilariae in tissue sections of skin and the adult worms in the subcutaneous nodules.

The cardinal manifestations are subcutaneous nodules, dermatitis and eye disease.

Nodulectomy removes adult worms in palpable nodules. Suramin kills adult worms but has dangerous side effects. Oral diethylcarbamazine (Hetrazan) kills microfilariae. A new drug, ivermectin, kills microfilariae but with a lesser allergic reaction than diethylcarbamazine.

TREMATODIASIS

The diseases caused by trematode helminths constitute trematodiasis. Some of the most common and widespread diseases caused by trematodes are as follows :

1. Schistosomiasis

Schistosomiasis (Bilharziasis) is caused by the parasitic infection of flukes of three principal species namely *Schistosoma mansoni, S. japonicum* and *S.haematobium*. Schistosomiasis is increasing in prevalence, affecting about 10 per cent of the world's population and ranking second only to malaria as a cause of morbidity and mortality. *S. mansoni* is found in tropical Africa, parts of Southwest Asia, South America and Caribbean island ; *S. japonicum* in parts of Japan, China, Philippines, India and several countries of Southeast Asia, and *S. haematobium* in large regions of tropical Africa and parts of Southwest Asia. The blood flukes pair, migrate to the small venule, where the female fluke deposits immature eggs. *S. mansoni* and *S. japonicum* lay eggs in the intestine and *S. haematobium* in the urinary bladder. Embryos develop during the passage of eggs through the tissues and the larvae are mature when the eggs pass through the wall of intestine or the urinary bladder. The eggs hatch in freshwater and liberate miracidia and get into the snail. Here these develop into cercariae which leave the snail, swim freely in water and penetrate the skin of man. Through the blood circulation the cercaria reach the lungs to become adult flukes. The adult flukes then get into the blood stream.

Intestinal schistosomiasis caused by *S. mansoni* and *S. japonicum* is associated with granulomas in the lamina propria and submucosa. The flukes cause dysentery and liver diseases followed by fever, sweating, diarrhoea, weightloss and lack of appetite. Urinogenital schistosomiasis is caused by *S. haematobium*. In this disease, the eggs are enormous in the bladder, ureters and seminal vesicles, they may also reach the lungs, colon and appendix, Eggs in ureter can cause obstructive uropathy. There is high incidence of carcinoma of the bladder in patients with urogenital schistosomiasis. The diagnosis is made by finding characteristic schistosome eggs in the faeces and urine.

Chemotherapy is now highly effective. The drugs having specific actions on the schistosomes are nitrothiazole compound nitridazole, nilodin, hycanthone and antimony compounds are recommended.

2. Opisthorchiasis (= Clanorchiasis)

Opisthorchiasis or clanorchiasis is caused by the infection of *Opisthorchis* (=*Clanorchis*) *sinensis* (Chinese liver fluke). This disease is widespread in China, Japan, Korea, Vietnam and India. Human infection is acquired by eating raw or undercooked fish which harbour metacercariae. Adult worms are flat and transparent, live in the bile ducts, and pass eggs to the intestine and finally come out in the faeces. After ingestion by an appropriate snail, the egg hatches in a miracidium. Cercariae escape from the snail and seek out certain fish which they penetrate and in which they encyst. When human host eat the fish the cercariae emerge in the duodenum, enter the common bile duct and mature in the distal bile ducts to an adult fluke.

The symptoms vary from mild to severe depending upon the number of flukes. An onset with chills and fever indicate bacterial infection from biliary obstruction. Patients with opisthorchiasis may die from a variety of complications including biliary obstruction, bacterial cholangitis, pancreatitis and cholangiocarcinoma. With massive infection the liver may be up to three times of the normal size. The diagnosis is made by identifying the eggs of *O. sinensis* in the stools.

Antimony compounds, chloroquine and bithionol have been found to be effective remedy for opisthorchiasis.

3. Paragonimiasis

Paragonimiasis is caused by an infection of the oriental lung fluke *Paragonimus westermani*. The infection is widespread in Asia, Africa and South America. In India it is reported from Bengal, Assam and South India. Adult flukes live in the respiratory tract (lungs) of man. Human hosts acquire the infection by eating raw or undercooked infected crustaceans (crabs and crayfishes). *Paragonimus* eggs are coughed up from the lungs, swallowed and passed in the stool. Miracidia emerge in water and infect a snail intermediate host after which a sporocyst and two generations of rediae being finally transformed into cercariae. Infective cercariae emerge and penetrate the gills of a crustacean (freshwater crab and crayfish), the second intermediate host. The cercariae migrate to soft tissue and encyst. After a human host ingests the cyst, a metacercaria emerges and penetrates the wall of the stomach, migrates to the diaphragm, bores through the pleura and settles in the lungs, where it matures into an adult worm, which survives for 20 years.

The lung flukes cause chronic cough with recurring attacks of haemoptysis and eggs in sputa and stool. Night sweats, severe chest pain and pleural effusions are common. Although the adult flukes cause pulmonary disease, the larvae occasionally produce lesions in the brain, liver, gut, skeletal muscles, testes and lymph nodes. In generalized paragonimiasis there is a fever, generalized lymphadenitis and cutaneous ulceration. Diagnosis may be made by the presence of eggs in sputa or stools.

Emetine and chloroquine have both been used for paragonimiasis. Bithionol has been found to give encouraging results. Praziquantel, the drug of choice, is effective against pulmonary paragonimiasis.

4. Fasciolopsiasis

Fasciolopsiasis is caused by an infection of *Fasciolopsis buski*, the giant intestinal fluke. It has been reported from China, Thailand and Malaysia, Bengal, Assam and other oriental regions. The adult worm lives in the small intestine of man and pig. The normal host is pig which serves as the reservoir of infection for man. It is the largest trematode parasitising man and measures 2.2 to 7.5 cm in length and 8.0 to 20.0 mm in breadth. Intermediate host is a snail in which it passes through an elaborate developmental cycle, producing metacercariae that leave the snail to be located on freshwater plants particularly the water nuts. Man, the definitive host, acquires the infection of fasciolopsiasis by eating uncooked aquatic vegetables contaminated with the encysted cercaria of *F. buski*. The flukes attach to the duodenal and jejunal wall. The point of attachment may ulcerate and become infected, causing pain that resembles to that of a peptic ulcer. Acute symptoms may be caused by intestinal obstruction or by toxins released by large numbers of worms. This is followed by chronic diarrhoea, nausea, and vomiting. Diagnosis is made by identifying the eggs of *F. buski* in the stool.

Specific antihelminthic drug, tetrachloroethylene, is useful in the eradication of intestinal flukes. Praziquantel is used for the treatment of fasciolopsiasis.

5. Fascioliasis

Fascioliasis is caused by the infection of *Fasciola hepatica*, the sheep liver fluke. This disease is cosmopolitan. Human may acquire the infection wherever sheep are raised. The eggs, passed by sheep in their faeces, require two weeks in freshwater before a miracidium emerges. Miracidium infect a molluscan intermediate host (lymnaeid snail), after which infective cercariae emerge from the snail and encyst on submerged vegetation. Humans become infected by eating vegetation that is contaminated by the cysts. Metacercariae encysts in the duodenum, pass through the wall in the peritoneal cavity, penetrate the liver and migrate through hepatic parenchyma into the bile ducts. The larvae mature to adults and live in hepatic bile ducts. Later the adult flukes penetrate through the wall of the bile ducts and wander back into the liver parenchyma where they feed on liver cells and deposit eggs. The eggs lead to abscesses formation, followed by a granuloma. The flukes induce hyperplasia of the lining epithelium of the bile ducts, portal and periductal fibrosis, proliferation of the bile ductules and varying degrees of biliary obstruction. Eosinophilia, vomiting and acute epigastric pain are the main symptoms. Severe untreated infection may be fatal. The diagnosis is made by recovering eggs from stool or from biliary tract.

Early diagnosis and aggressive treatment with praziquantel prevents irreparable damage to liver. Bithionol is now the drug of choice for fascioliasis.

CESTODIASIS

Cestodiasis is caused by cestodes (tapeworms). Some of the most common and widespread diseases caused by cestodes are as follows :

1. Taeniasis

Taeniasis is caused by the species belonging to the genus *Taenia*, which include mainly *T. solium* (pork tapeworm) and *T. saginata* (beef tapeworm). Man acquires the infection by eating raw or undercooked pork or beef that contains the cysticerci. The cysticerci develop into adult tapeworms in the intestine of man.

The presence of tapeworms in the intestine causes gastro-intestinal disorders. Occasionally they may be responsible for vague abdominal discomfort, chronic indigestion, anaemia and intestinal disorders such as diarrhoea alternating with constipation. Anaemic conditions may also develop. Diagnosis may be made by stool examination for segments and eggs of the tapeworm.

The drug of choice is mepacrine (Átebrin). Other antihelminthic drugs are dichlorophen and yomesan, a chlorosalicylamide derivative (for *Taenia* segments).

2. Echinococcosis (Hydatid cyst)

Echinococcosis is an infection caused by larval cestode, hydatid worm of *Echinococcus granulosus*. The definitive hosts of this tapeworm are dog, wolf, fox and jackal. The eggs of this tapeworm are set free in the intestine of the definitive host. The eggs are released in the faeces and develop into onchospheres. Man acquires infection on eating food or drinking water contaminated with onchosphere-containing eggs. Larvae released from the eggs penetrate the wall of the gut, enter the blood stream and disseminate to deep organs such as liver, lungs and other organs where they grow to form hydatid cysts containing brood capsules and scolices.

Echinococcosis is most common in liver but also involves the lungs, less commonly brain, kidney, spleen, muscle and soft tissue. The larvae enlarge in situ to become cysts which grow silently for years, usually producing no symptoms until they reach a size of 10 cm or more. Because of their size hydatid cysts of the liver often produce hepatomegaly and may lead to obstructive jaundice. Rupture of a cyst may provoke an acute hypersensitivity reaction. Traumatic rupture of hydatid cysts of abdominal organs results in severe diffuse pain resembling that of peritonitis and ruptured cyst in the lung may cause pneumothorax and empyema. The diagnosis is made by identifying the hydatid cyst.

No effective drug has been established for echinococcosis, although mebendazole has shown mixed results. The treatment of choice is surgical removal of the hydatid cyst.

REVISION QUESTIONS

1. Write as essay on "helminths and human diseases".
2. Describe some of the human diseases caused by nematodes.
3. Give an account of some human diseases caused by trematodes.
4. Describe two human diseases caused by cestodes.

52

Phylum Entoprocta (Endoprocta)

The Entoprocta are solitary or colonial, stalked sessile pseudocoelomates with a distal circlet of ciliated tentacles, with flame bulb protonephridia, and with a looped digestive tract of which both mouth and anus open inside the tentacular circlet.

GENERAL CHARACTERS

The Entoprocta are sessile organisms and their body is divided into a rounded or oval mass known as calyx. Calyx contains all the viscera. The slender stalk, that bears the calyx, is attached basally to some object or to another animal. On the free edge of the calyx is borne a circlet of tentacles ciliated on their inner faces. The surface of the calyx bordered by the tentacles is regarded as ventral and, hence, the convex surface from which stalk extends is dorsal. Mouth and anus open on the free surface of the calyx inside the tentacles at opposite ends of sagittal axis and the digestive tract is strongly curved into a U-shape. The central part of the nervous system consists of a ganglionic mass located in the concavity of the digestive tract. There is a pair of protonephridia, each provided with a single flame bulb. The majority of the Entoprocta are dioecious but a few species are hermaphroditic. The two gonads lie in the pseudocoel to either side of the terminal part of the intestine and open by a common gonopore shortly anterior to the anus. The yolky egg develops in a brood chamber formed of the calyx surface around the gonopore into a trochophore type of larva that after being set free attaches and undergoes a process of metamorphosis into the adult condition. Extensive reproduction by asexual processes is characteristic of the phylum. The Entoprocta are solitary or colonial, free-living or epizoic. They are marine with the exception of the genus *Urnatella* found in freshwater and are widely distributed. There are about 60 known species.

STRUCTURE

The Entoprocta are small, almost microscopic animals below 5 mm in length. They either grow singly or in colonies and are found attached to objects or to other animals and having the general appearance of hydroid polyps. The main features of the entoproct are the crown of tentacles, the body mass or calyx, the stalk and the basal attachments of the stalk.

The calyx is somewhat flattened laterally, the tentacular crown is oval or elliptical in outline. The number of tentacles ranges from 8 to 30 in different species. The tentacles are usually of the same length throughout the crown but in some loxosomatids, there are four longer tentacles at the oral end of the crown. The tentacles are evenly spaced except that there is a wider gap at the oral and anal ends and this confers a bilateral symmetry upon the tentacular crown. The tentacles are ciliated on their inner surfaces and this ciliation is related to a ciliated vestibular groove that runs along the inner side of the tentacular bases. Outwardly the tentacular bases are connected by a tentacular membrane that forms the edge of the calyx.

The calyx or body mass is slightly compressed laterally and is oriented either at right angles to the stalk obliquely to it. Its free flattened or concave surface is ventral and the convex attached surface is dorsal. Mouth and anus open on the ventral surface at opposite ends of the sagittal axis, inside the tentacles. When the calyx is placed obliquely on the stalk, the downward

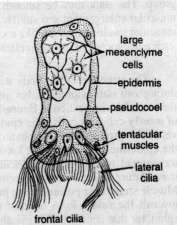

large mesenclyme cells

epidermis

pseudocoel

tentacular muscles

lateral cilia

frontal cilia

Fig. 52.1. *Pedicellina.* T.S. through tentacle.

tilt is towards the mouth and the anus may attain still greater elevation by being mounted on an **anal cone.** Posterior to the mouth in the sagittal axis is located the nephridiopore and posterior to that the gonopore. The concavity between the mouth and anus is called **vestibule** (also atrium) and the part of this that lies between gonopore and the anus serves as brood chamber for the developing eggs. The outer or dorsal surface of the calyx is usually smooth.

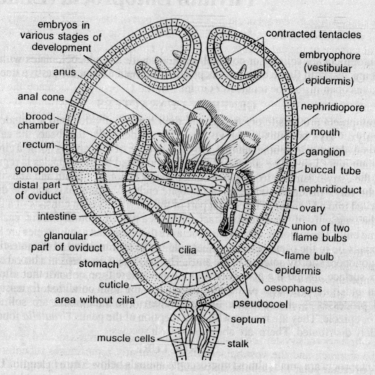

Fig. 52.2. *Pedicellina.* Median sagittal section of calyx.

The stalk is an outgrowth or elongation of the calyx, It offers much variation throughout the group. The stalk may be smooth or spiny. In several genera the stalk base shows a pronounced muscular enlargement and similar enlargements may occur along the stalk and near the calyx. These muscular swellings, acting like sockets, permit the odd flicking, bowing movements characteristic of such entoprocts and are also related to asexual reproduction.

BODY WALL

The structure of the body wall is typically pseudocoelomate type and is practically the same throughout stalk, stolons, calyx and tentacles. The body surface is clothed with a cuticle except on the tentacles and vestibule. Beneath the cuticle lies the cellular epidermis consisting of a single layer of mostly cuboidal cells. The epidermis is taller on the inner surface of the tentacles and along the vestibular groove in which locations it is also heavily ciliated. Numerous large gland cells occur in the epidermis of the calyx in loxosomatids. They are of two types : a granular opaque type and a transparent type filled with vacuoles. To the inner side of the epidermis occurs the body wall musculature in the form of longitudinal fibres. This musculature is sparsely present in the calyx. Muscle strands are present along the inner wall of the tentacles and enable these to be curved inward towards the vestibule. A band of muscle fibres causes within the tentacular membrane forming a sphincter that contracts this membrane over the tentacular crown when the latter is curled into the vestibule.

PSEUDOCOEL

The pseudocoel occupies the interior of tentacles, stalks, stolons and the space in the calyx between body wall and digestive tract. It is everywhere filled with a gelatinous material containing mesenchyme cells. The pseudocoel of tentacles is filled with large rounded cells, free amoeboid cells are also present. The pseudocoel of the calyx is separated from that of the stalk not only by the septum but also by plug of cells blocking the central hole in the septum. The pseudocoel of the stalk and stolons contains some wandering amoeboid cells but is mostly filled long, fusiform, more or less rigid cells known as tube cells.

DIGESTIVE SYSTEM

The U-shaped digestive tract occupies the greater part of the interior of the calyx. It is bilaterally symmetrical with respect to the sagittal plane of the calyx. The mouth is situated at the anterior end of the ventral surface of the calyx. It is a transversely elongated ciliated aperture located just within the tentacles. The mouth leads into a funnel-shaped buccal cavity that narrows into the tubular oesophagus. Oesophagus opens into the enlarged sacciform stomach, the most conspicuous organ of the entoproct, occupying most or part of the curve of the U. From the stomach the narrow intestine proceeds ventrally and is usually separated by a constriction from the terminal rectum. The rectum opens by the anus at the posterior end of vestibular surface, well inside the tentacles. The anus is often mounted on a projecting eminence, the anal cone. The digestive tract consists throughout of a one-layered ciliated epithelium of varying height. The digestive tract lacks a muscular coat but there is a limited amount of musculature associated with it. The fibres originating on the calyx wall and inserted on the lower lip act to expand the mouth opening. The oesophagus can be constricted by fibres that encircle it and extend from its posterior surface to the calyx wall and expanded by other fibres from this surface to the lateral calyx wall. Sphincter fibres occur at the junction of intestine and rectum and around the anus.

EXCRETORY SYSTEM

The Entoprocta are provided with a single pair of flame bulbs in each calyx, lying ventral to the stomach between the oesophagus and the subenteric ganglion. The intra-cellular canal from each bulb forms a channel through a few enlarged cells often provided with amoeboid extensions and apparently functioning as athrocytes. The two ducts then converge and unite before opening by a single nephridiopore situated in the median line shortly posterior to the mouth.

NERVOUS SYSTEM

The central nervous system consists of one main ganglionic mass located ventral to the stomach, between the stomach and the vestibular wall. It apparently represents a subenteric ganglion. The ganglion is of rectangular to bilobular shape and consists peripherally of ganglion cells, centrally of fibres. From the ventral surface of the ganglion three pairs of nerves proceed to supply the crown of tentacles. Their branches each terminate in a large ganglion cell or group of cells situated in the tentacular membrane between the tentacle bases. From each such ganglion nerves are given off into adjacent tentacle. From the dorsal surface of the subenteric ganglion spring a pair of nerves to the calyx wall, a pair to the stalk and a small pair to the adjacent gonads.

SENSE ORGANS

Sensory nerve cells of tactile type, consisting of one or more bristles proceeding from a nerve cell situated beneath the epidermis and piercing the latter are abundant on the outer surface of the tentacles and along the calyx margin. In loxosomatids either throughout life or in larval stages only, there occurs on the sides of the calyx near its oral end a pair of sense organs bearing a remarkable resemblance to the antennae of rotifers. Each consists of a tuft of bristles lined by a ganglion, from which a nerve proceeds to a ganglionic mass connected in turn with the subenteric ganglion.

REPRODUCTIVE SYSTEM

Some entoprocts are hermaphroditic and others are dioecious. But it is suspected that at least some apparently dioecious species may be actually protandric hermaphrodites. The gonads are a single pair of sacciform bodies located ventral to the liver region of stomach, either anterior or posterior to the ganglion. In hermaphroditic species, there is a pair of testes posterior to the pair of ovaries. From each gonad a short duct proceeds medially and unites with its fellow to open on the ventral surface of the calyx by a common gonopore. In hermaphrodites the sperm duct unites with the oviduct of that side prior to the formation of the common duct. The gonoducts are beset with eosinophilous unicellular glands or have an area of glandular epithelium. In males the common sperm duct may present an enlargement, the seminal vesicle, for the storage of ripe sperms. The sperms are flagellate type. The common gonopore is medially located behind the nephridiopore at the base of a pronounced elevation so that calyx surface between this elevation and the anal cone forms a considerable depression, the genital recess, which in females and hermaphrodites, acts as a brood chamber for the developing eggs.

ASEXUAL REPRODUCTION

All entoprocts proliferate extensively by asexual budding. In the Loxosomatidae buds arise on the sides of the calyx near its oral end in a pair of bilaterally symmetrical areas. In the Pedicellinidae buds are produced only by the stolons and stalks, never by the calyces and as the buds remain attached colony formation results. The bud begins as an epidermal proliferation which cuts off into the interior as an epithelial vesicle. This soon constricts into two vesicles of which the outer one becomes the free surface of the calyx and the tentacular crown and proliferates the ganglion from its inner wall and the inner vesicle develops into the digestive tract. The muscles, gonads and other mesodermal structures arise from the parental mesenchyme included in the bud. A constriction then separates the outgrowth into calyx and stalk. In the asexual reproduction the entire organism originates from the ectoderm and mesoderm without any participation of the endoderm.

REGENERATION

The entoprocts possess good powers of regeneration. Under adverse conditions colonies shed their calyces but the stalks and stolons remain alive for considerable periods and regenerate new calyces upon return of favourable conditions.

SEXUAL REPRODUCTION AND DEVELOPMENT

The small but rather yolky eggs are fertilized in the ovaries or gonoduct. During their passage through the gonoduct the eggs are covered with the secretion of the eosinophilous glands. This secretion forms a loose membrane over the eggs and embryos and is drawn out into a stalk of attachment. These stalks adhere to the embroyophore or brood chamber which is the name given to the anal cone. During brooding of the embryos, the wall of the brood chamber becomes thick and filled with food inclusions that are later ingested by the embryos. As new eggs issue from the gonopore, the already attached embryos are pushed forward so that there is a regular succession of stages in the brood chamber. Development proceeds in the brood chamber to the production of free-swimming larva.

AFFINITIES

According to Hyman (1951) the union of the Entoprocta and the Ectoprocta cannot be maintained although supported by Marcus (1939). The insuperable difficulty in the way of this union is the pseudocoelomate nature of the body cavity of the Entoprocta, whereas the Ectoprocta are typical coelomate animals. The Entoprocta are, thus, of a much lower grade of structure than are the Ectoprocta and cannot be united with them in the same phylum. The Entoprocta was linked with Ectoprocta because of some common features, *viz.*, a crown of ciliated tentacles and a looped digestive tract. However, the occurrence of tentacular structures on the distal end is common in sessile animals as a food catching device. As regards other anatomical features the two groups are quite dissimilar. The larval similarities of the two groups seem the best ground for postulating relationship. But in their further development the two larvae differ altogether. Thus, it is presumed that the similarities between the larvae are because of the pelagic habits of both.

The Entoprocta was also related with the annelid-molluscan types because of the similarity of the trochophore larva but it has been observed that the entoproct larva bear no great resemblance to a trochophore either superficially or as to structural details. The formation of coelom also takes place in a different manner in both the groups. The body cavity of Entoprocta is of a pseudocoelomate type.

Among the pseudocoelomate groups the Rotifera come close to the Entoprocta. The loxosomatid resembles the collothecacean rotifer in the following : (1) Both have a trumpet-shaped body with the free surface bordered by ciliated or bristle bearing projections that are simple extensions of the body wall. (2) The stalk in both is a post-embryonic outgrowth provided with pedal glands at least temporarily. (3) In both the mouth lies within the crown of tentaculate projections and in both the digestive tract makes a decided curve. In the rotifers this curvature of the digestive tract begins among the sessile forms and gets more and more pronounced with greater assumption of the sessile life. Although even in the most evolved of the collothecacean rotifers the anus still remains outside the coronal projections, it is clearly getting nearer and nearer to the mouth. However, no great importance can be placed on this point because a looped digestive tract is a common feature of sessile animals.

Besides this, the parts of the digestive tract are similar in both the groups and it may be noted that the mastax, of which no trace occurs in the Entoprocta, is in the process of degeneration among the collothecacean rotifers. (4) Both groups have protonephridia of flame-bulb type. (5) A pair of eyes is present in both loxosomatid and collothecacean young ones. (6) The ciliary rim of the ventral surface of the entoproct larva is probably a remnant of an originally completely ciliated ventral surface, as is the rotifer corona. (7) The pair of preoral organ of the entoproct larva and the loxosomatid adult is homologous with the lateral antennae of rotifers. In the loxosomatid adults they are situated towards the free end of the calyx. In the collothecacean rotifers too they have migrated to an anterior position. Therefore, it can be easily concluded that the Entoprocta are pseudocoelomate animals with nearest affinities with the rotifers.

REVISION QUESTIONS

1. Describe the internal anatomy of *Pedicellina*.
2. Discuss the affinities of Entoprocta.

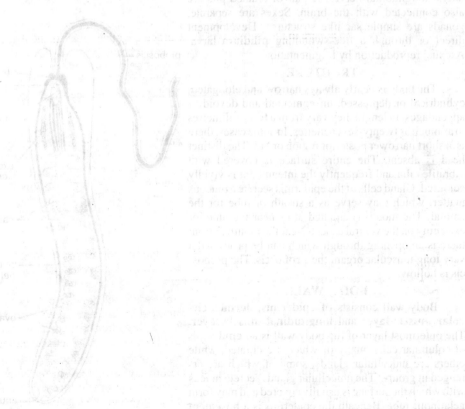

53
Phylum Nemertinea

Nemertines are elongated, vermiform, flattened and acoelomate Bilateria possessing anus,circulatory system, flame bulbs, simple ductless gonads and an eversible proboscis lodged in a tubular sheath, the rhynchocoel situated dorsal to the digestive tract.

GENERAL CHARACTERS

The nemertines are non-parasitic unsegmented worms, most of which are marine, only a few forms living on land or in freshwater. Body slender, worm-like, soft, highly contractile, unsegmented, bilaterally symmetrical, triploblastic and acoelomate. The ectoderm is ciliated. Eversible proboscis lying in a sheath on the dorsal side of the gut. The gut is straight, complete with lateral diverticula and terminates in posterior anus. True coelom and respiratory organs are absent, body spaces are filled with gelatinous mesenchyme. Circulatory system is closed. Paired, excretory tubules provided with flame cells. Nervous system comprises a well differentiated brain from which arises a pair of

lateral longitudinal nerves. A pair of ciliated pits are also connected with the brain. Sexes are separate, gonads are simple sac-like structures. Development direct or through a free-swimming pilidium larva. Asexual reproduction by fragmentation.

STRUCTURE

The body is nearly always narrow and elongated, cylindrical or depressed, unsegmented and devoid of appendages. In length they vary from a few millimetres to as much as twenty-seven metres. In some cases, there is a short narrower posterior region or tail. The distinct head is absent. The entire surface is covered with vibratile cilia and frequently the integument is vividly coloured. Gland cells of the epidermis secrete a mucous matter, which may serve as a sheath or tube for the animal. The mouth is situated at or near the anterior extremity on the ventral aspect. Near the mouth in front there is an opening through which can be protruded a very long muscular organ, the proboscis. The proboscis is hollow.

BODY WALL

Body wall consists of epidermis, dermis, circular muscle layer and longitudinal muscle layer. The outermost layer of the body wall is an epidermis of columnar cells, many of which are ciliated, while others are unicellular glands, some of which are arranged in groups. The unicellular glands secrete mucus with which the surface is usually covered and may form gelatinous tube. Beneath the epidermis is a basement membrane, very thin in most cases. Then follows the dermis forming a connective tissue layer. Beneath

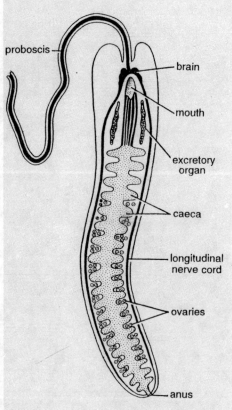

Fig. 53.1. Diagram of a generalized nemertine.

432

dermis is a thick muscular layer. In some nemertines there are only two layers of muscle fibres, an outer circular and an inner longitudinal, in the rest a third (longitudinal) layer is superadded. The gland cells are scattered irregularly between the narrower portions of the ciliated columnar epidermal cells. Besides the unicellular glands many nemertines have cluster of gland cells opening at the surface by a common duct, these are known as the packet glands. The packet glands may be included within epidermis as in paleonemertines or they may sink into the subepidermal tissue as in the heteronemertines.

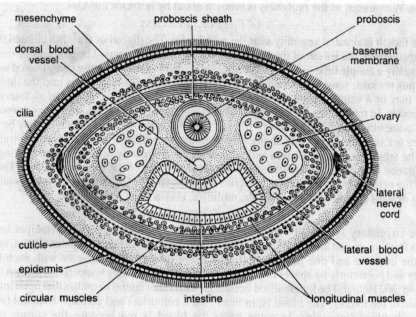

Fig. 53.2. Nemertine. Diagrammatic transverse section.

BODY CAVITY

The coelom is absent, the interspaces between the organs being filled with parenchyma.

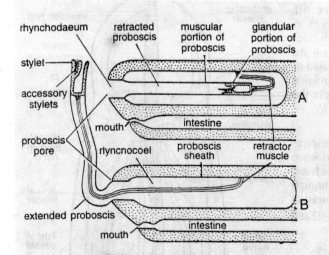

Fig. 53.3. Diagrammatic representation of the anterior end of a nemertine. A—Proboscis retracted ; B—Proboscis extended.

PROBOSCIS

The proboscis is the most characteristic feature of nemertines. It is an elongated, coiled, hollow and muscular organ opening in front and closed behind. It lies within the proboscis sheath and retractile in nature. When retracted it lies within the body in a fluid-filled cavity called rhynchocoel which is completely shut off from the exterior. The muscular walls of the rhynchocoel form the proboscis sheath. The epithelial cells of the proboscis, in most cases, secrete rods identical with the rhabdites of Turbellaria. The blind end of proboscis is attached to the posterior end of the sheath by a retractor muscle which checks the eversion of the proboscis beyond a certain point, and by means of which also it is retracted. The part of the proboscis in front of the brain is called rhynchodaeum which opens to the exterior through the proboscis pore. The proboscis may be armed or unarmed, if armed with stylets at the tip. The lining epithelium of the proboscis closely resembles the surface epidermis from which it is derived. The muscle layer of proboscis and those of the proboscis sheath repeat the body wall musculature. The proboscis is shot out with explosive force through muscular contraction exerting pressure in the fluid of the rhynchocoel. As this is done the proboscis turns inside out (everts) and protrudes. Withdrawal of the proboscis is brought about by retractor muscles.

DIGESTIVE SYSTEM

The mouth is situated ventrally near the anterior tip. The digestive tract is a ciliated tube which extends throughout the length of the body from the mouth to the anus. The first part of the digestive tract is usually a simple tube–oesophagus (stomodaeum) but may be more complicated and divided into various regions, sometimes with paired diverticula. Posteriorly it opens into the intestine. The intestine may be a simple unconstricted tube or may be only slightly constricted at intervals by the paired gonads. In most cases the constrictions corresponding to the gonads are very deep so that the intestine comes to be provided with two rows of lateral diverticula or caeca which may be branched. The caeca are separated from one another by incomplete transverse septa of dorsoventral muscular fibres. The arrangement of the caeca and septa with the alternately arranged gonads bringing about an appearance of imperfect metamerism as observed in some of the Platyhelminthes. The intestine opens to the exterior by an anus at the posterior end of the body. The nemertines feed usually at night on living or dead animals mainly annelids, molluscs, crustaceans and fishes, etc.

CIRCULATORY SYSTEM

The circulatory system of nemertines is closed type. There are three principal longitudinal trunks : a median dorsal and two lateral. The longitudinal trunks lie in the parenchyma, one on each side of the intestine and one just above it. The lateral vessels communicate with each other both anteriorly and posteriorly by spaces lined by only delicate membranes respectively known as cephalic lacuna and anal lacuna. The longitudinal vessels give off other lateral branches that open into a system of lacunae in the tissues. The blood is, in most cases, colourless and contains rounded or elliptical, usually colourless corpuscles. In some cases the blood is red because the corpuscles contain haemoglobin. Circulation in nemertines is primitive in several respects. There is no pumping organ or heart. The circulation is brought about by general movement of the body.

EXCRETORY SYSTEM

The excretory system consists of a pair of longitudinal vessels which give off branches. Each longitudinal vessel opens to the exterior by a nephridiopore on each side. The fine terminal branches of the system are provided with ciliary flames each situated in the midst of a group of cells, not in the interior of a single flame-cell as in most cases in the flatworms.

RESPIRATORY SYSTEM

There are no special organs of respiration in any of the group. But there is evidence that this function is carried out, in part at least, by taking in and giving out of water through the mouth by the oesophagus. Respiration also takes place by the diffusion of oxygen through the general body surface.

NERVOUS SYSTEM

The nervous system consists of brain. The brain is composed of two pairs of ganglia, dorsal and ventral. The ganglia of each pair being connected together by commissures,

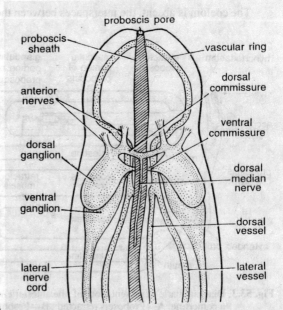

Fig. 53.4. Diagram of the anterior end of a nemertine to show the nervous system in dorsal view.

the dorsal situated above and the ventral below. From the brain pass backwards a pair of thick longitudinal nerve cords which run throughout the length of the body. Usually these are lateral in position, sometimes approximated dorsally and sometimes ventrally. The lateral nerve cords generally meet posteriorly in a commissure usually situated above, but in one genus below, the anus. A third median dorsal nerve of smaller size than the lateral nerve cords extends backwards from the dorsal commissure of the brain. The position of brain and lateral nerve cords, or the system of commissures and nerve branches varies in different groups.

SENSE ORGANS

The sense organs of nemertine consist of sensory nerve cells, sensory pits and eyes. The special organs of the sense are mostly restricted to the anterior part of the body but the sensory nerve cells are found scattered in the epidermis of anterior as well as posterior ends. The sensory nerve cells are slender-like in appearance, each bearing a hair-like process on the outer side. They are tactile in function. Sensory pits are found all over the body. Eyes are present in majority of nemertines and in the more highly organised species occur in considerable numbers. Sometimes they are of extremely simple structure, in other cases they are more highly developed, having a spherical refractive body with a cellular vitreous body and a retina consisting of layer of rods enclosed in a sheath of dark pigment. Each rod has a separate nerve branch connected with it. Statocysts containing statoliths have been found in only a few of the nemertines.

REPRODUCTIVE SYSTEM

Most nemertines are dioecious but some may be hermaphroditic. The gonads are simple, tubular, sac-like structures, situated in the intervals between the intestinal caeca. The ovary or testis is a sac lined by cells which give rise to ova or spermatozoa ; when these are mature each sac opens by means of a narrow duct leading to the dorsal, rarely to the ventral surface, or which it opens by a pore.

DEVELOPMENT

In nemertines the development is of two types : (i) direct and (ii) indirect. The characteristic larval form is the pilidium. This is a helmet-shaped body with side lobes like ear-lappets, and a bunch of cilia representing a spike. In the metamorphosis a number of ectodermal invaginations growing inwards around the intestine, fuse together and form the integument and body wall of the future worm, which subsequently frees itself from its investment and develops into the adult form. In the others there is a ciliated creeping larva called the larva of Desor in the interior of which the larval form is developed much as in the case of the pilidium.

AFFINITIES

The position of nemertines is very difficult to settle. They show affinities with lower chordates, vertebrates and the Platyhelminthes.

Affinities with lower Chordates. Nemertines possess several characters in common with a typical lower chordate, such as *Balanoglossus*. These are : (1) Elongated vermiform body. (2) No external metamerism. (3) Skin smooth, containing unicellular glands. (4) Ectodermal nerve plexus. (5) Terminal anus. (6) Simple metamerically situated gonads. (7) Retractile proboscis of nemertines is equivalent to the non-retractile proboscis of *Balanoglossus*.

Affinities with Vertebrates. Nemertines are considered to be the ancestral forms of vertebrates on account of the following similarities : (1) Dorsal nerve resembles the spinal cord of vertebrates. (2) Lateral nerves resemble the nerves of lateral lines of fishes. (3) Cerebral ganglion resembles the brain of vertebrates. (4) Proboscis sheath suggests the notochord of vertebrates.

Affinities with Platyhelminthes. Nemertines are often united with the Platyhelminthes. They are supposed to be related to the Turbellaria and were previously included in that class. The following similarities are found in both the groups : (1) The shape of the body is flat, ribbon-like or tape-like without external segmentation. (2) Body is completely covered with a ciliated epithelium containing gland cells. (3) Just below the integument are thick, highly contractile muscles. (4) The space between the body wall and the gut is filled with mesenchyme. The coelom is absent. (5) Excretory system comprises flame cells. (6) Nervous system is similar to that of flatworms.

However, nemertines differ from the flatworms in several features. Of these the most noticeable are : (1) Defined body wall. (2) Complete digestive tract with a second opening, the anus. (3) Vascular system of higher organization. (4) Higher organization of organs and tissues in general. (5) Massive brain forming a ring around the digestive tract. (6) Presence of proboscis independent of the gut.

On the basis of above similarities and dissimilarities it is advisable to place them in a separate phylum.

REVISION QUESTIONS

1. Describe the general characters and affinities of Nemertinea.
2. Give an account of the general anatomy of a nemertine.

The Acanthocephala are endoparasitic, pseudocoelomate, vermiform Bilateria without a digestive tract and with the anterior end formed of an invaginable proboscis armed with hooks.

GENERAL CHARACTERS

The Acanthocephala are endoparasitic worms of slender cylindroid or slightly flattened form and hollow construction. They live as adults in the intestine of vertebrates and as larvae in arthropods. The diagnostic feature of the phylum is the organ of attachment consisting of an invaginable proboscis that forms the anterior end. This proboscis is armed with rows of recurved hooks. The body wall consists of cuticle, syncytial epidermis permeated with spaces and subepidermal musculature. In connection with the proboscis apparatus the epidermis forms two elongated bodies termed lemnisci that hang down into the trunk. Mouth, anus and digestive tube are completely wanting. There is no circulatory system. Excretory organs when present are of the nature of protonephridia and open into the terminal part of the reproductive system. The nervous system consists of a ganglion near the proboscis and two lateral cords extend posteriorly from the ganglion along with numerous minor nerves. The sexes are separate, the females are generally larger than the males, the males are provided with a copulatory apparatus and the terminal part of the female apparatus is also somewhat complicated. The eggs develop within the maternal body into a larva that requires an intermediate invertebrate host for its further development. There are over 500 known species. *Echinorhynchus* is the chief genus of Acanthocephala and it is described here in detail.

HABIT AND HABITAT

The genus *Echinorhynchus* is a common parasite in the intestine of mammals, birds, reptiles, amphibians and fishes. The largest species *E. (Gigantorhynchus) gigas* is found in the pig and has once been recorded in the human being. It may attain the length of 50 to 65 cm.

EXTERNAL CHARACTERS

The body is cylindrical and ends in front in a protrusible portion, the proboscis, which is cylindrical and is covered with many rows of recurved chitinous hooks. In many species the body is ringed or constricted at regular intervals and so presents a more or less segmented appearance. Such segmentation reaches the highest degree in certain

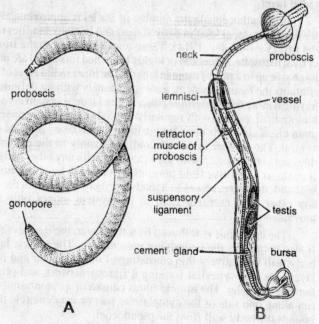

Fig. 54.1. *Echinorhynchus gigas*, A—Male; B—Female.

species of *Moniliformis* and *Mediorhynchus*. In all these forms it is difficult to distinguish dorsal from ventral surface from external appearance when the body is curved, the concave surface is ventral and when the proboscis is covered with unequal size of hooks, the larger hooks are ventrally located, but in most cases dorsoventrality can be determined with the help of internal structure.

The body is divisible into the short slender forebody or presoma and the much longer stouter trunk. The presoma is composed externally of the proboscis that bears the hooks and a neck region without hooks. Internally the proboscis includes the receptacle or sheath into which it invaginates or withdraws the lemnisci and the main ganglion of the nervous system. The neck is generally short but sometimes much elongated. The trunk may be cylindroid, flattened, curved or coiled with a smooth, wrinkled or segmented surface. In several genera the trunk is more or less noticeably differentiated into a broader foretrunk and a slender hindtrunk in varying proportions in different species. There is no trace of mouth, anus or excretory pore. The gonopore occurs at or near the posterior extremity.

BODY WALL

The body wall is covered with stout cuticle of homogeneous structure. Beneath cuticle lies the remarkable epidermis or hypodermis. The epidermis is a thick layer of fibrous syncytial construction comprising three fibrous strata : an outer layer, only slightly thicker than the cuticle, of parallel radial fibres, a middle somewhat thicker feltwork of layers of fibres running in different directions and an inner layer of radial fibres. The inner layer is the thickest of the three and by many authors is regarded as the epidermis proper, while the outer radial and the felt layers are assigned to the cuticle. The fibres of the epidermis do not appear to be the nature of connective tissue but rather seem to be protoplasmic strands. There are no indications of cell walls and the entire epidermis forms a syncytium. The nuclei and the lacunar systems are situated in the inner radial layer.

In Acanthocephala the number of nuclei is approximately constant for each species, at least in early stages, and in many families throughout the life (Van Cleave, 1914). These nuclei range in shape from globose or oval to rosette, amoeboid or highly branched forms and are of relatively large size up to 2 mm or more in length. The inner radial layer of epidermis contains the lacunar system, a set of channels without definite walls but having a more or less definite pattern. The lacunar system consists of two longitudinal vessels with regularly spaced transverse connections. The main channels in this case are medially located, *i.e.*, they are dorsal and ventral. The lacunar system is confined mainly to the epidermis and it does not communicate with the exterior or with any other body structure. It contains a nutritive fluid presumably obtained by absorption from the host and, therefore, serves as a food-distributing system in the absence of any other. The nutritive fluid in the system moves only with body movements.

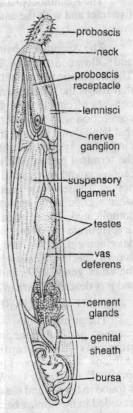

Fig. 54.2. *Echinorhynchus.* Dissection of male.

The epidermis is followed by a thin layer, the dermis (also called basement or binding layer). It also permeates the underlying musculature. The muscle layer forming the innermost coat of the body wall is relatively thin consisting of outer circular and inner longitudinal fibres. These muscle layers are also syncytial forming a fibrous network and probably contain a more or less definite number of nuclei. The muscle fibres consist of a cytoplasmic and a fibrillar portion ; the fibres may run along one side of the cytoplasmic part or may encircle the latter. No definite lining membrane bounds the body wall from the pseudocoel.

PROBOSCIS APPARATUS

The everted proboscis varies from a short cylindrical to globose shape to a long cylinder. It is armed with recurved hooks that are similar in shape but varied in size and arrangement (Van Cleave,1941). They are most commonly arranged in alternating radial rows but may be concentric or irregular ; they may be of even size over the proboscis. The hooks may be largest at the summit and decrease gradually toward the base or often are largest in the middle region decreasing towards the end. The number of rows, the number per row, and the size pattern of the hooks are fairly constant for each species, and in fact the proboscis armature constitutes one of the most important taxonomic characters of the phylum. The larger hooks have roots sunk into the proboscis wall and some authors reserve the term hooks for these, calling the smaller, rootless members of the armature spines. The hooks and spines are of unknown chemical nature but apparently consist of the same material as the dermis from which they seem to originate. They are covered with cuticle.

The proboscis is invaginable and withdrawable into a muscular sac, the proboscis receptacle, that is fastened in a circle to the inner surface of the proboscis wall and hangs into the pseudocoel. It is composed in some groups of a single muscle layer, in others of two layers. Proboscis and receptacle are operated by special muscle bands. From the proboscis summit there extends posteriorly along the proboscis interior a muscle or group of muscles termed the retractor, invaginator or invertor muscle. This inserts on the receptacle wall and also passes through this wall to continue as the dorsal and ventral receptacle retractors that terminate on the trunk wall. In the more complicated types there are also a number of dorsal, ventral and lateral receptacle protrusors that originate in a circle from the neck wall and insert on the rear part of the receptacle. Finally generally distributed in the Acanthocephala there are the retractors of the neck that originate near the posterior boundary of the neck and insert on the trunk. The retractors of the neck encircle all the other proboscis muscles and embrace the lemnisci as compressors of lemnisci.

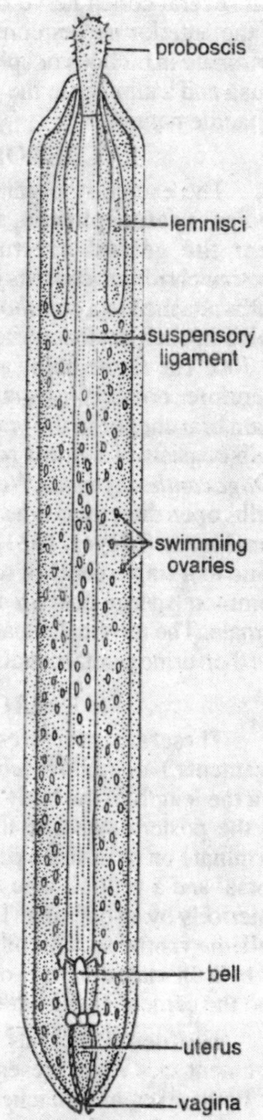

From the posterior part of the neck region there extend posteriorly into the trunk pseudocoel a pair of projections of the inner radial layer of the epidermis known as lemnisci. The lemnisci are generally long slender bodies, they are supplied by vessels of the lacunar system and contain either a limited and definite number of fragmented nuclei. They are externally covered by the dermis and are well supplied with the lacunar system. At certain levels the lemnisci are enclosed in the neck retractors. The function of the lemnisci is that they act as reservoirs for the fluid of the lacunar system of the presoma when the proboscis is invaginated.

NERVOUS SYSTEM

The nervous system consists of the cerebral ganglion, the branches from this, and in the male a pair of genital ganglia with branches. The cerebral ganglion, often called simply the ganglion, is a large cellular mass enclosed in the proboscis receptacle in contact with its ventral walls. It consists of a central fibrous mass embraced by ganglion cells, 86 in *Macracanthorhynchus*, 80 in *Hamanniella* and 73 in *Bolbosoma*. In the first two genera, the ganglion gives off two single and three pairs of nerves, in *Bolbosoma* one single and five pairs of nerves. The former comprise : an anterior median and a ventral anterior nerve to the musculature and sensory papillae of the proboscis, a pair of lateral anterior nerves to the lateral protrusors, a pair or lateral medial nerves to the receptacle wall, and the pair of main lateral posterior nerves that proceed to the posterior end of the animal. The lateral posterior nerves pierce the receptacle wall, proceed laterally to the body wall of the trunk into which they give branches, and then run posteriorly in the lateral body wall in the longitudinal muscle layer to the posterior end, giving off genital branches in females. In males, however, branches from these nerves enter a pair of genital ganglia situated in the penis base and connected with each other by a ring commissure. From the genital ganglia branches proceed anteriorly along the male genital tract and posteriorly into the bursa where some terminate in bulbous sense organs.

SENSE ORGANS

Organs of special sense are not developed in correlation to entoparasitic life. The known sense organs comprise three in the proboscis and several in the male bursa and penis. In the proboscis there

Fig. 54.3. *Echinorhynchus* Dissection of female.

is a sensory organ in the centre of the tip and in some genera one on each side in the neck. The terminal sense organ consists of a small pit beneath which there is a fusiform nerve ending of a nerve fibre that makes a coil just below its termination. The pair of lateral proboscis sense organ is similar except that several coiled nerve fibres are involved. These proboscis sense organs are supplied by certain of the anterior nerves coming from the cerebral ganglion. In males fibres from the genital ganglia terminate in bulbous or spherical sense organs of which there are seven or eight around the rim of the bursa and a number in the penis. It is usually supposed that all the acanthocephalan sense organs are of tactile nature.

EXCRETORY ORGANS

The excretory organs consist of a pair of small bodies, protonephridia, situated at the posterior end near the genital aperture. In most genera each protonephridium consists of a branching mass of flame bulbs attached to a common stem. The number of flame bulbs in each protonephridium ranges from about 250 to 700. The flame bulbs are devoid of nuclei and are, therefore, not cells ; usually three nuclei occur in the main branches or in the wall of the chamber. The flame bulb consists of a linear row of cilia. In certain genera (*Oligacanthorhynchus, Nephridiorhynchus*), the flame bulbs open directly into a sac from which the nephridial canal leads (Meyer, 1931). In any case the two canals unite to a single canal or to a bladder and this joins the common sperm duct in the male and uterus in the female. The terminal canals of the reproductive system are then urinogenital canals in the Archiacanthocephala.

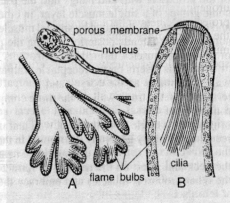

Fig. 54.4. *Echinorhynchus.* A—L.S. through terminal twigs of a protonephridium; B— L.S. of a flame cell.

LIGAMENT SACS AND LIGAMENT STRAND

These are structures peculiar to the Acanthocephala. The ligament sacs (formerly called ligaments) are hollow tubes of connective tissue with or without accompanying muscle fibres that run the length of the body interior and enclose the reproductive organs. Anteriorly they are attached to the posterior end of the proboscis receptacle or the adjacent body wall and posteriorly they terminate on or in some part of the reproductive system. In the female there are two ligament sacs, a dorsal and a ventral, whose medial walls make contact in the frontal plane and which communicate anteriorly by an opening. The dorsal ligament sac attaches posteriorly to the anterior rim of the uterine bell, the ventral sac extends to the posterior end of the body, opening en route into the ventral aperture of bell. In males there is only one sac, the ventral sac is wanting. The dorsal sac encloses the testes and the cement glands and posteriorly becomes continuous with the genital sheath.

Haffner (1942) has reported the ligament strand, a nucleated strand found between the two ligament sacs when present or situated along the ventral face of the single ligament sac. The gonads in both sexes are attached to this strand. According to Haffner's analysis, the ligament strand represents the endoderm midgut. The ligament sacs are regarded by Hyman as separated parts of the pseudocoel.

PSEUDOCOEL

The pseudocoel is a cavity, not provided with any lining membrane, between the body wall and the ligaments. It is small in forms with two ligament sacs but attains considerable size in those with one sac only. It also extends into the presoma between the muscle bands. As the cavity lacks a lining membrane, it is obviously not a coelom. As the ligament strand apparently represents the endoderm, the body cavity is a space between the endoderm and the body wall and, hence, classified as a pseudocoel. The pseudocoel is filled with a clear fluid.

REPRODUCTIVE SYSTEM

The greater part of the body is occupied by the reproductive organs. The sexes are separate and the female is larger than the male. In both the sexes the gonads and their ducts are connected with a ligament strand which extends backwards from the end of the proboscis sheath. In males there are two oval, rounded or elongated testes enclosed in the ligament sac and attached to the ligament strand.

From each testis a sperm duct proceeds posteriorly inside the ligament sac. Small enlargements representing spermiducal vesicles may occur along the sperm ducts. A cluster of unicellular gland cells known as cement glands (usually six or eight in number and of variable shape–rounded, pyriform, clavate or tubular) open into the sperm duct shortly behind the more posterior testis. The ducts of these cement glands, either separately or after union into one or two main ducts, enter the common sperm duct. The sperm ducts, the cement ducts and the protonephridial canals (when present) are all enclosed in a muscular tube, the genital sheath. The genital sheath terminates on the muscle cap of bursa. Inside the genital sheath, the two sperm ducts unite to a common sperm duct which may present a saccular enlargement, the seminal vesicle, the cement duct enter the common sperm duct and the common protonephridial canal, when present, also unites with common sperm duct. The urogenital canal so formed penetrates the centre of the penis, a short conical protrusion. The penis projects into hemispherical or elongated cavity the bursa, that is eversible to the exterior and grasps the rear end of the female in copulation. The bursa is composed of interned body wall of which the muscular layer is greatly thickened in the proximal part of the bursa, forming the muscular cap. The sperms are long filaments without definite heads.

The female reproductive system departs from the usual in many ways. The original single or double ovary breaks up into fragments termed ovarian walls that float free in the dorsal ligament sac but as the latter sac soon ruptures the balls occupy the pseudocoel. The ligament sacs lead to the first part of the female canal termed the uterine bell. The uterine bell is a muscular, funnel-shaped or tubular organ that by peristaltic contractions engulfs the developing eggs and passes them onward. The bell has a single(or a pair of) posterior ventral openings through which the immature eggs, which are spherical, pass back into the body cavity. At its posterior end the bell narrows to a uterine tube composed of several large cells with conspicuous nuclei and bearing two bell pouches that extend anteriorly. The uterine tube enters the uterus a muscular tube of some length and this is followed by the short non-muscular vagina opening to the exterior. The nephridia lie along side the uterine bell, the two protonephridial ducts run in the dorsal wall of the bell and the common canal formed by their union opens into the beginning of the uterine tube. The ovarian balls consist of central syncytium from which ovogonia separate, passing to the periphery for further development.

COPULATION AND DEVELOPMENT

In copulation the everted male bursa grasps the posterior end of the female and the penis enters the vagina and discharges sperms into the uterus. This is followed by the discharge of the cement secretion which sets as a plug in the gonopore and as a cap over the whole posterior tip, preventing escape of the sperms. The mature ova are elliptical and surrounded by a membrane. Fertilization takes place in the body cavity and after fertilization a membrane arises inside the original egg membrane. In the meantime the eggs have escaped from the ovarian balls and continue development in the pseudocoel or inside the dorsal ligament sac until a larval stage provided with a rostellum arrived with hooks is reached. Meanwhile, a third membrane, usually termed shell, has formed between the two membranes already present around the embryo. These ovic larvae are engulfed by the uterine bell and passed towards the uterine tube, those not sufficiently mature may be returned through the ventral bell aperture into pseudocoel or ventral ligament sac. The ripe ones proceed into the bell pockets and then along the uterus and vagina to the exterior. These elliptical ovic larvae must be ingested by the proper invertebrate host before they can develop further.

AFFINITIES

Because of many peculiarities of structure of Acanthocephala and the parasitic degeneration or alternation of some of their systems, determination of their affinities poses a difficult problem. The acanthocephalan worms were noticed about the beginning of the 18th century but were clearly distinguished from other intestinal worms until 1771 when Koelreuther proposed the name *Acanthocephalus* for one from fish. In 1776, Zoega and O.F. Muller without knowledge of Koelreuther's work gave the name *Echinorhynchus* to a similar fish parasite. Zeder (1803) gave these worms a common name"Haken wurmer" (hooked worms) and Rudolphi (1809) changed this into the form Acanthocephala (Greek, *akantho*=spiny; *kephalo*=pertaining to the head) by which the group has since been known.

Cuvier included the acanthocephalan worms with the flat worms in his group of parasitic worms. Vogt (1851) first clearly distinguished the flatworms from the roundworms upon which Gegenbaur gave the name Nemathelminthes to the roundworms. The position of Acanthocephala, however, has remained uncertain. At the present time there are only two views that need be seriously considered, those associating the Acanthocephala with the Platyhelminthes or with the Aschelminthes. The best way to decide between these two possibilities is to discuss, system by system, the similarities and dissimilarities between the three groups, something that has also been done by Chitwood(1940) and Van Cleave(1941).

Similarities with Platyhelminthes.The Acanthocephala resemble with the Platyhelminthes in the following respects: (1) An armed and protrusible proboscis occurs in certain cestodes and the proboscides of *Trypanorhyncha* and Acanthocephala is similar so far as the shape and arrangement of hooks is concerned. (2) Presence of cuticle and syncytial nucleated epidermis. (3) Musculature with circular as well as longitudinal fibres. (4) Protonephridia of flame-bulbs are present. (5) Reproductive system, particularly in male, resembles that of many flatworms. (6) Embryology is like that of cestodes. (7) Serological tests indicate a relationship of Acanthocephala with cestodes rather than nematodes.

Similarities with Aschelminthes : The following similarities are noteworthy : (1) The division of the body into the presoma and the trunk as in priapulids and the gordiacean larva. (2) An armed proboscis is found among the Aschelminthes in echinoderids, priapulids and gordiacean larva. (3) Superficial segmentation, sometimes involving musculature, is also conspicuous in rotifers, echinoderids, priapulids and nematodes, etc. (4) Clothing of body with cuticle and syncytial nucleated epidermis. (5) Division of pseudocoel by partitions and tissues resembling mesenteries. (6) Reduction of gut to a strand is found in male rotifers. (7) Flame-bulb protonephridia present. (8) A close relationship of nephridial and reproductive systems is common in priapulids and rotifers.

Differences from Nematoda. Acanthocephala, however, differ from the Nematoda in the following points : (1) Presence of proboscis. (2) Absence of digestive tract. (3) Presence of circular muscles. (4) Presence of ciliated excretory organs. (5) Peculiarities and complexities of reproductive system.

The foregoing comparisons do not furnish a decisive answer to the question whether the Acanthocephala are allied to the Platyhelminthes or to the Aschelminthes. The general structure is rather on the aschelminthic side, whereas the embryology presents more points of resemblance with the Platyhelminthes. Chitwood(1940) and Van Cleave (1941) favour a platyhelminth affinity, and on this basis Chitwood(1940) has proposed a superphylum Parenchymata to embrace the flatworms, nemertines and acanthocephalans. Leaving apart the fact that the Acanthocephala are not parenchymatous animals, one doubts the utility of the superphylum concept. On present evidence, raising the Acanthocephala to the rank of an independent phylum appears the best disposition of the group.

REVISION QUESTIONS

1. Describe the general characters of Acanthocephala and external features of *Echinorhynchus*.
2. Describe the general anatomy of *Echinorhynchus*.
3. Discuss the affinities of Acanthocephala.

55

Phylum Rotifera

The rotifers, or wheel animalcules, are microscopic, mostly free-living Aschelminthes with the anterior end formed into a ciliary apparatus, the corona, with a differentiated pharynx provided with jaws and with typical flame-bulb protonephridia.

HABIT AND HABITAT

The rotifers are among the most common inhabitants of freshwaters everywhere. Some also live in brackish water and a few in the ocean or on land in damp sites. They have adopted a variety of habitats and ways of life. Thus, there are creeping, swimming, pelagic and sessile types, as well as carnivores and bacteria feeders. Although the rotifers are generally solitary, some of the sessile species form spherical swimming colonies in which, however, the individuals have no organic continuity.

EXTERNAL CHARACTERS

Rotifers or wheel animalcules are minute animals ranging from 0.04 to 2 mm in length and most of them do not exceed 0.5 mm. The rotifer body is generally of elongated form and is divisible into the broad or narrowed or lobed anterior end, usually provided with a ciliary apparatus, an elongated

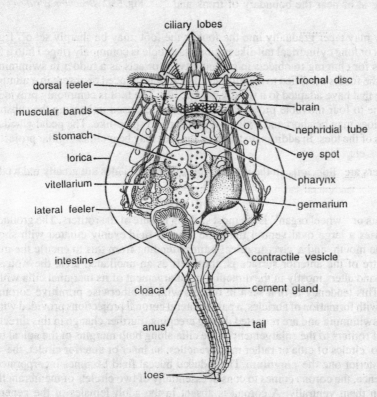

Fig. 55.1. *Brachionus rubens.* (Female).

443

trunk, often enlarged and a slender terminal region, the tail or foot. The body is covered with an evident yellowish cuticle that is often ringed throughout or in certain regions. The cuticle may be thickened, chiefly on the trunk to form a hard encasement, the lorica, of one to several plates, that may be variously ornamented.

The anterior end bearing the mouth corona and various projections is not definitely delimited as a head but may be called so for convenience. It is typically broad and truncate or slightly convex, presenting an unciliated region, the apical field, encircled by a ciliated zone, the corona. The head may also bear a pair of prominent lateral ciliated projections, known as auricles. Eyes (pigment spot ocelli) appearing as red flecks, occur singly or paired in the brain, as lateral paired eyes in or near the corona and as paired frontal eyes on the apical field or on the rostrum. The mouth is located in the corona in the mid-ventral line of the head and often coronal protrusion serves as lower lip.

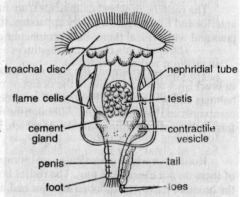

troachal disc — nephridial tube

flame cells — testis

cement gland — contractile vesicle

penis — tail

foot — toes

Fig. 55.2. *Brachionus rubens.* (Male).

The trunk may be cylindrical or variously flattened and broadened and is frequently enclosed in a lorica, often ornamented or spiny. Characteristic trunk structures of rotifers are the dorsal and lateral antennae or palps. The dorsal antenna, usually single, sometimes and probably originally paired, is commonly situated in the mid-dorsal line of the anterior end of the trunk and when well-developed is a finger-like projection tipped with sensory hairs. The anus is found in the mid-dorsal line at or near the boundary of trunk and foot.

The body may taper gradually into the foot or the foot may be sharply set off from the stout trunk as a short or long cylindrical tail-like region. Its cuticle is commonly ringed into a few to many joints. It serves for clinging to objects in creeping types or acts as a rudder in swimming types. In sessile forms, the foot is modified to a long stalk. The foot is reduced or absent in a number of forms, specially those that have adapted to a wholly pelagic life. The foot is commonly provided at or near its end with one to four movable projections known as toes, used in holding the substratum while creeping. The toes may be short and conical or slender and spine-like. The pedal glands commonly open at the tips of the toes. In addition to the toes, the foot may bear either similar projections known as styles, spurs, etc.

The rotifers are dioecious. In the majority of rotifers the males are greatly reduced in size and morphology.

CORONA

The corona or "wheel organ" is the most striking feature of the rotifers. The ground plan of the corona comprises a large oval ventral field, the buccal field evenly ciliated with short cilia and surrounding the mouth, and a circumapical band extending from this to encircle the margin of the head. The centre of the anterior surface is, thus, left as an unciliated area, the apical field. The circumapical band alters mostly in the direction of enlargement of its marginal cilia with loss of the interior cilia. This tendency is first seen in rotifers with an otherwise primitive corona ; as many notammatids, with formation of auricles, a pair of lateral coronal projections provided with long cilia. They assist in swimming and are retracted during creeping. Further change in this direction leads in some groups of rotifers to the enlargement of the cilia along both margins of the apical band, so that there result two circles of cilia or rather membranelles, an inner or anterior circlet, the trochus and an outer or posterior one the cingulum. The reduced buccal field becomes incorporated into these circlets and, hence, the corona comes to consist essentially of two circlets of membranelles, with the mouth between them ventrally. A corona is absent in the adult females of the genera *Atrochus, Cupelopagis* and *Acyclus* but is present in normal form in the males and young females of these genera. The corona of male rotifers usually differs from that of females of the same species, being usually less modified.

BODY WALL AND ASSOCIATED GLANDS

The body wall consists of cuticle, epidermis and subepidermal muscles. The cuticle, secreted by the epidermis, is not chitinous and presumably consists of scleroproteins. It is frequently divided into rings or segments that lend flexibility permitting a variety of body movements. In many rotifers the trunk cuticle is thickened and hardened into a lorica that, however, is slightly flexible. The lorica may consist of several pieces or two dorsal or two ventral plates or two dorsal and one ventral or of single dorsal and ventral plates or of one piece with or without a longitudinal suture. Loricate forms are often dorso-ventrally or laterally flattened; the margins of the lorica may project as teeth or spines and these are subject to much variation within a single species. The part of the lorica covering the neck region may be marked off from the general trunk lorica by a groove which is known as head shield.

The epidermis is a thin syncytium containing scattered nuclei bilaterally arranged and constant in position and number for each species. Around each nucleus or group of nuclei the cytoplasm is heaped up into an elevation projecting into the pseudocoel.

The principal glands attached to the epidermis are the retrocerebral organ and the pedal glands. The retrocerebral organ is situated above and behind the brain and consists typically of a median retrocerebral sac and a pair of lateral subcerebral glands. The duct of the sac forks and forks along with the outlets of the glands open on the apical field, often on a single or paired papilla. Sac and gland vary much in relative and absolute size in different rotifers. There may be a single sub-cerebral gland or the sac may occur without glands or the glands without the sac. Sac and glands consist of a syncytium and secrete droplets give them a vacuolated appearance. The sac and sometimes also the glands contain strongly diffractive granules, red pigment grains may be present. The function of the retrocerebral organ is uncertain.

The pedal glands are unicellular glands or multinucleate syncytia located in the foot. They are numerous, less numerous and reduced to a single pair and often rudimentary or absent in the adults of the sessile orders. They open by ducts on the tips of toes or at sides or base of the toes or on the spurs or at the foot end. The pedal glands secrete an adhesive material used for permanent attachment or in creeping and also in the construction of tubes and cases.

MUSCULAR SYSTEM

In rotifers the subepidermal muscles consist of a number of muscles found in different parts of the body. In typical cases they are circular and longitudinal muscles. In addition to these body wall muscles there are cutaneovisceral muscles that extend to the viscera, especially the digestive tract, from the body wall, and visceral muscles in the walls of the viscera themselves. The circular musculature of the body wall consists of a single muscle band, mostly three to seven, widely spaced running close to the underside of the epidermis in a circular direction. These bands form complete rings but are often very incomplete ventrally, frequently also dorsally, so that they may consist chiefly of short lateral arcs. They occur in neck and trunk, generally absent from the foot and reduced in forms with a well-developed lorica. The circular bands contain no nuclei, hence, are really part of the epidermal syncytium. The contraction of the circular muscles serves to extend the body. The circular musculature is specially developed in the head directly behind the corona where it forms the coronal sphincter composed of one to several broad bands and serves to close the neck over the retracted corona. A similar pedal sphincter may occur at the junction of trunk and foot. The longitudinal body wall muscles consisted originally of bands running the body length directly under the circular bands and attached at frequent intervals to the epidermis. By loss of many of these insertions the longitudinal bands come to run more directly through the pseudocoel and to act primarily on head and foot as retractors. The principal head retractors are the central, dorsal, lateral and ventral pairs. The lateral is commonly subdivided into three bands, superior, median and inferior. The longitudinal retractors serve to retract the head and corona and foot into the trunk region. The longitudinal retractors have one or more nuclei.

PSEUDOCOEL

The pseudocoel is often a spacious cavity lying between the body wall and the digestive tract and other viscera. This space has none of the characteristics of coelom. The pseudocoel is filled with fluid and a loose network formed by the union of branched amoeboid cells into a syncytium.

DIGESTIVE SYSTEM

The mouth is rounded, slit-like or triangular, situated ventrally on the head, Beneath the mouth the cingulum may form a definite lower tip. In forms with a large buccal field, the posterior end of the field may project as the so-called chin. The mouth may open directly into the pharynx or may lead to the latter by way of ciliated tube, the buccal tube. The pharynx or mastax is characteristic and peculiar to rotifers. It is a highly muscular, rounded, trilobed or elongated organ of complicated form and structure, whose inner wall bears the masticatory apparatus composed of hard cuticularized pieces, the trophi. The trophi consist of seven main pieces the unpaired fulcrum and the paired rami, unci and manubria. The trophi occur in several different types that are correlated with different modes of life. The trophi are of the following types : malleate type, virgate type, cardate type, forcipate type, incudate type, ramate type, uncinate type, fulcrate type. The salivary glands are two to seven in number, occur in the mastax wall in many rotifers as uninucleate or syncytial masses with granular or vacuolated cytoplasm. The function of the salivary glands is uncertain but presumably concerns ingestion or digestion. The mastax is followed by a short or long tube, the oesophagus. The oesophagus is lined with cuticle or ciliated throughout or at the posterior end only. The oesophagus is devoid of glands. The oesophagus is followed by the stomach. It is an enlarged thick-walled sac or tube. The stomach is provided with muscular layer consisting of muscle cells or if the stomach wall is syncytial there are syncytial muscle fibres. At the junction of oesophagus and stomach occurs a pair of gastric glands, composed of a syncytium having a constant number of nuclei and opening into the stomach by a simple pore on each side. The secretion comprises droplets or granules aggregated around the pore and presumably enzymatic. The stomach is followed by the intestine. In one case the intestine is tubular and in other bladder-like. The stomach and intestine are attached to the body wall by the usual cutaneovisceral muscles.

NERVOUS SYSTEM

The nervous system consists of a main bilobed mass, the brain or cerebral ganglia, sensory and motor nerves from this to adjacent parts, some additional ganglionic masses and two main ventral nerve cords. The brain is a rounded, triangular or quadrangular body lying dorsal to the mastax. A number of paired sensory nerves extend to the brain from the various sense organs of the head : the eyes, the sensory bristles and pits on apical field, the rostrum and the dorsal antenna. The brain also sends motor nerves to the anterior parts of the various muscles, as the dorsal, lateral and central retractors and to the salivary glands. The main ventral nerves are ganglionated cords that spring from the sides of the brain and proceed backward in latero-ventral position into the foot. Near the brain they bear an anterior ganglion and farther posteriorly a geniculate ganglion. Posteriorly the ventral cords terminate in ganglia serving the urinary bladder and foot. These ganglia may be fused in one mass, the caudovascular ganglion.

SENSORY STRUCTURES

The rotifers are richly supplied with sensory cells and sense organs. These occur abundantly on the anterior end in the form of sensory membranelles and styles, ciliated pits, sensory papillae, etc. The sensory membranelles or styles are single stiff bristles situated near the inner edge of the circumapical band and named from their position dorsolateral, lateral and ventrolateral styles. Similar apical styles occur on the apical field and oral styles may be present near the mouth. These styles seem to be tactile organs and each is underlined by one or two sensory nerve cells from which fibres go to brain. Paired ciliated pits, apparently chemo-receptors, may occur on the apical field. Conical or finger-like palps tipped with sensory hairs or without hairs may also be present on the apical field. Ocelli,seen as red pigment spots, are of common occurrence. Usually there is a single, less often paired, cerebral eye, embedded in the dorsal and ventral surface of the brain. Cerebral and apical or cerebral and lateral eyes may be present simultaneously. A sensory organ constantly present in rotifers is the dorsal antenna or tentacle. This is typically a movable papillae or finger-like projection provided at its tip with one or more tufts of sensory hairs.

EXCRETORY SYSTEM

The excretory system consists of a pair of typical protonephridial tubules provided with flame-bulbs and opening posteriorly into a common urinary bladder. The main tubules extend lengthwise the animal, one on each side,commonly in coils and loops and often fork into an anterior and a posterior branch. The flame bulbs, usually two to eight on each side, open into a ciliated capillary that enters the end of the main tubule or its branches and may run alongside the main tubule for some distance. A similar capillary, known as Huxley's anastomosis may run transversely between the anterior terminations of the main tubules and may receive additional flame bulbs. The flame bulbs vary from a tubular to a flattened triangular form and contain a slender to triangular membranelle of fused, kept in constant motion. The thickened cap-like end frequently bears one to several protoplasmic filaments that anchor the bulb mostly to the body wall. The flame bulbs are not cells and usually contain no nucleus but are part of the general nephridial syncytium. Posteriorly the tubules open separately into a urinary bladder situated ventral to the cloaca or they unite to a common stem that enters the ventral wall of the cloaca.

REPRODUCTIVE SYSTEM

The rotifers are exclusively dioecious. In rotifers, there exists a marked sexual dimorphism. The greatest sexual dimorphism is seen in the order Flosculariacea and Collothecacea where the free swimming males are one-tenth or less the size of the females and have a simple ciliated anterior end in place of the elaborate coronal lobes of the female. The reduction of males is most pronounced in pelagic and sessile rotifers and appears to be adaptation to ensure fertilization under these conditions of life. The minute size of males results from the facts that they come from smaller eggs and do not grow after hatching.

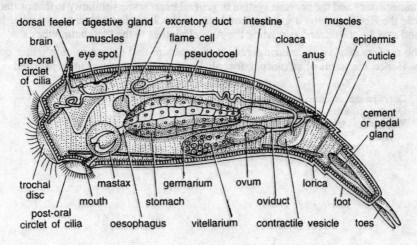

Fig. 55.3. Diagram of a rotifer showing the internal structures.

In the majority of rotifers, the female reproductive system consists of a single syncytial ovary and syncytial vitellarium bound together in a common membrane that continues to the cloaca as a simple tubular oviduct. The male reproductive system consists of a single large sacciform testis from which a ciliated sperm duct receiving a pair, sometimes more, of prostatic glands proceeds to the genital pore. The posterior end of the sperm duct is eversible as a cirrus and is lined with hardened cuticle ; or it may bear a cuticular tube protrusible as a penis ; or the body wall around the gonopore can assume a tubular form and so act as copulatory organ.

AFFINITIES

The rotifers have been allied in turn to almost every invertebrate group, specially the arthropods and annelids. The idea of arthropod affinity, was based on certain resemblances such as (i) cuticularized surface, (ii) apparent segmentation and (iii) the appearance of jaws and at the same time was strengthened by the discovery of *Pedalia* whose movable bristle bearing arms suggest the appendages of a crustacean larva. Hatschek propounded his trochophore theory which maintains that the living rotifers are closely related to the ancestral Mollusca, Annelida and certain other groups. This theory compares rotifers with the trochophore larva and concludes that rotifers are simple annelids that have remained in a larval state. At present this hypothesis is based chiefly on the rotifer *Trochosphaera* whose ciliary girdle, bent intestine and excretory organs resemble topographically the similar parts of the trochophore. But *Trochosphaera* is merely a peculiar rotifer with a modified girdle type corona only superficially resembling the prototroch of the trochophore is a highly modified corona. On the other hand the primitive corona was a large ventral ciliated field in no way resembling the ciliary circlets of the trochophore. The annelid theory must, therefore, be regarded as without foundation, as concerns the trochophore resemblance.

The embryology of rotifers suggests that these animals are primitive, not derived by the retrogression on higher forms. No trace is seen in the development of a coelom or an entero-mesoderm. The anatomy and embryology both incline to the origin of the rotifers from some low-grade creeping bilateral type such as a primitive flatworm. The primitive type of corona may be the remnant of a former complete or ventral ciliation such as found in the Turbellaria. The formation of cuticularized parts as the trophi is comon among the Turbellaria. The strongest point of resemblance between rotifers and turbellarians is, however, the protonephridial system which is practically identical with that of the rhabdocoels. The presence of this type of excretory system practically precludes the derivation of the rotifers from any higher group since none of the higher groups have protonephridia with flame-bulbs. The retrocerebral organ is probably homologous with the frontal organ of Turbellaria. The division of the female gonad into ovary and vitellarium is, another resemblance to flatworms. On the other hand the rotifers differ from flatworms in the presence of anus and the lack of a subepidermal muscle sheath and of the subepidermal nerve plexus so characteristic of the Turbellaria. Their small size, however, probably makes such an accessory nerve plexus unnecessary and the nervous system in general bears some similarity to that of flatworms. On the whole the Rotifera show a great resemblance to the Turbellaria than to any other invertebrate group and may be considered as relating the Aschelminthes to the Platyhelminthes.

The rotifers display an amazing variety in structure and do not resemble any one group of animals. Hence, the status of an independent phylum to rotifers appears to be justified.

REVISION QUESTIONS

1. Describe the structure of a rotifer.
2. Discuss affinities of Rotifera.
3. Write notes on : Corona; Lorica.

56

Phylum Ectoprocta (Bryozoa)

Ectoprocta are microscopic, sessile, colonial, unsegmented coelomate animals that are fastened permanently in exoskeletal cases or gelatinous material of their own secretion with a circumoral ring, crescentic lophophore and a U-shaped digestive tract bringing the anus near the mouth but without nephridia and circulatory system.

The Ectoprocta form colonies known as "Sea-mats" or 'Corallines" which in many cases bear a general resemblance to hydroid coelenterates. The ectoprocts exhibit slight structural diversities and a typical genus *Bugula* has been described here as an example of Ectoprocta.

HABIT AND HABITAT

Bugula avicularia, the common Bird's Head Coralline occurs in brown or purple bushy tufts, 5.0 to 7.0 cm long, found attached on rocks, piles of jetties and similar situations on the shore in all the parts of the world. The ectoprocts are strictly benthonic and pelagic only in larval stages. *Bugula* is a ciliary feeder and lives on micro-organisms, specially the diatoms.

EXTERNAL STRUCTURES

An ectoproct colony superficially resembles to a hydroid coelenterate but a closer examination reveals that it has a much higher type of organisation. A complete ectoproct colony is called zoarium. It is composed of several individuals or units called zooids.

The colony of *Bugula* consists of dichotomously branched narrow stem, which are rooted by a number of slender root filaments. Each stem is composed of a number of elements, the zooecia of the colony, which are closely united together and arranged in four longitudinal rows. The zooecia are cylindrical in shape, but broader distally than proximally, five times as long as broad and have, near the distal end, a wide crescentic aperture, the mouth of the zooecium, on either of which is a short blunt spine. A rounded structure–the ooecium, in many parts of the colony lies in front of each zooecium. On each zooecium except a few, is a remarkable appendage, the avicularium. The avicularium has appearance of bird's head supported on a very short stalk. The chitinous wall of the zooecia is the har-

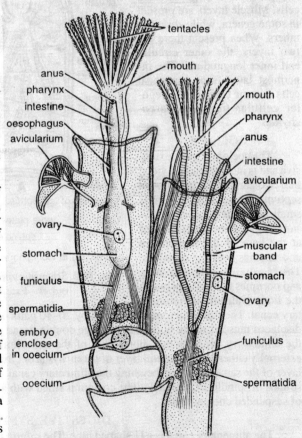

Fig. 56.1. *Bugula avicularia.* Two zooids magnified.

dened and thickened cuticle of zooids, having beneath it the soft body wall. The anterior region of the body of the zooid forms an introvert. When the introvert is everted it is seen to bear at its anterior end a circlet of usually fourteen long, slender, filiform tentacles on a circular ridge or lophophore surrounding the mouth of the zooid. The tentacles are densely ciliated except along their outer surfaces. The cilia of the tentacles vibrate in such a way as to drive currents of water and with them food particles towards the mouth. The tentacles are capable of being bent in various directions. In the interior of each tentacle is a narrow prolongation of the coelom. Besides bringing minute food particles to the mouth of the zooid by the action of their cilia, the tentacles are tactile and also act as organs of respiration. When retracted they become enclosed by the walls of the introvert or by a sheath, the tentacle sheath. A pair of bands of muscle fibres, the parieto-vaginal muscles passing to the introvert from the body wall serve to retract the introvert tentacles. The main body of the zooid is the trunk which is immovably attached inside the zooecium. It contains the coelom and other internal organs.

BODY WALL

The body wall consists of cuticle, epidermis, two muscular layers and parenchyma. The cuticle forms the covering of the zooecium. Beneath the cuticle lies the epidermis composed of a single layer of large flattened cells. Muscle layers are present in some genera, while absent in others. When present there are two layers, the outer circular and inner longitudinal. The innermost layer is of peritoneal cells in some cases or of irregular cellular tissue or parenchyma.

COELOM

The coelom is quite extensive and is incompletely divided into two parts by an incomplete septum. The anterior coelom is small and called the ring coelom. The ring coelom is situated at the base of the lophophore and extends into the tentacles. The trunk coelom is quite large and occupies the space between the body wall and the alimentary canal.

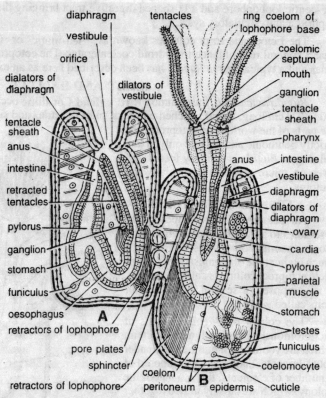

Fig. 56.2. Schematic zooids in an ectoproct colony, A—Retracted zooid; B—Extended zooid.

The trunk coelom is traversed by 20–40 pairs of muscle fibres which are regarded as the displaced muscles of the body wall. A large double strand passes from the proximal or aboral end of the alimentary canal to the aboral wall of the zooecium, is the funiculus. The coelom is lined externally either by the parietal layer of parenchyma or ciliated peritoneum and internally by visceral layer of the same tissue, ensheathing the alimentary canal. Coelom is crossed by numerous radiating strands of spindle-shaped cells. The coelom is filled with a colourless fluid containing several kinds of suspended coelomocytes.

DIGESTIVE SYSTEM

The alimentary canal is a U-shaped tube. The mouth is situated at the centre of the lophophore. The mouth leads into a wide chamber the pharynx which passes into the oesophagus. The oesophagus leads into stomach. The stomach gives off a long conical prolongation or caecum passing towards the aboral end of zooecium to which it is attached by the funiculus. The intestine comes off from the oral aspect of the stomach. The intestine terminates in a rounded anus situated near the mouth but outside the lophophore. The entire alimentary canal is lined by an epithelium which is ciliated throughout except in a portion of the stomach. A pair of slender muscles passing from the body wall to the stomach act as retractors of the alimentary canal when the introvert is drawn back.

CIRCULATORY SYSTEM

There are no blood vessels in the ectoprocts and the circulatory system is entirely absent.

EXCRETORY SYSTEM

Definite excretory organs do not occur in ectoprocts. The function of excretion (*i.e.,* the collection of nitrogenous waste matters) being apparently carried on by the leucocytes and the cells of the funicular tissue.

NERVOUS SYSTEM

The nervous system consists of a small round ganglion situated in the ring coelom between the mouth and anus. This ganglion gives off nerves to various parts of the body. The ganglion is continuous with the nerve ring surrounding the pharynx. The nerve ring gives two ganglionated motor and sensory nerve fibres to each tentacle. Special organs of sense are absent.

REPRODUCTIVE SYSTEM

Bugula is hermaphrodite. Ovary and testis are found to occur together in the same zooid. Both ovary and testis are formed from specially modified cells of the parenchyma, either of the funiculus or of the body wall. The testis develops from the cells of the funicular tissue and gives origin to the spherical masses of cells, the spermatidia which develop into sperms with very long motile tails. These become free from one another and move about in the body cavity or in its prolongations into tentacles. There is no sperm duct and it is doubtful if the sperms pass to the exterior. The ovary is a small rounded body formed from the parietal layer of the parenchyma about the middle of the zooecium. It consists of only a small number of cells of which only one at a time becomes a mature ovum, certain smaller cells forming an enclosing follicle. The mature ovum is perhaps fertilized in the coelom. It passes into the interior of a rounded outgrowth of the zooecium, the ooecium lined with parenchyma and forming a sort of brood pouch ir. which it undergoes development.

DEVELOPMENT

Self-fertilization has been observed in *Bugula*. The fertilized egg undergoes cleavage which is holoblastic (complete) and nearly regular. The plane of cleavage is of radial type. A coeloblastula is formed which eventually transforms into a gastrula by the process of delamination. During the process of production of 64–128 blastomeres, four elongated cells become cut off into the blastocoel. These are actually endomesodermal cells which give endoderm and mesenchyme. The larva is called cyphonautes. The cyphonautes larva in *Bugula* shows few specialized features, *viz.,* oval shape, absence of alimentary canal and delimitation of the apical organ by a circular groove.

ASEXUAL REPRODUCTION

Ectoprocta reproduce asexually by budding statoblasts, hybernacula, brown bodies and regeneration.

AFFINITIES

The phylogenetic relationships of Ectoprocta are uncertain and controversial. The controversy is due to their structural similarities with other groups of animals.

Affinities with Phoronida. Caldwell (1888) emphasised the affinities between Ectoprocta and Phoronida. This idea was based on the following similarities : (1) Both are provided with horse-shoe-shaped lophophore. (2) Presence of epistome. (3) U-shaped alimentary canal. (4) Similar disposition of the coelom and the presence of a septum separating the mesocoel and metacoel. (5) The nerve centre is located in the mesocoel and is supraenteric. But the detailed study of the two groups exhibited many structural differences between them. They differ widely in their anatomical organisation. The embryology also exhibits many differences. The noteworthy differences are as follows : (1) The origin of coelom is different. (2) The region between the mouth and anus is dorsal in position in Phoronida and ventral in Ectoprocta. (3) The circulatory system and nephridia are absent in Ectoprocta, while in Phoronida both the systems are present. Due to the above-mentioned differences the affinities between Ectoprocta and Phoronida cannot be established.

Affinities with Brachiopoda. There are many similarities between Ectoprocta and Brachiopoda. These similarities are : (1) Both have similar body organisation. (2) Bivalved shell of cyphonautes larva of Ectoprocta can be compared to the shell of Brachiopoda. (3) Presence of coelomic septum between the mesocoel and metacoel. (4) Alimentary canal is U-shaped. Besides the above similarities, there are many structural differences between these two groups. The main differences are as follows : (1) The brachiopod shell cannot be compared to the exoskeleton of Ectoprocta. (2) In Brachiopoda the shell is dorso-ventrally placed, while in ectoproct larva the shell is laterally placed (3) The chitinous setae present in Brachiopoda are absent in Ectoprocta. (4) The nervous system is mainly supraenteric in Ectoprocta, while in Brachiopoda it is subenteric. Because of lack of specific relationships between them, the affinities between these two groups cannot be established.

Affinities with Endoprocta. Previously Ectoprocta and Endoprocta were linked together as two classes under the phylum Bryozoa or Polyzoa because of the following similarities : (1) Presence of a crown of ciliated tentacles. (2) Presence of looped alimentary canal. (3) Similarity in larval stages. But such features occur in common in all the sessile animals. A careful examination of the structural organisation reveals that these two groups are fundamentally different from each other. They exhibit many differences. The main differences are as follows : (1) The tentacular crown surrounds only the mouth in Ectoprocta, but in Endoprocta both the mouth and anus are enclosed by the tentacles. (2) The ectoprocta possess true coelom, whereas in Endoprocta the true coelom is absent. (3) The nephridia and gonoducts are absent in Ectoprocta, while in Endoprocta both of them are present. Considering these features it is quite apparent that Ectoprocta is highly organised than the Endoprocta.

From all the information of anatomy and embryology available for Ectoprocta, it is convenient to place the ectoprocta under a separate phylum having phylogenetic relationship with the two other lophophorate coelomates, *i.e.,* Phoronida and Brachiopoda.

REVISION QUESTIONS

1. Describe habit,habitat and external features of *Bugula.*
2. Describe the disposition of zooids in an ectoproct colony.
3. Discuss the affinities of Bryozoa.

57

Phylum Brachiopoda

The Brachiopoda or "lamp-shells" are coelomate Bilateria that are enclosed in a bilaterally symmetrical bivalve shell attached directly or by way of stalk (peduncle)and composed of dorsal and ventral valves lined by a mantle lobe of the body wall and that are provided with a lophophore, an open circulatory system with a dorsal contractile vesicle and one or two pairs of metanephridia, also acting as gonoduct.

The structural organisation in all the brachiopods is more or less similar except the articulation of two shell valves. Here *Magellania* has been described as a typical example of the phylum Brachiopoda.

HABIT AND HABITAT

Magellania is a marine and benthonic animal like all other brachiopods. Brachiopods are found in all seas at different depths from between tide marks to 2900 fathoms. The larger number lives at moderate depths, down to 500 or 600 fathoms. *Magellania* includes several species which are widely distributed but are quite abundant off the coast of New Zealand. They remain attached by peduncle to rocky ground. They are ciliary feeders with lophophore as the food catching apparatus. They comprise minute marine organisms specially diatoms.

EXTERNAL STRUCTURES

Shell. The body is entirely covered by a bivalved shell of oval form and pink colour. The valves are separate, bilaterally symmetrical but more or less dissimilar in size and are dorsal and ventral in position. Both valves are deeply concavo-convex of a pinkish or brown colour outside and white within. The ventral valve is produced posteriorly into a beak terminating in a foramen for the peduncle. The distal margin of the foramen is left incomplete by the shell proper but is closed by a small double plate, the deltidium. Immediately anterior to the beak is the curved hinge-line along which the valve articulates with its fellow and just anterior to the hinge-line the inner surface of the shell is produced into a pair of massive irregular hinge-teeth. On the inner surface of the valve towards its posterior end, are certain shallow depressions making the attachments of muscles.

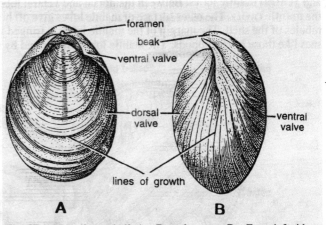

Fig. 57.1. *Magellania* shell. A—Dorsal aspcet ; B—From left side.

The dorsal valve has no beak, but its posterior edge forms a hinge-line which is produced in the middle into a strong cardinal process with a folded surface. When the valves are in position this process fits between the hinge-teeth of the ventral valve, the hinge-teeth in their turn being received into depressions placed on each side of the cardinal process. The inner surface of the dorsal valve is produced into a median ridge or septum, continuous posteriorly with the cardinal process. Attached on either side of the base of the cardinal process are the two ends of a delicate calcareous ribbon, the shelly loop which projects freely into the cavity enclosed between the two valves. The shelly loop has the form of a simple loop bent upon itself. The inside of the dorsal valve also has muscular impressions.

The valves externally present a series of concentric ridges, the lines of growth. The shell is made up of prismatic rods or spicules of calcium carbonate placed obliquely to the external surface made up of chitinous substance mixed in the carbonate of lime and called periostracum. The calcareous spicules are separated from one another by a thin layer of membrane. Further the shell is traversed by perpendicularly disposed delicate tubules closed on the outer surface.

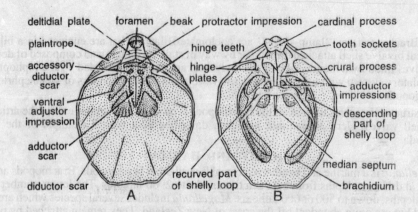

Fig. 57.2. *Magellania* shell. A—Interior of ventral valve ; B—Interior of dorsal valve.

INTERNAL STRUCTURES

Mantle. The body proper is situated inside the posterior end of the shell. Just below the shell valves or closely applied to the shell valves are present corresponding folds of integument, the **dorsal** and **ventral mantle lobes.** Between the dorsal and ventral lobes is enclosed a wedge-shaped space, the **mantle cavity.** The outer surface of mantle lobes give off hollow processes which extend into the tubules of the shell. The margin of the mantle lobes is fringed with minute setae lodged in muscular sacs like those of chaetopods. The mantle lobes are formed by reduplication of body wall.

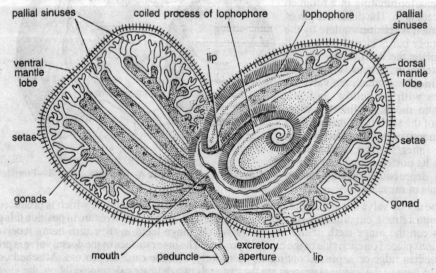

Fig. 57.3. *Magellania.* Body removed from the shell.

Body wall. The body wall comprises three layers; an outer epidermis consisting of single layer of cells, middle layer composed of connective tissue of varying thickness which is more or less cartilaginous at many places and a layer of ciliated coelomic epithelium lining the body-cavity.

Body-cavity or Coelom The body-cavity is the true coelom. It is quite spacious and is divided into three compartments—protocoel, mesocoel and metacoel. These compartments are partially separated from each other. The coelom contains mesenteries and muscles. The mesocoel gives large arm canals to the lophophore. The metacoel constitutes the main body cavity containing major part of the alimentary canal, shell muscles, nephridia and gonads, etc. It is also continued into the mantle lobes as mantle canal. The coelom is lined by a ciliated epithelium. It is filled with a fluid containing several types of free coelomocytes. The coelom communicates to the exterior through a pair of metanephridia.

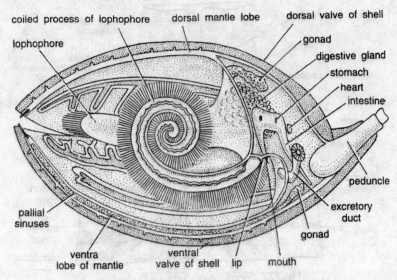

Fig. 57.4. *Magellania*. Sagittal section of the entire animal.

Lophophore. The mantle cavity is largely occupied by a large lophophore. The lophophore is an outgrowth of the anterior body wall that projects into the mantle cavity and fills the greater part of this cavity, being usually quite voluminous relative to the size of the body of the animal. The lophophore is the most conspicuous horse-shoe-shaped structure consisting of two spirally coiled tentacular arms. The two arms of the lophophore curve inwards and coil to fit into the mantle cavity. The middle of the concave edge, which is dorsal in position, is produced into a spirally coiled offshoot, and lies coiled towards the dorsal side between the two arms. The lophophore is hollow internally containing a spacious cavity or sinus, Its two main arms also receive prolongations of the coelom into which project the digestive glands.The lophophore is fringed throughout its whole extent with long ciliated tentacles which form the outer boundary of a ciliated food-groove, bounded on the inner side by a wavy ridgeor lip. By the action of the cilia microscopic particles are swept along the food-groove to the mouth. The lophophore is supported by internal skeleton called the brachidium or brachial support.The brachidium comprises a pair of prongs called the crura. Inside the lophophore the crura are continued forward as calcareous ribbon which form a loop. This long curve loop is present on the dorsal side. The loop is not attached with the dorsal valve. The calcareous support of the lophophore develops from the inner lamina of the dorsal mantle lobe.

MUSCULAR SYSTEM

The muscular system is well-developed. Two large adductor musclesarise on each side from the dorsal valve, and passing downwards, unite with one another so as to have a single insertion on the ventral valve. The action of these muscles is to approximate the valve and so to close the shell. A large and a small pair of divaricatorsarise from the ventral valve and are inserted into the cardinal process, which they depress, as this process is situated posteriorly to the hinge-line, its depression raises the rest of the dorsal valve and so open the shell. Two pairs of muscles arising, one from the ventral and the other from the dorsal valve, and inserted into the peduncle, are called adjustors.The peduncle being fixed, the adjustors serve to alter or adjust the position of the animal as a whole by turning it in various directions.

DIGESTIVE SYSTEM

The mouth is a narrow crescentic slit-like aperture situated in the middle of the lophophore. It is bounded dorsally by the brachial fold or lip and ventrally by the tentacular fringe of the lophophore. The alimentary canal is U-shaped and lined with ciliated epithelium. The mouth leads into the **oesophagus** which opens into a large **stomach.** On each side of the stomach and opening into it by a duct is a large, branched **digestive glands** or **liver.** The stomach passes into a narrow and straight **intestine** which is directed downwards and backwards towards the ventral surface and ends blindly. The anus is absent.

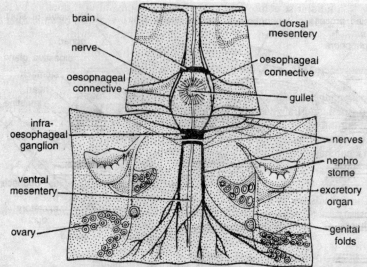

Fig. 57.5. *Terebratula.* Nervous System.

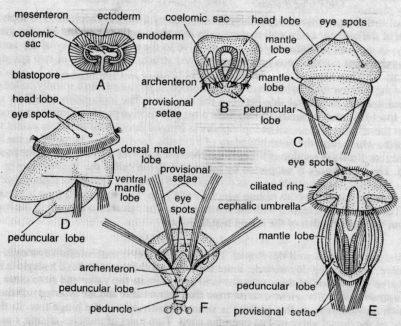

Fig. 57.6. Embryology of brachiopod. A—Formation of coelomic sacs; B—Embryo with three segments and commencing mantle fold with setae; C—Older embryo with same features and eye spots: D—Division of mantle lobe; E—Free swimming larva with cephalic umbrella; F—Attached larva with mantle lobes bent anteriorly.

CIRCULATORY SYSTEM

The circulatory system is simple and of open type. It consists of a contractile vesicle called heart and found attached to the dorsal mesentery. The blood channels arising from the heart supply the various parts of the body. The blood channels have no definite wall. These are merely spaces inside the mesenteries. The blood is colourless and cell free fluid. It is coagulable.

EXCRETORY SYSTEM

The excretory system consists of a pair of large metanephridia situated in the metacoel. Each metanephridium is a tubular structure, one end of which opens into the coelom by a wide funnel-shaped nephrostome, while the other end extends anteriorly and opens into the mantle cavity, the nephridiopore, situated one on each side of the mouth. The metanephridia also act as gonoducts.

NERVOUS SYSTEM

The nervous system (Fig. 57.5) comprises a supra-oesophageal ganglion in front of the mouth and a larger infra-oesophageal ganglion behind the mouth both connected by oesophageal connective. The infra-oesophageal ganglion gives off nerves to the dorsal mantle, dorsal arms, and adductor muscles and two small ganglia which supply the ventral mantle lobe and the muscles of the peduncle. The ganglia and commissures are in immediate contact with the ectoderm. No special sense-organs are known so far in *Magellania*, but in other brachiopods sense organs are represented by statocysts, eyes and sensory patches.

REPRODUCTIVE SYSTEM

The sexes are separate. There are two pairs of gonads, one pair dorsal and one pair ventral, near the intestine. The gonads are in the form of irregular organs sending off branches into the pallial sinuses. When the gametes become mature they are discharged into the metacoel from where they are conveyed to the exterior through metanephridia which act as gonoduct.

Fertilization is external. The cleavage is holoblastic and occurs along the radial plane. A coeloblastula is formed which eventually becomes a gastrula by emboly. Coelom is enterocoelous in this case. Mesoderm differentiates as a single sac which becomes separated off from the posterior end of the archenteron by a developing partition. After subsequent developmental stages, a free swimming ciliated larva emerges out which resembles closely to the annelidian trochophore larva. After short free swimming phase the larva fixes itself with the substratum by the peduncular region and metamorphoses into an adult.

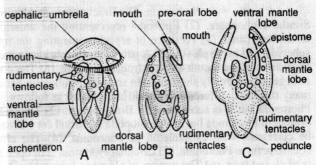

Fig. 57.7. Stages in metamorphosis. A—Free swimming larva; B—Transitional stages with reduced preoral lobe ; C—Young brachiopod after the turning forward of a mantle lobe.

AFFINITIES

Brachiopoda shows affinities with Mollusca, Annelida, Ectoprocta, Chaetognatha and Phoronida.

Affinities with Mollusca. Presence of bivalved shell and mantle lobes surrounding the body and trochophore-like larval form led many zoologists to include the brachiopods within the Mollusca. But the shell valves are dorsal and ventral in Brachiopoda in contrast with the lateral valves in Mollusca. They also differ in peduncle, internal structure of arm and embryology, their affinities cannot be advocated.

Affinities with Annelida. The Brachiopoda and Annelida have many structural similarities. These similarities are : (1) Indication of segmentation of body. (2) Presence of setae. (3) Presence of a well-developed perivisceral coelom. (4) Presence of metanephridia which also act as gonoducts. (5) The larva resembles a trochophore. The larval segmentation is comparable in both the Annelida and Brachiopoda.

In the light of these affinities, the Brachiopoda may be regarded as annelids with three segments marked in the embryo by the annular constriction of the integument. Thus, the Brachiopoda may be considered segmented annelids like *Cephalobranch* or *Oligonereis* which have become fixed and transformed their tubes into a pair of calcareous scales (valves) adhering to the epidermis. Segmentation of brachiopods is only superficial and there is no segmentation of the body cavity or genital organs or nervous system or segmental organs in the adult. Therefore, the resemblances of Annelida with Brachiopoda do not carry much weight and the Brachiopoda differ from Annelida basically.

Affinities with Ectoprocta. The Brachiopoda is related to Ectoprocta by possessing many similarities. These similarities are : (1) Both Brachiopoda and Ectoprocta have similar body plan. (2) A coelomic septum is present between mesocoel and metacoel. (3) U-shaped alimentary canal in both. (4) The bivalve shell of cyphonautes larva of Ectoprocta is comparable to the shell of Brachiopoda. Since these common features are due to the descendence from a common lophophorate ancestor, the above mentioned affinities are unsatisfactory due to the following main differences : (1) The nervous centre is mainly supra-enteric in Ectoprocta, but in Brachiopoda it is sub-enteric. (2) The Brachiopoda shell cannot be compared to the exoskeleton of Ectoprocta. (3) The shell is laterally placed in Entoprocta, but in Brachiopoda the shell is dorso-ventrally placed. (4) The chitinous setae are present in the brachiopods but in Ectoprocta no such setae have been observed. (5) The coelomic septum is poorly developed in most brachiopods. (6) The anus is lacking in some brachiopods.

Affinities with Chaetognatha. Lemeere (1931) considered closer affinities between Chaetognatha and Brachiopoda. The affinities are based chiefly on the presence of longitudinal, dorsal and ventral mesenteries and the enterocoelic mode of origin of coelom and mesoderm in both the groups but probably without any phylogenetic significance. Even if phylogenetic significance may be given to the development it will be seen that in the present case only the appearance of mesoderm has some similarity between the two and the further development is quite different and so is the organization of the adult.

Affinities with Phoronida. The Brachiopoda and Phoronida have many similarities such as (1) Similar lophophore. (2) Epistome representing the anterior segment of the body. (3) U-shaped alimentary canal. (4) Presence of septum separating the mesocoel and metacoel. (5) Presence of subepidermal nerve plexus. (6) A pair of metanephridia in the metacoel acting also as gonoducts ; (7) Derivation of the mouth directly from blastopore. (8) The dorsal surface between the mouth and the anus becomes greatly shortened. In spite of the above-mentioned similarities, these two groups have many structural differences. The differences are as follows : (1) The nerve centre is supra-enteric in Phoronida but it is sub-enteric in Brachiopoda. (2) Two sets of tentacles (larval and definite) are present in Phoronida but in Brachiopoda the larval set is absent. (3) The shell of Brachiopoda cannot be correlated with exoskeleton of Phoronida. (4) The chitinous setae in Brachiopoda have no counterparts in Phoronida. (5) Circulatory system is of open type in Brachiopoda but in Phoronida it is of closed type. (6) The pattern of cleavage is spiral in Phoronida but in Brachiopoda it is not so. Because of such differences the two groups are placed in separate phyla. The similar features are due to remote connection with the ancestral stalk.

The recent knowledge of the anatomy and development of brachiopods suggests that the group may be assigned the position of an independent phylum.

REVISION QUESTIONS

1. Describe the habit, habitat and external features of *Magellania*.
2. Describe the internal structures of *Magellania*.
3. Give an account of the embryonic development and metamorphosis of a brachiopod.
4. Discuss the affinities of Brachiopoda.
5. Write notes on lophophore.

58

Phylum Phoronida

Phoronida are tubicolous, hermaphrodite, vermiform, coelomate Bilateria with a terminal tentaculated horse-shoe-shaped lophophore, a dorsal anus and one pair of metanephridia also serving as gonoducts.

The Phoronida has two genera under it. The genera are : *Phoronis* and *Phoronopsis*. There are about 15 species known ; of these a majority are included in the genus *Phoronis*. The typical representative of this phylum, *Phoronis* is described here in detail.

HABIT AND HABITAT

Phoronis is exclusively marine and is found sparingly over a wide geographical range. It lives in sandy bottom in shallow seas. In the adult stage, it is sedentary becomes enclosed by a membranous or leathery tube, within which the animal is capable of being retracted. It is a ciliary mucous feeder obtains food in the form of small, marine creatures by way of tentacular ciliary currents.

TUBE

All phoronids occupy a cylindrical tube of their secretion in which they can move freely. These tubes usually occur in aggregations that in some species result from asexual reproduction. It is not definitely known whether the secretion comes from the entire surface of the worm or from some part thereof when freshly formed. The secretion is fluid, transparent and sticky but on contact with water sets into a firm condition. The secreted part of the tube is chitinous. During the sticky phase there adhere to the secretion various objects of the environment as sandgrains, minute pebbles, sponge spicules, shell fragments that give the tube its definite appearance although often a short length of the clear tube free of adhered objects remains at the top.

EXTERNAL STRUCTURES

The body of *Phoronis* is cylindrical, elongated and unsegmented. It is colourless and transparent but sometimes yellowish or greenish. The body is differentiated into an anterior lophophore and a posterior trunk.

Lophophore. The lophophore is horse-shoe-shaped tentacular crown lying at the anterior oral end. It consists of two prominent ridges, outer and inner, between which is a groove leading into the median mouth. There are numerous slender hollow ciliated tentacles present on the lophophore. The tentacles are arranged in two rows, of which the one on the inner side of the lophophore is incomplete in the middle line. The tentacles are non-retractile, supported by mesodermal exoskeleton and serve to catch the food particles. The tentacles of each row are basally fused to form a membrane continuous with the lophophoral ridge bordering the mouth. Overhanging the mouth a broad lobe called the upper lip or epistome is present. Both mouth and anus are situated at the tentacular extremity of the body separated from one another by only a short space. Near the anus open two ciliated nephridial tubes.

Trunk. The trunk region of the body is narrow, slender, cylindrical and is devoid of appendages. The trunk is demarcated from the lophophore by a slight groove. The trunk is of uniform diameter throughout the length except the posterior end which becomes enlarged to form the end bulb. The trunk exhibits faint annulations.

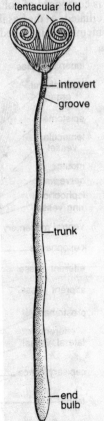

Fig. 58.1. *Phoronis australis.* Entire animal.

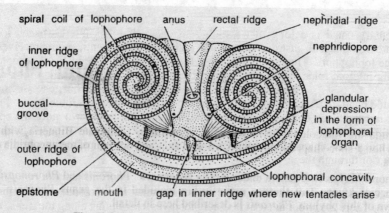

Fig. 58.2. *Phoronis australis.* Lophophore magnified.

BODY WALL

The body wall consists of cuticle, epidermis, basement membrane, muscular layers and coelomic epithelium. The cuticle is well-developed in the region of the lophophore. The epidermis is composed of columnar cells, neurosensory cells and gland cells. In the tentacles the epidermis is ciliated. At the basal part of the epidermis throughout the body, lies the nervous layer. The basement membrane is placed between the epidermis and the muscular layer. The muscular layer is composed of a thin outer circular muscles and thick inner longitudinal muscles. The coelomic epithelium is syncytial in nature.

COELOM

The coelom is spacious. The coelom is divided into two unequal parts by a partition or mesentery which runs across just behind the tentacles. The anterior part of coelom includes the cavities in the tentacular epistome and lophophore. This part of coelom is devoid of external openings. The posterior trunk coelom (metacoel) is quite extensive and occupies the whole length of the trunk. The metacoel, in the adult, is usually divided into four longitudinal compartments by mesenteries, two dorso-lateral and two ventro-lateral. The posterior trunk coelom is communicated with the exterior through the nephridia. The coelomic fluid-is a colourless, albuminous fluid and contains coelomocytes, red blood corpuscles, spindle bodies and pigment cells. The coelom is lined with a coelomic epithelium.

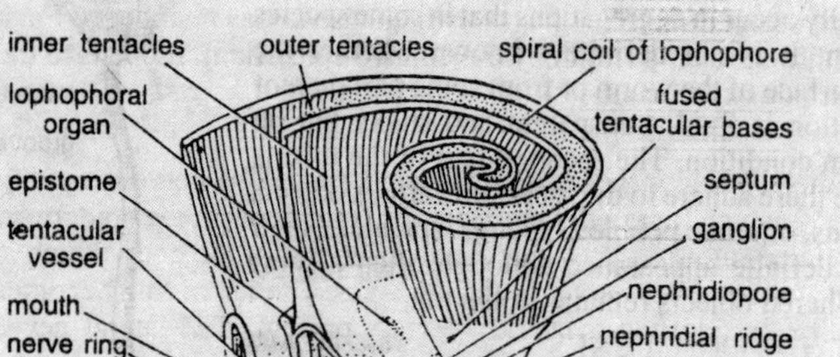

Fig. 58.3. *Phoronis australis.* Anterior and posterior ends of the body cut vertically to show the internal organisation.

DIGESTIVE SYSTEM

The alimentary canal is a long tube which bent on itself to form a U-shaped loop. It is differentiated into oesophageal, gastric and intestinal regions. The crescentic mouth receives ciliated grooves from the lophophore. The mouth leads into the oesophagus. The walls of oesophagus are thick and contain internal folds. The oesophagus proceeds into a long descending tube called the prestomach or proventriculus. The prestomach is devoid of muscular layer but possesses an internal mid-dorsal ciliated band. In the end bulb the prestomach is dilated to form a roundish stomach. The stomach has an inner ciliated epithelium in the middle region, but at the two sides the epithelium becomes syncytial. A constriction marks the stomach from the ascending intestine which is differentiated into proximal wider region and distal narrow region. The intestine passes into the rectum and opens to the exterior through the anus.

CIRCULATORY SYSTEM

The blood vessels are closed tubes with contractile walls. These blood vessels subserve the functions of heart. There are two main longitudinal blood vessels running along the trunk. A dorso-median or afferent vessel lies between the two limbs of alimentary canal. Anteriorly it forms an afferent ring vessel in the region of lophophore giving off one branch to each tentacle. In it the blood runs anteriorly. The ventro-lateral or efferent vessel runs along the left side of the oesophagus. Anteriorly it bifurcates before joining the efferent ring vessel of the lophophore. Blood flows in it posteriorly. Aborally, the dorso-median and ventro-lateral vessels communicate with the haemal plexus of the stomach wall. The blood contains only red blood corpuscles suspended in a colourless blood plasma.

EXCRETORY SYSTEM

The excretory system consists of a pair of metanephridia which also act as gonoducts. Each nephridium is a U-shaped tube lined throughout its length by the ciliated epithelium. It opens to the exterior through nephridiopore on the side of the anus.

NERVOUS SYSTEM

The nervous system lies immediately below the cells of the epidermis. The nervous system consists of nerve fibres and nerve cells which form a distinct nervous layer beneath the epidermis. This nervous layer becomes differentiated into nerve ring at the anterior end of the body which is regarded as the pre-oral nervous field and it gives nerves to the tentacles. The nerve ring becomes thickened and broadened mid-dorsally. In addition a lateral nerve is present. The lateral nerve innervates the trunk musculature.

SENSE ORGANS

There are no organs of special sense except the neurosensory cells in the epidermis. A pair of ciliated pits called lophophoral organs may be present dorsally in the concavity of the lophophore. They are considered glandular by some and sensory by others.

REPRODUCTIVE SYSTEM

Phoronis is hermaphrodite, although some species are dioecious. Specialized cells on the inner coelomic wall produce sperms and ova. The gonads are loose indefinite masses located posteriorly. Usually the testis occurs to the ventral side and ovary to the dorsal side of the lateral vessel. The mature cells are released in the body cavity and pass out through the nephridia to reach the concavity of the lophophore enclosed by the tentacles. Fertilization occurs either in the body cavity or in the lophophoral cavity where reproductive cells are brought out through the nephridiopores.

DEVELOPMENT

Fertilized ova undergo earlier stages of development while attached to the tentacles. The lophophoral cavity serves as a brood pouch containing ova and embryos in all the stages of development. The development is indirect. Cleavage is complete (holoblastic) and slightly unequal. The cleavage results into the formation of coeloblastula. The vagetal pole of the coeloblastula becomes flattened and invagination starts in typical embolic fashion. The mesoderm is budded off from the endoderm. The coelomic spaces arise as diverticula from the enteric wall. After the completion of development, a ciliated larva is produced. The larva is a free swimming form and has an oval body. The preoral lobe becomes expanded and bent forward. The alimentary canal is differentiated into oesophagus, stomach and intestine. As the larva develops, the cilia becomes restricted to certain areas of the body. The full developed larva is known as actinotrocha larva. It is free swimming, planktonic and has a gelatinous transparent body. It is elongated ranging from 1–5 mm in length. Overhanging the mouth of the larva there is a hood-like hollow pre-oral lobe and a circlet of ciliated tentacles. An apical plate with eye spots is present in the pre-oral lobe of the larva. A pair of excretory organs with solenocytes is present. There is present another post-oral ciliated ridge below the mouth. A girdle of slender tentacles arising from the pre-oral lobe surrounds the anterior part of the larva. Actinotrocha larva settles down to the bottom and transforms into an adult. This larva bears close resemblance with the tornaria larva of *Balanoglossus*.

AFFINITIES

The affinities of Phoronida have long been a subject for speculation and difference of opinion. Due to the peculiar anatomical organisation and structural resemblances with other groups, Phoronida has been a controversial issue since its discovery. Brachiopoda and Ectoprocta resemble very closely with the Phoronida. The Phoronida, Brachiopoda and Ectoprocta are collectively called the lophophorate coelomates. Hyman (1959) has suggested the term lophophorate for these groups because of the presence of lophophore.

Affinities with Brachiopoda. The Phoronida shows close resemblances with Brachiopoda. The resemblances are : (1) Presence of horse-shoe-shaped lophophore. (2) Presence of an epistome. (3) Presence of U-shaped alimentary canal. (4) Presence of a coelomic septum separating the mesosome and metasome, although poorly developed in Brachiopoda except *Crania* where the septum is complete. (5) Presence of sub-epidermal nerve plexus forming a nerve centre in the mesocoel. (6) Presence of a pair of metanephridia. (7) The mouth originates directly from the blastopore in both.(8) Dorsal surface between mouth and anus is extraordinarily shortened in both the cases. The Phoronida and Brachiopoda, though possess many similarities, have many structural differences which do not support the affinities of Phoronida with Brachiopoda. The main differences are as follows : (1) The nerve centre is supra-enteric in Phoronida, while sub-enteric in Brachiopoda. (2) In Phoronida two sets of tentacles are present, one is the larval set and the other is the definitive set, while in Brachiopoda larval tentacles are wanting. (3) The Brachiopoda shell cannot be correlated with the exoskeleton of Phoronida. (4) The chitionous setae in the larval and adult Brachiopoda have no counterparts in Phoronida. (5) The circulatory system of Phoronida is more developed than the Brachiopoda. In phoronids the blood vascular system is closed type, while in brachiopods it is open type. (6) In Phoronida, the cleavage pattern is spiral, while in Brachiopoda the cleavage is not spiral.

Affinities with Ectoprocta. Caldwell (1882) emphasised the affinities of Phoronida with Ectoprocta. The idea was based on the existence of the following similarities. (1) Same body and coelomic regionation with a definite septum between mesocoel and metacoel. (2) Presence of horse-shoe-shaped lophophore. (3) Presence of an epistome. (4) Presence of U-shaped alimentary canal. (5) The nerve centre is situated in the mesocoel and supraenteric in both. But a detailed study of two groups shows many structural dissimilarities. They differ widely from both anatomical and embryological point of view. The differences are : (1) The origin of coelom is different. In Phoronida the coelom is endomesodermal in origin, while in Ectoprocta it is ectomesodermal. (2) The region between the mouth and anus is dorsal in Phoronida but in Ectoprocta it is ventral. (3) Circulatory system and nephridia are absent in Ectoprocta but in Phoronida both the systems are present and well-formed. (4) The developmental sequences vary quite greatly.

Because of the presence of wide structural differences,the relationship between Ectoprocta and Phoronida cannot be justified. Of the three lophophorate coelomates, the phoronids are nearer to the lophophorate ancestor because they resemble each other in the following points : (1) Muscular vermiform body with crescentic lophophore. (2) Existence of a septum between an anterior lophophore bearing part and posterior trunk. (3) Circulatory system is of closed type with dorsal and ventral vessels. (4) Trochophore type of larva has protonephridia.

Affinities with Annelida. The affinities of Phoronida with Annelida are mainly based on the larval similarities. Because of their resemblances the Actinotrocha is regarded by many authors to be modified Trochophore larva. The similarities are as follows : (1) The tentaculate lophophore of Phoronida corresponds to the tentacular crown of *Sipunculus*. (2) In both Phoronida and Annelida the mature germ cells pass out through the nephridia. (3) The Actinotrocha larva and the Trochophore larva possess many common features : (i) Both of them are free swimming ciliated pelagic forms with distinct pre-oral lobe. (ii) The girdle of larval tentacles develops from the ciliary band. The cilia bordering the pre-oral lobe of Actinotrocha represent the metatroch and prototroch of Trochophore respectively. The disposition of telotroch is similar in both. (iii) A thickening of the ectoderm of the pre-oral lobe in Actinotrocha represents the apical plate of Trochophore. (iv) A pair of solenocytic nephridia is present. (v) In both the larval forms the alimentary canal is similarly placed and has similar divisions. But closer examination reveals that the Annelida and Phoronida are fundamentally different in their organisation. The most important point lies in the development of mesoderm. In Actinotrocha the mesoderm is endomesodermal and occurs as mesenchyme. The body of Phoronida is unsegmented, but in Annelida segmentation is the main criterion in their organisation. In Trochophore mesoderm is arranged in teloblastic bands. The affinities of Phoronida and Annelida cannot be justified critically, but the larval similarities are quite striking. These larval similarities may be due to their adaptive convergence.

Affinities with Hemichordata. Masterman (1897) tried to establish the affinities between Phoronida and Hemichordata on the grounds of similarities in the larval forms between the Actinotrocha larva of Phoronida and Tornaria larva of Hemichordata. The similarities are as follows : (1) The division of body of Hemichordata (proboscis, collar and trunk) corresponds to the body division of Phoronida (epistome, mesosome and trunk or metasome). (2) A pair of glandular pockets opening into the proximal end of the stomach of Phoronida is supposed by Masterman to be the paired notochord. (3) Presence of a septum between the middle and posterior sectors of the body in both the forms. (4) The position of tentaculate lophophore is similar to the tentaculate arms of *Cephalodiscus,* an example of Hemichordata. (5) Presence of superficial similarities in the disposition of coelom in the larval forms. But the thorough study reveals the following differences : (1) The three divisions of the body of Phoronida are not justified by embryological studies. As a matter of fact, Phoronida has two divisions in the body. The epistome of Phoronida is not the body region and does not contain coelom like that of proboscis of Hemichordata. (2) The mesocoel of Phoronida communicates to the exterior through the metanephridia which are absent in Hemichordata. (3) The coelom in Actinotrocha is divided in three compartments, while in Trochophore, the collar coelom and trunk coelom are paired. (4) The notochordal nature of glandular pockets in Phoronida is difficult to establish. From the above discussion it is quite apparent that most of the arguments forwarded by Masterman to establish the affinities between the Phoronida and Hemichordata are not supported by embryological facts, therefore, the affinities between these groups cannot be established.

Members of Protostomia (Platyhelminthes, Nemertines, Sipunculoidea, Echiuroidea, Annelida and Mollusca, etc.) appear to be related to one another as they show spiral cleavage, formation of mouth at the site of or as a part of blastopore. endomesodermal origin of coelom and free-swimming larvae that are Trochophores. On the other hand Deuterostomia (Hemichordata, Echinodermata,etc.)have body divisions into three regions, blastopore becoming anus, enterocoelous mode of origin of coelom and larva called dipleurula. Because of its dualistic affinities with the Protostomous phyla on one hand and the Deuterostomous phyla on the other, it appears that Phoronida forms a sort of connecting link between Protostomous phyla and Deuterostomous phyla.

REVISION QUESTIONS

1. Give an account of the internal organization of *Phoronis.*
2. Discuss in detail the affinities of Phoronida.

59
Phylum Mollusca

Mollusca (L., *mollis*=soft) comprise the second largest phylum of invertebrates in the number of species, over 80,000 living species have been described, and in addition about 35,000 fossil species are known. Possession of hard shell increases the chances of preservation, this has resulted in a rich fossil record of molluscs which came into existence in the early Cambrian. Mollusca appear to be a heterogeneous group with great diversity of form, but all of them are built on the same fundamental plan.

Mollusca are primitively bilaterally symmetrical animals with soft short bodies which show no segmentation, bilateral symmetry may be lost in some. The body has an anterior head, a dorsal visceral hump, a ventral muscular foot modified for crawling, burrowing or swimming. Around the body is a fleshy mantle which secretes a calcareous shell, the shell is usually external, though it may be internal, reduced or absent. The shell may be of one piece and called univalve, or of two parts and known as bivalve. Between the mantle and the body is a mantle cavity into which the anus and kidneys open, and in which lie a pair of ciliated gills or ctenidia having an axis bearing leaf-like branches on both sides, but the number of gills may be much larger in some molluscs. The schizocoelic coelom is reduced to cavities of pericardium, gonads and kidneys, the main body cavity is a haemocoele. The large amount of blood in the haemocoele can be manipulated by body wall muscles, this brings about change of shape, dilation of foot, and extension of proboscis and head. There is a dorsal heart with one or two auricles and a single ventricle, the respiratory pigment is haemocyanin. Respiration occurs by the mantle, epidermis, one to several ctenidia or by a lung in the mantle cavity. Sexes are usually separate, development is either direct or there is a modified trochosphere called a veliger larva.

Mollusca are mostly marine, though some are found in freshwater and a few are terrestrial. The members of this phylum show a great diversity of form, they include such familiar animals as chitons, snails, slugs, clams, oysters, squids and octopods.

Pila is commonly known as apple snail. The genus *Pila* is confined to the Oriental and Ethiopian regions. In the Oriental region it is found in India (except Punjab and Sindh), Burma, Sri Lanka, Thailand, Malaya, Indonesia, Vietnam and Philippines and in Ethiopian region it is found in Africa, Arabia and Madagascar. The common species found in Northern India (except Punjab)is *Pila globosa*, formerly known as *Ampullaria globosa* and that of South India are *P. virens, P. nevililana* and *P. theobaldi*. However, present chapter deals with the study of *Pila globosa*.

PILA GLOBOSA
SYSTEMATIC POSITION

Phylum	....	**Mollusca**
Class	....	**Gastropoda**
Subclass	....	**Prosobranchia**
Order	....	**Megagastropoda**
Genus	....	*Pila*
Species	....	*globosa*

HABIT AND HABITAT

Pila globosa or the apple snail is one of the largest freshwater molluscs. It is commonly found in freshwater ponds, pools, tanks, lakes, marshes, rice fields and sometimes even in streams and rivers. They occur in those areas where there is a large amount of aquatic vegetation like *Vallisneria, Pistia,* for food. They are amphibious being adapted for life in water and on land.

The animal creeps very slowly by its ventral muscular foot, covering about five cm per minute. The movement of the animal is like the gliding movement of planarian. During the rainy seasons *Pila* comes out of the ponds and makes long terrestrial tours, thus, respiring air directly. It can overcome long periods of drought in a dormant condition and buried in the mud ; this period of inactivity is called aestivation or summer sleep.

EXTERNAL FEATURES

Shell. The shell of *Pila*, as in other Gastropoda, is univalve but coiled around a central axis in a right-handed spiral. The top of the shell is the apex which is formed first and growth of shell takes place from it, the apex contains the smallest and the oldest whorl. Below the apex is a spire consisting of several successively larger whorls or coils followed by penultimate **whorl** and the largest whorl or body whorl which encloses most of the body. The lines between the whorls are called sutures. Internally all the whorls of the shell are freely communicated with one another; such a shell is called unilocular. The body whorl has a large mouth or opening, the margin of the mouth is called a peristome from which the head and the foot of the living animal can protrude. When viewed from the ventral side with the peristome facing the observer, the mouth lies to the right of the columella and the

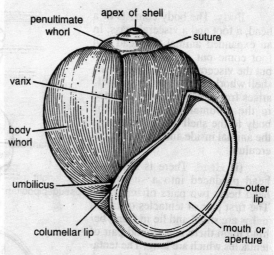

Fig. 60.1. *Pila globosa*. Shell seen from ventral surface.

shell is spiralled clock-wise, then it is spoken of as being right-handed or dextral. The outer margin of the mouth is called an outer lip, and the inner margin as inner or columellar lip.

In the centre of the shell runs a vertical axis or **columella** around which the whorls of the shell are coiled; the columella is hollow and its opening to the exterior is known as an **umbilicus**. Shells with an umbilicus are **umbilicate** or **perforate**. The lines of growth of shell are visible, some of them appear as ridges known as **varices**. The shell of *Pila* varies in colour from yellowish to brown or even blackish.

Operculum. Fitting into the mouth of the shell is a calcareous **operculum**, its outer surface shows a number of rings of growth around a nucleus ; the inner surface has an elliptical **boss** for attachment of muscles, the boss is creamcoloured and is surrounded by a groove. The operculum is,

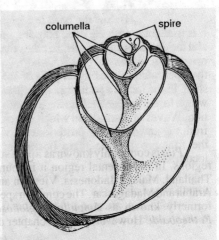

Fig. 60.2. *Pila globosa.* Shell seen from dorsal surface.

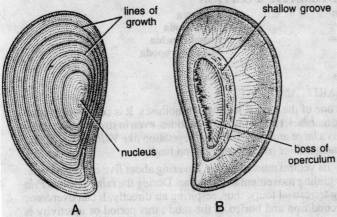

Fig. 60.3. *Pila globosa.* Operculum. A—Outer view; B—Inner view.

in fact, secreted by the glandular cells of the foot.

Microscopic structure of shell. The shell of *Pila* consists of an outermost pigmented layer called **periostracum** made of a horny organic conchiolin, below this is a **prismatic layer** made of crystalline calcareous plates running vertically, the innermost **nacreous layer** is made of calcareous plates running longitudinally. Shells of Gastropoda display an infinite variety of shapes, sculpturing, patterns, and colours. Inside the shell is the **mantle** which secretes the shell.

Body. The body consists of a head, a foot and a visceral mass. In an expanded animal the head and foot come out of the shell-mouth but the visceral mass lies inside the shell whorls. A **collumellar muscle** arises from the foot and is inserted in the columella, it attaches the body to the shell and it withdraws the animal inside and closes the operculum.

(i) Head. There is a distinct head produced into a **snout**, the head bears two pairs of **tentacles**. The first pair of tentacles or **labial palps** are small and lie in front, behind them there is a second pair of tentacles which are long. The tentacles are hollow and capable of much extension and contraction. Behind the tentacles the head has a pair of eyes borne on stalks or **ommatophores.**

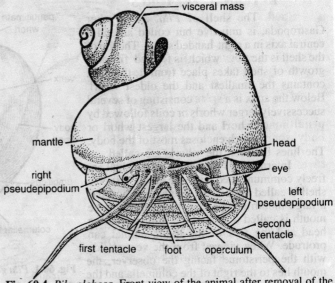

Fig. 60.4. *Pila globosa.* Front view of the animal after removal of the shell.

(ii) Foot. Below the head is a large muscular foot, its lower surface is gray and flattened sole. It is triangular with the apex pointing backwards, it is used for creeping ; its upper surface is spotted and the dorsal posterior surface bears the operculum. When the foot is withdrawn the operculum closes the mouth of the shell. In the foot is a pedal mucous gland which forms a slime trail during locomotion. Waves of contraction which sweep from the anterior to the posterior end of the foot provide the main power for locomotion.

In fact, the head and the foot together constitute the head-foot complex which is connected to the visceral mass by an inconspicuous neck.

(iii) Visceral mass. Above the head-foot complex is a visceral mass containing the main organs, it fills all the whorls of the shell and it is spirally-coiled like the shell. The visceral mass exhibits the phenomenon of torsion which is distinct from coiling. It is soft and grey to dark brown in colour.

(iv) Mantle. The mantle, also referred to as pallium, covers the visceral mass and it forms a hood over the

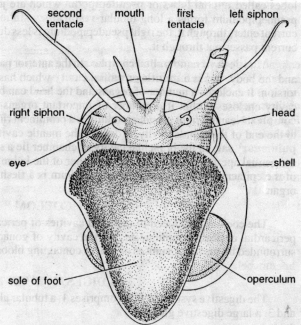

Fig. 60.5. *Pila globosa.* A living animal seen from the ventral side showing the elongated siphon formed by the left pseudepipodium.

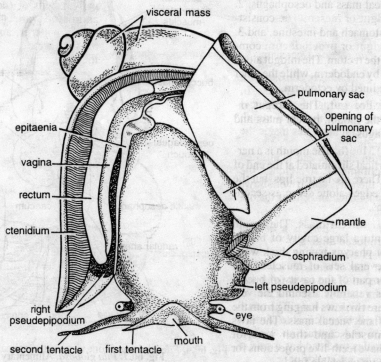

Fig. 60.6. *Pila globosa.* A female individual dissected to show the organs of the pallial cavity.

animal when it is withdrawn. The edge of the mantle is thick and contains shell glands which secrete the shell, above the thickened edge there is a supra-marginal groove. The mantle also has two fleshy lobes called nuchal lobes or pseudepipodia which are joined on either side of the head. The left pseudepipodium forms a long tubular respiratory siphon for aerial respiration and a respiratory current enters through it, the right pseudepipodium is less developed and not a regular tube, respiratory current passes out through it.

Mantle cavity and pallial complex. In the anterior part there is a large space between the mantle and the body, this is a mantle or pallial cavity which has been shifted to the front by a process of torsion. It encloses a number of organs and the head can be withdrawn into it. The mantle or pallial cavity encloses within it a number of important organs which are collectively known as pallial complex. Near the right pseudepipodium is a prominent ridge or epitaenia which runs backwards up to the end of the mantle cavity, it divides the mantle cavity into a right branchial cavity and a left pulmonary sac. In the branchial cavity or chamber lie a single gill or ctenidium, rectum and anus, the genital aperture and the anterior chamber of the kidney as a reddish mass near the posterior end of the epitaenia. Near the left pseudepipodium is a fleshy osphradium a typical molluscan sense organ.

COELOM

The coelom is reduced to unpaired cavities of pericardium, kidney and gonad. The renal and pericardial cavities communicate, but the cavity of gonad is unconnected. The visceral organs are surrounded by means of sinuses or spaces containing blood. These blood-filled spaces constitute the haemocoel.

DIGESTIVE SYSTEM

The digestive system of *Pila* comprises 1. a tubular alimentary canal, 2. a pair of salivary glands and 3. a large digestive gland.

Alimentary Canal

The alimentary canal is distinguished into three regions, *viz.,* 1. the foregut or stomodaeum including the buccal mass and oesophagus, 2. the midgut or mesenteron consisting of stomach and intestine, and 3. the hindgut or proctodaeum comprising the rectum. The midgut alone is lined by endoderm, while the other two are lined by ectoderm.

1. Foregut. The foregut includes the mouth, buccal mass and oesophagus.

(i) Mouth. The mouth is a narrow vertical slit situated at the end of snout. There are no true lips but the plicate edges alone serve as secondary lips.

(ii) Buccal mass. The mouth leads into a large cavity of buccal mass or pharynx having thick walls with several sets of muscles. The anterior part of the cavity of buccal mass is vestibule. Behind the vestibule are two jaws hanging from the roof of the buccal mass. The jaws bear muscles and their anterior edges have teeth-like projections for cutting up vegetable food.

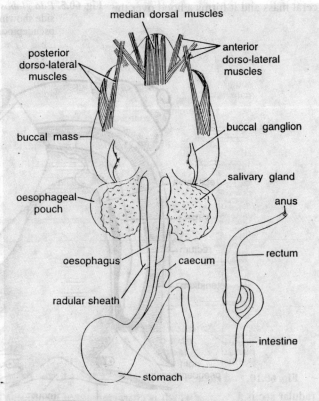

Fig. 60.7. *Pila globosa.* Alimentary canal.

Buccal cavity. Behind the jaws is a large buccal cavity. On the floor of the buccal cavity is a large elevation called odontophore. The front part of odontophore has a furrowed subradular organ which helps in cutting food. The odontophore has protractor and retractor muscles and two pairs of cartilages, a pair of triangular superior cartilages which project into the buccal cavity, and a pair of large S-shaped lateral cartilages.

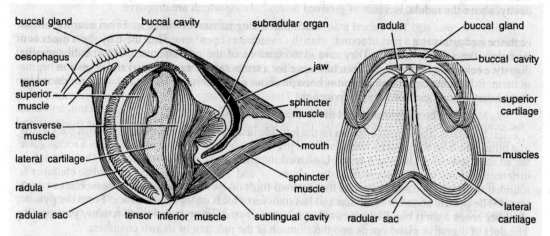

Fig. 60.8. *Pila globosa.* Vertical longitudinal section of the buccal mass about the middle.

Fig. 60.9. *Pila globosa.* Buccal mass in T.S.

Radula. Above and behind the odontophore is a bag-like radular sac which is a diverticulum of the buccal cavity. The radular sac has transverse rows of cells called odontoblasts. Inside the

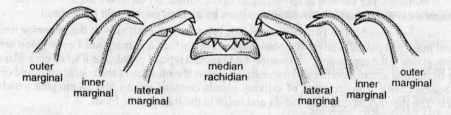

Fig. 60.11. *Pila globosa.* A single row of radular teeth.

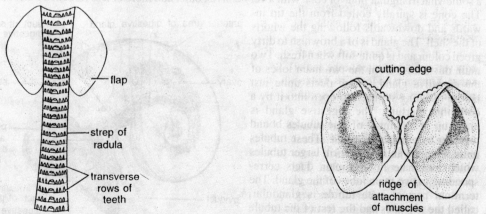

Fig. 60.10. *Pila globosa.* The radula.

Fig. 60.12. *Pila globosa.* Jaws.

radular sac is a radula which is characteristic of Mollusca. The radula is made of many transverse rows of horny teeth. Each row has seven teeth, two marginal and one lateral tooth on each side and a central or rachidian tooth in the middle, thus, giving a formula 2,1,1,1,2. The radula moves forward and backward on the odontophore for rasping food particles; these movements of radula are called chain saw movements. The teeth are made of chitin which is reinforced by hardened protein, they have sharp cutting projections which act like a file and rasp vegetable food. The teeth of the radula are worn off in front and new teeth are formed all the time by odontoblasts. On the roof of buccal cavity, above the radula, is a pair of grooved buccal glands which are digestive.

(iii) Oesophagus. The buccal mass leads into a long narrow oesophagus. From near the origin of the oesophagus arise a pair of round, whitish oesophageal pouches. They arise by short ducts and lie below the salivary glands. They are prolongations of the oesophagus, they probably secrete digestive enzymes. Oesophageal pouches serve for a temporary storage of food and digestion begins in them. Some extracellular digestion is brought about in the stomach by the enzymes produced by the salivary glands and oesophageal pouches.

2. Midgut. The midgut includes the stomach and intestine.

(i) Stomach. The stomach begins on the left side just below the pericardium and runs backwards as a blind pouch on the postero-lateral sides of the main whorl of the visceral mass. It is a rectangular sac of dark red colour having a broad U-shaped internal cavity of rose-red colour. The stomach is differentiated into two chambers— cardiac chamber and pyloric chamber. The cardiac chamber is rounded in appearance and possesses longitudinal folds on its inner surface. The oesophagus opens into it. The pyloric chamber is tubular and has transverse folds on its inner surface. From the pyloric chamber arises a short bag-like caecum but it has no crystalline style as found in many gastropods. The duct of digestive gland opens into the stomach at the junction of its two chambers.

(ii) Intestine. From the pyloric chamber arises an intestine which runs along its anterior edge and further along the digestive gland beneath the posterior renal chamber. It then turns upwards and backwards in the visceral mass where it forms $2\frac{1}{2}$ or 3 coils between the gonad in front and the digestive gland behind, before joining the rectum.

3. Hindgut. The rectum or terminal part of the alimentary canal is a thick-walled tube. It enters the mantle cavity and passes downwards to open by an anus on the right of the head.

Salivary glands. The two salivary glands lying one on each side of the posterior limit of the buccal mass and partially cover the oesophagus. The surface and margins of each gland are greatly cut up, giving it the appearance of a somewhat branched type of gland. The duct of each gland begins near its internal anterior corner and immediately enters the muscles of the buccal mass and opens into the buccal cavity. The secretion of salivary glands contains mucus and an enzyme which digests starch. The mucus lubricates the radula and helps in the transport of food.

Digestive gland. The digestive gland, often referred to as liver or hepatopancreas, of *Pila* is a somewhat triangular plate or cone with a very convex outer and more or less flattened inner surface.

The cone is spirally coiled from the tip inwards and downwards following the whorls of the shell. The gland is of a brownish to dirty green colour and is quite soft when fresh. Two main ducts arise from the two main lobes of the digestive gland; these ducts unite just before reaching stomach to open into it by a common aperture. The digestive gland is made up of a number of fine tubules bound together by connective tissue. These tubules unite with one another to form larger tubules which terminate in two main ducts corresponding to two main lobes of the gland. The terminal part of each tubule is glandular, called the alveolus and the rest of the tubule is ciliated. The alveoli have three kinds of cells, they are secretory, resorptive and calcareous cells or lime cells. The secretory cells

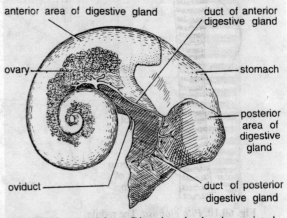

Fig. 60.13. *Pila globosa.* Digestive gland and associated structures seen from inner side.

produce a brown liquid containing an enzyme which dissolves cellulose of plants in the stomach converting in into pulp. The resorptive cells produce a proteolytic enzyme. This enzyme brings about intracellular digestion of cellulose pulp. The calcareous cells store phosphate of lime.

Food and Feeding

The food consists of aquatic plants of succulent nature like *Vallisneria* and *Pistia* which are cut by jaws and the odonotophore, then the radula moves forwards and backwards filing the food into small particles exactly like the chain-saw mechanism. Thus, the food is cut up and masticated inside the buccal cavity.

Digestion

The salivary glands pour their secretion by means of their ducts into the buccal cavity where it mixes with the food. It helps in digesting the starch by converting it into sugar. In the stomach the food is digested by the secretion of digestive gland. Secretion of digestive gland digests various kinds of food but cellulose is digested inside the resorptive cells only. Thus, both extracellular and intercellular digestion occur. The stomach is the site of extracellular digestion and the digestive gland is the site of intracellular digestion and absorption, this is characteristic of Mollusca. Absorption of digested food takes place mainly in the digestive gland and some in the intestine.

RESPIRATORY SYSTEM

Pila leads an amphibious life and, therefore, it exhibits dual modes of respiration, *i.e.*, aquatic and aerial. For these, it possesses a ctenidium or gill (for aquatic respiration) and a pulmonary sac or lung (for aerial respiration).

Respiratory Organs

The respiratory organs consist of a single ctenidium or gill, a pulmonary sac or lung and a pair of nuchal lobes.

1. **Ctenidium or gill.** The ctenidium or gill is the organ of aquatic respiration. The ctenidium is situated on the dorso-lateral wall of the branchial chamber of the mantle cavity. It is composed of

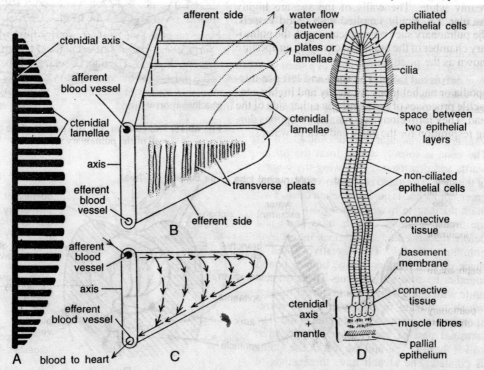

Fig. 60.14. *Pila globosa.* Respiratory organs. A—A monopectinate ctenidium ; B—Stereogram to show water current through gill-lamellae ; C—A single lamella to show flow of blood within it ; D—A lamella in T.S.

a long series of thin triangular leaflets or lamellae, lying parallel to each other, which are attached to the mantle wall by their broad bases but have their apices hanging free in the branchial chamber. The line of attachment of the lamellae to the wall of the mantle forms the ctenidial axis. The ctenidial axis is provided with an afferent blood vessel (carrying deoxygenated blood) and an efferent blood vessel (carrying oxygenated blood) from gills to heart. All the gill lamellae are not of the same size; these are largest in the middle and gradually smaller towards the two ends. Such a gill is known as monopectinate gill. Each lamella bears transverse ridges or pleats on both its anterior and posterior surfaces. These pleats are low ridges gradually decreasing in size from the base of the lamella to its apex. Each ridge contains branches of blood vessels. Each lamella has a smaller right side, which receives blood from the afferent vessel, is called the afferent side and a longer left side, from which blood goes into the efferent vessel, is called the efferent side.

The ctenidium of *Pila*, though situated on the right side of the animal, is morphologically the gill of the left side, which has shifted to the right on account of the development of an extensive pulmonary sac on the left side. This is shown by the blood supply and the innervation of the ctenidium and is further confirmed by the situation of the osphradium which still retains its original position on the left side of the animal.

Histologically, each lamella appears to be a hollow cavity lined on either side by the epithelium containing non-ciliated columnar cells, ciliated columnar cells and a few glandular cells. The epithelial layer is followed by a thin basement membrane below which are found connective tissue cells having scattered nuclei and oblique muscle fibres.

2. **Pulmonary sac or lung.** The pulmonary sac or lung is a closed cavity like a bag which hangs from the dorsal wall of the mantle in the pulmonary chamber. The dorsal wall of the pulmonary sac is densely pigmented, while the ventral wall is creamy white. The walls of the sac are highly vascular, *i.e.*, richly supplied with blood vessels. The pulmonary sac communicates with the pulmonary chamber of the branchial cavity by an aperture known as the pneumostome.

3. **Nuchal lobes.** The right and left pse-ude-pipodia or nuchal lobes are fleshy and highly contractile processes of the mantle on either side of the head. They form elongated funnels or siphons during respiration for the entry and exit of water.

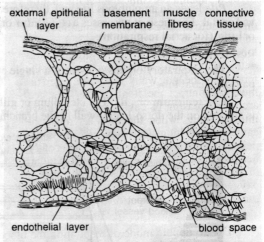

Fig. 60.15. *Pila globosa.* T.S. of a portion of the outer wall of the pulmonary sac.

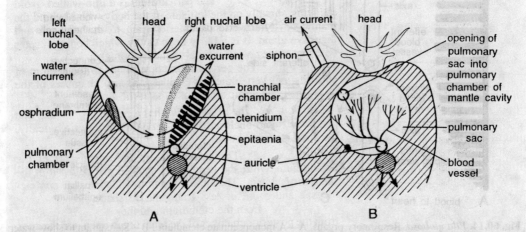

Fig. 60.16. *Pila globosa.* Diagrams showing mechanism of respiration. A—During aquatic respiration; B—During aerial respiration.

Mechanism of respiration. There are two types of respiration in *Pila* which are as follows :

1. Aquatic respiration. True aquatic respiration takes place when the snail lies at the bottom of a pond or aquarium, when it is floating or lying suspended in mid-water and when it is attached to plants or weeds in water. At this time the head and foot is fully extended and the two nuchal lobes further increase in size and the left lobe takes the form of a distinct gutter in which a current of water flows. In aquatic respiration a current of water enters the left nuchal lobe and first comes in contact with the osphradium which tests the nature of the water. It enters the mantle cavity and passes over the epitaenia into the branchial chamber to bathe the ctenidium, then the current passes out through the right nuchal lobe (Fig. 60.16 A). The ctenidium takes in oxygen from the current of water and gives out carbon dioxide which diffuses into water.

(ii) Aerial respiration. The pulmonary sac or lung is used in aerial respiration in two ways. When the snail comes to the surface of water its left nuchal lobe projects as a tube above the water and air is drawn into it, the air goes to the pulmonary chamber and then into the lung ; the branchial chamber being shut off by the epitaenia pressing against the mantle. When the snail comes on land it takes in air directly into its lung through the mantle cavity and no siphon is formed by the left nuchal lobe. In both types of aerial respiration alternate contractions and relaxations of the muscles of the lung walls take place, when the muscles contract the floor of the lung gets arched increasing its cavity and air is drawn into the lung, when the muscles relax the cavity of the lung decreases and air is expelled, inward and outward movements of the head and foot also help in the process of taking in air. The blood vessels in the lung take in

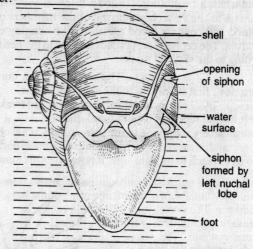

Fig. 60.17. *Pila globosa* with its siphon up for breathing air.

oxygen from the air and give out carbon dioxide (Fig. 60.16 B). *Pila* also respires by its pulmonary sac during aestivation period by means of the air already imprisoned in the pulmonary sac.

BLOOD VASCULAR SYSTEM

Due to double mode of respiration the blood vascular system of *Pila* has become very much complicated. It is of open type. It consists of (i) pericardium, (ii) heart, (iii) arteries, (iv) sinuses, and (v) veins, through which the blood flows.

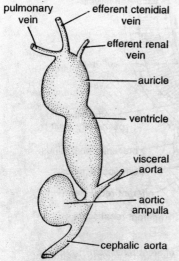

Fig 60.18. *Pila globosa*. Heart.

(i) Pericardium. The pericardium is a thin-walled ovoid sac lying dorsally on the left side of the body whorl behind the mantle cavity. It extends anteriorly up to the stomach and digestive gland. It is a fairly deep cavity which communicates with that of the posterior renal chamber through a reno-pericardial aperture. The pericardium corresponds to the coelom of annelids and vertebrates. It encloses the two chambers of the heart, the main aortic arches and the aortic ampulla.

(ii) Heart. The heart of *Pila* has a single auricle and one ventricle found enclosed in the pericardium. Physiologically, the heart is said to be myogenic.

(a) Auricle. The auricle lies in the dorsal part of the pericardium, while the ventricle is situated just below it in the same vertical axis. The auricle is a thin-walled, highly contractile sac and more or less triangular in shape. The efferent ctenidial vein from the ctenidium and the efferent renal vein from the posterior chamber of the renal organ open into the apex of the auricle, while the pulmonary vein from pulmonary sac opens at a slightly lower level at its anterior end. The auricle communicates with the ventricle by an aperture auriculo-ventricular opening having two semi-lunar valves, so arranged as to allow the blood from the auricle to flow into the ventricle but not in the reverse direction.

(b) Ventricle. The ventricle is ovoidal in shape and has thick spongy wall formed of a large number of muscular strands forming a meshwork which greatly reduces the cavity of the ventricle. The aortic trunk arises from the lower end of the ventricle and divides immediately into two branches, the cephalic aorta and visceral aorta. The opening between ventricle and aortic trunk is guarded by two semi-lunar valves which prevent the flow of blood from back into the ventricle.

(iii) Arteries. From the ventricle arises an aorta or aortic-trunk which divides into two branches, a cephalic aorta and a visceral aorta. The cephalic aorta has a bulbous outgrowth called aortic ampulla, a characteristic of the members of the family Pilidae, which aids in circulation of blood and controls blood pressure. The opening of aortic ampulla into cephalic aorta is devoid of valves. The cephalic aorta sends arteries to the head and buccal mass, the visceral aorta forms arteries going to the visceral mass.

(a) Cephalic aorta. The cephalic aorta, immediately beyond aortic ampulla, gives out three arteries ; first supplying to the skin, the cutaneous artery second supplying to the oesophagus, the oesophageal artery and third being stout and thick supplies to the left side of the mantle (organs like left nuchal lobe and osphradium), the left pallial artery. The cephalic aorta on its inner side gives out an artery supplying to the pericardium, renal chambers and to a portion of the genital organs, the pericardial artery. The main trunk of cephalic aorta then runs ahead and crosses over the oesophagus so as to reach to its right side. It now gives off numerous small branches to the oesophageal area and

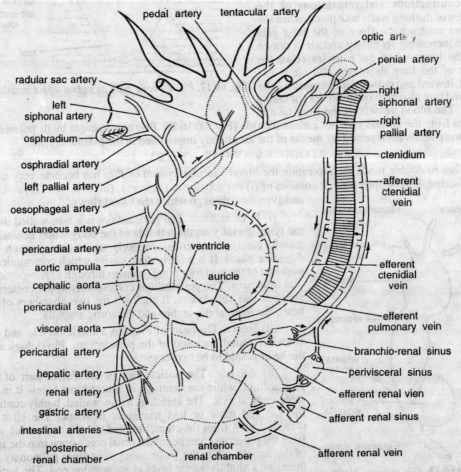

Fig. 60.19. *Pila globosa.* Heart and blood-vascular system.

a large branch to the right side which finally gives out a right pallial artery, supplying to the right part of mantle, a right siphonal artery, supplying to the right nuchal lobe and a penial artery, supplying to the copulatory organ. The main trunk of cephalic aorta, however, also branches to give a radular sac artery supplying to radular sac, an optic artery supplying to the eyestalks and eyes, a tentacular artery supplying to the tentacles and pedal arteries supplying to the foot.

(b) Visceral aorta. As mentioned earlier, the visceral aorta runs into the visceral mass and supplies to its different organs by giving off many branches. These branches are : a pericardial artery to the pericardium, skin and digestive glands, a gastric artery to the stomach, many small intestinal arteries to the intestine, many renal arteries to the roof of the posterior renal chamber, a hepatic artery to the digestive gland and gonad, several small arteries to the tip of the genital duct and then finally the visceral aorta terminates in the rectal wall.

(iv) Sinuses. The blood after being distributed to the various parts of the body through the arteries and their branches passes into small lacunae, which in turn unite to form large sinuses. There are four chief sinuses in the body : (a) anterior peri-visceral sinus, (b) anterior peri-intestinal sinus, (c) branchio-renal sinus and (d) pulmonary sinus.

(a) Anterior peri-visceral sinus. It lies above the foot and beneath the floor of the pallial cavity surrounding the anterior part of the alimentary canal. It collects blood supplied by the cephalic aorta, except pericardial artery, and some branches of visceral aorta.

(b) Anterior peri-intestinal sinus. It lies on the columellar axis next to the intestine and the terminal part of the genital duct and runs along the coils of the intestine up to the junction of the anterior and posterior renal chambers. It collects blood from viscera mainly distributed by visceral aorta.

(c) Branchio-renal sinus. It lies along the right side of the anterior renal chamber. It collects blood from renal chambers.

(d) Pulmonary sinus. It lies in the walls of the pulmonary sac. It collects blood from pulmonary sac.

(v) Veins. The veins carry venous blood from different parts of the body to the auricle directly or through the gill, mantle and kidney. The chief veins are as follows :

(a) Afferent ctenidial vein. It lies above the rectum and receives branches from the rectum, terminal part of the genital duct, peri-visceral sinus and branchio-renal sinus. It sends blood through numerous branches, to the gill-lamellae for purification.

(b) Efferent ctenidial vein. It lies along the roof of the anterior renal chamber and carries blood from ctenidial leaflets, mantle and conveys to the auricle.

(c) Afferent renal vein. It is situated on the roof of posterior renal chamber, and originates from the peri-intestinal sinus. It pours its blood into the posterior renal chamber.

(d) Efferent renal vein. It carries the blood of the posterior renal chamber to the auricle.

(e) Pulmonary vein. It collects blood from the walls of the pulmonary sac and opens into the auricle.

Blood. The blood of gastropods contains a respiratory pigment called haemocyanin which is a compound of copper and protein, haemocyanin is dissolved in the plasma and gives a faintly blue colour to the blood. But in a few gastropods, such as *Planorbis,* hemoglobin is found in place of haemocyanin. In the blood plasma are stellate amoebocytes which are phagocytic, they remove waste substances and some of them carry on intracellular digestion.

Course of Circulation

All parts of the body are supplied with blood from the ventricle through the cephalic and visceral aortae. The cephalic aorta carries blood to the head and its associated structures, a part of the mantle, the buccal mass, the oesophagus, the copulatory organ and the collumellar muscle. The visceral aorta supplies the whole of the visceral mass. The blood is collected from the various parts of the body into two main sinuses the peri-visceral and peri-intestinal. From these sinuses, the blood passes either into the ctenidium, pulmonary sac or into the renal organ. During aquatic respiration the blood from the peri-visceral sinus goes to the ctenidium and is purified ; an efferent ctenidial vein then takes this blood into the auricle. During aerial respiration the blood from the peri-visceral sinus goes to the lung and is purified; a pulmonary vein takes this blood into the auricle. The blood from the peri-intestinal sinus takes two courses, it either goes from this sinus to the anterior renal chamber and from there to the ctenidium and is purified, then through the efferent ctenidial vein it goes to the auricle. Or the blood from the peri-intestinal sinus goes to the anterior renal chamber, then to the posterior renal chamber (blood from the peri-intestinal sinus can also go direct to the posterior renal chamber without going to the anterior renal chamber); in any case the blood from the posterior renal chamber goes through an efferent renal vein into the auricle. Thus, the auricle receives pure blood from the ctenidium or the lung and impure blood from the posterior renal chamber, this mixed blood enters the ventricle and is distributed to the arteries. The renal chambers, however, remove waste substances from the blood.

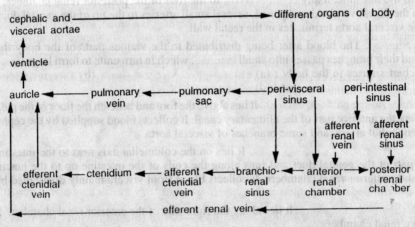

Fig. 60.20. *Pila globosa*. Diagrammatic representation of the course of circulation.

EXCRETORY SYSTEM

There is a single large **renal organ** or **kidney** or **organ of Bojanus** lying behind the pericardium. It is a thick-walled sac which is much folded within. The renal organ consists of two distinct chambers: a right **anterior renal chamber** and a left **posterior renal chamber**. The renal organ of *Pila*

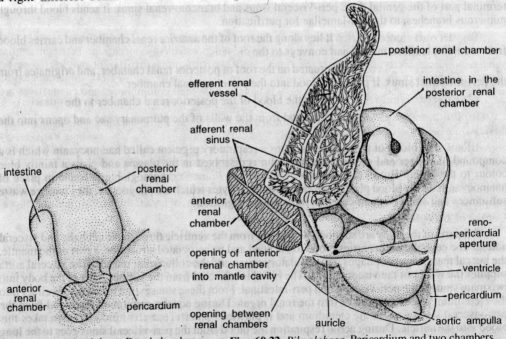

Fig. 60.21. *Pila globosa*. Renal chamber seen from above.

Fig. 60.22. *Pila globosa*. Pericardium and two chambers of renal organ.

corresponds to the left kidney of Diotocardia, while the right kidney in this order has been modified to form the genital duct.

Anterior renal chamber. It is a reddish organ somewhat ovoidal in outline, situated in front of pericardium and the posterior renal chamber. It projects into the mantle cavity and opens into it in a deep crypt through an elongated opening lying to the right of the epitaenia. The upper surface of the chamber shows shallow grooves corresponding to the internal lamellae, which hang downwards from the roof into the cavity of the chamber. The lamellae on the roof are arranged on either side of a median longitudinal axis, the efferent renal sinus. The lamellae on the floor are arranged on either side of a similar median axis, the afferent renal sinus which is the branch of the peri-intestinal sinus. It breaks up into numerous branches to supply the lamellae on both the sides.

Posterior renal chamber. The posterior renal chamber is a broad, somewhat hook-shaped area of a brownish to dusky grey colour, situated behind the anterior renal chamber in between the rectum on the left and pericardium and digestive gland on the right. It contains a large cavity in which a genital duct and a few coils of intestine lie. The roof of the chamber is richly supplied with blood vessels resulting from a repeated division of the afferent and efferent renal vessels of this chamber. The posterior renal chamber communicates with the pericardium by a reno-pericardial aperture at one end and with the anterior renal chamber through an aperture at the other end. The floor of the posterior renal chamber consist of a thin lining of tissue which separates its cavity from the organs which project into it.

Physiology of Excretion

Both the renal chambers in *Pila* have a true excretory function and excrete nitrogenous waste products. Owing to a single external opening, the excretory products from the posterior chamber are collected and emptied into the anterior chamber, from where they are discharged into the pallial cavity through the external renal opening. The kidney is a coelomoduct communicating at one end with the coelom (pericardium) and at the other end with the exterior (mantle cavity). The kidney removes nitrogenous waste from the blood, waste is discharged into the mantle cavity. Excretory matter contains mostly ammonia, and some ammonium compounds, urea and uric acid. In order to conserve water ammonia is converted into the relatively insoluble uric acid. This adaptation for water conservation is particularly striking in *Pila* which is seasonally amphibious, during its aquatic phase it excretes ammonium compounds, but during its terrestrial phase it excretes uric acid.

In most Gastropoda the digestive gland plays a role in excretion because it contains some excretory cells that take up waste which is eliminated by way of the stomach and intestine.

NERVOUS SYSTEM

The nervous system of *Pila* consists of paired and unpaired ganglia with their commissures and connectives. The commissures are the nerves which establish connections between similar ganglia, while connectives are the nerves which connect two dissimilar or different ganglia. However, the paired ganglia of *Pila* are cerebral, buccal. pleural, pedal and visceral, while unpaired ganglia are supraintestinal and infraintestinal. These ganglia with their commissures and connectives are described below :

1. Cerebral ganglia. There are two triangular cerebral ganglia, one on each side above the buccal mass, they are connected to each other by a thick cerebral commissure running transversely above the buccal mass, and by a thin labial commissure lying below the buccal mass. Each cerebral ganglion is further connected with the buccal ganglion of its side through a very slender cerebro-buccal connective. Thick band-shaped cerebro-pleural and cerebro-pedal connectives serve to connect each cerebral ganglion with the corresponding pleural and pedal ganglia. Each cerebral ganglion gives off several nerves supplying anteriorly the skin of snout, the tentacle and the buccal mass; and posteriorly the tentacle, the eye and the statocyst.

2. Buccal ganglia. At the junction of the buccal mass and oesophagus are two buccal ganglia. They are connected to each other by a transverse buccal commissure. They are also connected to the cerebral ganglia by a cerebro-buccal connective on each side, the connectives lie above the buccal mass. Nerves from each buccal ganglion supply the buccal mass, radular sac, salivary glands, oesophagus and the oesophageal pouches.

3. Pleuro-pedal ganglionic mass. In fact, the pleural and pedal ganglia of each side join together to form a pleuro-pedal ganglionic mass situated below the buccal mass. In a pleuro-pedal ganglionic mass, the pleural ganglion is placed towards the outer side and the pedal ganglion to the inner side.

The pleuro-pedal ganglionic mass is connected to the cerebral ganglion of its side by a **cerebro-pleural connective** and cerebro-pedal connective. The two pedal ganglia are connected to each other by two pedal commissures lying closely parallel to each other. The right pleuro-pedal mass has an infra-intestinal or a sub-intestinal ganglion also fused with it. A slender, loop-like infra-intestinal nerve behind the pedal commissure, connects the pleural ganglia of both the sides. A statocyst is connected by a band of connective tissue, to each pedal ganglion.

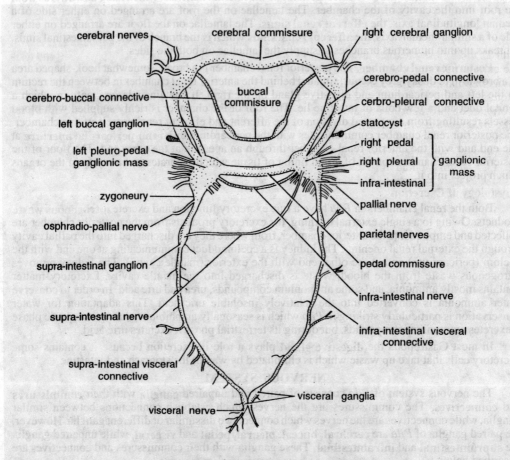

Fig. 60.23. *Pila globosa.* Nervous system.

4. Supra-intestinal ganglion. The supra-intestinal is a slightly swollen, more or less fusiform ganglion lying in a sinus about a quarter of an inch behind the pleuro-pedal mass of the left side. It is connected with the pleuro-pedal mass by a stout connective, called zygoneury. It gives off on the inner side a thin supra-intestinal nerve which runs anteriorly above the intestine to the right side to join the right pleural ganglion. The supra-intestinal ganglion also sends off posteriorly a branch, the left visceral connective which connects it with the visceral ganglion.

5. Visceral ganglion. The visceral ganglion is formed by the fusion of two spindle-shaped ganglionic masses. It lies near the base of the visceral mass close to the anterior lobe of the digestive gland and to the right of the pericardium. The visceral ganglion is connected with the supra-intestinal ganglion by a stout supra-intestinal or left visceral connective. It is further connected with the fused right pleural and infra-intestinal ganglion through the infra-intestinal or the right visceral connective.

Nerves from the cerebral ganglia go to the head, tentacles and eyes. The buccal ganglia send nerves to the buccal mass. Nerves from the pedal ganglia innervate the foot, and those from the pleural ganglia go to the mantle, ctenidium and siphons. From the visceral ganglion nerves go to the intestine, kidney and gonads. These nerves constitute the peripheral nerves.

Characteristics of nervous system. The nervous system of *Pila* shows two characteristics, firstly most of the ganglia, except the visceral, are concentrated near the buccal mass, secondly the visceral loop is twisted into a figure of 8 due to torsion. The twisted condition of the nervous system is a primitive feature, because in most gastropods there is a secondary bilateral symmetry shown by the ganglia and connectives.

SENSE ORGANS

In *Pila*, the special organs of sense are : a single osphradium, paired eyes, statocysts, and tentacles.

1. **Osphradium.** Osphradium hangs from the mantle near the left pseudepipodium. It is oval with 22 to 28 fleshy leaflets arranged on the sides of a central axis. It is a chemoreceptor and tests the current of water which enters the mantle cavity through the left pseudepipodium, it also exercises selection over the food taken in. The evolution of gastropod osphradium parallels that of ctenidia, in primitive forms an osphradium is present for each ctenidium, in prosobranchs which have one ctenidium there is only a single osphradium ; the osphradium disappears in those gastropods which have lost the ctenidia, or have a reduced mantle cavity, or have become pelgic.

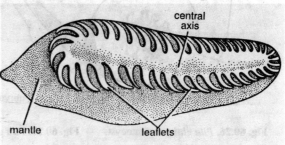

Fig. 60.24. *Pila globosa.* Osphradium.

2. **Statocysts.** Located in the foot near each pedal ganglion lies a statocyst in a depression. It is a round capsule lined with epithelial cells and surrounded by connective tissue. In the cavity of the capsule are small calcareous statoconia. The statocysts receive nerves from pedal and cerebral ganglia, they are organs of equilibrium and regulate the position of the snail.

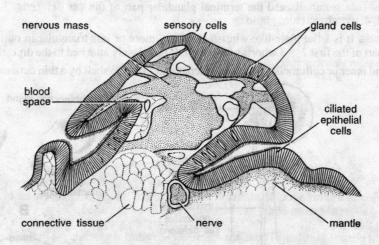

Fig. 60.25. *Pila globosa.* T. S. of osphradium.

3. **Eyes.** There is a pair of eyes, each borne on an ommatophore. An eye is an oval capsule, its wall is the retina made of pigmented sensory cells, it is continued in front as a thin, non-pigmented, transparent cornea. The overlying epidermis is transparent; in the interior of the capsule is a clear ovoidal lens surrounded by a dense vitreous body. An optic nerve innervates the retinal cells. Eyes are sensory to light.

4. **Tentacles.** The tentacles and foot are liberally supplied with nerves, they are sensory to contact, tentacles contain both tactile and chemoreceptor cells and probably gustatory also. The first pair of tentacles are olfactory.

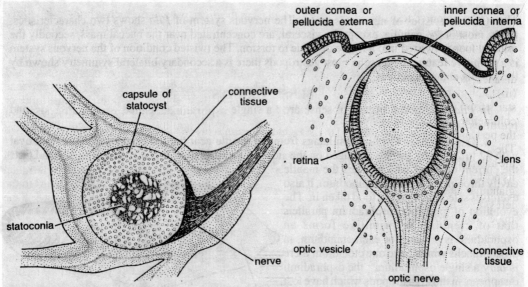

Fig. 60.26. *Pila globosa.* Statocyst.   **Fig. 60.27.** *Pila globosa.*Horizontal longitudinal section of the eye.

REPRODUCTIVE SYSTEM

In *Pila*, the sexes are separate, *i.e.,* **dioecious** and there is a definite sexual dimorphism. The shell of the male is usually smaller in size and less swollen than the female. There is a well developed copulatory organ in the male but it is quite rudimentary in the female.

Male Reproductive Organs

The male reproductive organs consist of 1. testis with its fine vasa efferentia, 2 vas deferens with the vesicula seminalis and the terminal glandular part of the vas deferens, 3. penis with its **sheath** and, 4. hypobranchial glands.

1. **Testis.** It is a flat plate-like whitish structure, more or less triangular in outline, situated in the upper part of the first $2\frac{1}{2}$ –3 whorls of the shell. It lies closely attached to the digestive gland along its upper and inner or collumellar edge and is separated from the shell by a thin cutaneous membrane.

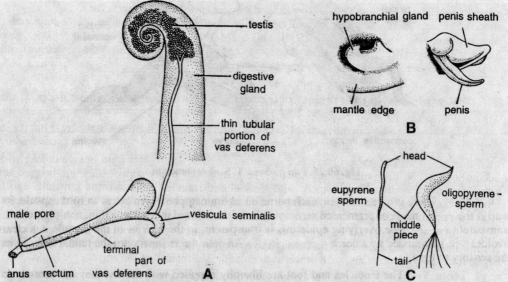

Fig. 60.28. *Pila globosa.* A—Male reproductive organs; B—Male copulatory organs in surface and ventral view; C—Sperms.

The cream-coloured testis is easily distinguished from the digestive gland which is brownish or dirty green. Minute ducts the vasa efferentia lead downwards from the different parts of the testis and may unite with one another before opening into the vas deferens.

2. Vas deferens. From the posterior end of testis arises a thin vas deferens. It consists of three distinct parts : (i) proximal thin tubular portion leading from the testis, (ii) vesicula seminalis and (iii) thick glandular portion which opens into the mantle cavity near the anal opening. The vas deferens starts from the posterior end of the testis and runs immediately beneath the skin along the inner or columellar edge upto the postero-renal chamber. It then turns to the left and on reaching the level of the pericardium turns upwards and to the right to open into the vesicula seminalis on its ventral side. The vesicula seminalis lies to the right of the pericardium immediately below the line of junction of the anterior and posterior renal chambers. It is slightly curved and has a flask-shaped appearance with its posterior blind end broadly rounded. The vesicula seminalis opens on the left side into the terminal glandular part of the vasa deferens. In the mantle-cavity, the vas deferens lies closely attached to the left side of the rectum and ends in a prominent claw-shaped structure the genital papilla having the male genital aperture a little behind the anus.

3. Penis sheath and penis. The edge of the mantle bears on its inner surface a thick glandular flap of a yellowish colour. The flap is attached on its right-side but is free on its left ; its edges are slightly rolled in to form a spout-like sheath, penis sheath for the penis. The penis is a long and stout flagellar structure, about half an inch long arising from the attached right side of the flap of the mantle. It is seen as a slightly curved structure lying within its sheath. It is swollen at its point of attachment but gradually tapers to the free tip, bearing a deep groove all along its length on its inner surface. The penis is capable of extension.

4. Hypobranchial gland. At the base of penis sheath is an oval hypobranchial gland. It consists of tall cells containing small basal nuclei. The surface of the glandular area is somewhat pleated but there is no duct and the secretions of the gland cells are apparently poured directly on the surface.

The spermatogenesis of *Pila globosa* has been worked out by Sharma, G. P., Gupta, Brj Lal, and Mital, O.P. (1959) and they have reported that the spermatozoa of *Pila* are of two kinds : (i) **eupyrene sperms** and (ii) oligopyrene sperms. The eupyrene sperms are hair-like having an elongated spirally twisted nucleus with a small conical acrosome in front, and a mitochondrial middle piece behind, followed by the end piece in the form of a long vibrating tail. The anterior and posterior limits of middle piece are marked by the proximal ring-shaped centrosome and distal granular centrosome respectively. The axial filament springs up from the proximal centrosome ; in the region of the middle piece the axial filament is enseathed by the mitochondrial material, but in the end piece the filament is naked. These sperms move actively forward in a spiral course, measure about 25 μ in length and 1.2 μ in breadth and they can only fertilize the eggs. The oligopyrene sperms on the other hand, have a very sluggish and serpent-like movement. The acrosome is poorly developed, the nucleus is elongated, broad and curved but not spirally coiled ; the middle piece is short and the number of axial filaments varies from 4–8. These sperms measure about 32.5 μ in length and 3 μ in width and they cannot fertilize the eggs; these are probably having some secondary function.

Female Reproductive Organs

The female reproductive organs consist of 1. ovary with numerous minute ducts, 2. main oviduct, 3. receptaculum seminis, 4. uterus, 5. vagina and, 6. hypobranchial gland.

1. Ovary. The ovary in the female lies in the same position as the testis in the male but it is not so extensive. It occupies the upper and inner surfaces on the first 2– $2\frac{1}{2}$ whorls and is covered over by a thin but stout skin-coat. Ovary is a much branched structure of a light orange colour which becomes darker in fully mature individuals. The branches of ovary consist of single-layered acini which are more or less flask-shaped, with their closed rounded ends directed outwards and the elongated necks of the flasks descending to meet those of the adjacent acini to form minute ducts which in their turn open into the main oviduct.

2. Oviduct. The narrow and transparent oviduct originates from about the middle of the ovary. It runs anteriorly just below the skin along the inner margin of the digestive gland. Near the renal organ it turns downwards and then upwards to enter the receptaculum seminis.

3. Receptaculum seminis. It is a bean-shaped structure, lying in the cavity of the posterior renal chamber closely attached to the uterus. A thin-walled pouch arises directly from the wall of the uterus and is called the pouch of the receptaculum.

4. Uterus . It is a large pear-shaped structure, deep-yellow in colour. It lies inside the body whorl below the intestine and the right of the renal chambers. The apex of the uterus points forwards and is continued as the vagina, while its basal portion is broad and rounded and is connected on its outer side with the receptaculum seminis.

5. Vagina. The vagina is a white or cream coloured, band-like structure lying immediately beneath the skin. It extends from the uterus to the upper end of the columellar muscle. The vagina enters the mantle cavity at its right posterior corner and continues forwards to the female genital aperture situated on a small papilla, a little behind the anus.

6. Hypobranchial gland. The hypobranchial gland of female is poorly developed. There is a rudimentary glandular thickening in the area of hypobranchial gland.

7. Copulatory apparatus. The female has a **rudimentary penis** lying beneath the glandular fold at the edge of the mantle. It is a thin flagellar structure with a rudimentary groove along its inner surface. The flagellum is about a quarter of an inch in length and has nearly the same thickness throughout except the tip where it is slightly pointed. There is no trace of the foldings of the penis sheath.

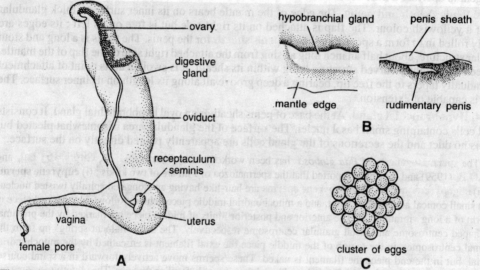

Fig. 60.29. *Pila globosa*. A—Female reproductive organs ; B—Female copulatory organs in surface and ventral view ; C—Eggs.

COPULATION

Copulation in *Pila globosa* (Fig. 60.30) occurs either in water or on land, it lasts for 3 hours. Male and female *Pila* come together facing each other. The penis of the male is expanded and gets attached to the genital papilla by its base. Then the penis and its sheath are inserted into the mantle cavity of the female. The tip of the penis is put into the female genital aperture and spermatozoa are transferred through the vagina into the receptaculum seminis.

FERTILIZATION

Eggs are fertilized in the uterus and oviposition starts a day or two later. The fertilized eggs are laid in masses of 200 to 800 in moist earth near ponds and lakes.

DEVELOPMENT

In their development Mollusca pass through two larval stages, there is a **trochosphere larva** which soon grows into a **veliger larva.** The development of the trochosphere is the same as in polychaete Annelida. The typical trochosphere develops in *Patella*. A free-swimming trochosphere is found only in some primitive gastropods, such as Diotocardia, but in all others the trochosphere stage is reduced and passed within the egg. More characteristic of marine gastropods is a free swimming veliger larva which hatches from the egg. The veliger is a modified trochosphere but represents a more advanced stage of development, its organs show greater degree of development than those in the trochosphere larva. It has a ciliated apical organ on the head, a curved gut, larval nephridia and a ciliated pre-oral prototroch ; but it has organs not found in the trochosphere. The prototroch develops into a characteristic swimming organ, the velum which is a bilobed circlet with strong cilia, it is formed as an outward extension of the prototroch. The velum causes a current which brings food into the mouth, and it serves as an organ of locomotion for the free-swimming veliger. On the dorsal side of the veliger is an embryonic shell gland which secretes a shell, the shell soon loses its simple form and assumes a spiral shape due to unequal growth ; larval retractor muscles are formed. On the ventral side is a foot lying between the mouth and the anus. On the dorsal side between the velum and the anus the ectoderm forms a mantle. The mesoderm forms two bands which do not segment but break up into cells, some of which form muscles. Torsion takes place during the veliger stage, the shell and visceral mass are rotated through 180 degrees in relation to the head and the foot, but coiling of the visceral hump usually precedes torsion. Torsion may be very rapid taking only a few minutes, or it may be a gradual process taking several days. A stage is reached when the veliger cannot only swim by its velum but it can also creep by its foot. Gradually the velum becomes smaller.

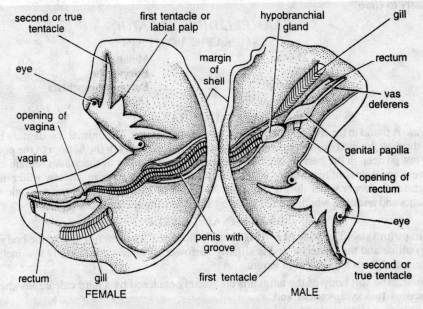

Fig. 60.30. *Pila globosa.* Copulation.

In freshwater and terrestrial Mollusca there is no free-swimming larva, both the trochosphere and the veliger stages are passed within the egg shell, and a tiny snail hatches from the egg shell.

REVISION QUESTIONS

1. Describe habit, habitat and external features of *Pila globosa*.
2. Describe the digestive system of *Pila globosa*.
3. Give an account of the respiratory organs and mode of respiration of *Pila globosa*.
4. Describe the blood vascular system of a snail you have studied.
5. Give an account of the nervous system of *Pila globosa*.
6. Describe the reproductive system of *Pila globosa*.
7. Draw labelled diagram to show the organs of pallial complex.
8. Write notes on : (i) Osphradium ; (ii) Veliger larva ; (iii) Radula.

61

Lamellidens (=Unio) (Freshwater Mussel)

Freshwater mussels are found in most parts of the world partly buried in the mud of rivers and lakes. *Unio* is found all over the world and *Lamellidens marginalis* in Indian rivers and other parts of the world. *Anodonta* is common in many parts. The description given will apply to all these genera but mostly to *Unio*.

LAMELLIDENS (= UNIO)
SYSTEMATIC POSITION

Phylum	....	**Mollusca**
Class	....	**Pelecypoda**
Order	....	**Eulamellibranchiata**
Genus	....	*Unio*

HABIT AND HABITAT

Unio is found in freshwater ponds, lakes, streams and rivers. The animal is sedentary but ploughs slowly through the mud or sand by its wedge-shaped muscular foot at the bottom of the pond or river. It does not go deep in the burrow because the posterior extremities of the valves remain exposed for the ingress and egress of respiratory water current. *Unio* usually stays in shallow water during night but migrates to deeper water during day time. The food of *Unio* comprises microscopic organisms, both plants and animals, which are fed upon by filter-feeding mechanism.

EXTERNAL FEATURES

Shape and size. The body of *Unio* is laterally flattened. The anterior side of the body is roughly oval in outline and the posterior end is slightly narrower. *Unio* has a bilaterally symmetrical body. The size varies from 5 to 10 cm in length.

Shell. The soft body of the animal is completely enclosed by a hard calcareous **shell**. Shell is composed of two symmetrical and equal halves called valves and known as right and left valves. The two valves are united by a dorsal elastic band called a **hinge ligament** which is continuous with the two shell valves but is made of uncalcified conchiolin, it is elastic and causes the valves of the shell to open. Near the hinge ligament are teeth and sockets which fit into each other to form an efficient inter-locking arrangement to prevent a fore and aft displacement of the two shell valves. At the anterior end of the hinge ligament on each side, is a swelling

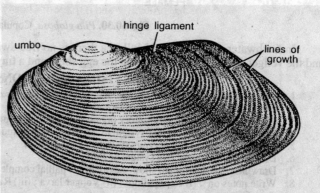

Fig. 61.1. *Unio.* Entire animal with shell (Lateral view).

called **umbo** which is the oldest part of the shell and is first formed in a young animal. Below the umbo are concentric lines of growth of the shell valves. The shell valves are rounded anteriorly but somewhat pointed posteriorly. The umbo is directed anteriorly making it possible to determine the right and left shell valves of the animal. In most Pelecypoda the two shell valves are similar and equal in size, but in some sessile families (oysters) the upper or left valve is always larger than right valve by which the animal is attached.

If a shell valve is removed from the mantle lobes, its inner surface is seen which shows marks of insertion of muscles running transversely between two valves. The insertion of the edge of the mantle marks a pallial line. Anteriorly is an impression of an **anterior adductor muscle**, posteriorly is a larger impression of a **posterior adductor muscle**; close to these impressions are marks of an **anterior retractor muscle** and a **posterior retractor muscle**. Near the anterior adductor is also an impression of a **protractor muscle**. The adductor muscles close the shell valves tightly by pulling them together, the retractors pull in the foot, and the protractor pushes out the foot. The hinge ligament acts antagonistically to the adductor muscles and causes the shell valves to open when the adductors relax. Primitively the two adductor muscles are equal in size, but in many families the anterior adductor becomes reduced, and in oysters and scallops it disappears completely, then the posterior adductor moves to the centre of the shell valves. All muscles are unstriped, they gradually shift with growth of the animal, their faint lines may be traced to the umbo.

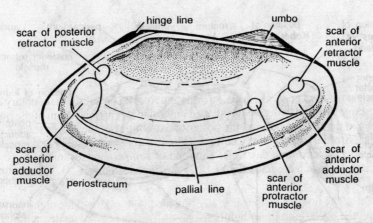

Fig. 61.2. *Unio.* Inner view of the left shell valve to show the muscle scars.

Microscopic structure of shell. In section the shell has three layers, an outer brown, horny layer, the **periostracum** which is protective and is made of a horny organic material called conchiolin.

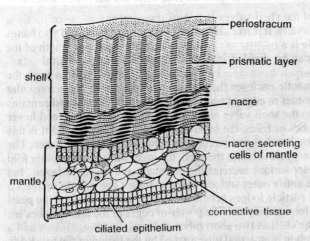

Fig. 61.3. *Unio.* Cross section of shell and mantle.

Below it the middle layer is a thick **prismatic layer** made of vertical crystals or prisms of $CaCO_3$ separated by conchiolin. The innermost **nacreous layer** or the "mother-of-pearl" layer is made of alternate layers of $CaCO_3$ and conchiolin. The hinge ligament is made of uncalcified conchiolin, it is continuous with the periostracum. Reserve calcium carbonate for the two inner layers of the shell is stored in certain cells of the digestive gland. The nacreous layer is thickest at the umbo and thinnest at the shell margin, it is used for manufacturing buttons. In formation of the shell the periostracum is laid down by the outer lobe of the mantle, while the prismatic and nacreous layers are secreted by the entire outer surface of the mantle, though the nacreous layer is also secreted by the thickened lower edge of the mantle.

INTERNAL STRUCTURES

Body. The body is elongated but laterally compressed. The head is lost, in the upper half is a visceral mass which passes into a mid-ventral, wedge-shaped, laterally-compressed foot directed anteriorly, this is an adaptation for burrowing. The foot has a large sinus which gets filled with blood when the foot is extended by blood pressure and muscular action of a pair of pedal protractor muscles, the protractors extend transversely from each side of the foot to the opposite shell valve. The foot becomes swollen and turgid, it is then used for ploughing through mud in burrowing. Withdrawal of the foot is effected by pair of anterior and a pair of posterior retractor muscles attached to the foot on one side and to the shell valves on the other, and also by the muscle fibres within the foot itself. A pair of fleshy, flattened lobes, called labial palps are situated just below the anterior protractor muscles. In the depression formed by labial palps, between anterior adductor muscle and the foot, is a transverse slit-like aperture, the mouth. On each side the body is produced into a mantle lobe, the space between the mantle lobes is mantle **cavity** into which hangs a ctenidium on each side. The mantle cavity is large and extends on each side of the body, it protects the ctenidia and prevents their clogging with silt, and it allows a current of water to pass in and out in definite directions.

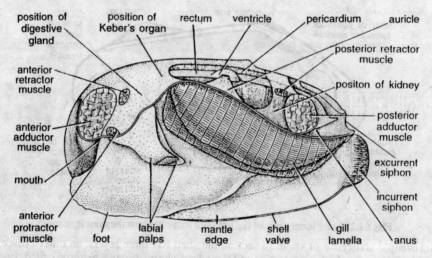

Fig. 61.4. *Unio.* Internal organs seen after the removal of the left shell valve and left mantle lobe.

Mantle. Lining the inner surface of the shell valves is a semi-transparent mantle or pallium which is made of two lobes continuous dorsally. It is like skin, it encloses the soft parts and also hangs down like a skirt. Enclosed by the mantle is a mantle cavity which extends the entire length of the body on each side. The mantle cavity can be divided into two chambers, a large ventral infra-branchial chamber and a small dorsal supra-branchial chamber. The bases of ctenidia mark the partition between these chambers. The mantle encloses the body in the upper half, and a muscular **foot** on the mid-ventral side. The lower border or edge of each mantle lobe is thickened and contains muscles, the muscles attach the mantle to the shell valve along a pallial line. The thickened lower border of the mantle has three parallel lobes or folds, the innermost fold is the largest and it is this fold which contains muscles which are both radial and circular, it controls the flow of water. The middle fold is sensory in function. The outer fold secretes the shell, the inner surface of the outer fold lays down the periostracum, while its outer surface secretes the prismatic and nacreous layers, but the nacreous layer is also secreted by the entire outer surface of the mantle . The mantle secretes a pearl in many bivalves when any foreign particle lodges between the shell and the mantle, the pearl is formed in concentric layers around the foreign particle. The posterior edges of the mantle lobes are also thickened and they project outside the shell as two short tubes, a dorsal exhalant siphon and a ventral inhalant siphon. The exhalant siphon is an actual tube formed by the fusion of the two lobes of the mantle, but the inhalant siphon is a temporary tube formed by approximation of mantle lobes, it has delicate fimbriae at its edges. Water enters through the inhalant siphon and after circulating it passes out through the exhalant siphon.

Histologically, the mantle has outer epithelium of one layer of cells in contact with the shell, it has branches of blood vessels, inside this is connective tissue with blood vessels, nerve cells and fibres, unicellular mucous glands, and nacreous glands which secrete the nacreous layer of the shell. On the innermost side is a single cell layer thick ciliated epithelium.

COELOM

Coelom is schizocoelic having been formed in molluscs by splitting of the mesoderm, but the coelom is reduced to the paired cavities of kidneys and gonads and a pericardium which encloses a heart. Originally all three cavities are intercommunicated, but there has been a progressive separation so that only the cavities of kidneys and pericardium communicate, the cavities of gonads have separated completely. However, the general body cavity is the haemocoel filled with haemolymph.

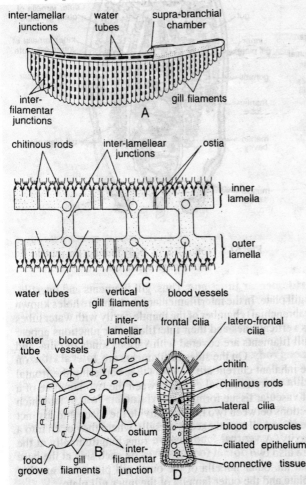

Fig. 61.6. *Unio*. Structure of gill. A—A demibranch seen from outside ; B—A portion of gill lamina in T.S. ; C—A portion of gill (A) enlarged ; D—Cross section of one gill filament.

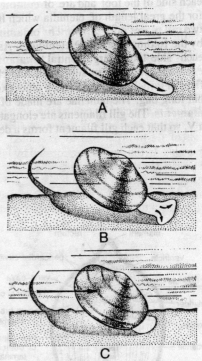

Fig. 61.5. *Unio.* Stages in locomotion.

LOCOMOTION

The muscular foot is the chief locomotory organ. When the *Unio* walks, the foot is thrust forward between the two valves of the shell and burrows like plough-share through the mud. This permits blood to flow into the many sinuses of the foot, causing it to swell and, thus, form an anchor. As the retractor muscles contract, the *Unio* is drawn forward an inch or so. The blood then is forced out of the foot so that it thins down again and can be withdrawn from the mud or sand. The process is repeated with each step and wedge-shaped path is left behind.

RESPIRATORY SYSTEM

Unio is an aquatic animal, hence, it respires by the oxygen dissolved in water, *i.e.*, the mode of respiration is aquatic exclusively. So, for performing this life activity, *Unio* possesses a pair of ctenidia or gills; mantle also helps in this activity. The gills of *Unio* are, in fact, supposed to be highly modified and specialized derivatives of its mantle.

1. **Ctenidia.** There is a single pair of elongated ctenidia or gills, one on

each side of the foot and are of eulamellibranch type. The large mantle cavity has made it possible for the great length of ctenidia which lie laterally. Each ctenidium appears double but it is made of two gill plates or demibranchs or laminae, an outer and an inner gill plate which have been derived by the folding of a single ctenidium. As mentioned earlier, the ctenidia divide the mantle cavity on each side into a large ventral inhalant chamber or infrabranchial chamber and a smaller dorsal exhalant chamber or suprabranchial chamber. Each gill plate or lamina is formed of two similar flaps or lamellae joined to each other except dorsally, thus, two lamellae of a gill plate form a narrow but long bag. The lamellae are made of a number of vertically parallel gill filaments or branchial filaments. The gill filaments are elongated, they pass downwards and are then reflected upwards like a V, so that each gill filament forms a descending and an ascending limb. Adjacent gill filaments are

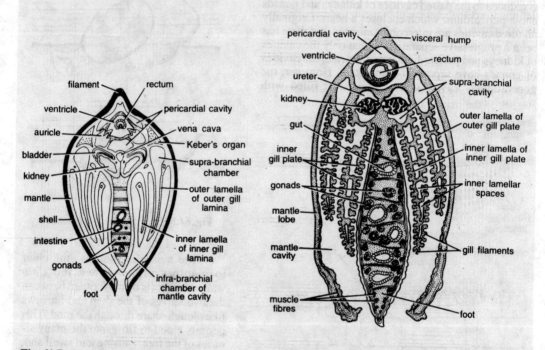

Fig. 61.7. *Unio.* T.S. of body through anterior region of gills.

Fig. 61.8. *Unio.* T.S. of body through the middle region of gills and foot.

joined by the fusion of tissues forming interfilamentar junctions. Thus, gill filaments and interfilamentar junctions form the two lamellae of a gill plate. In the interfilamentar junctions are holes known as ostia which connect ventral inhalant (infrabranchial) chamber of the mantle cavity with water tubes in the laminae. The gill filaments appear as vertical lines and their interfilamentar junctions appear as horizontal striations on a lamella. The gill filaments are covered with various kinds of cilia, and each gill filament is supported by two chitinous rods. On the sides of filaments are lateral cilia, on the distal surface which first encounters the inhalant current are frontal cilia, bordering the frontal cilia on both sides are long laterofrontal cilia or frontolateral cilia. Between the two lamellae of a gill plate a space divided by vertical bars of vascular tissue forming interlamellar junctions which contain blood vessels. The interlamellar junctions between two lamellae divide the space into distinct compartments called water tubes which are closed all round except dorsally where they open into a suprabranchial chamber of the mantle cavity. A ventral food groove runs longitudinally at the lower edge of each inner gill plate. There are also two dorsal food grooves on each side at the base of a ctenidium, one between the mantle and the outer lamella of the outer gill plate, and another between the inner lamella of the outer gill plate and the outer lamella of the inner gill plate.

   Attachment of ctenidia. The dorsal attachment of gill plates shows that the outer lamella of the outer gill plate is attached to the mantle, the inner lamella of outer gill plate and the outer lamella of inner gill plate are joined together to the visceral mass, the inner lamella of inner gill plate is attached to the visceral mass anteriorly, but further back it is free, and behind the foot it is joined to its fellow of the other side, so that the inner lamellae of inner gill plates are united with one another.

Blood supply of ctenidia. The ctenidia are supplied by afferent branchial vessel carrying deoxygenated blood from the kidneys and divides to give rise branches into the interlamellar junctions. These branches unite to open into the efferent branchial vessel which carries away oxygenated blood to the heart. In fact, during the flow of blood from the branches of afferent branchial vessel (in the interlamellar junctions)to the efferent branchial vessel, the blood is oxygenated.

Course of Water Current

Constant beating of the cilia of gill filaments causes a continuous current of water to enter the inhalant siphon lying posteriorly and ventrally from where it goes to the mantle cavity. The lateral cilia pass the water current in, and through the ostia it enters the water tubes of gill plates, then it goes to suprabranchial chambers and passes out through the exhalant siphon situated posteriorly and dorsally. The latero-frontal

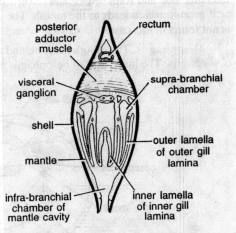

Fig. 61.9. *Unio.* T.S. of body through posterior region of gills.

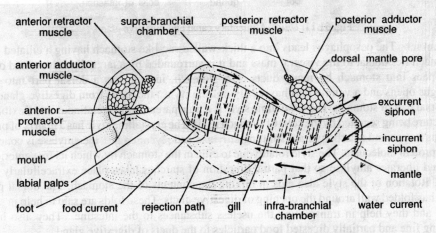

Fig. 10. *Unio.* Diagram showing water and food currents.

cilia form a flexible comb bordering the ostia, this comb forms a sieve to prevent large particles from entering ostia. The current transports not only oxygen to the ctenidia but also brings in food, the outgoing current carries away products of excretion and faeces in addition to carbon dioxide.

2. **Mantle.** In addition to shell secreting function, mantle also helps in respiration. It is richly supplied with the blood vessels and it remains in contact with water, hence, gaseous exchange takes place through its thin wall.

Physiology of respiration. When water passes through the water tubes in the gill, gaseous exchange takes place ; in fact, carbon dioxide from the blood is diffused out in the water and dissolved oxygen from water is diffused in the blood. Thus, deoxygenated blood becomes oxygenated which is carried to the heart for distribution.

DIGESTIVE SYSTEM

Digestive system consists of the alimentary canal and a pair of digestive gland.

Alimentary canal. It is a long coiled tube and comprises the mouth, oesophagus, stomach, intestine and rectum.

Mouth. It is a transverse slit-like aperture situated in the anterior end of the body ventral to the anterior adductor muscle. On each side of the mouth is a pair of triangular fleshy, flattened and ciliated labial palps, one in front and one behind the mouth. The labial palps are jointed to their fellows of the other side and form upper and lower lips. The two labial palps of each side enclose a ciliated oral groove which leads to the mouth. The characteristic buccal mass with jaws and radula of *Pila* is not found in this case.

Oesophagus. The mouth leads behind and dorsally into a short narrow tubular passage, called oesophagus. The inner wall of oesophagus is ciliated.

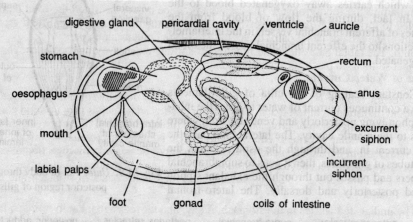

Fig. 61.11. *Unio*. Alimentary canal and digestive gland.

Stomach. The oesophagus leads into a thick-walled sac-like stomach having a ciliated lining. The stomach lies dorsal to the visceral mass and it is surrounded by a large digestive gland or liver which opens into stomach by many ducts. The stomach, in fact, has a dorsal part into which oesophagus opens and a ventral part having crystalline style ; the ducts from digestive gland open in the dorsal part of stomach. The crystalline style is a transparent, solid, gelatinous and flexible rod-like structure being secreted by the cells of stomach itself. The crystalline style has a matrix of protein, it contains mucus and a carbohydrate-splitting amylase and glycogenase; the amylase is condensed over the protein molecules. The style rotates due to cilia in the stomach by which its free anterior end erodes and liberates amylase so that partial digestion of starches takes place extracellularly in the stomach. Rotation of the style also aids in mixing the contents of the stomach. The dorsal part of stomach has folded wall around the opening of digestive ducts. These folds are said to help in storing the food and they help in transporting the useless substances to the intestine. They also help in conducting fine and partially digested food particles to the ducts of digestive gland.

Intestine. The posterior end of stomach leads into the intestine which goes down and forms a coil in the visceral mass where it is surrounded by the gonad, and finally comes up again. Near the stomach the intestine turns back into rectum.

Rectum. The rectum passes backwards through the pericardium, it traverses through the ventricle and opens by an anus above the posterior adductor muscle into the exhalant siphon serving as cloaca.

The lining of the alimentary canal forms two ridges or folds in the posterior part of the stomach and first part of the intestine, there is also a similar ridge in the rectum, these ridges are called typhlosoles.

Digestive gland. Liver is the only digestive gland which surrounds the stomach from lateral and posterior sides. It is a large paired structure of dark brown or green colour. As mentioned, it opens into the dorsal part of stomach by many ducts. It secretes digestive enzymes and its cells are capable of ingesting food particles where intracellular digestion also occurs. In fact, fine food particles enter into the digestive ducts to reach its cells where they are ingested and intracellulary digested.

Food and Feeding

The food of *Unio* comprises minute plants, Protozoa and organic debris. *Unio* is a filter or ciliary feeder and ctenidia have assumed the function of obtaining food. The respiratory current brings in particles of food into the mantle cavity. On entering the mantle cavity the current of water becomes slow and heavier particles sink down and pass to the posterior region. Smaller particles pass with the current over the gill filaments of ctenidia. The different cilia of gill filaments perform various functions. The lateral cilia cause the food-laden current to enter the mantle cavity, the latero-frontal cilia deflect the fine food particles on to the face of the filaments and they prevent large particles from clogging the ctenidia. Then the frontal cilia collect and pass the particles up or down the surface of ctenidia into the food grooves. The ctenidia produce mucus in which the food particles become entangled to form string-like masses which pass along the dorsal and ventral food grooves towards the mouth. The cilia of labial palps direct the food-laden mucus along the ciliated oral grooves into the mouth. The labial palps have the function of sorting and conveying food to the mouth, they can also reject some food particles and deflect them towards the outgoing current.

Digestion, Absorption and Egestion

Digestion is both intracellular and extracellular. The digestive glands produce enzymes which bring about digestion in the stomach. The cells of the digestive glands take up solid particles of food and intracellular digestion of proteins and perhaps further digestion of carbohydrates take place by means of intracellular enzymes. The crystalline style is made of protein and mucus, its material is mixed with food in the stomach and it produces an amylytic enzyme for digestion of carbohydrates. Amoeboid wandering leucocytes ingest food and also digest it, and they also transport digested food to all parts of the body. Absorption of digested food takes place in stomach and also from the digestive gland.

The undigested wastes in the stomach, if any, and those sent back into stomach from digestive gland pass into the intestine → rectum → anus → exhalant siphon. Intestine and rectum are believed to absorb water from the wastes passing through them.

BLOOD VASCULAR SYSTEM

The blood vascular system is well developed and is of open type. It comprises, the blood, heart, pericardium, arteries, sinuses and veins.

Blood. It is the circulatory medium and consists of plasma and corpuscles. The plasma is colourless probably in all lamellibranchs but in some species it is slight bluish in colour due to the presence of a respiratory pigment, the haemocyanin. Haemocyanin is a copper containing respiratory pigment (hence, imparts bluish colour to the plasma) in contrast to haemoglobin which is iron containing respiratory pigment. However, some bivalves like *Solen* possess haemoglobin as respiratory pigment. A large number of colourless stellate amoebocytes or corpuscles, also referred to as

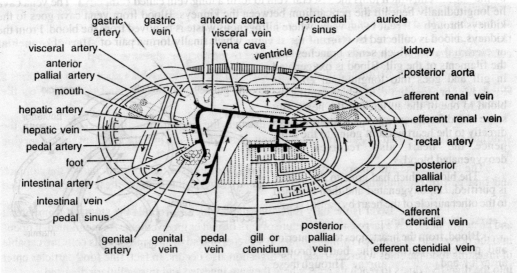

Fig. 61.12. *Unio.* Blood circulatory system.

leucocytes, are found in the plasma. The leucocytes are granular as well as non-granular in nature. The granular leucocytes leave the blood spaces and enter the body where they are phagocytic and remove waste. The blood performs its usual function of distribution of oxygen and nutrients to the parts of the body and carbon dioxide and nitrogenous wastes to the desired organs.

Heart and pericardium. The heart of *Unio* is three-chambered and found enclosed in a thin-walled triangular sac, called pericardium. It is situated in front of the posterior adductor muscle and placed mid-dorsally. The pericardium has a pericardial cavity filled with pericardial fluid; it represents a part of original coelom. The pericardium, however, communicates with the supra-branchial chamber through the kidneys.

As mentioned, the heart is three-chambered having one ventricle and two auricles. The auricles are thin-walled, highly distensible, triangular chambers one on either side of the ventricle. These are attached to the pericardium with their broad bases but open dorsally into the ventricle. Each auricle opens into the ventricle by auriculo-ventricular aperture guarded by a valve which allows the flow of blood from auricle to ventricle but do not permit the blood to go back into the auricle from ventricle. The auricles, however, receive blood from the ctenidia, kidneys and mantle, and pour it into the ventricle. The ventricle is thick-walled, muscular and horizontal chamber surrounding the rectum. In most lamellibranchs the ventricle has become folded around the rectum so that the pericardium encloses not only the heart but also a part of the alimentary canal. The heart beats about 20–100 times per minute.

Arteries. Each end of the ventricle is continued into an aorta , the anterior end into anterior **aorta** and the posterior end into posterior aorta. The anterior aorta passes over the rectum, while posterior aorta below the rectum and they give off a number of small arteries to supply blood into the different parts of the body. In fact, the anterior aorta gives off three main arteries ; (i) anterior pallial artery to supply the mantle, (ii) pedal artery to supply the foot, and (iii) visceral artery which gives off a gastric artery to stomach, a hepatic artery to liver or digestive gland, an intestinal artery to intestine and a gonadial artery to gonad. The posterior aorta gives fine arteries to the pericardium and kidneys, a branch from it supplies to the rectum and finally it continues as posterior pallial artery to supply the mantle.

Sinuses. The arteries end in ill-defined sinuses and lacunae which lack the epithelial lining of true blood vessels. There are no capillaries in molluscs, except in cephalopods, the blood from the arteries seeps into lacunar spaces in the connective tissue from where blood is taken up by the veins. Therefore, *Unio's* circulatory system is said to be open type.

Veins. The venous blood from visceral organs is collected by smaller veins ; gonadial vein from gonad, intestinal vein from intestine, hepatic vein from liver and gastric vein from stomach. All these veins together form the visceral vein. The blood from pedal sinus in the foot is collected by the pedal vein which joins the visceral vein to form a long vein called vena cava. The vena cava lie longitudinally beneath the pericardium between the kidneys. Blood from vena cava goes to the kidneys through afferent renal veins where nitrogenous waste is removed from the blood. From the kidneys, blood is collected by efferent renal veins which finally form a pair of afferent branchial or ctenidial vein which sends branches into the filaments of the gill. Blood is oxygenated in gill and goes into longitudinal efferent branchial or ctenidial vein which returns the blood to one of the auricles of the heart. But some blood from vena cava and kidneys goes directly to the heart without going to the gills, hence, the heart also receives some deoxygenated blood.

The blood which had gone to the mantle is purified, *i.e.,* oxygenated and then returned to the other auricle of the heart by pallial veins.

Course of Circulation

Blood, from the heart, goes to the anterior and posterior parts of the body through anterior and posterior aortae. Through these aortae, a part of blood goes to mantle where

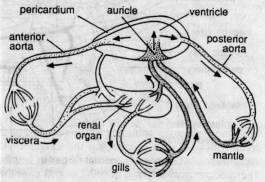

Fig. 61.13. *Unio.* Course of blood circulation.

oxygenation occurs and finally oxygenated blood is conveyed to the auricle through pallial vein. The other parts of the body are supplied by different branches of these aortae where it becomes deoxygenated. The deoxygenated blood is finally collected into vena cava through several veins. The vena cava gives blood to kidney where nitrogenous wastes are removed and the blood then goes to the gills for oxygenation. The oxygenated blood from the gills is conveyed to the heart by efferent branchial or ctenidial veins. Thus, circulation is completed and the heart again starts distributing the blood to the various organs. In this way the cycle goes on. However, the course of circulation of blood in the body of *Unio* may be graphically represented in the following way :

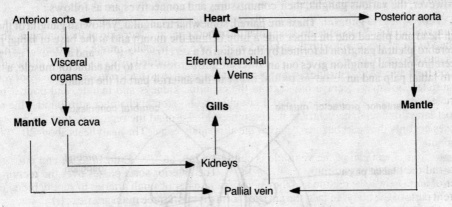

Fig. 61.14. *Unio*. Outline of course of blood circulation.

EXCRETORY SYSTEM

The excretory system of *Unio* consists of a pair of kidneys or organs of Bojanus and the Keber's organ.

Organs of Bojanus. The chief excretory organ of *Unio* is a pair of kidneys or nephridia, often referred to as the organs of Bojanus; these are named so after the name of discoverer. These are situated one on each side of the body below the pericardium. Each kidney consists of a tube bent upon itself forming a U-shaped structure. The lower limb of the tube is a thick-walled, spongy, brown-coloured glandular part of the kidney, the upper limb of the tube is a thin-walled, non-glandular and ciliated, called the urinary bladder. The bladders of two kidneys communicate by an oval aperture. Each kidney opens at one end into the pericardium by a minute reno-pericardial aperture, and at the other end it opens by an excretory or renal pore into the suprabranchial chamber of the mantle cavity. Each kidney is an enclosed part of the coelom or renocoel, and is equivalent to a coelomoduct leading from the coelom to the exterior.

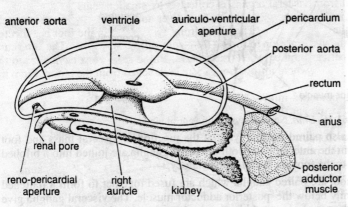

Fig. 61.15. *Unio*. Excretory system.

Physiology of excretion. The glandular part of kidneys removes nitrogenous excretory wastes from the pericardial fluid and blood supplied to them. The ciliated cells lining the urinary bladder create outward current carrying the excretory fluid from the glandular part of kidneys to the suprabranchial chamber of the mantle cavity and finally goes out of the body through exhalant siphon. There occurs reabsorption of inorganic salts in the kidneys. Kidneys also remove large amounts of water to maintain their blood concentration. Therefore, in addition to excretory function, the kidneys are osmoregulatory also.

Keber's organ. In front of the pericardium is another excretory organ called Keber's organ or pericardial gland. It is formed from the epithelium of the pericardium. It is a large reddish-brown glandular mass which discharges waste into the pericardium. Nitrogenous waste consists mainly of ammonia and amino compounds, but traces of urea and uric acid have also been found.

NERVOUS SYSTEM

The nervous system of *Unio* consists of only paired ganglia, commissures, (nerves connecting two similar ganglia), connectives (nerves connecting two dissimilar ganglia) and nerves. In fact, the nervous system of *Unio* is reduced to a great extent because of its sedentary and sluggish mode of life. However, the various ganglia, their commissures and connectives are as follows :

Cerebro-pleural ganglia. These are paired, somewhat triangular, yellowish ganglia of the size of a pin head and placed one on either side a little behind the mouth and at the base of labial palps. Each cerebro-pleural ganglion is formed by the fusion of a cerebral ganglion and a pleural ganglion. Each cerebro-pleural ganglion gives out an anterior adductor nerve to the adductor muscle, a labial nerve to labial palp and an anterior pallial nerve to the anterior part of the mantle.

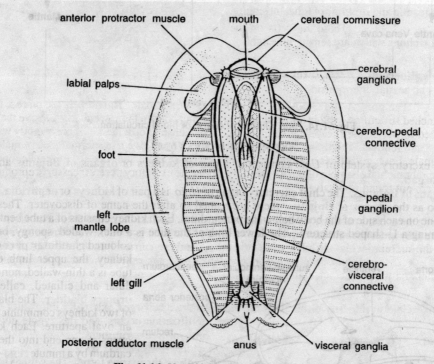

Fig. 61.16. *Unio.* Nervous system in ventral view.

Pedal ganglia. These are also paired ganglia lying at the junction of visceral mass and foot about one-third of its length from the anterior end. Both the pedal ganglia are joined into a bilobed mass. The pedal ganglia supply to the foot, its muscles and statocyst.

Visceral ganglia. These, too, are paired ganglia which are fused together to form a flattened X-shaped mass lying mid-ventrally below the posterior adductor muscle. The visceral ganglia give out the pallial nerve to the mantle, renal nerve to kidneys, ctenidial nerve to the gills and adductor nerve to the posterior adductor muscle.

Commissure. The cerebro-pleural ganglia of both the sides are connected together by a thin, transverse, loop-like nerve passing over the oesophagus; this nerve is called cerebral commissure. No other commissures are found in *Unio*.

Connectives. All the three ganglia are connected with somewhat stout nerves representing the connectives ; the cerebro-pleural is connected to pedal by cerebro-pedal connective, cerebro-pleural is connected to visceral by cerebro-visceral connective. All these connectives are paired. However, there is no connective between the pedal and visceral ganglia.

SENSE ORGANS

The sense organs are poorly developed. The eyes and tentacles are altogether absent. The main sense organs are : 1. osphradium, 2. statocyst, 3. tactile cells, and 4. photoreceptors.

1. **Osphradium.** It is a group of yellow-coloured sensory cells found near each visceral ganglion, they are chemoreceptors and test the water current entering the inhalant siphon.

2. **Statocyst.** There is a statocyst lying near each pedal ganglion in the foot. It is globular being formed as a pit of the skin. It is surrounded by several layers of cells and contains a calcareous statolith. The statocyst receives a nerve from the cerebro-pedal connective. Statocysts are organs of equilibrium.

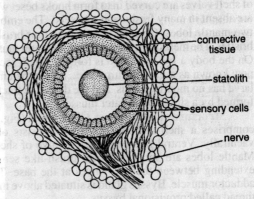

Fig. 61.17. *Unio.* T.S. of statocyst.

3. **Tactile cells.** Tactile cells occur on the edge of the mantle and fimbriae of inhalant siphon.

4. **Photoreceptors.** These are cells on the margins of siphons which are sensitive to light.

REPRODUCTIVE SYSTEM

Unio is **dioecious**, *i.e.*, the sexes are separate but there is no sexual dimorphism.

Gonads. The gonads are testes in male and ovaries in female. The gonads are paired, large, highly branched structures lying in and around the intestinal coils in the visceral mass above the foot. During breeding period they become greatly enlarged and conspicuous; the testes are brightly whitish and ovaries are reddish. The lining of the gonads proliferates to give rise spermatozoa in male and eggs in female. Each gonad has a short duct, vas deferens in male and oviduct in female, opening into the suprabranchial chamber of the mantle cavity near the excretory pore. Accessory reproductive structures are not found in bivalves.

FERTILIZATION

In male the sperms pass out through the exhalant siphon and are carried to the surrounding water from where they enter the inhalant siphon of the female and reach its ctenidia. In female the eggs are shed into the suprabranchial chamber of mantle cavity and are carried into water tubes of ctenidia where fertilization and early development occur. Fertilized eggs generally develop in the outer gill plates of ctenidia which become enlarged to form a brood pouch or marsupium.

DEVELOPMENT

Unlike *Unio* in majority of bivalves the sex cells are discharged externally into water where fertilization occurs, and the zygote develops into a free-swimming trochosphere larva which is succeeded by a veliger larva, specially in the marine forms. The veliger larva is symmetrical in pelecypods. In freshwater family Unionidae (which includes *Anodonta* and *Lamellidens*) there is an indirect but much specialized development. The veliger stage is formed in the marsupium of ctenidia, this veliger is highly modified and is known as a glochidium larva in this family.

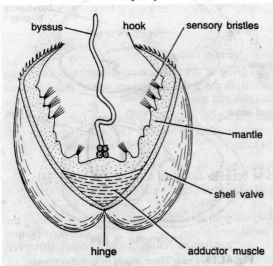

Fig. 61.18. *Unio.* A glochidium.

Early development. The zygote undergoes complete but unequal cleavage to form a morula having small micromeres and large macromeres. Gastrulation occurs by macromeres invaginating into micromeres, but the archenteron so formed remains small for a long time. The gastrula has micromeres or ectoderm, macromeres or endoderm, a large blastocoele and a small archenteron. It is enclosed in vitelline membrane. Some cells of the gastrula are budded in to the blastocoele to form mesoderm. A deep invagination occurs to form a shell gland which is characteristic of Mollusca. The shell gland marks the dorsal surface of the embryo, the posterior end is marked by a tuft of long cilia. The shell gland secretes an unpaired shell which is soon replaced by a triangular bivalved shell, the shell valves enclose a larval mantle. The lower parts of shell valves are curved in to form hooks beset with spines (in *Anodonta* and *Lamellidens*, but hooks are absent in many freshwater mussels). The embryo is cleft in the middle to form a dorsal body and two mantle lobes. On each mantle lobe four brush-like sense organs arise, each having a cluster of bristles. The mesoderm forms a large adductor muscle which runs between two shell valves anteriorly. On the body a byssus gland is formed which secretes a sticky thread called byssus. The embryo is now known as a glochidium larva. So far the embryo is nourished on yolk present in the egg. The larva has no mouth or anus and the digestive tract is not yet formed. Thousands of glochidia may be formed by a single freshwater mussel.

Structure of glochidium. Glochidium (Fig. 61.18) is a minute larva measuring 0.1 to 4.0 mm, comprises a shell and mantle. Shell consists of two triangular valves united dorsally and free vaentrally. Ventral free end of each valve of shell is produced into a curved hook bearing spines. Mantle lobes are small and bear brush-like sensory organs. Adductor muscle is well developed extending between the two valves at the base. The closure of the valves is effected by the large adductor muscle. Byssus gland is situated above the adductor muscle which gives rise to a long sticky thread called provisional byssus.

The glochidium is nourished in the marsupium which contains a large number of glochidia which are, thus, ectoparasitic. The glochidia are set free from the ctenidia and pass out through the exhalant siphon into water and sink down at the bottom. They get attached to gills or fins of fresh-water fishes by their byssus and shell valves. Some glochidia require only certain species of fish as hosts, but others can parasitize a large range of host fishes. The glochidia which do not get a suitable host die in due course. Adult fish are not harmed by parasitic glochidia. Larvae become encysted in a few hours by growth of cells of the host, the tissues of the host are stimulated to grow around the parasite forming a cyst. The glochidia feed by absorbing juices of the fish by the mantle, the larval mantle contains phagocytic cells which obtain nourishment for the developing mussel, thus, they lead an ectoparasitic life for about 10 weeks during which time metamorphosis takes place.

METAMORPHOSIS

The sense organs, larval adductor muscle, larval mantle, and byssus disappear and the adult organs begin to form. The ectoderm invaginates to form the stomodaeum and proctodaeum which open into the archenteron to form the alimentary canal. A foot arises as an elevation behind the mouth. On each side of the foot arise two papillae which form gill plates. The cyst weakens and the young animal opens and closes its shell valves and extends its foot. It escapes from the cyst and drops to the bottom to become free-living, then it assumes the adult form and mode of life.

Significance of glochidium. The glochidia, as ectoparasite on fishes, may reach to far off places with the fish. Thus, they

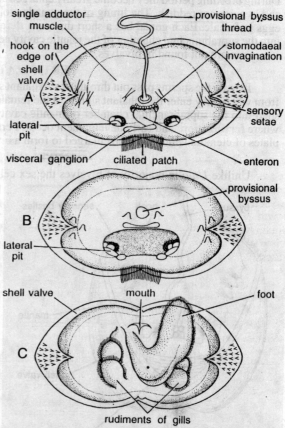

Fig. 61.19. *Unio.* Three stages in metamorphosis.

help in the dispersal of *Unio* to far off places because *Unio* is a sedentary and sluggish animal having very poor power of locomotion.

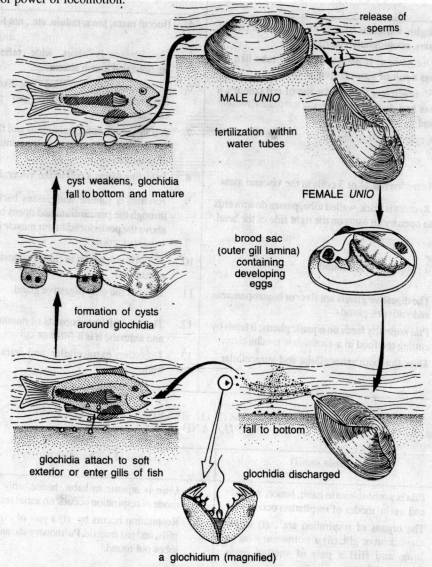

MALE *UNIO*

release of sperms

fertilization within water tubes

FEMALE *UNIO*

cyst weakens, glochidia fall to bottom and mature

brood sac (outer gill lamina) containing developing eggs

formation of cysts around glochidia

fall to bottom

glochidia attach to soft exterior or enter gills of fish

glochidia discharged

a glochidium (magnified)

Fig.61.20. *Unio.* Life cycle.

TABLE 61.1. COMPARISON OF DIGESTIVE SYSTEMS OF *PILA* AND *UNIO*

Pila (Apple snail)	*Unio* (Freshwater mussel)
1. The digestive system of *Pila* consists of the alimentary canal and digestive glands.	1. The digestive system of *Unio* consists of the alimentary canal and digestive gland.
2. The alimentary canal begins with mouth which is a vertical slit-like aperture at the tip of snout and provided with a pair of tentacles.	2. The alimentary canal begins with mouth which is a transverse slit-like aperture; no snout and tentacles.
3. Labial palps are absent, no true lips.	3. A pair of flap-like ciliated labial palps from the upper and lower lips.

Pila (Apple snail)	Unio (Freshwater mussel)
4. Highly muscular buccal mass having a pair of jaws, odontophore and radula.	4. Buccal mass, jaws, radula, etc., not found.
5. Oesophagus is narrow elongated tube-like ; it has a pair of oesophageal pouch.	5. Oesophagus is short wide tube-like ; oesophageal pouch absent.
6. Stomach is a rectangular sac of red colour ; it has two distinct chambers – cardiac chamber and pyloric chamber.	6. Stomach is thick-walled sac-like; not differentiated into cardiac and pyloric chambers.
7. Crystalline style absent.	7. A transparent, solid, gelatinous and flexible crystalline style present in the ventral part of stomach.
8. Intestine has $2\frac{1}{2}$ or 3 coils in the visceral mass.	8. Intestine forms a coil in the visceral mass.
9. Rectum is thick-walled tube, passes downwards to open by an anus on the right side of the head.	9. Rectum is tubular and passes backwards through the pericardium and opens by anus above the posterior adductor muscle into the exhalant siphon.
10. Typhlosole is not found.	10. Typhlosole present as ridge in intestine and rectum.
11. The digestive glands are liver or hepatopancreas and salivary glands.	11. Liver is the only digestive gland.
12. Pila normally feeds on aquatic plants; it feeds by cutting the food in a chain-saw mechanism.	12. The food of Unio consists of minute plants and animals; it is a filter or ciliary feeder.
13. Digestion both extracellular and intracellular.	13. Digestion extracellular and intracellular both.

TABLE 61.2. COMPARISON OF RESPIRATORY SYSTEMS OF PILA AND UNIO

Pila (Apple snail)	Unio (Freshwater mussel)
1. Pila is amphibious in habit, hence, aquatic and aerial modes of respiration occur.	1. Unio is aquatic in habit, hence, only aquatic mode of respiration occurs; no aerial respiration.
2. The organs of respiration are : (i) single ctenidium or gill, (ii) a pulmonary sac or lung, and (iii) a pair of nuchal lobes forming siphons.	2. Respiration occurs by (i) a pair of ctenidia or gills, and (ii) mantle. Pulmonary sac and nuchal lobes not found.
3. The single ctenidium lies on the right side of the branchial chamber.	3. The ctenidia are paired lying one on either side of the foot.
4. The ctenidium is simple being made of a large number of gill plates or lamellae; these are triangular and attached with the ctenidial axis by their broad bases and tips hang freely in the branchial chamber.	4. Each ctenidium is made of two gill laminae, each lamina is made of two gill lamellae; total being four lamellae in a ctenidium.
5. The gill lamellae are arranged in a row, parallel to one another , such an arrangement is called monopectinate.	5. The gill lamellae of one lamina are folded to form 'V' shaped structure; all the four gill lamellae of both the laminae of one side are united in a way to form 'W' shaped structure; such an arrangement is called eulamellibranch.

Pila (Apple snail)	*Unio* (Freshwater mussel)
6. Water tubes and ostia not found.	6. Two lamellae of one lamina unite together by interlamellar junctions to form many water tubes. The lamellae are provided with many ostia leading to the water tubes.
7. The gill filaments forming a lamella are covered by ciliated epithelium at their free ends; their basal parts are formed of glandular and non-ciliated cells.	7. Many vertically placed gill filaments form a lamella; these are covered by different types of cilia all along their outer border, supported internally by chitinous rods and filled with blood.
8. Suprabranchial chamber is not found.	8. Water tubes of each gill lamina open dorsally into a suprabranchial chamber.
9. Pulmonary sac (lung) is modified mantle, highly vascularized; it helps in gaseous exchange from air during aerial respiration.	9. Pulmonary sac is not found ; the mantle itself is highly vascularized and helps in gaseous exchange during aquatic respiration.
10. Nuchal lobes paired, one on either side of the head ; they form siphons during the process of respiration.	10. Nuchal lobes are not found ; exhalant and inhalant siphons distinctly present.
11. During aquatic respiration water enters the branchial chamber through left nuchal lobe, ctenidium is bathed, gaseous exchange takes place and the respired water goes out by the right nuchal lobe.	11. During aquatic reapiration water enters the branchial chamber of mantle cavity through inhalant siphon, then into the water tubes of gill laminae through ostia and then into the supra-branchial chamber—>exhalant siphon—>out . During the course of water in gill laminae gaseous exchange takes place.
12. The flow of water is maintained by alternate raising and lowering of the floor of mantle cavity.	12. The flow of water is maintained by the action of the cilia of gill filaments.
13. During aerial respiration left nuchal lobe forms respiratory siphon which receives air, air then enters the pulmonary sac where gaseous exchange takes place. The respired air goes out through right nuchal lobe.	13. Aerial respiration does not occur.

TABLE 61.3. COMPARISON OF NERVOUS SYSTEMS OF *PILA* AND *UNIO*

Pila (Apple snail)	*Unio* (Freshwater mussel)
1. The nervous system of *Pila* consists of paired and unpaired ganglia with their commissures and connectives. It is well developed but asymmetrical due to torsion.	1. The nervous system of *Unio* consists of only paired ganglia with their commissures and connectives. It is greatly reduced due to its sedentary mode of life but symmetrically arranged on the both sides of the body.
GANGLIA	
2. The paired ganglia are : (i) cerebral, (ii) buccal, (iii) pleural, (iv) pedal, and (v) visceral. The unpaired ganglia are (i) supra-intestinal, and (ii) infra-intestinal.	2. The paired gangula are : (i) cerebral and pleural, (ii) pedal, and (iii) visceral, which has fused to form a rectangular mass. Unpaired ganglia not found.

Pila (Apple snail)	*Unio* (Freshwater mussel)
3. Cerebral ganglia are somewhat triangular lying at the anterior dorso-lateral sides of the buccal mass, pleural ganglia not fused with it.	3. Cerebral ganglion not free but it is fused to pleural ganglion of its side to form a somewhat triangular cerebro-pleural ganglia lying at the base of labial palps antero-dorsally.
4. Pedal ganglion is fused with pleural ganglion to form pleuro-pedal ganglionic mass, one on each side lying posterior to the buccal mass ventro-laterally.	4. Pedal ganglia are free, both the pedals lie very close forming X-shaped structure and placed in the foot near visceral mass.
5. Visceral ganglia are fused to form a bilobed mass lying close to the anterior lobe of digestive gland and to the right of the pericardium.	5. Both the visceral ganglia are fused to form a rectangular ganglionic mass lying at the ventral end of the posterior adductor muscles.
6. Buccal ganglia are situated at the junction of buccal mass and oesophagus.	6. Buccal ganglia are absent.
7. Supra-intestinal ganglion is spindle-shaped lying below and behind the left pleuropedal ganglionic mass.	7. Supra-intestinal ganglion is absent.
8. Infra-intestinal ganglion is fused with right pleuropedal ganglionic mass	8. Infra-intestinal ganglion is not found.

COMMISSURES

9. Various commissures are (i) cerebral commissure, (ii) buccal commissure, and (iii) pedal commissure	9. Only cerebral commissure is found, others are not found.
10. The cerebral commissure is thick and band-like.	10. The cerebral commissure is very thin and delicate.

CONNECTIVES

11. Various connectives are: (i) paired cerebro-pleural, (ii) paired cerebro-pedal, (iii) paired cerebro-buccal, (iv) single supra-intestinal, (v) single infra-intestinal, (vi) single zygoneury, (vii) single supra-intestinal visceral, and (viii) single infra-intestinal visceral connective.	11. Various connectives are : (i) paired cerebro-pedal and (ii) paired cerebro-visceral connectives. Others are not found.

REVISION QUESTIONS

1. Give an account of the external features of *Unio*.
2. Describe the internal anatomy of a freshwater mussel you have studied.
3. Give an account of the respiratory system and mode of respiration in *Unio*.
4. Describe the ctenidia of *Unio*. Give a comparative account of respiratory system of *Pila* and *Unio*.
5. Explain the digestive system of *Unio*.
6. Describe the blood vascular system of *Unio*.
7. Give a comparative account of the digestive system of *Pila* and *Unio*.
8. Describe the nervous system of *Lamellidens* and compare it with that of *Pila*.
9. Give an account of development and metamorphosis of a *Lamellidens* you have studied.
10. Draw labelled diagrams only :
    (i) Inner view of shell valve of *Unio* (ii) T.S. *Unio* passing through the middle of foot region.
11. Write short notes on :
    (i) Mantle, (ii) Organ of Bojanus, (iii) Keber's organ, (iv) Glochidium larva.

62

Mollusca : Characters, Classification and Types

DEFINITION

Molluscs are soft-bodied, bilaterally symmetrical, unsegmented, coelomate animals; usually shelled having a mantle, ventral foot, anterior head and a dorsal visceral mass

GENERAL CHARACTERS

1. Molluscs are essentially aquatic mostly marine, few freshwater and some terrestrial forms.

2. The body·is soft, unsegmented, bilaterally symmetrical and consists of head, foot, mantle and visceral mass.

3. The body is clothed with one layered often ciliated epidermis.

4. Body is commonly protected by an exoskeletal calcareous shell of one or more pieces, secreted by the mantle.

5. Head is distinct, bearing the mouth and provided with eyes, tentacles and other sense organs except in Pelecypoda and Scaphopoda.

6. Ventral body wall is modified into a muscular flat or plough-like surface, the **foot** which is variously modified for creeping, burrowing and swimming.

7. Mantle or pallium is a fold of body wall that leaves between itself and the main body mass, the mantle cavity.

8. Visceral mass contains the vital organs of the body in a compact form taking the form of a dorsal hump or dome.

9. Body cavity is haemocoel. The true coelom is generally limited to the pericardial cavity and the lumen of the gonads and nephridia.

10. Digestive tract is simple with an anterior mouth and posterior anus but in gastropods, scaphopods and cephalopods the intestine becomes U-shaped bringing the anus to an anterior position.

11. Pharynx contains a rasping organ the radula except in Pelecypoda.

12. Circulatory system is open except in cephalopods which shows some tendency towards a closed system.

13. Respiratory organs consist of numerous gill or ctenidia usually provided with osphradium at the base. Lung is developed in terrestrial forms. Respiratory pigment is usually haemocyanin.

14. Excretory system consists of a pair of metanephridia which are true coelomoducts and communicate from pericardial cavity to the exterior by nephridiopore.

15. Nervous system consists of paired cerebral, pleural, pedal and visceral ganglia joined by longitudinal and transverse connectives and nerves.

16. Sexes usually separate (dioecious) but some are hermaphroditic.

17. Fertilization is external or internal.

18. Development is either direct or with metamorphosis through the trochophore stage called veliger larva.

CLASSIFICATION

The classification is adopted from Hyman, L.H. (1957) with certain modifications from Parker and Haswell (1965).

CLASS 1. APLACOPHORA OR SO-LENOGASTERS

. (Gr., *a*=not + *plax* = plate + *pherein* = bearing)

1. Body worm-like, bilaterally symmetrical and cylindrical.
2. Head, mantle, foot, shell and nephridia are absent.
3. Body covered with cuticle beset with numerous calcareous spicules.
4. Mouth and anus are terminal or subterminal at opposite end.
5. Digestive tract straight generally provided with a radula.
6. A pair of coelomoducts in the form of gonoducts opening into the terminal part of intestine or independently.
7. A mid-dorsal longitudinal keel or crest is often present.
8. Sexes united (hermaphroditic) or separate (dioecious).

Order 1. Neomenioidea

1. Mid-ventral longitudinal groove present.

    Examples : *Neomenia Proneomenia, Lepidomenia*

Order 2. Chaetodermatoidea

1. Mid-ventral longitudinal groove absent.

    Examples : *Chaetoderma, Prochaetoderma.*

CLASS 2. POLYPLACOPHORA

(Gr., *poly* = many + *plax* = plate + *pherein* = bearing)

1. Mostly bilaterally symmetrical, dorsoventrally flattened molluscs.
2. Body elliptical, convex dorsally and flattened ventrally.
3. Head distinct without eyes and tentacles.
4. Shell composed of a logitudinal series of eight calcareous pieces.
5. Foot flat and ventral, laterally bordered by a groove containing gills.
6. Radula well developed comprising 17 teeth.
7. Intestine coiled with a terminal anus.
8. A pair of nephridia extending from pericardium to the lateral groove.
9. A pair of gonoducts without relation to the pericardium.
10. Sexes are separate (dioecious).

Order 1. Lepidopleurida

1. Valves of the shell without insertion plates, or if present without insertion teeth.

Examples : *Lepidopleurus, Hanleya.*

Order 2. Chitonina

1. Valves of the shell with insertion plates and teeth.

    Examples : *Tonicella, Chiton, Cryptochiton, Choneplex.*

CLASS 3. MONOPLACOPHORA

(Gr., *monos* = one + *plax* + plate + *pherein* = bearing)

1. Body bilaterally symmetrical and segmented.
2. Shell comprises single piece or valve.
3. Head without eyes and tentacles.
4. Foot flat and ventral.
5. Mantle encircles the body as a circular fold of the body wall.
6. Gills external and serially arranged.
7. Five pairs of nephridia serially arranged.
8. Sexes separate (dioecious).

    Examples : *Neopilina galatheae.*

CLASS 4. GASTROPODA

(Gr., *gaster* = belly + *podos* = foot)

1. Gastropods are marine, freshwater, terrestrial and few parasitic on echinoderms.
2. Body unsegmented, asymmetrical typically with a univalve, spirally coiled shell.
3. Head distinct bearing tentacles, eyes and mouth.
4. Foot is ventral, broad, flat and muscular forming the creeping sole and often bearing dorsally a hard piece, the operculum on its posterior end.
5. Visceral mass spirally coiled exhibiting torsion.
6. Mantle is a collar-like fold of body wall, lining the body whorl leaving a space, the mantle cavity, between itself and the body.
7. Buccal cavity contains an odontophore with a radula bearing rows of chitinous teeth.
8. Digestive system comprises a muscular pharynx, long oesophagus, stomach, long coiled intestine and anteriorly placed anus.
9. Respiration by gills (ctenidia) in most forms, through the wall of the mantle cavity in some forms and in many by lungs.
10. Circulatory system is open and the heart is enclosd in a pericardium.
11. Excretory organs comprise metanephridia which are paired in primitive forms and reduced to a single nephridia in most forms.

12. Nervous system comprises distinct cerebral and pleural besides buccal, pedal, parietal and visceral ganglia.

13. Sexes are separate (dioecious) in most forms, while in some forms united (hermaphroditic).

14. Development includes trochophore and veliger larval stages.

SUBCLASS I. PROSOBRANCHIA

1. Mostly marine, few freshwater or terrestrial forms.

2. Owing to torsion of the visceral mass, the visceral nerve commissures are twisted into a figure of "8".

3. Mantle cavity opens anteriorly in front of the visceral mass.

4. Shell is generally conical and spirally coiled with an operculum.

5. Head distinct with snout bearing a pair of tentacles and a pair of eyes.

6. Foot is muscular, forms the ventral part of the body.

7. Ctenidia or gills, if present, are situated in front of the heart.

8. Sexes are separate (dioecious).

Order 1. Archaeogastropoda

1. Prosobranchs without proboscis, siphon, penis and prostratic glands.

2. Operculum is also absent in many forms with few exceptions.

3. One or two bipectinate internal gills.

4. Heart mostly with two auricles.

5. Two osphradia usually present.

6. Two nephridia.

7. Nervous system not concentrated usually with pedal cords.

8. Sex cells discharged directly into the sea by way of the right nephridia.

   Examples : *Haliotis, Fissurella, Acmaea, Patella, Trochus, Asteraea, Turbo.*

Order 2. Mesogastropoda

1. Prosobranchs usually with siphon, penis and a non-calcified operculum.

2. Radula taenioglossate type having 7 teeth in each row.

3. One monopectinate gill.

4. Heart with one auricle.

5. Single ospharadium.

6. Single nephridium.

7. Nervous system concentrated without pedal cords.

   Examples : *Viviparus, Ampullarius, Pila, Valvata, Truncatella, Littorina, Hydrobia, Jonthina, Cypraea.*

Order 3. Stenoglossa or Neogastropoda

1. Shell with more or less elongated siphonal canal.

2. Radula consists of rows with two or three teeth in each row.

   Examples : *Murex, Magilus, Buccinum, Melongena, Conus, Terebra.*

SUBCLASS II. OPISTHOBRANCHIA

1. Exclusively marine gastropods.

2. Shell often reduced or wanting, when present often covered with mantle or pedal folds.

3. Operculum usually absent.

4. Single gill or often replaced by secondary branchiae in the form of dorsal outgrowths.

5. Heart with one auricle posterior to the ventricle.

6. Due to the detorsion the mantle cavity rotated to the right side or often lost.

7. Nervous system concentrated due to detorsion.

8. Hermaphrodite, *i.e.*, sexes united.

Order 1. Onchidiacea

1. Slug-like, naked or without shell opisthobranchs.

2. Mantle projects widely beyond the foot.

3. Head bears a pair of retractile tentacles each tipped with an eye.

4. Pulmonary sac, anus and female gonopore located at the posterior end.

5. Male gonopore placed anteriorly.

   Examples : *Onchidium, Onchidella.*

Order 2. Cephalaspidea

1. Shell is generally present but may be partly or wholly enclosed by mantle.

2. Parapodial lobes present or absent.

3. Head with tentacular shield.

   Examples : *Acteon, Hydatina, Bulla.*

Order 3. Anaspidea or Aplysiacea

1. Found mostly in tropical and subtropical waters.

2. Shell small, more or less covered by mantle.

3. Parapodial lobes well developed.
4. Anterior end bears a pair of tentacles, a pair of rhinophores and a pair of eyes.
5. Sperm duct open, running the body length to the penis located anteriorly.
   Examples : *Aplysia, Akera.*

Order 4. Pteropoda

1. Pelagic snails with or without shell.
2. Swim by a pair of lateral expansions.
3. Protandrous, hermaphrodite with an open sperm groove.
   Examples : *Spiratella, Cavolina, Peraclis, Clione.*

Order 5. Acochlidiacea

1. Minute without shell or naked snail.
2. Gills, parapodia and visceral sac projecting behind the foot.
3. Sexes united or separate in few.
   Example : *Acochlidium.*

Order 6. Philinoglossacea

1. Minute naked snails.
2. Head appendages absent.
3. Gills are absent.
4. Visceral mass separated from the foot only by a shallow groove.
   Example : *Philinoglossa.*

Order 7. Saccoglossa

1. With or without shell.
2. Pharynx suctorial.
3. Sperm duct is closed.
4. Parapodia and cerata present.
   Example: *Oxynoe.*

Order 8. Notaspidea

1 Shell present or absent.
2. Parapodia absent.
   Gills bipectinate and osphradium on the right side.
4. Mantle present but devoid of mantle cavity.
   Examples : *Tylodina, Pleurobranchus.*

Order 9. Nudibranchia

1. Shell absent or naked.
2. Internal gill or ctenidium and osphradium absent.
3. Mantle or mantle cavity absent.
4. Respiration by secondary branchiae usually arranged in a circlet around the anus.

Examples : *Doris, Tritonia, Armina, Eolis.*

Order 10. Rhodopacea

1. Vermiform snail.
2. Without external appendages.
3. Nephridia protonephridial type.
   Example : *Rhodope.*

Order 11. Pyramidellacea

1. Shell spirally twisted.
2. Long invaginable proboscis.
3. Operculum absent.
4. Gills and radula absent.
   Examples: *Turbonilla, Odostomia.*

Order 12. Parasita

1. Endoparasitic gastropods found in the interior of holothurians.
2. Extremely degenerated snails.
   Examples : *Entoconcha, Thyonicola.*

SUBCLASS III. PULMONATA

1. Mostly freshwater or terrestrial, a few marine members.
2. Shell typically spiral or reduced or absent, if present partly or completely concealed by mantle.
3. Operculum is absent.
4. Mantle cavity transformed into a pulmonary sac with a narrow pore on the right side, gill absent.
5. Heart with one auricle anterior to the ventricle.
6. Nervous system secondarily symmetrical owing to the shortening of connectives and concentrartion of ganglia into a circum-oesophageal ganglionic complex.
7. Hermaphroditic.

Order 1. Basommatophora

1. Freshwater, brackish water and marine forms.
2. Shell delicate with a conical spire and large aperture.
3. One pair of non-invaginable tentacles with the eyes at their bases.
4. Male and female gonopore generally separate.
   Examples : *Siphonaria, Lymnaea, Planorbis.*

Order 2. Stylommatophora

1. Terrestrial pulmonates.
2. Shell with a conical spire, internal or absent.

3. Two pairs of invaginable or retractile tentacles with the eyes at the tips of the poste- rior pair.
4. Male and female gonopores usually united.

Examples : *Limax, Helix, Partula, Retinella.*

CLASS 5. SCAPHOPODA
(Gr., *scapha* = boat + *podos* = foot)

1. Exclusively marine.
2. Body is bilaterally symmetrical, elongated and enclosed in a tusk-like shell open at both ends.
3. Eyes, tentacles and gills are absent.
4. Mantle tubular completely enclosing the body.
5. Mouth surrounded by lobular processes or outgrowths.
6. Foot is reduced, used for digging.
7. Heart rudimentary.
8. Sexes separate (dioecious).

Example : *Dentalium.*

CLASS 6. PELECYPODA
(Gr., *pelekys* = hatchet + *podos* = foot)

1. Aquatic, mostly marine, some freshwater forms.
2. Body is bilaterally symmetrical and laterally compressed.
3. Shell consists of two lateral valves, hinged together mid-dorsally.
4. Head is not distinct; pharynx, jaws, radula and tentacles are absent.
5. Foot is ventral, muscular which is ploughshare.
6. Mantle is bilobed, consiting of paired, right and left lobes.
7. Gills or ctenidia are paired, one on each side.
8. Coelom is reduced to a dorsally placed pericardium.
9. Alimentary canal is coiled with large paired digestive glands.
10. Heart is contained within pericardium and comprises median ventricle and two auricles.
11. Excretory organs are paired nephridia or kidneys open at one end into pericardium at the other end to the exterior.
12. Nervous system consists typically of four pairs of ganglia, *viz.*, cerebral, pleural, pedal and visceral.

13. Cerebral and pleural of each side usually fused into a single cerebro-pleural ganglion.
14. Sense organs are statocyst and osphradia.
15. Sexes are separate or united.
16. Development is accompanied by metamorphosis which usually includes a trochophore larva.

Order 1. Protobranchia

1. Single pair of plate-like ctenidia each consisting of two rows of flattened gill filaments.
2. Foot is not compressed but has a flattened ventral surface or sole for creeping.
3. Two adductor muscles present

Examples : *Nucula, Solenomya.*

Order 2. Filibranchiata

1. Single pair of plume-like gills formed of distinct V-shaped filaments.
2. Inter-filamentar junctions are either absent or formed by groups of inter-locking cilia.
3. Inter-lamellar junctions are either absent or non-vascular.
4. Two adductor muscles present, anterior may be reduced or absent.
5. Foot small and poorly developed.

Examples : *Mytilus, Arca.*

Order 3. Pseudolamellibranchiata

1. Gills are plaited so as to form vertical folds.
2. Inter-filamentar junctions may be ciliary or vascular.
3. Inter-lamellar junctions vascular and non-vascular.
4. Single large posterior adductor muscle present.
5. Shell valves are frequently equal.
6. Foot rudimentary or feebly developed.

Examples : *Pecten, Ostraea, Melagrina.*

Order 4. Eulamellibrnachiata.

1. Gills are firm and basket-like.
2. Gill filaments are united by vascular inter-filamentar and inter-lamellar junctions.
3. Two equal sized adductor muscles present.
4. Siphon of small or large size present.
5. Foot large, byssus small or absent.

Examples : *Anodonta, Unio, Cardium, Venus, Mya, Teredo.*

Order 5. Septibranchiata

1. Gills reduced to a horizontal muscular partition dividing the mantle cavity.

2. Two adductor muscles present.

3. Foot long and slender and byssus rudimentary or absent.

4. Sexes united.

Examples : *Poromya, Cuspidaria.*

CLASS 7. CEPHALOPODA
(Gr., *kephale* = head + *podos* = foot)

1. Exclusively marine.

2. Body bilaterally symmetrical with head and trunk.

3. Shell spiral, chambered or usually with or without reduced shell embedded in the mantle.

4. Head bears large eyes and mouth.

5. Trunk consists of symmetrical and uncoiled visceral mass.

6. Mantle encloses posteriorly and ventrally a large mantle cavity.

7. Foot altered into a series of sucker bearing arms or tentacles encircling the mouth.

8. Mouth bears jaws and radula.

9. Two or four pairs of bipectinate gills.

10. Circulatory system closed, heart with two or four auricles.

11. Excretory system comprises two or four pairs of nephridia.

12. Nervous system is highly developed and the principal ganglia are concentrated around the oesophagus.

13. Sexes are separate.

14. Development meroblastic without metamorphosis.

SUBCLASS I. BELEMNOIDEA OR DI-BRANCHIATA

1. Shell usually internal and reduced, enveloped by the mantle, when external its cavity is not divided by septa.

2. Main part of the foot is modified into 8 or 10 sucker bearing arms encircling the mouth.

3. Funnel forms a complete tube.

4. Two ctenidia or gills, two kidneys, two auricles and two branchial hearts present.

5. Ink gland duct and chromatophores are present.

6. Eyes are complex in structure.

Order 1. Decapoda

1. Body is generally elongated often with lateral fins.

2. Arms are 10 of which 8 short and 2 long. Two longer arms or tentacles are retractile bearing suckers at their distal ends. Eight smaller arms bear stalked suckers provided with horny rims.

3. Shell is internal and well developed.

4. Nidamental glands are usually present.

5. Heart enclosed in the well developed coelom.

Examples : *Sepia, Loligo, Spirula.*

Order 2. Octopoda

1. Body usually globose and devoid of lateral fins.

2. Eight arms with sessile suckers and devoid of horny rims.

3. Shell is absent except in female *Argonauta.*

4. Nidamental glands absent.

5. Heart does not lie in the reduced coelom.

Examples : *Octopus, Agronauta.*

SUBCLASS II. NAUTILOIDEA OR TETRABRANCHIATA

1. Shell is external, spiral and chambered.

2. Main part of the foot encircling the mouth, divided into lobes bearing numerous tentacles.

3. Funnel does not form a complete tube.

4. Four ctenidia or gills, four kidneys and four auricles are present.

5. Ink gland and chromatophores are absent.

6. Eyes are simple.

Example : *Nautilus.*

SUBCLASS III. AMMONOIDEA

1. Shell of various forms straight to spiral.

2. Siphon external and marginal siphuncle.

3. Usually with frilled septal edges. Extinct forms.

Example : *Ammonites*

REPRESENTATIVE TYPES OF MOLLUSCA

1. *Chiton.* Chiton (Fig. 62.1) is a sluggish, marine animal found attached to the rocks, empty shells and corals between tide marks. Body is elongated, bilaterally symmetrical and dorsoventrally compressed and consists of shell, foot, mantle and the visceral mass. Shell is calcareous present on the dorsal side and composed of eight overlapping plates. Head is not distinct. Eyes and tentacles are

absent. Foot is ventral, muscular with a flat sole extending along the whole length of the body. It serves for creeping and adhering to the substratum. Mantle covers greater part of the body and partly

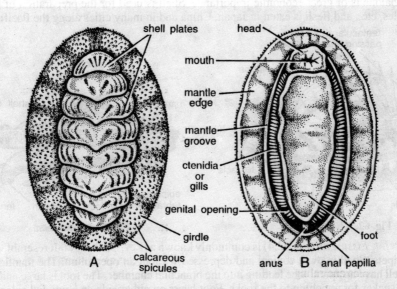

Fig. 62.1. *Chiton..* A—Dorsal view ; B—Ventral view.

covers the edges of the shell plates. Mouth and anus are at opposite ends. Numerous pairs of bipectinate ctenidia lying on either side of the body in the mantle groove. Sexes are separate gonad is single and median and gonoducts are paired . Development includes a trochophore larva.

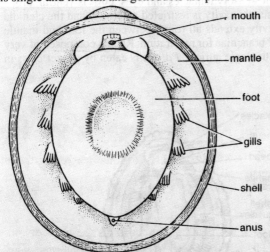

Fig. 62.2. *Neopilina galatheae.* (Ventral view).

2. *Neopilina galatheae.* *Neopilina galatheae* (Fig. 62.2) is one of very few living members of the Monoplacophora. *Neopilina* is a deep sea mollusc of special interest because it illustrates the primitive occurrence of metamerism in molluscs. *Neopilina* was discovered in 1952. In *Neopilina* the single symmetrical shell is low, somewhat patelliform and exogastrically coiled. The largest specimen known is 37 mm long 35 mm wide and 13 mm high. *Neopilina* appears somewhat chiton-like from the ventral surface. The central circular foot is separated from the encircling mantle by a pallial groove which contains five pairs of lamellated gills with a ciliated epithelium. The head is inconspicuous with two small pre-oral tentacles and two oral tentacle tufts around the mouth. Anterior to the mouth is a velar ridge with two flaps.

Unpaired anterior and posterior lips border the mouth. A feeding furrow extends between velar ridge and tentacle tufts. At the posterior end is the anus. Pharynx contains a radula. The stomach contains a crystalline style. The muscular system is complex. Six pairs of nephridia are located in the pallial fold. Sexes are separate. The food of *Neopilina* consists of radiolarians and other materials of the bottom.

3. Haliotis. Haliotis (Fig. 62.3) is marine and found attached to the rocks between tide marks. *Haliotis* is commonly called ear-shell. Shell is ear-shaped with small flattened spire, very large aperture and perforated by a series of marginal slits through which projects the tentacular process of the mantle. Operculum is absent. Eyes are borne upon stalks at the outer bases of tentacles. Foot very large with epipodia projecting through the shell. Mantle cavity is spacious and contains two bipectinate ctenidia or gills, the right being smaller. Two auricles and two nephridia are present. *Haliotis* or Abalone is of great economic importance. Shell is used for the preparation of beautiful buttons, buckles, etc., and flesh is eaten in Japan, China and in many cities along the Pacific coast.

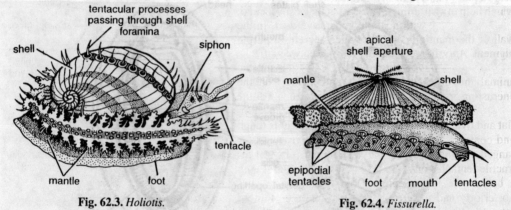

Fig. 62.3. *Holiotis.*   **Fig. 62.4.** *Fissurella.*

4. Fissurella. *Fissurella* (Fig.62.4) is commonly known as keyhole limpet. It resembles closely to the true limpets. Shell is oval, conical and depressed without an operculum. The mantle and the apex of the shell have an apical lobe leading into the branchial chamber. The foot is large and ventral; it is used as a sucker for attaching to the rocks. Foot bears on either side an epipodial ridge bearing a row of cirri.

5. Patella. *Patella* (Fig. 62.5) is a sluggish, marine gastropod, found attached to the rocks and feeding on minute algae. *Patella* a limpet, is a small oval gastropod. Shell is oval and rounded without operculum. Head is distinct; bears a pair of stout, sensory tentacles and eyes. Foot is ventral, broad and flat; used for creeping and adhering. True mantle cavity is restricted anteriorly and the ctenidia or gills have disappeared. Secondary mantle cavity extends all round between the foot and mantle and contains a series of pallial gills or secondary branchiae for respiration. Radula composed of very few, strong hooked teeth in each row. Heart with single auricle. *Patella* is eaten by poorer class in several countries like France, Italy and Ireland.

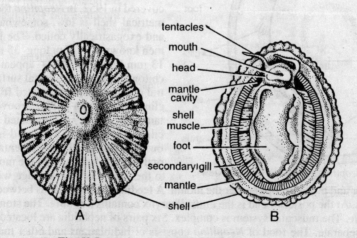

Fig. 62.5. *Patella.* A—Dosral view ; B—Ventral view.

6. Aplysia. *Aplysia.* (Fig. 62.6) is found crawling in sea weeds in most parts of the world from the Arctic to the Antarctic. *Aplysia* is commonly known as sea hare. The body is soft and lumpy with a thin flexible plate-like shell almost completely covered by mantle. Head bears two pairs of tentacles, the anterior being larger and ear-like, while the posterior pair is olfactory, each bearing an eye at

its base. Mantle cavity opens on the right side with the
ctenidium pointing backwards. Visceral mass is raised
into a prominent hump. Foot is broad and ventral and
bears a pair of lateral fleshy outgrowth, the parapodia
which help in swimming. Anus lies at the posterior end.
Hermaphrodite with a single generative duct. In the
wall of the mantle is a gland which secretes a purple
pigment. *Aplysia* feeds mainly on the sea weeds.

7. *Doris*. *Doris* (Fig. 62.7) is a sluggish marine
animal moving between weeds and feeding on the
encrusting organisms. *Doris* is commonly known as the
sea lemon. The body is bilaterally symmetrical, short,
flat and oval with convex dorsal surface. Skin is tough
and contains calcareous spicules of various types arranged symmetrically. Head bears a pair of short retractile tentacles or rhinophores. Foot is ventral with
a broad sole for creeping. Dorso-median anus lies
posteriorly and is surrounded by secondary plumose
retractile branchiae. Hermaphrodite. *Doris* exhibits

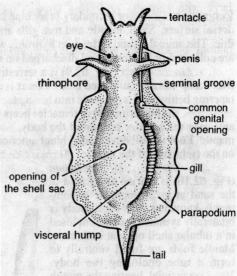

Fig. 62.6. *Aplysia.*

complete detorsion as shown by the
absence of shell mantle and ctenidium.

8. *Eolis*. *Eolis* (Fig. 62.8) inhabits shallow waters, found often
crawling on the underside of sea
weeds. *Eolis* is commonly known as
sea slug. Body is ovate, soft about
1–2 cm in length and orange with
brown spots in colour. Head bears
two pairs of cylindrical retractile tentacles and sessile eyes at the base of
the posterior pair of tentacles. Foot is
muscular and ventral and serves for

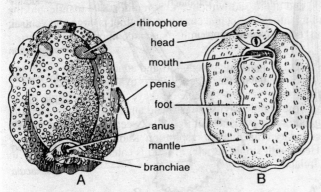

Fig. 62.7. *Doris.* A—Dorsal view; B—Ventral view.

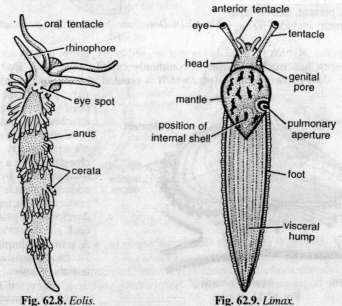

Fig. 62.8. *Eolis.*   **Fig. 62.9.** *Limax.*

locomotion. Cerata or secondary branchiae are numerous, cylindrical processes distributed over the dorsal surface. Shell, mantle and true gills are absent. Hermaphroditic, common gonad is protrandric. The animal is said to feed on hydroids which are digested and their undischarged nematocysts are collected in the cerata and discharged on irritation.

9. *Limax. Limax* (Fig. 62.9) is a terrestrial cosmopolitan in distribution and found in gardens over damp soil and cultivated lands. *Limax* is commonly known as gray slug. Body is elongated and tapering behind and is divisible into head, foot and visceral hump. Head bears two pairs of retractile tentacles, the posterior part of tentacles bears small black eyes at their lips. Mantle forms a shield-like area over the anterior portion of the body. Shell is internal, thin and rudimentalry lies embedded in mantle. **Foot** is well developed, blunt anteriorly and tapering posteriorly. Pulmonary aperture lies on the right side of the mantle. Hermaphrodite. Nocturnal and herbivorous.

10. *Dentalium. Dentalium* (Fig. 62.10) is marine and found in the sand at great depth. It is commonly known as tusk shell. Body is bilaterally symmetrical and enclosed in a tubular shell open at both ends. Mantle folds are fused ventrally to form a tube enclosing the body. Head is vestigial, bearing the mouth which is surrounded by a circlet of retractile tentacles, the captacula with sucker-like ends. Foot is long and conical, protrudes through the anterior opening of the shell and is used in burrowing. Well developed radula is present. Anus lies behind the base of foot. Gills are absent. Respiration by transverse folds in the lining of mantle. A pair of nephridia is present with their external openings on either side of the anus. Vascular system is poorly developed without distinct head. Nervous system simple and consists of cerebral, pleural and pedal ganglia. Eyes absent. Otocysts present. Sexes separate. Development includes veliger larva.

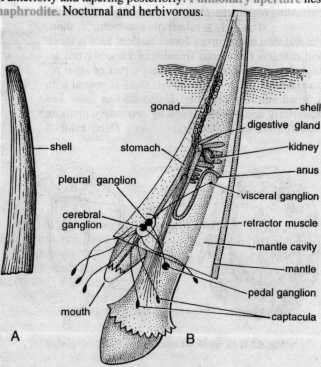

Fig. 62.10. *Dentalium.* A—Shell ; B—Structure of specimen in buried sand.

11. *Mytilus. Mytilus* (Fig. 62.11) is marine, sedentary, cosmopolitan and found attached to the rocks between tide marks. *Mytilus* is commonly called sea mussel. Body is enclosed in a wedge-shaped shell of two equal valves, which is pointed in front and rounded behind. Byssus

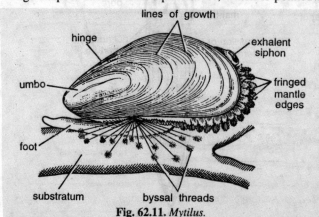

Fig. 62.11. *Mytilus.*

threads protrude from between two shell valves ventrally by which it is attached to stones and rocks. Mantle is bilobed and forms an exhalant siphon posteriorly. Foot is cylindrical, elongated with a ventral groove continuous with a byssus pit. Anterior adductor muscle is weaker, while posterior adductor muscle is strongly developed. A pair of gills is present, each gill is provided with filaments. A pair of simple eyes is present. Sexes are separate. Gonads extend into the mantle.

12. *Pecten. Pecten* (Figs. 62.12 and 62.13) is marine, free swimming

and cosmopolitan in distribution. *Pecten* is commonly known as scallops. Shell is beautifully ribbed by radiating lines. The two shell valves are unequal, the right being larger and more convex and the animal rests on this valve. Single large adductor muscle is divided into two parts and the larger of these serves for swimming movements. Foot is very much reduced. Two large and crescentic gills are present. Large number of stalked eyes are present at regular intervals along the edges of the mantle. Hermaphrodite. Ovary is pink and testis is cream coloured.

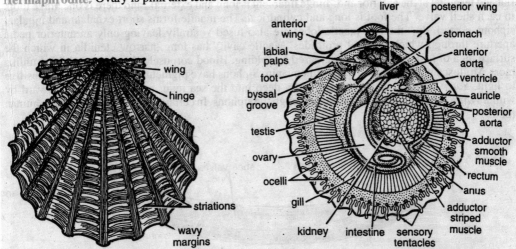

Fig. 62.12. *Pecten.* External view of entire animal.

Fig. 62.13. *Pecten.* Left valve, mantle and gill removed to show internal structures.

13. *Ostrea.* *Ostrea* is marine, sedentary animal found attached to rocks and stones, etc. *Ostrea* is commonly known as edible osyter. Shell surface is coarse, irregular and ruffled. Two valves of the shell are unequal, the left being larger and attached to the substratum. Single adductor muscle divided into two parts. Foot is absent. Heart with two fused auricles. Individuals function alternately as males and females. *Ostrea* is used as favourite food in many countries.

14. *Teredo.* *Teredo* (Fig. 62.14) is commonly known as ship worm. It is marine, found in burrows made in submerged wood of ships and boats. Body is elongated and vermiform. Mantle is tube-like and opens anteriorly. Foot is very much reduced. Shell is reduced and consists of two small valves enclosing only the anterior region of the body, provided with a rough and ridged surface. Siphons are long, the two siphons are united most of their lengths and provided with calcareous

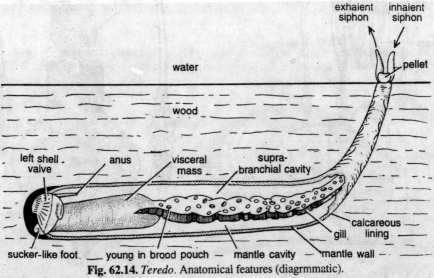

Fig. 62.14. *Teredo.* Anatomical features (diagrmmatic).

pellets for protection. Mantle cavity is long and contains a pair of elongated gills. *Teredo* bores into submerged wood reducing it into saw dust by the rotatory action of the two shell valves. Saw-dust is swallowed by the animal and digested by the enzymes secreted by the digestive gland.

15. *Solen.* *Solen* (Fig. 62.15) is commonly known as razor calm or razor shell. The shell is long and cylindrical, shell valves are narrow and straight, they gape at both ends, the umbones are flat and terminal at the anterior end, hinge ligament is long and external, and there is one hinge tooth in each shell valve. The foot is long and cylindrical. The mantle forms short exhalant and inhalant siphons posteriorly, the two mantle lobes are also fused ventrally leaving only an anterior pedal aperture through which the foot protrudes. Mantle cavity has long, narrow ctenidia in which the surface area of lamellae has been increased by folding. Blood corpuscles have hemoglobin, unlike most Mollusca in which blood has haemocyanin. Siphons have pigmented refractive cells sensitive to light. *Solen* burrows actively and rapidly deep into the sea mud, but it jerks itself forward by withdrawing the foot and ejecting water through the siphons. In certain areas clams are used as human food.

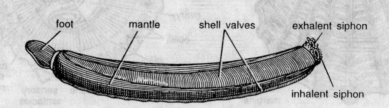

Fig. 62.15. *Solen.*

A similar razor clam *Ensis* is common in the Indian Ocean, its shell is about 20 cm long with a slight bend which makes the dorsal side concave and ventral side a little convex, the right shell valve has two hinge teeth and left one has three; siphons are very short.

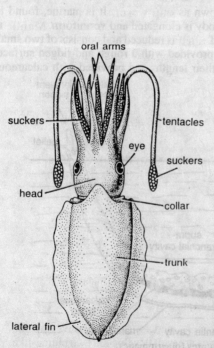

Fig. 62.16. *Sepia.* (Dorsal view).

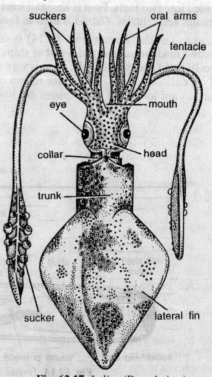

Fig. 62.17. *Loligo* (Dorsal view).

16. *Sepia.* Sepia (Fig. 62.16) is commonly known as cuttle fish. It is a marine form, found in the shallow waters and world-wide in distribution. Body is bilaterally symmetrical, dorso-ventrally flattened and is divisible into head, neck and trunk. Head bears a pair of large eyes and five pairs of arms surrounding the mouth. Of the five pairs of arms, four pairs are short and stout bearing four longitudinal rows of suckers on the inner flat surface. The fifth pair of arms is known as tentacles which are comparatively longer and narrower and provided with suckers only towards their free ends. Neck is constricted and connects the head with the trunk. Trunk is elongated and shield-shaped bordered by narrow lateral fold on either side. Mantle is thick and muscular enclosing a large mantle cavity on the ventral side which contains the viscera. Funnel is tubular opening into the mantle cavity. Shell is internal and enclosed in a shell sac in the mantle on the upper surface. Chromatophores are present in the deeper layers of integument over the entire surface. A pair of large plume-shaped ctenidia or gills, one each side of the mantle cavity performs the respiratory function. Single kidney is excretory organ. A pear-shaped ink sac lies over the posterior ventral surface. Sexes are separate. In male the left fourth arm is hectocotylised.

17. *Loligo.* Loligo (Fig. 62.17) is commonly known as squid. Body is spindle or torpedo-shaped and is divisible into head, foot and visceral hump. Head is short and bears a pair of large eyes and a central mouth surrounded by ten arms. Foot is modified into the funnel and the ten arms. Eight arms are short, stumpy and non-retractile, while two are long, slender and retractile tentacles used for capturing the prey. Inner surface of both arms and tentacles is provided with suckers. Funnel is muscular tube extending out beyond the edge of the mantle collar beneath the head. Visceral hump is long and pointed, bears two dorso-lateral triangular fins. Mantle is thick and muscular encloses the visceral mass and mantle cavity. Shell is internal, feather-shaped plate concealed beneath the skin on the anterior surface. Two elongated gills are present in the mantle cavity. Two nephridia or kidneys are also present. An ink sac is present and serves for defence. Sexes are separate. *Loligo* is used as food by Chinese and Italians and also as bait for marine fishing. *Loligo* is a marine form and has a world-wide distribution.

18. *Octopus.* Octopus (Fig. 62.18) is popularly known as devil fish. Body is globose with large head and trunk region. Head bears a pair of **eyes** and eight elongated equal arms webbed at the base which surrounded the mouth. Each arm bears suckers arranged in two rows. Third right arm in male is modified into a spoon-shaped structure which serves for transferring the spermatophores into the mantle cavity of the female for fertilizing the ova. Shell is absent. Mantle encloses the mantle cavity and the visceral mass. *Octopus* produces inky-fluid which diffuses in water and forms a smoky screen for defence from the enemies. *Octopus* is marine, cosmopolitan in distribution and found on the bottom of the sea.

19. *Argonauta.* Argonauta (Fig. 62.19) is commonly known as Paper Nautilus. Sexual dimorphism is remarkable and well marked. Male is small about 2.5 cm in length and without shell. Female is about 20 cm in length and possesses a thin, transparent unilocular shell which is secreted by extremities of two dorsal arms. Shell in female is used for protection of eggs. Mouth is surrounded by four pairs of elongated arms

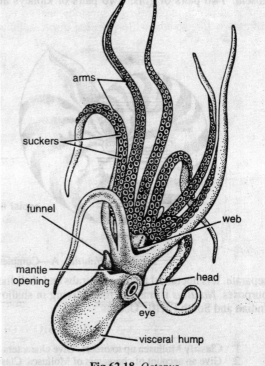

Fig.62.18. *Octopus.*

provided with suckers. Third arm in the male is hectocotylised and is used for conveying the spermatophores in the mantle cavity of female. Funnel and eyes are well developed. Two plume-like ctenidia and two kidneys are present. *Argonauta* is found in all warmer seas. Female lives in deep waters and comes up only at the spawning season.

20. *Nautilus. Nautilus* (Fig. 62.20) is commonly called as Pearly Nautilus. Body is enclosed in a calcareous spirally coiled many chambered shell. The animal occupies the outermost and largest chamber into which body can be withdrawn for protection. The chambers are separated by a system of septa which are perforated in the middle and traversed by narrow tubular vascular prolongations of the visceral mass, the siphuncles. Except the outermost chamber, all the chambers are filled with air so that the shell can float and animal can swim easily. Body of the animal consists of head bearing eyes and a system of tentacles and a sac-like trunk. Mouth is situated at the end of the head and surrounded by numerous lobes bearing two rows of retractile tentacles. Outer rows of tentacles are

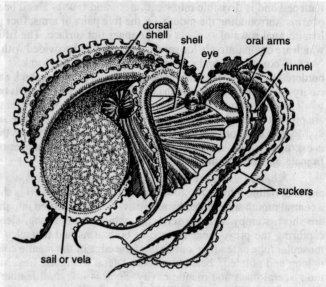

Fig. 62.19. *Argonauta* (Female).

borne on a muscular ridge forming the hood which serves as an operculum. Arms and suckers are absent. Two pairs of gills, two pairs of kidneys and two pairs of auricles are present. Sexes are

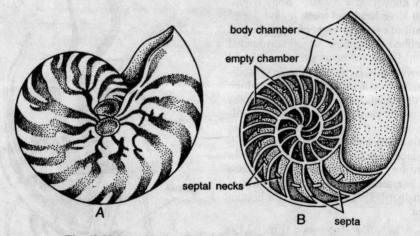

Fig. 62.20. *Nautilus*. A—Complete shell; B—Shell in section.

separate. It is nocturnal feeding on crabs and shell fishes. *Nautilus* is used extensively for ornamental purposes. *Nautilus* is marine, found living in shallow waters near the shores and coral reefs in the Indian and South Pacific Oceans.

REVISION QUESTIONS

1. Classify Mollusca up to orders. Give characters and examples.
2. Give an account of characters of Mollusca. Classify it up to orders and give examples.
3. Write short notes on :
   (a) *Chiton* ; (b) *Aplysia* ; (c) *Doris* ; (d) *Mytilus*; (e) *Teredo* ; (f) *Octopus* ; (g) *Nautilus* ; (h) *Loligo*.

63

Mollusca in General

ARCHIMOLLUSC

The molluscs are thought to be of pre-Cambrian in origin. But it is still a problem of debate and is to be decided that from which animal or animal group, the molluscs of today have descended . However, it is, therefore, presumed that today's molluscs have descended from a hypothetical ancestor which would had been very primitive. This primitive hypothetical ancestor is referred to as archimollusc which has given rise to the different classes of Mollusca of today. The characteristics of archimollusc are summarized in the following lines :

1. The archimollusc was a sluggish animal, creeping slowly over the hard surfaces in shallow water.

2. It had a flattened body which was perfectly bilateral in symmetry.

3. There was no trace of segmentation but it had an anterior mouth and a posterior anus.

4. It had a distinct head, situated antero-ventrally, with a pair of tentacles and a pair of eyes.

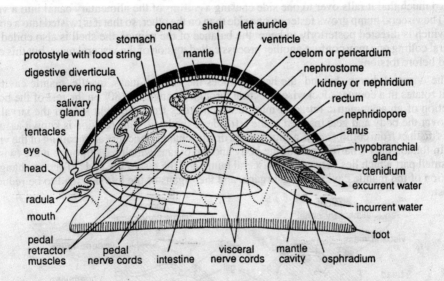

Fig. 63.1. Schematic lateral view of an archimollusc (hypothetical molluscan ancestor).

5. It had a large, muscular ventral foot; its edges were provided with small delicate tactile tentacles.

6. Its postero-dorsal part was raised into a hump.

7. Its visceral mass was covered in pallium or mantle.

8. Dorsally, it had an oval, convex shell secreted by the mantle.

9. Mantle cavity lying between the visceral mass and mantle was in direct communication to external environment.

10. Respiration was performed by one or more pairs of ctenidia or gills.

11. An olfactory organ, osphradium was present close to gills.

12. Its alimentary canal was somewhat straight; pharynx had horny jaws, odontophore was present which had chitinous radula.

13. It was microphagous and herbivore.

14. Its heart was three chambered, having one mid-dorsal ventricle and two ventro-lateral auricles.

15. The body cavity was haemocoel and original coelom in the form of pericardium and gonocoel.

16. It had a pair of tubular nephridia or kidneys for excretion.

17. Its nervous system was very simple; nerve ring around oesophagus, visceral and pedal nerve cords.

18. Paired tentacles, eyes, osphradium, statocysts were the sensory organs.

19. Sexes were separate and fertilization was external.

20. A free swimming trochophore larva developed during development which metamorphosed directly into adult without undergoing in veliger stage.

TORSION IN GASTROPODA

Mollusca are typically bilaterally symmetrical animals but this symmetry is lost in Gastropoda due to two processes called coiling and torsion. There is a tendency for digestion and resorption to be confined to a dorsal digestive gland or liver, the liver undergoes growth to form a projection which grows so much that it falls over to one side causing a coiling of the alimentary canal into a visceral hump. The visceral hump grows faster on one side than on the other, so that it is twisted into a compact spiral which is directed posteriorly to keep the balance of the animal, the shell is also coiled. With this spiral coiling one may confuse another process called torsion of the visceral mass, but this coiling evolved before torsion.

The visceral hump behind the head includes the visceral mass, mantle, mantle cavity, and foot ; it rotates in a counter-clockwise direction through an angle of 180° on the rest of the body by contraction of an asymmetric retractor muscle which arises from the right side of the larval shell, passes over the body and gets inserted to the left side of the head. This rotation is known as torsion which is distinct from coiling and is a much more drastic change, it occurs after coiling of the visceral hump. In torsion only a narrow part of the body and the organs which pass through it are twisted, it is that small part which lies between the visceral hump and the rest of the body. Torsion changes the orientation of the mantle cavity and its organs, and the organs of the left side tend to be reduced or even lost.

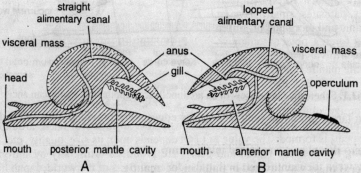

Fig. 63.2. A gastrpod showing torsion. A—Before torsion ; B—After torsion.

Before torsion the mantle cavity opens posteriorly, ctenidia point backwards, the auricles are behind the ventricle, the nervous system is bilaterally symmetrical, and the mouth and the anus are at opposite ends. After torsion the mantle cavity opens in front just behind the head, ctenidia come to lie in front and point anteriorly, the ctenidium of the right side comes to lie on the left and that of the left side on the right, the auricles become anterior to the ventricle, the auricle of the right side comes to lie on the left and vice versa, the nervous system is twisted into a figure of 8 by the crossing of the two long nerve connectives running to the viscera, and the digestive system becomes U-shaped so that the anus comes to lie in front near the mouth. The entire process of torsion generally takes only a few minutes.

In primitive Gastropoda there are two ctenidia, two auricles and two kidneys, but in more specialized forms the real left but topographically right ctenidium, right auricle and the right kidney fail to form; this absence of organs of the right side is a consequence of torsion. The number of auricles is directly related with the number of ctenidia present, and the loss of one gill leaves only one auricle. It is not clear whether torsion is an advantage or not to the animal, or if it has any evolutionary significance, but it takes place during the embryological development of gastropods, the larva is a first bilaterally symmetrical, then quite suddenly it undergoes torsion.

In some forms after the coiling of the visceral hump, torsion occurs by rotation only through 90°, so that the ctenidia and anus point laterally.

Detorsion. In some forms the changes brought about by torsion are reversed to a certain extent, while in others, *e.g., Aplysia* a complete reversal of torsion takes place which is known as detorsion, this occurs when the shell is lost or much reduced, the ctenidia liberated from their enclosing case point posteriorly again, their anterior position being of no advantage, and the visceral hump gets completely untwisted.

In Cephalopoda the body has become greatly elongated along the dorso-ventral axis, and as a result of change in the method of locomotion this axis has become the functional antero-posterior axis. A ring of tentacles lies at the anterior end of the body and the visceral hump is posterior, the original mantle cavity has become ventral.

PEARL FORMATION

Pearl is a valuable gem known to mankind since ancient times. The pearl, in fact, is of animal origin and produced by certain **bivalves** of Mollusca. The pearl producing bivalves are marine oysters of the genus *Pinctada*, though some freshwater bivalves of the genus *Unio* and *Anodonta* also produce pearl but of inferior quality and rarely of any use. Today, Japan produces the bulk of pearl in the world by using pearl culture technique. However, the culture of pearl, its fishing and its commercialisation, etc., constitute a separate story. Here we are concerned only with the way of the formation of pearl in the body of a bivalve.

The pearl is secreted by the **mantle** as a protective measure against foreign objects like sand particles, parasites, small larvae or any object of organic and inorganic origin. In fact, as soon as a foreign object, somehow, enters the body of a bivalve in between the shell and mantle, the mantle immediately gets irritated and at once encloses it like a sac. The mantle wall then starts secreting layers of **nacre** around the foreign object from defence

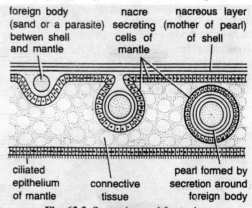

Fig. 63.3. Stages in pearl formation.

point of view. Thus, mantle wall secretes continuously several layers of nacre around the foreign object and finally pearl is formed. The value of pearl depends upon its size, quality, etc. Now a days, the pearl producing bivalves are reared and pearls are produced artificially by introducing some foreign objects between the mantle and shell in the different parts of the world; Japan has surpassed all other countries in this field.

ECONOMIC IMPORTANCE OF MOLLUSCA

Some Mollusca are indirectly harmful to man but most of them are beneficial. The harmful molluscs are slugs and shipworms. Slugs are injurious in gardens and cultivations, they not only eat the leaves but also destroy plants by cutting up their roots and stems. *Teredo*, the shipworm burrows into wooden structures immersed in the sea, it causes serious damage to wharves, piers and ships. But molluscs are a great source of human food in various parts of world, millions of maunds of clams, oysters, scallops and mussels are eaten in China, Japan, Malaya, Europe and America, oysters being regarded as a delicacy. Other bivalves, octopuses and cuttlefishes furnish large quantities of food in Europe. Shells of freshwater mussels are used in the pearl button industry in all parts of the world, they are made from the nacreous layer of shells, no other material stands laundering as these buttons. Shells of oysters are mixed with tar for making roads in America and lime from these shells is used in feeding poultry for formation of their egg shells. Lime is also used in buildings. In many parts of the world molluscan shells are used for making ornaments and jewellery, in some parts shells of *Cypraea* (cowrie) are used as money and as ornaments. Many freshwater clams and marine oysters produce pearls, but the most valuable natural pearls are produced by pearl oysters *Pinctada margaritifera* and *Pinctada mertensi* which inhabit the warmer parts of Indian and Pacific Oceans along the coasts of China, India, Sri Lanka and Japan. A pearl is made when a small foreign object, such as a particle of sand or a parasite, lodges between the shell and the mantle. The foreign object becomes a nucleus around which concentric layers of nacreous are laid by the mantle, in this manner a pearl is formed. But pearls are also produced by most pelecypods including freshwater clams. In Japan pearl culture is practised by artificially introducing a small solid or liquid irritant below the mantle of the oyster, the resultant one year old pearl is then transplanted to another oyster, a pearl of good size is obtained in three years after transplanting.

REVISION QUESTIONS

1. Give an account of torsion and detorsion in Gastropoda.
2. Write notes on :
   (i) Archimollusc; (ii) Pearl formation; (iii) Economic importance of Mollusca.

64

Phylum Annelida

The annelids were by early zoologists included with other worms in the group Vermes but were separated by Cuvier in 1798 from the unsegmented worms. The name Annelida was first of all used by Lamarck in 1809 for the higher segmented worms.

Annelida (L., *annellus* = little ring or F., *anneler* =to arrange in rings) are triploblastic, bilaterally symmetrical, coelomate and segmented Metazoa. Body is covered by a thin cuticle having chitinous setae in most. Body wall is covered with glandular epidermis, below which are muscles forming an outer layer of circular muscles and an inner layer of longitudinal muscles. The body is divided for the first time in the animal series into metamerically arranged segments or metameres arranged in a linear series, but the segments are integrated into a single functional unit. Perivisceral cavity is a schizocoelic coelom between two layers of mesoderm. The coelom contains a coelomic fluid which is imcompressible, consequently it acts as a hydraulic skeleton. There is a single pre-oral segment called prostomium and a similar post-segmental region posteriorly known as a pygidium. The nervous system has a pair of pre-oral ganglia or brain, and paired ventral nerve cords ganglionated in each segment. There is a closed circulatory system. The digestive tract is more or less straight but differentiated into well-defined regions; digestion is entirely extracellular. Organs of excretion are metameric ectodermal nephridia, besides which there are tubular mesodermal coelomoducts used for passage of reproductive cells. The larva, if present, is a trochosphere. The members of the phylum are modified for sedentary, active, or ectoparasitic life, they occur on land, in freshwater, or in the sea. The phylum contains over 8,600 known species and is divided into four classes called Polychaeta, Oligochaeta, Hirudinea, and Archiannelida. But in some systems of classification Echiuroidea, Sipunculoidea, Priapulida, and Myzostomaria have also been included as classes, while in other systems these classes have been considered as appendix to phylum Annelida or to some of its classes.

65

Neanthes (=Nereis) (Clamworm)

Neanthes (old name *Nereis*) is commonly known as sandworm because it is found buried in sand or clamworm as it is found along with clams but has no ecological relationship with them or ragworm. *Neanthes* is one of the largest and most common typical marine annelid with most of the characteristics of the phylum. *Neanthes* has a great number of species which are found in different parts of the world but resemble greatly with each other from the morphological point of view. Few important and common species are : *N. dumerilli, N. diversicolor, N. irrorata, N. cultrifera, N. virens, N. pelagica, N.caudata, N. limbata* and *N. limnicola*. However, description given hereunder pertains to *N. virens* which applies nearly to all species.

NEANTHES VIRENS (THE CLAMWORM)

SYSTEMATIC POSITION

Phylum	....	**Annelida**
Class	....	**Polychaeta**
Order	....	**Errantia**
Genus	....	*Neanthes (Nereis)*
Species	....	*virens*

HABIT AND HABITAT

Neanthes is found on the sea-shore in the shallow water in rock crevices, hidden under the stones or sea weeds. Some live in tubular U-shaped burrows lined by mucus in sand or mud at tide level. It is carnivorous as it feeds on small insects, molluscs and worms. It is very active during night and passive during the day, *i.e., nocturnal*. During night they come out from their hidden places and start crawling over the sand and swimming by lateral wriggling of the body either for the purpose of feeding or reproduction but during day time they go to their burrows or hidden places with their heads protruding for feeding. When breeding period approaches it leaves the burrow and comes at the water surface to lead a pelagic life, then it is called heteronereis.

DISTRIBUTION

Neanthes is cosmopolitan in distribution. It is found abundantly in Europe, North Pacific, America, Alaska and other places.

EXTERNAL FEATURES

Shape and size. The body is long, narrow, slender, bilaterally symmetrical, tapering posteriorly and relatively broad anteriorly. It is approximately dorsoventrally flattened with rounded or convex dorsal surface and flat ventral surface. The size varies from species to species, it may range from 30 to 40 cm in length and 2 to 6 mm in width.

Colouration. The colouration of body varies in different species, and it may also vary even in the individuals of same species of different age and sexual maturity. However, *N. plelagica* is reddish brown, *N. cultrifera* is greenish, *N. limnicola* is brownish in colour, while *N. virens* is bluish-green in colour having orange or red tinge on the appendages.

Segmentation. The anterior end of *Neanthes* is differentiated into a distinct head and the rest of the body is divided by a series of ring-like narrow grooves into a series of segments or metameres or somites arranged in a linear series. All the metameres are nearly alike except the last one which is rounded. The number of metameres varies from species to species. In *N. dumerilli* and *N. cultrifera*, the number of segments is nearly 80, while in *N. virens* the number of metameres reaches up to 200.

Division of body. The body of *Neanthes* is divisible into three well marked regions, *viz.*, head, trunk, and pygidium.

1. **Head.** The anterior end of the body possesses a distinct, prominent and well developed head which consists of two main parts, prostomium and peristomium.

(i) **Prostomium.** (Gr., *pro* = before; *stoma* = mouth). Prostomium is an anterior narrow, nearly triangular fleshy outgrowth. It is situated mid-dorsally in front of the mouth. It is not the true segment of the body as it is derived from pre-oral lobe of the larva.

(ii) **Peristomium.** (Gr., *peri* = around ; *stoma*-mouth). Peristomium is a large ring-like structure carrying ventrally the transverse mouth. The peristomium is formed by the fusion of first two body segments, it forms the lateral and ventral margins of the mouth.

Sensory appendages and organs of head. Various sensory appendages and organs are found on the head of *Neanthes*. These are as follows :

(i) **Prostomial eyes.** Prostomium bears four simple, black and rounded eyes on its dorsal surface. These are sensitive to light.

(ii) **Prostomial tentacles.** There is a pair of short cylindrical prostomial tentacles projecting forward from the anterior border of the prostomium. These are probably tactile in function.

(iii) **Prostomial palps.** These are also two in number but somewhat stout and longer. These are two jointed appendages present on the ventral side of the prostomium but posterior to tentacles. These are also supposed to be tactile organs.

(iv) **Nuchal organs.** These are ciliated pits of doubtful nature lying one on each side of the prostomium.

(v) **Peristomial cirri.** These are long slender structures present on the anterior side of the peristomium. Four peristomial cirri, two dorsal and two ventral are present on each lateral side of the peristomium. These are tactile organs. These are probably homologous with the parapodial cirri of other body segments.

2. **Trunk.** Posterior to the head, the rest of the body which is metamerically segmented (having 80–120 segments) is called trunk. The segments are known as metameres or somites which bear a pair of parapodia are nearly alike except the last.

3. **Pygidium.** The last segment of the body called variously as tail, anal segment or pygidium, is elongated, swollen and bears a terminal anus. It bears no parapodia but has a pair of elongated anal cirri which are ventral cirri and several minute sensory papillae. The pygidium represents the posterior part of the larva, and the body segments are formed in front of it.

Parapodia. (Gr., *para*=side+*podus*=foot). Each segment of the body, except the peristomium and the anal segment, bears on either lateral side a flat, fleshy,

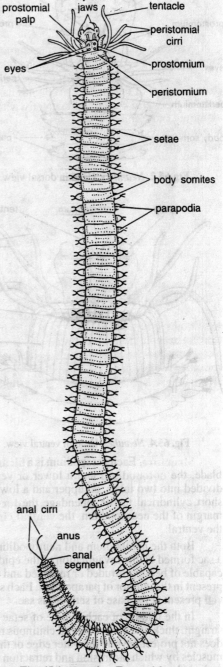

Fig. 65.1. *Neanthes.* External features.

hollow and vertical flap-like out-growths, the parapodia. Huxley first of all gave the name parapodia to these fleshy outgrowths.

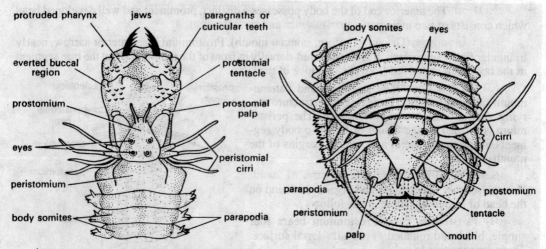

Fig.65.2. *Neanthes.* Head in dorsal view.   Fig 65.3. *Neanthes.* Head in frontal view.

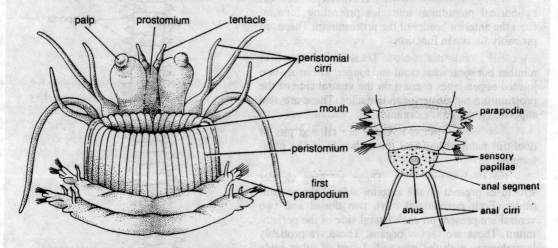

Fig. 65.4. *Neanthes.* Head in ventral view.   Fig.65.5. *Neanthes.*Hind end of the body.

Structure. Each parapodium is a biramous structure consisting of two parts–an upper or dorsal blade, the notopodium and a lower or ventral blade, the neuropodium. Each of these is further divided into two lobes, an upper and a lower. The dorsal margin of notopodium is produced into a short, cylindrical, tactile appendage, the dorsal cirrus and a similar structure is produced at the ventral margin of the neuropodium, the ventral cirrus. Of the two cirri, the dorsal one is much larger than the ventral.

Both the notopodium and neuropodium have a bundle of bristle-like setae or chaetae lodged in a sac formed by the invagination of the epidermis, the setigerous or chaetigerous sac. The setae are capable of being protruded or retracted and turned in various directions by strands of muscular fibres present in the interior of parapodium. Each seta of the bundle originates from a single large formative cell present at the base of setigerous sac.

In the middle of each bundle of setae and deeply embedded in the parapodium is found stout, straight, thick and dark coloured chitinous rod the aciculum which projects only a short distance but does not project beyond the outer edge or the parapodium. At its inner end the aciculum has attached muscles by which protrusion and retraction of the parapodium occurs. The two acicula constitute the endoskeleton of parapodium and serve to support and for attachment of the setal muscles.

The parapodia are the largest in the mid-region of the body and decrease in size towards the anterior and posterior ends of the body. The first two parts of parapodia have no notopodial setae. The parapodia are highly muscular, well vascularised and glandular structure.

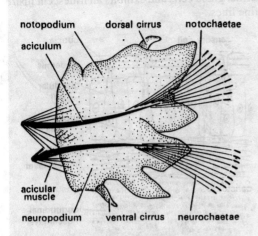

Fig. 65.6. *Neanthes.* Parapodium.

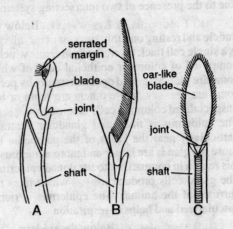

Fig.65.7. *Neanthes.* Kinds of setae. A—Typical ;
B—Long blade; C—Oar-shaped seta
of *Heteronereis.*

Functions. The parapodia are primarily the organs of locomotion, used both in creeping and in swimming. Since the parapodia are highly vascularised, hence, they also serve the function of respiration.

Setae or Chaetae. The setae or chaetae are fine but stiff chitionous rods which help in the locomotion by acting as minute paddles; these are protective used for offense and defence and they also provide hold on the smooth surface of the burrow. Each seta consists of two movable articulated parts—the basal shaft or stalk and the distal blade which can be retracted into the shaft. There are three types of setae, *viz.*, (i) having a small slender shaft and the terminal long blade which is nearly straight, pointed and serrated at one edge, (ii) having a large stout shaft and short and slightly hooked blade and (iii) having the oar-shaped blade.

Nephridiopores. In each segment on the ventral side of the body near the bases of parapodia are found laterally a pair of minute openings, the excretory opening or nephridiopores by which excretory materials are removed.

LOCOMOTION

Locomotion is brought about by the combined action of parapodia, body musculature and to some extent the coelomic fluid. *Neanthes* shows generally two types of locomotion, *viz.*, slow creeping and fast creeping but sometimes it swims in water.

(i) Slow creeping. Slow creeping movements of *Neanthes* are carried out by the action of parapodia only. During locomotion each parapodium performs two strokes : an effective or back stroke and recovery or forward stroke. In the effective stroke, the aciculum of parapodium is extended so that the parapodium is lowered to come in contact with the substratum and moves backwards against the substratum. In the recovery stroke, the aciculum is retracted so that the parapodium is lifted above and moves forward. The combined effective and recovery strokes of numerous parapodia propel the worm forward. The parapodia of the two sides work alternately causing successive waves along each side of the worm.

(ii) Fast crawling. In addition to the parapodial locomotion, undulatory movements of the body cause the worm to crawl or swim rapidly. Body undulations are caused by waves of contractions in the longitudinal muscles of the body wall. These contractions coincide with the alternating waves of parapodia on the two sides. The longitudinal muscles of one side contract when the parapodia of that side are moved, the muscles relax when parapodia sweep backwards.

BODY WALL

The body wall is thick and consists of the following layers :

(i) **Cuticle.** It is thin, tough, chitinous, and non-cellular layer covering the body externally. It is perforated by numerous pores, the openings of epidermal gland cells and exhibits an iridescent lustre due to the presence of two intersecting systems of fine lines.

(ii) **Epidermis or hypodermis.** Below the cuticle and resting on a thin basement membrane is a single cell thick layer, the epidermis which is composed of columnar epithelial cells of which some are glandular and open externally by pores, some are sensory while others are more or less unspecialized columnar cells or supporting cells. The epidermis is thick and glandular ventrally particularly near the bases of the parapodia because the glands are larger and more numerous in this region in comparison to the dorsal epidermis. The gland cells produce mucus which lines the burrows of the animal. The epidermis is richly vascularized and helps in respiration.

(iii) **Musculature.** Below the epidermis are present the muscles which are of three types, *viz.*, circular, longitudinal and oblique. Circular muscles lie just below the epidermis and form a thin continuous layer around the body. Contrac-

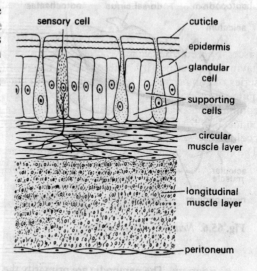

Fig. 65.8. *Neanthes* V.S. of body wall.

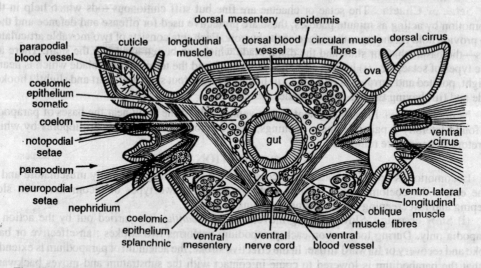

Fig. 65.9. *Neanthes.* Transverse section of a segment with right and left halves into different planes.

tion of these muscles makes the body longer and thinner. Below the circular muscles are present the longitudinal muscles which are better developed than the circular muscles. They do not form any continuous layer around the body but are arranged in four separate longitudinal bundles—two dorsolateral and two ventrolateral. Contraction of these muscles makes the body shorter and thicker. There are two pairs of oblique muscles in each segment which originate from the median ventral line and pass dorsolaterally to be inserted into the circular muscles on the base of parapodium. Each oblique muscle is made up of two bundles of muscle fibres, one bundle goes to the dorsal part of the base of parapodium and the other to the ventral part. The function of these muscles is to retract the parapodium. Protrusion of parapodium is largely due to the pressure of coelomic fluid. But each parapodium has other muscles also, the largest parapodial muscles arise from the circular muscles of the body wall and are joined to the acicula, they extend the acicula and parapodium. All muscle layers are syncytial tissue.

(iv) Peritoneum. A parietal peritoneum is the innermost layer of the body wall, which lines the musculature internally and forms the lining of coelom; it secretes coelomic fluid.

COELOM

The coelom is an extensive perivisceral cavity having an outer parietal peritoneum and an inner visceral peritoneum which encloses the alimentary canal. The coelom is schizocoelic in annelids having been formed by splitting of the mesoderm into two layers. Coelom is divided into a linear series of compartments by intersegmental septa which pass inwards from the body wall but do not quite join the alimentary canal, the septa also have apertures, hence, the coelomic compartments communicate. Each septum has a double layer of coelomic epithelium containing muscles and connective tissue. The coelom is filled with a coelomic fluid containing amoeboid corpuscles or coelomocytes, and during the breeding season reproductive cells in various stages of development. The coelom communicates with the outside by nephridia and coelomoducts.

Functions of coelomic fluid. The functions of coelomic fluid may be counted as under :

1. It provides turgidity to the body which aids in locomotion.

2. It helps in the protection of the body by absorbing external shocks, if any, and acts as a hydraulic skeleton.

3. It helps in the distribution of various nutritive materials and respiratory gases to the whole body.

4. It helps in removing excretory wastes from the body.

DIGESTIVE SYSTEM

Alimentary canal. The alimentary canal is a straight and unbranched tube from mouth to anus. It has two openings to the exterior, an anterior one, the mouth by which food is ingested and a posterior one, the anus through which undigested food remains are removed. The alimentary canal is differentiated into three regions on the basis of its lining– stomodaeum or foregut, mesenteron or midgut and proctodaeum or hindgut.

1. Stomodaeum or foregut. It is the anterior region of alimentary canal, lined internally by ectoderm and cuticle. It consists of buccal cavity and pharynx.

(i) Mouth. The mouth is a transverse slit, lies ventral to the prostomium. It is bordered laterally and ventrally by the peristomium which forms a buccal ring. The mouth opens into a wide chamber, the buccal cavity.

(ii) Buccal cavity and pharynx. The buccal cavity is a short but wide chamber situated inside the peristomium. The buccal cavity leads into a muscular protrusible pharynx extending up to fourth segment. The buccal cavity and pharynx are bound together by a muscular sheath and internally they are lined with thick cuticle. Buccal cavity has several small dark-brown denticles or paragnaths which are regularly arranged. The

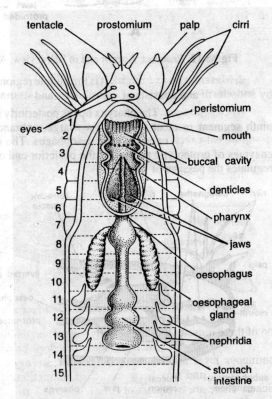

Fig. 65.10. *Neanthes.* Anterior end of the body dissected dorsally to show the alimentary canal and nephridia.

cavity of pharynx is narrow and its posterior part is greatly muscular and thick-walled with a pair of large, powerful, dark, movable, chitinous and laterally placed jaws with serrated edges, embedded in it. Each jaw has a rounded hollow base embedded in the muscles and an anterior pointed incurved apex, its inner edge is provided with teeth. The whole of buccal and pharyngeal region can be turned completely inside out. Running from peristomial wall to the pharynx are bands of protractor muscles which can evert the buccal cavity and pharynx as a proboscis or introvert, the pressure of coelomic fluid also helps in everting, the proboscis is turned completely inside out and this causes the two jaws to open wide in front of the proboscis, with the jaws it catches small animals. Such eversion takes place during normal feeding and is also common at death. The proboscis may be everted at times only partly, revealing only the buccal cavity, this happens when the worm is digging or feeding on the surface mud, this is brought about by the pressure of the coelomic fluid. From the posterior end of the pharynx to the body wall are retractor muscles which retract the proboscis, this makes the jaws to close and cross one another by which they effectively hold small animals for food, the jaws kill and tear apart such animals for food which are pulled in when the pharynx is withdrawn.

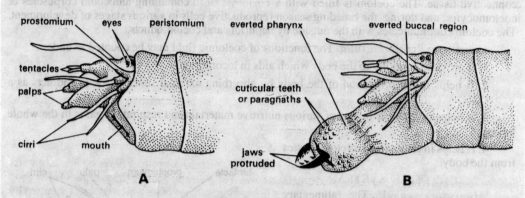

Fig. 65.11. *Neanthes.* Anerior end in lateral view. A—Pharynx retracted ; B—Pharynx everted.

2. Mesenteron or midgut. It is the middle region of the alimentary canal and it is lined internally by endoderm and consists of oesophagus and stomach-intestine.

(i) Oesophagus. The pharynx opens posteriorly into a narrow oesophagus which runs up to the ninth segment in most species. Two large, unbranched, laterally placed glandular pouches, the oesophageal caeca open into the oesophagus. The oesophageal caeca probably secrete digestive enzymes of proteolytic nature. At the posterior end of the oesophagus is a sphincter muscle which regulates the passage of food.

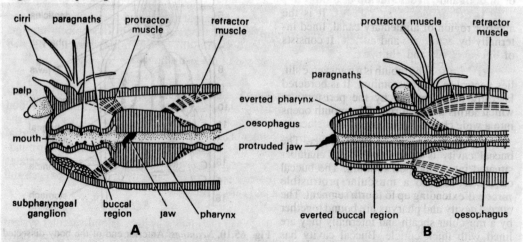

Fig. 65.12. *Neanthes.* Diagrammatic representation of the action of proboscis or introvert. A—Proboscis or introvert at rest ; B—Proboscis or introvert protruded.

(ii) Stomach-intestine. The oesophagus opens posteriorly into stomach-intestine. Stomach-intestine is a wide tube extending through the remaining length of the body. It is straight, thin-walled tube segmentally constricted by septa, and its internal epithelial lining possesses scattered gland cells which secrete digestive enzymes. The stomach-intestine is the principal site of digestion and absorption. The stomach-intestine opens into a rectum which lies in the last segment. A distinct stomach is, however, not found.

3. Proctodaeum or hindgut. It is the posteriormost part of the alimentary canal, lined internally by ectoderm and cuticle and consists of rectum only.

(i) Rectum. Rectum is a short tube-like structure lying in the anal segment and it opens posteriorly through the terminal anus.

Histology of gut wall. Histologically, the gut wall consists of an outer layer of parietal layer of peritoneum, a layer of longitudinal muscles followed by a layer of circular muscles and finally by an enteric epithelium which is, as mentioned earlier, ectodermal in fore- and hindguts and endodermal in the midgut; however, the fore- and hindguts are lined internally by the cuticle.

Food. *Neanthes* is a carnivorous animal and feeds on small animals such as crustaceans, molluscs, sponges, larvae, and other worms and animals.

Feeding mechanism. Generally the prey is captured by the eversion of buccal cavity and protrusion of pharynx. Protrusion of pharynx brings out the jaws in front to grasp the prey. The everted buccopharyngeal region forms a kind of proboscis or introvert. Buccal cavity is everted due to pressure of coelomic fluid, while protrusion of pharynx is due to contraction of protractor muscles. Retraction is effected by the contraction of retractor muscle. This retraction brings the jaws close and cross one another to hold the prey and to carry into the pharynx.

Neanthes feeds in two different manners, *viz.,* feeding in burrows and feeding at surface.

(i) Feeding in burrows. When *Neanthes* lives in U-shaped burrow, it feeds by ejecting out a cone of mucus in front of the mouth and creates a current of water by beating the parapodia. The food particles coming along with the current of water are held in mucous cone which are later ingested by *Neanthes*. This type of mode of feeding is known as filter feeding.

(ii) Feeding at surface. When *Neanthes* is on the surface outside the burrow, it feeds by pulling out the buccopharyngeal region. When small animals come close to *Neanthes* it suddenly everts its proboscis to catch the prey which is dragged inside the buccal cavity during the course of inversion or retraction. This type of mode of feeding is known as raptorial feeding.

Digestion, absorption and egestion. The ingested food first of all undergoes mastication in the buccopharyngeal region as it is provided with numerous denticles meant to masticate the food. The masticated food is pushed onwards inside the gut by rhythmic waves of contraction passing over the wall of alimentary canal from anterior to posterior end. Digestion is mainly extracellular and the food is digested by the digestive juices secreted by the oesophageal glands and the gland cells of the epithelial lining of stomach-intestine. Absorption of digested food also occurs in the stomach-intestine by the diffusion. The undigested part of the food passes on to the rectum from where it is egested through the terminal anus situated on the posterior end of the anal segment.

RESPIRATION

Gills or any other special organs of respiration are lacking in *Neanthes*. The parapodia with their rich blood supply and body wall with its plexus of blood vessels subserve the function of blood respiration. Gaseous exchange takes place at the surface of these organs. Oxygen diffuses from the surrounding water into the blood through the integument or parapodial surface due to great partial pressure in comparison to blood. Similarly from the blood carbon dioxide diffuses into the surrounding water due to great partial pressure than the surrounding water. Blood of *Neanthes* contains respiratory pigment erythrocruorin which increases the absorptive capacity of blood for oxygen and carbon dioxide. Blood is the carrier for oxygen and carbon dioxide.

BLOOD VASCULAR SYSTEM

Neanthes has a well developed and closed type of circulatory system. Blood vascular system mainly includes a system of blood vessels running to all parts of the body. The blood vessels are filled with blood of a bright red colour. The red colour of the blood is due to the presence of a respiratory pigment erythrocruorin, which is like hemoglobin in its plasma.

Blood vessels. On the basis of their functional activity, the blood vessels are of two types, *viz.*, distributing vessels and collecting vessels. The distributing vessels distribute the blood to different parts of the body, while collecting vessels collect the blood from different parts of the body. Distributing vessels communicate with the collecting vessels by means of fine network of microscopic capillaries. The vessels have muscular walls and the constant circulation of blood is maintained by peristaltic waves passing over the walls of the large blood vessels. In *Neanthes,* there are two main longitudinal vessels, one median dorsal and the other median ventral to the gut.

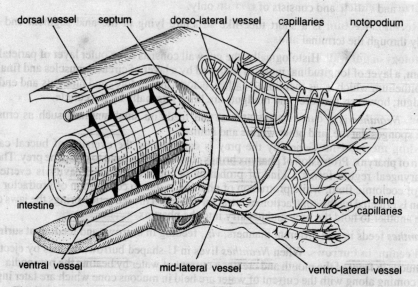

Fig.65.13. *Neanthes.* Diagrammatic representation of blood circulation in a segment.

(i) **Dorsal blood vessel.** It is a collecting and contractile vessel, lies in the mesentery just dorsal to the gut, running from posterior to the anterior end. It carries the blood from behind forwards. Anteriorly the dorsal vessel bifurcates and forms a plexus on the oesophagus, then it joins with the ventral vessel in the fifth segment. As it is mainly a collecting vessel in the region of stomach-intestine it receives blood from the stomach-intestine by means of two pairs of short vessels—dorsointestinals or efferent intestinals in each segment. It also collects blood from body wall, parapodia, and nephridia through lateral vessels. But in the oesophageal region it acts as a distributing vessel and supplies blood to oesophagus through its branches.

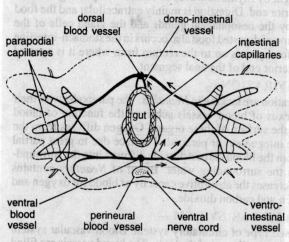

Fig.65.14. *Neanthes.* Diagrammatic representation of main blood vessels in a segment.

(ii) **Ventral blood vessel.** It is mainly a distributing and non-contractile vessel, lying mid-ventrally below the alimentary canal from the fifth segment to the last. It carries the blood from anterior end to the posterior end. As it is a distributing vessel so it supplies the blood to the stomach-intestine through a pair of short vessels–the ventrointestinals or afferent intestinals in each segment. It also supplies blood to the body wall, parapodia and nephridia through lateral vessels. Posteriorly it joins the dorsal vessel by circumrectal ring in the anal segment.

The dorsal and ventral vessels are connected on either side by a pair of loop-like transverse vessels or lateral vessels in each segment, except the first five segments. These vessels are known as laterals or commissural vessels which take the blood from the ventral to the dorsal but not directly. First they take the blood to body wall, parapodia and nephridia by afferent cutaneous, afferent parapodial and afferent nephridial vessels respectively and then collect blood from these organs by efferent cutaneous, efferent parapodial and efferent nephridial vessels which open into dorsal vessel. Afferent and efferent vessels are joined by an extensive network of capillaries or plexus. In each segment there is a pair of circumintestinal vessels or ventrointestinal vessels taking blood from the ventral vessel to the dorsal vessel. The circumintestinal vessels form a network of capillaries in the stomach-intestine.

(iii) Subneural vessel. A thin subneural vessel runs below the nerve cord. Blood flows in it from anterior end to posterior end. It collects blood from the lower body wall and supplies blood to the ventral vessel.

EXCRETORY SYSTEM

Excretory organs. In *Neanthes* the excretion is carried out by means of special type of coiled tube-like structures, the nephridia, one pair of which is found in each segment except the first and the last segment.

Structure of nephridium. Each nephridium has an oval syncytial mass of protoplasm containing a long, convoluted, ciliated canal, the nephridial tubule. The syncytial protoplasm is differentiated into a body and a neck. The main body is an irregular, oval and compact gland-like mass directed transversely in the segment. It contains highly convoluted and mostly ciliated tubule. The nephridial tubule passes through the septum into the anterior segment where it opens by a ciliated funnel or nephrostome. Posteriorly the tubule opens by a contractile nephridiopore located ventrally at the base of parapodium near the origin of ventral cirrus. The nephridial tubule is an excavation in the mass of protoplasm. Such an open type of nephridium with a ciliated nephrostome is called a metanephridium.

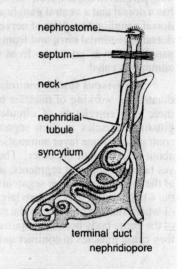

Fig.65.15. *Neanthes.* A nephridium.

Physiology of excretion. The chief nitrogenous waste in polychaetes is ammonia. Nephridia collect waste from coelomic fluid and blood by diffusion, the cilia of the nephridial tubule cause the liquid waste to pass out of nephridiopores. The waste laden coelomocytes or amoeboid corpuscles are probably removed from the coelomic fluid by the ciliated nephrostomes.

The nephridia of *Neanthes* also possess the power of osmoregulation. Its blood and body fluids are isotonic to its surrounding environment over a wide range of salt concentrations, but below a certain limit *Neanthes* maintains a salt concentration greater than that of the surrounding environment. This maintenance is due to an active intake of salts. Nephridia play an important role in maintaining salt and water balance in the body of *Neanthes*.

NERVOUS SYSTEM

Neanthes has a well developed nervous system which is bilateral and metameric in its arrangement. It includes the central, peripheral and visceral nervous system.

Central nervous system. Cerebral ganglia or brain is a large bilobed mass, situated in the prostomium above the buccal cavity. The brain has numerous nerve cells or neurons and nerve fibres and is large in size due to an active life. The middle region of the brain has two small lobes called corpora pedunculata which are association centres and coordinate all the impulses coming to brain. From the brain arise a pair of stout circumpharyngeal connectives which encircle the pharynx and meet below it in the third segment; close to the brain each circumpharyngeal connective has a ganglion. Where the circumpharyngeal connectives meet a subpharyngeal ganglion formed by the fusion of two pairs of ganglia, it is continuous with a ventral nerve cord made of two cords enclosed in a common sheath. The nerve cord lies below the ventral vessel, it has a double ganglion in each segment beginning from the fourth.

Peripheral nervous system. The peripheral nervous system mainly includes the nerves coming directly from the brain and nerve cord to supply the different regions of the body. The brain gives out four short optic nerves to the eyes, two tentacular nerves to the prostomial tentacles, and two palpal nerves to the palps. From the small ganglion of circumpharyngeal connectives two pairs of nerves go to the ventral peristomial cirri on each side. From the subpharyngeal ganglion a pair of nerves goes to the first parapodia. Three pairs of nerves arise from each ganglion of the nerve cord, the first goes to the anterior segment and the remaining two pairs innervate the organs of the segment, parapodia and body wall.

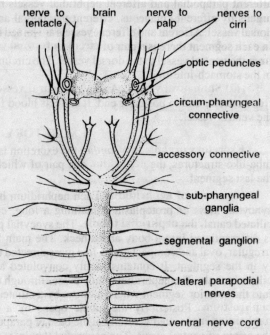

Fig.65.16. *Neanthes*. Nervous system.

Visceral nervous system. The visceral nervous system has two main nerves originating from the subpharyngeal ganglion and running parallel to the connectives, each of them has a dorsal and a ventral ganglion ; from the dorsal ganglion two pairs of nerves go to the dorsal peristomial cirri, and from the ventral ganglion nerves go to the front part of the alimentary canal.

The nervous system controls and co-ordinates the working of muscles by reflexes, there is a correlation of circular and longitudinal muscles in each segment so that contraction of one layer automatically brings about relaxation of the other. There are nerves between adjacent segments, and excitation of a muscle layer in one segment leads to excitation of the same layer in other segments. In the nerve cord are five longitudinal giant fibres running along the whole length, they are two large lateral fibres, one large median fibre, and two smaller fibres each of which runs on one side of the median fibre. The giant fibres bring about immediate co-ordination of the entire body because impulses travel rapidly in them from one end of the body to the other, and they cause muscles to contract quickly.

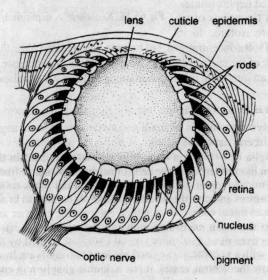

Fig. 65.17. *Neanthes*. V.S. of entire eye.

SENSE ORGANS

In *Neanthes* the sense organs are specialized and well developed. On the basis of the function they are of the following types :

1. **Tactile sense organs.** It has been mentioned earlier that the prostomial tentacles, prostomial palpi and peristomial cirri of head are the main tactile sense organs as they are sensitive to touch.

2. **Chemoreceptors.** It has already been referred to that nuchal organs are a pair of pits on the prostomium, they are lined with ciliated columnar epithelium with some gland cells. These organs are of doubtful nature but some have regarded them as chemoreceptor and olfactory sense organs as being sensitive to taste and smell respectively.

3. Photoreceptors. There are four simple eyes on the dorsal surface of prostomium which are sensitive to light. Each eye has a cup made of pigmented retinal cells produced inwards into clear rods, the opening of the cup is a pupil. In fact, each retinal cell has three distinct parts : an outer nucleated part with nerve fibres, a highly pigmented main body and an inner part of transparent cuticular rod. The external cuticle forms a transparent cornea. Inside the cup is a transparent, gelatinous, refractive lens. The retinal cells are joined to nerve fibres of the optic nerve. The eyes are photoreceptive ; they are not related to the formation of image but they help in detecting charges in light intensity.

REPRODUCTIVE SYSTEM

Neanthes is dioecious, *i.e.*, sexes are separate. The gonads (testes in male and ovaries in female) are neither permanent nor distinct; they are seasonal and develop only during the breeding season, *i.e.*, in the summer months.

Gonads. The gonads are formed by the proliferation of the cells of coelomic epithelium and can be seen as groups of masses of germ cells. These groups of germ cells are found particularly on the ventral side in the coelomic space of nearly all segments except a few anterior segments of the body.

However, in male *Neanthes dumerilli* there is only one pair of testes lying in any one segment between the nineteenth and twenty-fifth segments. But in *N. virens* and *N. diversicolor* the testes extend in many segments. In the female the ovaries lie in many segments around blood vessels. Gonads have no gonoducts. The germ cells from the masses, in male, separate in the coelomic fluid as sperm mother cells, they keep on floating in the

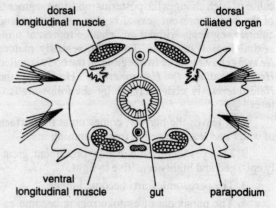

Fig.65.18. *Neanthes.* T.S. of a segment to show ciliated organs.

coelomic fluid, divide rapidly and undergo maturation division to form spermatids which transform into sperms. A mature sperm has a rod-shaped head and a long vibrating tail. Ova are also formed in the same way in female. An ovum contains yolk granules and is rounded in shape surrounded by a vitelline membrane.

The body of a sexually mature *Neanthes* is, thus, packed with gametes. Since gonoducts are absent in *Neanthes*, hence, gametes are discharged out either by the rupture of body wall or by the nephridia. Such nephridia, acting both as excretory and genital ducts, are called mixonephridia (Goodrich, 1945).

Dorsal ciliated organs. A pair of dorsal ciliated organs is found in each segment situated close to the dorsal longitudinal muscles. Each ciliated organ is a small, ciliated tract of coelomic epithelium and much folded funnel-shaped structure; it opens into the coelom by a wide opening but it has no external opening. These are believed to be the coelomoducts of other polychaetes and open temporarily to the exterior during breeding season performing the function of gonoducts. However, the true nature of ciliated organs is still to be known.

Neanthes virens and *N. dumerilli* are extremely variable species, if a number of specimens are examined they show individual variations, these differences are in colour and number of segments. Appearance of orange or reddish colour is the greatest in females during breeding season. Increase in the number of segments takes place by formation of new segments just anterior to the caudal one. Besides these there may be change in the shape of parapodia, number of their setae, length of the tentacles, and in the number and arrangement of denticles.

Generally a sexually mature *Neanthes* resembles more or less with non-sexual *Neanthes* from the morphological point of view. But in some species certain variations or structural modifications have been recorded in the body of sexually mature *Neanthes* which are completely lacking in non-mature *Neanthes*. Such species exhibits two distinct phases in life cycle ; a non-sexual or *Neanthes* phase and sexual or *Heteronereis* phase. This phenomenon is called epitoky.

EPITOKY AND *HETERONEREIS* OR *HETERONEANTHES*

Epitoky is a reproductive phenomenon being characteristic of nereids and other annelids like syllids and eunicids. Epitoky is the formation of sexual individual or epitoke which differs from the parent non-sexual individual or atoke. In fact, these forms differ in such a wide range that sometimes they are considered to be of different genera. Malamgren has recognized that in *N. virens*, at sexual maturity, the posterior body segments having packed with gametes undergo morphological and anatomical changes. These changes are induced by hormones secreted into a plexus of blood vessels lying below the brain. Because of such changes the posterior modified segments of the body represent sexual region or epitoke and anterior segments without any change represent non-sexual region or atoke. Thus, the sexually mature *Neanthes* having these two regions in the body is called *Heteroneanthes* (= *Heteronereis*). However, the *Heteronereis* is characterised by the following features :

1. It leaves the burrow, comes up at the surface of water and leads an active free swimming life.

2. The eyes become much more prominent, greatly enlarged and highly sensitive to light.

3. The peristomial cirri become longer.

4. The parapodia of epitoke region become enlarged, develop additional foliaceous outgrowths, setae become oar-shaped and highly vascularized.

5. The intestine in the epitoke region becomes compressed due to the development of gonads and finally it becomes functionless.

6. The anal segment (pygidium) develops sensory papillae.

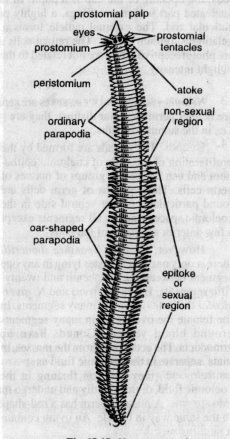

Fig.65.19. *Heteronereis* phase.

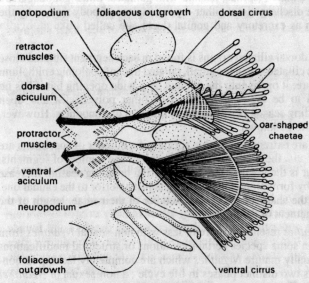

Fig. 65.20. Parapodium of *Heteronereis*.

Parapodium of *Heteronereis*.
The parapodia of epitoke region differ considerably from the parapodia of atoke region. The parapodia of atoke region resemble the parapodia as described earlier but the parapodia of epitoke region become greatly enlarged, foliaceous, develop additional lobes, dorsal and ventral cirrus are highly enlarged, setae become oar-shaped and arranged in fan-like manner, it becomes highly vascularised. The original parapodial muscles break down and are digested by leucocytes, then new muscles are formed. Modification of parapodia is an adaptation to a swimming habit and their larger surface serves for more rapid respiration during swimming.

TABLE 65.1. DISTINCTION BETWEEN *NEANTHES* AND *HETERONEANTHES* (=HETERONEREIS)

Neanthes (=Nereis)	*Heteroneanthes* (=Heteronereis)
1. Lives in burrows, under stones, etc., and creeps at the bottom of the sea.	1. Swims actively at the surface of the sea.
2. Eyes are small and indistinct.	2. Eyes are prominent, enlarged and highly sensitire to light.
3. Body not differentiated into regions.	3. Body differentiated into anterior non-sexual, atoke region and posterior sexual, epitoke region.
4. Sensory papillae on the anal segment indistinct.	4. Sensory papillae on the anal segment very prominent.
5. Sexually immature.	5. Sexually mature.
6. Intestine tubular and functional.	6. Intestine of epitoke region compressed and non-functional.
7. All parapodia are alike.	7. Parapodia of atoke and epitoke regions differ.
8. Setae on parapodia normal ; pointed at the tips.	8. Parapodial setae oar-shaped and arranged fan-like to provide effective swimming.
9. Notopodia and neuropodia are normal bilobed.	9. Notopodia and neuropodia are flattened with more lobes.
10. Dorsal and ventral cirrus are short.	10. Dorsal and ventral cirrus are well enlarged.

Significance of *Heteronereis*. As mentioned, *Neanthes* is the non-sexual phase and lives in the burrow or creeps at the bottom of the sea, while *Heteronereis* (= *Heteroneanthes*) is the sexual phase, swims actively at the surface of sea-water. So, it discharges gametes to far off places in the sea and, thus, helps in the dispersal of species.

SWARMING

The fully sexually mature clamworms leave their burrows in groups and come up at the surface of sea-water to swim freely, it is called swarming. This phenomenon probably occurs to facilitate fertilization. Some species of clamworms are said to perform nuptial dance in which males and females swim rapidly in small circle. However, swarming occurs at night during a particular lunar phase but the physiological causes and periodicity of swarming are still to be understood. Workers like Clark and Hess (1940) have emphasized that tidal activity and turbidity of sea-water suppress swarming.

FERTILIZATION

Fertilization is external and takes place in open sea-water. During swarming, the female *Heteronereis* produces a substance called fertilizin which attracts the male *Heteronereis* and it is also responsible for stimulating and shedding of sperms by the males that in turn stimulates female for shedding of ova or eggs (Barnes, 1968). After shedding of gametes the parent worms die.

DEVELOPMENT

The development of *Neanthes* is indirect and can be discussed under the following headings :

1. Early embryonic development. For making the description easily understandable, it can be discussed as under :

A. Egg. The newly discharged egg of *Neanthes* is spherical in shape and possesses two membranes ; a thin outer membrane which is delicate, followed by a thick radially striated membrane called zona radiata which encloses the ooplasm having yolk spherules, oil droplets and female nucleus. An egg is surrounded in a thick, transparent, gelatinous coat. However, immediately after fertilization, several changes occur in an egg; the zona radiata disappears, yolk spherules aggregate at the lower end of the egg leaving a clear zone in the upper end. The lower end, thus, becomes to be known as vegetal pole and the upper end as animal pole; the egg is, thus, telolecithal. Two small polar bodies are extruded towards the animal pole and the zygote undergoes cleavage.

B. Cleavage and formation of germ layers. The zygote undergoes cleavage in which the first two divisions are equal producing four cells which are equal and lie in the same plane, these cells are

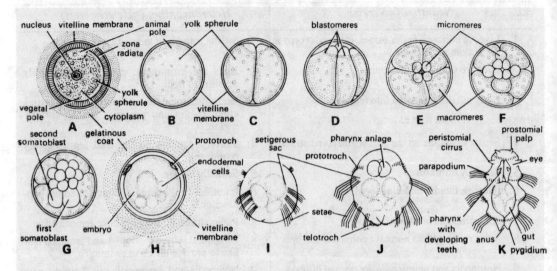

Fig. 65.21. *Neanthes.* Stages in development. A—Unfertilized egg ; B—Fertilized egg ; C,D, E—2, 4, 8-celled stages ; F—First somatoblast formed ; G—Second somatoblast formed ; H—Young trochophore before hatching ; I, J—Post-trochophore larva with setigerous sacs ; K—Later larva with parapodia and setae after three weeks.

A, B, C and D. Each cell gives rise to one of the quadrants of the embryo. D is larger than the others and forms the dorsal side of the embryo, B is ventral, and A and C are lateral. The succeeding cleavages are unequal and at right angles to the first two divisions, they form three quartets of micromeres which are divided off from the fourth quartet of macromeres, the micromeres lie towards the animal pole and the macromeres at the vegetal pole. The micromeres are not directly over the macromeres, but one quartet is displaced to the right, the next is displaced to the left, and the next to the right again. This pattern of division is called spiral cleavage in which any one cell lies between two blastomeres or below it, and at first the cleavage planes are oblique to the polar axis (axis between animal and vegetal poles). Later the successive cleavage planes are at right angles. Spiral cleavage is determinate, if at the 4-cell stage the blastomeres are separated, then each will form only one quarter of the embryo, that

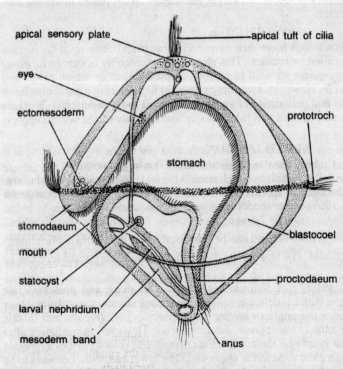

Fig. 65.22. A typical trochophore larva.

is the fate of blastomeres is predetermined, this is known as determinate cleavage. The fate of blastomeres is fixed and each will give rise to a particular tissue only. The cells of the first three quartets give rise to the ectoderm of the larva and the adult. At the next cleavage a fourth quartet is separated from the macromeres, one of the cells of the fourth quartet known as a somatoblast produces the entire mesoderm, while the remaining three cells reinforce the macromeres and all of them form the endoderm. The cells eventually form a gastrula, then the three germinal layers are formed.

Structure of trochophore and its metamorphosis. The gastrula develops into a trochosphere or trochophore larva. The trochosphere is not only characteristic of Polychaeta, but it also occurs is Mollusca, Archiannelida, and polyclad Turbellaria. The trochosphere (Fig. 65.22) is rounded and transparent, it has a thin external ectodermal epithelium which is thickened at the two ends and along an equatorial ring. There is a curved gut with a mouth, ectodermal oesophagus or stomodaeum, an endodermal stomach, and an ectodermal hindgut opening by an anus. It feeds on micro-organisms.

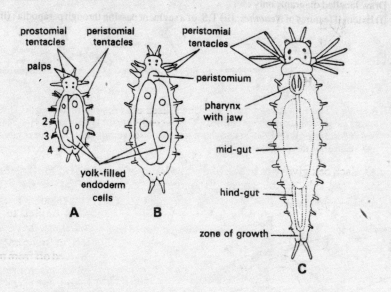

Fig. 65.23. *Neanthes.* Diagrams showing metamorphic changes and growth.

On the thickened parts of the ectoderm is an anterior ciliated apical organ with an apical ganglion below which is an eye spot, at the posterior end are some large cilia and on the equatorial ring is a pre-oral ciliated band or prototroch. Between the ectoderm and gut is a large cavity, the blastocoel having mesencyme cells, larval mesoderm and a pair of larval nephridia, each made of two hollow cells, one of which contains a flame of cilia, there is an otocyst near the nephridia. The trocosphere is pelagic, it drifts about in the sea swimming by its prototroch ; organs of the adult begin to form. The apical organ forms the prostomium with brain, tentacles and eyes. The part immediately behind forms the peristomium. The larva grows from the anal end as an elongated cylinder which forms segments of the body by metameric segmentation. The larval nephridia are replaced by permanent ones, larval setae are dropped, tentacles, palps and parapodia are formed. The advanced larva consists of the adult head and body segments separated by the body of the larval trochosphere, this larval region shrivels up, and the head and body segments are drawn together and joined to metamorphose the larva into a young worm. The young worm, thus, resulted, settles at the botom of the sea and starts forming its burrow and gradually attains adulthood.

However, it is interesting to note that a typical free-swimming trochophore, as described above, occurs only in some polychaetes. In *Neanthes*, this stage is passed inside the egg membrane and the larva which hatches out of the egg is advanced trochophore larva referred to as nectochate which undergoes metamorphosis to become a young worm in the same way as described above.

REVISION QUESTIONS

1. Describe habits, habitat and external morphology of *Neanthes*.
2. Describe the structure of parapodium of *Neanthes* and compare with that of *Heteronereis*.
3. Describe the alimentary canal of *Neanthes* and add a note on its food and feeding mechanism.
4. Give an account of blood vascular system of *Neanthes*.
5. Give an account of excretory organs and physiology of excretion in *Neanthes*.
6. Describe the nervous system of *Neanthes*.
7. What is *Heteronereis* ? How does it differ from *Nereis* ? Compare their parapodia.
8. Give an account of the process of reproduction in *Neanthes*.
9. With the help of suitable labelled diagrams explain the development of *Neanthes*.
10. Write short notes on :
    (i) Locomotion in *Neanthes* ; (ii) Coelom and coelomic fluid of *Neanthes* ; (iii) Significance and swarming of *Heteronereis* ; (iv) Trochophore larva ; (v) Epitoky.
11. Draw labelled diagrams only :
    (i) External features of *Neanthes:* (ii) T.S. of a segment passing through parapodia ; (iii) *Heteronereis*.

Pheretima (Earthworm)

The name *Pheretima* for common earthworm was used first by Kingberg (1857) and later adopted by Mechaelsen in the same year. There are nearly more than a thousand species of earthworms known today. *Lumbricus* is a common earthworm of Europe and North America. Many earthworms are known from India. *Megascolex* and *Drawida* from Southern India, *Eutyphoeus* from the Gangetic plain of India. *Pheretima* is yet another genera represented by nearly 500 species from the South-East Asia, Japan. Sri Lanka and Australia. Out of these nearly 13 species belong to India, some of them are : *P. posthuma, P. hetrochaeta, P. rubusta, P. elongata, P. compalata, P. planata, P. marrisi,* etc. The description of earthworm, hereunder refers largely to *Pheretima posthuma,* a common Indian earthworm, is based on the contributions of an Indian worker Late Prof. K. N. Bahl.

PHERETIMA POSTHUMA (THE INDIAN EARTHWORM)

SYSTEMATIC POSITION

Phylum	....	**Annelida**
Class	....	**Oligochaeta**
Order	....	**Opisthopora**
Genus	....	*Pheretima*
Species	....	*posthuma*

HABIT AND HABITAT

The earthworms are burrowers. They are found in the soil rich in decaying organic matters usually in gardens, pastures, lawns, irrigated farm lands, near the banks of the ponds, lakes and rivers. The do not prefer to live in sandy, clay and acid soils which are deficient in organic matters. They generally inhabit an upper layer of earth to a depth of about 30 to 45 cm and even they go down up to 3 meters or more during summer in search of moisture. The rainy season is the most favourable time for the earthworms, during this season they live in the superficial soil of the earth and they are often seen crawling on the surface in abundance. The earthworms are nocturnal in habit; during night hours they come out of their burrows in search of food, reproduction and exploring fresh habitat. They breed during the rainy season. They are cold-blooded or poikilothermal animals as their body temperature fluctuates with the fluctuation in the surrounding temperature. The way of the excavation of their burrows is very interesting ; as the worm eats on the soil, so it goes on eating the soil progressively down- wards, the organic contents of the soil are digested and absorbed in the gut, while residual soil

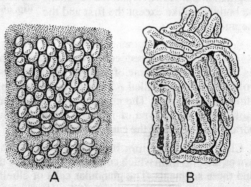

Fig. 66.1. Castings of earthworms. A—*Pheretima* ; B—*Eutyphoeus.*

is discharged by its anus at the opening of the burrow as castings. Thus, the presence of earthworms is inferred by their castings. The castings of *Pheretima* form little heaps of small round pellets lying separately near the burrows, while in *Eutyphoeus* they form large cylindrical structures of 5 cm in height. The natural life span of earthworms varies from three and a half years to ten years.

EXTERNAL FEATURES

Shape and size. *Pheretima posthuma* has long, elongated, cylindrical narrow body which is bilaterally symmetrical. The anterior end is tapering, while the posterior end is more or less blunt.

The dorsal surface of the body is marked by the presence of dark median line of dorsal blood vessel which runs throughout the length of the body just below the skin, while the ventral surface is marked by the presence of genital openings and papillae in the anterior part of the body. Size of earthworm varies from species to species and individual to individual of the same species. A mature earthworm may attain the size up to 150 mm in length and 3–5 mm in width.

Colouration. The earthworm is slimy to touch and glistening dark-brown in colour due to the presence of a pigment—porphyrin in its body wall which protects the body from otherwise effect of the bright light. The dorsal surface of its body is darker than the ventral surface.

Segmentation. The body of earthworm consists of about 100–120 small ring-like segments or somites or metameres. It exhibits true segmentation, *i.e.,* the external segmentation corresponds with internal segmentation. In other words, the whole surface of the body is divided into many ring-like segments by a distinct series of annular grooves or furrows representing the external segmentation. Similarly, the interior of the body is divided by intersegmental septa or coelosepta into small chambers representing internal segmentation. However, all the segments of the body are alike except the first and the last segments.

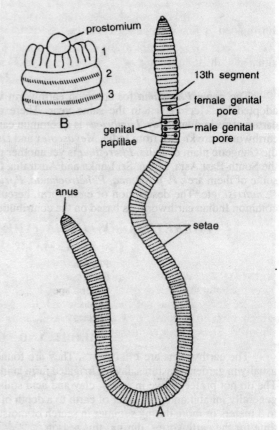

Fig. 66.2. A—*Pheretima posthuma* in ventral view ; B—Anterior end in dorsal view.

Setae. In all the segments of the body except the first, last and clitellum there is a ring of chitinous setae lying embedded in the middle of each segment which project backwardly. Each seta arises from a setigerous **sac** of the skin and is a pale-yellow curved S-shaped pointed rod-like with a swollen middle part called nodulus. The setae help in locomotion by holding the earth since they are directed backwards. The movement of setae is controlled by special type of muscles. With the help of these special type of muscles the setae can be moved in any direction and extended or withdrawn at the will of the earthworm.

Clitellum or cingulum. In a mature worm, there is a prominent circular band of glandular tissue known as the clitellum which completely surrounds the segments from 14th to 16th forming a girdle around these segments. The glandular cells of clitellum secrete mucus, albumen, and material for forming cocoons which assist in fertilization as the eggs are laid in them. Due to the presence of clitellum the body of earthworm is divided into following regions :

(i) Pre-clitellar region. This is the anterior part of the body from segment 1st to 13th. The first segment is characteristically called peristomium (*peri*=around+*stoma*=mouth) which surrounds the mouth. At the anterior end of peristomium there is a small fleshly lobe called prostomium (*pro*=before+*stoma*=mouth). The prostomium is not a segment and remains separated from the peristomium by a groove. In fact, the prostomium is an extension of the peristomium at its dorsal side and ventral to it is a mouth.

(ii) Clitellar region. This region is formed by segments 14th, 15th and 16th as described earlier.

(iii) Post-clitellar region. This region is represented by all the segments of the body after clitellum, *i.e.,* it starts from 17th segment up to the last segment of the body.

External Apertures

1. Mouth. It is a crescentic aperture situated just below the prostomium on the ventral side surrounded by first segment of the body—the peristomium or buccal segment.

2. Anus. It is the exit of the alimentary canal by which undigested wastes are removed. It is situated at the terminal end of the last body segment referred to as the anal segment.

3. Genital openings. Earthworm is hermaphrodite, so male and female generative apertures are found in the same individual.

(i) Male genital apertures. A pair of male genital apertures are situated latero-ventrally in the 18th segment. These are crescentic openings through which the male reproductive bodies are discharged.

(ii) Female genital aperture. It is a median aperture situated at the ventral side in the 14th segment through which the female reproductive bodies are discharged.

4. Spermathecal pores. There are four pairs of small ventrolateral spermathecal apertures lying intersegmentally between the grooves of the segments 5/6, 6/7, 7/8 and 8/9.

5. Nephridiopores. A large number of very minute nephridiopores are found situated throughout the body of earthworm except few anterior segments. These pores are the apertures of integumentary nephridia, through which metabolic wastes of the body are removed. These pores are found scattered all over the surface of the body.

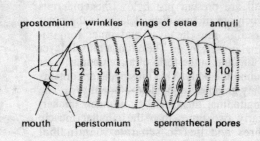

Fig. 66.3. *Pheretima.* Anterior region in lateral view.

6. Dorsal pores. These pores are situated along the mid-dorsal line in the intersegmental grooves as minute openings and lead directly into the body cavity. The first dorsal pore lies in the furrow between segments 12th and 13th, while there is a pore in each of the succeeding intersegmental furrows of the worm, except the last. Through these pores coelom communicates with the exterior.

Genital or copulatory papillae. In the same line, with the male pores, on the ventral side of each of the 17th and 19th segments there is a pair of circular and raised papillae; these are the genital or copulatory papillae. Each genital papilla bears a cup-like depression at the top but not any aperture. During copulation, the genital papillae function as suckers.

BODY WALL

The body wall of earthworm is very thin, soft, shiny and elastic which consists of the following layers :

1. Cuticle. It is a thin, elastic, non-cellular and iridescent layer covering the body externally. It is made of two layers of collagenous proteins forming fibres and a polysaccharide with a small amount of gelatin. It is secreted by the columnar epithelial or supporting cells of the epidermis and remains perforated by many minute pores through which integumentary nephridia and epidermal glands open out. This layer is protective in function.

2. Epidermis. The cuticle is followed by a single layer of tall columnar cells forming the epidermis. The epidermis consists of the following four types of cells :

(i) Supporting cells. These are long columnar cells constituting a major part of the epidermis and they have an oval nucleus nearly in their middle.

(ii) Gland cells. These cells are situated between the supporting cells and are of two types :

(a) Mucous gland cells. The cells are club-shaped and are in large numbers. They secrete mucus which keeps the body moist. Thus, it prevents the animal from desiccation and helps in locomotion by lubricating the body. The mucus secreted by these cells cements the wall of the burrows to keep them lubricated and smooth. The mucous gland cells are also known as goblet cells and they open at the surface of the cuticle by minute pores.

(b) Albumen gland cells. These cells are cylindrical, fewer in number and have uniformly distributed fine granules. These cells secrete albumen.

(iii) Basal cells. These cells are small and undifferentiated which fill up the spaces between the inner ends of the other epidermal cells. The cells later differentiate to form the supporting and gland cells, hence, they may be called replacing cells.

(iv) Sensory cells. These cells are cylindrical and lie in groups having sensory hair-like protoplasmic processes at their outer free ends. These cells are also known as epidermal receptor cells.

3. Muscles. The muscles of the body wall are present just below the epidermis which are of two distinct layers—the outer circular muscle layer and inner longitudinal muscle layer. The circular muscle layer is thin and in the form of a continuous layer around the body. This muscle layer contains many granules of pigment—porphyrin. The longitudinal muscle layer is much thicker, nearly two times than the circular muscle fibres and lies in separate longitudinal bundles. These bundles are separated together by thin connective tissue septa. The contraction of circular muscles makes the body

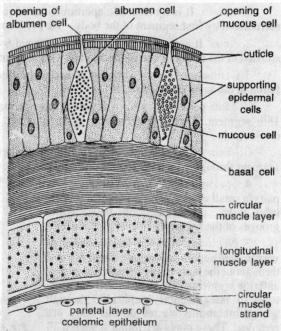

Fig. 66.4. *Pheretima.* T.S. of a portion of body wall.

long and narrow, while that of the longitudinal muscles makes the body short and broad. The longitudinal muscle layer is further followed by a very thin strip of circular muscle fibres. The musculature of the body wall consists of smooth muscle fibres.

4. Coelomic epithelium. The musculature of the body wall is lined internally by a thin layer of coelomic epithelium. It is a membranous layer consisting of thin flattened squamous cells of mesodermal origin. Since, this layer forms the outer boundary of coelom, hence, it is called parietal peritoneum or parietal layer of coelomic epithelium.

Functions of the body wall. The body wall of earthworm performs the following functions :

1. It forms an outer covering of the body to protect the internal more delicate organs from injury.

2. It provides definite shape to the body.

3. The mucus secreted by the mucous gland cells of epidermis keeps its body smooth and moist to assist in locomotion and respiration.

4. The mucus also keeps the burrow smooth and moist which assists in checking desiccation and cementing the wall of the burrow.

5. The sensory cells of the epidermis are the only receptors to receive stimuli.

6. The setae which are locomotory structures are found lodged in it.

7. The contraction and relaxation of the muscles of the body wall, assisted by setae, bring about locomotion in this animal.

8. The thin, soft and moist body wall helps in gaseous exchange which facilitates respiration.

9. The coelomic epithelium or peritoneal layer secretes the coelomic fluid.

10. The cuticle checks excess evaporation.

Setae, setal sac and associated structures. As referred earlier, the setae are found in every segment of the body except the first, last and clitellar segments. In *Pheretima* nearly 80–120 setae are found embedded in the middle of each segment arranged in a ring. Such an arrangement of setae is called perichaetine. In *Lumbricus*, the setae occur in two pairs on either side of a segment. This is

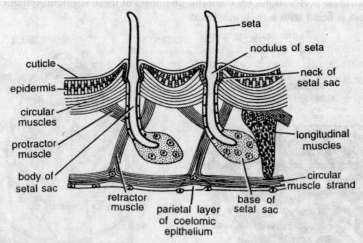

Fig. 66.5. *Pheretima.* T.S. of a part of body wall through a setal ring.

called lumbricine arrangement. Each seta is found lodged in a setal sac. The seta is secreted by a single large epidermal cell situated at the bottom of the setal sac. The setae are composed of chitin and scleroprotein. The setae are pale-yellow, curved S-shaped pointed rod-like structures with swollen middle part called nodulus. Two sets of muscles are found attached at the base of each setal sac : the protractor and retractor muscles. The protractor muscle radiates outwards from the base of the setal sac to join the circular muscles, while the retractor muscle runs inwards and joins the inner thin strip of circular muscle band situated just above the parietal peritoneum. These muscles serve to protrude and withdraw the setae respectively. The setae fall out of the body wall when worn out and are replaced by new ones repeatedly.

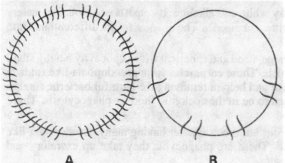

Fig. 66.6. Arrangement of setae. A—Perichaetine; B—Lumbricine.

COELOM

It is a large spacious cavity between the body wall and alimentary canal and encloses all the internal or visceral organs of the body, hence, it is also called perivisceral cavity. This cavity is lined by parietal epithelium on the outer side and visceral epithelium on the inner side. Actually, this cavity of earthworm is a true coelom derived by the splitting of embryonic mesoderm, such a coelom is called schizocoel. The outer lining of coelom, lying below the body wall, is called parietal layer or somatic layer and that around the alimentary canal is called visceral or splanchnic layer. Many cells of the splanchnic layer containing yellow granules, are called chloragogen cells.

The spacious coelom of earthworm is divided into small compartments due to the development of intersegmental septa which grow from the intersegmental grooves of the body wall to the alimentary canal. Each septum is a sheet in interlacing muscle fibres and surrounded from both the sides by peritoneum. However, the first four segments are without intersegmental septa, hence, they have a continuous coleom. The first intersegmental septum is located between 4th and 5th segments, it is thin and membranous. The next five septa are thick, muscular and obliquely placed between segments 5/6, 6/7, 7/8, 8/9 and 10/11. These are cone-shaped. Contraction of these cone-like septa increases the pressure on the coelomic fluid by which the anterior segments become turgid and are used for digging the burrow. Intersegmental septum between 9/10 is absent. The remaining septa from 11/12 to the posterior end are thin, membranous and transverse ; the first three of them (11//12, 12/13 and 13/14) are complete with no apertures, thus, isolating their coelomic chambers. The remaining septa from 14/15 to the posterior end are perforated by many minute apertures, these apertures are surrounded by sphincters of unstriped muscles. Such septa are characteristic of *Pheretima*. With these perforations, the coelomic chambers of these segments remain in communication. The coelom is filled with a coelomic fluid.

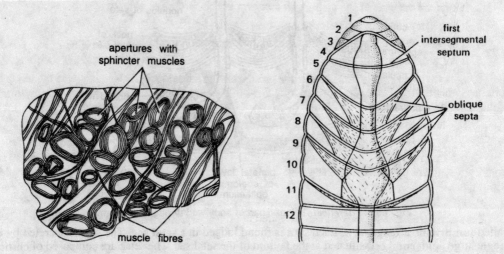

Fig. 66.7. *Pheretima.* A part of intersegmental septum.   **Fig. 66.8.** *Pheretima.* Arrangement of septa in the anterior segments.

The coelomic fluid of earthworm is milky white and alkaline. It consists of colourless watery matrix the plasma and a large number of coelomic corpuscles. The corpuscles are differentiated into four types :

(i) **Granulocytes.** These are numerous, large-sized and spherical with a concavity having small nucleus. They have many granules of fat droplets. These corpuscles form pseudopodia-like folds to act as phagocytes. These are probably nutritive and help in removing the harmful bacteria, foreign particles and other microorganisms that happen to be in the coelomic fluid by phagocytosis. These are also called eleocytes.

(ii) **Amoebocytes.** These are also numerous but much smaller having many pseudopodia-like processes. They look like stars and nucleated. These are phagocytic, they take up excretory and foreign matter and act as defence against parasites.

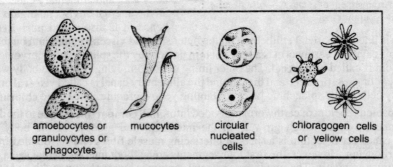

Fig. 66.9. *Pheretima.* Coelomic corpuscles.

(iii) **Mucocytes.** These cells are elongated, vase-shaped with an expanded end like a fan and the other end being narrow. The narrow end bears nucleus. Their function is not definitely known.

(iv) **Leucocytes.** These are small, flattened disc-shaped and nucleated cells. They are fewer in number, nearly 10 per cent of the corpuscles. They have clear cytoplasm and their functions are still uncertain.

The coelomic fluid flows from anterior to posterior on the ventral side and from posterior to anterior on the dorsal side.

Functions of coelomic fluid. The coelomic fluid performs following functions :

1. It oozes out through the dorsal pores and keeps the body moist which facilitates respiration.

2. It kills the bacteria of the soil which come on the body surface of the worm.

3. It helps in removing the excretory wastes from the body.

4. It helps in the transportation of materials from one part of the body to the other.

5. It helps in destroying harmful bacteria, micro-organisms and foreign materials.

6. It also helps in fixing the setae into the ground during locomotion. This is achieved by making certain segments turgid and stiff by restricting coelomic fluid in them by closing sphincter apertures of the septa between them.

7. The luminosity produced by some earthworms is due to the coelomic fluid.

LYMPH GLANDS

These are small paired glandular structures present in the coelom on the sides of the dorsal vessel from 26th segment up to the last. They also contain phagocytes which ingest foreign materials and digest them.

LOCOMOTION

No specialized locomotory organs are found in earthworms, even then these are very active and they crawl rapidly when out of burrows. The process of locomotion is, in fact, a cumulative effect of contraction and relaxation of both the muscle layers of body wall aided by setae and the hydrostatic pressure created by the coelomic fluid.

The forward locomotion is brought about by an increase in the hydrostatic pressure of the anterior segments of the body (usually first nine segments) and at the same time contraction of circular muscle layer begins at the anterior end and passes backwards. This results the anterior region to extend forward and at the same time making it thinner in diameter. The extending and thinning passes backwards as a wave of contraction at the rate of 2 to 3 cm per second ; by this means the body of the worm is pushed forward. The anterior end now grips the substratum and the setae act as hooks by their posteriorly directed points. After the wave of contraction of circular muscles has passed down the front half of the worm, the circular muscles relax and the longitudinal muscles of the body wall of the anterior segments contract in a wave beginning from the anterior end, this shortens and thickens the anterior end, causing the posterior body of the worm to be dragged forward. At this stage the segments in a state of longitudinal contraction do not move but remain anchored to the ground by the extended setae. The contraction of longitudinal muscles passes backwards like a wave. Again a wave of contraction of circular muscle starts from the anterior end making it thinner and extended forward. This wave starts before the

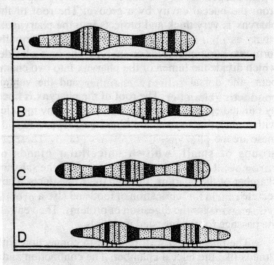

Fig. 66.10. Diagram to illustrate locomotion in an earthworm.

first one has reached to the posterior end. Thus, locomotion is brought about by alternate contractions of circular and longitudinal muscles causing wave of thinning and thickening to pass backward. This involves partly a pushing of the anterior end and partly a pulling of the posterior end, the setae playing only an accessory role. The worm moves at the rate of 25 cm per minute. The nervous system coordinates the activities of circular and longitudinal muscles so the contraction of any layer brings about relaxation of the other muscle layer.

The earthworms can move backward also, as they usually do during their withdrawal from the burrow and also during excavating it. The backward movement is brought about by reversing the direction of setae.

The coelomic fluid serves as a hydraulic skeleton because a decrease in its pressure results in the relaxation of muscles.

The earthworms can move on a smooth and hard surface like glass by using mucus for adhesion as the setae cannot anchor the substratum.

DIGESTIVE SYSTEM

The digestive system of earthworm consists of the alimentary canal and the digestive glands.

Alimentary canal. The alimentary canal runs as a straight tube throughout the length of the body from the mouth to the anus. It consists of the following regions :

1. Mouth and buccal chamber. The mouth is a crescentic aperture lying below the prostomium. The mouth leads into a short, thin-walled tube called buccal chamber or buccal cavity running up to the 3rd segment. The lining of the buccal cavity is folded and it is surrounded by muscular strands. The buccal cavity can be protruded through the mouth with the help of special muscles that run backwards from the buccal chamber to the body wall.

2. Pharynx. The buccal chamber is followed by the pharynx which extends up to the 4th segment. It is a pear-shaped broad and muscular structure separated from the buccal cavity by a groove. The roof of the pharynx is very thick and projects into the pharyngeal cavity as pharyngeal bulb, its lateral walls internally form two horizontal folds or shelves, one on each side, which divide the lumen of the pharynx into two chambers—the dorsal salivary chamber and the ventral conducting chamber. The roof of the pharynx is lined by ciliated epithelium, above which are many muscles with connective tissues and blood vessels and outside these are the pharyngeal or salivary glands. These are groups of small, whitish unicellular glands of chromophil cells. These glands open into the salivary chamber of the pharynx through their fine ducts. They secrete mucin for lubrication of food and also a proteolytic enzyme for the digestion of proteins. The ventral conducting chamber of the pharynx serves as the passage for the ingested materials.

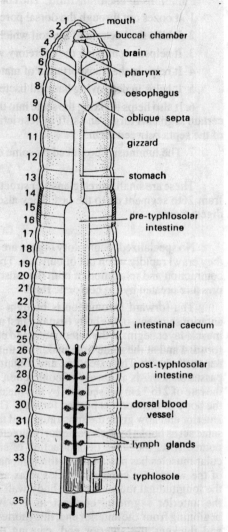

Fig. 66.11. *Pheretima.* Alimentary canal.

The pharyngeal wall remains in connection with the body wall by a thick mass of muscular strands like the buccal chamber. The contraction and relaxation of these muscular strands serve to compress or dialate the pharyngeal lumen. Thus, the pharynx acts as a pump during feeding. The mouth is pressed against the bits of humus of mud, then the pharynx undergoes a series of contractions resulting into the sucking of the food into the buccal chamber, and then pumping the same backwards into the oesophagus.

3. Oesophagus. Behind the pharynx is a short, narrow, thin-walled oesophagus running up to the 8th segment. The oesophageal wall is folded internally and devoid of any gland.

4. Gizzard. The oesophagus is followed by the gizzard. The gizzard is a prominent oval, hard, thick-walled and highly muscular organ lying in the 8th or 8th and 9th segments. It has a thick wall of circular muscles lined by columnar cells which is further lined by cuticle. The gizzard grinds the food into a fine state.

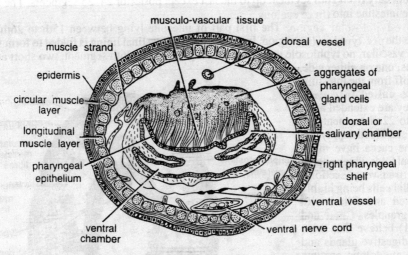

Fig. 66.12. *Pheretima.* T.S. through the pharyngeal region.

5. Stomach. The gizzard is followed by a short, narrow, thin-walled tubular stomach extended up to 14th segment. The anterior and posterior openings of stomach are sphinctered. Its thin wall is highly glandular and vascularised but less muscular. Its internal wall is folded transversely. The glandular cells situated in the epithelial lining of stomach secrete a proteolytic enzyme. Some calciferous glands are found in the epithelial lining which produce calcium and CO_2. The calcium probably neutralizes the contents of the alimentary canal. Calciferous glands are excretory and remove ions of calcium and carbonate from the blood when the level of these ions becomes excessive, they are excreted as calcite into the stomach from where it passes out with mud through the anus.

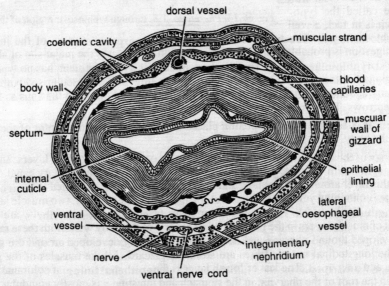

Fig. 66.13. *Pheretima.* T.S. through the gizzard.

6. Intestine. The stomach is followed by the intestine. It is a long, wide and thin-walled tube extending from 15th segment up to the anus. It has a beaded appearance due to constrictions corresponding to septa but bulging in each segment. The lining of intestine has ciliated and glandular cells. The intestinal lining is folded to form villi, one of these villi becomes larger and well developed than the others to form the typhlosole. The typhlosole, thus, hangs in the lumen of intestine and runs mid-dorsally from 26th segment up to the last except posterior 24, 25 segments. The typhlosole divides the intestine into three regions :

(i) Pre-typhlosolar region. The first part of intestine lying between 15th to 26th segments constitutes the pre-typhlosolar region. In this region the intestinal lining is folded to form villi which are highly vascular, no typhlosole is found in this region. In the 26th segment, two short and conical outgrowths, one on either side, are given off from the intestine. These are called intestinal caeca. They are extended anteriorly up to 22nd segment and have a special blood supply; internally the caeca have many longitudinal folds which appear as villi in transverse sections, the epithelial cells being highly vascularised and filled with secretory granules. Chen and Puh (1941) believe that these caeca are digestive glands and secrete an amylolytic enzyme for the digestion of starch. Usually active digestion occurs in this region.

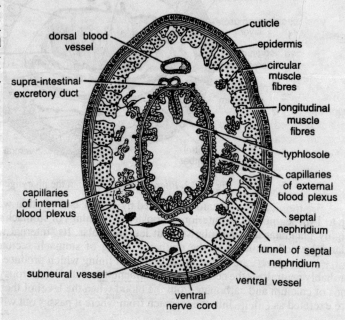

Fig. 66.14. *Pheretima*. T.S. through typhlosolar region of the intestine.

(ii) Typhlosolar region. This is the second part of intestine lying between 26th to the last segment except posterior 24, 25 segments. This region is provided with an internal median fold of the dorsal wall of intestine called the typhlosole, which is in fact, a well developed intestinal villi. The typhlosole increases the absorptive surface of the intestine. The process of digestion is probably completed in this region, hence, it is the major site of absorption.

(iii) Post-typhlosolar region. The intestine, in the last 24, 25 segment, has no typhlosole. It is the third region of intestine and is called the rectum. It is thin-walled, vascularised without villi and glandular cells. It contains small pellets of mud which are passed out from the anus as faeces at the opening of burrows. These are actually the castings of *Pheretima*.

7. Anus. It is a small circular opening placed at terminal end in the centre of the last or anal segment of the body.

Histology of the alimentary canal. The alimentary canal is made of four layers; an outer layer of visceral peritoneum which forms the outermost covering layer of alimentary canal. The most of the cells of this layer around the stomach and intestine are modified and called chloragogen cells or chloragocytes containing yellow granules of chloragosomes. Next to this, two muscle layers—outer layer of longitudinal muscle fibres and inner layer of circular muscle fibres are found. The arrangement of muscle layers in the gut wall is just reverse to the body wall. Both these muscle layers are well developed around pharynx and oesophagus but poorly developed around the stomach and intestine. The longitudinal muscle fibres are absent in gizzard. All the muscles of the gut wall are involuntary and unstriped. The last or fourth layer is the epithelial lining of columnar cells which are ciliated in the roof of the pharynx, in the stomach and intestine it is mostly glandular and ciliated to form villi in the intestine. In the gizzard, it mostly secretes cuticle.

Food and Feeding Mechanism

The earthworms are omnivorous; they feed upon all sorts of organic humus, decaying matters, small protozoans, nematodes, insects and other microorganisms found in the soil. They commonly ingest soil in large quantities and that is why their gut is always full of soil. During feeding the buccal chamber is everted out and the food is drawn into the mouth by sucking action of the muscular pharynx as stated earlier.

Digestive Glands

The pharyngeal or salivary gland cells, glandular cells of stomach, intestine and the intestinal caeca are supposed to be the various digestive glands which secrete the digestive enzymes for the digestion of food.

Physiology of Digestion

Various types of enzymes are said to be secreted by the digestive glands of earthworms for the digestion of food due to their omnivorous mode of feeding habit.

The swallowed soil passes through the buccal chamber into the pharynx where it receives the salivary secretion from the salivary gland cells. The salivary secretion contains mucin and a proteolytic enzyme. The mucin lubricates the food and food passage, while the proteolytic enzyme hydrolyses the proteins into peptones and proteoses. Then the food comes into the gizzard through oesophagus. The gizzard further grinds the food and soil due to the action of the contraction of its well developed circular muscles into a fine state so that the enzymes of stomach, intestine and intestinal caeca can act upon it. Firstly, after reaching the food in fine state into the stomach, it is subjected to the action of more proteolytic enzymes secreted by the glandular cells of this region. This results in the conversion of proteins into peptones, as mentioned above. Then the food reaches into the intestine where it comes across the enzymes secreted by the glandular cells of intestine and intestinal caeca. Usually, these enzymes are—proteases which hydrolyse peptones into amino acids, lipase hydrolyses fats into fatty acids and glycerol, amylases acting upon the carbohydrates and converting them into monosaccharides, cellulase hydrolyses the cellulose if any and chitinase hydrolysing the chitin present in the food. Digestion occurs in stomach and fully completed in the intestine.

Absorption. The digested food is absorbed by the intestinal viili, more particularly by the typhlosole which increases the absorptive area of intestine. The absorbed food passes into the blood stream through the well developed capillary network of the intestine, from where transported to the tissues. The coelomic fluid also serves to transport the digested food to the tissues.

Egestion. After digestion and absorption of food, the undigested remains and the soil are passed out through the anus as castings at the opening of the burrows.

Chloragogen cells. As referred to earlier, that some of the cells of visceral peritoneum around the stomach and intestine are modified as chloragogen cells having yellow granules—the chloragosomes in them. These cells are believed to be of vital importance in the metabolism and they play a role similar to that of the liver in vertebrates. However, these cells take up waste from the blood and probably from coelomic fluid and store it as yellow granules of chloragosomes. When these cells become filled with such granules, they either pass out through dorsal pores or excretory organs or the excreta remains permanently in chloragogen cells throughout life. These cells are the chief centre of synthesis and storage of glycogen and fat. They manufacture glycogen from fatty acids and store it as reserve food and pass it on to the coelomic fluid when needed. Thus, these cells are excretory as well as they serve for storing the reserve food. These cells are also related with the deamination of amino acids, and the formation of ammonia, synthesis of urea, etc.

BLOOD VASCULAR SYSTEM

The blood vascular system of *Pheretima* is of closed type. It consists of the blood vessels, hearts, loops, capillaries and the blood glands.

Blood

The blood of *Pheretima* is red coloured due to the presence of a respiratory pigment haemoglobin in it. The haemoglobin is not contained in the corpuscles like the vertebrates but it is found dissolved in the plasma. The plasma also contains many corpuscles which are colourless and nucleated.

Blood Vessels

The blood vessels are of two types: collecting blood vessels and distributing blood vessels which are closed tubes with definite walls and they break up into capillaries to ramify in the different parts of the body. The arrangement of blood vessels in the anterior thirteen segments is somewhat different from that behind the thirteen segment, *i.e.*, in the region of intestine. Therefore, for convenience the blood vessels can be described under the following two heads :

    A. Blood vessels and their arrangement in the segments behind 13th, *i.e.*, intestinal region.

    B. Blood vessels and their arrangement in the anterior thirteen segments.

A. Blood Vessels and their Arrangement in the Segments behind 13th, *i.e.*, Intestinal Region

    The blood vessels of this region include :

    1. Median longitudinal blood vessels;

    2. The intestinal blood plexus;

    3. The commissural vessel;

    4. The integumentary vessel; and

    5. The nephridial vessels.

1. Median Longitudinal Blood Vessels

    (i) **Dorsal vessel.** It runs mid-dorsally above the alimentary canal from the posterior to the anterior end of the body. It is the thickest vessel with contractile muscular walls visible from outside as a dark line through the thin and semitransparent body wall. The direction of flow of blood in this vessel remains from behind to forward (from posterior to anterior). It is contractile and pulsates rhythmically to force the blood from posterior to anterior side. In each segment it has a pair of valves internally which check the backward flow of blood. It is the main collecting vessel behind the 14th segment, but in front it distributes the blood. From the posterior segment up to the 14th segment it receives two pairs of dorsointestinal vessels from the intestine in each segment and a pair of commissural vessels from the subneural vessel. The commissural vessels form a loop behind each septum and they receive blood from the body wall, nephridia and prostrate glands. The commissural vessels also give out blood in each segment through a septointestinal branch to the intestine.

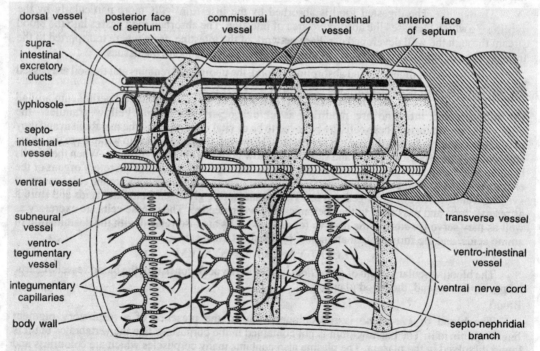

Fig. 66.15. *Pheretima.* Blood vascular system in the segments behind 13th. A part of body wall on the left side has been cut and reflected in order to expose the blood vessels in position.

    (ii) **Ventral vessel.** It is also a long vessel and runs ventrally below the alimentary canal and above the ventral nerve cord from second segment up to the last segment of the body. It is thin-walled without muscles and valves. The direction of flow of blood in this vessel remains from anterior to the posterior side or from in front to backwards. It is a distributing vessel. It gives out a pair of ventrotegumentary vessels, one on each side in front of the septum in all segments. The ventro-tegumentary vessels run upwards along the body wall and supply blood to the body wall, integumen-tary nephridia, septal nephridia, gonads, seminal vesicles and spermathecae. The ventral vessel also gives out a ventrointestinal vessel in each segment behind the 13th segment, these take blood to the lower part of the intestine. The branches in intestine form blood plexuses consisting of two networks in the intestinal wall.

(iii) Subneural vessel. It is also a long but thin vessel extending from anterior 14th segment up to the last segment situated mid-ventrally below the ventral nerve cord. It is without muscular walls and internal valves. The direction of flow of blood in this vessel remains from anterior to posterior side and it is mainly a collecting vessel. It receives a pair of slender branches in each segment which bring blood from the ventral body wall and the nerve cord. It gives a pair of commissural vessels in each segment which join the dorsal vessel, as already mentioned while describing the dorsal vessel. Thus, it collects blood from the ventral body wall and supplies some blood to the intestine.

2. Intestinal Blood Plexus

The intestine of *Pheretima* is richly supplied with blood capillaries which form a close network. The intestinal blood plexus consists of a close network of capillaries in the wall of intestine. In fact, there are two capillary networks in the intestine : (i) the external and (ii) the internal.

(i) The capillary network which is present at the outer surface of intestine is known as external plexus which receives blood from the ventral vessel through ventro-intestinal and passes it on to the internal plexus.

(ii) The capillary network which is present between the circular muscle layer of intestine and its internal epithelial lining is known as internal plexus which serves to absorb the nutrients from the gut and is connected with dorsal blood vessel through the dorsointestinals.

3. Commissural Vessels

These vessels connect the dorsal and subneural vessels. These vessels receive blood from nephridia, body wall and reproductive organs through capillaries and then they send it to dorsal blood vessel.

4. Integumentary Vessels

These vessels coming from ventral vessels supply the blood to integument for aeration and the aerated blood is collected by numerous capillaries of commissural vessel in each segment. Thus, there is a close parallelism between venous and arterial capillaries throughout the body wall.

5. Nephridial Vessels

These vessels originate from the ventro-tegumentary vessels of ventral vessel and supply the blood to the nephridia.

B. Blood Vessels and their Arrangement in the Anterior 13 Segments

The blood vascular system in the first thirteen segments is modified considerably and differs markedly from that of the intestinal region. It consists of the following :

1. Median longitudinal vessels;

2. Hearts and anterior loops;

3. Blood vessels of the gut.

The function of collecting blood from the anterior region of the gut is taken over by a new vessel supra-oesophageal, while the blood from the peripheral structures is collected by the right and left lateral oesophageals.

1. Median Longitudinal Blood Vessels

(i) Dorsal vessel. This blood vessel becomes the distributing vessel in these segments instead of collecting vessel. Structurally, it retains its original identity as it was in the posterior segments. But is has neither dorso-intestinals nor commissural vessels opening into it. It sends out all the collected blood from the posterior region of the body into hearts and the anterior region of the gut where it divides into three branches distributed over the pharyngeal bulb and the roof of the buccal chamber. However, it supplies to stomach, gizzard, oesophagus, pharynx and other related parts.

(ii) **Ventral vessel.** This blood vessel remains distributing in these segments also but extends only up to the second segment. The ventro-intestinals are absent, hence, it does not supply to the alimentary canal in this region. However, the ventro-tegumentary vessels, a pair in each segment, supply blood to the integument, nephridia, septa and reproductive organs.

(iii) **Supra-oesophageal vessel.** It is the shortest longitudinal vessel extending from 9th to 13th segment situated above the stomach. It receives blood from the lateral oesophageals by two pairs of anterior loops that encircle the stomach in the 10th and 11th segments. It sends its collected blood by the latero-oesophageal hearts in segments 12th and 13th to the ventral vessel.

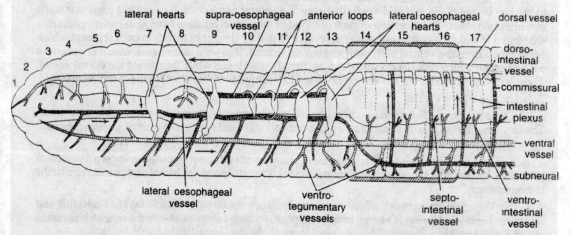

Fig. 66.16. *Pheretima.* The blood vascular system in the anterior 13 segments in the body.

(iv) **Lateral oesophageals.** In fact, the subneural vessel bifurcates in the 14th segment to form two lateral oesophageals. These vessels are considerably thick and situated along the ventro-lateral margins of alimentary canal in the anterior thirteen segments. These vessels are closely attached to the wall of the stomach from 10th to 13th segments and communicate with the ring vessels. But in the region of gizzard and further forwards, they remain free from the wall of the alimentary canal even though they receive branches from it in each segment. These vessels receive a pair of branches in each segment bringing blood from the body wall and the septum. They also collect blood from the reproductive organs and nephridia, thus, functioning like the subneural and commissural vessels of the posterior region, *i.e.,* these are collecting vessels.

2. Hearts and Anterior Loops

In the posterior segments behind 13th the dorsal and ventral blood vessels have no direct connections but anteriorly both these vessels are connected together by 4 pairs of pulsatile hearts which are neurogenic, *i.e.,* the heart beat originates in the nerve cells of the hearts. The hearts are contractile and encircle the alimentary canal, they are in the segments 7th, 9th, 12th and 13th. The hearts of segments 12th and 13th are joined above to both the dorsal and the oesophageal vessels, these are called latero-oesophageal hearts. These hearts have thick muscular walls and a pair of valves at each junction with the dorsal vessels and supra-oesophageal vessel, and another pair of valves at the ventral end. These valves allow blood to flow downwards only. The other hearts of the segment 7th and 9th are called lateral hearts. These connect the dorsal vessels to the ventral vessel. They have four pairs of valves which allow blood to flow only downwards.

Besides four pairs of hearts there are two pairs of loop-like vessels in the 10th and 11th segments which connect the supra-oesophageal with the lateral oesophageals. These vessels are neither muscular nor pulsatile and are called **anterior loops.** These are devoid of valves. The blood from lateral oesophageals flows through these loops into supra-oesophageal which sends all its collected blood into ventral vessel through the hearts of 12th and 13th segments.

3. Blood Vessels of the Gut

On either side of stomach are situated ring-like vessels which connect the supra-oesophageal and lateral-oesophageal vessels. Through these vessels blood flows upwards from the lateral-oesophageals into the supra-oesophageal. Buccal cavity, pharynx and gizzard receive their blood supply from dorsal blood vessel directly.

Circulation of Blood

The blood collected by the dorsal vessel through the dorso-intestinals, blood plexuses of intestine, and commissurals is given out partly to the anterior alimentary canal, but mainly through the hearts to the ventral vessel. In the ventral vessel the blood flows forwards to the anterior region in front of the hearts, but the main portion of blood flows backwards, this is distributed through ventro-tegumentaries to the body wall and the organs in the coelom, and through the ventro-intestinal vessels to the alimentary canal. In other words all parts receive blood from the ventral vessel. From the ventral body wall blood is collected by the subneural which also receives some blood through the lateral-oesophageal from the anterior region. This blood passes from the subneural to the dorsal vessel through the commissurals. The lateral-oesophageals also

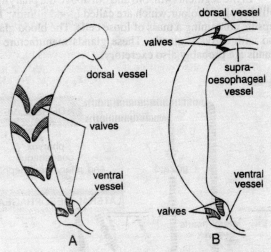

Fig. 66.17. *Pheretima*. A—Lateral heart ; B—Latero-oesophageal heart.

send blood through the anterior loops to the supra-oesophageal vessel which then passes it through the latero-oesophageal hearts to the ventral vessel. The course of circulation of blood in *Pheretima* has been shown in Fig. 66.20.

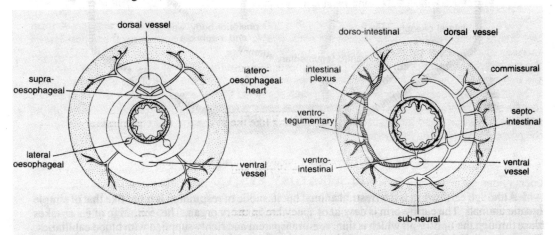

Fig. 66.18. *Pheretima*. T.S. through latero-oesophageal hearts.

Fig. 66.19. *Pheretima*. T.S. through a segment on the left and through a segment on the right.

Functions. The blood distributes digested food to various body regions, and it collects waste substances like nitrogenous waste and CO_2 which are given up to nephridia, skin and the coelomic fluid. Respiration in almost all aquatic and terrestrial oligochaetes takes place by diffusion of gases through the integument which in larger forms contains a capillary network in the outer epidermal layer. In terrestrial species the film of moisture necessary for diffusion of gases is supplied by mucous glands, coelomic fluid, and nephridial excretions. The haemoglobin of plasma extracts O_2 from the capillaries of the skin, but there must be a moist skin where O_2 can combine with haemoglobin to be transported by the blood. Haemoglobin is an efficient pigment and it can take up O_2 either from the surrounding air or from an environment comparatively deficient in oxygen. Hence, earthworms can live in well aerated water and are not drowned. They can also live for several hours without O_2, in this condition they probably carry on anaerobic respiration.

Blood Glands

In the segments 4th, 5th and 6th above the pharyngeal mass are several groups of small rounded follicles of red colour,which are called blood glands. The follicles have a syncytial wall enclosing a capsule containing a mass of loose cells. The blood glands are connected with pharyngeal nephridia and with salivary glands. These glands manufacture blood corpuscles and haemoglobin. These glands are probably also excretory.

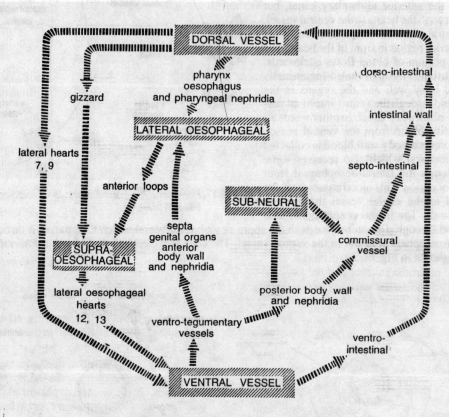

Fig. 66.20. *Pheretima.* Course of circulation of blood.

RESPIRATORY SYSTEM

Although earthworm is a terrestrial animal but its mode of respiration is more like that of simple aquatic animals. The earthworm is devoid of special respiratory organ. The exchange of gases takes place through the body wall which is thin, semitransparent and richly supplied with blood capillaries. The tegumental glands and coelomic fluid make the surface of the skin moist with their secretions to assist in gaseous exchange. It has been observed that if its skin dries the worm dies of suffocation, *i.e.*, asphyxia.

As mentioned earlier the blood of earthworm contains a respiratory pigment—haemoglobin in a dissolved state in its plasma. The epidermis of the body wall acts as a permeable membrane through which the atmospheric oxygen diffuses in its capillaries and combines with haemoglobin to form oxyhaemoglobin. The oxyhaemoglobin is circulated by the blood into the tissues where oxygen tension is very less and CO_2 tension is high. The oxyhaemoglobin breaks up to release oxygen to the tissues and haemoglobin in a reduced state. This oxygen is utilized in the tissues for the oxidation of foodstuffs to release energy needed for performing the vital activities of life and carbon dioxide. At the same time, CO_2 from the tissues diffuses into the blood due to its high tension. The CO_2 is carried by the blood generally in a dissolved condition and when it reaches to the epidermal capillaries the CO_2 from the blood diffuses out in the atmosphere due to low CO_2 tension at this level and again oxygen diffuses in the blood due to its high tension and combines with haemoglobin to form oxyhaemoglobin once again. Thus, respiration is affected in earthworm.

EXCRETORY SYSTEM

The excretory organs of earth-worms are segmentally arranged slender coiled tubules called nephridia which are ectodermal in origin. In *Pheretima* there is a large number of small-sized nephridia in each segment which are called micronephridia or mesonephridia. The nephridia are found in all segments except the first three. These are of three types according to their location in the body :

1. Septal nephridia;
2. Integumentary nephridia; and
3. Pharyngeal nephridia.

1. Septal nephridia. These are found situated on the intersegmental septum between 15th and 16th segments to the posterior side of the body. Each septum bears nephridia on both the surfaces arranged in semicircles around the intestine, two rows in front of the septum and two behind it. Each septum has about 40 to 50 nephridia in front and the same number behind, so that each segment possesses 80 to 100 septal nephridia except

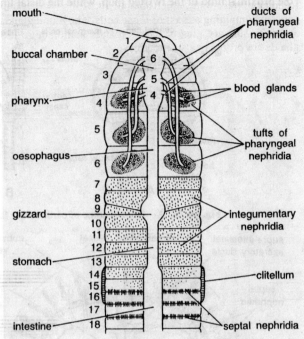

Fig. 66.21. *Pheretima.* Different types of nephridia and general plan of their distribution.

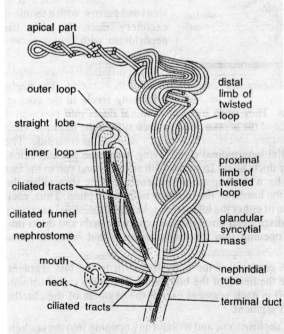

Fig. 66.22. *Pheretima.* A septal nephridium.

the 15th segment which has only 40 to 50 nephridia. These are not found in the segments up to 14th.

Structure. The septal nephridia may be considered typical of all the nephridia of *Pheretima*. Each septal nephridium (Fig. 66.22) consists of nephrostome, neck, body of nephridium and the terminal duct.

(i) Nephrostome. It is also known as ciliated funnel or nephridiostome. It is the proximal flattened funnel-shaped structure of the nephridium lying in the coelom. It has an elliptical mouth-like opening leading into an intracellular canal of the large central cell, the margins of the opening are surrounded by a large upper lip and a smaller lower lip. The lips are provided with several rows of small ciliated marginal cells and the central canal is also ciliated.

(ii) Neck. The nephrostome leads into a short and narrow ciliated canal forming the neck. It joins the nephrostome to the body of nephridium.

(iii) Body of nephridium. The body of nephridium has two parts : a short straight lobe and a long twisted loop. The loop is formed by two limbs—the proximal limb and the distal limb. Both these limbs are twisted spirally around each other, the number of twists varies from nine to thirteen. The neck of nephridium and the terminal duct join together and remain connected with the proximal limb of the twisted loop, while the distal limb becomes the straight lobe.

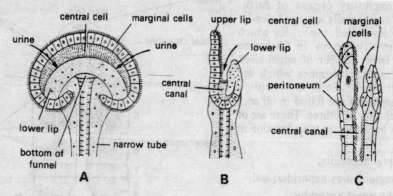

Fig. 66.23. A—Nephrostome of earthworm ; B and C—L. S. of nephrostome.

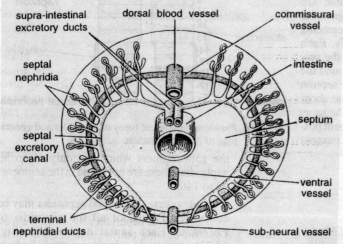

Fig. 66.24. *Pheretima.* The arrangement of septal nephridial system in relation to the intestine.

Internally the nephridium is made of a connective tissue matrix having long coiled nephridial duct forming loops. There are four such canals in the straight lobe, three in the lower part and two in the upper part of the limbs of twisted loop. Two canals of the straight lobe out of the four are ciliated like the ciliated canal of the neck.

(iv) **Terminal duct.** It is short and narrow with a terminal excretory duct. It joins the nephridium with septal excretory canal.

Relation of septal nephridia with intestine. The nephridia hang freely in the coelom and are attached only by their terminal ducts. They open by their terminal ducts into two septal excretory canals lying on the posterior surface of the septum, one on each side of the intestine, each begins ventrally but dorsally it opens in the supra-intestinal excretory duct of its own side. The supra-intestinal excretory ducts are two parallel longitudinal canals lying above the gut and below the dorsal vessel (Fig. 66.24). These excretory ducts begin from the 15th segment and run to the last segment, they communicate with each other for a short space behind each septum, then either the right or the left duct opens by a ductule into the lumen of the intestine near the septum. Thus, each segment has one such opening into the intestine of either the left or the right supra-intestinal excretory duct. The waste collected by the nephridia is discharged through the excretory canals and ducts into the lumen of the intestine. Such nephridia opening into the intestine are called enteronephric nephridia.

2. **Integumentary nephridia.** In each segment of the body from 7th to the last segment, numerous nephridia are found attached inside the lining of the body wall. These are called integumentary nephridia which are about 200–250 in each segment except the segment of the clitellar region where they number 2000–2500 in each segment.

These nephridia are small-sized, without nephrostome and without any opening into the coelom. Hence, they are called closed type of nephridia. Each integumentary nephridium is V-shaped with a short straight lobe and a twisted loop, its lumen has two ciliated canals. Each nephridium opens by a nephridiopore on the outer surface of the body wall directly. Since the integumentary nephridia discharge the excretory wastes directly outside, hence, they are called exonephric nephridia.

3. Pharyngeal nephridia. These nephridia lie in three paired tufts, one on either side of the anterior region of the alimentary canal in the segments 4th, 5th and 6th. The tufts of pharyngeal nephridia also contain blood glands (Fig. 66.21).

Each pharyngeal nephridium is about the size of a septal nephridium but it is of the closed type having no funnel or nephrostome. It has a short straight lobe and a spirally twisted loop, its lumen has ciliated canals. Ductules arise from each nephridium and unite to form a single thick-walled duct on each side in each segment. The two ducts of nephridia of segment 6th open into the buccal cavity in segment 2nd and the paired ducts of nephridia of segments 4th and 5th open into the pharynx in segment 4th (Fig. 66.21). These nephridia also discharge their wastes into the alimentary canal and are, therefore, enteronephric but such enteronephric nephridia which open into the anterior region of the alimentary canal (buccal cavity and pharynx) are called peptonephridia because they may have taken the function of digestive glands. Recently it has been reported that the pharyngeal nephridia of *P. posthuma* produce a variety of enzymes like amylase, chimosin, prolinase, prolidase, dipeptidases, aminopeptidase, lipase, etc., which hydrolyse various foodstuffs. Thus, such nephridia work like the salivary glands.

Physiology of Excretion

Like other animals, in earthworms also, the protein catabolism results in the formation of nitrogenous waste substances like certain amino acids, ammonia and urea. Uric acid is not found in the earthworms. However, the amino acids are degraded to form free ammonia and the urea is synthesized in the chloragogen cells which are released into the coelomic fluid and also in the blood for its removal. Free amino acids are not excreted but traces of creatinine occur in the urine. Moreover, the nitrogen excreted in different forms in a well fed worm is about 72% NH_3, 5% urea and remaining other compounds, while in a starved worm NH_3 8.6%, urea 84.5% and remaining being other compounds. But generally, the excretion is 42% NH_3, 50% urea, 0.6% amino acids and remaining being other compounds. So, we can say that in a well fed earthworm, NH_3 predominates the nitrogenous excretory wastes, hence, it is ammonotelic, while a starved one is ureotelic.

An earthworm excretes the nitrogenous wastes in the form of urine which generally contains urea, water, traces of ammonia and creatinine. Nephridia excrete these substances from the body of earthworm. The various excretory wastes from the coelomic fluid are drawn into the nephrostomes of septal nephridia or into the excretory canals of other nephridia along with some other useful substances. These products are either discharged into the intestine (by enteronephric nephridia) or outside by the nephridiopores (by exonephric nephridia). The body of nephridia also absorbs some wastes. However, the useful substances are reabsorbed and the passing out waste remains concentrated for various nitrogenous compounds. The excreted waste substances are removed out from the body with faeces. The nephridia, in addition to excretory, are also osmoregulatory in function. The nephridia help in conserving water by reabsorption from the excreted products during summers and winters, so they pass hypertonic urine in relation to blood. During rainy season, the urine is dulute due to lesser reabsorption of water. The enteronephric nature of nephridia provides another device for conserving water.

NERVOUS SYSTEM

The nervous system of *Pheretima* is well developed, concentrated and consists of the **central, peripheral** and **sympathetic** or **autonomic** divisions.

1. Central nervous system. It consists of the nerve ring or brain ring and the ventral nerve cord.

Nerve ring. A pair of cerebral or supra-pharyngeal ganglia is found fused together to form the so-called brain which lies dorsally in the 3rd segment in the groove between the buccal chamber and the pharynx. From the brain a pair of circum-pharyngeal connective arise, one on each side, they encircle the pharynx and meet ventrally in the 4th segment by a pair of fused sub-pharyngeal ganglia. Thus, a nerve collar is formed around the pharynx which is called the nerve ring or brain ring.

Nerve cord. A nerve cord originates from the sub-pharyngeal ganglia and runs on the mid-ventral side beneath the ventral vessel but above subneural vessel extending up to the posterior end of the body. The nerve cord is double and is made of two longitudinal cords fused together. In each segment from 5th to the last the nerve cord has a pair of ganglia fused together as swellings representing the segmental ganglia. The nerve cells are distributed all over the nerve cord and are not confined to ganglionic swellings.

Structurally, the double nerve cords of *Pheretima* are solid and enclosed in a common sheath called perineurium consisting of three layers—the outer peritoneum, middle longitudinal muscle layer and inner thick fibrous layer of epineurium. The nerve cords are solid consisting of the nerve cells and the fibres. Both the nerve cords are separated internally by a vertical epineurium. The ventro-lateral regions of nerve cord contain bipolar and tripolar nerve cells all along the length, and the middle region has many nerve fibres with supporting neuroglia. Running longitudinally in the upper part of the nerve cord are four giant nerve fibres surrounded by epineurium, they are all tubular and filled with homogeneous plasma-like matter. These are responsible for rapid conduction of impulses throughout the nerve cord. However, in the region of segmental ganglia the partition between the two nerve cords is absent.

2. Peripheral nervous system. From the brain 8 to 10 pairs of nerves arise which supply to the prostomium, buccal cavity and pharynx. Two pairs of nerves arise from the circumpharyngeal connectives which supply to the first segment and buccal cavity. From the subpharyngeal ganglia three pairs of nerves arise to supply 2nd, 3rd and 4th segments. The

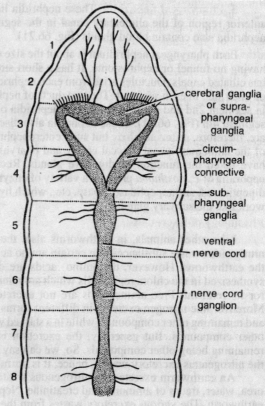

Fig. 66.25. *Pheretima*. Nervous system in dorsal view.

nerve cord and ganglia of each segment give out three pairs of nerves which supply the various parts of the segment in which the ganglia are situated. Thus, the nerves originating from the central nervous system to supply the different parts of the body constitute the peripheral nervous system.

3. Sympathetic nervous system. It includes the nerve plexuses situated in the wall of the alimentary canal and some other internal organs. Such plexuses are connected with the peri-pharyngeal connectives by

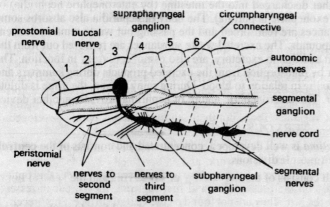

Fig. 66.26. *Pheretima*. Anterior end in lateral view to show the disposition of nerve ring and nerve cord.

fine nervules and help in co-ordinating the functions of the related organs.

Working of the Nervous System

The nervous system of *Pheretima*, like those of higher animals, has both sensory and motor neurons. The nerves of the nerve cord, therefore, have both sensory and motor fibres, *i.e.*, mixed. The stimuli from the skin are transmitted by sensory fibres to the nerve cord and the stimulus is transferred either to an association neuron first, or it may go to the muscles (effectors) which cause them to contract. This circuit of stimuli or impulses forms a simple reflex arc. The movements of circular and longitudinal muscles are co-ordinated, so that contraction of one brings about relaxation of the other. The impulses are conducted more rapidly in the giant fibres resulting into sudden contraction of the whole body of earthworm.

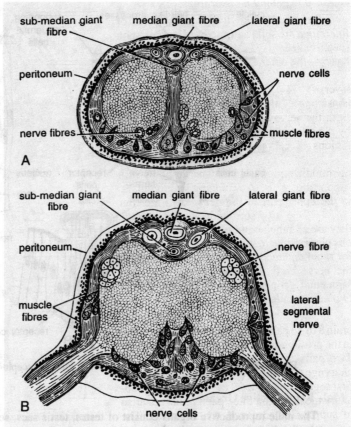

SENSE ORGANS

Pheretima reacts to a number of external stimuli with the help of three types of sense organs or receptors : epidermal receptors, buccal receptors and photoreceptors.

1. **Epidermal receptors.** Epidermal receptor (Fig. 66.28A) consists of an ovoid group of tall cells in the epidermis which cause an elevation of the cuticle. These cells are separated from each other by spaces. Each cell has a nucleus near the middle and it ends above in slender hair-like processes which penetrate the cuticle and project beyond it. The lower ends of these cells are supplied with nerve fibres. The epidermal receptors are found all over the epidermis but are more numerous in the lateral and ventral regions. They are tactile in function, *i.e.,* tangoreceptors and also perceive thermal and chemical stimuli. Hence, earthworms are very

Fig. 66.27. *Pheretima.* A—Section of ventral nerve cord ; B—Section of ventral nerve cord at the region of the origin of segmental nerves.

sensitive to touch and to vibrations transmitted through solid objects, though they cannot hear at all.

2. **Buccal receptors.** These are found in the epithelium of buccal cavity in large numbers, they consist of groups of tall cells which project beyond the epithelial cells. These cells (Fig. 66.28B)have sensory hair-like processes and their nuclei lie below the middle part of the cells. These receptors serve to smell, *i.e.,* olfactoreceptors and taste food, *i.e.,* gustatoreceptors. These cells can distinguish between the tastes of different vegetable foods but their sense of smell is poorly developed, though earthworms can smell different types of decaying leaves used as food.

3. **Photoreceptors.** A photoreceptor (Fig. 66.28C) is a single ovoid cell in the inner part of epidermis, it has a nucleus and cytoplasm with a network, and an optic cell (phaosome or lens) generally of curved shape and made of a hyaline substance. One or two nerve fibres enter this optic cell. Photoreceptors are found mostly on the prostomium and first segment, they occur in lesser numbers in other segments including the last. They are not found on the ventral surface. Photoreceptors are sensitive to light and also called little eyes or ocelli. Actually the network of a photoreceptor is formed by branching and rebranching of the nerve fibre entering into it and characteristically called retinella. The earthworms show a negative response to even a very weak light, hence, they retreat into their burrows during day and come out at night, *i.e.,* they are nocturnal in habit.

REPRODUCTIVE SYSTEM

The *Pheretima* is monoecious or hermaphrodite having both male and female reproductive organs in the same individual. But cross-fertilization occurs as a rule because of the relative position of male and female genital apertures and also because earthworms are protandrous, the male gametes mature first and earlier than the female gametes, so that self-fertilization is prevented. *Pheretima* reproduces sexually only and no asexual reproduction occurs.

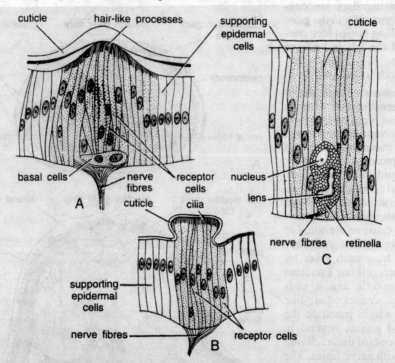

Fig. 66.28. *Pheretima.* Sense organs. A—An epidermal receptor ; B—A buccal receptor ; C—A photoreceptor.

Male Reproductive Organs

The male reproductive organs consist of testes, testis sacs, seminal vesicles, vasa deferentia, prostate glands and accessory glands.

Testes and testis sacs. The testes are two pairs, very minute, whitish and lobed structures situated one pair each in segment 10th and 11th found attached with the posterior surface of 9/10 and 10/11 intersegmental septa. Each testis consists of 4 to 8 finger-like lobules projecting from a compact base. Each lobule of the testis contains rounded cells in masses called spermatogonia. The testes are well developed only during the young stage of the worm and become degenerated in the adult worm. The testes of each segment are found enclosed in a thin-walled, wide bilobed and fluid-filled sacs called testis sacs. Thus, there are two testis sacs situated in the segments 10th and 11th on the ventrolateral sides of the ventral nerve cord beneath the stomach. Behind each of the four testes, in the testis sacs, is a large spermatic funnel having folded and ciliated margins. The testis sacs remain in communication with the seminal vesicles. The spermatogonia are shed into the testis sacs and pass on into the seminal vesicles where they undergo maturation and form spermatozoa.

Seminal vesicles. These are two pairs of large, white, sac-like bodies, one pair each in the segments 11th and 12th into which the testis sacs open by narrow ducts. The anterior seminal vesicles are smaller than the posterior ones. The seminal vesicles of the.11th segment are found enclosed in the posterior larger testis sac, while those of the 12th segment are exposed in the coelomic cavity. These are also placed ventro-laterally beneath the stomach and since they develop as septal outgrowths, hence, they are also known as septal pouches.

Vasa deferentia. Each spermatic funnel (posteriorly) leads into a thin, narrow, thread-like sperm duct or vas deferens. Thus, the two vasa deferentia of each side run very closely and laterally to the nerve cord beneath the alimentary canal on the ventral body wall, up to 18th segment where they join the prostatic duct.

Prostate glands. These are a pair of large, white, solid and irregularly-shaped glandular masses situated one on either side of the gut in the segments from 16th or 17th to 20th or 21st. Each prostate gland consists of a maximum glandular region and a small part of non-glandular region. From each prostate gland emerges a thick curved prostatic duct in 18th segment. This duct joins the two vasa deferentia of its side and these three ducts are enclosed in a common sheath to form a common prostatic spermatic duct which opens separately through a male genital aperture on the ventral side of the 18th segment. Thus, each genital aperture has three separate apertures—two of the vasa deferentia and one of the prostatic gland. The function of the secretion of prostatic duct is not definitely known.

Accessory glands. These are two pairs of rounded structures situated one pair each in the segments 17th and 18th on the ventral body wall at the lateral sides of the nerve cord. These glands open to the out side by a number of small ductules on the two pairs of genital papillae situated on the either side of the mid-ventral line in 17th and 19th segments externally. The secretion of these glands is believed to keep together the two worms during the process of copulation.

As mentioned earlier, the spermatogonia from the testes are shed into the testis

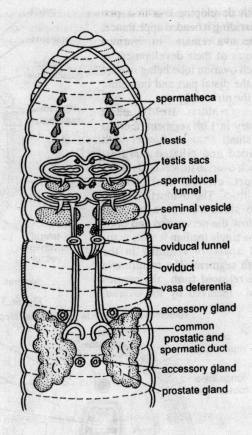

Fig. 66.29. *Pheretima.* Reproductive system.

sacs and pass on to the seminal vesicles where spermatogenesis is completed and tailed spermatozoa are formed Now, these spermatozoa again enter the testis sacs and through the spermatic funnels go down the vasa deferentia and are discharged through the male genital apertures along with the secretion of prostate glands.

Female Reproductive Organs

Female reproductive organs consist of the ovaries, oviducts and spermathecae.

Ovaries. There is a pair of white, small, lobulated ovaries, one on either side of the ventral nerve cord in the 13th segment attached with the posterior face of the inter-segmental septum of 12/13 segments. Each ovary has several finger-like processes

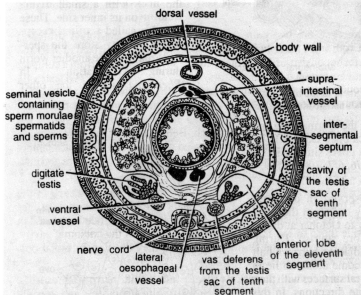

Fig. 66.30. *Pheretima.* T.S. passing through the testis sacs, testes and seminal vesicles in the anterior region of 11th segment.

with developing ova in a row providing it beaded appearance. The ova remain in various stages of their development in each ovarian lobe being mature in the distal part and immature in the proximal part.

Oviducts. Below each ovary in 13th segment, there is a small ovarian funnel with folded and ciliated margins. Each ovarian funnel leads into a short, conical and ciliated oviduct. The oviducts of both the sides converge to meet below the nerve cord and open by a single median female genital aperture ventrally in the 14th segment. The mature ova are released from the ovaries and received by the ovarian

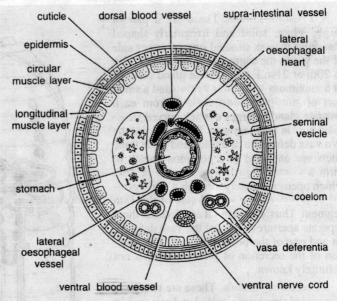

Fig. 66.31. *Pheretima.* T.S. 12th segment of body.

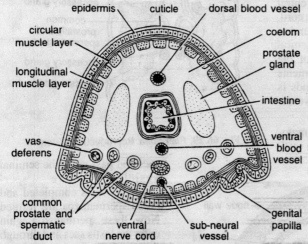

Fig. 66.32. *Pheretima.* T.S. 17th segment of the body passing through prostate glands and genital papillae.

funnel, pass through the oviducts and which go out through the female genital aperture.

Spermathecae. These are four pairs, one pair each in the segments 6th, 7th, 8th, and 9th situated ventro-laterally. Each spermatheca is flask-shaped, the main body is the ampulla which is continued into narrow duct— the neck with a small diverticulum on its inner side. These are also called seminal receptacles as they store the spermatozoa from the another worm during copulation. In *Pheretima.* unlike the other

earthworms, the diverticula store the spermatozoa and not the ampulla. The spermatheca open externally by their small ducts as spermatheca pores situated intersegmentally between segments 5/6, 6/7, 7/8 and 8/9.

Copulation, Cocoon Formation and Fertilization

Copulation has been observed in different species of earthworms. It usually occurs in the rainy season during the months of July to October at dawn, *i.e.,* in the morning hours before sunrise. During copulation two earthworms of adjacent burrows half emerge from their burrows and come closer to lie in contact to each other by their ventral surfaces with their anterior ends pointing in opposite directions. In this position the male genital apertures of each worm lie opposite the spermathecal pores of the other. The areas

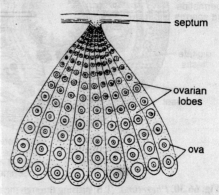

Fig. 66.33. *Pheretima.* Ovary.

of the male genital apertures are raised into papillae and inserted into the spermathecal pores, so that there is a mutual exchange of spermatozoa and prostatic fluid between the two copulating worms. Copulation lasts for about an hour or so, then the worms separate and recede into their burrows.

Cocoon or ootheca formation starts after copulation when ovaries mature. The epidermis of clitellar segments, *i.e.,* 14th, 15th and 16th segments contain three kinds of glands, they are unicellular mucous glands which produce mucus for copulation, cocoon-secreting glands secrete the wall of the cocoon and albumen glands produce albumen in which eggs are deposited in the cocoon. A membranous girdle is secreted by cocoon-secreting glands of the clitellum, this girdle soon hardens, then albumen is deposited between the girdle and the body wall. The worm starts withdrawing itself backwards from the girdle. As the girdle passes over the female genital aperture it receives eggs, and when it passes over the spermathecae sperms are extruded into it through spermathecal pores. Lastly, the girdle is thrown off from the anterior end of the worm and soon the elasticity of its wall closes up its two ends to form a cocoon or ootheca. Several cocoons are formed after each copulation because the spermatozoa contained in the spermatheca do not

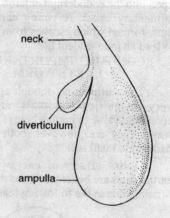

Fig. 66.34. *Pheretima.* Spermatheca.

pass out all at one time. The cocoons are oval, light yellow in colour and are about 2 to 2.4 mm long and 1.5 to 2 mm broad.

Fertilization takes place inside the cocoon and generally there is only one embryo in a cocoon. Cocoons are laid from August to October in damp situations.

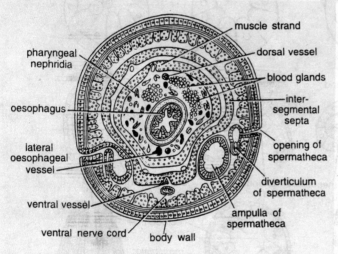

Fig. 66.35. *Pheretima.* T.S. passing through the region of spermathecae.

DEVELOPMENT OF EARTHWORM

The cocoon contains fertilized egg and albuminous substance secreted by the glands of the clitellum for nourishment of the embryo. Development (Fig. 66.38) occurs in the cocoon with no larval stage.

The zygote undergoes holoblastic and a modified spiral cleavage resulting into a hollow ball of cells, the blastula, enclosed into a vitelline membrane. The lower cells of blastula are endodermal and those of upper cells are ectodermal. Gastrulation occurs by invagination of endodermal cells into ectodermal cells to form a cylindrical gastrula with an archenteron cavity and a blastopore which narrows to become the mouth. Two large mesoblast cells are differentiated early

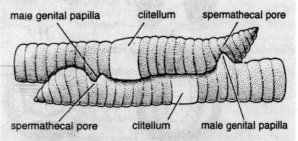

Fig. 66.36. *Pheretima.* Two earthworms in copulation.

and they give rise to the mesoderm band. The embryo escapes from the vitelline membrane and begins to feed on albuminous substance in the cocoon. The embryo elongates, the mesoderm band extends between the ectoderm and endoderm and it gets divided into segments. Each segment of the mesoderm acquires a coelomic cavity. The ectoderm cells form thick rows behind a large cell known as teloblast, the innermost row forms the nerve cord, and the next two rows of ectoderm give rise to nephridia. The mouth and anus open into the endodermal enteron to form the alimentary canal. A young earthworm is, thus, formed which escapes from the cocoon to lead an independent life.

ECONOMIC IMPORTANCE OF EARTHWORM

The earthworms, though appear to be very insignificant animals, are of great economic value to human beings in different ways. They are, however, both useful and harmful to mankind.

Useful affairs of earthworms. The earthworms are better known as the friend of farmers due to the following reasons :

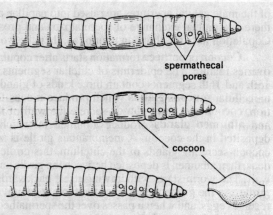

Fig. 66.37. Formation and release of a cocoon in earthworm.

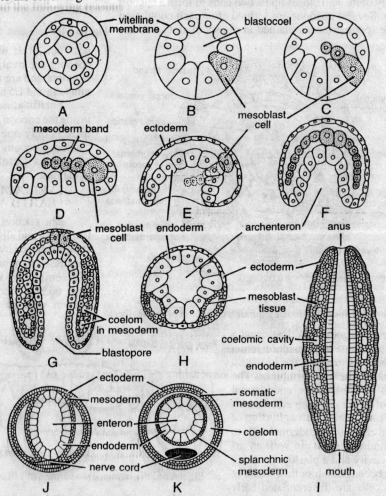

Fig. 66.38. Development of an earthworm. A—Blastula ; B—T.S. blastula with mesoblast cell ; C—T.S. blastula with growth of mesoblast ; D—L.S. of early gastrula ; E—Lateral view of gastrula showing invagination ; F—T.S. gastrula ; G—L.S. early embryo ; H—T.S. early embryo ; I—L.S. late embryo after the formation of mouth and anus ; J—T.S. late embryo and K—Later embryo in T.S.

1. The earthworms improve the fertility of soil in different ways and, therefore, they are of utmost importance in agriculture. Actually, the burrowing and soil feeding habits of earthworms make the soil porous wnich permit both aeration and quick absorption of water. It also permits easy and deep penetration of the plant roots. They also bring the fresh subsoil to the surface which is still finer and rich in organic matters Charles Darwin has estimated that an acre of earth is inhabited by nearly 50,000 earthworms (a recent estimate suggests that their number may reach up to 25,00,000 per acre) which may bring more than 18 tons of deeper subsoil to the surface in one year. This may in 20 years form a layer of 7.5 cm thick surface on the earth in the form of their castings. The castings of earthworm contain fine soil having mixed with its nitrogenous wastes and faeces of nice manurial value. The faeces of earthworm contain nitrate, calcium, magnesium, potassium and phosphorus which constitute an important component of the humus essential for plant growth. They also reduce the alkalinity and acidity of the soil to provide better canditions for plant growth. After their death and decomposition, they increase the organic constituents of the soil. Thus, the earthworms make the soil fertile to a great extent. Thus, these worms are also known as natural ploughmen or tillers of the soil.

2. These are used as bait and food. As bait they are used in fishing. The earthworms were used as food by so many uncivilized people of the world and they are still used as food by Macrea people. The earthworms are eaten upon by frogs, toads, moles, hedgehogs and birds which are of many uses to mankind.

3. Many people earn their livelihood by catching these worms and supplying to scientific laboratories.

4. Ayurvedic and Unani system of therapy suggests that these worms were used in making medicines for the cure of diseases like bladder stones, jaundice, pyorrhoea, piles, rheumatism, etc. Even today, these are used in making various medicines of vital importance in India as well as other countries.

Harmful affairs of earthworms. They may damage young and tender plants by eating them bit by bit. They also damage the grass lands by making tunnels in the ground when present in huge numbers. They are also said to help soil erosion. Some earthworms act as secondary hosts for the completion of life stages of some parasites which are directly or indirectly harmful to mankind.

REVISION QUESTIONS

1. Give an account of the alimentary canal of *Pheretima* and its mode of feeding.
2. Describe the circulatory system of earthworm in the anterior thirteen segments.
3. Describe the structure of the body wall of earthworm and write down its functions.
4. Give an account of the coelom and coelomic fluid of earthworm. Describe the function of coelomic fluid.
5. Describe the excretory system and physiology of excretion of *Pheretima*.
6. Give an account of the nervous system of earthworm.
7. Describe the reproductive system of *Pheretima*.
8. Earthworms are farmer's friend, discuss.
9. Draw well labelled diagrams only.
   (i) T.S. earthworm passing through pharynx; (ii) T.S. earthworm passing through typhlosole;
   (iii) Septal nephridium of earthworm ; (iv) Reproductive system of earthworm.
10. Write short notes on :
   (i) Chloragogen cells; (ii) Locomotion of earthworm ; (iii) Typhlosole ; (iv) Pharyngeal nephridia ;
   (v) Spermatheca.

67

Hirudinaria (Indian Cattle Leech)

Hirudinaria, commonly called Indian cattle leech, belongs to class Hirudinea which contains over 300 species of leeches. Leeches are the most specialized annelids and have evolved from oligochaetes. *Hirudinaria* has a great number of species. The common Indian species are : *Hirudinaria granulosa, H.viridis, H. javanica,* and *H. manillensis.* These species are also common in Burma, Pakistan, Bangladesh and Sri Lanka. *H. medicinalis,* and *H. australis* are the common leeches of Britain and Australia respectively. *Haemadipsa* is a land leech of the hills of Southern India. The most common Indian cattle leech, *Hirudinaria granulosa* is described here in detail.

HIRUDINARIA GRANULOSA (THE COMMON INDIAN LEECH)
SYSTEMATIC POSITION

Phylum	....	**Annelida**
Class	....	**Hirudinea**
Order	....	**Gnathobdellida**
Genus	....	*Hirudinaria*
Species	....	*granulosa*

HABIT AND HABITAT

Hirudinaria is a common Indian leech found in freshwater tanks, ponds, lakes, swamps, and slow streams. It prefers shallow water and remains concealed under weeds, logs and stones. It is sanguivorous (blood-sucking), sucking the blood of fishes and frogs, and also of cattle or human beings when they enter the pond.

Leeches show a great diversity in their habits and habitat. Some species are marine, some are freshwater, while others are terrestrial. Though many species are blood-suckers (ectoparasitic) yet a large number are not ectoparasitic but are predatory and feed on worms, snails and insect larvae.

EXTERNAL FEATURES

Shape and size. The body of *Hirudinaria* is soft, vermiform, elongated, bilaterally symmetrical and metamerically segmented. In a state of extension the body is dorsoventrally flattened and appears almost strap-shaped but in a state of contraction, the body becomes more or less cylindrical. The body is broadest near the posterior end, while narrowest near the anterior end. It has geat power of contraction and expansion. A full grown specimen may attain the length of 30 to 35 cm.

Colouration. The body is beautifully coloured with characteristic markings. The dorsal surface is generally olive-green and the ventral surface is orange-yellow or orange-red and the two sides bear distinct stripes of orange or yellow and black. On the dorsal side is a median longitudinal black stripe.

Segmentation. The body of leech is divided metamerically into segments or somites but metamerism is much reduced and the number of segments, unlike other annelids, is fixed in leeches, they always have 33 segments or somites. In case of leech the external segmentation does not correspond with the internal segmentation. But the original segmentation is obscured by secondary external annulation. Each segment is broken up externally by grooves into rings called annuli. The first and second segments have one annulus each, the third has two annuli, segments fourth to sixth have three annuli each, segments seventh to twenty-second are broad having five annuli each, segments twenty-third to twenty-sixth have two annuli each, segments twenty-seventh to thirty-third have one annulus each, they form the posterior sucker. However, segments with less than five annuli are referred to as incomplete, while those with five annuli are called complete segments. Each annulus of a segment is divided into small rectangular areas by longitudinal wrinkles. Each such area has a sort of papilla-like structure bearing sensory organ called annular receptor; there are 18 such receptors both on the dorsal and ventral surfaces of each annulus. Besides these, the first annulus of each segment bears larger sensory organs called sensillae or segmental receptors; these are four pairs on the dorsal side and three on the ventral side. Due to this the first annulus of each segment is called sensory annulus.

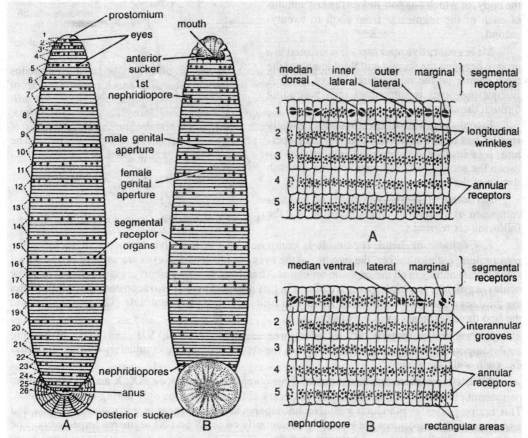

Fig. 67.1. *Hirudinaria granulosa*. External features. A—Dorsal view ; B—Ventral view.

Fig. 67.2. *Hirudinaria*. A segment from middle region of the body showing the receptors. A—Dorsal view; B—Ventral view.

Suckers. Each end of the body of leech bears a hollow muscular organ, the sucker. The anterior sucker or cephalic or oral sucker is formed by the fusion of the prostomium with a few somites of anterior region. It is oval in outline and is placed on the ventral surface of anterior end. It also possesses a ventrally directed cup-like hollow structure, the pre-oral chamber, which leads into the mouth. The posterior sucker or anal sucker is circular in outline and forms the highly muscular disc at the posterior end of the body of leech. It is formed by the fusion of last seven segments. It is much better developed and larger in size than the anterior sucker. Both suckers are directed ventrally, the leech can firmly grip the substratum by its suckers. The two suckers are primarily meant for adhesion and locomotion.

Clitellum. During breeding season a girdle-like clitellum is formed around segments ninth to eleventh, rest of the year there is no clitellum.

Eyes. On the dorsal side are five pairs of eyes, one pair on each of the first and second segments, and one pair on the first annulus of the segments third, fourth and fifth.

External apertures. External apertures in the body are as follows :

Mouth. It is a narrow triradiate aperture situated in the centre of the funnel-like pre-oral chamber of the anterior sucker.

Anus. It is a very small aperture situated mid-dorsally on the twenty-sixth segment at the root of the posterior sucker.

Nephridiopores. There are seventeen pairs of nephridiopores lying on the ventral surface of the body, of which one pair lies on the last annulus of each of the segments from sixth to twenty-second.

Male generative aperture. It is situated in a groove between the second and third annuli of the tenth somite on the mid-ventral line of body. A filamentous penis is sometimes seen protruding through this aperture.

Female generative aperture. It is usually smaller and less conspicuous than the male aperture. It is situated mid-ventrally in a groove between the second and third annuli of the eleventh somite of the body.

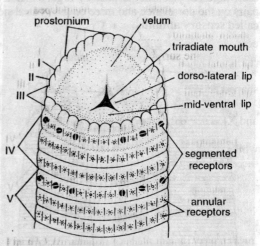

Fig. 67.3. *Hirudinaria.* Cephalic region (Ventral view).

Divisions of body. The body of leech is composed of 33 somites and is divisible into the following six regions :

1. Cephalic or head region. It is composed of the first five segments. It includes the prostomium, anterior sucker, the mouth and the eyes ; in fact a pair of eyes are situated on the dorsal side of first annulus in all the cephalic segments. Therefore, these segments are also referred to as the ocular segments. Nephridiopores are absent in this region. The first two segments are uniannulate, the third segment is biannulate and fourth and fifth segments are triannulate. The prostomium and the first three segments form the upper lip.

2. Preclitellar region. It includes three segments, *i.e.,* VI, VII, and VIII, all bearing nephridiopores. Somite VI is triannulate but the remaining two are completely quinquannulate, *i.e.,* each with five annuli.

3. Clitellar region. It is composed of three complete segments, *i.e.,* IX, X and XI. There is no permanent clitellum in *Hirudinaria* but temporary clitellum develops only during breeding season. This region possesses glandular wall. Nephridiopores are also present in this region, the male and female generative apertures are situated mid-ventrally on the X and XI segments respectively. The segments of clitellar region are quinquannulate.

4. Middle region. It is the largest region of the body and consists of eleven complete somites (XII to XXII). All the segments of this region are quinquannulate and possess nephridiopores.

5. Caudal region. This region is short and consists of four incomplete somites, *i.e.,* XXIII to XXVI. Segment XXIII is triannulate but the remaining three are biannulate. Segment XXVI bears the anal aperture on the dorsal side. There are no nephridiopores.

6. Posterior sucker. It is composed of seven segments (XXVII to XXXIII) arranged in concentric rings and each represented by a single annulus. These seven segments are completely fused and their intersegmental furrows are greatly suppressed.

BODY WALL

The body wall consists of five layers, *viz.,* cuticle, epidermis, dermis, muscular layer, and botryoidal tissue.

Cuticle. The cuticle is the outermost, thin, delicate, transparent, colourless and moderately elastic protective covering. It is thicker slightly on the dorsal surface than on the ventral surface. It is perforated throughout by which epidermal glands open out. It is secreted by the underlying epidermis and is cast off in the form of thin transparent spreads periodically.

Epidermis. The epidermis is a single-cell layer of hammer-shaped cells, some epidermal cells form several kinds of unicellular tubular and pear-shaped glands, the gland cells are sunk into the dermis, they secrete mucus which covers the body.

Epidermal glands. Several epidermal glands are found in the epidermis which are as follows:

1. Slime glands. These are distributed all over the body and secrete a slimy mucus that covers the whole body. These glands are either tubular or pear-shaped and sunken deep into the dermis. However, these glands are better developed on the dorsal surface than the ventral surface.

2. Sucker glands. These glands are distributed only in the suckers and are clustered. These are pear-shaped in the anterior sucker, while rounded or spherical in the posterior sucker. Their secretion smoothens the surface for locomotion.

3. Prostomial glands. These are found distributed only in the prostomium. These are pear-shaped and lie in groups. Their secretion forms plugs of the ootheca or egg-case.

4. Clitellar glands. These glands are found distributed only in the clitellar segments, *i.e.,* IX,X and XI. They become active only during the breeding season and are of two types : the chitogenous glands and the albumen glands. The secretion of chitogenous glands forms the wall of the ootheca, while albumen secreted by albumen glands is filled in the ootheca constituting the nourishment of the developing embryo. The chitogenous glands are situated between the circular and oblique muscles, while albumen glands lie in the longitudinal muscles in groups.

Dermis. Below the epidermis is a dermis made of connective tissue with muscle fibres, capillaries, fat and pigment cells. The glands lie in the dermis but open on the surface.

Musculature. The musculature below the dermis has a thin layer of circular muscles and a thicker layer of longitudinal muscles. The longitudinal muscles are powerfully developed and their fibres converge into the two suckers. Circular muscles are arranged concentrically in the suckers. Between the circular and longitudinal muscles leeches have an additional double layer of oblique muscles directed spirally around the body like a coil. There are also dorso-ventral muscles arranged segmentally throughout the body, they run from the dorsal to the ventral side in each segment. There are some radial muscles whose fibres radiate from the alimentary canal to the skin, they take the place of septa. The muscle fibres of leech have a characteristic structure, each fibre has an outer striated and contractile cortex or myoplasm, and an inner unmodified protoplasm called medulla or sarcoplasm.

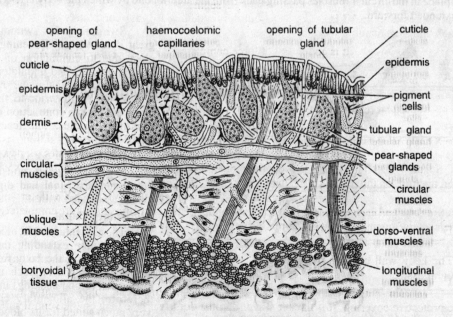

Fig. 67.4. *Hirudinaria.* T.S. of body wall.

Botryoidal tissue. The mesenchyme of leeches is a characteristic botryoidal tissue made of pigmented and richly vascularized cells which are large and arranged end to end, the cells contain a dark brown pigment and have intra-cellular branching capillaries filled with fluid. The botryoidal tissue is probably excretory, it almost completely fills the body cavity. Within the botryoidal tissue are two types of cells characteristic of leeches, they are fat cells and yellow cells. Fat cells contain fat droplets and some glycogen, yellow cells are filled with yellow, brown, or green granules, these cells appear to be excretory.

Functions of body wall. The body wall of leech performs the following functions :

1. It protects the internal delicate organs from mechanical injury.

2. The cuticle and slimy coat check evaporation and help in easy escape from the grip of enemies.

3. It is richly supplied with haemocoelomic capillaries, hence, respiratory in function.

4. It is sensory due to the presence of various types of receptors on it.

5. The gland cells present in the wall of prostomial segment secrete plugs of the ootheca.

6. The gland cells in the clitellar segments secrete ootheca and albumen ; albumen being the food of the developing embryo.

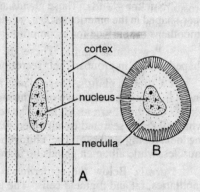

Fig. 67.5. *Hirudinaria*. A muscle fibre. A—L.S.; B—T.S.

LOCOMOTION

The leech has two types of locomotion, creeping, looping or crawling and swimming.

Creeping or crawling. In creeping the suckers are alternately fixed to the substratum and the body contracts and extends. When the anterior sucker is fixed, a wave of contraction takes place in the longitudinal muscles shortening the animal and moving the posterior sucker forward, by this the body contracts and is pulled forwards, then the posterior sucker is fixed and a wave of contraction takes place in the circular muscles passing back from the anterior end by which the body is lengthened and extended forward.

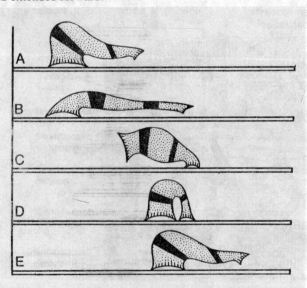

Fig. 67.6. *Hirudinaria*. Stages in locomotion.

Swimming. In swimming a great dorso-ventral flattening takes place due to contraction of dorso-ventral muscles and undulatory waves pass in a vertical plane over the body from the anterior to the posterior end due to contraction of longitudinal muscles. The leech is a swift swimmer.

DIGESTIVE SYSTEM

Digestive system consists of the alimentary canal and digestive glands associated with it.

Alimentary Canal

The alimentary canal of leech is a straight tube extending throughout the length of the body from the mouth to the anus. Leech is sanguivorous (blood-sucking) in habit, therefore, the alimentary canal is very much suited for its blood sucking habit as the most portion of the alimentary canal serves to store uncoaguolated blood, while only a small portion serves for its digestion and absorption. The alimentary canal consists of the stomodaeum (lined with ectodermal epithelium and covered by cuticle), the mesenteron (lined with endodermal epithelium and no cuticle covering) and the proctodaeum (lined with ectodermal epithelium and covered by cuticle).

1. Stomodaeum. It consists of preoral chamber, buccal cavity and pharynx.

(i) Pre-oral chamber. It is a cup-shaped depression on the ventral side of the anterior sucker. At the base of the pre-oral chamber lies the **tri-radiate mouth** guarded by the **velum,** which forms an almost complete partition between the pre-oral chamber in front and the buccal cavity behind. The prostomium and the first four segments of the body form the roof of the pre-oral chamber, while the circular rim of the sucker forms its outer boundary.

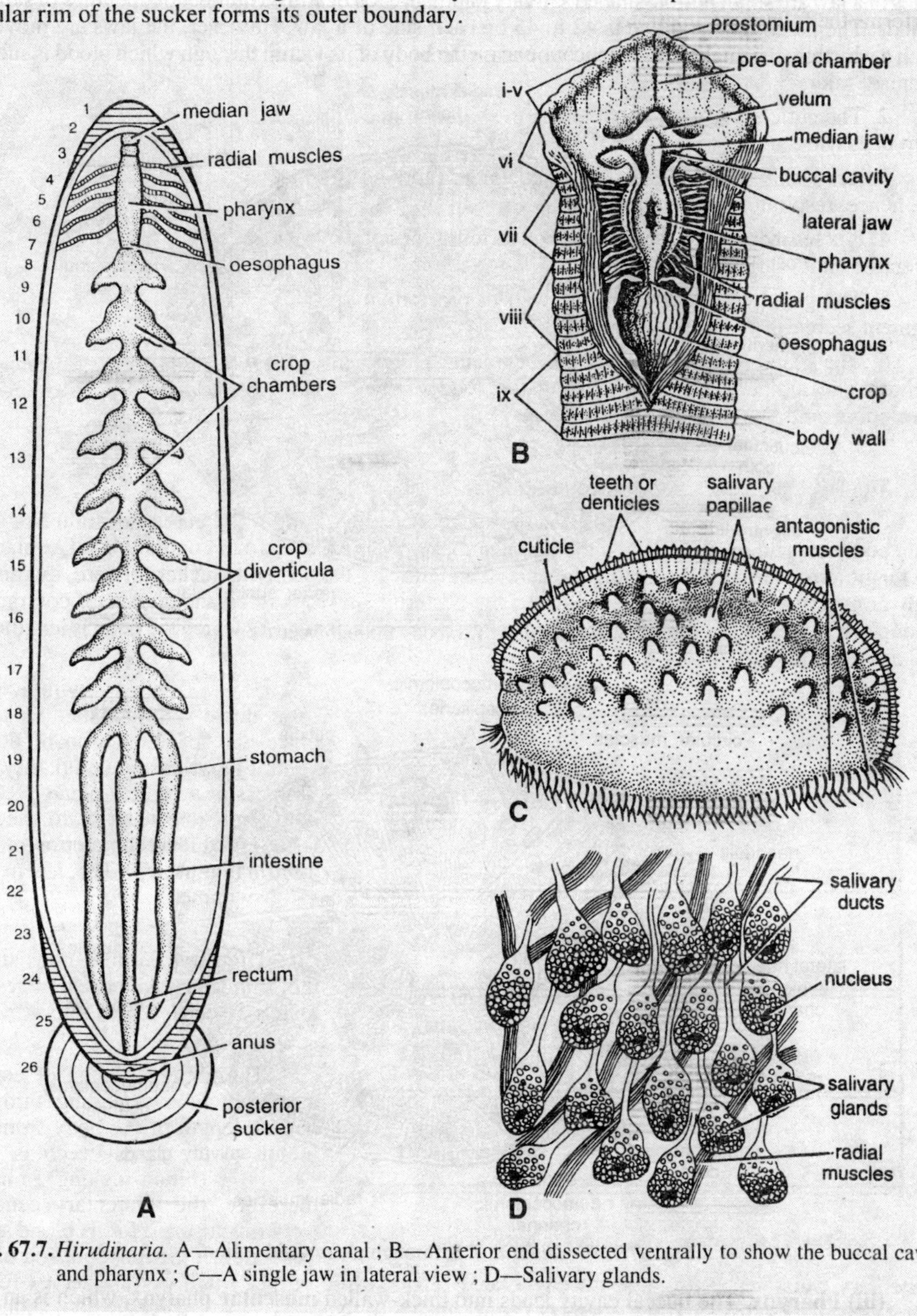

Fig. 67.7. *Hirudinaria.* A—Alimentary canal ; B—Anterior end dissected ventrally to show the buccal cavity and pharynx ; C—A single jaw in lateral view ; D—Salivary glands.

(ii) Buccal cavity. The triradiate mouth leads into very short chamber, the buccal cavity. In the mucous membrane of buccal cavity are embedded three crescentic **jaws,** one mid-dorsal and the other two are ventro-lateral in position. Each jaw is a laterally compressed cushion, covered with a fine cuticle which is thickened at the free edge to form a dentigerous ridge bearing a row of minute teeth (denticles). As these teeth form a single series on each jaw, the jaw is termed as monostichodont. The median jaw bears 103 to 128 teeth, while the lateral jaws bear 85 to 115 teeth each. On both the sides of a jaw are small button-shaped salivary papillae, each bearing a number of openings of salivary glands. The number of papillae is 42 to 45 on each side of a jaw. However, the jaws are moved in such a way that they make a Y-shaped wound on the body of its victim through which blood is sucked.

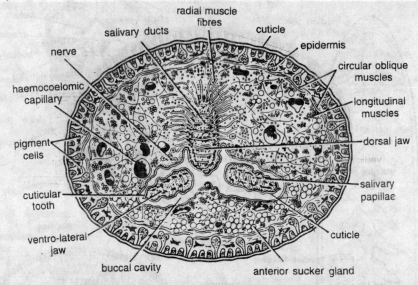

Fig. 67.8. *Hirudinaria.* T.S. body through buccal cavity.

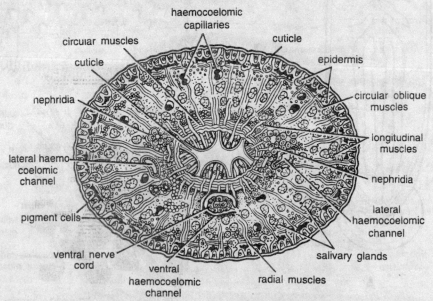

Fig. 67.9. *Hirudinaria.* T.S. through pharyngeal region.

(iii) Pharynx. The buccal cavity leads into thick-walled muscular pharynx, which is an oval sac running from the fifth to the eighth segment. The lumen of the pharynx varies in outline in different regions. The muscles of the pharynx are circular and radial which join the pharyngeal wall to the body wall; radial muscles dilate the pharynx producing a pump-like action for sucking blood. Large masses of unicellular pyriform salivary glands surround the pharynx, their ducts open between the teeth of jaws. The secretion of salivary glands contains a substance called hirudin or anticoagulin which prevents the coagulation of blood of the host when the leech is sucking.

2. Mesenteron. The mesenteron consists of oesophagus, crop, stomach and intestine.

(i) Oesophagus. It is a short narrow tube, through which the pharynx leads into the crop. The lumen of oesophagus is very narrow and its epithelial lining is produced into numerous folds.

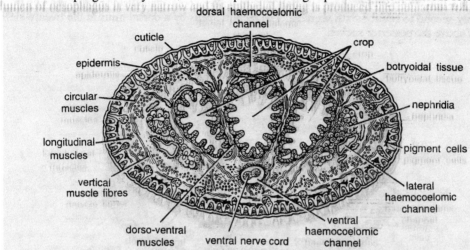

Fig. 67.10. *Hirudinaria.* T.S. body through crop and its diverticula.

(ii) Crop. The crop is the largest region of the alimentary canal extending from the ninth to the eighteenth segment. It has ten thin-walled chambers, one in each segment and they are connected with one another by more or less circular apertures surrounded by sphincters. Each chamber consists of a small anterior and a broad posterior part which is produced into a pair of lateral outgrowths, the caeca. The chambers and the caeca go on gradually increasing in size towards the posterior side. The last chamber of the crop is the largest and its caeca are prolonged backwards up to the twenty-second segment. The crop and its caeca are greatly extensible and used for storing blood, one cropful of blood lasts for several months and digested slowly.

(iii) Stomach. It is a small heart-shaped structure lying in the nineteenth segment. The opening of crop into the stomach is narrow having sphincter muscles which regulate the flow of food. The stomach has both secretory and absorptive epithelial cells and its inner lining is produced into numerous transverse folds which anastomose with one another.

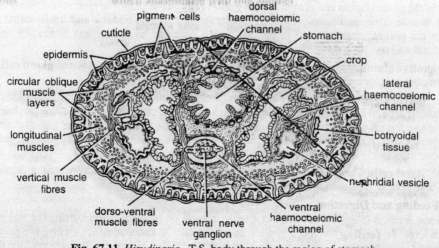

Fig. 67.11. *Hirudinaria.* T.S. body through the region of stomach.

(iv) Intestine. The stomach leads into the intestine which is not clearly differentiated externally from the stomach. The intestine is a thin-walled, straight and narrow tube extending from the nineteenth to twenty-second segment. Its inner lining is thrown into numerous longitudinal and transverse folds resembling the spiral villi to increase the absorptive surface.

3. Proctodaeum. Proctodaeum consists of rectum only.

(i) Rectum. The intestine opens into a short, thin-walled somewhat ciliated rectum running from the twenty-second to twenty-sixth segment. The rectum opens by a dorsal anus in the twenty-sixth segment above the posterior sucker.

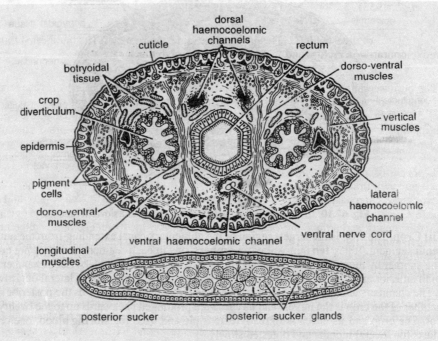

Fig. 67.12. *Hirudinaria.* T.S. body through rectum and posterior sucker.

Histology of alimentary canal. Histologically, the wall of alimentary canal is made of a layer of columnar epithelium resting on a basement membrane layer which is followed by the layer of connective tissue. The epithelial layer of stomodaeum and proctodaeum is lined by cuticle; it is ciliated in the proctodaeum and provided with goblet cells in the crop. The connective tissue contains circular muscle fibres and haemocoelomic capillaries, it contains circular and longitudinal muscle fibres in the preoral chamber and in the pharynx it contains all the muscle fibres, *i.e.,* circular, longitudinal and radial.

Digestive glands. These include the salivary glands and some other isolated gland cells found in the mucous membrane of the gut wall.

A. Salivary glands. As mentioned earlier, these are unicellular, pyriform, glandular mass of cells situated around and behind the pharynx. Each glandular cell has elongated fine ductule which finally enters the jaws to open in raised salivary papillae. The secretion of these glands contains an anticoagulant substance called hirudin; hirudin prevents coagulation of blood so that the leech can suck blood effectively and for longer duration to fill up its crop and caeca.

B. Gland cells. These are in the form of goblet cells, found scattered throughout the lining of crop. These secrete mucus in the crop.

Food, Feeding and Digestion

Since, leech is sanguivorous in habit, hence, it feeds on blood of cattle visiting the water source where it lives. In feeding the leech applies its oral sucker to the skin of its victim, the jaws move towards and away from each other, they painlessly puncture the skin, pump-like action of the pharynx sucks in large quantities of blood to fill the crop, secretion of hirudin prevents coagulation of blood. In the crop, the blood is haemolysed in which corpuscles burst, haemoglobin gets dissolved in the plasma and the blood becomes dark red ; this blood passes slowly through the sphincter aperture into the stomach where it turns green and is digested, but the haemoglobin of ingested blood is absorbed directly by the cells of the stomach, it is the globin of ingested blood which is mainly used as food. However, the process of digestion is very slow; a cropful of blood takes ten to fourteen months for complete digestion.

Abderhalden and Heise (1909) found a peptolytic ferment which hydrolyses proteins in an alkaline medium. However, digestion has been reported to occur entirely by gut bacteria in *Hirudo* (Busing *et al.*, 1953).

Absorption and Egestion

Absorption of digested food takes place in intestine and stomach. The undigested food, if any, is stored temporarily in rectum and egestion occurs through the anus.

COELOM

The perivisceral coelom of general annelids has been lost in leeches, it is invaded and almost obliterated by botryoidal tissue, what is left is reduced to four intercommunicating haemocoelomic channels, their branches and some coelomic sinuses. The haemocoelomic channels are dorsal and ventral channels with thin walls, and two lateral channels which have acquired muscular walls secondarily. All four longitudinal channels are lined with coelomic epithelium. The haemocoelomic channels have many branches, the most prominent are those of the ventral channel which form bag-like swellings enclosing ciliated organs, these swellings are perinephrostomial ampullae. All channels and their branches contain red haemocoelomic fluid, because of this the channels are called haemocoelomic channels and not blood vessels, their fluid is not blood, but coelomic fluid coloured red due to dissolved haemoglobin. Coelomic sinuses are spaces within testes sacs and ovisacs which enclose the gonads, and around the vasa deferentia. They are lined with coelomic epithelium which gives rise to gonads, they contain colourless coelomic fluid with no haemoglobin, suggesting the fact that the coelomic sinuses are remnant of original coelom and they separate very early before haemoglobin develops in the coelomic fluid.

HAEMOCOELOMIC SYSTEM

There is no true blood vascular system and the coelomic space and fluid have been modified to form the circulatory system, it consists of much-reduced coelom containing red coelomic fluid with haemoglobin in solution and colourless amoeboid corpuscles. This system is spoken of as a haemocoelomic system, and the red coelomic fluid as a haemocoelomic fluid, the channels in which it flows are called haemocoelomic channels.

The haemocoelomic system consists of four longitudinal haemocoelomic channels, their branches, and some networks formed by capillaries. The longitudinal haemocoelomic channels are one dorsal channel, one ventral channel, and two lateral channels. The haemocoelomic fluid flows from posterior to anterior side in the dorsal and lateral channels, and it flows from the anterior to posterior side in the ventral channel. All four channels are joined to each other in the posterior region. The dorsal and ventral channels are distributing channels, the lateral channels are both distributing and collecting channels.

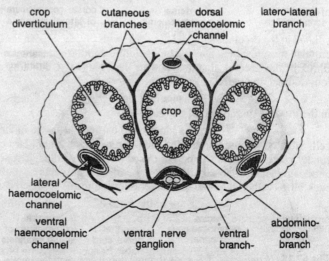

Fig. 67.13. *Hirudinaria*. T.S. body through dorso-abdominal branches.

Longitudinal Channels and their Branches

Dorsal channel. The dorsal channel runs mid-dorsally below the body wall and above the alimentary canal. It has a thin wall, which is non-contractile being made of eonnective tissue and coelomic epithelium. In each segment the dorsal channel gives off two pairs of **dorso-laterals** taking the haemocoelomic fluid to the dorsal and dorso-lateral regions of body wall and several **dorso-intestinals** going to the alimentary canal. The dorsal channel bifurcates in the twenty-second segment and these two branches join the ventral channel posteriorly. Anteriorly the dorsal channel forms a network above the alimentary canal from the sixth to the first segment. In the dorsal channel there is no valve and haémocoelomic fluid flows **behind forwards.**

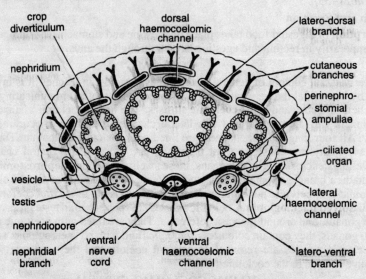

Fig. 67.14. *Hirudinaria.* T.S. body through nephridial branches.

2. Ventral channel. The ventral channel, like the dorsal channel, has non-contractile thin wall being made of connective tissue and coelomic epithelium. It lies mid-ventrally below the alimentary canal extending from the anterior to the posterior end. It is broad and encloses the central nervous system within it. It gives off two pairs of branches in each segment, the **first branch** or **cutaneous branch** divides on each side into two branches, a **ventral branch** going to the ventral body wall, and an **abdomino-dorsal** branch which passes vertically upwards to the dorsal body wall. The **second branch** of the ventral channel in each segment is a pair of **nephridial branches**, each nephridial branch runs outwards and enlarges into a **perinephrostomial ampulla** which encloses the ciliated organ. The nephridial branch is found only in eleven segments which contain testes, these branches take the haemo- coelomic fluid to nephridia, body wall and ciliated organs around which they form bag-like perinephrostomial

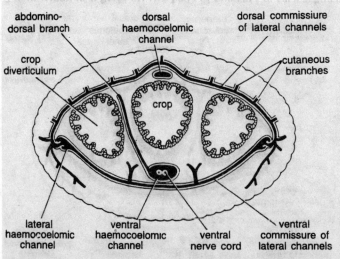

Fig. 67.15. *Hirudinaria.* T.S. body through dorsal and ventral commissures of the lateral haemocoelomic channels.

ampullae. Like dorsal channel, the ventral channel has no valve but haemocoelomic fluid flows from anterior to posterior side of the body.

3. Lateral channels. The lateral channels run symmetrically one on each side of the alimentary canal. They are large in diameter and become even larger in the posterior third of the body. The lateral channels have contractile muscular walls and they contain valves which allows the haemocoelomic fluid to flow from behind forwards only. A lateral channel gives out one branch and receives two branches in each segment. It gives out a latero-ventral branch which bifurcates into an anterior and a posterior branch and each joins its fellow of the opposite side mid-ventrally to form a rhomboidal swelling, *i.e.,* ventral commissure of laterals in each segment, then they take the haemocoelomic fluid to the alimentary canal, nephridia and reproductive organs. Each lateral channel receives a latero-lateral branch in each segment from the skin and nephridium of its side, and a latero-dorsal branch from the skin and the viscera ; the latero-dorsals of both lateral channels are connected together dorsally above the dorsal channel by dorsal commissure of the laterals, Thus, the branches of the lateral channels supply the haemocoelomic fluid to the skin, nephridia, reproductive organs, alimentary canal and lower body wall ; and they collect the haemocoelomic fluid from all parts, *i.e.,* from upper and lower body wall, skin, alimentary canal, nephridia and reproductive organs. Anteriorly the lateral channels break up into capallaries in fifth segment, and posteriorly they join the ventral channel.

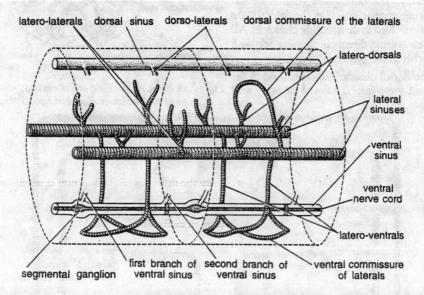

Fig. 67.16. *Hirudinaria.* Diagrammatic representation of the haemocoelomic system of two segments.

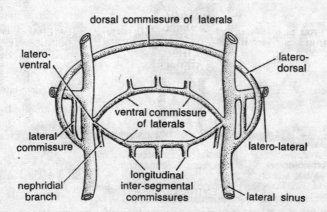

Fig. 67.17. *Hirudinaria.* Diagrammatic representation of the lateral channels and their branches in a segment.

Capillary System

The four channels not only communicate with each other but they form capillaries in the skin, muscles and botryoidal tissue. This **capillary system** has three main sets, a set of botryoidal capillaries forming a network in the botryoidal tissue. This condition of communication with capillaries of botryoidal tissue is unique, it may be compared to vertebrates in which the lymphatic system communicates both with the coelom and the blood system. The second part of the capillary system is an intra-muscular set of capillaries in the muscles. The third is a set of cutaneous capillaries in skin.

Course of Blood Circulation

Of the four longitudinal channels, the fluid in the dorsal and two lateral channels moves from behind forwards, while in the ventral it runs from anterior to posterior end of the body. The dorsal and ventral are the distributing channels, while the laterals are collecting as well as distributing channels. All the channels are in direct communication with one another at the posterior end.

The dorsal channel supplies fluid to the dorsal and dorso-lateral parts of the body wall

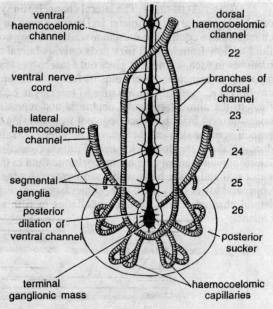

Fig. 67.18. *Hirudinaria.* Hind end of the body showing union of the four longitudinal haemocoelomic channels.

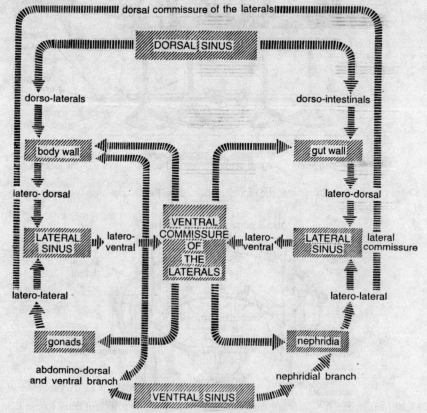

Fig. 67.19. *Hirudinaria.* Diagrammatic representation of the course of blood circulation.

and the entire alimentary canal, from where it is collected by latero-dorsals, which carry the fluid to the lateral channels.

The ventral channel supplies the fluid to the ventral, ventro-lateral and median dorsal region of the body wall, ciliated organs, nephridia and the atrium. From all these parts the fluid is collected by the latero-lateral branches of the lateral channels.

Lateral channels supply the fluid to the nephridia, genital organs, gut and ventral body wall through the latero-ventrals and is collected back through the latero-lateral and latero-dorsal branches.

RESPIRATORY SYSTEM

There are no special respiratory organs in *Hirudinaria*. In addition to its primary role of a protective covering, the skin also serves a respiratory function. It is provided with a rich supply of haemocoelomic fluid in an extensive system of capillaries and capillary loops, which penetrate into the spaces between the inner ends of the epidermal cells. The epidermis acts as a permeable membrane through which the CO_2 of the haemocoelomic fluid in the capillary loops is exchanged for the O_2 dissolved in water. Leeches live in water or in damp soil, and, thus, the skin is always kept wet by the surrounding water, while the mucus secreted by the epidermal slime glands also prevents it from drying on exposure to the atmosphere.

EXCRETORY SYSTEM

The excretory system (Fig. 67.27) consists of segmentally arranged seventeen pairs of nephridia lying in segments from sixth to twenty-second. The first six pairs of nephridia are situated

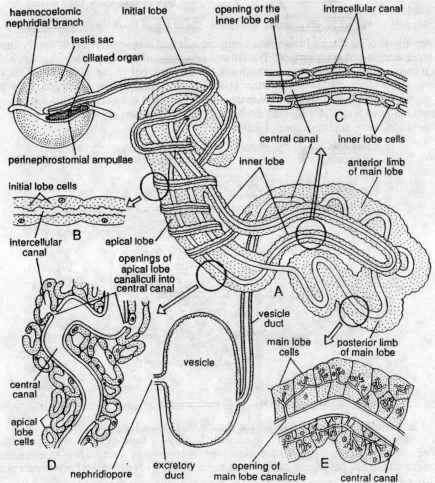

Fig. 67.20.*Hirudinaria.* A—A complete testicular nephridium ; B—A portion of initial lobe in L.S.; C—A portion of inner lobe in L.S. ; D—A portion of apical lobe in L.S. ; E—A portion of main lobe in L.S.

in the pre-testicular segments (sixth to eleventh), while the remaining eleven pairs are situated in the testicular segments (twelfth to twenty-second). The nephridia lying in the pre-testicular segments and the testicular segments are termed pre-testicular and testicular nephridia respectively.

Testicular nephridium. A typical testicular nephridium (Fig. 67.20) has a horse-shoe-shaped structure. Beginning with the inner coelomic end a typical testicular nephridium consists of six parts, *viz.,* (i) ciliated organ, (ii) initial lobe, (iii) apical lobe, (iv) main lobe, (v) inner lobe, and (vi) vesicle-duct and the vesicle.

(i) Ciliated organ. A ciliated organ is completely enclosed within the perinephrostomial ampullae which is a dilation of the haemocoelomic system. A ciliated organ has a central reservoir which is perforated, around which are innumerable ciliated funnels. The reservoir is a more or less spongy structure with an outer wall formed of single layer of cells and a central mass consisting of connective tissue cells which manufacture corpuscles. Each ciliated funnel is like an ear-lobe, with

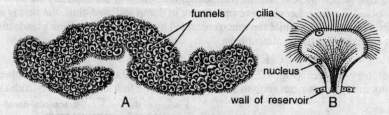

Fig. 67.21. *Hirudinaria.* A—Entire ciliated organ; B—A single funnel.

about one-fourth of its margin incomplete along one side and is covered with outwardly directed cilia on its outer margin and inner surface. The ciliated organ manufactures coelomic amoeboid corpuscles. Ciliated organs are joined to nephridia in the embryo, but in the adult animal they have no connection with nephridia. This shows that originally the ciliated organ belonged to a nephridium, but in the adult having no connection with the nephridium. It is not excretory but has become a part of haemocoelomic system for making corpuscles. Ciliated organs correspond to coelomoducts of Polychaeta and not to nephrostomes of nephridia.

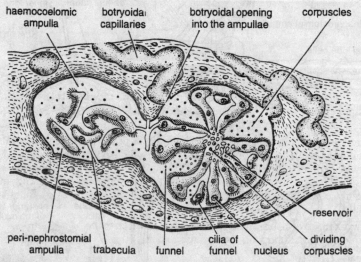

Fig. 67.22. *Hirudinaria.* T.S. through the ciliated organ enclosed within perinephrostomial ampullae.

(ii) Initial lobe. The initial lobe or the testicular lobe is a long and slender cord-like structure which twines around the apical lobe, then ends blindly in front close to the perinephrostomial ampullae and its posterior end joins the main lobe. It consists of a single row of elongated hollow cells placed end to end having the intracellular canal which gives off several diverticula in each cell.

(iii) Apical lobe. The posterior limbs of the main lobe pass forward to form a stout lobe, the apical lobe, which lies in the antero-posterior position beneath the gut. The apical lobe is fairly stout and its anterior end is bent on itself like the handle of a walking stick. The cells of the apical lobe are much larger than those of the initial lobe and are traversed by numerous regular intracellular canals.

(iv) **Main lobe.** The main lobe, forming the horse-shoe proper, lies in a ventro-lateral position between the adjacent diverticula of the crop. It consists of two unequal limbs, one longer and anterior in position, and the other smaller and posterior. The cells of the main lobe are the largest in the nephridium and are polyhedral in shape.

(v) **Inner lobe.** The inner lobe is narrow and lies all along the inner concavity of the main lobe and also runs forwards along the outer border of the apical lobe for about half of its length. Its cells are long and tubular, the lumen in each cell is very large and makes a big excavation in the cell, cytoplasm contains a small nucleus.

(vi) **Vesicle duct and vesicle.** From the lower end of the anterior limits of main lobe arises a thin vesicle duct which passes over and joins a large thin-walled oval bag called vesicle or bladder. Bhatia (1940) has described that the lining of bladder is ciliated but a later worker B. Dev is of the view that the so called cilia are nephridial microflora consisting of non-motile bacteria ranging from 2.8 μ to 7 μ in length. From the vesicle emerges a short excretory duct which opens externally by a rounded aperture, the nephridiopore in the last annulus of the segment in which the nephridium lies.

A nephridium is made of a cord of cells, the initial lobe has no canal but an intercellular ciliated canal starts from the apical lobe, goes into the inner lobe, then passes through the main lobe to enter the vesicle duct.

Pre-testicular nephridia. The first six pairs of nephridia, called pre-testicular nephridia, resemble the testicular nephridia in structure; but they lie in the segments from sixth to eleventh in which testis sacs, perinephrostomial ampullae, and ciliated organs are absent. The initial lobes of these nephridia end loosely in the general connective tissue on either side of the ventral nerve cord.

Central canal of nephridium. As mentioned, the cells of initial lobe, apical lobe and inner lobe possess intracellular canals, all these open into a central canal originating from the anterior part of apical lobe. The central canal is, thus, a long continuous passageway traversing through the different lobes of nephridium and finally enters the vesicle duct near anterior limb of the main lobe. Thus, this canal carries the excretory products secreted by the glandular cell masses of the nephridium and finally discharges into the vesicle through vesicle duct.

Physiology of Excretion

The ciliated organ is completely separated from the nephridium in the adult. It has no excretory function but manufactures coelomic corpuscles of the haemocoelomic system. The nephridium proper is truly excretory in function and serves to eliminate excess of water and nitrogenous waste. Nitrogenous waste consists mainly of ammonia and small quantities of urea, hence, leech is ammonotelic. Nephridia act as excretory as well as osmoregulatory organs. The nephridium is richly supplied with branches of haemocoelomic channels and the gland cells separate waste products from the haemocoelomic fluid. The excretory fluid is finally collected in the vesicle of nephridium to be discharged through the nephridiopore.

As referred to, nephridium is also osmoregulatory in function because it is related to maintain water balance in the body ; the osmotic pressure of body fluid is always higher than the surrounding water, hence, water enters its body continuously. The nephridia, however, removes excess water. The leeches are also said to possess a special mechanism in their epidermis for taking in Na and Cl ions to compensate those lost in the metabolism. This helps in maintaining a constancy in the body fluid osmotic pressure.

Several workers have also assigned an excretory function to the botryoidal tissue, the capillaries of which are in communication with the haemocoelomic fluid.

NERVOUS SYSTEM

The nervous system is of usual annelidan type except there is a fusion of ganglia at the anterior and posterior ends. It consists of three parts : (1) central nervous system, (2) peripheral nervous system, and (3) sympathetic nervous system.

1. **Central nervous system.** The central nervous system consists of five parts, *viz.,* (i) a pair of cerebral ganglia, (ii) a pair of peri-pharyngeal connectives, (iii) a sub-pharyngeal ganglionic mass, (iv) a ventral nerve cord, and (v) terminal ganglionic mass. The entire central nervous system is enclosed within the ventral haemocoelomic channel.

A pair of fused cerebral ganglia or supra-pharyngeal ganglia form a small brain above the pharynx in the fifth segment. The brain has shifted back due to a reduction in size of prostomium. From the brain, peri-pharyngeal connectives (one on either side of the pharynx) arise and join a sub-pharyngeal ganglionic mass lying below the pharynx in the fifth segment, this is formed by fusion of four pairs of ganglia. Thus, the cerebral ganglia and sub-pharyngeal ganglionic mass represent the ganglia of first five segments of the body.

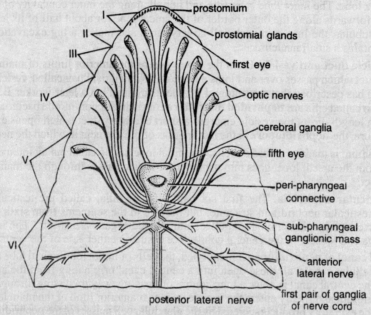

Fig. 67.23. *Hirudinaria.* Nervous system in the first six segments.

A double ventral nerve cord, being covered in a protective sheath called neurilemma, runs along the mid-ventral line, from the sub-pharyngeal ganglionic mass to the terminal ganglionic mass lying within the posterior sucker. It has twenty-one double ganglia, each lying within the first annulus of its own somite, from the sixth to the twenty-sixth segment.

The terminal ganglionic mass is a large ovoid body composed of seven pairs of ganglia fused together, each pair belonging to a segment of the sucker.

2. Peripheral nervous system. It consists of paired nerves given off from the various ganglia of the central nervous system, which innervate all parts of the body.

A pair of stout nerves arises from the brain which runs forward to supply the first pair of eyes, the prostomium and the roof of the buccal chamber. The subpharyngeal ganglionic mass gives out four pairs of nerves which go to the second, third, fourth and fifth pairs of eyes and also to segmental receptors of the first five segments, roof of the buccal cavity and the muscles of body wall. From each ganglion of ventral nerve cord arise two pairs of stout nerves, the anterior laterals and posterior laterals. The anterior laterals arise from the anterior part of the ganglion, branch and innervate the vas deferens, nephridium, the nephridial vesicle, muscles of body wall, ventral nerve receptors and two outer dorsal receptors of their own side. The posterior laterals arise from the posterior part of the ganglion just behind the anterior laterals. The posterior laterals branch and innervate the viscera, median dorsal region of body wall and the central pair of the dorsal segmental receptors. The terminal ganglionic mass sends off several nerves supplying the receptor organs and other structures found within the posterior sucker.

3. Sympathetic nervous system. It forms extensive nerve plexuses beneath the epidermis, within the muscle layers of body wall and on the wall of the alimentary canal. It is connected, on the one hand, with certain cells on both sides of the peripharyngeal connectives and, on the other, with multipolar ganglion cells, irregularly distributed over the entire alimentary nerve plexus.

SENSE ORGANS

The sense organs or receptors of leech consist of specially modified epidermal cells. There are four types of receptors : (i) free nerve endings (ii) annular receptors, (iii) segmental receptors, and (iv) eyes.

(i) **Free nerve endings.** The free nerve endings are found all over the body, between the epidermal cells, with their ganglion cells lying beneath the epidermis. They are probably **chemoreceptors.**

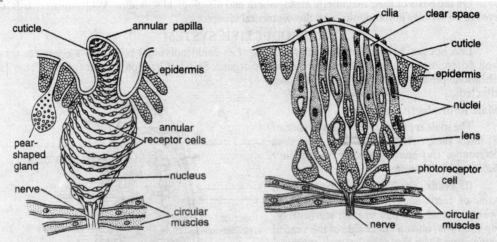

Fig. 67.24. *Hirudinaria.* V.S. of an annular receptor.   **Fig. 67.25.** *Hirudinaria.* V.S. of a dorsal segmental receptor.

(ii) **Annular receptors.** These are arranged in a line across the middle of each annulus of a segment. Each annulus of the body bears 36 very minute annular receptors, 18 on the dorsal side and 18 on the ventral side. Each receptor projects as a small papilla and consists of many flat overlapping cells which receive nerve fibres from the lateral branches. Annular receptors are **tactile organs** or **tangoreceptors.**

(iii) **Segmental receptors.** These are small whitish patches elevated on the elliptical papillae borne upon the first annulus of every body segment. They lie in four pairs on the dorsal surface and three pairs on the ventral surface in each segment. Each receptor consists of a group of long slender cells, 10 to 15 in number which are separated from one another by clear spaces. There are 5 to 10 long, slender tactile cells, separated from one another and provided with five hair-like processes at their outer free ends. The photoreceptor or light perceiving cells, found only in the dorsal receptors, contain a crescentic hyaline substance, the **optic organelle** or lens, in their cytoplasm. Each receptor receives a nerve branch from one of the lateral nerves and functions as **tangoreceptors** and **photoreceptors.**

(iv) **Eyes.** There are five pairs of eyes lying in a semicircle of black spots on the dorsal surface of the anterior sucker, one pair in the first annulus of each of the first five segments. Each eye is cylindrical or cup-like in shape with its long axis perpendicular to the body surface. Each eye consists of a long pigmented cup covered externally by transparent epidermis and cuticle forming a cornea. Inside the cup are refractive

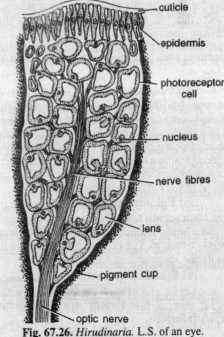

Fig. 67.26. *Hirudinaria.* L.S. of an eye.

cells arranged in several longitudinal rows. Each refractive cell contains a crescentic hyaline substance, the optic organellae or lens surrounded by a very thin peripheral layer of cytoplasm containing a small rounded nucleus. An optic nerve enters each eye basally and runs along its median axis distributing branches to all photoreceptor cells. All the eyes are not of equal size ; the first and second pairs are the largest, while the remaining pairs are comparatively smaller in size, the fifth pair being the smallest. The eyes are differently directed and each eye can receive the light only from one direction. It is not known whether the eyes are able to form images of external objects ; probably they can distinguish light from darkness and enable the leech to locate the direction of the source of light.

On the basis of their metameric arrangement and histological structure, Whiteman regards the eyes to be serially homologous with the segmental receptors.

<h1 style="text-align:center">REPRODUCTIVE SYSTEM</h1>

Leeches are hermaphrodite (monoecious), *i.e.,* each individual possesses a complete set of well differentiated male and female reproductive organs. Self-fertilization does not occur. Cross-fertilization, preceded by copulation, is being effected.

Male Reproductive Organs

The male reproductive organs consist of (i) testis sacs, (ii) vasa efferentia, (iii) vasa deferentia, (iv) epididymes, (v) ejaculatory ducts, and (vi) atrium.

(i) Testis sacs. There are usually eleven pairs of testis sacs in segment twelfth to twenty-second, one pair in each segment, lying ventrally, one on either side of the ventral nerve cord. Each testis sac is small spherical coelomic sac, from the walls of which spermatogonia or sperm-mother cells are budded off. The spermatogonia float in the coelomic fluid within each testis-sac and develop into spermatozoa.

(ii) Vasa efferentia. From the posterior border of each testis-sac arises a short sinuous duct, the vas efferens, through which the mature spermatozoa are passed into the vas deferens. All the vasa efferentia of one side open into the common vas deferens of that side.

(iii) Vasa deferentia. They are a pair of slender longitudinal ducts running forward, from twenty-second to the eleventh segment, lying along the ventral body wall on either side of nerve cord. Each vas deferens is enclosed within a tubular coelomic space which contains amoeboid corpuscles similar to those of the haemocoelomic fluid.

(iv) Epididymes. Each vas deferens, in the tenth segment, swells to form closely convoluted and compact mass, the epididymis or sperm-vesicle. The two epididymes serve to store the spermatozoa.

(v) Ejaculatory ducts. From the inner and anterior end of each epididymis arises a short narrow ejaculatory duct or ductus ejaculatorious.

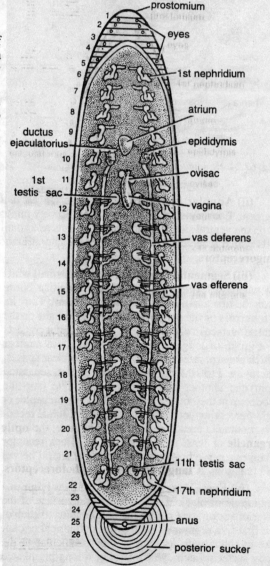

Fig. 67.27.*Hirudinaria.* Reproductive and nephridial system.

(vi) **Atrium.** It is a pyriform sac situated in the ninth and tenth segments, to which join the ejaculatory ducts of both the sides. The atrium is made of an anterior prostate chamber and a posterior penis sac. The prostate chamber possesses thick muscular walls covered over with several layers of unicellular prostate glands. The penis-sac is an elongated muscular chamber and contains a tubular coiled penis which can be everted and is often seen protruding out through the male genital aperture on the ventral side of the second annulus of tenth segment.

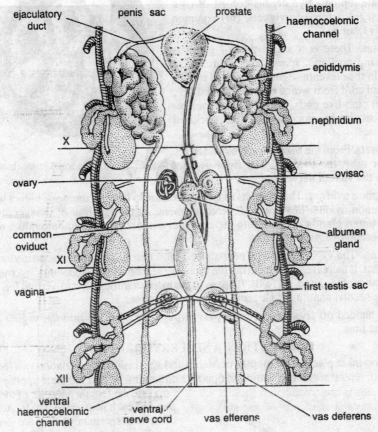

Fig. 67.28. *Hirudinaria.* Reprodctive organs of X, XI and XII segments of body.

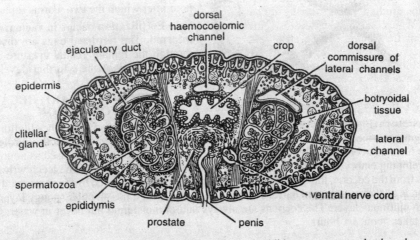

Fig. 67.29. *Hirudinaria.* T. S. of body through the region of epididymes , prostate glands and penis-sac.

The spermatozoa produced in testis-sacs are stored in the epididymes. From the epididymis of each side the spermatozoa pass into the prostatic chamber where they are glued together by a secretion of the prostate glands to form bundles called spermatophores. The spermatophores pass into the narrow canal of the penis, through which they are transferred into vagina of other leech during copulation.

Female Reproductive Organs

The female reproductive organs consist of (i) a pair of ovisacs, (ii) a pair of oviducts, (iii) common oviduct, and (iv) vagina.

(i) Ovisacs. There is a single pair of globular ovisacs enclosing coelomic spaces and an ovary in each, situated in the eleventh segment. Each ovary is a coiled nucleated cord from which ova are budded off ; it terminates in club-like ends. The coiled ovaries remain floating in the haemocoelomic fluid enclosed within the ovisacs.

(ii) Oviducts. From the base of each ovisac arises a short slender tube, the oviduct. The right oviduct passes beneath the ventral nerve cord.

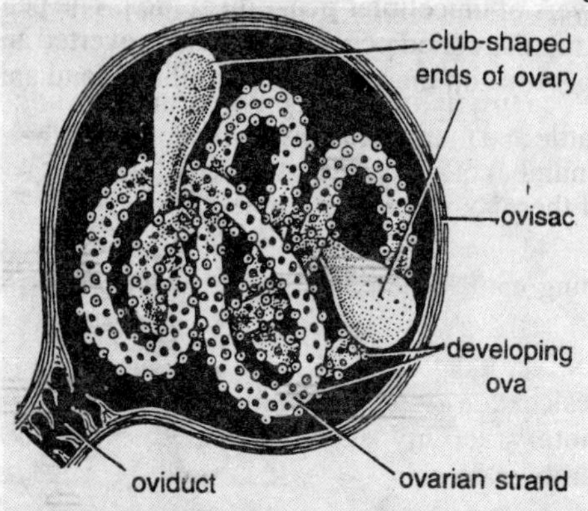

Fig. 67.30. *Hirudinaria.* Ovisac dissected to show the ovary.

(iii) Common oviduct. The oviducts of two sides unite to form a common oviduct which is like an S. The common oviduct lies in the eleventh segment. At the junction of oviducts is a mass of unicellular albumen glands opening into the common oviduct. The common oviduct opens into a pear-shaped muscular vagina.

(iv) Vagina. The vagina is a large pear-shaped muscular bag lying in the posterior part of the eleventh segment. It increases in size during the breeding season and also becomes internally thrown into a large number of longitudinal folds. It opens to the exterior through a mid-ventral female genital aperture in the second annulus of eleventh segment.

The ova, budded off from the ovaries, pass through the oviducts into the vagina where they remain for some time.

COPULATION AND FERTILIZATION

Copulation takes place in the months of March and April ; during copulation two leeches come together by their ventral surfaces pointing in opposite directions, so that the male aperture of each is opposite the female aperture of the other. The penis of each is inserted into the vagina of the other and spermatophores are deposited, so that there is mutual insemination. Copulation may occur on land or in water, it lasts for an hour after which the two worms separate.

Fertilization occurs in vagina, *i.e.,* it is internal. The fertilized eggs are discharged through the female genital aperture into the cocoon (ootheca)where further development occurs.

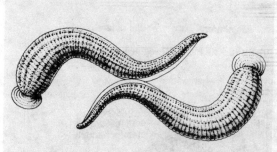

Fig. 67.31. *Hirudinaria.* Two leeches in copulation.

COCOON OR OOTHECA FORMATION

The cocoons (Fig. 67.32)of *Hirudinaria* are formed in April, May and June. The clitellum forms around segments nine to eleven during breeding season, its glands secrete a frothy girdle which hardens to form a cocoon, the clitellar glands secrete albumen into the cocoon used as nourishment by the developing embryo. The fertilized eggs are extruded into the cocoon. The leech wriggles out backwards from the cocoon, the two ends are closed by polar plugs secreted by the prostomial glands. The cocoon is an amber-coloured barrel 30 mm × 15 mm in size. It has an outer spongy layer and an inner tough chitinous layer. The cocoons are always laid in moist mud but never in water. Cocoon formation takes about six hours.

DEVELOPMENT

Development of young proceeds within the cocoon. In each cocoon one to twenty-four embryos develop and swim in the cocoon feeding on albumen, they finally escape from the cocoon. Development is direct, there is no larva, and it is completed in about fourteen days.

PARASITIC ADAPTATIONS IN *HIRUDINARIA*

Hirudinaria, the common Indian cattle leech, leads a parasitic life as it feeds on the blood of cattle and man. For parasitic mode of life, there are a number of adaptive features in it. However, some of these features are as under :

1. Its long, flattened , limbless swift swimming nature and slimy body is well suited for its aquatic life.

2. Its slimy body covering protects it from desiccation ; reduces friction in water during locomotory activity and also facilitates respiration through the skin.

3. Its preference to live in shallow waters of the pond, tank, lake and stream ensures food as the cattles and man frequently visit these water reservoirs for drinking or bathing. It also provides concealment under weeds, logs and stones lying at the bank of these water reservoirs.

4. Anterior and posterior suckers are the organ of attachment ; particularly posterior sucker is much more powerful and muscular.

5. Since it is sanguivorous in habit, hence, it must attach itself to the body of the host. So, its suckers help in doing so.

6. It possesses denticulated jaws in the buccal cavity ; the jaws make wounds on the body of victim so that victim's blood vessels are exposed and blood starts oozing out.

7. It possesses a muscular suctorial pharynx; the oozing blood from the victim's body is sucked by the pumping action of the pharynx.

8. Its saliva contains hirudin, an anticoagulant, that prevents blood clotting so that the leech may suck the blood for longer duration, as getting a host is a chance.

9. Its ten chambered crop with caeca help in storing the blood ; it is believed that leech can suck blood several times more of its own weight in a single meal. So, this blood is stored in crop and caeca.

10. Its one full meal is supposed to be enough for many months and even for a year because the process of digestion is very slow.

11. Since special respiratory organs are not found in leech, hence, its skin is richly supplied by haemocoelomic capillaries to ensure proper exchange of gases from the surroundings.

12. Its well developed receptors provide better chances of survival.

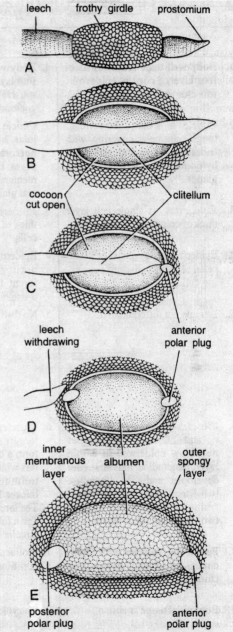

Fig. 67.32. *Hirudinaria.* Stages in cocoon formation. A, B—Formation of frothy girdle; C—Formation of anterior plug; D—Formation of posterior plug; E—Cocoon seen in section.

13. Its hermaphroditic sexuality has doubled the rate of reproduction as all individuals are capable of laying eggs in contrast to only 50 per cent individuals of unisexual forms.

14. Development occurs in ootheca or cocoon ; the coccon provides protection to developing young ones.

15. A short span of developmental period, *i.e,* a fortnight, and formation of several (up to 24) individuals in a single cocoon ensure to maintain its regular population.

TABLE 67.1. COMPARISON OF THE BODY WALL OF *NEANTHES, PHERETIMA* AND *HIRUDINARIA*

Neanthes (= Nereis) (Clamworm)	Pheretima (Earthworm)	Hirudinaria (Leech)
1. Body wall thick and consists of four layers : cuticle, epidermis, muscles and peritoneum.	1. Body wall thin and consists of four layers : cuticle, epidermis, muscles and peritoneum or coelomic epithelium.	1. Body wall thicker and consists of five layers : cuticle, epidermis, dermis, muscles and botryoidal tissue.
2. Cuticle is a thin, non-cellular, tough, chitinous covering with iridescent lustre and perforated by numerous pores of epidermal glands.	2 Cuticle is thin, elastic, non-cellular and iridescent layer and perforated by many minute pores through which integumentary nephridia and epidermal glands open out.	2. Cuticle is thin, delicate trans-parent, colourless moderately elastic and perforated by which epidermal glands open out.
3. Epidermis is single cell layer thick of columnar epithelial cells.	3. Epidermis is single cell layer thick of tall columnar epithelial cells.	3. Epidermis is single cell layer thick of hammer-shaped cells.
4. Epidermal cells consist of gland cells, sensory cells, and supporing cells.	4. Epidermal cells consists of supporting cells, gland cells of different types, basal cells and sensory cells	4. Epidermal cells consist of slime glands, sucker glands, prostomial glands and clitellar glands.
5. Dermis not differentiated.	5. No distinct dermis.	5. A distinct dermis below epidermis present; it consists of connective tissue, muscle fibres, haemocoelomic capillaries, fat and pigment cells. The epidermal glands are sunken in the dermis but open on the surface.
6. Muscles are circular, longitudinal and oblique; circular muscles lie below epidermis in a thin layer, longitudinal muscles better developed and in 4 bundles: two dorsolateral and two ventrolateral. Oblique muscles two pairs in each segment.	6. Muscles are only circular and longitudinal ; circular muscles form a thin layer below epidermis which is continuous, longitudinal muscle layer much thicker lie in separate bundles. The longitudinal muscle layer is again followed by a thin sheet of circular muscle fibres	6. Muscles are circular, longitudinal and oblique; circular muscle is a thin layer below dermis, followed by oblique muscles. The longitudinal muscles form major part of body musculature.
7. Parapodial muscles arise from circular muscles and inserted into chaetigerous sacs.	7. Protractor and retractor muscles constitute the setal musculature.	7. Parapodial and setal musculature not found because these structures are not found.
8. Botryoidal tissue is absent.	8. Botryoidal tissue is absent.	8. Botryoidal tissue characteristic, found beneath the longitudinal muscles surrounding the alimentary canal.

Neanthes (=Nereis) (Clamworm)	Pheretima (Earthworm)	Hirudinaria (Leech)
9. Coelomic epithelium or peritoneum lines the muscle layer internally.	9. Coelomic epithelium lines the musculature internally.	9. This layer is not found.

TABLE 67.2. COMPARISON OF THE DIGESTIVE SYSTEM OF *NEANTHES*, *PHERETIMA* AND *HIRUDINARIA*

Neanthes (=Nereis) (Clamworm)	Pheretima (Earthworm)	Hirudinaria (Leech)
Digestive system consists of the alimentary canal and digestive glands.	Digestive system also consists of the alimentary canal and digestive glands.	Digestive system also consists of the alimentary canal and digestive glands.
Alimentary Canal		
1. It is a striaght tube and extends from anterior to the posterior end of the body; it is held in the coelomic cavity by dorsal mesentery and intersegmental septa.	1. It is also a straight tube and extends from one end of the body to the other end; it is held in the coelomic cavity by intersegmental septa.	1. It is also a straight tube and extends from end to end in the body; it is held inside the body by botryoidal tissue and septa.
2. It is differentiated into the followng parts : mouth, buccal cavity, pharynx, oesophagus, stomach, intestine, rectum and auns.	2. Its alimentary canal is differentiated into the following regions : mouth, buccal cavity, pharynx, oeso- phagus, gizzard, stomach, intestine, rectum and anus.	2. Its alimentary canal has following parts : pre-oral chamber having mouth, buccal cavity, pharynx, oesophanus, crop, stomach, intestine, rectum and anus.
3. Mouth is a transverse slit-like aperture lying ventrally to the prostomium and bordered by peristominum.	3. Mouth is a crescentic aperture lying below the prostomium.	3. Mouth is a tri-radiate aperture lying at the base of cup-shaped pre-oral chamber on the ventral side of anterior sucker and guarded by the velum.
4. Buccal cavity is a short wide muscular chamber lined by cuticle having denticles.	4. Buccal cavity is a short thin-walled chamber without cuticular lining..	4. Buccal cavity is a short chamber and contains three jaws.
5. Pharynx is a wide muscular chamber having cuticular denticles and a pair of jaws.	5. Pharynx is a pear-shaped, muscular chamber with a pharyngeal bulb; its lumen is divided into a dorsal salivary and a ventral conducting chambers.	5. Pharynx is highly muscular, oval chamber and is provided with circular and radial muscles which join it with the body wall.
6. Pharynx and the buccal cavity are enclosed in a comman muscular sheath.	6. Phyranx and buccal cavity are separate.	6. Pharynx and buccal cavity are separate.
7. The buccal cavity and pharynx together are everted out as proboscis or introvert.	7. Only buccal cavity is protruded and retracted through the mouth.	7. Neither buccal cavity nor pharynx can be everted.
8. Oesophagus is a long, narrow tube and extends through five segments behind the pharynx up to ninth segment.	8. Oesophagus is a long a narrow tube and extends through four segments behind the pharynx up to seventh segment.	8. Oesophagus is very short and does not extend even through a complete segment.

Neanthes (=*Nereis*) (Clamworm)	*Pheretima* (Earthworm)	*Hirudinaria* (Leech)
9. Gizzard is not found.	9. A muscular gizzard lined by cuticle for crushing and grinding the food is present.	9. Gizzard is absent.
10. Grop is not found.	10. Crop is absent.	10. A ten chambered crop with lateral caeca is characteristically present for storing food as availability of host animal is uncertain.
Stomach and intestine not differentiated from each other. These are represented by segmentally constricted tube extending from eleventh segment to the last but one segment.	11 Stomach and instestine separate. Stomach extends up to fourteenth segment from gizzard; its both ends are sphinctered.	11. Stomach and intestine separate. Stomach is a narrow tube and folded internally; it extends nearly in one segment, *i.e.*, the nineteenth segment only. It opens by a sphinctered aperture into the intestine.
12. Separate intestine indistinct.	12. Intestine is a long tube of uniform diameter extending from fifteenth to the last segment of the body.	12. Intestine is thin walled, narrow and straight tube, it extends from nineteenth to twenty second segment.
13. Typhlosole and intestinal caeca not found.	13. Typhlosole and intestinal caeca present. Due to the presence of typhlosole the intestine is divisible into pretyphlosolar region(from 15th to 26th segment), typhlosolar region (from 26th to the last except 24, 25 segments) and the post- typholosolar region (last 24, 25 segments).	13. Typhlosole and intestinal cacea absent.
14. Rectum is very short tube situated only in the last segment of the body.	14. Rectum is a long tube extending into the last 24, 25 segments of the body.	14. Rectum is a narrow tube extending from twenty-second segment to twenty-sixth segment.
15. Anus is terminally placed in the last segment.	15. Anus is terminally placed in the last segment.	15. Anus is mid-dorsally placed on the twenty-sixth segment at the junction of body and posterior sucker.
Digestive Glands		
16. A pair of elongated pouch-like oesophageal glands or caeca opening into the oesophagus.	16. Oesophageal glands or caeca not found.	16. Oesophageal glands or caeca not found.
17. The epithelial lining of oesophagus, and stomach-instestine possess gland cells which are supposed to be digestive glands.	17. Gland cells present in the epithelial lining of stomach and intestine.	17. Gland cells found in the lining of crop, stomach and intestine.
18. Pharyngeal or salivary glands absent.	18. Pharyngeal or salivary glands present which secrete saliva.	18. Unicellular pharyngeal or salivary glands present which secrete hirudin, an anticoagulant substance.

Neanthes (=*Nereis*) (Clamworm)	*Pheretima* (Earthworm)	*Hirudinaria* (Leech)
Food and Feeding		
19. It is carnivorous feeding on small worms, crustaceans, larvae and molluscs.	19. It is omnivorous feeding on organic humus, decaying matter and micro-organisms of the soil.	19. It is sanguivorous feeding on the blood of cattle and man.
20. During feeding, the proboscis or introvert is everted with jaws to capture the prey.	20. During feeding, the buccal cavity is protruded out and the food is sucked by the pumping action of the pharynx.	20. During feeding, it attaches with the host body by its posterior sucker and applies its anterior sucker to the skin of the host. Its jaws form a Y-shaped wound on the victim's body and the oozing blood is sucked by the pumping action of the phaynx.

TABLE 67.3. COMPARISON OF EXCRETORY SYSTEM OF *NEANTHES*, *PHERETIMA* AND *HIRUDINARIA*

Neanthes (= *Nereis*) (Clamworm)	*Pheretima* (Earthworm)	*Hirudinaria* (Leech)
1. Excretory system consists of nephridia only.	1. Excretory system consists of nephridia and chloragogen cells.	1 Excretory system consists of nephridia and botryoidal tissue
2. Nephridia are segmentally arranged coiled tubes of considerably large size.	2. Nephridia are segmentally arranged coiled tubes of very minute size.	2. Nephridia are segmentally arranged coiled tubes of larger size.
3. Paired nephridia are found in all the segments except few anterior and posterior segments of the body.	3. Numerours nephridia are found in all the segments except the first two segments of the body.	3. Paired nephridia are found only in the segments from sixth to twenty-second;
4. All nephridia are alike.	4. Nephridia are of three types : (i) integumentary nephridia attached to the inner surface of the body wall in all segments except first two; (ii) pharyngeal nephridia found in the segments 4, 5 and 6; (iii) septal nephridia found attachea on the either sides of the intersegmental septa behind the 15th segments.	4 Nephridia are of two types : (i) pre-testicular nephridia, six pairs from segments sixth to eleventh; (ii) testicular nephridia, eleven pairs from segments twelfth to twenty second.
5. All nephridia are exonephric, *i.e.*, they open out by nephridiopores situated at the base of parapodium.	5 Integumentary nephridia are exonephric, pharyngeal and septal nephridia are enteronephric, *i.e.*, they open through ducts into the alimentary canal.	5. All nephridia are exonephric, opening directly to the exterior by nephridiopores.
6. All nephridia are provided with internal openings, the nephrostomes.	6 Septal nephridia only possess nephrostomes. Pharyngeal and integumentary nephridia are without nephrostomes.	6. Adult's nephridia without nephrostomes; these are probably represented by ciliated organs.

Neanthes (=*Nereis*) (Clamworm)	*Pheretima* (Earthworm)	*Hirudinaria* (Leech)
7. A typical nephridium is made of a small narrow neck and an oval main body.	7. A typical septal nephridium is made of a ciliated funnel or nephrostome, a main body and a short terminal duct.	7. A typical testicular nephridium is made of a main lobe, a vesicle with duct, an apical lobe, ar initial lobe and a ciliated organ.
8. Each nephridium is an oval irregular syncytial mass of protoplasm having a long convoluted and ciliated nephridial tubule ; the tubule is placed between the nephrostome and nephridiopore.	8. Each septal nephridium starts from nephrostome and terminates into the nephridiopore; the part of nephridium between these two structures is a coiled tabular portion which is generally ciliated but a syncytical mass of protoplasm is not found.	8. Each nephridium is horseshoe shaped, synctical mass absent and the basic structure is the same starting from the ciliated organ and terminating into the nephridiopore. The structure between the two is the different part of nephridium which is glandular.
9. The nephridial tubule forms a single loop inside synctial mass.	9. The tubular portion of nephridium forms two loops ; the stright lobe and spirally twisted lobe having proximal and distal limbs.	9. The tubular portion of nephridium forms main lobe, inner lobe, apical lobe and initial lobe.
10. Sac-like vesicle is not found.	10. Sac-like vesicle absent.	10. Sac-like vesicle or to say bladder present.
11. Nephridia remove excretory wastes from the blood and coelomic fluid.	11. All types of nephridia remove excretory wastes from the blood but septal nephridia also remove from coelomic fluid.	11. Nephridia remove excretory wastes from haemocoelonic fluid.
12. No other excetory organ is found.	12. The chloragogen cells are supposed to remove some excretory wastes from blood and coelonic fluid.	12. The botryoidal tissue is supposed to perform excretory function which removes wastes from the haemocoelonic fluid.

TABLE 67.4. COMPARISION OF REPRODUCTIVE SYSTEM OF *NEANTHES*, *PHERETIMA* AND *HIRUDINARIA*

Neanthes (=*Neries*) (Clamworm)	*Pheretima* (Earthworm)	*Hirudinaria* (Leech)
1. Dioecious with sexual dimorphism	1. Monoecious, hence, question of sexual dimorphism does not arise.	1. Monoecious, hence, question of sexual dimorphism does not arise.
2. Gonads are temporary organs ; they develop only during the breeding season.	2. Gonads are permanent organs found throughout the life.	2. Gonads are permanent organs found throughout the life
3. A sexually mature worm, referred to as *Heteroneanthes* or *Heteronereis* differs from sexually immature worm.	3. No differentiation between sexually immature and mature worms.	3. No differentiation between sexually immature and mature worms.
Male Reproductive System		
4. It consists of testes only.	4. It consists of testes, testis sacs, seminal vesicles, vasa deferentia, prostate glands and accessory glands.	4. It consists of testes, testis sacs, vasa efferentia, vasa deferentia ; epididymis or vesicula seminales, ejacula- tory ducts, atrium and prostate glands.

Neanthes (=Nereis) (Clamworm)	*Pheretima* (Earthworm)	*Hirudinaria* (Leech)
5. Testes lie in the anterior segments except the first few; these proliferate from coelomic epithelium as cell masses during breeding season only.	5. Testes two pairs, one pair each in the segments tenth and eleventh; these are permanent structures.	5. Testes eleven pairs, one pair each in the segments from twelfth to twenty-second; these are permanent structures.
6. Testis sacs not found.	6. Each testis is enclosed in a testis sac.	6. Each testis is in fact the lining of rounded testis sac.
7. Vas deferens, vas efferens and spermiducal funnel not found.	7. Vasa deferentia two pairs, each arising from spermiducal funnels and extends up to eighteenth segment. Vasa efferentia not found.	7. Vasa deferentia paired, each starts from twenty-second segment and travels up to eleventh segments. Each vas deferens receives vasa efferentia throughout the segments from twenty-second to twelfth. Spermiducal funnel absent.
8. Seminal vesicle absent.	8. Seminal vesicles two pairs; one pair each in the segments eleventh and twelfth. Maturation and storage of sperms occur in seminal vesicles.	8. Each vas deferens opens in a highly glandular seminal vesicle or vesicula seminalis also referred to as epididymis in tenth segment. It acts as storage organ for sperms.
9. Atrium and penis not found. Male genital aperture is not found, male gametes (sperms) are discharged by the rupture of the body wall.	9. Atrium not found but the terminal part of vasa deferentia and prostatic duct of each side act as penis. Male genital apertures are paired situated latero-ventrally in the eighteenth segment.	9. Atrium is a pyriform sac; it is differentiated into broad basal prostatic chamber and a narrow penis sac enclosing a filamentous penis. The penis sac opens out ventrally in the second annulus of tenth segment as male genital aperture.
10. Prostate glands or any other accessory glands are not found.	10. A pair of prostate glands are found as accessory reproductive glands in the segments from seventeenth to twenty.	10. Numerous unicellular prostate glands are found on the prostatic chamber of the atrium. Their secretion glues the sperms into bundles of spermatophores.

Female Reproductive System

11. It consists of ovaries only.	11. It consists of ovaries, oviducts, spermathecae or seminal receptacles.	11. It consists of ovaries, ovisacs, oviducts, common oviduct, vagina and albumen glands.
12. Ovaries many pairs and lie in all the segments except few anterior ones; these proliferate from coelomic epithelium only during the breeding season.	12. Ovaries paired only and lie in the thirteenth segment attached to intersegmental septum of 12/13; these are permanent structures.	12. Ovaries paired and lie in the eleventh segment; these are permanent structures.
13. Ovaries are in form of cell masses.	13. Ovaries contain numerous finger-like lobules.	13. Ovaries delicate, filamentous, coiled having club-like ends.
14. Ovaries not found.	14. **Ovaries are absent.**	14. Each ovary is found enclosed in an ovisac.

Neanthes (=*Nereis*) (Clamworm)	*Pheretima* (Earthworm)	*Hirudinaria* (Leech)
15. Oviducts absent, gametes are discharged out by the rupture of body wall.	15. An oviduct starts from each ovary behind, thus, both the oviducts unite in fourteenth segment and open mid-ventrally by a single female genital aperture; the oviducts to start with bear funnel-shaped oviducal funnels.	15. An oviduct starts from an ovisac, thus, the two oviducts unite to form a common oviduct which is S-shaped and lies in the eleventh segment
16. Vagina is absent.	16. Vagina is absent.	16. Vagina is a large pear-shaped muscular bag, it lies in the posterior part of eleventh segment and receives the opening of common oviduct in its middle. Vagina opens mid-ventrally in the second annulus by female genital aperture.
17. Spermathecae not found.	17. Spermathecae four pairs; one pair in each segment from sixth to ninth. These store sperms after copulation till fertilization takes place.	17. Spermathecae absent. The sperms are stored in the vagina after copulation till fertilization occurs.
18. Albumen glands are absent.	18. Albumen glands are not found.	18. Albumen glands are present at the junction of two oviducts from which common oviduct starts.
19. Copulation does not occur.	19. Copulation takes place.	19. Copulation takes place.
20. Fertilization is external, cocoon is not formed.	20. Fertilization takes place in cocoon or ootheca.	20. Fertilization takes place in cocoon or ootheca.
21. Development indirect involving a free-swimmng trochophore larval stage.	21. Development direct; free larval stage wanting.	21. Development direct ; free swimming larval stage wanting.

REVISION QUESTIONS

1. Give an account of the habits, habitat and external features of a leech.
2. Describe the alimentary canal of leech and add a note on its food and feeding mechanism.
3. What is haemocoel and haemocoelomic system ? Describe the haemocoelomic system of *Hirudinaria*.
4. Describe the excretory structure and mode of excretion of *Hirudinaria*.
5. Describe the sense organs of a leech.
6. Give an account of the reproductive system of *Hirudinaria* and add a note on the formation of cocoon.
7. Compare the body wall of leech, earthworm and clamworm.
8. Give a comparative account of the nephridial system of *Nereis, Pheretima* and *Hirudinaria*.
9. Compare the digestive system of *Nereis, Pheretima* and *Hirudinaria*.
10. Compare the reproductive organs of annelids you have studied.
11. Draw fully labelled diagrams only :
    (i) T.S. body wall of *Hirudinaria;* (ii) T.S. *Hirudinaria* through crop and its diverticula; (iii) A testicular nephridium of leech.
12. Write short notes on :
    (i) Segmentation of *Hirudinaria;* (ii) Botryoidal tissue; (iii) Coelom of leech; (iv) Ciliated organ; (v) Formation of ootheca in *Hirudinaria;* (vi) Parasitic adaptive features of *Hirudinaria*.

68

Annelida : Characters, Classification and Types

DEFINITION

Annelids are triploblastic, bilaterally symmetrical, metamerically segmented, coelomate worms with a thin flexible cuticle around the body.

GENERAL CHARACTERS

1. Annelida are mostly aquatic ; marine or freshwater, some terrestrial, burrowing or living in tubes, sedentary or free-living. Some are commensal and parasitic also.

2. Body triploblastic, bilaterally symmetrical, elongated and vermiform.

3. Body metamerically segmented ; externally by transverse grooves and internally by septa into a number of divisions ; each division is called a segment, metamere or somite.

4. Organ-system grade of body organization.

5. Outer covering of the body is cuticle secreted by the underlying epidermis.

6. Body wall is contractile, consisting of an outer epidermis, circular and longitudinal muscles.

7. Appendages when present are unjointed.

8. Locomotory organs are segmentally arranged paired setae or chaetae in most of the cases.

9. Presence of a true schizocoelous coelom usually divided into a large number of compartments by intersegmental septa.

10. Alimentary canal is tube-like, complete, extending from mouth to anus.

11. Respiration occurs through general body surface, in some cases by gills also.

12. Blood vascular system is closed .ype, blood is red due to the presence of haemoglobin or erythrocruorin found dissolved in the plasma.

13. Excretion by segmentally arranged nephridia which usually communicate the coelom to exterior.

14. Nervous system with a pair of cerebral ganglia, the brain and a double nerve cord having segmentally arranged ganglia.

15. The tactile organs, taste buds, statocysts, photoreceptor cells and eyes are the receptor organs.

16. Usually monoecious, *i.e.*, hermaphrodite; dioecious or unisexual forms also present.

17. Development direct in monoecious forms but indirect in dioecious forms.

18. A free-swimming trochophore larval stage is characteristic in case of indirect development, while in others this stage is passed during the development.

19. Asexual reproduction also occurs in some forms.

CLASSIFICATION

CLASS 1. POLYCHAETA
(Gr., *poly*=many+*chaete*=bristles)

1. Polychaeta are marine and carnivorous

2. Body is elongated and segmented.

3. Head consists of prostomium and peristomium and bears eyes, tentacles, cirri and palps, etc.

4. Setae are numerous and are borne up on lateral prominences of the body wall known as parapodia.
5. Clitellum is absent.
6. Cirri or branchiae or both may be present for respiration.
7. Coelom is spacious usually divided by interaegmental septa.
8. Alimentary canal is provided with an eversible buccal region and protrusible pharynx.
9. Excretory organs are segmentally paired nephridia.
10. Sexes separate, fertilization external, free swimming larval stage trochophore.
11. Asexual reproduction by lateral budding

Order 1. Errantia

1. Free-swimming, often pelagic, while some living in tubes.
2. All body segments are similar except at anterior and posterior ends.
3. Parapodia, provided with cirri, are equally developed throughout.
4. Head with distinct prostomium which is provided with eyes, tentacles and palps.
5. Pharynx is usually protrusible and armed with chitinous jaws and teeth.

Examples : *Nereis, Aphrodite, Glycera, Polynoe, Syllis.*

Order 2. Sedentaria

1. Burrowing and tube dwelling forms.
2. Body is divisible into two or more regions with unlike segments and parapodia.
3. Head is small or much modified, without eyes and tentacles, prostomium indistinct.
4. Pharynx is non-protrusible devoid of jaws or teeth.
5. Gills, when present, localized to the anterior segments.
6. Feeding on plankton or organic detritus.

Examples : *Chaetopterus, Terebella, Sabella, Arenicola, Serpula, Amphitrite, Spirórbis.*

CLASS 2. OLIGOCHAETA
(Gr., *oligos*=few+*chaete*=setae)

1. Mostly terrestrial or some freshwater forms.
2. Body with conspicuous external and internal segmentation.
3. Distinct head, eyes and tentacles are absent.
4. Parapodia are absent.
5. Setae are usually arranged segmentally.
6. Clitellum is usually present.
7. Pharynx is not eversible and without jaws.
8. Hermaphrodite, *i.e.*, sexes united.

9. Development is direct and takes place within cocoons secreted by clitellum; no free larval stage.

Order 1. Archioligochaeta

1. Mostly freshwater forms.
2. Body consists of few segments.
3. Setae are present in bundles.
4. Gizzard is poorly developed, non-muscular or absent.
5. Clitelium is simpler, consists of single layer of cells and situated far forwards.
6. Eye spots are frequently present.
7. Male reproductive openings lie in front of the female reproductive openings.
8. Reproduction asexual and sexual.

Examples : *Tubifex, Aelosoma.*

Order 2. Neooligochaeta

1. Usually terrestrial forms.
2. Body is large and many segmented.
3. Setae are arranged in lumbricine manner.
4. Gizzard is well developed.
5. Clitellum is composed of two or more layers of cells and never begins before twelfth segment.
6. Female genital apertures are always on the fourteenth segment and the male pore lies a few segments behind them.
7. Vasa deferentia are elongated extending over the three or four segments.
8. Eye spots are never developed.
9. Reproduction sexual. Asexual reproduction is not known

Examples : *Pheretima, Eutypheus, Megascolex, Lumbricus.*

CLASS 3. HIRUDINEA
(L., *hirudo* = a leech)

1. Mostly ectoparasitic and freshwater forms, while few are marine feeding upon fishes and other animals.
2. Body is elongated usually flattened dorso-ventrally or cylindrical.
3. Body consists of definite number of segments, each segment breaks up into 2 to 4 rings or annuli.
4. Parapodia and setae are absent.
5. Body is provided with an anterior and a posterior sucker, both situated ventrally.
6. Mouth opens on the ventral surface in the anterior sucker, while anus opens dorsal to the posterior sucker.
7. Hermaphrodite, *i.e.*, sexes united; reproduction sexual.
8. Asexual reproduction is not known.
9. Eggs are usually laid in cocoons.

10. Development is direct without free swimming larval stage.

Order 1. Acanthobdellida

1. Mostly parasitic on tne fins of salmon fishes.
2. Body comprises thirty segments only.
3. Anterior sucker is absent but posterior sucker is well developed and composed of four segments.
4. Anterior five segments are provided with double rows of setae.
5. Proboscis is short.
6. Body cavity is spacious and incompletely divided by septa.
7. Vascular system consists of dorsal and ventral vessel.
8. Nephridial opening situated on the surface between the segments.
9. Acanthobdellida forms a connecting link between Oligochaeta and Hirudinea.

Example : *Acanthobdellida.*

Order 2. Rhynchobdellida

1. Parasites on snails, frogs and fishes, marine and freshwater forms.
2. Each typical body segment consists of 3, 6 or 12 rings.
3. Mouth is small median aperture situated in the anterior sucker.
4. Proboscis is prostrusible; jaws are absent.
5. Blood is colourless.

REPRESENTATIVE TYPES OF ANNELIDA

1. *Aphrodite. Aphrodite* (Fig. 68.1) is commonly known as sea mouse. It burrows in the sea mud. There is a small head formed by prostomium and peristomium, the prostomium projects dorsally over the mouth. In front are two lateral palps and a short tentacle. The body is short and broad with an arched dorsal side, and a flat ventral side which is annulated to form a creeping sole. Thick long setae of the notopodium are irridescent, they are woven into a blanket which covers the back including the elytra. Between the blanket and the dorsal body wall is a space containing 15 pairs of elytra or scales formed from modified dorsal cirri. Pumping action of the dorsal body wall causes water to be filtered through the blanket of setae into the space below, elytra obtain oxygen from this water. The intestine has long branching segmental caeca which digest minute food particles which come in through a sieve lying between the intestine and caeca, in the caeca are several kinds of secretory and absorptive cells. Coelomic epithelium is ciliated which causes circulation, and projecting into the rectum are a series of strongly ciliated ridges.

6. Coelom is reduced to sinuses without botryoidal tissues.

Examples : *Pontobdella, Glossiphonia, Branchellion, Piscicola.*

Order 3. Gnathobdellida

1. Freshwater and terrestrial forms.
2. Each typical body segment consists of five rings or annuli.
3. Anterior sucker with three jaws, one median dorsal and two ventro-lateral.
4. Proboscis is absent.
5. Blood is red coloured.
6. Botryoidal tissue present.

Examples : *Hirudo, Haemopis, Hirudinaria, Herpobdella.*

CLASS 4. ARCHIANNELIDA
(Gr., *archi*=first)

1. Exclusively marine forms.
2. Body elongated and worm-like.
3. Setae and parapodia are usually absent.
4. External segmentation is slightly marked by faint, while internal segmentation is marked by coelomic septa.
5. Prostomium bears two or three tentacles.
6. Unisexual or hermaphrodite.
7. Larva is typical trochophore.

Examples : *Polygordius, Protodrillus, Nerilla, Saccocirrus.*

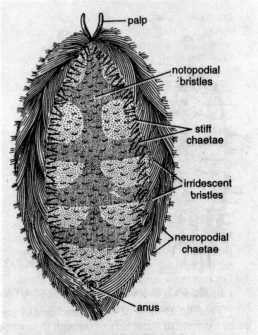

Fig. 68.1. *Aphrodite.*

2. *Glycera.* *Glycera* (Fig. 68.2) commonly known as smooth blood worm is a marine burrowing form. Body is elongated and cylindrical, consists of numerous segments. Prostomium is long and conical with four small tentacles at its tip. Proboscis is very large and prostrusible armed with four sharp teeth. Parapodia are reduced in size and bear compound setae. Blood vascular system absent. Special retractile gills are present.

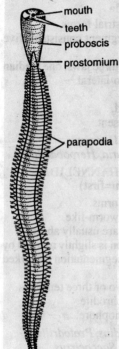

mouth
teeth
proboscis
prostomium

parapodia

Fig. 68.2. *Glycera.*

3. *Polynoe.* Body is short and compressed dorsoventrally. Head has a prostomium and peristomium. On the prostomium are three tentacles, two long palps, and four eyes. Peristomium has two pairs of tentacles or peristomial cirri. Body segments are few, each segment bears a pair of parapodia which have long golden setae. Covering the body dorsally are flat elytra formed by modified dorsal cirri. Elytra are phosphorescent and they can be cast off and replaced. *Polynoe* (Fig. 68.3) is carnivorous and its pharynx is everted in feeding.

4. *Chaetopterus.* It is 15–35 cm long, the stout body is divided into three regions, an anterior flattened region has a funnel-shaped peristomial collar with two rudimentary tentacles and a mouth. In the fourth segment setae are enlarged, tenth segment has a pair of wing-like aliform notopodia having ciliated epithelium and many mucous glands. On the dorsal side is a ciliated groove running from the mouth to a ciliated cup called dorsal cupule. Middle region has modified parapodia forming three pairs of fans which are like semi-circular wings, the fans fit against the cylindrical wall of the tube. Posterior region has smaller segments bearing parapodia. *Chaetopterus* is one of the most modified tubicolous worms, it lives permanently in a U-shaped parchment-like tube in the sea mud, the two ends of the tube are open but constricted, they project above the mud water. The tube lies buried in the intertidal zone being alternately exposed and covered by the tides. Ventral surface of the animal is fixed to the tube by suckers. The body secretes slime which lines the tube and covers the body, it makes the animal brilliantly phosphorescent in the dark, at times the slime disperses into water which produces luminescence in the sea. Tube-dwelling has made the body soft and helpless outside.

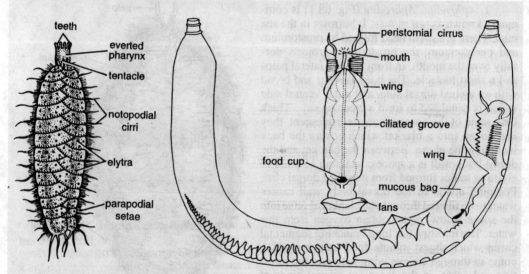

teeth
everted pharynx
tentacle
notopodial cirri
elytra
parapodial setae

peristomial cirrus
mouth
wing
ciliated groove
food cup
wing
mucous bag
fans

Fig. 68.3. *Polynoe.*

Fig.68.4. *Chaetopterus* in tube, feeding and diagram of anterior end.

Feeding. Beating of three paired fans of the middle region and of the cilia of the ciliated groove cause a current of water to flow through from one end of the tube to the other, this current is respiratory and brings in food. The aliform notopodia secrete a cylindrical sheet of mucus which forms a mucous bag which is streched like a net between the two notopodia. All water passing through the tube is filtered through the mucous bag which collects food particles consisting of plankton and detritus, only the very small particles are retained, the food-laden mucous bag comes down the ciliated groove and is rolled into a ball or **bolus** by the dorsal cupule. Beating of cilia in the dorsal groove is reversed periodically so that the ball is passed along the dorsal groove to the mouth and is swallowed. Beating of fans stops when the ball is being propelled to the mouth.

5. *Terebella.* *Terebella* (Fig. 68.6) is a tubicolous burrowing form. Body is long and vermiform. Prostomium is horse-shoe-shaped provided with numerous long tentacles which serve as gills. Peristomium is without cirri. Just below the head are found two pairs of branched gills. Parapodia are feebly developed. Nephridia are large and small and serve as both excretory and genital ducts.

6. *Amphitrite.* *Amphitrite* (Fig. 68.7) lives between tide marks inside tube made in the sea mud, the tubes are lined with mucus. The body is brown-coloured, cylindrical, and about 20–30 cm long, it forms three distinct regions, a head, thorax and abdomen. Head is formed by the prostomium and peristomium. The prostomium is flat and forms an upper lip of the anterior mouth. It bears no palps but there are numerous contractile tentacles in two large clusters, a tentacle is hollow containing coelomic fluid, it has a ciliated groove and mucous gland cells. Food is collected by the tentacles and passed along the grooves to the mouth. The peristomium forms a lower lip of the mouth. Thorax is long with broad segments. On the first three segments of the thorax are three pairs of gills of red colour, the gills are much branched respiratory organs, they are formed from modified dorsal cirri. Remaining segments of thorax bear notopodia with setae and neuropodia with hook-like uncini which are modified setae. The anterior thoracic segments have shield-shaped mucous glands on the ventral side, they secrete mucus for lining the tube. The abdomen is long and narrow with no setae, it has a terminal anus. Very often an errant polychaete scale worm *Lepidometria* lives in symbiotic relationship with *Amphitrite* in its tube.

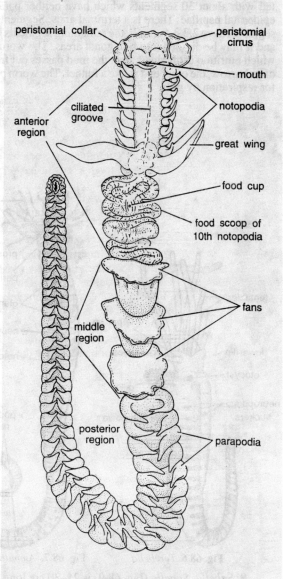

Fig. 68.5. *Chaetopterus.*

7. *Arenicola.* *Arenicola* (Fig. 68.8) is commonly known as **lug** or **lobe worm**. It is 20–40 cm long living in U-shaped burrows in the sea mud, burrows are lined with mucus. The body has three regions, an anterior region of eight segments, first is a small trilobed prostomium, the second is a peristomium. The prostomium, peristomium and the next segment form a small head. The remaining segments bear parapodia. At the anterior end is a mouth through which a buccal mass is everted as a **proboscis,** the proboscis is covered with small, curved vascular papillae, proboscis is used for feeding and locomotion. In feeding the proboscis is forced into sand and then retracted with a load of sand from which organic matter is digested. The middle region of the body has 13 segments of which the first eleven bear eleven pairs of gills. The gills are dorsal, they are much branched and of red colour,

gills are modified cirri of notopodia. In some species (*A. marina*) there are 13 pairs of gills. Segments of the middle region bear parapodia. A parapodium of anterior or middle region has a dorsal conical notopodium having a tuft of setae, and a ventral elongated neuropodium with a long slit in which there are hooks or uncini formed from modified setae. The posterior region of the body is a narrow tail with about 30 segments which have neither parapodia nor setae, but they may have irregular epidermal papillae. There is a terminal anus. Segments of the body are divided into annuli, first four segments have 2,2,3,4 annuli, the remaining segments have 5 annuli each. The epidermis is pigmented and it may be divided into polygonal areas. The worm ingests sand along with organic matter from which nutrition is obtained, then the mud passes out from its anus as long surface castings at one end of its burrow, the other end is like a funnel. The worm pumps water through the funnel into the burrow for respiration by gills.

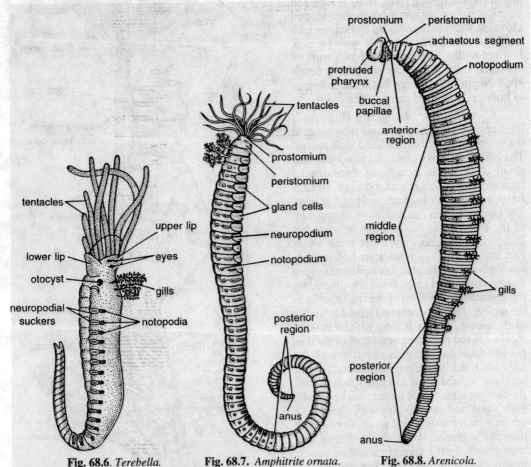

Fig. 68.6. *Terebella.*   Fig. 68.7. *Amphitrite ornata.*   Fig. 68.8. *Arenicola.*

  8. *Sabella.* Sabella (Fig. 68.9) is 25–30 cm long, body is cylindrical of orange-brown colour, it lives in a long membranous tube in the sea mud. The body is divisible into a head, thorax and abdomen. The head has two processes of the upper lip and two eyes on the prostomuim, it has a collar with two processes, it is formed of three segments, in front of which are ten pairs of tentacles forming ciliated branchiae which are about 4 cm long and green-coloured. Thorax has five segments having mucous glands and parapodia consisting of notopodia with setae and neuropodia with hooks. Abdomen is long with about 300 segments bearing parapodia wihch are like those on the thorax. Feeding : The branchiae extend from the tube into water like a crown, their cilia cause a current of water which is drawn along the grooves of branchiae into the mouth. At the base of the branchiae is a device by which smallest particles go into the mouth, medium particles are used for building the tube and the largest particles are rejected and thrown out.

9. *Serpula*. *Serpula* (Fig. 68.10) lives in a calcareous tube in the sea. Elongated body has a head, thorax, and abdomen. Prostomium is reduced but its appendages are long and modified into feathery tentacles, each tentacle has a long stem bearing two rows of short filaments ; the tentacles take food to the mouth. An enlarged branch of a tentacle forms an **operculum** which closes the mouth of the tube when the animal is retracted. Peristomium is like the thoracic segments, but it is produced into a **collar** which folds backwards. The collar secretes the tube and its hoop-shaped rings. There is a lateral thoracic membrane which is probably respiratory. A median **ciliated groove** runs from the anus along the ventral side of the abdomen, then it turns towards the dorsal side of the thorax, it removes faeces through the opening of the tube. Body segments bear parapodia. Muscular movements pump water in and out of the tube.

10. *Spirorbis*. *Spirorbis* (Fig. 68.11) lives in small spiral calcareous tubes attached to the shells or other objects. The worm is minute measuring 0.8 to 1.5 cm in length. Body of the worm is divisible into an anterior thorax or trunk and posterior abdomen. Mouth is surrounded by numerous gill filaments, one of the gill filaments is greatly enlarged terminally into an operculum which closes the mouth of the tube when animal is withdrawn inside the tube. Operculum is grooved on the side which serves as a brood sac. The peristomium is similar to the other segments of the thorax but it forms the collar which secretes the tube. Hermaphrodite, anterior abdominal segments producing the ova, while the posterior ones sperms.

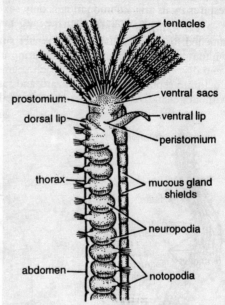

Fig. 68.9. *Sabella.*

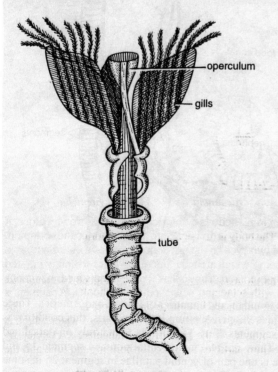

Fig. 68.10. *Serpula.*

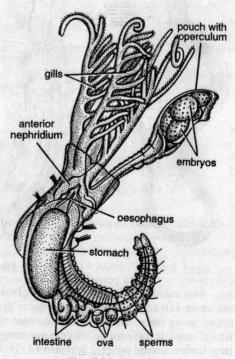

Fig.68.11. *Spirorbis.*

11. *Tubifex*. Most freshwater oligochaetes are found in shallow water, but *Tubifex* (Fig. 68.12) is an exception since it inhabits the bottom of deep lakes in very large numbers. It lives in tubes made of mud and minerals cemented together with mucus. It is 4 cm long, cylindrical, red-coloured worm which resembles an earthworm. A clitellum is formed in segments 11 and 12, there are contractile hearts in segment 8. On the body are numerous short setae in dorsal and ventral bundles, the setae have branched ends. Male genital pore is in segment 11 and female genital pore in segment 12. It respires by its tail. Reproduction is only sexual.

12. *Aelosoma*. *Aelosoma* (Fig. 68.13) is a freshwater worm found in freshwater ponds or attached to or in the liver of freshwater snails. Body is transparent, dorso-ventrally flattened and without external segmentation measuring up to 100 mm long. Prostomium is provided with cilia ventrally. Setae are arranged in each segment. The number of setae in each bundle is indefinite. Coelomic septa are absent. Gizzard and lateral vascular commissures are absent. Hermaphrodite without generative ducts. Reproduction predominantly asexual.

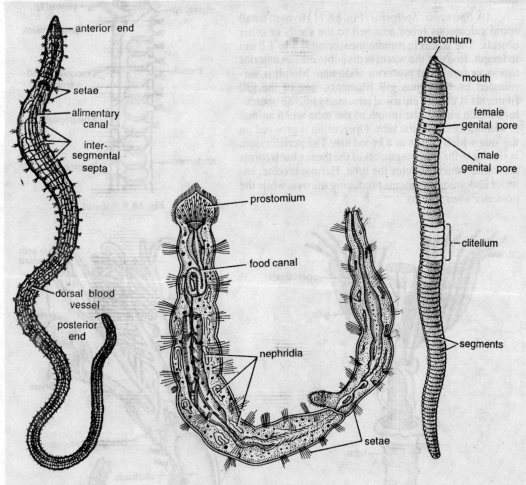

Fig. 68.12. *Tubifex*.   Fig. 68.13. *Aelosoma*.   Fig. 68.14. *Lumbricus*.

13. *Lumbricus*. *Lumbricus* (Fig. 68.14) is found in cold countries of Europe and America. There are about 150 segments. The prostomium divides the peristomium into two parts, this condition is called **tanylobous**. Clitellum is permanent in segments 33 to 37, but it is found only on dorsal and lateral sides, being incomplete mid-ventrally. There are two male genital pores in segment 15 and two female genital pores in segment 14. There is one pair of genital papillae in segment 26 in some species. There are two pairs of spermathecae with no diverticula, there are three pairs of seminal vesicles. Each segment has four pairs of setae in the lower half. In copulation two worms come together by their ventral surfaces and each gets enveloped in a mucous sheath. The clitellum of one adheres closely and embraces segments 9 and 10 of the other worm, and the setae are thrust into the body wall of the partner. Spermatozoa pass out of the male genital aperture and travel along the seminal grooves into the clitellum, then they enter the spermathecae of the other worm when the cocoon is being slipped over.

14. *Glossiphonia or Clepsine. Glossiphonia* or *Clepsine* (Fig. 68.15) is a freshwater leech. The anterior sucker is fused with the body and lies behind the mouth. The body is broad, flattened and of greenish-yellow colour. It feeds on snails and is carnivorous. The segments have an average of three annuli each. Clitellum does not become prominent even in the breeding season. Intestine has four pairs of lateral caeca. There is no pharynx but there is a proboscis which can be produced or retracted through the mouth. Coelomoducts join nephridia to form compound segmental organs called nephromixium which are excretory and may also serve as genital ducts. *Glossiphonia* deposits large spermatophores on the back of another, they sink through the skin and reach the ovaries, this is called hypodermic impregnation. The young on hatching attach themselves to the ventral surface of the mother.

15. *Pontobdella. Pontobdella* (Fig. 68.16) is 20 cm long and is green-coloured. It is marine and ectoparasitic on elasmobranch fishes. The anterior sucker is saucer-shaped and posterior sucker is cup-shaped. The anterior end forms a proboscis which can be everted. The skin is leathery with many rough knobs. There are no nephridia, but there is a complex network of tubes on the ventral side with a pair of ciliated nephrostomes and nephridiopores in each segment. It lays eggs in empty mollusc shells and guards them for over hundred days till they hatch.

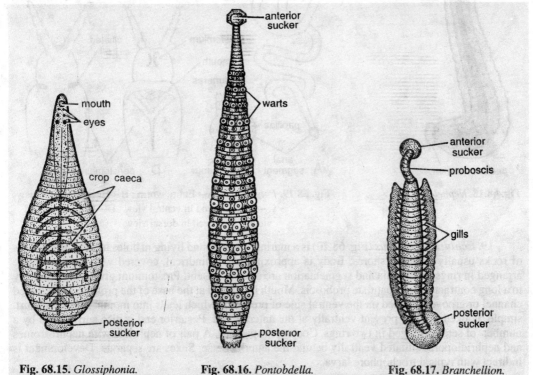

Fig. 68.15. *Glossiphonia.*   **Fig. 68.16.** *Pontobdella.*   **Fig. 68.17.** *Branchellion.*

16. *Branchellion. Branchellion* (Fig. 68.17) is an ectoparasite on the outer surface of the marine fishes especially skates and rays. Body is elongated and cylindrical, divided into a narrow anterior region, the neck and wide posterior region, the abdomen. Anterior region is produced into a long proboscis and an anterior sucker. Posterior region, the abdomen bears eleven pairs of lateral foliaceous (leaf-like) gills. Posterior sucker is well developed. Hermaphrodite. Sexual reproduction is common. *Branchellion* is worldwide in distribution but it is not reported from India so far.

17. *Napheles (Herpobdella).* *Napheles (Herpobdella)* (Fig. 68.18) is found in freshwater ponds and streams under stones and in vegetation. Body is slender about 8 cm in length and brownish black in colour. Anterior end is rounded and devoid of definite anterior sucker. Posterior end is flattened and bears a distinct small sucker. Each body segment has five annuli or rings. It is carnivorous, feeds on aquatic larvae, worms and snails.

18. *Polygordius.* *Polygordius* (Fig. 68.19) is a marine worm found in sand of European seas. Body is narrow, elongated and cylindrical, measuring about 4 cm in length. Externally the body segments are very faintly marked off though the internal division by means of septa is complete. Parapodia, setae, cirri and gills are entirely absent. Prostomium is small, bears a pair of short tentacles, while peristomium is large and bears a pair of sensory ciliated pits. Mouth is ventral to the prostomium. Anal opening is in the last segment and bears a pair of adhesive papillae. Excretory system consists of paired segmental nephridia. Sexes are separate. Fertilization is external. Development is indirect including Loven's larva resembling typical trochophore larva.

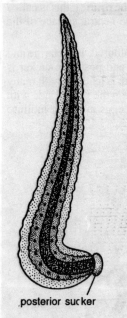
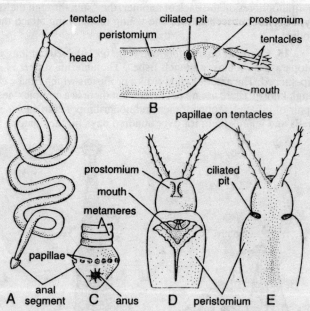

Fig. 68.18. *Napheles.*

Fig. 68.19. *Polygordius.* A—Entire worm ; B—Head in lateral view; C—Posterior end in ventral view ; D—Head in ventral view ; E—Head in dorsal view.

19. *Echiurus.* *Echiurus* (Fig. 68.20) is a marine worm, found living in holes in sand, in crevices of rocks usually near sea shores. Body is approximately cylindrical, covered with small papillae arranged in rings. Parapodia and segmentation are entirely absent. Prostomium gives rise anteriorly to a long contractile and spatulate proboscis. Mouth is situated at the base of the proboscis. A ciliated channel or groove is placed on the ventral side of proboscis which leads into mouth. A pair of short, simple, hooked setae is present ventrally at the anterior end. Posterior end is also surrounded by a number of setae arranged in two rings. Coelom is spacious. A pair of nephridia with nephrostomes and nephridiopores situated ventrally behind the anterior setae. Sexes are separate. Development is indirect with typical trochophore larva.

20. *Bonellia.* *Bonellia* (Fig. 68.21) is a marine worm, found living in crevices of rocks. *Bonellia* exhibits dimorphism.

Female. Body is ovoid in shape about 5 cm long and green in colour. Body is covered with large papillae which are not arranged in rings. Proboscis is very long, extensible and bifurcated terminally. Mouth is situated at the base of the proboscis. Two ventral setae are present behind the mouth. Single greatly enlarged nephridium which acts as uterus.

Male. It is minute turbellarian-like. Body is ciliated about 0.5 mm in length. Proboscis is absent. Alimentary canal is reduced without mouth and anus. In the young condition the male enters the pharynx of the female and after attaining sexual maturity lives permanently in the nephridium.

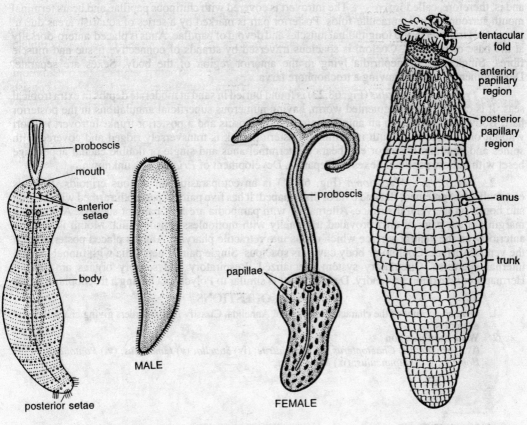

| **Fig. 68.20.** *Echiurus.* | **Fig. 68.21.** *Bonellia.* | **Fig. 68.22.** *Sipunculus.* |

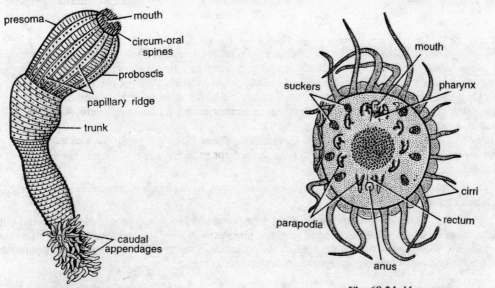

Fig. 68.23. *Priapulus.*

Fig. 68.24. *Myzostoma.*

21. *Sipunculus.* **Sipunculus** (Fig. 68.22) is found in burrows in sand or crevices of rocks at moderate depth off the coast in most countries outside the tropics. It is elongated and cylindrical worm without segmentation. Parapodia and setae are absent. Anterior part of the body is slightly narrower than the posterior part. The narrower anterior part can be drawn into larger posterior portion and is, therefore, called introvert. The introvert is covered with chitinous papillae and bears terminal mouth surrounded by tentacular folds. Posterior part is marked by a series of squarish areas due to crossing of transverse and longitudinal muscles and devoid of papillae. Anus is placed antero-dorsally at the base of introvert. Coelom is spacious traversed by strands of connective tissue and muscle fibres. Single pair of nephridia lying in the anterior region of the body. Sexes are separate. Development is indirect having a trochophore larva.

22. *Priapulus.* **Priapulus** (Fig. 68.23) is found buried in sand at moderate depths in extra tropical seas. It is cylindrical unsegmented worm, having numerous superficial annulations in the posterior half. Body is divisible into an anterior introvert, proboscis and a posterior trunk. Introvert is short without oral tentacles. Mouth is terminal. Posterior trunk is transversely ridged and covered with spines and papillae. Posterior end bears the terminal anus and single or double caudal appendage beset with hollow papillae. Sexes are separate. Development of *Priapulus* is unknown.

23. *Myzostoma.* **Myzostoma** (Fig. 68.24) is an ectoparasitic on various crinoids. Body is externally unsegmented, flat and oval or disc-shaped. It has five pairs of parapodia armed with acicula and hooks on the ventral surface. Alternating with parapodia are four pairs of suckers. Around the margin are ten pairs of cirri provided terminally with motionless sensory cilia. Mouth is situated anteriorly on the ventral surface which opens into retractile pharynx. Anus is placed posteriorly on the ventral surface. Coelom or body cavity is spacious. Single pair of nephridia with funnel-shaped internal apertures. Circulatory system specialized. Respiratory and sensory organs are absent. Hermaphrodite exhibit protandry. Development is similar to Polychaeta having a trochophore larva.

REVISION QUESTIONS

1. Give an account of the characters of phylum Annelida. Classify it up to orders giving characters and examples.
2. Write short notes on :
   (i) *Aphrodite;* (ii) *Chaetopterus*, (iii) *Amphitrite*; (iv) *Sabella;* (v) *Lumbricus;* (vi) *Pontobdella;* (vii) *Bonellia;* (viii) *Sipunculus;* (ix) *Myzostoma.*

69

Annelida in General

METAMERISM IN ANNELIDA

Development of a coelom is bound up with the formation of a series of gonadial coelomic sacs lying on both sides of the gut, but in most coelomate animals the coelom is a large perivisceral cavity, yet traces of the segmental nature of coelom are evident, it is divided into compartments by intersegmental septa and many other systems are also segmentally arranged, thus, in Annelida the body consists of linear series of segments built, more or less, on the same plan and resembling each other. Animals whose bodies conform to such a plan are said to be metamerically segmented or to show metamerism. In metamerism not only is there a serial repetition of homologous parts (*e.g.*, nephridia, blood vessels, nerves, reproductive organs, muscles), but each of these parts works in co-operation with all the others, the segments being integrated into a single functional unit, the segmental structures are interdependent. Annelida show metameric segmentation of the main organs and of the entire body which is divided into a series of segments by transverse partitions. The youngest segments occur at the posterior end, and new segments are formed in front of the last segment or pygidium.

COELOM IN ANNELIDA

The coelom in Annelida is a perivisceral cavity between the body wall and alimentary canal, it is formed from segmental vesicles of the mesoderm, it is lined on the outer side by a parietal layer of mesoderm and on the inner side by a visceral layer of mesoderm, these mesodermal layers form the peritoneum. The walls of the coelom give rise to reproductive cells and to coelomoducts which carry sperms or eggs from the coelom to the exterior. Excretory organs lead from the coelom to the outside. In some Polychaeta the coelomic peritoneum gives rise to excretory yellow cells. Coelom contains a coelomic fluid having amoeboid corpuscles, this fluid absorbs nourishment and permits transport of materials in solution.

The coelom in Polychaeta and Oligochaeta is a well developed space. In Polychaeta the coelom is perivisceral, but it is divided by a series of transverse septa lying intersegmentally from the body wall towards the gut. A septum is a double fold of peritoneum enclosing muscle fibres. The coelomic chambers are serial and they communicate through spaces around the alimentary canal where the septa are not complete. In *Arenicola* there are only first three septa and some at the posterior end so that the coelom is almost an uninterrupted space. In *Aphrodite* there is a spacious coelom lined with cilia which bring about circulation, it has developed at the expense of the blood system.

In Oligochaeta the large perivisceral coelom is divided into compartments by septa lying intersegmentally from the body wall to the alimentary canal. The first septum in *Pheretima* lies between segments 4 and 5, so that the coelom of the first four segments is continuous. The next eight septa have no apertures so that their coelomic chambers are shut off from the others, from the fourteenth segment to the end the septa have many apertures with sphincter muscles, hence, all these coelomic chambers communicate with each other.

In Hirudinea the coelom has been obliterated as a perivisceral cavity by formation of botryoidal tissue. Only one primitive leech (*Acanthobdella*) has a perivisceral coelom in the anterior region with septa. In *Hirudinaria* it is represented by four longitudinal haemocoelomic channels, their branches, and by spaces enclosing gonads and vasa deferentia. The coelomic fluid in the longitudinal channels and their branches is red due to dissolved haemoglobin, but it is not coloured in other coelomic spaces. Archiannelida have a large coelom divided into chambers by transverse septa.

NEPHRIDIA AND COELOMODUCTS

Annelida have segmentally repeated tubes called segmental organs, they are nephridia and coelomoducts.

Nephridia

Nephridia are coiled tubes formed by invagination of ectoderm, they lie in the coelom, their ciliated lumen is intracellular. A nephridium opens into the coelom by a ciliated funnel or nephrostome either in the same segment in which it lies or in the segment just in front; at the other end the nephridium opens to the exterior by a nephridiophore. Nephridia remove waste from the coelom, but their original function was probably removal of water from the body.

Coelomoducts

Coelomoducts are segmentally repeated mesodermal tubes which open at one end into the coelom by a wide ciliated funnel (which is quite different from a nephrostome), and at the other end to the exterior, their lumen is intercellular. Coelomoducts may be excretory, or combine excretion with the function of conducting germ cells to the exterior, or only to conduct germ cells to the exterior which was perhaps their original function.

Nephridia and Nephromixia

Some Polychaeta have nephridia of closed tubes, their blind ends project into the coelom, this is a primitive condition. The blind end is fringed with solenocytes lying separately or in groups. The solenocytes are round ciliated cells connected to the nephridium by a thin tube each, in the lumen of

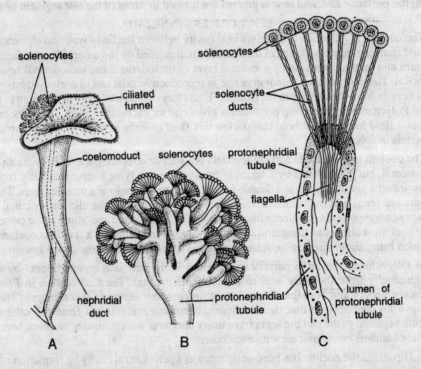

Fig. 69.1. Protonephridium and coelomoduct in *Phyllodoce paretti.* A—Relation of protonephridium and coelomoduct; B—Branched end of protonephridium; C—Solenocytes of one protonephrdial branch. (After **Goodrich**).

the tube is a long vibratile flagellum; solenocytes resemble flame cells of Platyhelminthes. Such nephridia are known as protonephridia, *e.g., Phyllodoce, Vanadis.* But in many Polychaeta and Oligochaeta the nephridia are of the open type, each having a ciliated nephrostome opening into the coelom, they are called metanephridia, *e.g., Neanthes, Lumbricus.* Some Polychaeta have compound excretory organs formed by the union of nephridia and coelomoducts, they are called

nephromixia. In these the functions of excretory organs and.genital ducts become combined. They are of three types : (a) Protonephromixium, the coelomoduct has combined with a closed protonephridium, *e.g.*, Aliciopidae, *Phyllodoce.* (b) Metanephromixium, coelomoduct is attached to an open metanephridium, *e.g., Hesione.* (c) Mixonephrium or Nephromixium, coelomoduct is attached to a nephridium in such a way that they form a single organ, the funnel being coelomoduct and the duct is nephridial, *e.g.,* Capitellidae, *Arenicola.* There is no hard-and-fast boundary between metanephromixium and mixonephrium.

In some Polychaeta, *e.g., Neanthes,* a part of the coelomoduct separates from the metanephromixium and becomes attached to the dorsolateral muscles as a dorsal ciliated organ, this keeps the coelomic fluid in circulation.

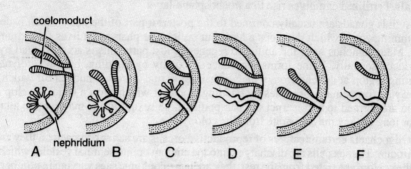

Fig. 69.2. Diagrammatic representation of nephridia and coelomoduct in various combinations in Polychaeta. A—Protonephridium and separate colemoduct (*Vanadis*); B—Protonephromixium (*Phyllodoce*); C—Protonephridium and ciliated organs (Nephthyidae and Glyceridae); D—Metanephridium and separate coelomoduct (Capitellidae); E—Mixonephridium (*Arenicola*); F—Metanephridium and ciliated organ (*Nereis*).

In some tubicolous worms, *e.g., Serpula* there is a division of labour, the nephridia of the anterior region are large and carry on excretion, and those of the posterior region are small and act as genital ducts exclusively.

In Oligochaeta and Hirudinea nephridia and coelomoducts are separate. There is generally one pair of metanephridia in each segment, but coelomoducts are restricted only to a few reproductive segments. Their nephridia may open to the outside of the body and are called exonephric nephridia (*e.g., Lumbricus*) or they may open into the gut and are known as enteronephric nephridia (*e.g. Pheretima*). In a majority of earthworms there is a pair of original large-sized metanephridia in each segment,they are called holonephridia or meganephridia, *e.g., Lumbricus.* But in *Pheretima* there is large number of small-sized nephridia in each segment, they are called meronephridia or micronephridia. It is assumed that the original pair of holonephridia has broken up to form a large number of meronephridia. In *Pheretima* there are three types of meronephridia : (a) Those of the anterior segments are many enteronephric meronephridia opening into the pharynx, they may have taken on the function of digestive glands and are called peptonephridia. (b) In every segment behind the sixth are integumentary exonephric meronephridia. (c) In all segments after the fourteenth there are enteronephric meronephridia which open into supra-intestinal excretory ducts having segmental opening into the intestine.

In Hirudinea the nephridia are generally like metanephridia of Oligochaeta, with a ciliated nephrostome opening into a coelomic space, *e.g., Hirudo.* In *Hirudinaria* the nephridia are coiled tubes opening into a bladder which leads to the exterior by a nephridiophore, the other end lies in a coelomic space but it has no nephrostome. In some Rhynchobdellida, *e.g., Pantobdella,* there is a complex network on the ventral surface of the body which gives out a pair of branches in each segment terminating in a ciliated funnel, and a similar pair of branches opening to the exterior.

Archiannelida have a pair of nephridia in each segment, they may be closed protonephridia with solenocytes, or they may be metanephridia with nephrostomes opening in the coelom, *e.g., Polygordius.*

REPRODUCTION IN ANNELIDA

In Polychaeta sexes are separate. The gonads are patches of coelomic epithelium and are repeated in most of the segments. The gonads become conspicuous during the breeding season and they proliferate a very large number of germ cells which detach and fill coelom where they undergo maturation in the coelomic fluid. When ripe the germ cells pass to the exterior either through segmental organs or by rupture of the body wall. Fertilization occurs in sea water. In many forms a phenomenon of swarming occurs, the crawling or burrowing worms rise to the surface to discharge their sex cells, then they sink to the bottom. Swarming habit is an adaptation for securing fertilization of the greatest possible number of eggs. Swarming is usually during definite periods and often coincides with lunar periods. Discharge of gametes is nearly always followed by death of the sexual individuals. Fertilized egg gives rise to a trochosphere larva.

In syllids gonads are usually confined to the posterior part of the body which is detached as a free-swimming zooid which develops a head but no jaws or pharynx, it lives for a time to produce gametes. Many annelids have the ability to regenerate lost parts, this is accompanied by a capacity to reproduce asexually. Some forms reproduce asexually by budding, but in *Autolytus* there is a proliferating region at the end from which a chain of sexual zooids is budded off which detach one by one. *Syllis* forms many branches by budding, some of which form a head, develop sex organs, notopodia are formed to reconstruct the parapodia, these sexual forms may remain attached to the parent for long or they may separate from the colony.

In Oligochaeta certain features of reproductive organs are salient characters, they are almost all hermaphrodite. The sex cells are discharged into the coelom or into seminal vesicles which are special parts of the coelom separated from the rest, they are large coelomic sacs varying in number in different genera; often a pair of seminal vesicles may coalesce to form a median sperm reservoir into which ciliated funnels of vasa deferentia open. Testes may be several but ovaries are never more than two. Spermathecae are usually present to receive spermatozoa of another worm during copulation. The clitellum is a glandular development of the epidermis for formation of cocoons and albumen for nourishment of the embryo. The clitellum may be permanent, as in earthworms, or it may develop only during the breeding season. Some Oligochaeta possess special copulatory setae. In some Oligochaeta asexual reproduction occurs, *e.g., Nais* and *Chaetogaster* multiply by proliferation of segments at the posterior end forming a chain of zooids which eventually separate and acquire sex cells.

Hirudinea are hermaphrodite with several pairs of testes but only two ovaries, gonads are completely shut off in closed coelomic vesicles, but they are continuous with their ducts in distinction from other Annelida. The spermatozoa unite in bundles to form spermatophores. Generally copulation occurs, though in some hypodermic impregnation takes place. The clitellum appears during breeding season, and eggs are laid in cocoons formed by clitellar glands.

Archiannelida are generally hermaphrodite, the ovaries occurring in anterior segments and testes behind them, so that gonads are restricted to a few segments. In *Polygordius* sexes are separate, the ovaries or testes develop in a few posterior segments, there are no ducts.

REVISION QUESTIONS

1. Give an account of nephridia and coelomoducts in Annelida.
2. Write a note on :
   (i) Reproduction in Annelida; (ii) Metamerism in Annelida; (iii) Coelom in Annelida.

70

Phylum Arthropoda

The phylum Arthropoda (Gr., *arthros*=jointed+*podos*=foot) is the largest group of the animal kingdom. Phylum Arthropoda surpasses all others both in number of individuals and in the diversity of their ecological distribution. They have undergone an adaptive radiation for aerial, aquatic, terrestrial, and parasitic environments filling every conceivable ecological niche. More than 8,00,000 species have been described, thus, Arthropoda are approximately 80 per cent of all known animals.

Arthropoda are bilaterally symmetrical, metamerically segmented Metazoa. Their metameres are not alike but are specialized, and their number is generally fixed. Either all or some segments bear paired appendages which are jointed, at least one pair of appendages function as jaws. The head is well developed. The schizocoelic coelom is much reduced and replaced by a perivisceral haemocoele which is filled with blood. Circulatory system is of the open type. Coelom is replaced by a haemocoele because a hydraulic turgescence of the body wall is no longer needed, and a consequence of reduction of coelom is the loss of nephridia. True nephridia are absent but coelomoducts act as gonoducts and often as excretory organs. Muscles are mostly striped, they are separate, unlike the continuous muscle layers of Annelida. There are no cilia in the body. There is an exoskeleton made of chitinous cuticle which is often thick and hard, but in places on the trunk and limbs it is flexible to provide movable joints. The thick cuticle has brought about several changes, it causes a necessity of joints in limbs. In order to move the hard piece of exoskeleton the muscles are separate. Thick cuticle prevents a loss of water, this has enabled Arthropoda to invade land, they are the only invertebrates which have adapted to living on land on a highly successful scale, hence, there are more terrestrial forms than in any other invertebrate phylum. But the presence of a hard exoskeletal covering of cuticle has created two problems which had to be overcome in the evolution of arthropods, they are the problems of growth and locomotion. Problem of growth has been solved by periodic moultings so that the animal can increase in size before the new cuticle becomes hardened. The problem of locomotion was removed by division of the cuticle of the body and appendages to form separate plates or sclerites, with thin, soft and flexible articular membranes between any two sclerites which permit bending and locomotion. Arthropoda have evolved from annelids or at least from some common ancestor.

71

Palaemon (=*Macrobrachium*) (Prawn)

Palaemon (now known as *Macrobrachium*) is commonly known as prawn. A large number of species of the genus *Palaemon* are distributed in freshwater streams, rivers, lakes, and ponds all over India. The common Indian species of *Palaemon* are : *P. malcolmsonii, P. carcinus, P. idae, P. rudis* and *P. lamarrei*. Several species of *Palaemon* are also found outside India, *e.g., P. jamaicensis* in West Indies and *P. heterochirus* in Mexico, while a number of other species range over the isles of the Pacific and Australia. *Palaemon malcolmsonii,* which is studied in most of the Indian Universities as a typical representative of the class Crustacea, is described here in detail. The description of *P. malcolmsonii,* given under, is largely based on the work of Patwardhan (1937).

PALAEMON (= MACROBRACHIUM)
SYSTEMATIC POSITION

Phylum	....	**Arthropoda**
Subphylum	....	**Mandibulata**
Class	....	**Crustacea**
Subclass	....	**Malacostraca**
Order	....	**Decapoda**
Genus	....	*Palaemon* (=*Macrobrachium*)
Species	....	*malcolmsonii*

HABIT AND HABITAT

Palaemon inhabits freshwater streams, rivers, lakes and ponds. It is a nocturnal creature and lies hidden at the bottom during the day and comes to the surface during night in search of food. It prefers slow moving clean water and feeds on algae, mosses and other weeds, small insects and the debris, *i.e.,* omnivorous. It walks slowly at the bottom with the help of walking legs and swims actively at the surface with the help of swimmerets (pleopods). *P. malcolmsonii* breeds in May, June and July and the females carry eggs attached to their pleopods (abdominal appendages).

EXTERNAL FEATURES

Shape and size. The body of *Palaemon* is elongated, more or less spindle-shaped and bilaterally symmetrical. The size of the adult *Palaemon* varies considerably in different species. *P. carcinus* from Travancore measures 90 cm, *P. malcolmsonii* from Central Provinces and Madras is generally 25 to 38 cm and *P. lamarrei,* another common species in lakes and ponds, is only 2.5 to 5 cm in length.

Colouration. The young specimens are trasparent, pale yellow or perfectly white in appearance, but the older specimens are differently tinted according to the species. The colour is generally pale blue or greenish with brown or orange-red patches and bands of different patterns. The preserved specimens assume deep orange-red colour on a white or yellow background.

Division of body. The body of adult *Palaemon* is consisting of nineteen appendage bearing segments having two distinct regions : an anterior rigid cephalothorax and a posterior movable abdomen.

(i) Cephalothorax. The cephalothorax is somewhat cylindrical in shape and is unjointed; no external segmentation is marked. It is formed by the union of head comprising five appendage-bearing segments and the thorax comprising eight segments.

(ii) Abdomen. The abdomen, rounded dorsally but compressed laterally, is jointed, *i.e.,* external segmentation is clearly marked and composed of six movable segments having a terminal conical piece, telson. The abdomen is often turned downwards. Each segment of the abdomen carries a pair of jointed appendages called pleopods or swimmerets.

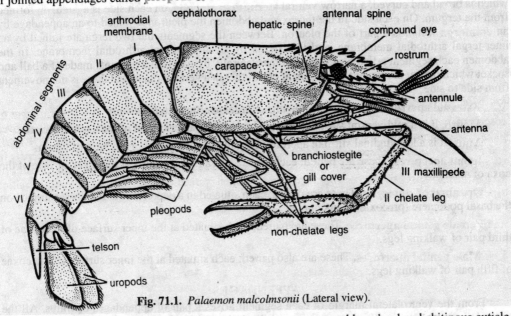

Fig. 71.1. *Palaemon malcolmsonii* (Lateral view).

Exoskeleton. The entire body and the appendages are covered by a hard and chitinous cuticle which forms exoskeleton. The exoskeleton is hardened by deposit of salts of lime and is coloured with various pigments. The hard pieces of exoskeleton are called sclerites which are joined by softer cuticle forming arthrodial membrane. The cephalothorax consists of a head and thorax, the head is covered with a dorsal plate and thorax with a carapace. The dorsal plate and carapace are completely fused to form a continuous dorsal shield. The dorsal shield is produced in front into a rostrum which is laterally compressed and is serrated. At the base of rostrum, on either side is an orbital notch which accommodates the stalk of compound eye. The dorsal plate has two short spines on each side, they are an antennal and a hepatic spine. The carapace hangs down on the sides of the thorax as a branchiostegite or lateral plate which encloses the gill chamber. On the ventral side of head and thorax are chitinous sclerites called sterna. The cephalothorax is joined to the abdomen by a calcified hardened arthrodial membrane.

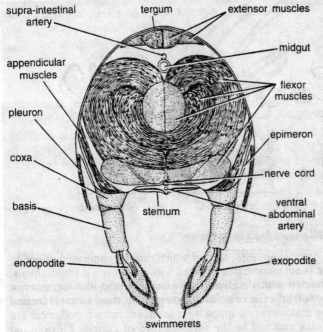

The dorsal shield covers the head and thorax dorsally and laterally. On the ventral side are sterna, they are an anteriormost ophthalmic sternum, behind it an antennular sternum, followed by an antennal sternum or epistome to which a medium labrum is attached. The third and fourth segments have no sterna. The sterna of segments 5 to 13 have

Fig. 71.2. *Palaemon.* A diagrammatic hand section passing transversely through an abdominal segment to show the sclerites.

fused to form a floor. On the sides of segments 5 to 13 are 9 pairs of chitinous sclerites called epimera, one epimeron on each side of a segment. In the abdomen each segment has a dorsal tergum or tergite which is broad and curved, a narrow ventral sternum or sternite, on each side is a pleuron formed from the tergum. On each side in the thorax and abdomen the pleuron is joined to an appendage by an epimeron which is a part of the pleuron. Between the segments the two terga are joined by an inter-tergal arthrodial membrane, and two sterna by an inter-sternal arthrodial membrane. In the abdomen each segment articulates with the other laterally by pair of hinge-joints made of a ball and socket which permit movement of a segment on another in a vertical plane, but there is no movement from side to side.

External apertures. There are following external apertures in *Palaemon* :

Mouth. It is a mid-ventral slit-like aperture lying at the anterior end of the cephalothorax.

Anus. It is a longitudinal slit-like aperture lying at the ventral end of the base of telson.

Renal apertures. These are paired; each situated on a raised papilla at the inner surface of the coxa of antennae.

Openings of statocysts. These are paired; each situated in a depression at the dorsal surface on the basal podomere (precoxa) of antennules.

Female genital apertures. These are paired; each situated at the inner surface of the coxae of third pair of walking legs.

Male genital apertures. These are also paired; each situated at the inner surface of the coxae of fifth pair of walking legs.

APPENDAGES

From the ventrolateral margin of each segment arises a pair of appendages or limbs. All the appendages are biramous (L., *bi*=two+*ramus*=branch), except the first pair which are uniramous (L., *uni*=one +*ramus*=branch). Each appendage has a basal stalk or protopodite made of two joints or podomeres, a lower coxapodite or coxa and an upper basopodite or basis. From the protopodite arise

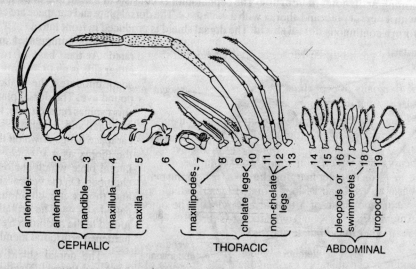

Fig. 71.3. Appendages of *Palaemon*.

two rami, an inner endopodite and an outer exopodite, each of which may be composed of one to several podomeres. The first appendage is not comparable in detail with the others, it is uniramous. Each appendage has a cuticular exoskeleton which is divided in most into tube-like segments or podomeres connected to one another by soft articular or arthrodial membrane, thus, a joint is created at each junction, these joints enable the podomeres of appendages to move. In each podomere are two protractor and two retractor muscles attached to the inner surface of cuticle. Flexion and extension of appendages are brought about by the muscles, with the muscles and cuticle acting together as a lever system. This co-ordination of muscular and skeletal systems for locomotion is essentially the same as in vertebrates, the only difference is that in arthropods muscles are attached to the inner surface of an exoskeleton, whereas in vertebrates the muscles are attached to the outer surface of an endoskeleton. Generally all the appendages are one of the following two types : (a) Stenopodium is a slender limb, its endopodite and exopodite are set on a common stalk, the protopodite. (b) Phyllopodium is broad and leaf-like with thinner cuticle, the endopodite and exopodite do not form a fork.

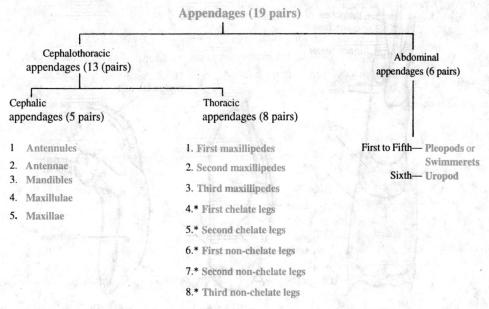

Appendages (19 pairs)

Cephalothoracic appendages (13 (pairs)

Abdominal appendages (6 pairs)

Cephalic appendages (5 pairs)

Thoracic appendages (8 pairs)

Cephalic	Thoracic	Abdominal
1 Antennules	1. First maxillipedes	First to Fifth— Pleopods or Swimmerets
2. Antennae	2. Second maxillipedes	Sixth— Uropod
3. Mandibles	3. Third maxillipedes	
4. Maxillulae	4.* First chelate legs	
5. Maxillae	5.* Second chelate legs	
	6.* First non-chelate legs	
	7.* Second non-chelate legs	
	8.* Third non-chelate legs	

* These five pairs of thoracic legs are called walking legs.

In *Palaemon*, however, as referred to, all the appendages are built on a biramous plan (except the first) but they are modified variously ; it is because of their different functions.

A. Cephalic Appendages

Of the five pairs of cephalic appendages, first two, *i.e.*, antennules and antennae are pre-oral, while mandibles, maxillulae and maxillae are post-oral.

1. Antennules. The antennules are situated, one on either side, immediately below the bases of eye-stalks. Antennules are uniramous. Each antennule consists of a protopodite having three podomeres, precoxa, coxa and basis and a pair of slender many jointed feelers. The precoxa is very large and bears a depression, containing the opening of statocyst on its dorsal side and a spiny lobe called stylocerite on its outer margin. The coxa is short and cylindrical. The basis is longer than coxa. From the basis arises a pair of long, jointed feelers which are probably not homologous with the exopodite and endopodite of a typical appendage. The outer feeler is divided into two unequal branches. Antennule is tactile and its statocyst is for equilibration. Antennules are homologous with the antennae of other mandibulate classes.

2. Antennae. The antennae are situated, one on either side, just below and behind the antennules. The protopodite is considerably swollen due to the presence of the excretory organ within it, which opens by minute renal aperture on the inner margin of coxa. The exopodite is broad leaf-like plate, the squama, while the endopodite is long many jointed feeler. The squama bears setae along its inner and distal margin and probably serves the function of a balancer during swimming. The antennae are tactile, excretory and balancing in function.

3. Mandibles. The mandibles are short but stout appendages, lying one on each side of the mouth. The greater part of each mandible consists of the coxa which is differentiated into a proximal spoon-shaped apophysis and a solid distal head. The head consists of two parts : a molar process with five or six dental plates and a flat plate-like incisor process with three teeth. The outer margin

of the head carries a small three jointed mandibular palp. The proximal segment of the mandibular palp represents the basis of the protopodite, while the two distal segments represent the endopodite. The exopodite is absent. The mandibles are masticatory .n function.

4. **Maxillulae.** The maxillulae are small, thin and leaf-like appendages. Coxa and basis are broad, and project inwards as jaws or gnathobases (Gr., *gnathos* =jaw) fringed with bristles. Endopodite is curved and bifurcated terminally, it has small hooks. Exopodite is absent. The maxillulae are used for passing food to the mouth.

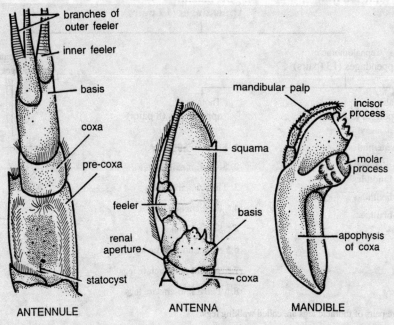

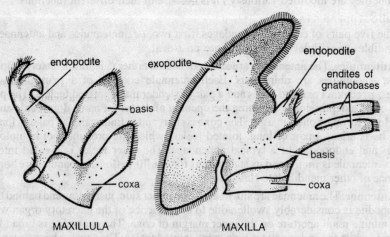

Fig. 71.4. *Palaemon.* Cephalic appendages.

5. **Maxillae.** The maxillae are also thin and leaf-like appendages. The coxa is very small and incompletely divided into two, while the basis is larger forming a bifurcated gnathobase with stiff setae at its inner end. The endopodite is small, while the exopodite forms a large fan-shaped scaphognathite or baler with plumose bristles along its border. The scaphognathite projects into a gill-chamber causing a current of water on the gills. Maxillae have both feeding and respiratory function.

B. Thoracic Appendages

The thoracic appendages consist of the anterior three pairs of maxillipedes (Gr., *maxilla*=jaw+*podos*=foot)or foot jaws and posterior five pairs of walking legs or paraeopods.

1. First maxillipedes. The first maxillipedes or foot jaws are thin and tend to be phyllopodium. Coxa and basis form flat leaf-like gnathobases or endites by its inner borders. On its outer side coxa bears a bilobed leaf-like epipodite which acts as a gill. The endopodite is small and unsegmented. The exopodite is longer and bears a thin plate-like expansion from its base. The margin of exopodite and endopodite are fringed with setae. First maxillipedes hold the food and also serve the function of tactile and respiratory organs.

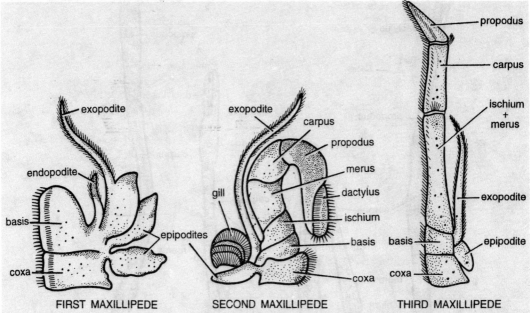

Fig.71.5. *Palaemon.* Maxillipedes.

2. Second maxillipedes. The coxa is small with an epipodite and a gill on its outer border. The exopodite is long and slender. The endopodite arises from the basis and consists of five podomeres called ischium, merus, carpus, propodus and dactylus. Of these propodus and dactylus lie parallel and form a cutting plate with bristles. Second maxillipedes are tactile, hold food and are respiratory.

3. Third maxillipedes. The third maxillipedes are distinctly leg-like in appearance. The coxa bears a small epipodite on its outer side. The basis is small and supports a slender unjointed exopodite and an elongated endopodite consisting of three podomeres. In the endopodite the first podomere represents fused ischium and merus, second is the carpus and third represents fused propodus and dactylus. The exopodite is thickly covered with setae all along its length. Third maxillipedes are tactile, hold food and are respiratory.

Walking legs. The five pairs of walking legs of *Palaemon* differ from the maxillipedes in the absence of the exopodites and epipodites. A typical walking leg, like the fourth, consists of a two jointed protopodite and a five jointed endopodite. The protopodite consists of a short ring-shaped coxa and a triangular basis. The endopodite consists of five podomeres, *viz.,* ischium, merus, carpus, propodus, and dactylus. All the seven podomeres are arranged in a linear series and are movably hinged together. In the first and second pairs of walking legs the propodus is prolonged distally beyond its articulation with the dactylus, so that the two podomeres work one against the other like the blades of a pair of forceps forming a chela or pincers with sharp terminal claws. In fact, dactylus is movably articulated to propodus. Such legs are called chelate legs or chelipeds, and are used to catch the prey and transfer it to the mouth and also serve as organs of offense and defence. The second chelate legs in male are larger and more powerful than in the female.

The third, fourth and fifth pairs of walking legs are typical and non-chelate. In female, each of the third leg bears a crescentic female genital aperture on the inner side of its coxa, while in male, each of the fifth leg bears a slit-like male genital aperture on its side of the arthrodial membrane connecting the leg and thorax.

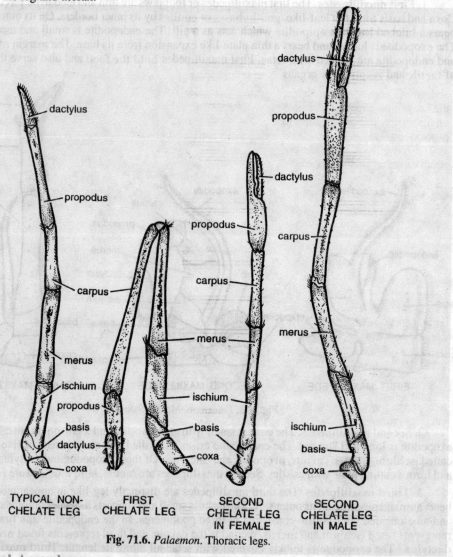

Fig. 71.6. *Palaemon.* Thoracic legs.

C. Abdominal Appendages

The six pairs of abdominal appendages are known as pleopods or swimmerets. Abdominal appendages are simple and typical biramous type. The third abdominal appendage may be taken as a typical type.

Third abdominal appendages. Protopodite consists of only two podomeres, a short ring-like proximal coxa and a long cylindrical distal basis. The basis bears flattened leaf-like smaller endopodite and larger exopodite. Closely applied against the inner margin of the endopodite, there is a short and slender, slightly curved rod called appendix interna with a knob-like head, bearing many hook-like processes. In the female , second, third, fourth and fifth abdominal appendages serve to carry eggs in the breeding season. The appendix interna of each of these appendages becomes interlocked with its fellow of the opposite side, thus, leading to the formation of a series of bridges on the ventral side of the abdomen which serve to carry the eggs. The remaining five abdominal appendages resemble this typical appendage in all essential features but there are small differences which are given below.

First abdominal append-ages. In the first abdominal appendages, the **endopodite** is greatly reduced and the **appendix interna** is totally absent.

Second abdominal appendages of male. In the second abdominal appendages of male, the appendix interna gives off on its inner side an additional process called **appendix masculina** lying in between the appendix interna and endopodite.

Uropod. The sixth or the last pair of abdominal appendages are very large and form broad flat plates and lie one on either side of the telson. These appendages are called **uropods** or **tail feet.** In the uropod, the coxa and basis are fused together to form a **sympod.** The exopodite and endopodite are oval and oar-shaped. The exopodite is broad and large and is divided into two unequal parts by a transverse suture. The endopodite is slightly smaller and is undivided. The margins of exopodite and endopodite, except the outer border of the exopodite, are fringed with long plumose setae. The two uropods with the telson form a fan-like **tail fin** which causes the strong and rapid backward spring of prawn in swimming.

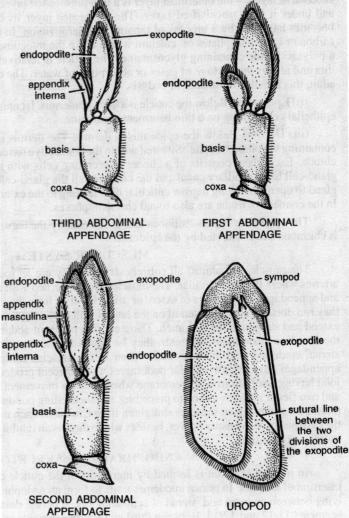

Fig. 71.7. *Palaemon.* Abdominal appendages.

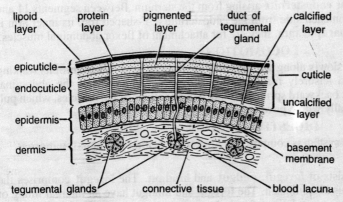

Fig. 71.8. *Palaemon.* T.S. of body wall.

BODY WALL

The body wall of *Palaemon* consists of an outer thick layer of **cuticle,** a middle single-layered **epidermis** and an inner **dermis.**

(i) Cuticle. The body is covered with a thick two-layered cuticle, the outer layer is a thin non-chitinous **epicuticle** and an inner layer is a thick laminated **endocuticle.** The **epicuticle** is made of an outer **lipoid layer** and an inner **protein layer.** It is produced into spines and setae of different forms and bears, at places, the fringes of setae. The endocuticle contains layers of chitin and has three successive layers—the outermost layer is a thin pigmented layer, below it is a thick calcified layer and under it is an uncalcified layer. The pigmented layer is dark due to protein deposits and it becomes hardened by a process of tanning or sclerotization. In the calcified layer are deposists of carbonates and phosphates of calcium which make the integument hard. The chitin is an acetate of a polysaccharide containing glycosamine. The cuticle is relatively impermeable, except where it is thin and allows the passage of gases or absorption of water. The cuticle is cast off once a year in the adult, this is called moulting or ecdysis.

(ii) Epidermis. Below the cuticle is a thick epidermis. It comprises a layer of glandular columnar epithelial cells resting on a thin basement membrane.

(iii) Dermis. Below the epidermis is dermis. The dermis is made of loose connective tissue containing the blood lacunae. Situated within the connective tissue layer are a number of tegumental glands. Each gland consists of a cluster of secreting cells with nuclei placed at their bases. Each gland-cell has a capillary canal and the canals of all the gland-cells join together in the centre of the gland to open into a long narrow cuticular duct leading to the exterior on the surface of the epicuticle. In the connective tissue are also found chromatophores.

The epicuticle is non-chitinous and is secreted by the tegumental glands, while endocuticle is chitinous and is secreted by the epidermis.

MUSCULAR SYSTEM

The muscles are almost all entirely striped, they are all longitudinal, except in the heart and arteries where they are circular. The muscles are concerned with extension and flexion of abdomen and appendages. Seven pairs of extensor muscles arise from the six abdominal segments and telson, they run dorsally and are inserted on the lateral wall of the thorax, when these muscles contract they extend and straighten the abdomen. There are five paires of abdominal flexor muscles arising from the first five abdominal segments, they lie ventrally and are very strong, they are inserted on the sterna, epidermis and thoracic wall. When flexor muscles contract they bend the abdomen. The appendages have hollow, tubular podomeres, two adjacent prodomeres being connected by a hinge joint having a soft arthrodial membrane which permits movement. Each podomere has two extensor and two flexor muscles joined to preceding and succeeding podomeres, the flexor muscles bend the podomere and extensor muscles straighten it. In Crustacea each muscle has only two to five nerves, they are motor and sensory nerves, besides which there is an inhibitory nerve which inhibits or checks muscles contraction.

ENDOPHRAGMAL SKELETON

An internal skeleton is formed by ingrowths of the cuticle called apodemes which serve for insertion of muscles. In prawn apodemes unite to form an endophragmal skeleton. It consists of rods lying between epimera and sterna of cephalothorax. It is best developed between segments 3/4 and segments 11/12 and 12/13. Between third and fourth segments are two large apodemes joined by a transverse fibrous strand, together they form a cephalic apodeme for attachment of mandibular muscles. In succeeding segments on each side there are two adjacent apodemes, an endopleurite arising from the epimeron, and ar endosternite arising from the sternum. Between segments 11 and 12, and 12 and 13 there arises on each side from the endosternite a Y-shaped rod, its inner arm is mesophragm and outer arm is paraphragm, they are for attachment of flexor abdominal muscles.

LOCOMOTION

Palaemon crawls or walks slowly along the bottom of the river or pond by means of its walking legs. It can swim forward in a leisurely manner by beating its swimmerets or the abdominal appendages. It may take a quick backward spring by sudden contractions of the muscles, which pull the uropods and the telson ventrally with a powerful stroke.

DIGESTIVE SYSTEM

In *Palaemon*, the digestive system is composed of alimentary canal and hepatopancreas.

Alimentary Canal

The alimentary canal consists of foregut, midgut and hindgut. The foregut comprises the mouth, buccal cavity, oesophagus and stomach. The foregut and hindgut have an internal lining of cuticle (intima) but the midgut has a soft lining of endoderm.

(i) Mouth. The mouth is a large slit-like aperture situated mid-ventrally below the anterior end of head between the third and fourth segments. It is bounded in front by a shield-shaped labrum, on the sides by the incisor processes of the mandibles, and behind by the labium which is cleft to form two lobes or paragnatha.

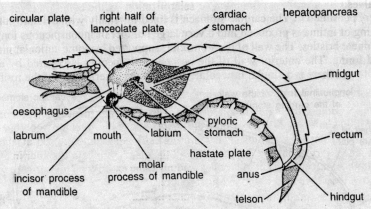

Fig. 71.9. *Palaemon.* Alimentary canal in lateral view.

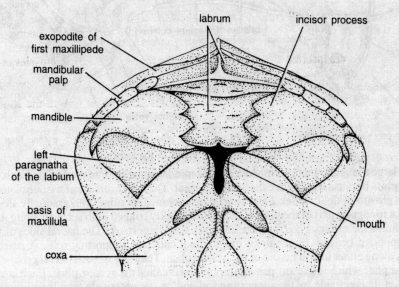

Fig. 71.10. *Palaemon.* Ventral view of the oral region.

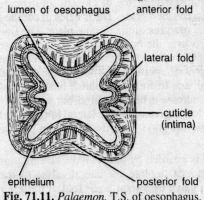

Fig. 71.11. *Palaemon.* T.S. of oesophagus.

(ii) Buccal cavity. The mouth leads into a short buccal cavity. It is antero-posteriorly compressed and has a thick chitinous lining which is thrown into irregular folds. The molar processes of the mandibles project into the buccal cavity from two sides to crush the food between them.

(iii) Oesophagus. The buccal cavity leads into short but broad oesophagus running almost vertically upwards from the buccal cavity to the stomach. Internally the thick muscular wall of the oesophagus is thrown into four prominent longitudinal folds projecting into the lumen. Of these folds, the anterior is short but the posterior and lateral folds are longer and more prominent. Each of the lateral folds being subdivided into two smaller unequal folds.

(iv) Stomach. The oesophagus leads into a spacious chamber, the stomach, which occupies most of the cephalothoracic cavity. It is surrounded laterally, ventrally and posteriorly by the hepatopancreas. The stomach is divided into two parts : (a) a large anterior bag-like cardiac stomach, and (b) a very small posterior pyloric stomach. Cardiac and pyloric stomach are separated by a number of valves.

(a) Cardiac stomach. The cardiac stomach is lined internally with delicate cuticle or intima. The inner lining of intima is produced into a very large number of inconspicuous longitudinal folds covered by minute bristles. The wall of the stomach is supported by some cuticular plates embedded in its internal lining. The anterior wall of the oesophageal opening is covered by a thin circular cuticular plate and there is a similar lanceolate plate on the anterior part of the roof of the cardiac

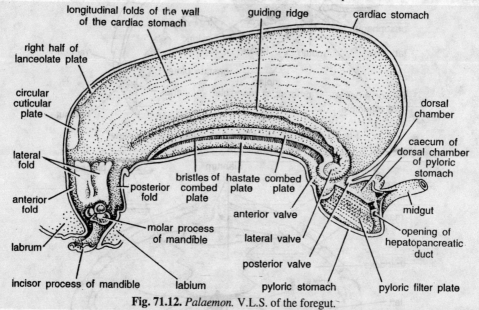

Fig. 71.12. *Palaemon.* V.L.S. of the foregut.

stomach. A large triangular plate is embedded in the middle of the floor of cardiac stomach, it is called the hastate plate because it looks like the head of a spear. The upper surface of hastate plate is covered with a thick growth of delicate setae and bears a distinct median ridge with gradually sloping sides. The posterior triangular part of the plate is depressed, thickly fringed with setae all along its posterior border and forms the anterior valve of the cardio-pyloric aperture. The lateral sides of the hastate plate are supported beneath by a pair of longitudinal cuticular supporting rods. A narrow lateral groove runs along either lateral border of the hastate plate. The floor of each lateral groove is covered by a cuticular plate which is like an open drain-pipe and is called the groove plate. Each lateral groove is bounded on its inner side by the supporting rod and on the outer side by a long cuticular ridged plate. The inner border of each ridged plate is forged all along with a row of closely set delicate bristles, forming a long comb-like structure, therefore, called a combed plate. The bristles of combed plate cover the lateral groove and partially overlap the lateral margins of the hastate plate. The fine bristles of the comb plate constantly keep moving to and fro over the outer margin of the hastate plate. The two combed plates united anteriorly, and completely enclose the hastate plate except that their incurved posterior ends remain separated by the cardio-pyloric aperture. Just outside the combed plates, the wall of cardiac stomach is folded on each lateral side to form two bluish black lateral longitudinal folds. These folds are low in front but gradually increase in height behind, but posteriorly the high walls of these folds bend inwards over the cardio-pyloric aperture. These lateral longitudinal folds are also known as guiding ridges because they guide the food towards the cardio-pyloric aperture.

The cardio-pyloric aperture is narrow X-shaped and is guarded by four valves. The anterior valve is formed by the low-lying posterior triangular area of hastate plate, the lateral valves by the large flap-like posterior ends of guiding ridges and posterior valve by a semi-lunar fold of posterior wall of cardiac stomach. The cardio-pyloric aperture leads into the pyloric stomach.

(b) Pyloric stomach. The pyloric stomach is a very small and narrow chamber lying below the posterior end of the cardiac stomach. Its walls are thick and muscular, they divide the lumen of the pyloric stomach into a small dorsal chamber and a large ventral chamber, the two communicating with each other by a narrow vertical slit-like aperture. The floor of the chamber is raised into a median

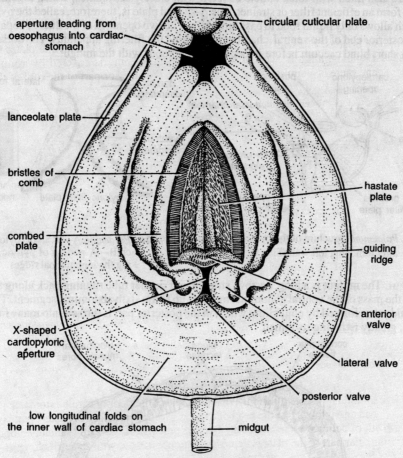

Fig. 71.13. *Palaemon.* Floor of cardiac stomach in dorsal view.

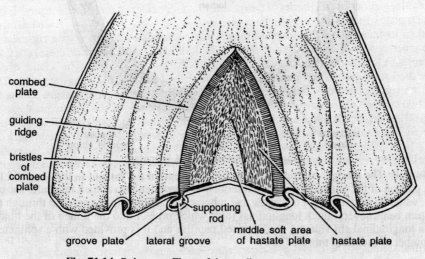

Fig. 71.14. *Palaemon.* Floor of the cardiac stomach cut across.

longitudinal ridge so as to divide its cavity into two lateral compartments. The floor of ventral chamber is covered by a Λ-shaped filter plate, each side of which is rectangular in outline and bearing a series of alternating longitudinal ridges and grooves. The ridges bear rows of horizontal comb-like bristles which form a felt-like covering over the grooves. The lateral walls of the ventral chamber are also lined with thick cuticle covered with closely set bristles, which together with the filter plate form an efficient filter or strainer. The Λ-shaped plate is, therefore, called the pyloric filter plate which allows only liquid food to pass through it. The two openings of the duct of hepatopancreas lie at the posterior end of the ventral chamber just behind the filtering apparatus. The dorsal chamber gives off a short blind caecum before it becomes continuous with the midgut.

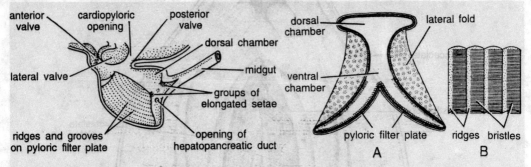

Fig. 71.15. *Palaemon.* Structure of the pyloric stomach after removing left wall (Side view).

Fig. 71.16. *Palaemon.* A—T.S. of pyloric stomach; B—A portion of pyloric filter showing the longitudinal ridges.

Midgut. The midgut is a long, narrow, straight and slender tube running back along the median line above the mass of the ventral abdominal muscles up to the sixth abdominal segment. The internal lining of midgut is formed by epithelium which in the posterior part is thrown into many longitudinal folds, thus, greatly reducing its lumen.

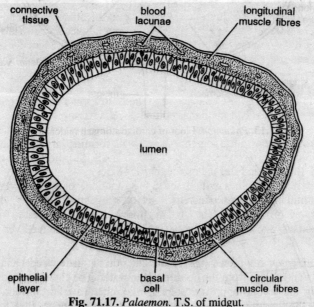

Fig. 71.17. *Palaemon.* T.S. of midgut.

Hindgut. The hindgut extends from the posterior end of the midgut to the anus and forms the shortest portion of the alimentary canal. Anteriorly it is swollen into a thick muscular sac called the rectum, while its posterior part is narrow and tubular which opens to the exterior through the anus. The rectum bears several thick longitudinal folds which project into the lumen of the hindgut. The anus is a longitudinal slit situated on the raised papillae and it is provided with a sphincter muscle and a number of radiating muscle fibres.

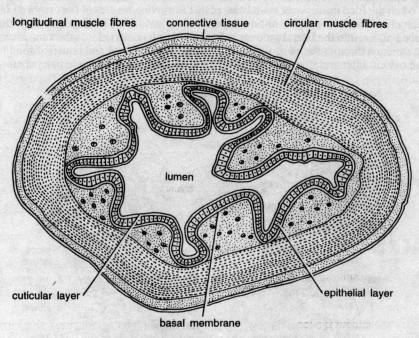

Fig. 71.18. *Palaemon*. T.S. of rectum.

Hepatopancreas

The hepatopancreas or the so called liver is a large bilobed, compact, orange-coloured glandular mass occupying a considerable area of cephalothoracic cavity. It lies immediately behind the cardiac stomach but a part of it lies around the floor and sides of the stomach. Dorsally it is covered over by the reproductive organs and the heart, while ventrally it overlies the nerve cord. Developmentally it is formed from one pair of lateral tubular outgrowths, the hepatic caeca, of the midgut. The hepatopancreas of adult consists of numerous glandular tubules branching in a racemose manner, the branches are held together by the connective tissue as to form a compact mass. The wall of the tubules is made of a single layer of columnar epithelial cells having granular cells, ferment cells, hepatic cells and basal or replacing cells. The epithelial cells rest on a basement membrane. The canals of the numerous tubules unite together at intervals forming larger and larger canals, finally forming the two large hepatopancreatic ducts which open into the ventral chamber of pyloric stomach just behind the pyloric filter plate, one on each side.

The hepatopancreas combines within itself the functions of the pancreas, liver and small intestine of higher animals. Like the pancreas it secretes digestive ferments which are capable of digesting carbohydrates, proteins and fats. Like the midgut it absorbs digested food material. It also serves as an important storage organ for glycogen, fat and calcium like the liver.

Food and Feeding

The food of *Palaemon* comprises algae, moss and other aquatic weeds, and occasionally some small aquatic insects and debris from the bottom of the water. The chelate legs pick up the food and take it to the mouth, the second and third pairs of maxillipedes hold the food in position for the mandibles, to cut up the food into small pieces by their incisor processes, then food is transferred to the mouth. In the mouth cavity the molar processes of mandibles crush the food which goes to the cardiac stomach through the oesophagus.

Digestion, Absorption and Egestion

The smaller particles of the food from the cardiac stomach are passed on to the pyloric stomach. The digestive secretion of the hepatopancreas is poured into the pyloric stomach through the hepatopancreatic ducts. Secretion reaches the cardiac stomach and mixes with the food. By the contraction and expansion of cardiac stomach the food is churned and also digested by the digestive ferments. When the food passes over the hastate plate the moving bristles of the combed plates cut it into fine particles. The food in the semi-liquid and semi-digested form is filtered through the bristles of the combed plates, into the lateral grooves below, whence it is carried into the ventral chamber of the pyloric stomach through the cardio-pyloric aperture. The digested and liquefied food is filtered through the pyloric filter and it again enters the hepatopancreas through the hepatopancreatic ducts

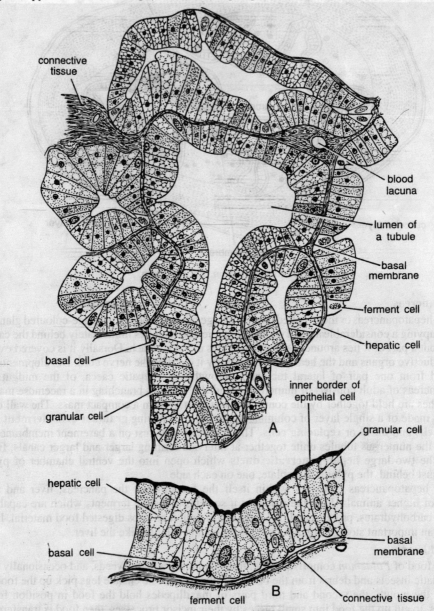

Fig.71.19. *Palaemon.* A—T.S. through a portion of the hepatopancreas ; B—T.S. of a portion of the wall of an hepatopancreatic tubule.

and then becomes absorbed. The hepatopancreas serves for digestion as well as for absorption. The residual food material, consisting of undigested particles, ascends up the dorsal pyloric chamber and from there enters the midgut. The remaining digested food is absorbed in the midgut. The undigested faecal matter passes on to the posterior side of the hindgut and ultimately expelled through the anus.

RESPIRATORY SYSTEM

In *Palaemon,* the respiratory organs are well developed and consist of 1. branchiostegites or gill covers, 2. three pairs of epipodites, and 3. eight pairs of gills or branchiae.

1. Branchiostegites. Each gill chamber is enclosed between the branchiostegite or carapace on the outer side and the thoracic wall on the inner side. The gill chambers open on all sides except dorsally. The inner linings of branchiostegites are thin, membranous and highly vascular containing blood lacunae. These are constantly bathed in freshwater, thus, forming the respiratory surfaces which absorb oxygen dissolved in water and give out carbon dioxide.

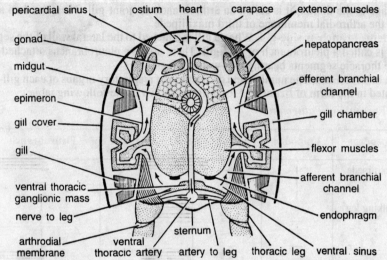

Fig. 71.20. *Palaemon.* A hand section through the cephalothorax to show gill chambers.

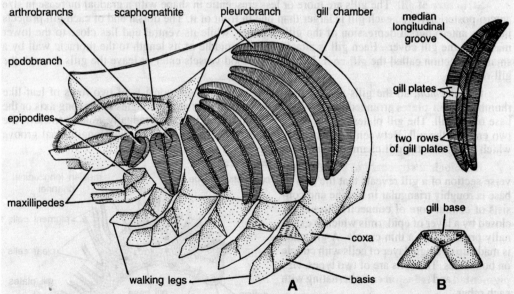

Fig. 71.21. *Palaemon.* A—Left gill-chamber exposed after the removal of the branchiostegite to show the gills ; B—A phyllobranch.

2. Epipodites. There are three pairs of simple, leaf-like and highly vascular epipodites which are the outgrowths of the coxal podomeres of three maxillipedes. The epipodites lie in the anterior part of the gill-chamber below the scaphognathite. The epipodites serve as respiratory organs like the primitive gills.

3. Gills. There are eight gills or branchiae lying inside each gill-chamber but only seven of them are exposed at once on the removal of gill-cover as the eighth lies hidden beneath the dorsal part of the second gill.

Types of gills. Gills are named according to their place of origin and attachment. There are three kinds of gills which are as follows :

(i) **Podobranch or foot-gill.** When a gill is attached to the coxa of an appendage, it is known as podobranch or foot-gill. There is **one** podobranch attached to the coxa of each second maxillipede.

(ii) **Arthrobranch or joint-gill.** When a gill is attached to the arthrodial membrane connecting the appendage to the thorax, it is called an arthrobranch or joint-gill. There are **two** arthrobranchs attached to the arthrodial membrane of third maxillipede.

(iii) **Pleurobranch or side-gill.** When a gill is attached to the lateral wall of the segment having the limb, it is called a pleurobranch or side-gill. There are five pleurobranchs attached to the lateral walls of the thoracic segments bearing five walking legs.

Branchial formula. The number and dispostiton of respiratory organs of each gill-chamber can · be represented in the form of branchial formula as shown in the following table :

Branchial Formula of *Palaemon*

Appendage	Epipodite	Podobranch	Arthrobranch	Pleurobranch	Total
I Maxillipede	1	—	—	—	1
II ,, ,,	1	1	—	—	2
III ,, ,,	1	—	2	—	3
I Walking leg	—	—	—	1	1
II ,, ,,	—	—	—	1	1
III ,, ,,	—	—	—	1	1
IV ,, ,,	—	-	—	1	1
V ,, ,,	—	—	—	1	1
Total	3	1	2	5	11

Structure of gill. The gills are more or less crescentic in shape with a gradual increase in size antero-posteriorly, *i.e.*, each gill is larger than one in front of it. The dorsal end of each gill projects into the antero-dorsal depression of the gill chamber, while its ventral end lies close to the lower margin of the gill cover . Each gill is attached in the middle of its length to the thoracic wall by a small connection called the gill-root. Nerves and blood vessels enter or leave the gills through the gill-roots.

In *Palaemon*, all the gills are phyllobranch, *i.e.*, each gill consists of two rows of leaf-like rhomboidal gill-plates arranged like the leaves of book and lie at right angles to the long axis or the base of the gill. The gill plates are largest in the middle but become gradually smaller towards the two ends of the gill. Between the two rows of gill-plates runs a deep median longitudinal groove which opens into the gill-chamber at both the dorsal and ventral ends of the gill.

Histological structure of gill. A transverse section of a gill reveals that the axis or base is roughly triangular in outline and consists of central core of connective tissue enclosed by a layer of epidermis which is externally protected by a thin cuticle. A gill plate is made up of single layer of cells with cuticle on both sides. The cells are of two types, *viz.*, pigmented and transparent, alternating with each other.

Vascular supply of the gills. Three longitudinal blood channels run through each gill base. There are two lateral longitudinal channels, running along the lateral margins, one on each side. The third is a median longitudinal channel, which runs through the

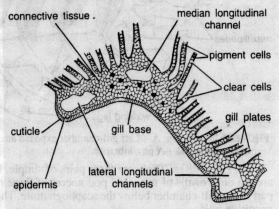

Fig. 71.22. *Palaemon.* An oblique T.S. of a gill.

apex of gill base below the median groove of the gill. The two lateral longitudinal channels are connected with each other by a series of small transverse connectives which present a ladder-like appearance. At the place of attachment of each gill-plate on the axis, a slender marginal channel is given off from each lateral longitudinal channel which runs all along the margin of its gill-plate and opens into the median longitudinal channel.

Course of blood in a gill. Non-aerated or impurified blood from the body is brought to the gill by an afferent branchial channel which opens into a transverse connective lying immediately against the root of the gill. The blood then flows into both the lateral longitudinal channels and passes through the marginal channels and reaches the median longitudinal channel. During this course the blood gets oxygenated. From the median longitudinal channel of each gill all the oxygenated blood is carried by an efferent branchial channel to the pericardial sinus and heart.

Mechanism of Respiration

The scaphognathite of each maxilla vibrates constantly causing a current of water in the gill chamber. The freshwater enters the gill chamber from behind in the form of a current along the posterior and ventral margins of the gill cover. The water then flows

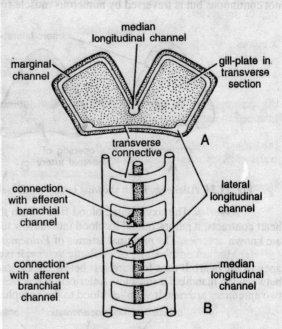

Fig. 71.23. *Palaemon.* A—Blood supply in gill-plates; B— A diagrammatic representation of the ladder of blood channels in a gill.

over the gills and epipodites and reaches the antero-dorsal depression of the gill chamber wherefrom it is expelled out at the anterior end by the baling action of the scaphognathite. The gills and epipodites are richly supplied with blood and exchange of gases takes place on the surface of gills and epipodites. The oxygen dissolved in water is taken in by blood and carbon dioxide diffuses out in the water. The action of scaphognathite is supplemented by the movements of the exopodites of maxillipedes.

BLOOD VASCULAR SYSTEM

In *Palaemon*, the blood vascular system is of the open type. It comprises : 1. pericardium, 2. heart, 3. arteries, 4. sinuses or blood-lacunae, and 5. blood channels. There are no veins and capillaries in *Palaemon*.

1. **Pericardium or pericardial sinus.** It is a wide spacious sinus lying just below the dorsal wall of the thorax and above the reproductive organs and hepatopancreas. The floor of pericardium is in the form of a thin horizontal pericardial septum which is attached in front and behind to the dorsal body wall and on the two sides to the lateral walls of the thorax. The pericardium is incompletely filled with blood which it gets from the channels and passes into the heart, enclosed within the pericardium.

2. **Heart.** The heart is a muscular triangular structure with its apex in front and base behind. It is enclosed in the pericardium in the median dorsal part of thorax dorsally to the alimentary canal. A median longitudinal cardio-pyloric strand runs from the apex of the heart to the pyloric stomach and two lateral strands, each extending from the lateral angle of the heart to the body wall. These strands keep the heart in position inside the pericardium. The thick and muscular wall of the heart is perforated by five pairs of apertures or ostia (L., *ostium*=a door). Each ostium is a small, slit-like opening and its lips act as valves allowing blood to flow only in one direction, *i.e.*, from pericardial sinus into the heart and not vice versa. The ostia are so distributed that the first pair lies mid-dorsally, second pair mid-ventrally, the third pair posteriorly, the fourth pair antero-laterally and the fifth

pair postero-laterally. In a transverse section, the heart appears like a thick spongy meshwork of muscle fibres, the small cavities of which represent the cavity of the heart. The cavity of the heart is not continuous but is traversed by numerous muscle fibres.

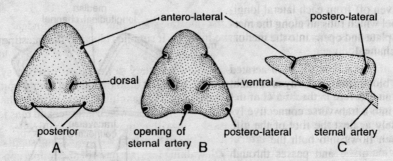

Fig. 71.24. *Palaemon.* Heart showing ostia. A—Dorsal view; B—Ventral view; C—Lateral view.

3. Arteries. The oxygenated blood flows from the pericardial sinus into the heart. When the heart contracts, it pumps out all its blood into narrow tubes which are thick, strong and muscular and are known **arteries.** The principal arteries of *Palaemon* are as follows :

(i) Median ophthalmic or cephalic artery. It is a single slender artery, which arises from the apex of the heart. It runs forward just below the carapace along the mid-dorsal line of the renal sac between the mandibular muscles. Anteriorly it reaches the roof of the oesophagus where it joins the two antennary arteries. It supplies blood to the oesophagus, cardiac stomach and the head.

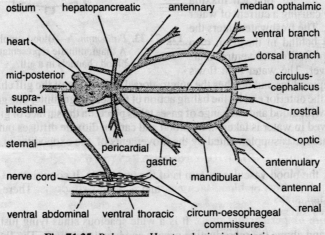

Fig. 71.25. *Palaemon.* Heart and principal arteries.

(ii) Antennary arteries. A pair of **antennary arteries** arise from the apex of the heart, one on each side of the median ophthalmic. Each antennary artery runs obliquely forwards passing along the outer side of the mandibular muscle. It gives off three branches, *viz.,* (a) a **pericardial branch** to the pericardium, (b) a **gastric branch** to the cardiac stomach and (c) a **mandibular branch** to the mandibular muscles. Each antennary artery passes forwards and again divides into a **dorsal** and **ventral branch.** The **dorsal branch** divides into two sub-branches, of which the outer, the **optic artery** supplies the eye, while the inner meets its fellow of the opposite side and the median ophthalmic artery to form a loop-like artery, the **circulus cephalicus** which gives off a pair of **rostral arteries** to the rostrum. The **ventral branch** also divides into two sub-branches, one of which supplies the antennule, the **antennulary artery** and the other re-divides into two, supplying the renal organ, the **renal artery** and antenna, the **antennal artery.**

(iii) Hepatic arteries. A pair of **hepatic** or **hepatopancreatic arteries** arise from the heart of the ventro-lateral sides, one on each side just behind the antennary. Each of them soon after its origin plunges downwards into the hepatopancreas and ramifies within it.

(iv) Median posterior artery . From the middle of the postero-ventral surface of the heart arises a short stout median artery which immediately bifurcates into two branches : a slender **supra-intestinal artery** and a stout **sternal artery**.

(a) Supra-intestinal artery. The supra-intestinal artery or dorsal abdominal artery passes straight backwards along the dorsal surface of the intestine extending up to the hindgut, where it divides into two branches, one on each side of the hindgut. It supplies blood to the intestine and the dorsal muscles of the abdomen.

(b) Sternal artery. The sternal artery is the stoutest artery in the blood vascular system of *Palaemon.* It runs obliquely downwards passing either to the left or to the right of the midgut. It then pierces through an aperture in the middle of the ventral thoracic ganglionic mass to reach the ventral side where it divides into two branches · (i) **Ventral thoracic artery** which is larger and runs forwards and supplies blood to the sternal region of the thorax, maxillae, maxillulae, maxillipedes and first three pairs of walking legs. (ii) **Ventral abdominal artery** which runs backwards and supplies blood to the ventral region of the abdomen, fourth and fifth walking legs, six pairs of abdominal appendages and the hindgut.

4. Blood sinuses or lacunae. The arteries repeatedly branch into capillaries in the various organs of the body. The veins are entirely absent in *Palaemon,* therefore, arteries open into the blood sinuses or lacunae of the haemocoel. All the sinuses of the body eventually meet into a pair of elongated and ill-defined ventral sinuses which are situated below the hepatopancreas and the flexor muscles of the thorax. The ventral sinuses communicate with each other at several places.

5. Blood channels. From each ventral sinus blood is carried to the gill of that side by means of six afferent branchial chan-

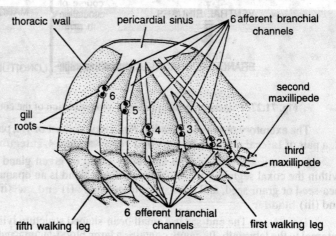

nels. As there are two ventral sinuses, the blood channels of both the sides are six pairs. These channels are lacunar in nature and lie just on the inner side of the lateral thoracic wall and innervate the gills through the gill-roots. The first channel supplies blood to the two arthrobranchs and podobranch of the second maxillipede and the remaining five channels supply blood to the pleuro-branchs. The aerated blood from the gills of each side returns to the pericardial sinus through another series of six efferent branchial channels which also leave the gills through their gill-roots.

Fig. 71.26. *Palaemon.* Lateral view of the thoracic wall showing the pericardial sinus and branchial channels.

Course of Circulation of Blood

Due to the rhythmic contraction of the heart, the blood is pumped out of the heart into the arteries which carry the aerated blood to all the parts of the body. The course of circulation of blood in the body of *Palaemon* can be diagrammatically represented by the Fig. 71.27.

Blood

In *Palaemon,* the blood is a colourless, thin, watery fluid containing floating colourless leucocytes or the white amoeboid corpuscles, which are phagocytic in nature. The respiratory pigment is haemocyanin which is dissolved in the plasma of the blood. Haemocyanin is a compound of copper and protein. When oxidised it is bright blue, but is colourless when deoxidised. The blood has the power of coagulation.

EXCRETORY SYSTEM

Excretory organs of Crustacea are two pairs of glands, antennary glands opening at the base of antennae, and maxillary glands opening at the base of maxillae. Generally, both glands do not function at the same time in one animal, one gland may succeed the other during the life history. In most Crustacea antennary glands are found in the larva, while maxillary glands are functional in adult, but in Decapoda antennary glands are functional in adult and they sometime use the maxillary gland during larval period.

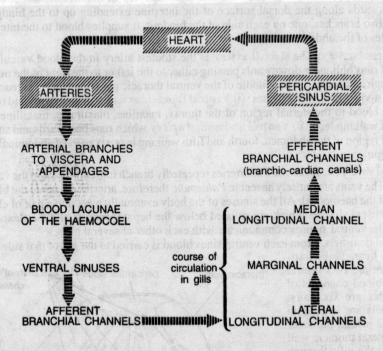

Fig. 71.27. *Palaemon.* A diagrammatic representation of the course of circulation of blood.

The excretory organs of the adult *Palaemon* consist of 1. a pair of antennary or green glands, 2. a pair of lateral ducts, 3. an unpaired renal sac, and 4. integument.

1. Antennary glands. The antennary gland or green gland of adult *Palaemon* lies enclosed within the coxal segment of each antenna. Each gland is an opaque-white structure of the size of a pea-seed or gram-seed, and consists of three parts : (i) end sac, (ii) labyrinth or glandular plexus, and (iii) bladder.

(i) **End-sac.** The end-sac is a small bean-shaped structure lying in the anterior part of the gland internal to the labyrinth. Its cavity contains a large blood-lacuna and communicates with the labyrinth by a single aperture. The wall of the end-sac consists of two layers, the outer thick layer consists of connective tissue containing numerous blood lacunae and the inner thin layer consists of large excretory epithelial cells having finely granular cytoplasm and large nuclei. The wall of the end sac is produced into a number of radial septa which project into the cavity of end-sac.

(ii) **Labyrinth or glandular plexus.** The labyrinth is very much larger in size than the end-sac and lies on its outer side. It consists of a mass of highly convoluted and branching excretory tubules which open, on the one hand, into the end-sac by a common opening and, on the other, into the bladder by several openings. The wall of each tubule consists of a single layer of excretory epithelial cells. Each tubule has a small lumen while the intertubular spaces between adjoining tubules are filled with connective tissue containing blood lacunae.

(iii) **Bladder.** The bladder or urinary bladder is a thin-walled sac, lying on the inner side of the end-sac. Its outer wall lies against the end-sac and the labyrinth, while the inner wall forms a short excretory duct or ureter which opens to the outside by a small rounded renal or excretory aperture situated on a papilla on the inner side of the coxal joint of the antenna and in front of the labrum. The wall of the bladder consists of a single layer of epithelial cells resembling closely those of the excretory tubules.

2. Lateral ducts. From the bladder of each antennary gland runs posteriorly a narrow lateral duct. The lateral ducts of both the sides are connected by a transverse connective. These lateral ducts open into an elongated renal sac or nephroperitoneal sac.

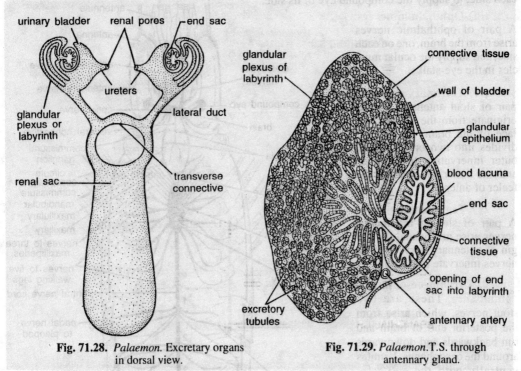

Fig. 71.28. *Palaemon.* Excretary organs in dorsal view.

Fig. 71.29. *Palaemon.*T.S. through antennary gland.

3. Renal sac. It is a large median elongated, thin-walled sac situated above the cardiac stomach and just below the carapace. Posteriorly it extends up to the gonads, while anteriorly it communicates with the bladder of each side by the lateral duct. The wall of renal sac is made of a single layer of flattened excretory epithelial cells.

Physiology of Antennary or Green Glands

The antennary glands are complex nephridia-like and extract nitrogenous waste products and excess of water from the blood in the same manner as the vertebrate kidneys do. These glands also perform the function of osmoregulation. The end-sac removes ammonia compounds, but uric acid and other nitrogenous waste matters are removed by other parts. The excretory fluid is first collected in the urinary bladders and then expelled outside through the renal apertures.

4. Integument. The integument is regarded to be an important excretory organ. The non-living nitrogenous waste product, which is deposited over the integument, is cast off at each moult or ecdysis.

NERVOUS SYSTEM

The nervous system of *Palaemon* consists of : 1. central nervous system, 2. peripheral nervous system, and 3. sympathetic nervous system.

1. Central Nervous System

Central nervous system consists of : 1. brain or a pair of supra-oesophageal ganglia, 2. a pair of circum-oesophageal commissures, 3. ventral thoracic ganglionic mass, and 4 a ventral nerve cord.

1. Brain or supra-oesophageal ganglia. The brain or supra-oesophageal ganglion is a bilobed structure which lies at the base of rostrum, anterior to the oesophagus. It is embedded in a thick mass of fat. It is formed by the fusion of several ganglia as it appears from the fact that several nerves arise from it to innervate the eyes, antennules, antennae and labrum etc. However, from segmentation point of view it is supposed to be formed of protocerebrum, paired optic ganglia, mesocerebrum and metacerebrum. The following nerves originate from the brain :

(i) **Antennulary nerves.** A pair of antennulary nerves arise from below the origin of optic nerves. Each nerve enters the antennule of its side into which it sends a statocystic branch to statocyst.

(ii) **Optic nerves.** A pair of stout optic nerves arise from the dorsal surface of the brain, one on each side, to supply the compound eye of its side.

(iii) **Ophthalmic nerves.** A pair of ophthalmic nerves arise from the brain, one on each side, and supply the ocular muscles in the eye-stalks.

(iv) **Antennary nerves.** A pair of stout antennary nerves originate from the ventral surface of the brain. Each nerve divides into two branches, the outer innervating the squama and the inner innervating the feeler of antenna.

(v) **Tegumental nerves.** A pair of slender tegumental nerves arise just behind the origin of antennary nerves. These nerves innervate the labrum.

2. Circum-oesophageal commissure. These are two stout nerves, which arise from the posterior end of brain and run backwards and downwards around the oesophagus. It unites ventrally with the sub-oesophageal ganglia which form the indistinguishable anterior part of the ventral thoracic ganglionic mass. Each commissure bears a small commissural ganglion near its anterior end, and gives off small nerve to the mandible of its side. The two circum-oesophageal commissures are connected with each other by a slender transverse commissure near the posterior end.

3. Ventral thoracic gan-

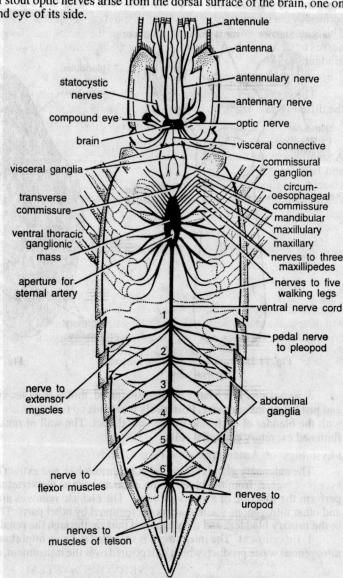

Fig. 71.30. *Palaemon.* Nervous system in dorsal view.

glionic mass. The ventral thoracic ganglionic mass is an elongated oval structure situated immediately above the thoracic sternal plates in the mid-ventral line. It is a composite mass which is formed as a result of fusion of the eleven pairs of ganglia. It gives off eleven pairs of nerves on the lateral sides. The first three pairs are of cephalic nerves, supplying the mandibles, maxillulae and the maxillae respectively. The last eight pairs are of the thoracic nerves, of which the first three pairs give off branches to the three pairs of maxillipedes respectively and the remaining five pairs supply the five pairs of walking legs. Each nerve to a leg becomes bifurcated before entering the leg.

4. Ventral nerve cord. The ventral thoracic ganglionic mass is continued posteriorly into the ventral or abdominal nerve cord. It runs posteriorly along the mid-ventral line of the abdomen up to the last segment. In each abdominal segment there is an abdominal ganglion. The ventral nerve cord and the abdominal ganglia are double. Each of the first five abdominal ganglia gives off three pairs of nerves in its segment, (i) a pair of pedal nerves supplying the pleopods, (ii) a pair of nerves to the extensor muscles of its segment, and (iii) a pair of nerves to the flexor muscles of the succeeding segment. The last or sixth adbominal ganglion or stellate ganglion is comparatively large and is formed by the fusion of paire⁻ᵈ ganglion of the sixth segment with a number of post-abdominal ganglia. This ganglion supplies two pairs of nerves to the flexor muscles of the sixth segment, two pairs of nerves to the uropods, two pairs of nerves to the telson, and a single median nerve to the rectum and hindgut.

2. Peripheral Nervous System

The various nerves originating from the central nervous system, as discussed above, to innervate the different pats of the body constitute the peripheral nervous system.

3. Sympathetic Nervous System

The sympathetic or visceral nervous system is represented by a few small ganglia and nerves. A small nerve arising from the posterior part of the brain, runs on the roof of the cardiac stomach and bears two visceral or oesophageal ganglia, one anterior and another posterior. The anterior visceral ganglion is joined with the two commissural ganglia by a pair of connectives. The posterior visceral ganglion is free and gives off two pair of nerves to the muscles of the wall of oesophagus and the cardiac stomach.

SENSE ORGANS

The sense organs of *Palaemon* are of four types, *viz.*, 1. compound eyes, 2. statocysts, 3. tactile organs, and 4. olfactory setae.

1. Compound Eyes

Structure. In *Palaemon*, there is a pair of black and hemispherical compound eyes. Each eye is borne on a short two-jointed movable stalk lying in an orbital notch. Each eye is a composite structure made of a large number of structural and functional visual units called ommatidia or ocelli lying radially. This type of eyes, made up of hundreds or thousands of ommatidia, are termed as the compound eyes and are found in majority of arthropods.

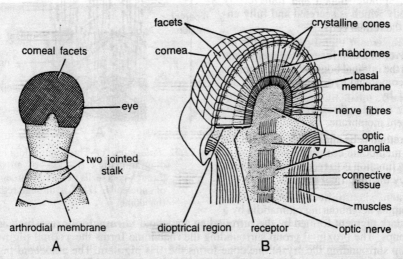

Fig. 71.31. *Palaemon.* A—Compound eye; B—A diagrammatic L.S. of compund eye showing arrangement of ommatidia.

The eye is covered with a transparent chitinous covering of cuticle forming a cornea. The cornea is divided into a large number of square facets placed in juxtaposition like squares of a graph paper. Each facet corresponds to a single ommatidium and below each facet lies one ommatidium inside the eye. All ommatidia are simple and are arranged radially lying side by side and separated by dark pigment cells.

Structure of ommatidium. Each ommatidium is composed of a number of cells arranged end to end along a central axis. However, it comprises the following structures :

(i) **Cornea.** As mentioned above, the outermost layer of an eye is the transparent cuticle forming cornea which is divided into a large number of square-like facets. These facets are thickened in the centre to give them the appearance of a biconvex lens. Thus, each corneal facet behaves like a lens and sheds off at the time of moulting, again secreted by the underlying cells.

(ii) **Corneagen cells.** Each corneal facet is followed by a group of two cells; these cells are modified epidermal cells called corneagen cells. Their function is to secrete cornea when it is moulted off.

(iii) **Cone cells or vitrellae.** These are a group of four much elongated cells situated beneath the corneagen cells. These cells secrete and enclose a transparent and refractile crystalline cone which works like a second lens. The inner end of cone cells is long and tapering.

The cornea, corneagen cells and cone cells together constitute the dioptrical region, whose function is to focus the light rays on the inner sensitive region.

(iv) **Retinal cells.** The cone cells are followed by a group of seven elongated cells forming the proximal part of the axis of an ommatidium. These cells are elongated and provided with distally placed dilations having nuclei.

(v) **Rhabdome or optic rod.** It is an elongated, spindle-shaped and transversely striated body which is secreted and fully enclosed by the retinal cells.

(vi) **Basement membrane.** It is the innermost layer of a thin fenestrated membrane that marks the internal boundary of the ommatidia in a compound eye. The ommatidia are innervated by optic nerve fibres, coming from optic ganglia, through the fenestrae in the basement membrane.

The retinal cells and rhabdome up to the basement membrane constitute the receptor region; its function is to receive the light rays focussed by the dioptrical region.

Pigment sheath. Each ommatidium is cut off from its neighbouring ommatidia by a

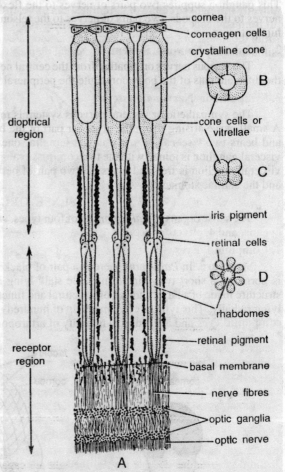

Fig. 71.32. *Palaemon.* A—Three ommatidia in L.S. (semi-diagrammatic); B—T.S. of an ommatidium through cone-cells ; C—T.S. through basal ends of cone-cells ; D—T.S. through retinal cells and rhabdome.

sheath of dark pigment formed by the surrounding amoeboid chromatophores which are arranged in two groups. The proximal group surrounding the rhabdome forms the retinal pigment and the distal group surrounding the crystalline cone forms the iris pigment. The amoeboid pigment cells take up different positions according to the changes in the intensity of light.

Working of the compound eye. The working of the compound eye is very complex. In the formation of an image, several adjacent ommatidia take part and light enters through them. Each ommatidium is capable of producing a separate image of a small part of the object seen. Therefore, the whole image formed in a compound eye is actually made of several small pieces contributed by the several adjacent ommatidia. On this account the vision effected through a compound eye is called mosaic vision.

In diurnal crustaceans the compound eyes are adapted for bright light and it produces an apposition or mosaic image. But in nocturnal forms, like *Palaemon*, it is adapted for seeing in weak light and superpostion image is formed.

Formation of apposition or mosaic image. In the bright light, during the day time, the pigment cells spread in such a way that they completely separate optically one ommatidium from the adjacent ommatidia. In this condition, rays of light, which strike the cornea obliquely, are absorbed by the pigment cells, therefore, they cannot produce a visual effect. Only those rays of light, which pass directly through the centre of the cornea, can travel through the ommatidium and reach the rhabdome to from an image of a part of an object. These small parts, placed together like the parts in a mosaic, from the image of the entire object. This is known as a mosaic vision in which the rays are received simultaneosly by distinctly separate visual elements, *i.e.*, ommatidia and the image is made up of

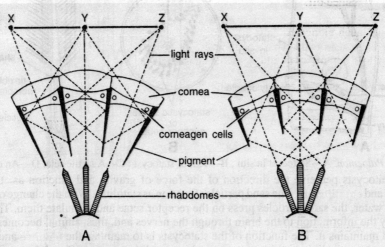

Fig. 71.33. *Palaemon.* Diagrammatic representation of image formation by a compound eye. A—Apposition or mosaic image; B—Superposition image.

several components placed in juxtaposition. Such an image is called an apposition image. The sharpness of the image depends upon the number of ommatidia involved and the degree of their isolation from one another ; the larger number of ommatidia and more complete their isolation from one another, the sharper the image. However, an eye adapted for this type of image formation functions best at short distances only; it is, therefore, most of the arthropods are short-sighted. Such arthropods are usually night blind, *e.g.*, butterflies.

Formation of superposition image. In the dim light, the pigment cells migrate towards the distal and basal parts of the ommatidia and the neighbouring ommatidia work in unison. In this condition, even the oblique rays of the light are capable of forming a point of image, after passing through a number of ommatidia. As a result, an overlapping of the adjacent points of image takes place and, thus, a continuous image is formed. Such an image is called superposition image. In this case, the vision is not distinct but the animal is able to have some sort of idea of its surrounding objects, specially of their movements . In some insects, like fire-flies and some moths, the eyes are permanently set in the way that they are adapted for vision in the dim light, *i.e.*, at night but they are day-blind, *e.g.*, moths and fireflies.

It is probable that the *Palaemon* like most of the arthropods can adjust its eyes so as to form both the types of images according to the intensity of light available.

2. Statocyst

The statocysts are a pair of small white, cuticular, hollow, sub-spherical structures. Each statocyst lies inside the precoxa of each antennule, attached to its dorsal wall. The base of each statocyst is slightly depressed and the neck opens to the outside by a minute aperture situated on the concave roof of the precoxa of antennule. The opening is covered by a small fold of integument. The statocyst is innervated by a small statocystic branch of the antennulary nerve. On cutting a section of the statocyst, its cavity is found full of minute sand-particles. On removing the sand-particles, it is found that there is an oval ring of elongated delicate receptor setae, which are attached to the inner wall of the statocyst in an oval outline. Each receptor seta consists of a swollen base and a filamentous shaft which is sharply bent about the middle of its length. The base of seta is attached to the wall of the sac by a very thin arthrodial membrane and the shaft bears fine bristles beyond the bend. Each receptor seta is innervated at its base by a fine branch of statocystic nerve.

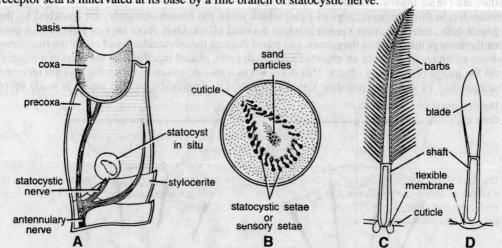

Fig. 71. 34. *Palaemon.* A—Statocyst in situ ; B—T.S. of statocyst ; C—A tactile seta; D—An olfactory seta.

The statocysts perceive the direction of the force of gravity and function as the organs of orientation and equilibrium. The sand particles function as statoliths. With the change of the position of prawn in water, the sand particles press on the receptor setae and stimulate them. The stimulated setae convey the information to the brain through the nerves and, thus, animal becomes aware of its position and maintains it. The function of the statocysts is to maintain the balance and position. In moulting of prawn, the lining of the statocyst and its statoliths are cast off and then renewed.

3. Tactile Setae

Tactile setae are found on the feelers of antennae and are abundant on the borders of the flattened portions of the appendages like the rami of the pleopods. Each tactile seta is a hollow cuticular outgrowth containing a slender prolongation of the ectoderm and the muscle fibres and also supplied with a nerve fibre and consists of two segments. The proximal segment or shaft is slightly swollen at its base and is attached to the integument by a flexible membrane. The distal segment gradually tapers at its free end and is provided with a pair of linear rows of small barbs. Tactile setae are sensory to water current and to the substratum. They are stimulated only on being moved and not on being touched.

4. Olfactory Setae

Olfactory setae are found in a longitudinal groove on the small middle feeler which lies between the two feelers of each antennule. Each seta consists of a proximal shaft which is attached to the integument by a flexible membrane, and a distal segment or blade which is bluntly rounded at its free end and covered with a thin membrane. Each seta is innervated with a single nerve-fibre from the olfactory branch of the antennulary nerve. The function of these setae is olfactory.

REPRODUCTIVE SYSTEM

Sexual Dimorphism

Palaemon is dioecious, *i.e.,* sexes are separate and the sexual dimorphism is well marked. The males and females can be distinguished from each other by a number of external characters which are as follows :

1. The males are larger in size than the females.

2. In males, the bases of the thoracic legs are more closely approximated than in the females.

3. Males possess narrower abdomen than those of females.

4. In the males, the second pair of chelate legs are more elongated and more profusely covered with spines and setae than in the females.

5. In the males, each second pleopod bears an additional process, the appendix masculina which lies between the appendix interna and the endopodite.

6. In the males, the epimera of the abdominal segments are smaller than in the females, where they are bigger in size for carrying eggs.

7. In the males, the paired genital apertures are situated on the coxae of the fifth pair of walking legs, while in the females the paired genital apertures are situated on the raised papillae on the coxae of the third pair of walking legs.

Reproductive Organs

Reproductive organs consist of gonads which are similar in shape, size, position, and general disposition in both the sexes. They are situated in the posterior region of the thorax dorsally above the hepatopancreas and below the pericardium. Gonads are the hollow enclosing remains of coelom, they are continuous with their ducts because of the reduction of coelom.

Male reproductive organs. The male reproductive organs consist of a pair of testes, a pair of vasa deferentia, and a pair of vesiculae seminales.

(i) Testes. The two testes are soft, white, elongated structures lying above the posterior half of the dorsal surface of the hepatopancreas and below the pericardial sinus and the heart. Anteriorly they extend as far as the renal sac and posterioly as far as the first abdominal segment. At their anterior ends, the two testes fuse to form a common lobe, while posteriorly they remain separate. In the middle region, the two testes are separated apart so as to enclose a space through which extends the cardio-pyloric strand.

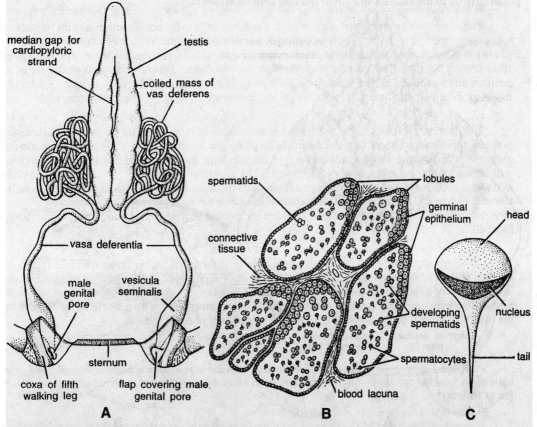

Fig. 71.35. *Palaemon.* A—Male reproductive organs in dorsal view ; B—T.S. of a portion of testis ; C—A spermatozoon magnified.

Histologically, testis reveals that it consists of a large number of lobules compactly held together by the connective tissue. Each lobule has a thin wall consisting of an outer limiting membrane and an inner single layered epithelium enclosing a large central cavity. The lumen of the lobules is always filled with spermatocytes. Each spermatocyte gives rise to a single spermatozoon. A mature sperm consists of a hemispherical cytoplasmic mass containing a large, dark, crescentic nucleus and a short blunt tail-like process.

(ii) **Vasa deferentia.** From the posterior end of each testis arises a long coiled and narrow tube, the vas deferens. Soon after emerging from the testis, each vas deferens forms a much coiled mass and then runs vertically downwards between the thoracic wall on the outer side and the abdominal flexor muscles on the inner side.

(iii) **Vesicula seminales.** On reaching near the coxa of the last pair of walking legs, each vas deferens swells into a small club-shaped structure, the vesicula serminalis, in which the sperms are stored in the form of white compact bodies called the spermatophores. Each vesicula seminalis opens to the outside by a male genital aperture on the arthrodial membrane of the coxa of the fifth walking leg of its side. Each male genital aperture is covered by a small flap of integument.

Female reproductive organs. The female reproductive organs consist of a pair of ovaries and a pair of oviducts.

(i) **Ovaries.** The two ovaries are white compact and sickle-shaped structures. They are situated above the hepatopancreas and below the pericardial sinus and heart. Both the anterior and posterior ends of the ovaries touching each other and leaving a gap in the middle for the passage of the cardio-pyloric strand. The shape and size of the ovaries vary considerably according to the age of the prawn and the season of the year. Like the testes, the ovaries extend anteriorly up to the renal sac and posteriorly up to the anterior margin of the first abdominal segment.

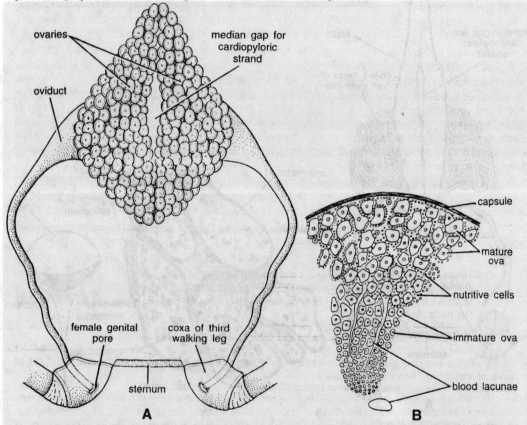

Fig. 71.36. *Palaemon.* A—Female reproductive organs in dorsal view ; B—T.S. of a portion of ovary.

Histologically, ovary shows that it is composed of a number of radially arranged rows of ova in various stages of development. The immature ova lie towards the centre, while the mature ones towards the periphery. Each developing ovum is being surrounded by a number of small nutritive cells. A mature ovum has a rounded appearance with a large nucleus and a cytoplasm full of yolk-granules. Each ovary is enclosed within in a membranous capsule.

(ii) **Oviducts.** Both the oviducts are short, wide and thin-walled tubes. Each oviduct arises from the ovary at about the middle of its outer border having a broad funnel at its commencement. It runs vertically downwards and opens by a female genital aperture on the inner side of the coxa of the third walking leg of its side.

FERTILIZATION AND DEVELOPMENT

The breeding season in *Palaemon malcolmsonii* is during the months of May, June and July. Fertilization is external. In copulation a male puts the female down on her back and deposits sperms on the ventral surface near the female genital pores. As the eggs come out of the female genital pores, they are fertilized by the sperms already present there. The female lays eggs in large numbers. The eggs are large with much yolk forming a central core, the yolk is surrounded by peripheral protoplasm. The fertilized eggs are fastened to the pleopods by a sticky secretion of the tegumental glands. During breeding season a single female prawn is found to carry several hundreds of eggs and developing embryos.

The development is direct and the embroys remain attached to the pleopods until they hatch. A newly hatched embryo looks like a small prawn with all its appendages except the last abdominals, *i.e.,* sixth abdominals. The adult form is reached after a series of moults.

ENDOCRINE SYSTEM

Palaemon, like other crustaceans, produces a large number of hormones. It is believed that the sinus gland at the base of the eye-stalk is known to have a number of hormones. They are supposed to control the spread of pigment in the chromatophores of the epidermis and in the compound eyes. They also seem to have some regulatory power over moulting and affect the deposition of lime salts in the exoskeleton. The blood probably distributes the hormones like the higher forms.

The exact mechanism by which the physiological processes are carried out is still very obscure. Extensive research indicates that there is an X–organ in the eye-stalk along with the sinus gland. Neurosecretory cells in the X-organ and in the brain produce a moult-preventing hormone which is stored in the sinus gland. When eye-stalks are removed experimentally from a non-moulting specimen, moulting will occur in a few days because the inhibiting effect of the hormone is removed; when eye-stalks from non-moulting specimen are implanted into the body of an eye-stalkless specimen, moulting is delayed. A Y-organ, which produces a moult-accelerating hormone, has been described in some crustaceans. The interaction of the moult-preventing and moult-accelerating hormones may be the regulatory device in the moulting process.

For the expansion and contraction of the pigments into and out of the chromatophore processes, certain chromatophorotropic hormones in the sinus gland appear to be responsible as revealed by the removal of the eye-stalks (darkening effect) or by the injection of eye-stalk extracts (paling effect).

A specific hormone from the sinus gland is known to control the retinal pigment movements also.

REVISION QUESTIONS

1. Give an account of the habits, habitat and external features of *Palaemon.*
2. Enumerate the appendages of prawn. Describe the abdominal appendages.
3. What is a biramous appendage ? How would you justify that the cephalic appendage are derived from this basic plan.
4. Describe the digestive system of *Palaemon.*
5. Give an account of respiratory organs and mode of respiration in *Palaemon* .
6. Give an illustrated account of the circulatory system of prawn.
7. What is a compound eye ? Describe the structure and mode of working of the compound eye of *Palaemon.*
8. Give an account of the nervous system of prawn.
9. What is sexual dimorphism ? Describe the sexual dimorphic characters of prawn and give an account of its reproductive organs.
10. Write short notes on :
    (i) Chelate legs; (ii) Hastate plate; (iii) Green gland; (iv) Statocyst.
11. Draw labelled diagrams only :
    (i) Appendages of prawn; (ii) T.S. of prawn through cephalothorax : (iii) Branchiostegite cut open to show the structures of gill chamber, (iv) Nervous system of prawn; (v) T.S. of testis of prawn.

72

Scorpion

Scorpions are the oldest known terrestrial arthropods, their fossils are found from the Silurian period. Today the scorpions are restricted to tropical and subtropical regions. There are 7 families and nearly 700 species of scorpions. Some of the common living genera are : *Palamneus, Buthus, Parabuthus, Microbuthus, Scorpio, Isometrus, Euscorpius, Pandinus* and *Vejovis,* etc. All the scorpions are essentially alike, but the description given here under generally relates to *Palamnaeus* which will apply to all of them.

PALAMNAEUS

SYSTEMATIC POSITION

Phylum	....	**Arthropoda**
Subphylum	....	**Chelicerata**
Class	....	**Arachnida**
Order	....	**Scorpionida**
Genus	....	*Palamnaeus* (Scorpion)

HABIT AND HABITAT

Scorpions are nocturnal animals. During the day they hide under wood, stones, loose bark, in sand, crevices and holes, and in the debris on the ground, etc. They come out of their abodes at night to hunt for food. They are carnivorous and predaceous, feeding for the most part on insects, spiders and other small animals. They catch their preys by the chelate pedipalpi, kill them with the sting and finally suck their juices. Cannibalism has also been found in them as they devour young ones of their own kind.

In walking, scorpions carry their pedipalps horizontally in front, using them partly as feelers and partly as raptorial organs. As regards the body, the attitude varies considerably. In some cases it is raised high upon the legs and the tail or metasoma is curved forward over the back, but in others the body is held low and the tail is dragged along behind, the end only being slightly curled. In scorpions, the sense of touch is well developed. The pectines are said to be special tactile organs. Their sight is poor, and they are deaf. The effect of scorpion's poison is not serious. In man and other large animals, the poison causes pain, local swelling and discolouration. A scorpion's poison has no effect upon itself.

Scorpions are solitary creatures and never live in groups. If two scorpions are found under the same stone, one is engaged in eating the other. All scorpions are viviparous and the females carry the newly-hatched young on their backs.

DISTRIBUTION

Scorpions are inhabitants of warm countries all over the world. However, they are not found in New Zealand, South Patagonia and the Antarctic islands. Scorpions are fairly common in hilly regions of India particularly on slopes of hills. *Palamneus* is an Indian scorpion found all over from India to Philippines. It has many species, of which *Palamneus bengalensis* is common in North India.

EXTERNAL FEATURES

Different species of scorpions differ from one another in size, colour, distribution and details of morphology, but the general structure is more or less similar.

Shape and size. The body of scorpion is elongated, narrow and dorso-ventrally flattened. The size varies from species to species. The smallest scorpion, *Microbuthus pusillus* is about 1.3 cm in length, while the largest species *Pandinus imperator* is about 20 cm in length. In India, the adult of *Buthus tamulus* measures about 7 to 9 cm in length, while the largest Indian scorpion *Palamneus swammerdami* measures up to 15 cm in length.

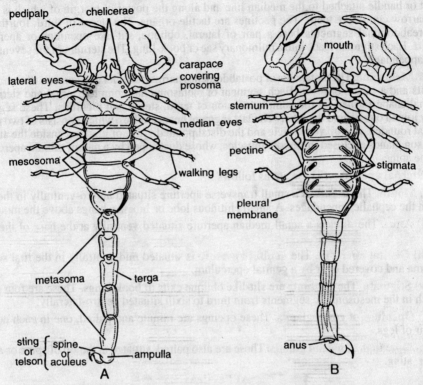

Fig. 72.1. Scorpion. A—Dorsal view ; B—Ventral view.

Colouration. The colour is variable, usually corresponding with the habitat of the animal which is generally blackish dorsally and slightly light coloured ventrally. The species, which are living in tropical jungles, are of shining black colour, and the species which are found in the sand are pale-yellow in colour usually the dorsal surface is much darker in colour than those of the ventral surface.

Division of body. The elongated segmented body is divisible into two major regions : (i) prosoma or cephalothorax and (ii) opisthosoma or abdomen.

(i) Prosoma. The prosoma or cephalothorax is the anterior short, broad, and flat region of the body. It is formed by the fusion of head and thorax. It is made up of six segments, each of which bears a pair of appendages on the ventral side. Dorsally the prosoma is covered by a single, thick and square-shaped cephalothoracic shield or dorsal carapace. The dorsal carapace is formed by fusion of terga of this region. The anterior margin of the dorsal carapace has a deep notch forming right and left frontal lobes. The carapace bears a pair of median eyes in the middle and two to five pairs of smaller lateral eyes on the antero-lateral margins. All the eyes are simple in structure. On the ventral surface of the prosoma there is a single median, small triangular plate, the sternum, lying between the coxae of third and fourth pairs of legs. The sternum is greatly reduced due to the enormous development of the coxae of thoracic appendages.

(ii) Opisthosoma. The prosoma is followed by a long opisthosoma. It is distinguished into two parts : (a) an anterior broad mesosoma or preabdomen and (b) a posterior narrow metasoma or postabdomen.

(a) Mesosoma. The mesosoma or preabdomen consists of seven segments. It is as broad as the prosoma anteriorly but slightly narrow posteriorly. Each segment of mesosoma is covered dorsally by a tergal plate or tergum and ventrally by a sternal plate or sternum and the two are joined with each other laterally by a pleural or arthrodial membrane. The sternum of the first mesosomal or preabdominal segment is small and bears the median genital aperture which is covered by a plate-like, rounded, bifid and movable lid or genital operculum. The sternum of second segment bears a pair of comb-like appendages, the pectines. Each pectine consists of a three segmented stem or shaft or handle attached to the median line and along the posterior margin of which is a row of 4 to 36 narrow comb-like teeth. The pectines are tactile organs. The sterna of third, fourth, fifth and sixth preabdominal segments bear a pair of lateral, oblique, slit-like openings or apertures, the stigmata. Each stigmata leads into a pulmonary sac or book-lung. The sternum of the seventh segment has no appendage.

(ii) Metasoma. The metasoma or postabdomen is narrow, slender and consists of five cylindrical segments and a telson or sting. Each segment of metasoma has complete tergal and sternal arcs of octagonal shape formed by the complete fusion of terga, sterna and pleurons. These segments are flexibly joined one behind the other. The last segment bears a telson which consists of two parts—the proximal rounded ampulla or vesicle and the distal pointed spine or aculeus. Inside the ampulla are two poison glands enclosed in smooth muscles, whose ducts open by a pair of minute apertures at the tip of the spine.

External apertures. These are as follows :

(i) Mouth. The mouth is a small transverse aperture situated antero-ventrally in the prosoma between the cephalic appendages. A small chitinous lobe or labrum hangs above the mouth.

(ii) Anus. The anus is a small median aperture situated ventrally at the base of the telson or sting.

(iii) Genital aperture. The genital aperture is situated mid-ventrally in the first segment of mesosoma and covered over by a genital operculum.

(iv) Stigmata. The stigmata are slit-like oblique exits of book-lungs. These are four pairs; one pair each in the mesosomatic segments from third to sixth situated ventro-laterally.

(v) Openings of coxal glands. These opeings are minute and paired, one in each coxa of the third pair of legs.

(vi) Openings of poison glands. These are also paired, situated at the tip of spine or aculeus of telson or sting.

APPENDAGES

In scorpion, there are six pairs of appendages in the cephalothorax. These are a pair of chelicerae, a pair of pedipalpi and four pairs of walking legs.

1. Chelicerae. The chelicerae are the anterior-most and preoral appendages, situated close to each other on either side of the mouth. Chelicerae are homologous with antennae of crustaceans. Each chelicera is a small, three jointed and chelate appendage. The first or basal segment is small, triangular piece, lying concealed beneath the carapace. The two distal segments form the chela or small pincer. The second segment is large, swollen and bears at its anterior end on the inner side a projection which forms the immovable finger of the chela. The third segment or movable finger is articulated on the outer side of the second segment.

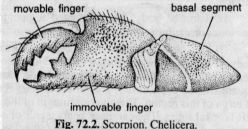

Fig. 72.2. Scorpion. Chelicera.

Both the fingers are armed with teeth. The chelicerae are prehensile and are used for holding and tearing up the body of prey.

2. Pedipalpi. Behind the chelicerae are a pair of powerful and clawed appendages called pedipalpi which are post-oral in position. Each pedipalp is made of six segments, *viz.*, coxa, trochanter, humerus, brachium, manus and movable finger. The coxa is small and situated on the side of the pre-oral cavity beneath the carapace. On each coxa there is a gnathobase towards the mouth. The gnathobases of both sides serve as jaws, protruding in the pre-oral cavity and help in squeezing and

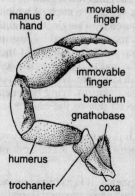

Fig. 72.3. Scorpion. Pedipalp.

crushing the body of the prey. The trochanter is also a small segment bearing at right angles to the longitudinal axis, the powerful humerus. Then follows the brachium directed forward. The last two segments are opposed to one another and form the chela. The manus or hand is the longest and most developed segment. It forms a powerful chela with the movable finger which is movably articulated on its outer in the middle. The biting edges of the movable and immovable fingers of pedipalpi are provided with rows of minute teeth which help in catching the prey. The pedipalpi move in the horizontal plane.

3. Walking legs. There are four pairs of walking legs attached to the cephalothorax. These are all alike and are used for walking. Each leg consists of seven segments or podomeres, *viz.* coxa, trochanter, femur, patella, tibia, protarsus and tarsus. The coxae of the first three pairs of legs of both the sides are comparatively small, triangular pieces, while those of the fourth are longer. The coxae of first two pairs of legs are movable and provided with forwardly directed triangular maxillary processes or gnathobases. The two coxae of the first pair of legs do not meet each other, those of second pair meet each other, while those of the third and fourth pairs are separated from each other by the sternum. The coxae of the third and fourth legs of the same side are immovable and fused with each other. The trochanter is a short and stout segment, moving in all directions. The femur is long, straight segment moving freely upwards and liltle outwards. The patella is also long and moves downwards. The tibia is elongated and provided with a tibial spur at its lower distal extremity. The protarsus and tarsus are not so much long. The protarsus bears a pair of dark tipped claw-like spurs, the pedal spurs. The tarsus bears three movable curved pointed claws, of which two are dorsal or superior and one is ventral or inferior. The inferior claw is generally worn out and, thus, only two are usually seen.

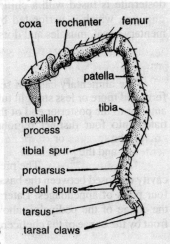

Fig. 72.4. Scorpion. First walking leg.

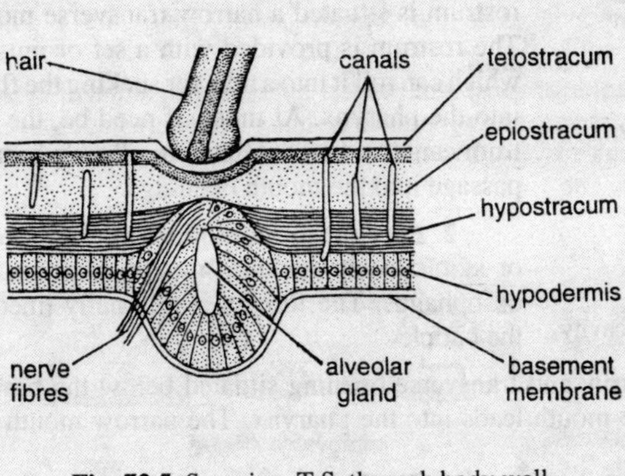

BODY WALL

The body wall of scorpion consists of three layers, *viz.,* cuticle, hypodermis and basement membrane.

The cuticle is the outer, non-living chitinous layer, which is brilliant in colour. It is secreted by the underlying layer of hypodermis and consists of three distinct layers, an outer superficial layer or tetostracum, a middle layer or epiostracum and an inner layer or hypostracum. The cuticle is traversed by numerous canals which open to the outside at its surface. The hypodermis consists of a single layer of columnar cells filled with pigment granules. Some of the hypodermis cells are modified so as to form hairs which project above the cuticle and are sensitive to touch. The basement membrane is a thin and structureless layer, situated below the hypodermis.

Fig. 72.5. Scorpion. T.S. through body wall.

BODY CAVITY

In scorpion, the body cavity is haemocoel as in cockroach. It is filled with blood surrounding the heart, alimentary canal with its associated glands, gonads and other internal structures.

MUSCULATURE

In scorpion, there is one pair of muscles in the cephalothorax and eight pairs of dorso-ventral muscles in the preabdomen, extending from dorsal to the ventral surfaces on either lateral sides of body wall.

ENDOSKELETON

In scorpion, there is an endoskeleton known as endosternite lying somewhat obliquely at the junction of the prosoma and mesosoma. It lies inside the body dorsally to the nerve cord and ventrally to the alimentary canal. It is triangular in structure and produced into several paired processes, the anterior, posterior and horizontal which provide surface for the attachment of muscles. Posteriorly, the body of endosternite is fused with a chitinous plate called diaphragm, which is perforated by the nerve cord, alimentary canal, muscles and dorsal aorta.

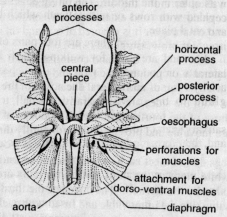

Fig. 72.6. Scorpion. Endosternite and diaphragm.

DIGESTIVE SYSTEM

Alimentary Canal

The alimentary canal of scorpion is a fairly uniform and more or less straight tube extending from the anterior to the posterior end of the body. It is differentiated into four distinct regions, *viz.*, the pre-oral cavity, the foregut or stomodaeum, midgut, or mesenteron and the hindgut or proctodaeum.

1. Pre-oral cavity. The pre-oral cavity is a small cavity enclosed between the basal segments of the first four pairs of appendages. Laterally, it is bounded by the coxae of the pedipalpi, above by the rostrum, in front by the coxae of the chelicerae and below by the two pairs of the maxillary processes of the coxae of the first two pairs of walking legs. All these structures bear bristles or hairs which protrude into the pre-oral cavity. A laterally compressed cushion-like structure called rostrum or buccal appendage protrudes into the pre-oral cavity from the posterior side. Below the base of the rostrum is situated a narrow transverse mouth. The rostrum is provided with a set of muscles which can roll it into a tube for sucking the fluids into the pharynx. At times, if need be, the rostrum can also be contracted to allow a broader passage into the mouth opening.

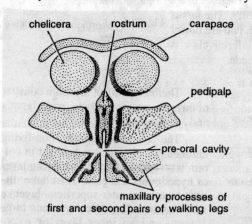

Fig. 72.7. Scorpion . T.S. through the pre-oral cavity.

2. Foregut or stomodaeum. The foregut or stomodaeum includes mouth, pharynx and oesophagus. The foregut is internally lined by the cuticle.

(i) Mouth. The mouth is a small, narrow and transverse opening situated below the base of rostrum and behind the pre-oral cavity. The mouth leads into the pharynx. The narrow mouth can only admit juices and pulps.

(ii) Pharynx. The pharynx is a pear-shaped, bulbous and muscular structure situated obliquely below the mouth. It is provided with a thick chitinous internal lining and numerous muscles outside. The muscles are distinguished into sphincters and dilators. The sphincter muscles keep the pharynx contracted, while the dilator muscles dilate it considerably. Therefore, the pharynx acts as a powerful sectorial organ for sucking the liquid food.

(iii) Oesophagus. The pharynx is followed by a small narrow and delicate tube, the oesophagus which passes through the nerve ring and opens into the midgut or mesenteron. It is also provided with an internal chitinous lining. At its posterior end, it protrude a short distance into the lumen of stomach so as to form a sleeve valve which prevents the regurgitation of food into the pharynx. This function is also supplemented by the presence of sphincter muscles at the posterior end of the oesophagus.

3. Midgut or mesenteron. The midgut or mesenteron is differentiated into the **stomach** and intestine with the two digestive glands. The mesenteron is lined internally by the epithelium and devoid of internal chitinous lining.

(i) Stomach. The stomach is slightly dilated thin-walled part of the alimentary canal situated in the cephalothorax and extending between the oesophagus and diaphragm. It is covered above and on sides by an irregular brownish gland called stomach gland or the gastric gland. This gland comprises three lobes—two lateral and one median dorsal and opens into the stomach by a pair of short lateral ducts. Huxley regarded this gland to be salivary gland but Blanchard and Pavlovsky have shown that it cannot be considered a salivary gland either by reason of function or position and, therefore, modern workers called it stomach gland.

(ii) Intestine. The intestine is the longest part of the alimentary canal extending from the diaphragm to the last segment of the body where it passes into the hindgut. It is divisible into two regions, the anterior preabdominal region or hepatopancreatic region or pars tecta intestine and the posterior postabdominal region or ileum or pars nuda intestine. The anterior preabdominal region is narrower and has a thin wall lined with glandular epithelial cells. It has the opening of five pairs of short hepatopancreatic ducts arising from hepatopancreas. At the junction of pre- and post-abdominal intestines, arise two pairs of Malpighian tubules.

The posterior, postabdominal region of intestine or ileum extends from the thirteenth segment to the eighteenth segment. It is comparatively wider, thin-

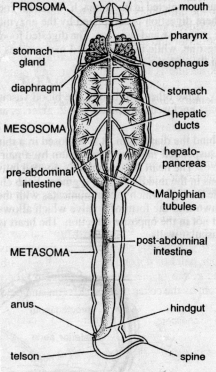

Fig. 72.8. Scorpion . Digestive system.

walled tube lined with tall epithelial cells arranged uniformly in the internal epithelium. The walls of the postabdominal intestine are feebly muscularized, only few circular and longitudinal muscular fibres are present.

(iii) Digestive glands. These are largely represented by the hepatopancreas or chylenteron, also referred to as liver. The hepatopancreas is a large, brownish and lobulated gland filling the whole of the preabdominal cavity. Its lobules penetrate the various internal organs. The wall of the lobules is composed of a layer of epithelium arranged on a thin membrane or tunica propria and a peritoneal covering. The cells of the epithelial layer are of two types; the more numerous large absorptive cells and the fewer smaller ferment cells.

4. Hindgut or proctodaeum. The hindgut is the smallest and bulbous part of the alimentary canal, situated in the last or eighteenth segment. It is lined internally by chitin and opens externally by the anal aperture situated on the ventral side between the last segment and the telson. The anus is surrounded by four chitinous plates which keep it normally closed.

Food and Feeding

Scorpions are carnivorous animals and the food consists of small insects and spiders. They live purely on the liquid food derived as juice from the body of the prey. The prey is seized by chelate (pincers) of pedipalpi and stung to death by the telson. The pedipalpi pass the killed prey to chelicerae, one chelicera holds the food and other rips it open. The coxae of the pedipalpi and first two pairs of legs now press up on the prey so that the entire body fluid is squeezed out into the pre-oral cavity. Meanwhile, the rostrum forms a groove which is applied to the prey and the liquid is sucked into pharynx and then it is driven into oesophagus and stomach.

Digestion, Absorption and Egestion

Inside the pre-oral cavity, the food is mixed with the secretion of the alveolar glands situated in the maxillary processes of the first two pairs of legs. This secretion contains proteolytic enzymes.

The proteins are proteolysed and the food is reduced into pulp. Thus, the food reaching the stomach is in a partly digested condition. In the stomach the partly digested food is mixed with the secretions of stomach gland containing the enzymes pepsin, erepsin and lipase, etc. Most of the digestion is, thus, completed in the stomach. When the food reaches the intestine, it passes into the hepatopancreas where digestion is completed by the enzymes already mixed with the food and those secreted here, *i.e.,* amylase and catalase. The digested food is absorbed in the hepatopancreas and the preabdominal intestine, while the undigested part reaches the postabdominal intestine and hindgut to be expelled out through the anus.

BLOOD VASCULAR SYSTEM

Like other arthropods, the blood vascular system in scorpion is of open type. It consists of 1. heart enclosed in pericardium. 2. arteries and 3. sinuses.

1. Heart and pericardium. The heart is an elongated and muscular tube extending back from behind the diaphragm. It is enclosed in a thin-walled membranous sac, the pericardium. The heart is suspended into the pericardium by a pair of connective tissue bands in each segment called **ali cordi.** The heart is incompletely divided into seven distinct chambers by means of shallow constrictions in the middle of each segment. Each chamber bears a pair of ostia (opening) in its dorsolateral side through which it communicates with the pericardial cavity. The wall of each ostium is slightly drawn into the form of a valve which allows the flow of blood from the pericardium into the heart but not in the opposite direction. The heart is able to perform slow peristaltic movements due to the muscular walls.

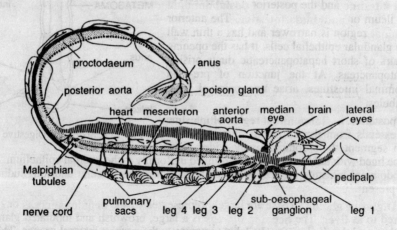

Fig. 72.9. Scorpion. Diagrammatic lateral view of the circulatory system and other internal organs.

2. Arteries. The heart is continued anteriorly as the anterior aorta and posteriorly as the posterior aorta. A pair of lateral systemic arteries are also given off from the each chamber of the heart.

(i) **Anterior aorta.** The anterior aorta arises from the anterior end of the first chamber of the heart and runs anteriorly along the dorsal surface of the alimentary canal. It is a short and wide vessel which gives off arteries to the different structures of the prosoma. The main arteries given off from the anterior aorta are as follows : (a) A pair of small visceral arteries which supply blood to the intestine and hepatopancreas. (b) Beyond the diaphragm but before the brain a pair of arteries arises from the anterior aorta which encircle the oesophagus and unite ventrally to form a supraneural artery which runs medially above the ventral nerve cord supplying the nerve cord and ventral muscles. (c) The anterior aorta, also gives off six pairs of arteries which supply the appendages of prosoma, brain and eyes, etc.

(ii) **Posterior aorta.** From the posterior end of the heart arises a posterior aorta or caudal artery which runs backwards on the dorsal side of the intestine up to the last segment. It gives off a pair of arteries in each segment of the postabdomen and then divides into three branches : (a) A median branch extends ventrally to join the suprarenal artery and (b) two lateral branches run into the posterior lobes of the hepatopancreas and supply the muscles of the fourteenth segment.

(iii) **Systemic arteries.** From each chamber of the heart arises on either side a systemic artery. These arteries form a network and supply the various parts of the preabdomen.

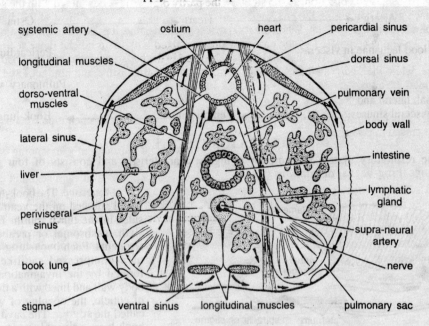

Fig. 72.10. Scorpion. T.S. passing through the middle region of the body showing pulmonary and main sinuses of the body.

3. **Sinuses.** All the arteries break up into numerous small branches and sub-branches and finally pour their blood into narrow spaces, the lacunae. From these lacunae the blood is collected into large spaces called sinuses. There are three important sinuses in the scorpion, *viz.*, ventral sinus, dorsal sinus and perivisceral sinus.

The **ventral sinus** extends along the whole length of the body below the ventral longitudinal muscles. It collects blood from the ventral part of the body. It also sends a diverticulum to each book-lung to supply blood to the latter.

The **dorsal sinus** runs along the dorsal side of the pericardial sinus or pericardium. It collects blood from the dorsal part of the body. It is connected to the ventral sinus through the lateral sinuses.

The **perivisceral sinus** surrounds the alimentary canal and is formed by the union of various lacunae between different visceral organs. It also communicates with the ventral sinus.

4. **Pulmonary veins.** From the book-lungs the oxygenated blood is sent back to the pericardial sinus by four pairs of pulmonary veins which are continued over the dorsal side of the book-lungs as lacunae.

Blood

The **blood** or haemolymph of scorpion is colourless and it contains non-nucleated amoebocytes or leucoytes. The respiratory pigment in blood is **haemocyanin** which is found dissolved in the plasma. The blood becomes bluish in colour when oxygenated due to the presence of respiratory pigment (haemocyanin) having copper metallic base in contrast to the haemogloblin with iron metallic base.

Course of Circulation

By the contraction of the ligaments, the cavity of the heart enlarges and the blood of the pericardial sinus passes on to the heart through ostia. Afterwards, the heart contracts and sends the blood into various organs and parts of the body through the anterior and posterior aortae and the systemic arteries which are connected with the blood lacunae. The impure or deoxygenated blood from the viscera is collected in the ventral sinus. From the ventral sinus blood passes to the book-lungs, enters the lamellae and is oxygenated. From the book-lungs the oxygenated blood is sent to the pericardial sinus by four pairs of pulmonary veins to enter the heart through ostia. The course of circulation of blood in scorpion can be diagrammatically represented as follows :

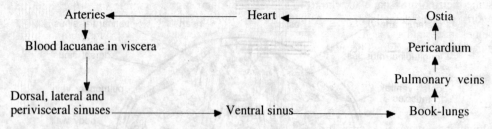

RESPIRATORY SYSTEM

The respiratory system of scorpion is highly characteristic and consists of four pairs of book-lungs (lung-books) or pulmonary sacs.

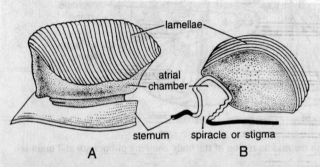

Fig. 72.11. Scorpion. A—book-lung in dorsal view; B—Book-lung in V.S.

Structure. The book-lungs are found situated on the ventro-lateral sides in the third, fourth, fifth and sixth mesosomal or preabdominal segments. Each book-lung consists of a compressed sac-like cavity formed by the invagination of the body wall and lined with a thin layer of cuticle, the opening of which is called the stigma. The cavity of the book-lung is divisible into two parts, the smaller proximal part is called the atrial chamber which opens to the outside by the stigma, while the larger distal part is the pulmonary chamber. Each pulmonary chamber contains about 150 vertical folds or leaf-like lamellae. These lamellae are attached to the inner posterior side of the chamber and are arranged like the leaves of a book. Each lamella is a hollow structure made of two thin layers of cuticle united at their edges. The outer side of the lamellae bear ridges and bristles which keep the adjacent lamellae apart and a little air space (inter-lamellar space) is left between them for the flow of air. The roof of the atrial chamber is perforated by many linear slit-like openings, set parallel with another. The atrial chamber communicates with the inter-lamellar spaces containing air through these openings.

The blood flows continuously in the spaces inside the lamellae, while the inter-lamellar spaces are filled with the air so that exchange of gases takes place through the thin walls of the lamellae which separate the blood contained in the lamellar cavities from the air in the inter-lamellar spaces.

Blood supply. The impure blood from ventral sinus is sent to each book-lung by a diverticulum from where it enters the lamellae at their bases. The blood is aerated or purified in the lamellae of each book-lung and is collected into a pulmonary vein which travels dorsally and opens into the pericardium.

Mechanism of Respiration

The inspiration and expiration of air in the book-lungs is controlled by the action of the dorso-ventral and atrial muscles. When the dorso-ventral muscles are contracted the pulmonary chamber is compressed

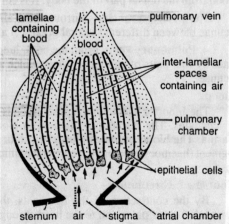

Fig. 72.12. Scorpion. Vertical section of book-lung to show the mechanism of respiration.

and the air in between the lamellae is forced out into the atrial chamber then to the outside through the stigma due to the contraction of atrial muscles. When the atrial muscles relax, the book-lungs resume their normal shape and the fresh air enters through stigma first into the atrial chamber and then into the inter-lamellar spaces. At this time dorso-ventral muscles relax and pulmonary chamber resumes its normal shape. The gaseous exchange takes place through the thin membranous walls of the lamellae and the blood becomes oxygenated and carbon dioxide is expelled out into the air.

EXCRETORY SYSTEM

The excretory organs of scorpion are : 1. Malpighian tubules, 2. coxal glands and 3. hepatopancreas, and 4. nephrocytes.

1. Malpighian tubules. There are two pairs of Malpighian tubules arising from the junction of preabdominal and postabdominal intestine. These tubules are tubular, anteriorly directed and endodermal in origin. They possess thin syncytial walls which remove the waste from the blood. The waste is then excreted into the lumen of the tubules as guanine crystals which pass out through the alimentary canal. The transverse section of Malpighian tubule reveals that a thin peritoneal sheath externally covering a few longitudinal and circular muscle fibres and excretory epithelial cells arranged on a basement membrane. The epithelial cells show striations at their bases.

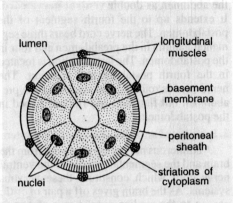

Fig. 72.13. Scorpion. T.S. of Malpighian tubule.

2. Coxal glands. There is one pair of coxal glands situated near the bases of the third pair of walking legs in the fifth segment of the prosoma. The coxal glands are shining white structures and are coelomoducts of coelomic origin. Each coxal gland consists of a large excretory saccule or vesicle or end sac and a much coiled tube, the labyrinth which dilates near its end to form a swollen bladder or reservoir. The reservoir opens outside by the excretory pore on the posterior face of the fifth walking leg. The saccule and labyrinth of each coxal gland collect excretory nitrogenous wastes from the blood and pass them outside through the excretory pore.

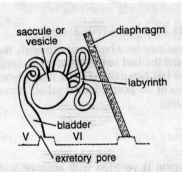

Fig. 72.14. Scorpion. Coxal gland.

3. Hepatopancreas. The hepatopancreas also acts as an excretory organ. Pavlovsky has shown that particles of ammonical carmine injected into the body of scorpion are picked up by the cells of hepatopancreas. Pearson believes that the ferment cells of the hepatopancreas also pick up excretory products. Thus, hepatopancreas also assists in the excretion.

4. Nephrocytes. Large nephrocytes and lymphatic organs are specialized excretory structures. These are found under the body wall in the mesosoma. These are believed to be excretory as well as phagocytic in function.

NERVOUS SYSTEM

The nervous system consists of : central nervous system and peripheral and visceral nervous system.

1. Central Nervous System

The central nervous system includes the brain or cerebral ganglion, circum-oesophageal connectives, sub-oesophageal ganglion and ventral nerve cord.

(i) Brain. The brain or cerebral ganglion is a small bilobed mass situated in the prosoma just beneath the median eyes. Microscopical and embryological studies reveal that the brain develops from the fusion of eight pairs of ganglia. A pair of optic nerves are given out from the brain to the median and lateral eyes; brain also gives off numerous fine nerves to rostrum, pharynx and oesophagus.

(ii) Circum-oesophageal connectives. From the brain arises a pair of thick, short and stout circum-oesophageal connectives which encircle the oesophagus and unite ventrally in a **sub-oesophageal ganglion.** In this way a thick nerve-ring is formed surrounding the oesophagus. From the connectives and ganglion six pairs of lateral nerves are given out to six pairs of cephalothoracic appendages.

(iii) Sub-oesophageal ganglion. It represents the first ganglion fused with sub-oesophageal mass.

(iv) Ventral nerve cord. The sub-oesophageal ganglion is continued backwards into the abdomen as double ventral nerve cord. It extends up to the fourth segment of the postabdomen. The nerve cord bears three segmental ganglia in the preabdomen and four in the postabdomen. The last ganglion is located in the fourth postabdominal segment. The nerve cord is rounded and slender in the preabdomen but flattened and ribbon-shaped in the postabdomen.

2. Peripheral and Visceral Nervous System

Numerous nerves are given out from the brain and the segmental ganglia of the ventral nerve cord which constitute these nervous systems. As the brain gives off a pair of optic nerves to the median eyes, a pair of nerves which branch and supply the chelicerae and the lateral eyes, a pair of nerves to the rostrum, a pair of nerve trunks to the pedipalpi and four pairs of nerves to the four pairs of walking legs. Besides these, the brain also supplies nerves to the pharynx, oesophagus and heart.

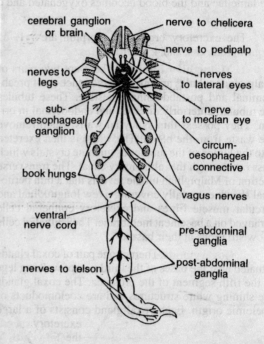

Fig. 72.15. Scorpion. Nervous system.

The sub-oesophageal ganglion may send two to four pairs of vagus nerves which run posteriorly into the preabdomen to supply the genital operculum, the pectines and the first two pairs of book-lungs. The segmental ganglia of the preabdomen send out nerves to the last two pairs of book-lungs, heart, and muscles of abdomen, while those from the segmental ganglia of the postabdomen supply nerves to the segmental muscles. The last ganglion also supplies the sting.

SENSE ORGANS

The sense organs and receptor organs of scorpion are sensory setae or sensillae, pectines and eyes.

1. Sensory setae or sensillae. The whole body of scorpion is covered with sensory setae (sensillae) and hairs which are generally much longer on the legs and tail. The sensory setae are tactile organs of scorpion. Each of the sensory setae is connected to a sensory cell located at its base which in turn is connected to a nerve fibre. On the podomeres of pedipalpi, the hairs are long and bristle-like and originate from cuticular integumental pits called setigerous, setal or bristle pores. The hairs are extremely sensitive to touch.

2. Pectines. The pectines are a pair of modified appendages lying attached to the sternum of the second segment of mesosoma joined to each other in the middle. Each pecten (Fig. 72.16) consists of a shaft or handle made of three pieces which bears a series of movable lamellae or teeth arranged like the teeth in a comb on the posterior margin of the shaft in the outer half. The number of teeth differs from species to species. The teeth of the pecten are sensitive either to touch or smell. Pocock observed a scorpion walking over a cockroach until the pectines come in contact with it when it suddenly withdrew and preyed upon it.

3. Eyes. There are four pairs of eyes in scorpion, a pair of median eyes and three pairs of lateral eyes.

(i) **Median eyes.** Median eye is like a cup covered externally by a cuticular lens or cornea which is continuous with the cuticle but is much thicker. Inside the pigmented cup are rhabdomes, each

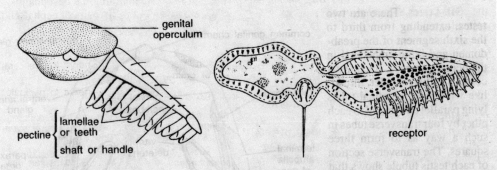

Fig. 72.16. Scorpion. Pectine.　　**Fig. 72.17.** Scorpion. T.S. through the pectine.

enclosed inside several retinal cells which receive nerve fibres of an optic nerve. Median eyes of scorpion are intermediate between compound and simple eyes of insects. They resemble a compound eye in having their retinal cells arranged in groups around each rhabdome as in ommatidia, but unlike the compound eyes of insects and crustaceans the sensory retinal cells both receive stimuli and transmit impulses. They resemble a simple insect eye in not being faceted but having a single lens. Both lateral and median eyes are sensitive to light changes but are incapable of forming images.

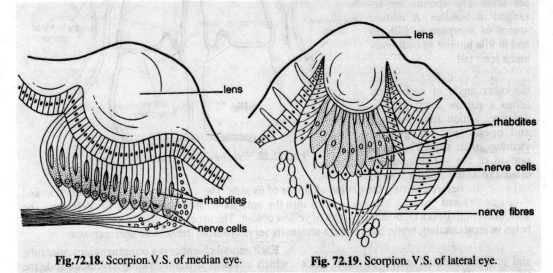

Fig.72.18. Scorpion. V.S. of median eye.　　**Fig. 72.19.** Scorpion. V.S. of lateral eye.

(ii) **Lateral eyes.** Lateral eyes are like simple eyes of insects. It is like a pigmented cup covered externally by a biconvex lens formed from transparent cuticle, inside the cup are several longitudinal optic rods called rhabdomes associated with retinal cell or retinulae. The retinal cells receive nerve fibres.

It is also regarded that in some species of scorpions, stridulating organs are found on the coxae of the pedipalpi or first pair of legs, in the form of ridges across which file-like surface can be drawn to produce sound. It indicates that scorpions probably have some perception of sound.

REPRODUCTIVE SYSTEM

The sexes are separate and scorpions show some sexual dimorphism. The male is generally smaller, has a narrower abdomen, longer pedipalpi, longer tail and a larger number of pectinal teeth. In male the operculum is formed of two flaps. The female is bigger having broader abdomen, smaller pedipalpi, shorter curved tail and fewer pectinal teeth.

Male Reproductive Organs

The male reproductive organs are a pair of **testes**, a pair of vasa deferentia, genital chambers, paraxial organs and common genital chamber.

(i) Testes. There are two testes, extending from third to the sixth segment of the preabdomen and lying embedded in the hepatopancreas. Each testis consists of two slender, threadlike whitish longitudinal tubes lying parallel and joined to each other by four transverse tubes in such a way as to form three squares. The transverse section of each testis tubule shows that it consists of an outer layer of connective tissue, a thin basement membrane and the germinal cells. The germinal cells are divided into several chambers by septa of connective tissue. In each chamber spermatogonia, spermatocytes and sperms are seen. The sperms are arranged in bundles. A mature sperm of scorpion is filiform and motile having an oval body and a long tail.

(ii) Vas deferens. From the outer angle of each testis arises a narrow duct, the vas deferens which runs forward and opens into the genital chamber of its side. The distal portion of the vas deferens is dilated so as to form the termi-

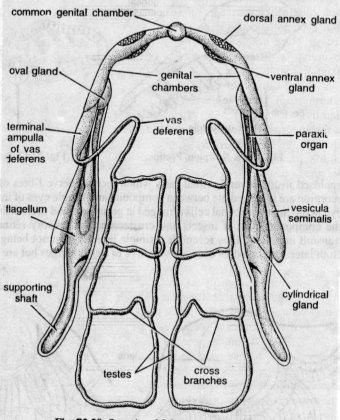

Fig. 72.20. Scorpion. Male reproductive organs.

nal ampulla before entering the genital chamber of its side. The accessory glands (cylindrical and oval glands) and vesicula seminalis open into the anterior terminal part of the vas deferens. The vesicula seminalis is a club-shaped organ of yellow colour. The accessory glands secrete a fluid which helps in reproduction, while the vesicula seminalis serves to store the mature spermatozoa.

(iii) Genital chamber and paraxial organ. Each genital chamber is a prominent muscular tube and produced behind into a paraxial organ which contains a tightly fitting chitinous rod, the flagellum. The structure of flagellum is different in different species of scorpions. It consists of a supporting shaft with a groove inside it. Few spines are also found on one side of the flagellum. The two flagella or chitinous rods together form the so-called double penis of scorpion which serve as claspers during copulation.

(iv) Common genital chamber. The two genital chambers continue forwards and open into a small, median common genital chamber which opens to the outside by a narrow male genital aperture, situated beneath the genital operculum on the sternum of first preabdominal segment.

Female Reproductive Organs

The female reproductive organs consist of the ovary, oviducts and common genital chamber.

(i) Ovary. The ovary is single which extends from the third segment to the sixth segment of the preabdomen and lies embedded in the hepatopancreas. It consists of three longitudinal hollow tubules (a median and two lateral) called the ovarioles which are interconnected by four narrow transverse tubules so as to form three pairs of squares. The ovarioles and their cross branches are lined by germinal epithelium, the cells of which form the ova. The mature ova project into hollow bud-like processes on the surface called the diverticula or the follicles.

The embryos start development inside the follicles as a result of which each follicle forms an elongated structure now called uterus. The uterus is differentiated into a proximal wider region or embryonic chamber and a distal narrow appendix terminating into an enlarged tip called the head of appendix. Thus, in a mature fertilized female several such uteri are seen emerging from each longitudinal and transverse tubules of the ovary. The shape of follicles varies in different species of scorpions and the size depends upon the size of the developing embryo within it. The follicles are fusiform in *Palamneus* and spherical in *Buthus*.

(ii) Oviducts. The two lateral ovarioles continue anterioly as the oviducts which converge towards the mid-ventral line to open into a small median common genital chamber. The common genital chamber opens to the outside by the female genital aperture situated beneath the bilobed operculum on the sternum of the first preabdominal segment.

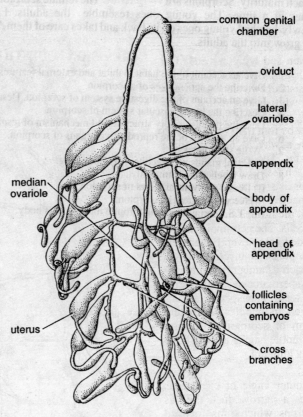

Fig. 72.21. Scorpion. Female reproductive organs.

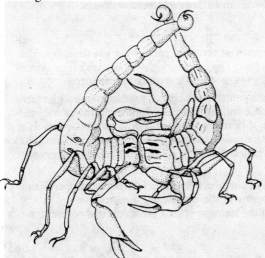

Fig. 72.22. Scorpion. Prior to a true copulation or to the transfer of a spermatophore to the female orifice.

COPULATION AND FERTILIZATION

The fertilization in scorpion is internal and it is followed by the courtship or copulation. Fabre has given a good account of the mating habits of scorpions. According to him, male and female scorpions stand face to face with raised tails which they intertwined. The male grasps the pedipalpi of the female with its own and the two scorpions go on moving hand in hand for an hour or more during which the animals turned several times. This is a sort of mating or nuptial dance termed as 'promenade a deux'' by Fabre. At length, the male would dig a hole in the neighbourhood of a stone and both would disappear into the hole under the stone. After mating, the female often devours the male. In India scorpions breed during monsoons.

DEVELOPMENT

In scorpions, the development is internal and very slow and some species take several years to reach maturity. Scorpions are viviparous. The female scorpions give birth to two to three dozen young ones at a time. The young ones resemble the adults. For some time the mother carries the newly-hatched young ones on its back and takes care of them. The young ones undergo several moults to grow into the adults.

REVISION QUESTIONS

1. Give an account of the habit, habitat and external features of a scorpion.
2. Describe the appendages of a scorpion.
3. Give an account of the digestive system of scorpion. Describe its food and feeding.
4. Describe the blood vascular system of scorpion.
5. Describe the respiratory structure and mechanism of respiration in scorpion.
6. Give an account of the reproductive organs of scorpion.
7. Write short notes on :
   (i) Coxal glands; (ii) Pectine; (iii) Book lung.
8. Draw labelled diagrams only :
   (i) Dorsal and ventral views of scorpion;
   (ii) Nervous system of scorpion;
   (iii) T.S. scorpion passing through middle of its body.

73

Periplaneta (Cockroach)

The cockroach is a typical insect and exhibits all the fundamental characteristics of class insecta. In fact, the cockroaches are very ancient insects and they are found practically all over the world except the polar regions. Nearly 2,600 species of cockroaches are known of which two species *Periplaneta americana* and *Blatta orientalis* are commonly found in India. *P. americana* is the largest species, measures about 4 cm in length and the both sexes possess well developed wings. It is a native of tropical America (Mexico) and has travelled with man to all parts of the world. *B. orientalis* is smaller, measures about 2 cm in length and black in colour. Its males possess wings which are shorter than body, while the wings of its females are vestigial. It is a native of tropical Asia and has spread to all parts of the world. The other species are *P. australasiae, P. brunnea, Blatella germanica* and *Nauphoeta cinerea.*

The description hereunder generally relates to *Periplaneta americana* which is commonly known as the American cockroach or ship cockroach.

PERIPLANETA AMERICANA (THE COMMON COCKROACH)

SYSTEMATIC POSITION

Phylum	....	**Arthropoda**
Subphylum	....	**Mandibulata**
Class	....	**Insecta**
Subclass	....	**Pterygota**
Order	....	**Orthoptera**
Genus	....	*Periplaneta*
Species	....	*americana*

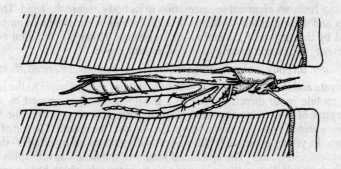

Fig. 73.1. Sectional view of a crevice showing a cockroach in resting condition.

HABIT AND HABITAT

Cockroach prefers to live in damp but warm places and generally found in kitchens, hotels, bakeries, restaurants, warehouses, grocer's shops, sewage, ships and public latrines, etc., where plenty of food is available. It is a nocturnal animal hiding in holes and crevices during the day and coming out at night when it tastes diverse objects like clothes, shoes, books and human food to feed upon. Thus, it is omnivorous in diet. It is a fast runner, *i.e.,* cursorial in habit. It can also fly but it flies very rarely. It is dioecious and oviparous and exhibits parental care.

EXTERNAL FEATURES

Shape, size and colour. Its body is narrow, elongated, compressed dorso-ventrally and bilaterally symmetrical. The adult cockroach measures from 2 to 4 cm in length and about 1 cm in width. The colour is reddish-brown. There are two dark patches surrounded by a light-brown margin in the first thoracic segment.

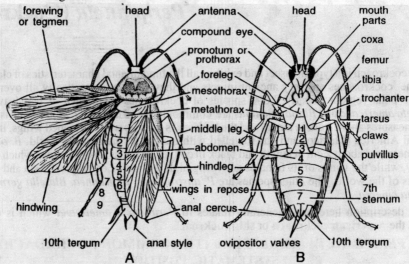

Fig. 73.2. *Periplaneta*. External features. A—Male in dorsal view; B—Female in ventral view.

Exoskeleton. The entire body of cockroach is covered by a hard brown-coloured exoskeleton. The exoskeleton of each segment has four separate sclerites which are joined together by delicate and elastic articular membrane. The sclerites of the dorsal side are called tergite, of ventral side are called sternite and those of lateral sides are called pleurites. The exoskeleton, in fact, consists of a thick and strong chitinous cuticle which provides protection to the body, prevents unnecessary water loss and points for the attachment of muscles.

Segmentation. It shows clear cut segmentation in its body except the head. The thorax consists of three segments and abdomen ten segments in adults which were eleven in embryo. The head is said to be formed by the fusion of six embryonic segments. However, the total body segments in embryo remain twenty but in adults only nineteen as said above.

Division of body. Its body is clearly divisible into three regions, *i.e.*, head, thorax and abdomen.

Head. It is ovate and flattened antero-posteriorly and lies at right angle to the longitudinal body axis. It is highly mobile in all directions due to a flexible neck. It is formed by the fusion of six segments. The tergites of these segments have fused to form a head capsule. The head bears a pair of compound eyes, a pair of antennae and appendages around the mouth. The top of the head capsule is called the vertex. In young cockroach, the vertex is divided by an inverted Y-shaped epicranial suture into two epicranial plates. The epicranial suture of the head capsule splits during moulting and it disappears in the adult. Below the vertex is a frons anteriorly which has a ventral clypeus. The sclerite of the head capsule forming vertex is called occiput and the lower part of clypeus forms the upper lip or labrum. On the sides of the head capsule is a gena below each compound eye. At the back of the head is a large triangular occipital foramen which connects the cavity of the head with that of the body.

A pair of kidney-shaped sessile compound eyes are situated at the dorso-lateral sides of the head. In the angle between the eyes and antennae are two small pale coloured areas called ocellar spots or fenestrae, they are undeveloped ocelli. A pair of antennae arise from membranous sockets, one on either side below the eyes. Each antenna has three parts, a large basal scape, followed by a smaller pedicel and a long filamentous, many- jointed flagellum. Such an antenna is called filiform antenna. The antennae possess small sensory bristles and it can be moved in all possible directions. The antenna belongs to the second segment of the head.

Mouth parts. The appendages around the mouth constitute the mouth parts which are of chewing or mandibulate or orthopterus type. The mouth parts consist of a labrum, a pair of mandibles, a pair of maxillae, a labium and a hypopharynx.

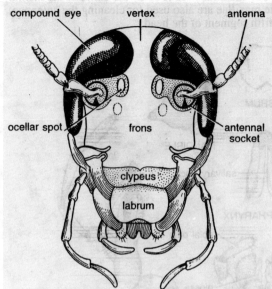

Fig. 73.3. *Periplaneta*. Head in dorsal view.

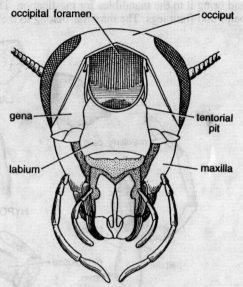

Fig. 73.4. *Periplaneta*. Head in ventral view.

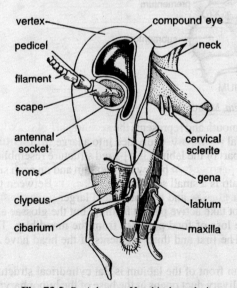

Fig. 73.5. *Periplaneta*. Head in lateral view.

1. Labrum. It is a membranous flat lobe suspended below the clypeus. It is movable due to the muscles inserted on its base. It lies in front of the mouth as the upper lip. On its ventral surface many sensory setae are situated which are possibly gustatoreceptors. Fused to the inner surface of labrum is a thin membranous plate, called the epipharynx.

2. Mandibles. These are suspended from the sides of the head capsule, one on either side of the mouth, and have a ball and socket attachment with the head. Each mandible is stout, heavily sclerotised having teeth-like cutting plates at its inner edge. On its upper inner edge is a softer prostheca. The mandibles are jaws used for crushing and cutting the food. The mandibles are movable with the help of adductor and abductor sets of muscles. The contraction of adductor muscles brings the mandibles closer so that their teeth are inter-fitted and in this position the food is broken down into small fragments. Then the abductor muscles contract and the mandibles get separated from each other. So, the cutting and chewing of food is affected by the alternate contraction and relaxation of these muscles. The mandibles belong to the fourth segment of the head.

3. Maxillae. These are two, one on either side of the head capsule behind the mandible. These are also attached with the head capsule by muscles and each of them consists of many podomeres. Each maxilla has a basal protopodite having cardo and stipes podomeres bent at right angle to each other. The cardo joins the maxilla with the head capsule. From the outer surface of stipes arises a five-jointed maxillary palp representing the exopodite, at the base of which is a small sclerite called

the palpifer. From the inner side of the stipes arises a double outgrowth consisting of an outer hood-like galea and inner lacinia which is a flat, tapering lobe ending in two sharp claw-like projections, its inner margin bears stout bristles. The maxillae hold food by the claws of the lacinia and bring it to the mandibles for mastication. The maxillae are also used for cleaning the antennae, palps and front legs. The maxillae belong to the fifth segment of the head.

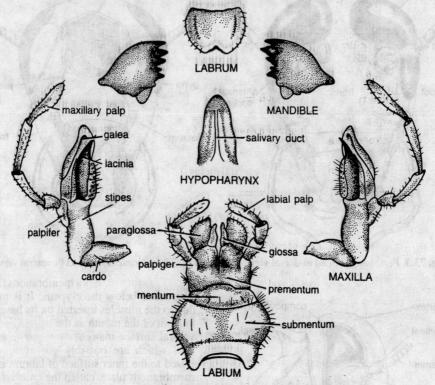

Fig. 73.6. *Periplaneta.* Mouth parts.

4. Labium. It is the lower lip lying behind the mouth and represents the second pair of maxillae which have fused together into one. It has a proximal postmentum divided into a large submentum and a small poorly sclerotized mentum. The distal part of the labium is a paired structure resembling a pair of maxillae united at their bases, it consists of prementum below the mentum and on each side it has a 3-jointed labial palp, at the base of each palp is a small sclerite, the palpiger. Between the labial palps are four lobes, two median and smaller glossae and two outer and larger paraglossae. The labial palps are sensory and the labium does not take active part in feeding, but the glossae and paraglossae together called the ligula prevents the loss of food particles from the mandibles. The labium belongs to the sixth segment of the head. The first and third segments of the head have no appendages.

5. Hypopharynx. Between the maxillae and in front of the labium is flat cylindrical structure called   hypopharynx or lingua. The common salivary duct opens at the base of the hypopharynx.

Neck. The neck or cervicum is a slender soft region supported by chitinous cervical plates, two dorsal and two ventral. The neck has muscles which retract and protract the head and turn it up or down or from side to side. The cockroach can also stretch its head like other insects.

Thorax. The thorax consists of three segments, the prothorax, mesothorax and metathorax. Each segment bears a pair of walking legs and the first pair of wings arise from the mesothorax, while the second pair from the metathorax. The prothoracic segment is the largest and due to the presence of three pairs of walking legs it is also called hexapoda.

The exoskeleton of each thoracic segment is formed by four chitinous sclerites, a dorsal tergite or tergum (the thoracic terga are also called nota in insects), laterally each side has a pleurite or pleuron and ventrally there is a sternite or sternum. Between the sclerites of each segment and between the sclerites of adjacent segments are thin, soft, flexible articular or arthrodial membranes which join the sclerites.

The prothorax has a large pronotum, its anterior margin overlaps the retracted head and the posterior margin covers the bases of the wings. The mesonotum and metanotum are smaller, they are flat and rectangular with irregular lateral margins. The thoracic pleura are divided into two parts each by a vertical groove, they are an epimeron and an episternum. Ventrally, the thorax is largely membranous, but in each segment the sternum is in the form of two plates, one anterior and the other posterior.

Walking legs. All the three pairs of walking legs are similar and they help the cockroach in its cursorial (fast running) habit. Each leg consists of five segments—a large basal coxa articulating with the thoracic segment between the pleuron and sternum, coxa is followed by a smaller trochanter which is freely movable on the coxa but is fixed to the next segment, the femur which is long and broad; this is followed by a long uniformly thick tibia which bears stout bristles, the tibial spurs; the last segment is a tarsus having five movable joints or podomeres or tarsomeres which have five bristles, and their lower sides have soft adhesive pads, the plantulae. The last tarsomere of the tarsus is often referred to as pretarsus and it terminates in two curved claws or ungues. Between the claws is a soft hollow lobe, the arolium having small bristles. The arolium is an adhesive organ for holding on the smooth surfaces.

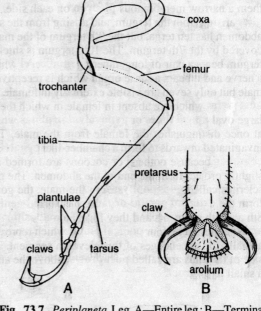

Fig. 73.7. *Periplaneta.* Leg. A—Entire leg ; B—Terminal parts of tarsus.

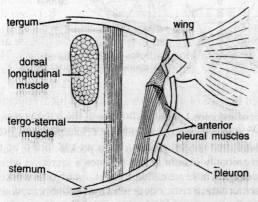

Fig. 73.8. *Periplaneta.* T.S. of thorax showing flight muscles.

Wings. As mentioned earlier the wings are two pairs, the first pair arises from mesothorax and second pair from metathorax. The wings are attached to the antero-lateral margin of the notum. The first pair of wings are heavily sclerotised and are known as elytra or tegmina. These are protective and cover the hind wings in a folded state, the left tegmen partly overlaps the right. The second pair of wings are membranous and larger, they lie folded below the tegmina when at rest. The wings are formed as outgrowths of the integument from between the notum and pleuron. Each wing has two membranous layers with tubular and chitinous prolongations of the haemocoel between them known as veins or nervures which contain blood in the early stages. Veins are strongly chitinized and enclose a small trachea ; the larger veins also contain a fine nerve fibre. The cockroach has a poorly developed set of wing muscles yet it can fly fairly well. In flight the wings are stretched horizontally, the anterior margins of the wings remain rigid but the rest of the wings yield to air pressure as the wings are moved up and down, so that when the wing moves downward, it is curved upwards and as the wing moves upward, it is bent downwards. Hence, by becoming deflected the wings encounter pressure from behind which propels the insect through the air. A longitudinal dorsal muscle lying below the terga raises the terga by which the wings move down. A tergosternal muscle running from the tergum to the sternum on each side of the thorax pulls the tergum down by which the wings are raised up.

Abdomen. Abdomen consists of ten segments. The exoskeleton of the abdomen is formed of hardened sclerites. A typical abdominal segment has a dorsal tergum, ventral sternum and between them a narrow membranous pleuron on each side. Each pleuron has three sclerites, two latero-ter-gites arising from the tergum, and arising from the sternum is a narrow latero-sternite. Dorsally, the abdomen has ten terga, but the 9th tergum of the male and 8th and 9th terga of the female are largely covered by the 7th tergum. The 10th tergum is shield-shaped with a deep cleft posteriorly. The 10th tergum bears a pair of long, tapering anal cerci which is fifteen jointed. Each cercus is traversed by a nerve and it bears a sense organ which is receptive to sound. Ventrally, there are nine sterna in the male but only seven are visible externally in female. The 9th sternum of the male has a pair of slender anal styles which are absent in female in which the 7th sternum is produced backward into a pair of large oval apical lobes or gynovalvular plates which form a keel-like structure. This rounded keel at once distinguishes the female from the male. The 8th and 9th sterna of the female have been invaginated inwards to form a chamber-like gynatrium whose posterior part constitutes the oothecal chamber because ootheca or cocoons are formed in it. In male a group of genital structures may slightly project from the end of the abdomen. The genital apertures of both sexes are surrounded by sclerites called gonapophyses. In the male, the gonapophyses belong to the 9th segment and they form the external genital organs or external genitalia. In female the gonapophyses belong to the 8th and 9th segments and they form an ovipositor. In the 10th segment just below the tergum is an anus supported by four podical plates which represent the vestiges of the 11th segment and cerci are actually the appendages of this eleventh segment. The podical plates form four lobes, one on each side of the anus are called paraprocts, above the anus is a rounded epiproct, and below the anus is a small hypoproct.

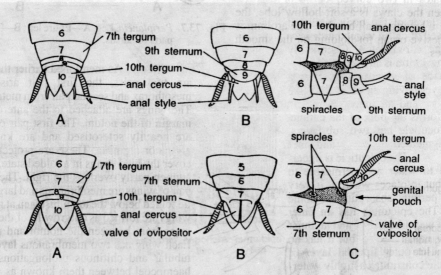

Fig. 73.9. *Periplaneta americana.* Posterior segment of abdomen. I of male. A—In dorsal view ; B—In ventral view ; C—In lateral view ; II of female. D—In dorsal view ; E—In ventral view, F—In lateral view.

The membrane between the 5th and 6th abdominal terga forms two deep pockets in the male, each pocket has two slit-like pouches which are probably glandular and produce a secretion which excites the female for copulation in the breeding season. These are called stink glands. Some workers suggest that the secretion of these glands possesses a characteristic odour which is probably repulsive for the enemies and helps the female in detecting the presence of its mate.

The male genital aperture is situated between the 9th and 10th sterna, while the female genital aperture is situated on the 8th sternum.

Spiracles. There are ten pairs of slit-like spiracles, two on the thorax and eight on the abdomen. The first pair of thoracic spiracles lies on the pleuron between the prothorax and metatorax and the second pair lies between the mesotorax and metathorax. The first pair of spiracles being larger than the other. The abdominal spiracles are smaller than the thoracic ones, the first pair lies dorsally in the first abdominal tergum, the remaining seven pairs lie on the pleuron of segments 2nd to 8th. These are the exit of respiratory system.

LOCOMOTION

Cockroach is a swift runner as well as a flier.

The six legs are helpful in walking or running. When the cockroach is at rest, the coxae of the legs lie back against the body and the first legs are directed forward, the hind legs are stretched out posteriorly and the middle legs take whatever position is convenient. During locomotion the first pair of leg is directed forward, they determine the course of the insect during walking or running. In locomotion on land the six legs are used as two tripods. The first and third legs of one side and the middle leg of the other side form a triangle on which the insect rests, while the other three legs are advanced and placed on the substratum. Then the first leg pulls and the third leg pushes, the middle leg of the opposite side acts as a pivot. The process is repeated by the other three legs and the insect moves in a zig-zag fashion.

The wings are used during flight. The fore-wings are held at right angles to the body axis and they do not beat. In fact, the beating of hind-wings with the help of flight muscles as mentioned earlier helps the cockroach in flying. The wings beat upward and downward alternately. The wings beat obliquely and at every downward beat, the wings push the air downwards and backwards. Due to this, its body is propelled upwards and forwards. Thus, by repeating this process in quick succession, cockroach flies.

INTEGUMENT OR BODY WALL

The body wall of cockroach consists of three distinct layers—an outermost cuticle, a cellular epidermis or hypodermis and a delicate basement membrane.

Cuticle. The cuticle is the outermost layer of the body wall and composed of chitin which hardens to form the exoskeleton. Chemically speaking, chitin is an acetate of polysaccharide of glycosamine. It is a thick layer having an outer film-like epicuticle and an inner procuticle which forms the bulk of the cuticle. The procuticle has two sub-layers, outer pigmented exocuticle and inner endocuticle. The epicuticle is impermeable to water and permeable to gases, but in places where it is very thin it permits absorption of some water. The epicuticle has an outer layer of wax-like lipoid and an inner layer of hard protein, but it has no chitin. The outer lipoidal layer of epicuticle constitutes a highly waterproofing mechanism which checks the evaporation of water and provides an effective protection of the

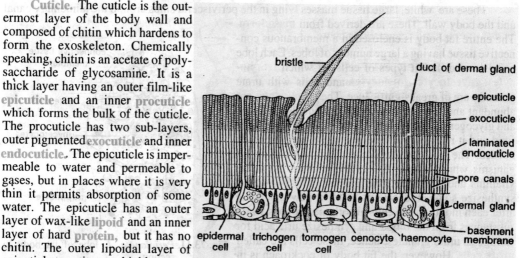

Fig. 73.10. *Periplaneta.* T.S. of body wall representing integument of insects in general.

soft tissues against desiccation. It also helps in absorbing some water from the humidity of the atmosphere. The epicuticle bears movable and fixed bristles. The procuticle is a thick, laminated, flexible layer of chitin. The upper part of procuticle is a laminated zone which has pigment and is sclerotized, this is often called exocuticle and it gives both rigidity and flexibility. The endocuticle is made of protein and chitin arranged in horizontal lamellae.

Epidermis. It is a single layer of columnar epithelial cells and secretes cuticle. Some cells of the epidermis or hypodermis are modified to give rise to the movable bristles, such cells are called trichogen cells. This layer contains some dermal glands which open at the surface of the cuticle through fine dermal ducts. There are some other cells like oenocytes in addition to the dermal glands in hypodermis.

Basement membrane. The basement membrane is thin and structureless membranous layer lining the inner surface of the epidermis.

Functions. 1. The body wall or integument is a protective covering for the delicate internal organs.

2. The cuticle forming the exoskeleton checks the loss of water from the body by evaporation and it also provides hard surface for the attachment of muscles.

3. Different types of outgrowths from the cuticle throughout the body act as sensory, feeding, filtering, copulatory and locomotory organs.

MUSCLES

The muscles are well developed and striated which provide quick movements to the body parts. The head and legs of cockroach are well muscularised, while abdomen is not so. The muscles are arranged in bundles, unlike the annelids where they constitute uniform layers in the body wall. However, the muscles are attached to the inner surface of the chitinous skeleton. The muscles of the legs, wings and jaws are very characteristic which provide an efficient movement mechanism to these parts.

BODY CAVITY

Though cockroach is a coelomate animal but its coelom is greatly reduced in the adults. The original coelom is represented by the cavities of the reproductive organs. However, the space between the body wall and gut represents the haemocoel which is filled with blood. The haemocoel is not true coelom and it is divided into three sinuses by two horizontal muscular diaphragms which are perforated; the pericardial, perivisceral and perineural sinuses. Actually, the haemocoel relates to the blood vascular system, hence, it will be discussed later.

FAT BODY OR CORPORA ADIPOSA

These are white, large tissue masses lying in the perivisceral sinus around the alimentary canal and the body wall. These are derived from mesoderm. The entire fat body is enclosed in a membranous connective tissue having a large number of lobes. Each lobe consists of different types of cells, of which trophocytes, mycetocytes, oenocytes and cells with urate granules are of great significance. The trophocytes are abundant and they store not only fats but also proteins and glycogen. Thus, this cell acts as stock of the reserve food and it releases the food into the blood whenever needed. The mycetocytes harbour symbiotic microorganisms which help in the synthesis of amino acids, vitamins and glycogen from glucose. The oenocytes synthesize some lipoproteins to form new epicuticle after each moult. Some cells absorb nitrogenous waste substances from the blood and synthesize uric acid for storage as urate granules, hence, these cells are called urate cells. However, the fat body of cockroach is in fact analogous to the vertebrate liver.

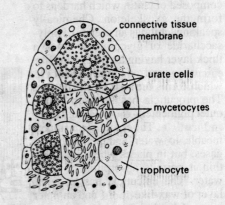

Fig. 73.11. *Periplaneta*. A lobe of fat body in section.

ENDOSKELETON

The exoskeleton, at several places most particularly in the head and thorax, extends into the body internally to form the endoskeletal elements. Such elements are called apodemes and meant for the attachment of muscles. The apodemes of the head constitute a characteristic structure called the tentorium (Fig. 73.12). It lies below the occipital foramen in the head capsule, it has a central space for the passage of nerves and three pairs of arms—the anterior, posterior and dorsal arms. The apodemes of the thoracic region are meant for the attachment of the muscles of the legs. The abdomen has no endoskeleton.

DIGESTIVE SYSTEM

The digestive system of cockroach consists of the alimentary canal and digestive glands.

Alimentary Canal

The alimentary canal starts from mouth and it consists of the preoral cavity, pharynx, oesophagus, crop and gizzard forming the foregut or stomodaeum; the mesenteron forming the midgut and the ileum, colon and rectum constituting the hindgut or proctodaeum. The stomodaeum and proctodaeum are ectodermal in origin and lined internally by the continuation of the exoskeletal cuticle, while the mesenteron is endodermal in origin and without cuticular lining.

Foregut. The so-called mouth is situated at the base of the pre-oral cavity or buccal chamber, also known as cibarium. The buccal chamber is a space in front of the mouth into which the food is received. This cavity is bounded in front by the labrum, posteriorly by the labium and on each side by a mandible and a maxilla. Inside this cavity a large tongue-like hypopharynx is present. The mouth opens behind into a short tubular pharynx which passes vertically upwards, then it bends

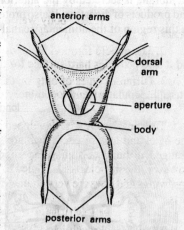

Fig. 73.12. *Periplaneta.* Tentorium.

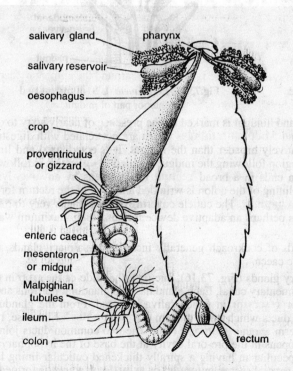

Fig. 73.13. *Periplaneta.* Digestive system.

backward into an oesophagus. The oesophagus is a narrow tubular passage which passes through the neck and gradually expands in the thorax, finally taking the shape of sac-like structure in abdomen. This sac-like structure is called crop which is thin-walled and muscular. The crop is followed by a gizzard or proventriculus. The gizzard is a round, thick-walled bulb-like structure. Structurally, it has an outer thick layer of circular muscles and its lumen gets considerably reduced due to the infolding of its wall. The gizzard can be divided into anterior armarium and posterior stomodaeal valve. The cuticular lining of armarium is thickened to form six highly chitinised plates called teeth. Behind the teeth, there are thin less chitinised plates which bear cushion-like pads covered with backwardly directed bristles. The deep grooves are also provided with fine bristles. The teeth help in grinding the food, while bristles help in straining the food to allow only well crushed food to pass on. The hind part of the gizzard projects into the midgut as a funnel, called stomodaeal valve which prevents the passage of food from midgut into the gizzard.

Midgut. The gizzard is followed by a narrow tube of uniform diameter representing the midgut or mesenteron. Its junctional region with the gizzard, which actually surrounds the stomodaeal valve, is called cardia. From this region, arise eight finger-like tubular blind processes called hepatic caeca or enteric caeca or mesenteric caeca. The midgut is formed of tall columnar endodermal cells which are glandular in nature. The internal lining of the midgut is thrown out into small but several folds forming villi and covered by a very thin layer of transparent peritrophic membrane. The peritrophic membrane is secreted by the anterior end of the cardia and it is permeable for enzymes and for the end products of digestion. It also protects the wall of the midgut. The process of digestion is completed in this region of the alimentary canal and the digested food is also absorbed in it.

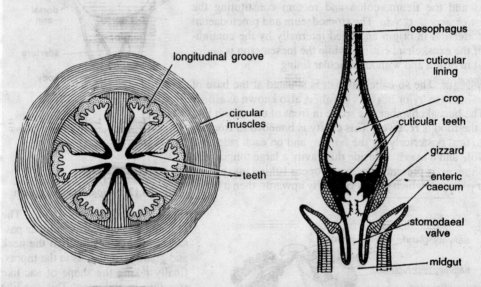

Fig. 73.14. *Periplaneta.* T.S. of gizzard.   **Fig.73.15.** *Periplaneta.* L.S. of foregut and
                                                              anterior part of midgut.

Hindgut. The junction of midgut and hindgut is marked by the presence of nearly sixty to one hundred fifty long, filamentous and blind Malpighin tubules which are not related with digestion but with excretion. The hindgut is relatively broader than the midgut. It is ectodermal and lined internally with the cuticle. Its anterior region following the midgut is called ileum which is followed by a long and coiled colon. The colon ends in a broad rectum which opens by an anus lying posteriorly below the 10th tergum. The lining of the colon is wrinkled and that of the rectum forms six thick longitudinal folds called rectal papillae. The cuticle covering the papillae is very thin but its underlying epithelium is thick, this is perhaps an adaptive device for absorbing maximum water from the passing out faeces.

Digestive glands. Digestive glands of cockroach generally include the salivary glands, the glandular cells of the midgut and hepatic caeca.

Salivary glands. A pair of salivary glands (Fig. 73.16), one on either side of the crop in the thorax, are found associated with the alimentary canal. Each gland has two glandular portions and a bag-like diverticulum or receptacle or reservoir in which saliva is stored. From the glandular portions of the two sides arise salivary ducts which unite to form a common duct. Likewise, two ducts from the reservoirs also join to form another common duct. The two common ducts join to form an efferent salivary duct which opens in the pre-oral cavity at the base of the hypopharynx. The ducts of glands and reservoir are peculiar in having a spirally thickened cuticular lining like trachea. Each salivary gland is made of several secreting lobules or acini. Each acinus is formed of two types of cells—zymogenic cells, packed with secretory granules and ductule containing cells with very less secretory granules but having plenty of mitochondria, rough endoplasmic reticulum and vesicular bodies.

The glandular cells of the internal lining of the midgut and hepatic caeca also produce juice containing digestive enzymes.

Food and feeding. As referred earlier, cockroach is omnivorous; it feeds on every type of animal and plant materials, though it prefers to feed on sugary and starchy substances but tastes almost everything it comes across. The presence of food is detected by the sensory receptors present on the antennae and maxillary palps. The maxillae pick up and bring food to the madibles for mastication. During the act of mastication the teeth of the mandibles bite and chew the food. The labrum and labium work like lips to prevent the loss of food from the mandibles at the time of mastication. The chewed food is pushed into the pre-oral cavity by maxillae, prostheca of mandibles and labium from where it is swallowed into the mouth. The function of hypopharynx is not certain in this connection.

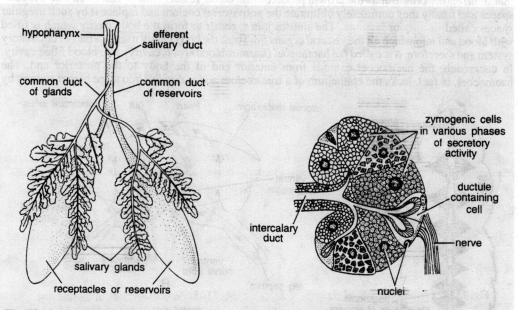

Fig. 73.16. *Periplaneta*. Salivary apparatus.   **Fig. 73.17.** *Periplaneta*. A salivary acinus in section.

Physiology of digestion. Since salivary glands open by their common duct in the pre-oral cavity at the base of the hypopharynx, hence, saliva mixes with the food during mastication. The saliva contains enzymes like amylase, chitinase and cellulase which hydrolyse different carbohydrates; some of them are converted into glucose. The saliva also moistens the food for its easy transport in the alimentary canal. However, such food is swallowed by the mouth and transported through the pharynx and oesophagus into the crop. After reaching into the crop, the digested carbohydrate in the form of glucose is absorbed and remaining food comes across the secretion of the glandular cells of the midgut. Actually, the digestive juice secreted by the glandular cells of the midgut ascends into the crop through the gizzard. This juice contains amylolytic enzymes like invertase, maltase and lactase to complete the carbohydrate digestion; proteolytic enzymes like trypsin, proteases and peptidases to digest proteins into amino acids; lipolytic enzymes for the digestion of fats into fatty acids and glycerine. Thus, maximum digestion occurs in crop and then the food descends down through the gizzard into the midgut. The gizzard grinds and crushes the food particles into finer ones and again it filters the food with the help of the fine bristles present at its posterior region. Thus, food coming into the midgut is very fine paste-like. The stomodaeal valves check the backward passage of food from the midgut into the crop. As mentioned earlier, the inner lining of the midgut—the peritrophic membrane is permeable to digestive enzymes and digestive nutrients, therefore, the digestive enzymes meet the food to complete the digestion which is already going on.

Absorption. The end products of digestion, *i.e.,* proteins as amino acids, fats as fatty acids and glycerine and carbohydrates as glucose are absorbed by the lining cells of the midgut and hepatic caecae and transported to the different parts of the body for their use. The excess food material is stored in the fat body as glycogen, fat and probably albumen.

Egestion. The undigested food passes into the hindgut. In the rectum, maximum of water is absorbed from it, hence, the undigested residue which remains here is almost solid. This is egested out in the form of small dry pellets through the anus.

BLOOD VASCULAR SYSTEM

The blood vascular system of cockroach is poorly developed and it is of open or lacunar type because the blood vessels open not into capillaries but into spaces so that the blood comes in contact directly with tissues, hence, the rate of circulation is low. However, the blood vascular system of cockroach consists of the haemocoel, blood which is called haemolymph and heart.

Haemocoel. In the embryonic stage of cockroach, a large perivisceral coelom is found like that of an earthworm. But as the growth proceeds, the blood vessels enlarge and swell into irregular spaces and finally they completely obliterate the perivisceral coelom and replace it by such irregular spaces called sinuses or lacunae. The sinuses join together to form the body cavity which is filled with blood and into which all the visceral organs lie. Thus, the body cavity itself is a part of circulatory system and therefore, it is called the haemocoel (*haema*=blood+*coel*=cavity), *i.e.,* blood filled cavity. In cockroach, the haemocoel extends from anterior end of the body to the posterior end. The haemocoel, in fact, lacks the epithelium of a true coelom and is divided into three bigger sinuses by

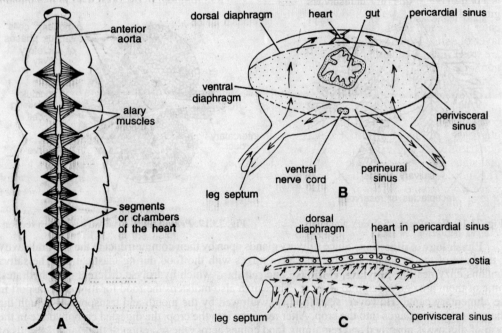

Fig. 73.18. *Periplaneta.* A—Heart in dorsal view; B—Course of circulation of blood in T.S. of thoracic segment; C—Course of circulation of blood in L.S. of body.

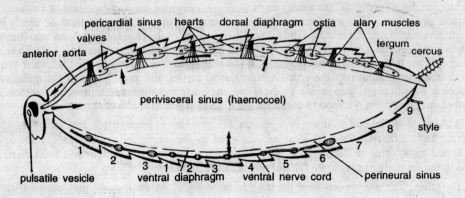

Fig.73.19. *Periplaneta.* Blood vascular system.

two horizontal septa. The septa are muscular membranous structures; one dorsal diaphragm and the other ventral diaphragm. The sinuses are upper dorsal sinus or pericardial **sinus** enclosing the heart, middle perivisceral sinus lodging the various visceral organs and ventral perineural sinus or sternal sinus enclosing the ventral nerve cord. Both the diaphragms are perforated so that the three sinuses remain in communication with each other. Attached to the dorsal diaphragm is a series of paired alary muscles, they are triangular in shape and their pointed outer ends are inserted into the terga.

Heart. The heart is an elongated tube with muscular wall, lying mid-dorsally beneath the terga of the thorax and abdomen consisting of thirteen segmentally arranged funnel-shaped chambers At the lateral side of each chamber is a pair of ostia, one on each side, the ostia are guarded by valves which allow blood to only enter the heart. The heart is made of a single layer of cells having striated muscles, the cells are lined both outside and inside by a delicate membrane. The first chamber of the heart is continued anteriorly into an anterior aorta which opens into haemocoel of the head. The alary muscles are twelve pairs whose alternate contractions and relaxations cause the dorsal diaphragm to raise and fall and so results the blood to flow from perivisceral sinus to pericardial sinus and finally into the heart as it beats. The muscular wall of the heart contracts in a wave from behind to forward and the blood is forced into the anterior aorta from where it re-enters the haemocoel and goes slowly to the organs and appendages including wings.

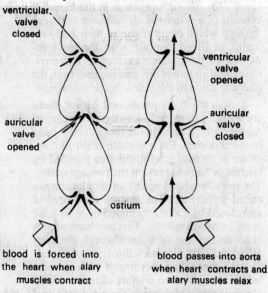

Fig. 73.20. *Periplaneta*. Diagrammatic representation of the working of valves in the heart.

In cockroach there is an accessory pulsatile vesicle at the base of each antenna which also pumps blood.

Haemolymph or blood. The haemolymph is the circulatory media in cockroach. It has colourless plasma and many corpuscles called haemocytes. No respiratory pigment is found in it. Hence, it does not help in the transport of respiratory gases. Its sole function is to transport various nutrients from one part of the body to the other and to carry nitrogenous waste substances from the tissues to the organ of excretion. The plasma contains about 70% water and a large number of organic molecules like free amino acids, uric acid, proteins, sugars and fats, etc. The haemocytes are of three types, *i.e.*, pro-haemocytes, transitional haemo- cytes and large haemocytes. According to some workers, only two types of haemocytes are found in *P. americana*, the plasmatocytes and coagulocytes or cytocytes. The plasmatocytes are polymorphic and constitute nearly 60—95% of the total haemocytes. The haemocytes are phagocytic in nature, help in coagulation and for healing the wounds.

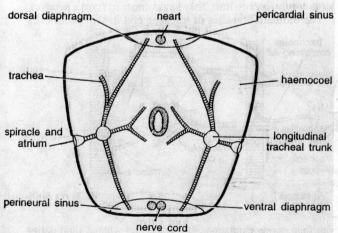

Fig. 73.21. *Periplaneta*. T.S. of thorax with respiratory organs.

Course of circulation of blood. Wave of contraction in the heart sets from posterior to anterior end, forces the haemolymph in the anterior aorta →haemocoel of the head →ventral and perivisceral sinuses →dorsal or pericardial sinus →heart. Complete circulation of haemolymph through the body takes nearly 30 to 60 minutes.

RESPIRATORY SYSTEM

The respiratory system of cockroach is well developed and elaborate like those of the other terrestrial insects to compensate the absence of respiratory pigment in the blood. It consists of a system of air tubes or tracheae through which every tissue of their body remains in direct contact with the environmental air for gaseous exchange. The environmental air enters into and escapes from the tracheae through the spiracles or stigmata.

Spiracles. As mentioned earlier, there are ten pairs of spiracles or stigmata arranged segmentally; 2 pairs in the thorax and 8 pairs in the abdomen. Each spiracle is slit-like aperture in an oval sclerotised area guarded by bristles or hairs to prevent the passage of dirt. The spiracle is bordered by an annular sclerite called peritreme. The spiracles are opened and closed by valves regulated by sphincter or spiracular muscles. This mechanism prevents undue loss of water through the spiracles and also regulates the flow of the air through them. The aperture of each spiracle leads internally into a short chamber called atrium from which arises the main tracheal trunk.

Tracheae. The haemocoel of terrestrial insects including cockroach contains a system of network of elastic, closed, branching and silvery white tubes called tracheae. The tracheae are formed by the inpushing of the ectoderm, hence, its wall consists of three

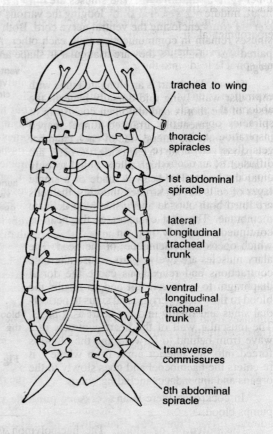

Fig. 73.22. *Periplaneta.* Tracheal system in dorsal view.

layers : taenidia or intima, basement membrane and epithelium. The intima is the cuticular lining in the form of spiral or ring-like thickenings which prevents the tracheae from collapsing. There are three pairs of large longitudinal tracheal trunks—one dorsal, one ventral and one lateral in position. All these trunks are connected by transverse commissures, thus, they anastomose to form a network which reaches to every part of the body. The ultimate branches of tracheae end in tracheole cells

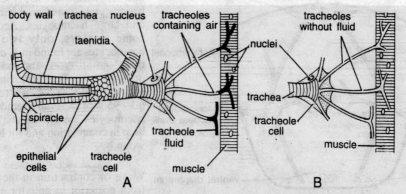

Fig. 73.23. *Periplaneta.* A—Tracheoles with fluid during expiration ; B—Tracheoles without fluid during inspiration.

from which arise very fine tubes called tracheoles. The tracheoles have thinned cuticle lining and they end blindly in the tissue cells. In a resting insect when respiratory activity is not high, the tracheoles are filled, not with air but with a tissue fluid of cells in which oxygen dissolves. By means of this system of tracheae the cells of the body or their fluids are in direct communication with the environmental air.

However, the thoracic spiracles lead into several tracheal trunks directly, while each abdominal spiracle leads into the lateral longitudinal trunks of their sides.

Mechanism of respiration. Inspiration and expiration take place through the spiracles ; expiration is an active process but inspiration is passive. In cockroach the first thoracic and first abdominal spiracles remain open all the time, but the second thoracic and last seven abdominal spiracles open during inspiration and close during expiration. Air enters the spiracles during inspiration and comes to the tracheae, then it comes to the tracheoles which contain fluids, the O_2 gets dissolved in these fluids and reaches the tissue cells. Opening of spiracles and subsequent diffusion of air occur due to the stimulation of spiracles by carbon dioxide. In expiration some carbon dioxide may pass out through the spiracles but the major part of it diffuses out through the cuticular covering of the body. Carbon dioxide also dissolves in the plasma and reaches the body surface which is permeable to gases and allows carbon dioxide to pass out.

When active movement takes place, as in running or flying, the metabolic rate is high and the osmotic pressure of the tissues increases, as a result of these the fluid is withdrawn from the tracheoles into the body cells. This withdrawal makes it possible for a column of air to extend deeply into tracheoles and directly reach the cells, and O_2 is taken by the fluid of the cells. In active movement the abdominal segments expand and relax, these movements are termed respiratory movements and they cause more air to be taken in through the spiracles.

Respiratory movements are co-ordinated by nerves in each segment, but these nerves receive impulses from thoracic ganglia which exercise a controlling influence over all respiratory activities. The co-ordinating centres in thoracic ganglia are stimulated and respond lack of oxygen and also to an excess of carbon dioxide.

EXCRETORY SYSTEM

Like other insects, Malpighian tubules are the main excretory organs of cockroach. In addition, fat body, nephrocytes, cuticle and uricose glands are also excretory in function.

Malpighian tubules. At the junction of midgut and hindgut a large number (usually sixty to hundred fifty) of thin, long, filamentous, thread-like yellow coloured structures are found attached, which are called Malpighian tubules. The Malpighian tubules arise in six groups and hang freely in the haemocoel without any external opening into it. These are ectodermal in origin like the nephridia of Annelida. Each Malpighian tubule is formed of a single layer of glandular ciliated cells having a characteristic brush border formed of cilia. These tubules excrete the nitrogenous wastes from the haemolymph of the haemocoel and empty the excreted substance into the gut. These are also osmoregulatory in function.

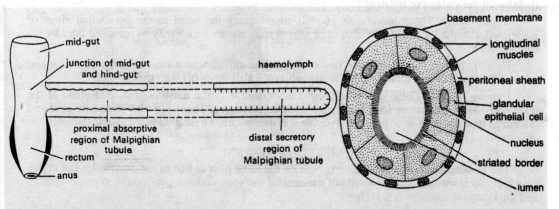

Fig. 73.24. *Periplaneta.* Diagram to show the relationaship of Malpighian tubule with the gut.

Fig. 73.25. *Periplaneta.* T. S. of Malpighian tubule.

Physiology of excretion. The physiology of Malpighian tubule has been widely studied in different insects and it appears that it functions essentially in the same way in all the insects. **Wigglesworth** has noticed two distinct regions in each tubule; a **distal** blind **secretory region** which hangs freely in the haemocoel and a **proximal absorptive region** which opens into the gut. The inner cells lining the distal region have well developed brush border, while in the proximal region they are less differentiated an called honey comb border.

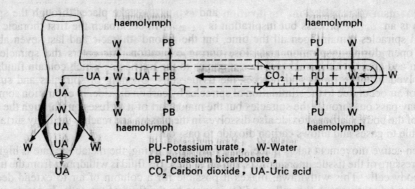

Fig. 73.26. *Periplaneta.* Diagrammatic representation of the working of Malapighian tubule.

The insects produce nitrogenous waste in the form of soluble **potassium urate** which is liberated into the haemolymph. These along with water are taken up by the glandular cells lining the distal region of the Malpighian tubule. In the cells of the tubule the potassium urate reacts with **water** and **carbon dioxide** (CO_2 present in the cells as a result of respiration) to form **potassium bicarbonate** and **uric acid.** The potassium bicarbonate is absorbed back into the haemolymph but uric acid is left out in the lumen of the tubule. As the uric acid in dissolved condition moves back into the proximal region of the Malpighian tubule, the water is reabsorbed in it and passed on into the haemolymph. The reabsorption of water occurs to such an extent that the basal part of this region becomes filled with solid crystals of uric acid. Water is further reabsorbed in the rectum, so that the passing out urine contains very little water and the bulk of it being nitrogenous waste as uric acid. Hence, the insects are physiologically called **uricotelic** animals. Thus, the Malpighian tubules are excretory as well as osmoregulatory in function because they help in conserving a sufficient amount of water which has helped the insects in leading effective life activities in terrestrial habitat.

Fat body. As referred earlier, the fat body completely fills the haemocoel and consists of many lobules. The lobules are formed of different types of cells, some of them are **urate cells** which store **uric acid** and **urate granules.** Thus, the fat body also works as excretory organ in addition to its usual function of the storage of nutrients.

Nephrocytes. These are chains of cells found along the heart in the pericardial sinus or associated with the fat body, they also store nitrogenous wastes which may be removed later by the haemolymph.

Cuticle. During the secretion of new cuticle, some nitrogenous wastes are deposited on it and when it sheds off during moulting, the waste substance also sheds off with the cuticle.

Uricose glands. These glands are found associated with the mushroom-shaped gland of the male reproductive organ as long blind tubules at its periphery. These can also store uric acid and discharge it at the time of copulation over the spermatophore. These glands are also called **utriculi majores.**

NERVOUS SYSTEM

The nervous system of cockroach is built on the same plan as that of the earthworm but in this case it is much specialised. It consists of the **central nervous system, peripheral nervous system** and the **sympathetic nervous system.**

Central Nervous System

The central nervous system consists of the **supra-oesophageal ganglion** or **brain, sub-oesophageal ganglion** and the **nerve cord.**

The supra-oesophageal ganglion or cerebral ganglion is a bilobed structure situated in the head in front of oesophagus, above the tentorium and almost between the bases of the antennae. It is formed by the fusion of three pairs of ganglia. It represents the brain and is concerned chiefly with sensory function. From the supra-oesophageal ganglia arise two cirum-oesophageal connectives which encircle round the oesophagus and meet below it with the sub-oesophageal ganglion. The sub-oesophageal ganglion is also situated in the head and formed by the fusion of 3 pairs of ganglia. Thus, the supra-oesophageal ganglion, circum-oesophageal connectives and sub-oesophageal ganglion together constitute the nerve ring round the oesophagus in the head capsule. The sub-oesophageal ganglion is the principal motor centre and controls the movements of muscles, mouth parts, wings and legs.

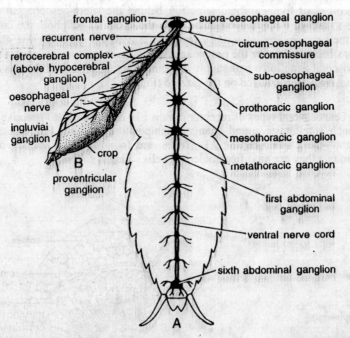

Fig. 73.27. *Periplaneta.* Nervous system. A—Central and peripheral nervous system ; B—Symphathetic nervous system.

From the sub-oesophageal ganglion arises a double nerve cord which travels through the thorax and abdomen below the alimentary canal on the ventral side up to the posterior end of the body. The nerve-cord has three large ganglia in the thorax, one each for pro-, meso-and metathoracic segments, therefore, they are called prothoracic, mesothoracic and metathoracic ganglia. Further the nerve cord has six ganglia in the abdomen which lie in the 1st, 2nd, 3rd, 4th, 5th and 7th segments. Each ganglion of the nerve cord is formed by the fusion of two ganglia except the ganglion in the 7th segment. The ganglion in the 7th abdominal segment is the largest of all the abdominal ganglia and probably formed by the fusion of 3 pairs of ganglia. Both the nerve cords run parallel and very close to each other but unlike earthworm they are not enclosed in a common sheath. But they are fused only at the place of the presence of ganglion and they are solid.

Peripheral Nervous System

The nerves originating from the nerve ring and ventral nerve cord to innervate different parts of the body constitute the peripheral nervous system. Three pairs of nerves originate from the supra-oesophageal ganglion—optic, antennary and labro-frontal nerves. The first two innervate the eyes and antennae but the third one divides into labral nerve supplying to the labrum and the frontal nerve which runs forwards to join the sympathetic nervous system. Similarly, three pairs of nerves originate from the sub-oesophageal ganglion—mandibular, maxillary and labial to innervate the mandibles, maxillae and labium respectively. Several pairs of nerves arise from each thoracic ganglion to supply the different parts of their own segment. A pair of nerves, however, from metathoracic ganglion innervates the 1st abdominal segment. The nerves originating from first five abdominal ganglia innervate the 2nd, 3rd, 4th, 5th and 6th abdominal segments. From the last abdominal ganglion three pairs of nerves are given off to supply the 7th, 8th, and 9th segments. It also gives a branch to innervate the cercus and other associated structures.

Sympathetic Nervous System

The autonomic or stomogastric or sympathetic or visceral nervous system of cockroach consists of some ganglia and their connectives. It includes the frontal, occipital, visceral or ingulvial and preventricular ganglia. The nerves from these ganglia are connected with the supra-oesophageal ganglion. The frontal ganglion is a small ganglion situated on the oesophagus in front of the supra-oesophageal ganglion. A pair of frontal connectives from the frontal ganglion is connected with the supra-oesophageal ganglion, a median recurrent nerve passes backward from it and connects the occipital or hypocerebral ganglion behind the supra-oesophageal ganglion.Three nerves, two lateral and one median originate from the occipital ganglion; the lateral nerves are connected with the corpora cardiaca and corpora allata which are endocrine glands, while the median nerve runs backwards over the oesophagus and joins the visceral ganglion situated on the crop. From the visceral ganglion a pair supply the alimentary canal, one of them is connected with the proventricular ganglion situated on the gizzard (Fig. 73.27).

RECEPTOR ORGANS

Cockroach bears several types of receptor organs liks other insects to perceive different types of stimuli like touch, smell, taste, sound, change in temperature and light. From these all, except the receptors for light—the photoreceptors, *i.e.*, eyes, are found situated in the epidermis of the integument and in fact they are modified epidermal cells called sensillae.

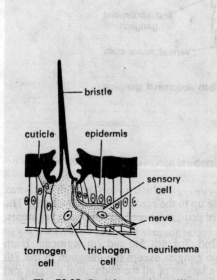

Fig. 73.28. *Periplaneta.* A sensilla.

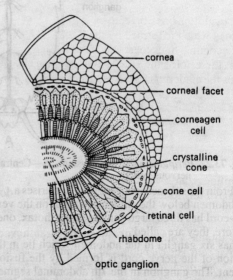

Fig. 73.29. *Periplaneta.* Gross V.S. of a compound eye.

Sensillae. A sensilla is the fundamental structure of a receptor. It has a modified sensory cell innervated by a nerve fibre, a trichogen cell for the secretion of spines or bristles and some tormogen or hair membrane cells. The receptors of touch, taste and smell have such isolated and simple sensillae, but those of hearing and sight have aggregations of sensillae which form elaborate organs.

The receptors for touch, *i.e.*, thigmoreceptors are located on the antennae and bristles of the legs, body, maxillary palps and cerci. The receptors for smell, *i.e.*, olfactoreceptors are found chiefly on antennae. The receptors for taste, *i.e.*, gustatoreceptors are found on the palps of maxillae and labium. The receptors for change in environmental temperature, *i.e.*, thermoreceptors are found mainly on the pads between the first four tarsal segments on the legs. The receptors for hearing, *i.e.*, auditory or chordotonal receptors are found on the anal cerci which respond to air or earthborne vibrations.

Photoreceptor organs. The photoreceptor organs of insects are simple eyes or ocelli and compound eyes. But in cockroach, usually compound eyes are found.

The compound eyes of cockroach are a pair of large, sessile, black, kidney-shaped structures situated at the dorso-lateral sides of the head capsule. It is a complicated structure and covered externally by the cuticle which is transparent. The transparent cuticle covering the compound eyes is divided into a large number of hexagonal compartments (2000 in cockroach) called corneal facets. These facets possess ectodermal structures beneath them arranged vertically and radially in the compound eyes. One facet and all the elements beneath it constitute an ommatidium which is in fact the visual unit. Thus, a compound eye consists of a large number of visual units or ommatidia and 2000 such visual units are found in a compound eye of cockroach.

Structure of an ommatidium. An ommatidium has a bioconvex lens or cornea which is formed by the cuticle becoming thickened and transparent, these form the facets. Below the lens the epidermis forms two clear corneagen cells or lenticular cells which secrete the lens. Below the corneagen cells is a transparent crystalline cone which functions as a second lens, it is surrounded by four vitrellae or cone cells. The vitrellae secrete the crystalline cone, they taper downwards. All this forms the focussing or

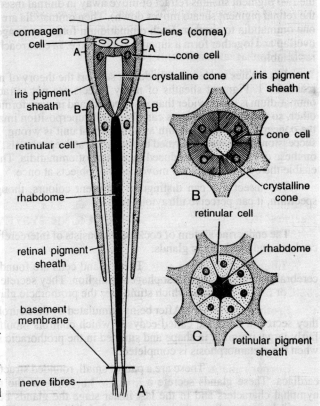

Fig. 73.30. *Periplaneta.* A—L.S. of an ommatidium ; B—T.S. through cone at A—A ; C—T.S. through rhabdome at B—B.

dioptrical region. Below the cone and in contact with it is a spindle-shaped refractive body, the rhabdome surrounded by seven photoreceptor retinular cells or retinulae which are elongated cells. The retinular cells secrete the rhabdome which is made up of seven rhabdomeres, one for each retinular cell. The rhabdome and retinulae constitute the receptor region, and below it is a basement membrane of the eye. Each retinular cell joins a nerve fibre at its base, and the fibres enter the optic nerve. Surrounding each ommatidium and separating it from its neighbours in many insects there are heavily pigmented cells arranged in two groups, an iris pigment sheath around the cone, and a retinal pigment sheath around the rhabdome and retinular cells. The retinal pigment sheath is absent in some insects.

Working of compound eye. Insects have two kinds of ommatidia. In nocturnal insects and many crustaceans the pigment is confined only around the cone cells, their retinulae and rhabdome do not touch the cone. Such eyes are called superposition eyes in which the ommatidia are not separated from each other by pigment. Their retinulae and rhabdome can be excited by light coming through their own as well as through neighbouring lenses, or light enters an ommatidium through several lenses. Each ommatidium forms a complete image of the entire field of vision, and all the images together form a continuous though partly overlapping superposition image. Superposition images are formed in dim light and are not sharp.

In diurnal insects the ommatidia are separated from each other by two pigment sheaths, their retinulae and rhabdome abut against the cone. Such eyes are known as apposition eyes in which only those rays of light can form an image which are parallel to the longitudinal axis of an ommatidium and pass directly through the centre of the lens. Each ommatidium forms a different but adjacent image, and all the ommatidia of a compound eye produce apposition images or mosaic vision composed of as many separate but adjacent images as there are ommatidia. But when the light is dim, the two pigment sheaths retract or move away in diurnal insects (the iris pigment sheath goes up and the retinal pigment sheath moves down). Then ommatidia are not isolated and light can pass through one ommatidia to another. Each ommatidium forms an image, and the images of all the ommatidia overlap and together form a superposition image. In cockroach, however, the pigment sheaths are not retractable.

But studies made recently do not support the theory of mosaic vision because of the following reasons : 1. Pigment sheaths of many insects are not retractable. 2. The field of vision of each ommatidium is much wider than is supposed, and images formed by adjacent ommatidia overlap each other, so that apposition eyes can also form superposition images contrary to previous ideas, hence, the concept of an ommatidium as a functional unit is wrong. 3. In each ommatidium, not one, but a succession of images are formed by focussing at deeper levels. The power of a compound eye depends on these deeper images produced by groups of ommatidia. The images are not very distinct but they enable the eyes to detect the movements of objects at once.

The insect eye can distinguish different colours, though it cannot see all the colours of a spectrum, it can perceive ultraviolet rays.

ENDOCRINE SYSTEM

The endocrine system of cockroach consists of intercerebral gland cells, corpora allata, corpora cardiaca and prothoracic glands.

Intercerebral gland cells. These gland cells are found situated in between the two lobes of cerebral ganglion or supraoesophageal ganglion. They secrete a neurohormone called prothoracotropic or brain hormone which stimulates the prothoracic glands to secrete their secretion.

Prothoracic glands. After being stimulated by the neurohormone from the intercerebral glands they secrete a hormone called ecdyson which controls moulting of the nymphs. These glands are fairly large, irregular in shape and situated in the prothoracic segment. These glands get degenerate when the metamorphosis is completed.

Corpora allata. These are a pair of small, rounded structures situated close behind the corpora cardiaca. These glands secrete a juvenile hormone in the nymphs which helps in retaining the nymphal characters and in the last instar stage the glands become inactive. Thus, the absence of juvenile hormone allows the appearance of adult characters. During the adult stage, these glands again become active to secrete the gonadotropic hormone. This hormone controls the development and functions of accessory reproductive glands and regulates the production of eggs in females. In a virgin female cockroach, these glands produce some volatile secretions which attract the male cockroach and, thus, it helps in finding the mate for copulation.

Corpora cardiaca. These are a pair of elongated structures situated on either side of oesophagus behind the brain. They secrete a hormone which increases the pulsatile rate of the heart, peristalsis of the hindgut but decreases the peristalsis of the foregut. It also regulates protein metabolism. However, hormone secreted by these glands is called growth hormone.

REPRODUCTIVE SYSTEM

The cockroaches are dioecious, *i.e.,* sexes separate. The sexual dimorphism is well marked, *i.e.,* males and females exhibit certain external features on the basis of which they can be reconised easily. The sexual dimorphic characters of the males and females are given in the following table :

	Male Cockroach		Female Cockroach
1.	Its body is smaller.	1.	Its body is relatively larger.
2.	Its abdomen is slender and the terminal abdominal segment pointed.	2.	Its abdomen is broader and the terminal abdominal segment blunt, boat-shaped.
3.	Its abdomen has nine distinct segments.	3.	Its abdomen has only seven distinct segments.
4.	Its seventh sternite has no cleft.	4.	Its sternite of seventh abdominal segment is divided into two lobes by a median cleft.

Male Cockroach	Female Cockroach
5. A pair of anal styles is present which emerge from 9th abdominal segment in addition to a pair of anal cerci.	5. Anal styles are not found, only a pair of anal cerci present.
6. Its wings are larger and extend beyond the hind end of the body.	6. Its wings are relatively smaller and extend only up to the hind end of the body
7. The second and third podomeres from the base of the antennae are equal sized.	7. The third podomere is comparatively larger than the second from the base in the antennae.

Male Reproductive Organs

The male reproductive system of cockroach consists of a pair of testes, vasa deferentia, an ejaculatory duct, utricular gland, phallic gland and the external genitalia.

Testes. There is a pair of three-lobed testes lying dorsolaterally in the 4th and 5th abdominal segments, being embedded in the fat body. The testes are well developed and elaborate structures in young cockroach and they are full of sperms. The testes become non-functional and reduced in old adults but some sperms may still be found in them.

Vasa deferentia. From each testis arises a thin thread-like, white vasa deferens. Both the vasa deferentia pass backwards almost to the posterior end of abdomen and then bend forwards to meet in the middle and open into an ejaculatory duct.

Ejaculatory duct. The ejaculatory duct is an elongated wide median duct which runs backwards in the abdomen and opens out by male gonopore situated ventral to the anus.

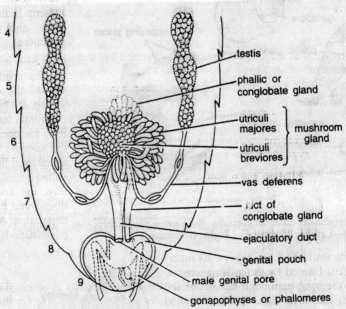

Fig. 73.31. *Periplaneta*. Male reproductive organs in dorsal view.

Utricular or mushroom-shaped gland. It is a large accessory reproductive gland, whitish in colour and situated at the junction of vasa deferentia with the ejaculatory duct. It has a mass of glandular tubules of three kinds, the peripheral long tubules or utriculi majores, the central tubules are small short tubules or utriculi breviores and behind the short central tubules are some short but more bulbous tubules forming the seminal vesicles filled with sperms.

Phallic or conglobate gland. It is a long and club-shaped accessory gland. Its anterior broader end lies in the 6th segment slightly to the right of the nerve cord. It narrows posteriorly into a tubular structure and finally tapers to open by a separate aperture located close to the male gonopore at the hind end of the body.

External genitalia. Some chitinous asymmetrical structures are found surrounding the male gonopore at the end of the abdomen. These are three phallomeres or male gonapophyses which constitute the external genitalia.

Right phallomere. It is mid-dorsal in position. It has two chitinous but membranous horizontal opposing plates and a broad serrate lobe with a saw-toothed edge and two large teeth, and at its posterior side it has a sickle-shaped hook.

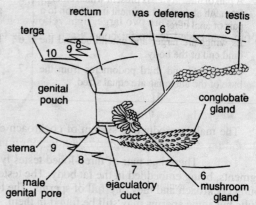

Fig. 73.32. *Periplaneta.* Male reproductive organs in lateral view.

Left phallomere. It has a broad base from which several structures arise, on the extreme left is a long slender arm with a curved hook called titillator, next to the titillator is a shorter and broader arm ending in a black hammer-like head called pseudopenis. Close to the pseudopenis are three small soft lobes, one of which bears a hook and is called an asperate lobe. The duct of the phallic gland traverses the left phallomere and opens between the asperate lobe and pseudopenis.

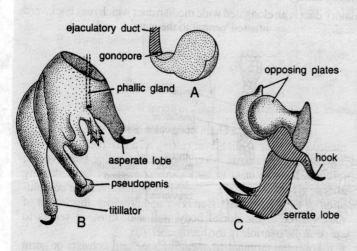

Fig. 73.33. *Periplaneta.* External genitalia. A—Ventral phallomere; B—Left phallomere ; C—Right phallomere.

Ventral phallomere. It is very simple in structure and lies partly below the right phallomere. It has a large brown plate and bears the male gonopore.

Spermatophore. The sperms produced from testes, while the cockroach is still young, are brought by the vasa deferentia into the seminal vesicles for storage. The sperms in the seminal vesicles are glued together in the form of bundles called spermatophores. Actually, the spermatophores are discharged by the male during copulation. A spermatophore is pear-shaped about 13 mm in diameter and its wall has three layers. Its innermost layer is first formed by the milky secretion secreted from the long peripheral tubules of the utricular gland. This layer then receives bundled sperms from seminal vesicle and a liquid from the short tubules of the utricular gland. Then this inseminated layer passes down the ejaculatory duct and it receives the second layer from the cells of ejaculatory duct. During mating, the two layered spermatophore, thus, formed is attached to the spermathecal aperture of the female and then the secretion of phallic gland is poured over it which hardens to form the third and outermost layer of the spermatophore.

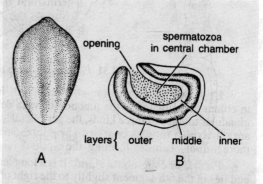

Fig.73.34. *Periplaneta.* A—Spermatophore; B—T.S. of spermatophore.

Female Reproductive Organs

The female reproductive system of cockroach consists of a pair of ovaries, vagina, genital pouch, collaterial glands, spermathecae and the external genitalia.

Ovaries. There are two large, light yellow-coloured ovaries lying laterally in the segment 4th, 5th, 6th, embedded in the fat body. Each ovary is formed of a group of eight ovarian tubules or

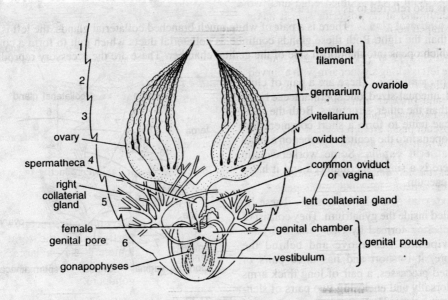

Fig. 73.35. *Periplaneta.* Female reproductive organs in dorsal view.

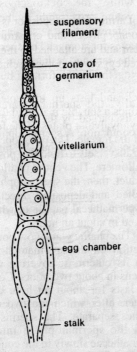

Fig. 73.36. *Periplaneta.* An ovariole in L.S.

ovarioles containing a chain of developing ova. An ovariole is made up of an epithelial layer resting on a basement membrane and enclosed externally in a connective tissue coat. However, an ovariole from in front to backwards consists of the following zones : (i) suspensory filament, it is thin, thread-like continuation of the connective tissue layer and provides attachment of the ovariole to the dorsal body wall and, thus, it serves to suspend the ovariole in the haemocoel, (ii) zone of germarium, it follows the terminal filamentous zone and consists of germ cells or oogonia and mature into oocytes and pushed downwards, (iii) vitellarium, this zone receives the oocytes from the zone of germarium one by one and constitutes the largest part of the ovariole, the oocytes become enclosed in a follicle of epithelium and increase progressively in size towards the posterior end which gives it beaded appearance, (iv) egg chamber, the vitellarium opens posteriorly into a small, thick, oval egg chamber which contains a single large mature ovum at a time, (v) stalk or pedicel, the egg chamber continues posteriorly into thin-walled, hollow stalk which opens into the lateral oviduct.

Oviducts. The stalk of all eight ovarioles on one side join to form an oviduct which is lateral, small and with muscular wall.

Vagina. Both the lateral oviducts unite to form a broad median common oviduct called vagina. The vagina opens by the female gonopore into the genital chamber.

Genital pouch. It is a large boat-shaped structure whose floor is formed by the 7th sternite, roof and sides are formed by the 8th and 9th sternites. The genital pouch can be divided into a genital chamber into which vagina opens and an oothecal chamber where oothecae are formed. The genital chamber also receives the accessory reproductive glands. The female gonopore is an aperture in the 8th sternum, which lies inside the genital chamber inflected above the 7th sternite. The 7th sternite is also produced backwards into two large oval gynovalvular plates or apical lobes. The genital pouch is also referred to as gynatrium.

Collaterial glands. There is a pair of white much branched collaterial glands, the left is much larger than the right. Both these glands continue as collaterial ducts which join to form a common duct which opens into the dorsal side of the genital chamber. These are the accessory reproductive glands.

Spermathecae. These are a pair of club-shaped, unequal-sized, one spermathecae being larger than the other, structures. Both the spermathecae unite to form a short common duct which opens into the genital chamber on a small spermathecal papilla. Some workers claim that there is a single spermatheca and it has a lateral caecum.

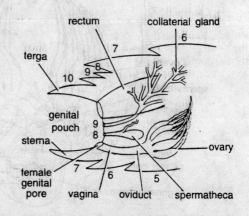

Fig. 73.37. *Periplaneta*. Female reproductive organs in lateral view.

External genitalia of female. These lie concealed inside the gynatrium. They consist of an ovipositor formed by two gonapophyses. The ovipositor lies above and behind the gonopore, it is short and has three pairs of elongated processes, a pair of long thick arms lying dorsally and enclosing two pairs of slender tapering arms. These two pairs of arms arise from a common base and they constitute the posterior gonapophyses, they belong to the 9th abdominal segment and are joined to the 9th tergum. The third pair of arms of the ovipositor is large, they converge and meet posteriorly lying below the posterior gonapophyses and constitute the anterior gonapophyses. These belong to the 8th abdominal segment and are attached to the outer margins of 8th tergum. The ovipositor is used only to conduct fertilized eggs to the oothecal chamber.

COPULATION

The active breeding season of cockroach starts from March and lasts up to September. Copulation occurs at night. During copulation, the male cockroach finds a suitable mate and the two partners come together by thin posterior ends. The male opens the gynovalvular plates of the female by its titillator and inserts its phallomeres into the genital chamber of the female. The pseudopenis of the male is then inserted into the gonopore of the female and rotated transversely to hold it in position. The anterior gonapophyses of the ovipositor are held by the right phallomere. The ventral phallomere moves to the right, thus, opening the gonopore of the ejaculatory duct, then, the spermatophore is expelled and deposited directly on the spermathecal papilla to which it is fixed in about an hour.

The phallic gland now pours its secretion on the spermatophore to form its outermost covering which hardens in about two hours. Copulation lasts for about an hour and a quarter, after which the two cockroaches separate. The sperms pass from the spermatophore into the spermathecae slowly in the course of the next 20 hours after which the empty spermatophore is discarded.

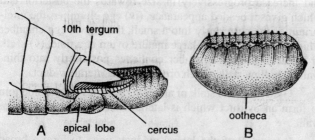

Fig. 73.38. *Periplaneta*. Ootheca formation. A—Abdomen of female showing the release of ootheca ; B—A released ootheca.

OOTHECA FORMATION

The eggs come alternately from the two ovaries into the common oviduct and pass through the female gonopore into the genital chamber where they are fertilized by sperms coming from the spermathecae. The two collaterial glands pour their different secretions on the fertilized eggs, these secretions combine to form a scleroprotein which hardens to form a dark brown ootheca around the eggs. The ootheca is shaped and moulded by the ovipositor and the walls of the oothecal chamber. The ootheca is 12 mm in length, on one side it has a straight crest with a serrated margin, it contains 16 fertilized eggs standing vertically in two rows, the position of eggs can be seen on the outer surface of ootheca. The ootheca is completed in about a day and it protrudes from the oothecal chamber, being held in place by the 10th tergum and gynovalvular plates. The female cockroach carries the ootheca for several days and finally drops it in some dark, dry place. Every female cockroach produces nearly 15 to 40 ootheca in its life span of about one to two years.

LIFE-HISTORY

The eggs of cockroach, like other insects, are called centrolecithal because the ooplasm is placed in the form of a thin film outside a central mass of yolk. The embryonic development occurs in the ootheca, which takes nearly 5 to 13 weeks. After the embryonic development is complete, the ootheca ruptures and the young ones hatch out. The young ones of cockroach resemble their parents in every respect except that they are smaller in size and without wings. These are called nymphs which undergo metamorphosis.

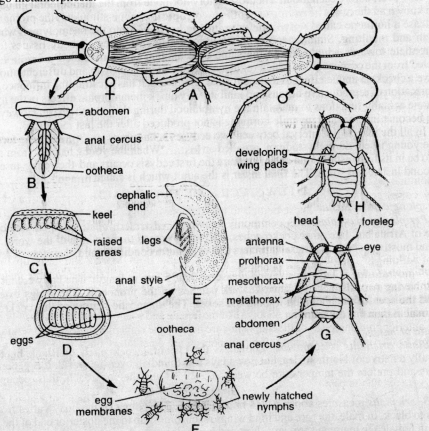

Fig. 73.39. *Periplaneta.* Life history. A—Copulation; B—Laying of ootheca ; C—A single ootheca ; D—Ootheca in section showing eggs; E—Early embryo; F—Hatching; G—Early nymph ; H—Late nymph with wing pads.

METAMORPHOSIS

The nymph of cockroach which resembles its adult in structure and feeding habit, but it is paler in colour, smaller in size, devoid of wings and the gonads are immature. As it feeds it grows, its outer exoskeleton is cast off, and this process of shedding the exoskeleton is known as moulting or ecdysis which is controlled by the hormonal activity.

During ecdysis, the hypodermis of the integument secretes an enzyme which erodes the lower surface of the old cuticle, thus, separating the cuticle from the hypodermis. Then the hypodermis secretes a new epicuticle which is impervious to the enzyme. Finally the hypodermis secretes a new procuticle. The epicuticle and procuticle form a new cuticle. The old cuticle is ruptured and is shed by the animal. Thus, the nymph forms a new exoskeleton by its hypodermis before the old one is cast off and growth can take place only before the new covering has hardened, because the tough exoskeleton does not allow increase in size. The cockroach nymph undergoes ten to twelve ecdyses to become an adult in about a year. During this period the nymph grows, wings are formed from the integument and gonads become mature. The ecdysis is, thus, closely associated with the growth also. However, summing up the whole processes it can be said that the nymph gradually develops further and further from ecdysis to ecdysis. After the last ecdysis no further increase in size, *i.e.*, growth occurs. This gradual assumption of adult characters with hardly any change is called paurometabolic metamorphosis.

Hormonal Control of Metamorphosis

As referred earlier, insects have three endocrine glands, out of these only two are directly related with ecdysis and growth.

However, before each moult a neurosecretory hormone from the intercerebral gland cells of the brain known as the brain hormone or prothoracotropic hormone stimulates the prothoracic glands to release a hormone called ecdyosone or moulting hormone into the haemolymph which induces growth and moulting. Simultaneously this hormone also stimulates all body tissues to grow and differentiate towards adulthood. At the same time another hormone called juvenile hormone is secreted from the corpora allata which regulates the rate of early growth and differentiation of tissues to have a check on undue effect of the ecdyosone. Therefore, it has a restraining influence and checks the formation of reproductive organs and inhibits very quick metamorphic effects in the nymph. This hormone actually functions to maintain the nymphhood during the growth phase. However, corpora allata become inactive and juvenile hormone is not produced after the last moulting.

In all the insects the interval between two ecdyses is known as stadium and the form assumed by the young insect during a stadium is called an instar. When the young hatches from an egg, it is said to be in its first instar, at the end of stadium the first ecdysis occurs and the young insect assumes its second instar, and so on. The final instar is the adult which is called imago.

A FEW SPECIES OF COCKROACH

1. *Periplaneta australasiae*

Periplaneta australasiae is commonly known as Australian cockroach. It was originally a native of Africa but, like other cockroaches, it has now spread to the whole of the world. In India it is found mostly in south. It generally prefers to live in warm conditions and, therefore, it is a common pest of buildings.

P. australasiae is large in size and measures 30–35 mm in length. The body colour is reddish brown having two distinct and separate dark patches on the pronotum. The wings extend a little beyond the apex of the abdomen in both the sexes. The diagnostic feature of this cockroach is the pale basal margins of the tegmina.

2. *Blatta orientalis*

Blatta orientalis is commonly known as the Oriental cockroach or Black beetle. It was originally a native of North Africa, but nowadays it is found all over the world. It is generally found indoors and prefers the temperature between 20°–29° C and the cockroach, thus, occupies cooler places.

B. orientalis measures about 20–24 mm in length. The colour of the body varies from reddish brown to black. In male, the fore and hind wings reach almost up to the posterior end of the abdomen, while in female the tegminae are very short and hind wings are absent. The colouration on pronotum is uniform. Both the sexes are devoid of power of flight.

3. *Blatella germanica*

Blatella germanica is commonly known as the German cockroach or Steamfly. It was originally a native of Africa but nowadays it is very common throughout the world. It prefers to live in warm and moist conditions and, hence, inhabits indoor places such as kitchens, restaurants and dining halls.

B. germanica is small in size and measures from 10–15 mm in length. The colouration of body is pale ochraceous buff to tawny with two dark longitudinal bands on the pronotum. The male is thin and slender and its wings do not reach up to posterior end of the abdomen, while the female is stout and robust and its wings reach up to the posterior extremity of abdomen. The female carries the ootheca for about 10–15 days or more until the eggs hatch. *B. germanica* does not fly but can run swiftly by gliding flight.

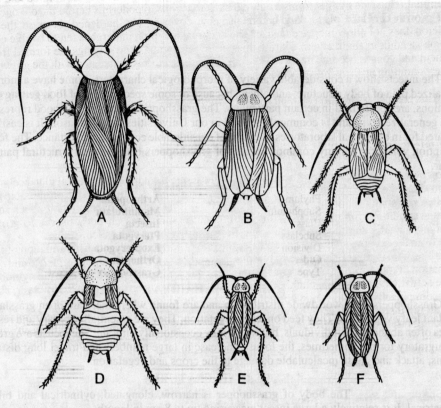

Fig. 73.40. A few species of cockroach. A—*Periplaneta americana* (male) ; B—*P. australasiae* (male); C—*Blatta orientalis* (male) ; D—*B. orientalis* (female) ; E—*Blatella germanica* (male) ; F—*B. germanica* (female).

REVISION QUESTIONS

1. Give an account of the habit, habitat and external features of *Periplaneta*.
2. Describe the mouth parts of cockroach.
3. Give an account of the digestive system and physiology of digestion in cockroach.
4. Give an account of the blood vascular system of cockroach.
5. Give an account of the respiratory system and mechanism of respiration in cockroach.
6. What are Malpighian tubules ? Describe the structure and function of such a tubule.
7. Describe the nervous system of cockroach.
8. Give an account of the structure and mode of working of the compound eye of cockroach.
9. Describe the reproductive organs of cockroach.
10. Draw only labelled diagrams of the following :
    (i) An ommatidium ; (ii) Salivary glands.
11. Write short notes on :
    (i) Sensilla; (ii) Tentorium; (iii) Endocrine glands of cockroach; (iv) Hormonal control of metamorphosis in cockroach; (v) Sexual dimorphism in cockroach.
12. Describe a few species of cockroach other than *Periplaneta americana*.

74

Grasshopper or Locust

The insects show a considerable variety of morphological characters. Some have a more or less generalized plan of body structure, and others, because of some special habit of food getting or living conditions, are specialized in certain particulars. The grasshopper, or locust, is a good representative of the generalized type and is commonly studied in our Universities for that reason. It is easily raised and cared for in biological laboratories. It is also of considerable economic importance. The following description will serve for any common species of grasshoppers because their structural patterns are similar.

SYSTEMATIC POSITION

Phylum	....	**Arthropoda**
Subphylum	....	**Mandibulata**
Class	....	**Insecta**
Subclass	....	**Pterygota**
Division	....	**Exopterygota**
Order	....	**Orthoptera**
Type	....	**Grasshopper** or **Locust**

HABIT AND HABITAT

Grasshoppers have worldwide distribution and are found where there are open grasslands and abundant leafy vegetation. They feed on leafy vegetation. They are essentially solitary and residential species often abundant as individuals, but which may occasionally migrate. The locusts are gregarious and migratory forms. Sometimes, the locusts increase in large numbers and travel long distances in swarms, attack and cause incalculable damage to the crops and vegetation.

EXTERNAL FEATURES

Shape and size. The body of grasshopper is narrow, elongated, cylindrical and bilaterally symmetrical. It is relatively a large insect measuring up to 8 cm in length

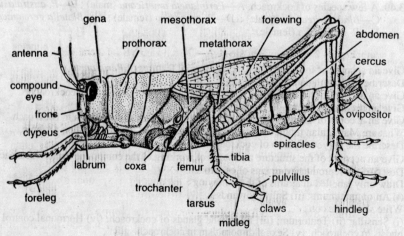

Fig. 74.1. Grasshopper (Lateral view).

Colouration. The usual body colour is yellowish and brownish with different markings and colour spots. The pigment in the chitin provides the protective colouration to the body matching the environment.

Exoskeleton. The body is covered by an exoskeleton that protects the delicate systems within. This exoskeleton is the cuticle which consists of chitin and is divided into a linear row of segments. The exoskeleton is formed into hard plates or sclerites separated by soft cuticle that permits movement of the body segments and appendages. The softer regions are known as sutures. Each segment is made up of separate pieces known as sclerites. Usually some of the sclerites of a typical segment cannot be distinguished and the sutures are, therefore, said to be obsolete or indistinct. The body wall consists of the cuticle beneath which is a layer of cells the hypodermis which secretes it and under this a basement membrane.

Division of body. In grasshoppers, the body is divided into three typical regions, *viz.*, the head thorax and abdomen.

Head. The head in grasshopper is more or less ventral, although it appears to be hypognathus while feeding. It is enclosed in a chitinous capsule and is attached to the body by means of a small neck having cervical sclerites. Six segments are fused together to form the head. The head is made up of a dorsal portion, the vertex; a region in front, the frons; and the sides, or genae. Below the frons is the plate, clypeus. On each side of the head is a compound eye. Three simple eyes or ocelli are located in the region between compound eyes. A pair of slender antennae are also found on the head. On the ventral side of the head are the mouth parts.

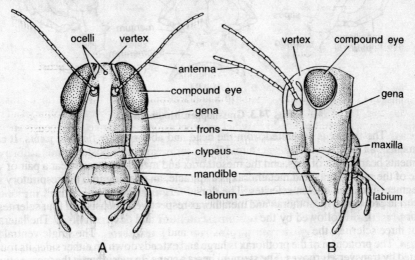

Fig. 74.2. Grasshopper. Head. A—Dorsal view ; B—Lateral view.

Appendages of the head. The head bears a pair of antennae, a pair of compound eyes, three simple eyes or ocelli and mouth parts.

Antennae. The antennae are filiform. Each antenna consists of a small piece called the scape, an undifferentiated pedicel and a sufficiently long flagellum composed of about twenty-five segments. Sensory bristles, probably olfactory in nature, are present on the surface of antennae.

Compound eyes. Two compound eyes are placed dorso-laterally on the first segment of the head. These are sessile as stalks are absent. Each compound eye is covered by a transparent part of the cuticle, the cornea which is divided into a large number of hexagonal facets. Each facet is the outer end of a unit known as an ommatidium. Such a structure gives mosaic vision.

Ocelli. Three simple eyes or ocelli are placed between the compound eyes. An ocellus consists of a group of visual cells the retinulae and a thick transparent lens which is the modification of cuticle.

Mouth parts. The mouth parts of grasshopper are chewing or mandibulate type. The mouth parts include the labrum, mandibles, maxillae, labium and hypopharynx. There is a labrum or upper lip attached to the ventral edge of the clypeus. Beneath this is a membranous tongue-like organ, the hypopharynx. On either side is a single, hard jaw or mandible with a toothed surface fitting for grinding. Beneath the mandibles are a pair of maxillae. Each maxilla consists of a basal cardo, central stipes, a long curved lacinia, a long rounded galea and a maxillary palp which arises from the palpifer. The labium or lower lip comprises a basal submentum, a central mentum, two movable flaps, the ligulae and a labial palp on either side.

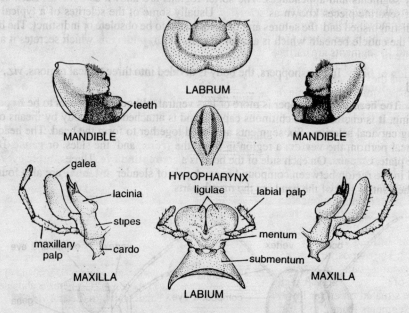

Fig. 74.3. Grasshopper. Mouth parts.

Thorax. The thorax is separated from the head and abdomen by flexible joints. It consists of three segments : an anterior prothorax, a middle mesothorax and a posterior metathorax. Each of these segments bears a pair of legs, and the mesothorax and metathorax each bear a pair of wings. On either side of the mesothorax and metathorax is a spiracle, an opening into the respiratory system. A typical segment includes eleven sclerites. The dorsal tergum (called pronotum, mesonotum and metanotum in prothorax, mesothorax and metathorax respectively) consists of four sclerites in a row, an anterior prescutum followed by the scutum, scutellum and postscutellum. The lateral pleuron consists of three sclerites, the episternum, epimeron and parapteron. The single ventral sclerite is the sternum. The pronotum of the prothorax is large and extends down on either side ; its four sclerites are indicated by transverse grooves. The sternum bears a spine. In mesothorax the mesonotum is small but the sclerites of pleuron are distinct. The sclerites of metathorax resemble the mesothorax.

Legs. Each thoracic segment bears a pair of jointed legs. Each leg consists of a linear series of five segments as follows : the coxa articulates with the body, then come the small trochanter fused with the femur, the tibia and the tarsus. The tarsus of each leg consists of three visible segments, the one adjoining the tibia has three pads on the ventral surface and the terminal segment bears a pair of claws between which is a fleshy lobe, the pulvillus.

Wings. In grasshopper, each of the mesothorax and metathorax bears a pair of wings. The forewings are narrow and mostly parchment-like. These may be coloured uniformly or with deepening shades towards the bases or may be spotted. This pair is also named as tegmina because in the position of rest it covers the abdomen and the hind pair of wings. The hind wings are broad and membranous and kept folded in fan-like manner having a number of longitudinal folds in alternating directions. Each wing develops as a sac-like projection of the body covering and flattens to a thin double membrane that encloses tracheae, nerves and blood sinuses. The cuticle thickens along the sinuses to form strengthening nervures or veins. Although these veins vary in their patterns among the different species, they are constant in individuals of certain species, where they serve for classification.

Abdomen. The abdomen is elongated and tapers towards the posterior end, where the terminal segment is specialized for copulation or egg-laying. It consists of 11 segments. Each segment typically has a dorsal tergum and a ventral sternum, there being no pleura. The sternum of first segment of the abdomen is fused to the thorax and its tergum bears on either side the oval tympanic membrane which covers the auditory sac. The terminal segments are modified in both the sexes for copulation and egg-laying. In the male the end of the abdomen is rounded, while in female it is pointed. In both the sexes, the terga of 9 and 10 segments are partly fused. In the male the tergum of 11 segment forms the supra-anal plate over the anus. A small process called the cercus projects on each side behind 10 segment and sternum of 9 segment is long and bears the sub-genital plate which terminates dorsally in two short projections. The subgenital plate covers the male genital apparatus. In the female the sternum of 9 segment is elongated and the abdomen terminates in two pairs of lobes or valves with a smaller pair hidden between the larger valves. The ovipositor is made up of these three pairs of valves. Eight pairs of spiracles are present, one spiracle situated on either lower side of the segments from 2 to 9.

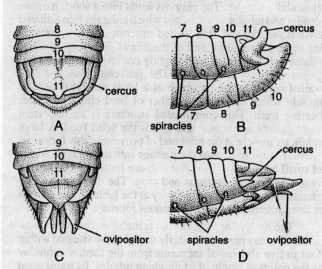

Fig. 74.4. Grasshopper. A—Male abdomen (Dorsal view) ; B—Male abdomen (Lateral view); C—Female abdomen (Dorsal view) ; D—Female abdomen (Lateral view).

INTERNAL ANATOMY

The internal cavity of grasshopper is a haemocoel, *i.e.*, contains blood and is not a true coelomic cavity. The systems of organs lie within the haemocoel.

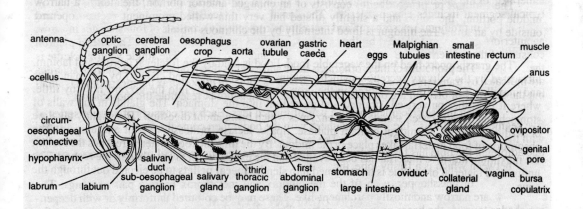

Fig. 74.5. Grasshopper. Longitudinal section showing the internal organs.

MUSCULAR SYSTEM

The muscles are of striated type, very soft and delicate but strong. The number of muscles is very large. They are segmentally arranged in the abdomen but not in the head and thorax. The most conspicuous muscles are those that move the mandibles, the wings, the metathoracic leg and the ovipositor.

DIGESTIVE SYSTEM

Alimentary canal. The alimentary canal of grasshopper consists of three principal regions, *viz.*, **foregut, midgut** and **hindgut.**

The **foregut** or **stomodaeum** starts at the **mouth** surrounded by the mouth parts and opening into a very short muscular **pharynx.** The pharynx leads into a short, narrow, slender and tubular **oesophagus** which enlarges into a dilated conical sac-like and thin-walled structure, the **crop** extending up to the posterior end of the thorax. The crop abruptly dilates to form a thick hard slightly conical structure, called **proventriculus** or **gizzard.** The proventriculus is thick-walled owing to the presence of a large powerful circular muscle which operates a number of hard chitinous plates bearing teeth. This complicated structure is an important **masticatory apparatus** and grinds the solid food. A large sphincter muscle at the hind end of proventriculus forms the **cardiac valve** to control the passage into the midgut. A pair of small branched **salivary glands** are found attached to the ventral side of oesophagus and crop. The ducts of salivary glands open into the mouth cavity at the labium. The foregut is lined internally with the chitinous intima.

The **midgut** or **mesenteron** is the **ventriculus** or **stomach.** It is a very prominent nearly straight tube situated within four to five abdominal segments from the cardiac sphincter to the points of origin of Malpighian tubules. Its transparent membranous walls are not lined with cuticle as in the foregut. A series of six double finger-shaped **hepatic caeca** or **gastric caeca** arise from its anterior end in two groups ; the first group of thick broad pointed tubes is directed forwards, while the second group of slender ones points posteriorly. These open independently into the anterior end of midgut. The **pyloric sphincter** located in the sixth abdominal segment marks the posterior end of mesenteron. A number of fine thread-like pale yellow Malpighian tubules take their origin from this area and may be seen floating about in the haemocoelomic cavity independently.

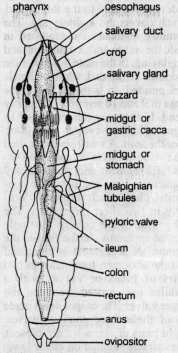

Fig 74.6. Grasshopper. Alimentary canal in dorsal view.

(Figure labels: pharynx, oesophagus, salivary duct, crop, salivary gland, gizzard, midgut or gastric cacca, midgut or stomach, Malpighian tubules, pyloric valve, ileum, colon, rectum, anus, ovipositor)

The **hindgut** or **proctodaeum** consists of an enlarged anterior portion, the **ileum,** a narrow middle portion, the **colon** and a slightly dilated but very thin-walled prominent **rectum** opening outside by an **anus.** The hindgut is lined internally by the chitinous intima.

Feeding and Digestion

The grasshoppers feed on the vegetable food. Food is held by the forelegs, labrum and labium, lubricated by the salivary secretion (which contains some enzymes) and chewed by the mandibles and maxillae. Chewed food is stored in the crop. It passes onwards into the gizzard little by little, where it is further pulverised, strained and passed on into the stomach. The glands in the walls of stomach and hepatic caeca secrete a few enzymes which bring about digestion. The slightly alkaline or acidic secretions of midgut contain maltase, lipase, lactase, protease, trypsin and erepsin. The absorption of food material takes place in the midgut. By the time the food material reaches the rectum the maximum nutritive material has been availed and the excess water is absorbed in the rectum. The undigested material or residue is transformed into slender **faecal pellets** to be ejected out through the anus.

CIRCULATORY SYSTEM

The circulatory system is an open one (lacunar), for there are no capillaries or veins. It is much reduced compared with many other arthropods. There is a single, slender, tubular and pulsatile **heart** lying mid-dorsally in the abdomen. It is suspended in a shallow pericardial cavity formed by a delicate transverse **diaphragm** which stretches across the concave inner surface of the tergites. The heart has a number of side-openings named **ostia** which are provided with valves to permit the flow of blood in one direction only. A number of muscular strands, the **alary muscles** are divergently spread out fan-wise over the diaphragm to enlarge and reduce the cavity of pericardium by their contraction and relaxation. Fibres of one muscle meet those of the corresponding muscle of the other side beneath the heart. In between the points of attachment of the alary muscles, there are spaces on either sides, through which the blood from haemocoelomic cavity passes into the pericardial sinus. A wave of contraction over the diaphragm closes the interspaces and pushes the valves of ostia to pump the blood into the heart. On pulsation of this structure the blood flows anteriorly into the head region through a long dorsal aorta and returns to the haemocoelomic cavity. Anatomically the heart and aorta can be distinguished by the presence of segmental dilations of the tube, known as chambers of the heart. There are generally such seven chambers in grasshoppers. Ostia are, thus, crescentic openings in their lateral walls. Aorta is the thoracic part of the dorsal vessel and after passing through the thorax, enters the head.

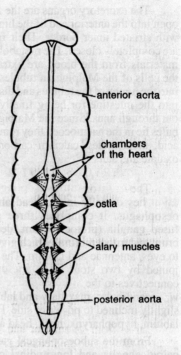

Fig. 74.7. Grasshopper. Circulatory system.

Besides the dorsal diaphragm, there is a ventral diaphragm which forms a continuous sheet from the prothorax to the end of the body and encloses a perineural sinus below. The blood circulates throughout even into appendages and wing veins, although closed veins or capillaries are wanting.

The blood plasma contains colourless blood cells which act as phagocytes to remove foreign organisms. The blood serves mainly to transport food and waste material. Fat bodies consist of loosely aggregated masses of yellow cells completely enveloping the various organs and nerve cord, more or less acting as a sheath. They store the food for use under adverse conditions.

RESPIRATORY SYSTEM

The respiratory system consists of a network of ectodermal tubes, the tracheae that communicate with every part of the body. The tracheae consist of a single layer of cells and are lined with cuticle. The largest tracheal tubes possess spiral threads of chitin, the taenidia which prevent them from collapsing. The spiracles on each side of the body lead by branches into a longitudinal trunk. The finest tracheae, the tracheoles are connected directly to the body tissues to deliver oxygen and carry away carbon dioxide. The small blind endings of the tracheoles, on the muscles and other organs, are filled with fluid. During activity of the muscle the concentration of substances in the body fluid around the tracheoles increases. This causes diffusion of water from the tracheole into the surrounding area, thus, bringing oxygen into closer proximity to

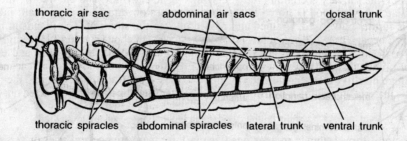

Fig. 74.8. Grasshopper. Respiratory system.

the site where it is being used as the air moves farther down into the blind tip of tracheole. After activity stops, the metabolic products that changed the osmotic pressure are disposed of and the water returns to the tracheole. There are also several thin-walled air sacs in the abdomen which pump air in and out of the tracheal system by the alternate contraction and expansion of the abdomen. In the grasshopper the action of spiracles is so synchronized that the first four pairs of spiracles are open at inspiration and closed at expiration, while the other six pairs are closed at inspiration and open at expiration.

EXCRETORY SYSTEM

The excretory organs are the Malpighian tubules which are coiled about in the haemocoel and open into the anterior end of the hindgut. The Malpighian tubules have a wall of a single layer of cells with striated inner border. Their free ends are completely closed. The metabolic waste materials from the blood are extracted by the cells of the Malpighian tubules, passed into the lumen of the tubules and discharged into the intestine for being finally ejected out through anus. Since the Malpighian tubules lie in the haemocoel, they remove uric acid, urea, urates, calcium carbonate and oxalate and salts.

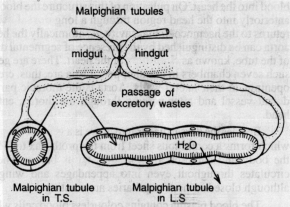

Fig. 74.9. Grasshopper. Malpighian tubule in T.S. and L.S.

NERVOUS SYSTEM

The brain or supraoesophageal ganglion lies dorsally in the head above the oesophagus. It comprises three pairs of fused ganglia (protocerebrum, deutocerebrum and tritocerebrum) which give nerves to eyes, antennae and labrum. The brain is joined by two stout circumoesophageal connectives to the suboesophageal ganglion, again formed by the fusion of three pairs of ganglia, *viz.,* mandibular, maxillary and labial. It is situated above the mouth parts in the middle of the head, slightly inclined to posterior side. From this eight paired nerves are given off to mandibles, maxillae, labium, hypopharynx, neck, head and salivary region.

From the suboesophageal ganglion extends posteriorly the ventral nerve cord made up of paired ganglia and longitudinal connectives. Each thoracic segment contains a pair of ganglia supplying nerves to the legs, wings and internal organs. There are only five pairs of abdominal ganglia which send nerves to various posterior organs.

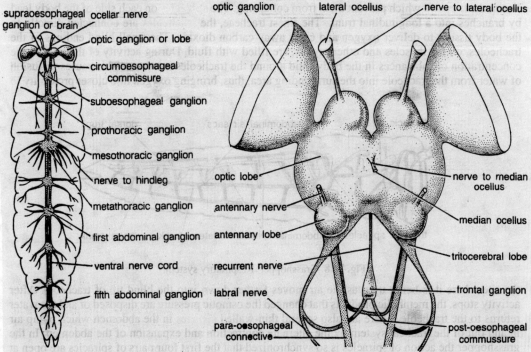

Fig. 74.10. Grasshopper. Nervous system (Dorsal view).   **Fig. 74.11.** Grasshopper.Brain (Dorsal view).

There is also a visceral or sympathetic nervous system, composed of an oesophageal portion or stomatogastric nervous system with ganglia and nerves connecting to the brain and supplying to the anterior part of the gut and a ventral sympathetic system supplying nerves to hindgut and reproductive system. A fine pattern of peripheral nerves lies beneath the epidermis of the body wall.

SENSE ORGANS

The sense organs of the grasshopper are adapted for receiving stimuli from the air and other environment in which it lives and to make adjustment to the external changes by the movement or other responses. This is achieved by the development of special cells of the body wall forming particularly designed structures called sensilla to receive the external stimuli, which are transmitted to the central nervous system through a mechanism of nerve tracts controlling motor tissues. Sense organs are widely distributed over the body surface and appendages occurring even in the anterior and posterior portions of alimentary canal. The following sense organs are met within grasshopper :

1. Tactile organs. They are in the form of setae, spines, hairs, cones and bristles, etc., scattered on the various parts of the body especially the antennae, mouth parts, legs, wings, genitalia, etc. Tactile organs are sensitive to touch.

2. Olfactory organs. Olfactory organs are sensitive to smell. The antennae are supplied with principal organs of smell.

3. Gustatory organs. Organs of taste occur in a form, similar to the olfactory organs, on the mouth parts specially palps, pharynx, antennae, and tarsi.

4. Visual organs. The grasshopper has a pair of large compound eyes and three ocelli. The compound eyes are concerned with vision and ocelli for light perception. An ocellus consists of a group of photoreceptor cells or retinulae, each ending in a nerve fibre which leads to the brain. The outer end of each photoreceptor forms a rhabdome. The cuticle covering the group of photoreceptor cells forms a thick biconvex, transparent lens. The real function of ocelli is not clearly known. The compound eyes are similar to those of cockroach, prawn or crayfish in structure as well as function.

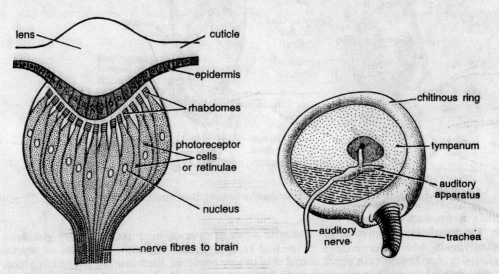

Fig. 74.12. Grasshopper. V.S. of an ocellus.   **Fig. 74.13.** Grasshopper. Tympanum and adjacent trachea (Interior view).

5. Auditory organs. It is supposed that grasshopper can hear because it creates particular sound with the stridulating apparatus. The pair of auditory organs are located on the sides of the tergite of the first abdominal segment. Each auditory organ consists of a tympanum or tympanic membrane stretched within an almost circular chitinous ring. It is set into movement by sound vibrations in the air. This in turn affects a slender point beneath the membrane which is connected to sensory nerve fibres.

REPRODUCTIVE SYSTEM

The sexes are separate and the distinction between male and female grasshopper can be determined by the posterior ends of abdomen. In the male it is round; in the female it is pointed because of ovipositor.

Male Reproductive Organs

The male reproductive organs consist of two testes, two vasa deferentia, two seminal vesicles, single ejaculatory duct, single penis and a pair of accessory glands. Both the testes lie embedded in a mass of fat bodies above the intestine. Each testis is composed of a series of slender tubules or follicles in which the spermatozoa develop. A convoluted tube called the vas deferens leads from each testis. Each vas deferens is dilated posteriorly into a sac-like structure called seminal vesicle. It narrows down posteriorly and meets a stout thick-walled prominent accessory gland of its own side. The size and shape of seminal vesicle and accessory gland differ in different species. The two seminal vesicles coming from either side meet together forming a common median ejaculatory duct. This duct opens at the end of a large ventral male copulatory organ, the penis or aedeagus. The accessory glands apparently secrete a fluid that helps in the transfer of spermatozoa to the female during mating.

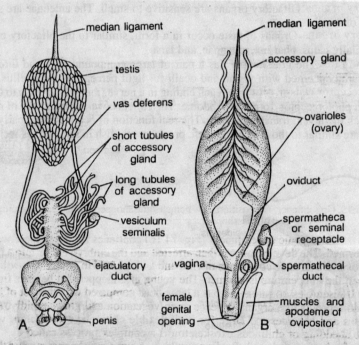

Fig. 74.14. Grasshopper. A—Male reproductive system; B—Female reproductive system.

Female Reproductive Organs

The female reproductive organs comprise a pair of ovaries, oviducts, accessory glands, a median vagina, and a spermatheca or seminal receptacle. Each ovary is composed of several ovarioles or ovarian tubules in which a number of ova are produced. Each ovariole is a tapering tube, the thickness of its walls increases posteriorly. Since ova are shed into its lumen and descend posteriorly as they grow in size, this tube gives a beaded appearance owing to varying dimensions of ova in various stages of development. The terminals of ovarioles are intertwined. Posteriorly the ovarioles meet together to form a common duct, the oviduct. Oviducts from either side meet together to form a median short vagina which is slightly thicker and muscular. It runs posteriorly and opens ventrally between the plates of ovipositor. A pair of prominent accessory glands meet the vagina independently. A small sac, the spermatheca or seminal receptacle, joins the vagina by means of a small narrow duct. During copulation the sperms are received and stored in the seminal receptacle. They fertilize the eggs as they pass through the vaginal region.

Copulation. The copulation occurs during late summer. In copulation, the male grasshopper clings to the back of female and inserts his penis into her vagina and transfers spermatozoa. The spermatozoa are stored in the seminal receptacle until the eggs are laid. Copulation may take place several times before the female starts to lay eggs.

Fertilization. The mature eggs, 3 to 5 mm long, pass down the oviduct. Each egg is enclosed by a delicate inner **vitelline membrane** and a brownish flexible shell or **chorion** that contains a minute pore or **micropyle** through which sperm enters during laying and fertilizes the egg. The sperm nucleus unites with the nucleus of the mature egg and a blastoderm is formed around the periphery of the egg from which an embryo develops.

Oviposition. Egg-laying begins a short interval after copulation and continues into the autumn. The female uses her ovipositor to form a short tunnel or hole in the ground in which eggs are deposited and surrounded by a sticky secretion that fastens them together as an **egg-pod.** The eggs are usually laid in lots of twenty and a single female may lay up to ten lots. The adults die some days after mating and egg-laying.

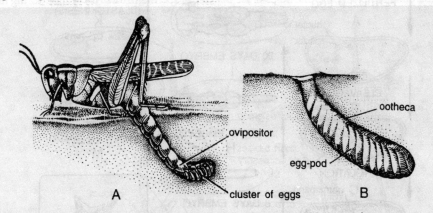

Fig. 74.15. Grasshopper. Oviposition. A—Female grasshopper laying eggs in ground ; B—Egg-pod of grasshopper.

Development. Embryonic development (Fig. 74.16) continues for about three weeks until the embryo is well formed. The development is then arrested and the embryo enters into a rest period, or **dipause,** to tide over the adverse conditions of cold and lack of food in winter. Growth begins again in the spring when the temperature is warmer. The young grasshopper that hatches from the egg is called a **nymph.** It resembles its parent but has a large head compared with the rest of the body and it lacks wings and reproductive organs. It feeds upon vegetation and grows rapidly. As the young grasshopper grows and becomes too large for its inflexible chitinous exoskeleton, which is shed periodically. The shedding of chitinous exoskeleton is a complex process called **moulting.** Wings gradually develop from wing-pads and after five moults the young grasshopper reaches the adult form. This type of development is called **simple** or **gradual metamorphosis.**

ECONOMIC IMPORTANCE OF GRASSHOPPER

As crop pests. Both nymphs and adults eat many kinds of vegetation, specially succulent types. They often migrate into new feeding grounds and may damage or ruin farm and garden plantings. Feeding is most active in the mid-morning hours of quite sunny days. When food is scarce, these insects will eat cotton or woollen fabrics, wood and disabled grasshoppers. Grasshoppers also feed on grasses and, thus, render heavy damage to range and pasture fields. True locusts which are also grasshoppers migrating in long hordes, are of a different kind and cause heavy damage to our crop fields and other vegetation. *Locusta migratoria,* the migratory locust found in eastern hemisphere, has caused famines since Biblical times. *Melanoplus maxicans,* the rocky mountain locust of North America give rise to a migratory phase called *M. maxicans spretus* which also cause great loss. The grasshopper *Camnula pellucida* is a serious pest. During favourable conditions and lack of enemies, it develops and hatches in May or June. It is a migratory form and can fly long distances. The swarms of this grasshopper destroy the green vegetation and were called **plague of grasshoppers** by Egyptians.

As food. The grasshoppers are also of some use to man and other animals. They are used as good fish bait, either living or dead. They are sometimes used even for human food. They are still used as food in such countries specially in Japan, Mexico and Philippines. They are commonly eaten by North American Indians and primitive tribes in other parts of the world. The Greeks ground the locusts by mortars and made flour of them and used the flour as food. The eggs, nymphs and adults of grasshoppers provide food for several predatory insects, spiders, frogs, reptiles, birds and mammals. In India also some people eat them as food either roasted or fried.

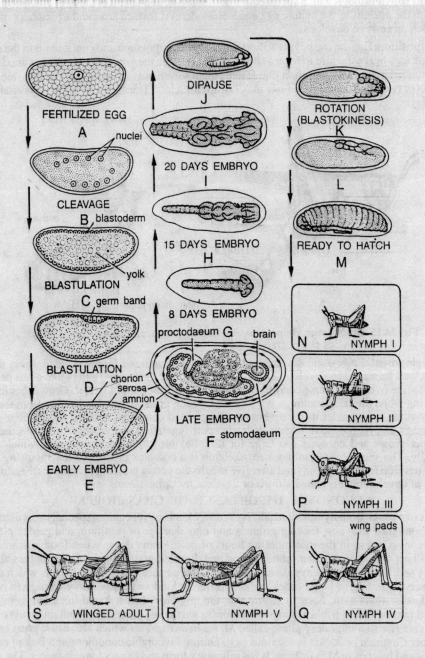

Fig. 74.16. Grasshopper. Development. A–M—Embryogeny; N–S—Metamorphosis.

CONTROL OF GRASSHOPPERS

The grasshoppers are controlled by natural as well as artificial or chemical means. The grasshopper eggs are eaten by some beetles, bee flies, moles, skunks, and mice, the nymphs by robber flies and digger wasps and both nymphs and adults by large predatory insects and by frogs, reptiles, birds and mammals. Eggs of grasshoppers are also parasitized by certain insects. Flesh flies (*Sarcophaga*) lay living maggots on adults, and tachinid flies deposit their eggs on grasshoppers in flight, the larvae of both burrow into their host and consume the fat tissues. Parasitized grasshoppers become logy and fail to reproduce or die. The parasitic insects, thus, constitute a factor in grasshopper control. Both fungus and bacterial diseases also destroy numbers of grasshoppers at times. Eggs of grasshoppers are killed in the ground during winter, if the soil is exposed to the sun by ploughing. In olden days the control of grasshoppers was done by giving them food mixed with arsenic or some other stomach poison. But now insecticides are generally used. Various insecticides are used in the form of sprays or dusts and poisoned baits that kill either by contact or when eaten. Some insecticides which are recently employed are : aldrin, dieldrin, chloradane, heptachlor and toxaphane. Methoxychlor is also now used as insecticide for protecting fruits and vegetables and pasture fields, as it does not leave any residue which is harmful to man or domestic animals.

REVISION QUESTIONS

1. Give an account of the habit, habitat and external features of a grasshopper.
2. Describe the mouth parts, food and feeding of a grasshopper.
3. Give an account of the digestive system of a grasshopper.
4. Describe the reproductive system of a grasshopper.
5. Write a note on the economic importance of grasshopper.

75

Culex and Anopheles : The Mosquitoes

Mosquitoes belong to the order Diptera. They possess short, elongated and slender body, long many segmented antennae, long slender legs and an elongated proboscis with piercing and sucking mouth parts. True mosquitoes differ from all flies in the proboscis being much longer than the head, and the nervures and posterior border of the wings being fringed with flat striated scales. The important genera of mosquitoes are *Culex, Aedes* and *Anopheles*. The following account deals in detail the morphology and life histories of *Culex* and *Anopheles*.

SYSTEMATIC POSITION

Phylum	.....	**Arthropoda**
Subphylum	.....	**Mandibulata**
Class	.....	**Insecta**
Subclass	.....	**Pteryogota**
Division	.....	**Endopterygota**
Order	.....	**Diptera**
Family	.....	**Culicidae**
Genus	.....	*Culex* and *Anopheles*

CULEX

HABIT AND HABITAT

Culex pipiens is found in temperate regions all over the world, and *Culex fatigans* throughout the tropics and sub-tropics. *Culex* lives in houses, in cities and farms, and is abundant also in rural areas. They are most abundant during spring, but hibernate during unfavourable climatic conditions, the adults hide in hollows of trees, caves, crevices, barns, etc. The life span of male mosquitoes is seldom more than three weeks, they die after fertilizing the females. The females live from four weeks to several months, but they die when all their eggs are laid. *Culex* has several generations in a year.

EXTERNAL FEATURES

Shape, size and colouration. The body of *Culex* is small, soft, and covered with small scales. *Culex* measures about 3 to 4 mm in length. The body colour is grey-black.

Division of body. The body is divisible into head, thorax and abdomen.

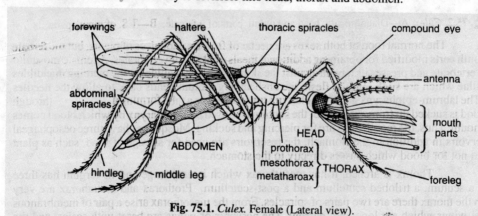

Fig. 75.1. *Culex.* Female (Lateral view).

1. Head. Head is globular and highly mobile on a slender neck. There are two very large black compound eyes, there are no ocelli. The top of the head has an epicranium below which is a clypeus which is thick and projects in front. There are two filiform antennae, each with 15 joints, the basal segment is the scape which is concealed by a very large globular second segment, the pedicel containing a Johnson's organ which is auditory in function, the other 13 joints form a flagellum having many bristles lying in rings. The bristles are longer and much more numerous on the antennae of males giving them a bushy appearance. In the female the antennae have rings of few, short bristles, thus, sexes can be distinguished readily by the antennae. The head bears two maxillary palps and a proboscis. The maxillary palps are stiff and have many bristles, the palps in the female are short and three-jointed, but in the male they are as long, or even longer than the proboscis, they are five-jointed.

Mouth parts. The proboscis is a straight, long tube formed by a fleshy ventral labium which has a deep groove on its upper side, in this groove is a long pointed and ventrally-grooved labrum epipharynx. At the distal end of the labium is a pair of small tactile labella which are reduced labial palps. The groove of the labium also contains five needle-like stylets in a female *Culex*, they are two mandibles, two maxillae, and a hypopharynx. The mandibles are finer than the maxillae, but both have saw-like edges on their tips. The hypopharynx is also needle-like and has a fine salivary duct running through it and opening at the tip, through this duct saliva is poured to prevent coagulation of blood of the victim. In the male the labrum-epipharynx and the labium are the same as in the female, but the mandibles and maxillae are very short and functionless and the hypopharynx is fused with the labium.

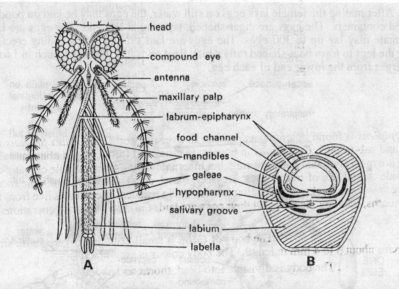

head
compound eye
antenna
maxillary palp
labrum-epipharynx
food channel
mandibles
galeae
hypopharynx
salivary groove
labium
labella
A
B

Fig. 75.2. *Culex.* A—Diagrammatic head and mouth parts of a female; B—T.S. of mouth parts.

Feeding. The normal food of both sexes are nectar of flowers and juices of plants, but the female has its mouth parts modified for obtaining additional meals of blood of vertebrates. A female mosquito sits on a vertebrate and presses its labella against the skin, they act as a guide for the piercing mandibles and maxillae which are sunk into the flesh; the ensheathing labium bends back to allow the needles to go in. The labrum-epipharynx and hypopharynx together act as a tube forming a food canal through which blood is sucked up from the wound; the suction is caused by the pharynx by which blood comes into the mouth. Thus, the mouth parts are for piercing and sucking. Mosquitoes have three oesophageal food reservoirs in addition to the stomach, the reservoirs are used for storage of food, such as plant juices, but not for blood which passes directly to the stomach.

2. Thorax. Thorax is arched, it has mesothorax which is very large and its tergum has three sclerites, a scutum, a trilobed scutellum and a post-scutellum. Prothorax and metathorax are very small. On the thorax there are two pairs of spiracles. From the mesothorax arise a pair of membranous functional wings which are long and narrow. The nervures of wings are beset with scales, and the posterior margin of the wings is fringed with bristle and scales. The wings of metathorax are reduced to form a pair of small haltferes, each of which has a swollen base or scabellum, a narrow stem or pedicel, and a distal swollen knob or capitellum. Halteres vibrate 300 times per second during flight, they probably act as balancers, but their function is doubtful, however, if halteres are removed flight becomes difficult or even impossible. From the thorax arise three pairs of legs which are very long and slender, they are fragile and have the usual parts of an insect leg, but the coxae are short and tarsi long with five joints ending in a pair of simple claws, below each claw is a pad-like pulvilus. The legs also have many scales and bristles.

3. Abdomen. Abdomen consists of 10 segments of which the first is vestigial and fused to the metathorox ; the second to the eighth are clearly seen, each has a pair of spiracles ; the ninth and tenth segments are partly telescoped into the eighth. In the female the 10th segment is blunt and bears a pair of cerci, between them is a small post-genital plate which is part of the tenth sternum. In the male the 9th and 10th segments are complex, they undergo a torsion of 180° as soon as the mosquitoes are born, so that the terga and anus become ventral and the sterna dorsal. The ninth segment in ring-like with a bilobed ventral tergum, it bears a pair of large claspers, each with a broad basal coxite followed by a narrow style which ends in a claw. The 10th segment has a bilobed dorsal sternum from which project two processes with curved and toothed tips, the male intromittent organ or aedeagus projects posteriorly, it is formed by fusion of gonapophyses of ninth segment. The ejaculatory duct opens into the aedeagus. During copulation the male holds the female by its claspers and the aedeagus is inserted into the vagina.

LIFE HISTORY

Eggs. After mating the female lays eggs on still water, the eggs may be laid on ponds, or pools, or rain-filled containers. The eggs are cigar-shaped, tapering at one end. The eggs are laid at night and one female may lay up to 300 eggs. The eggs are laid side by side standing erect, and glued together by the legs to form boat-shaped rafts which float on water. The eggs hatch in 1 to 3 days and a larva emerges from the lower end of each egg.

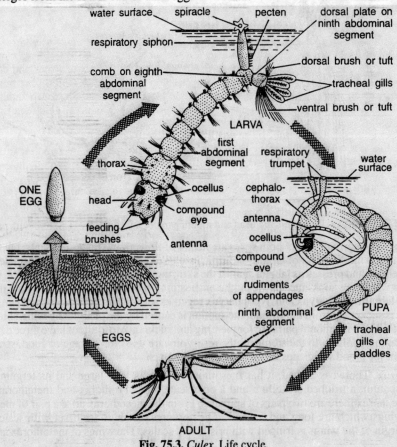

Fig. 75.3. *Culex.* Life cycle.

Larva. The larvae are called wrigglers because of their wriggling movements, they are microscopic on hatching. The larva leads an active life, it swims about, feeds and grows, and the larval life lasts from 3 to 14 days according to temperature. During this period it moults four times and grows larger after each moulting. The larva has a large chitinous head which is flattened dorso- ventrally, it has compound eyes developing, and closely behind each is a larval ocellus, it has a labrum, small toothed mandibles, a pair of maxillae with feeding bristles lying internally, labial plates, and a pair of jointed antennae. It has a mouth over which is a pair of rotary feeding brushes, formed of stiff bristles, the brushes cause a current of water by which small particles of food are wafted into the mouth. Food consists of algae and small organic particles, the larva feeds on these below the surface of water. Thorax is globular, its segments are fused together. On the head, thorax and abdomen are paired bristles, some of them forming bushy tufts, especially on the thorax. Abdomen is slender and has nine segments, on the first seven abdominal segments are tufts of bristles. The eighth segment has a chitinous and tubular respiratory siphon, at the tip of the siphon are two spiracles leading into tracheae. Around the spiracles are five leaf-like lobes which can close over the spiracles to prevent water from entering. The respiratory system is metapneustic in which only the last pair of abdominal spiracle is open. The larva though aquatic breathes air through the siphon and comes to the surface to take in air. When resting the larva pierces the surface film of water by its siphon which projects just above the surface and draws in air, and it hangs by the siphon with its head downwards, but it is inclined at an angle. The siphon on its ventral side has two tufts of bristles, and two rows of flat spines called pecten. On the eighth segment is a patch of small scales in one or two rows forming a comb. In some species of *Culex* the comb has scales in several rows. The ninth segment of the abdomen is slender and covered by a chitinous dorsal plate. At the end of the ninth segment is an anus surrounded by four leaf-like tracheal gills which differ from true gills in having tracheae instead of blood vessels. The ninth segment has a tuft of dorsal bristles at its tip, and ventrally a bushy tuft of bristles called ventral brush. The larva sinks in water being heavier, and it rises by wriggling movements of the abdomen. After the fourth moult the larva changes into a pupa.

Pupa. The pupa is comma-shaped and is called a tumbler. It has a large cephalothorax formed by the head and thorax. On the mid-dorsal side of the cephalothorax is a pair of tubular respiratory trumpets which are broader at the distal end, they communicate with an anterior pair of thoracic spiracles. By means of the trumpets the pupa hangs from the surface film of water and takes in air through their distal ends which project slightly above water. Inside the cephalothorax may be seen cases containing compound eyes, one pair of ocelli, antennae, wings, and legs of the adult. Behind the cephalothorax is a ventrally flexed abdomen formed of nine segments of which the first is very small but segments 2 or 9 are distinct and movable. On the abdomen are tufts of bristles. The last segment bears a pair of chitinous leaf-like paddles by which the pupa swims. The pupa is a resting stage, during this period it does not feed, but the pupae of mosquitoes are peculiar in not being quiescent, they are active and can swim about. Unlike the larva the pupa is lighter than water and requires a muscular effort to sink down. The pupal period lasts from two to seven days depending upon the temperature. During this time remarkable changes occur in the pupa while the adult insect called imago is being formed. When the imago is completed the skin of the pupa splits mid-dorsally along the back between the trumpets and the imago emerges, first the head, then body and appendages are extricated. The imago rests for some time on the pupal skin, it stretches and dries its wings, then flies off. It can start laying eggs in a week's time and, thus, repeat the life history.

Metamorphosis. The young one that hatches from an egg is quite different from the adult insect in structure and mode of life, it is known as a larva. The larva feeds, moves, moults, and grows, then it passes into a quiescent stage, the pupa which is different from both the larva and the imago. Finally the adult is formed in the pupa. This form of development is termed complete metamorphosis or holometabolus metamorphosis. It occurs in higher insects as seen in the mosquito. Growth and moulting up to the end of the larval period are controlled by the juvenile hormone of corpora allata. The pupa though quiescent undergoes very great internal changes in order to form the imago. Most of the larval organs in the pupa, except the central nervous system and developing genital organs, are broken down, the process of breaking down and disintegration of larval organs is called histolysis. The process of histolysis is brought about largely by blood corpuscles called phagocytes which feed upon the tissues of disintegrating organs, and their products of digestion pass into the blood to form new tissues. For the formation of organs of the imago groups of formative cells are set aside in the larva, they are called imaginal buds or histoblasts. The imaginal buds are found all over the body of the larva, close to its internal organs or in invaginations of the epidermis. The imaginal buds are the rudiments of future organs. The process of formation of new adult organs inside a pupa is known as **histogenesis.** Imaginal buds are dormant, they are stimulated by a hormone of **prothoracic endocrine glands,** these glands become active only during metamorphosis secreting a pupation hormone which causes imaginal buds to develop. By this process the imago develops inside the pupa; when development is completed the pupal covering splits and a perfectly formed imago emerges. The final moulting into an adult is also controlled by the hormone of prothoracic glands, it occurs only after the juvenile hormone of corpora allata is not being produced. Thus, in holometabolus metamorphosis the stages in the life cycle are, egg →larva →pupa →imago and the adult wings develop from inside from imaginal buds and are not visible externally. In hemimetabolous or heterometabolus metamorphosis, as seen in a cockroach the stages are, egg →nymph →imago, and the adult wings develop externally from the integument.

ANOPHELES

Several species of *Anopheles* are the carriers of **vectors** of a protozoan *Plasmodium* which causes malaria fever. The *Anopheles* transmit the parasite from one human being to another. *Plasmodium* also causes malaria in monkeys, hence, monkeys act as reservoir hosts of the malarial parasite. The female *Anopheles* when feeding on the blood of a malarial patient takes in gametocyte

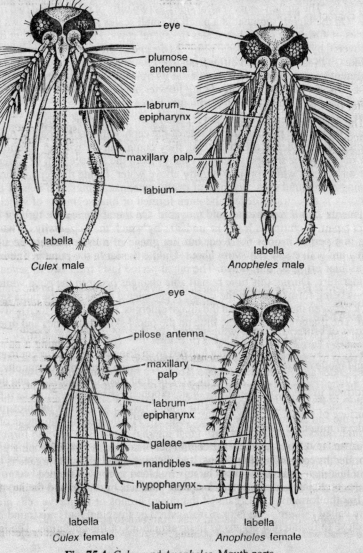

Fig. 75.4. *Culex* and *Anopheles*. Mouth parts.

stages of *Plasmodium* which develop and undergo sexual reproduction in the mosquito to form thousands of sporozoites. When this mosquito bites a person it transfers the infective sporozoites into his blood along with its saliva. *Anopheles* dwell in marshy places, but some species, like *A. stephensi, A. quadrimaculatus* invade human dwellings in suburban and rural areas. In India there are many species of malarial mosquitoes, the common ones are *Anopheles maculatus, A. culicifacies, A. fluvialitis* and *A. stephensi*. Besides these there are many other species responsible for malaria in the world.

HABIT AND HABITAT

Anopheles mosquitoes are generally active at twilight and early morning, but some species feed in the dark. Both sexes feed on honey and plant juices, but the females also suck the blood of vertebrates, usually at intervals of several days. Anopheline mosquitoes generally hibernate as adults, hiding in trees, rocks and caves, but some species hibernate as larvae which bury themselves under damp mud. Most species of *Anopheles* are of a sedentary habit and seldom fly more than few hundred yards. They breed mostly in natural waters, such as ponds, swamps, rice fields, and grassy ditches, but some species breed in flowing streams, like *A. listoni* in the sub-Himalayan streams, and *A. rossi,* in temporary rain-filled pools, and *A. stevensi* breeds in wells in India.

IDENTIFICATION

Anopheles resembles a *Culex* described before in many details of structure and life history, but it has certain characters by which it can be identified in all stages of development.

Anopheles imago has a slender body except when the abdomen is filled with blood. In male the maxillary palps are longer than the proboscis and are five-jointed, the last two joints are flat and broad so that the palps appear club-shaped. In the female the maxillary palps are always more than half as long as the proboscis, but usually as long as the proboscis. In *Culex* the maxillary palps of the male are usually as long as the proboscis but are not club-shaped; in the female they are always short and three-jointed. In the thorax the scutellum of *Anopheles* is crescentic with bristles on its posterior margin ; in other mosquitoes the scutellum is trilobed with a tuft of bristles on each lobe. The wings of *Anopheles* are marked with dark spots, while in others they are unspotted. *Anopheles* rests with its body at an angle to the surface, its proboscis being in line with the body ; *Culex* rests with its body parallel to the surface, and its proboscis is not in a straight line with its body. But some *Anopheles* have a resting position as in *Culex, e.g., Anopheles culicifacies*. In the abdomen of *Anopheles* the sterna have no scales, while in others both terga and sterna of abdomen are covered with scales.

LIFE HISTORY

Eggs. Female *Anopheles* lays 40 to 100 eggs at one time. The eggs are pointed at both ends and have a pair of lateral air floats. The eggs are laid singly and lie horizontally on water, and owing to surface tension they form geometrical patterns and they lie in loose clusters. In *Culex* the eggs are cigar-shaped with no air floats, they form boat-shaped rafts standing vertically. The larva of *Anopheles* hatches in 24 to 48 hours from the egg.

Larva. There is no respiratory siphon in the larva of *Anopheles* but on the eighth segment it has a raised chitinous quadrilateral plate with two spiracles, the spiracles are surrounded by five small leaf-like flaps. There are small bristles near the spiracles which form a pair of pecten. The comb formed by rows of bristles on the eighth segment in the larva of *Culex* is absent, except in the newly hatched *Anopheles* larva. The larva has palmate bristles or hairs forming a pair of tufts on each thoracic and most of the abdominal segments. A palmate bristle consists of a short stalk from which a number of slender and flat leaflets radiate. The larva hangs horizontally from the surface of water by means of the palmate bristles and the quadrilateral plate of the eighth segment, this is a characteristic resting position, in this position it touches the water surface at several places, and the spiracles project above the surface of water. The head of the larva is longer than broad, and it feeds on the surface of water. The development is slow and the larval life lasts from two to four weeks.

In *Culex* the larva has a tubular respiratory siphon having two pectens. On the 6th segment there is a comb formed by rows of small bristles. It has tufts of bristles on the thorax and abdomen but the bristles are not palmate. The larva hangs by its respiratory tube with the head downwards ; it touches the water surface only at one place by its siphon. The head is round and the larva feeds below the surface of water.

Pupa. In *Anopheles* the pupal period lasts from two to seven days. The respiratory trumpets are short and broad with a large terminal opening, from this opening a split or cleft runs down on one side ; while in other mosquitoes the respiratory trumpets are long and narrow, with a small terminal opening but with no split. The abdomen of the pupa of *Anopheles* is more strongly curved than in *Culex* . In *Anopheles* the abdominal paddles at their tips have one large and one small bristle, while in *Culex* there is a single large bristle. *Anopheles* pupa has a pair of peg-like spines at the posterior ends of all but the last abdominal segments ; while *Culex* pupa has a pair of tufts of fine, branched bristles on abdominal segments.

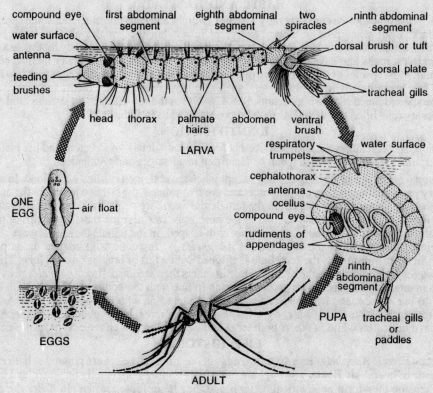

Fig. 75.5. *Anopheles*. Life cycle.

However, the life histories of *culex* and *Anopheles* have been compared in Table 75.1.

TABLE 75.1. COMPARISON OF THE LIFE HISTORIES OF *CULEX* AND *ANOPHELES*

Culex	*Anopheles*
A. OVIPOSITION	
1. It lays eggs usually 200–400 in number on the surface of dirty stagnant water sources.	1. It lays eggs usually 40–100 in number on the surface of clean and freshwater.
2. It lays eggs in clusters which are glued to form rafts.	2. It lays eggs singly.
B. EGGS	
3. The eggs are cigar-shaped.	3. The eggs are boat-shaped.
4. The eggs remain vertically placed in the rafts, enclosing air between their spaces which help in floating on the water surface. Floats are not found.	4. The eggs remain horizontal to the water surface and bear later air-filled floats which help in floating in the water.
5. The eggs with micropylar cap.	5 Eggs without micropylar cap.

Culex	*Anopheles*
C. LARVA	
6. It is comparatively larger and transparent.	6. It is smaller and somewhat opaque.
7. It is bottom feeder.	7. It is surface feeder.
8. It lies inclined obliquely at an angle with the water surface.	8. It lies parallel to the water surface.
9. Its head is somewhat rounded.	9. It is longer than the breadth.
10. On the 8th abdominal segment, it has a long conical respiratory siphon which projects out of the surface of water.	10. On the 8th abdominal segment the respiratory siphon is reduced much, it is in the form of quadrilateral plate having spiracles.
11. Body without palmate bristles.	11. The bristles on the body are palmate.
12. Comb bristles present.	12. Comb bristles absent in later larval instars.
D. PUPA	
13. Abdominal segments are not much curved.	13. Abdominal segments are very much curved.
14. Respiratory trumpets are long without clefts.	14. Respiratory trumpets are short with clefts.
15. The bristle on the paddle are long.	15. The bristles on the paddle are short and long both.
E. ADULT	
16. At rest it keeps its body parallel to the surface and its proboscis never lies in straight line to the longitudinal axis of the body.	16. At rest it keeps its body at an angle of 45° to the surface and its proboscis remains in straight line to the longitudinal axis of the body.
17. Its body longer and broader having stout legs.	17. Its body smaller and slender having delicate legs.
18. Bristles on the body sparse.	18. Britstles on the body dense.
19. Wings with uniform colouration.	19. Wings appear spotted.
20. In the thorax scutellum is trilobed with a tuft of bristles on each side.	20. The scutellum is crescentic with bristles on its posterior margin.
21. Maxillary palps either longer than proboscis or very short.	21. Maxillary palps are equal in length to proboscis.

MOSQUITOES AND DISEASE

When a mosquito bites a fungus is expelled from its oesophageal diverticula into the wound, the fungus causes a local swelling and irritation ; apart from this annoyance the mosquitoes are responsible for several diseases. They cause diseases in man and animals in two ways, first by their attacks directly they transmit a disease but there is no multiplication of the disease organism in mosquito. Secondly, they transmit disease-producing organisms which undergo development or multiplication in their bodies.

The diseases caused by mosquitoes in man are malaria, yellow fever, dengue, filariasis, encephalitis and dermatobia.

1. Malaria. Malaria is a deadly human disease. It is transmitted by *Anopheles;* malaria is caused by a parasitic protozoan *Plasmodium* which spends part of its life in man and part in the body of female *Anopheles;* and the mosquito acts as a vector. About two dozen species of *Anopheles* are important natural vectors of malaria in different regions of the world. In malaria there is high recurring fever accompanied by chills and shivering, sometimes with convulsions till the teeth chatter. The patient gets violent headache and nausea followed by sweating so profuse that clothes are wet, then the temperature drops till the next attack. Often relapses occur which may prove fatal.

2. Yellow fever. Yellow fever is confined to South America and Africa. It is due to a virus which causes sudden fever with severe headache and pains in the bones, the face is flushed and swollen, and the skin becomes dry. After some days severe jaundice, haemorrhage and vomiting of blood and bile occur. The mortality in yellow fever is very high. Forest animals serve as hosts for yellow fever virus and it is transmitted by *Haemogogus* and several species of *Aedes,* such as *A. aegypti, A. simpsoni, A. fluvialitis* and *A. albopictus;* of these mosquitoes *Aedes aegypti* has a world-wide distribution, and with modern airplane traffic the introduction of yellow fever is an ever present menace.

3. Dengue fever. Dengue or breakbone fever is caused by a virus, the disease is widely distributed in warm countries. There is sudden high fever with rash on the face and intense pain in the head, eyes, muscles, and joints. Dengue is not fatal, it is transmitted by *Aedes aegypti*, *Aedes albopictus* and *Culex fatigans*. Dengue often breaks out abruptly in an epidemic form which spreads rapidly.

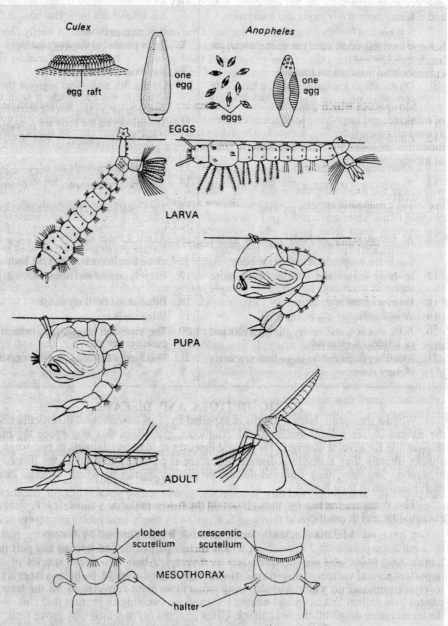

Fig. 75.6. *Culex* and *Anopheles*. Comparison of stages of life history.

4. Filariasis or Elephantiasis. Filariasis is caused in man by nematodes *Wuchereria bancrofti* and *W. malayi*. The intermediate hosts are several types of mosquitoes, like *Aedes*, *Culex*, and *Anopheles*. The larvae of *Wuchereria* called **microfilariae** are sucked up with the blood of infected persons by mosquitoes which serve as vectors. The microfilariae grow in mosquito and become infective. When a mosquito bites a man the larvae creep out from the proboscis on to the skin and penetrate inside, from where they go in deeper and cause inflammation of lymph glands, scrotum, arms, and legs. Filariasis may eventually cause **elephantiasis** but not always.

5. **Encephalitis.** Encephalitis is caused by a virus resulting in high fever, headache, drowziness, and inflammation of the brain. It chiefly effects horses and domestic animals, but human infections also occur, though they are not common. Encephalitis is transmitted by numerous species of *Aedes* and *Culex*.

6. **Dermatobia.** Dermatobia is a disease of the skin of man and cattle. A botfly *Dermatobia* lays her eggs on the body of a mosquito *Psorophora*. When this mosquito bites, the eggs of the botfly hatch quickly on the skin of the victim, and the larvae penetrate the skin causing swellings and cutaneous myiasis. *Psorophora* is confined to Central and South America.

CONTROL OF MOSQUITOES

Mosquitoes which transmit human diseases are among the most important and deadly enemies of mankind, and steps have to be taken for their destruction, but general measures will not be effective against all types, therefore, habits and breeding places of mosquitoes must be studied before effective measures are taken for their eradication. The following general methods may be used for the control of mosquitoes :

1. **Personal protection.** (a) In mosquito-infected area protective clothing may be used, such as will cover the exposed parts of the body, especially after sunset. (b) Mosquito repellents are also useful, like mosquito cream, citronella, odomos and Indalone which keep mosquitoes away. Repellent No. 448 of the American navy is very effective for long periods. (c) While sleeping fine mesh mosquito nets prevent them from biting and bed rooms or houses could be screened to prevent entry of mosquitoes. (d) Painting walls with creosote repels mosquitoes.

2. **Destruction of adults.** (a) Killing of mosquitoes can be done be spraying liquid insecticides like flit or D.D.T., the latter not only kills mosquitoes but also makes them leave a house. (b) Fumigation of dwellings with sulphur dioxide is also useful. (c) A mixture of water and 10% D.D.T. in oil sprayed from the air is very effective in killing large number of mosquitoes in towns, ponds, marshes and forests.

3. **Destruction of larvae.** It is easier and more effective to kill mosquitoes in their larval forms than as adults, and several methods are used with success. (a) Oiling: The breeding places of mosquitoes are sprayed with petroleum oils, the oil film formed on the surface of water does not asphyxiate the larvae, as is commonly believed, but is toxic to them, the oiling must be repeated to kill those larvae and pupae which will hatch later. (b) Panama larvicide is a mixture of caustic soda, resin, and phenol in water, it has been used most effectively in the Panama Canal region. The Panama larvicide mixes well with water and kills both the larvae and the algae on which they feed. One part of Panama larvicide is sufficient for 10,000 parts of water. (c) Paris green is a powder of arsenic mixed with fine dust, one part of powder with 100 parts of dust. This can be thrown in the wind and it will cover the surface of a pond ; it is insoluble in water and remains floating and is eaten by surface feeding larvae of *Anopheles;* it will kill the larvae but not pupae. It is effective only against those larvae which feed on surface. (d) Natural enemies: Fishes, minnows and *Gambusia* live on larvae and pupae of mosquitoes, and their introduction in a breeding place is helpful, but for this the brush and floating vegetation must be cleared so that the fish can reach the larvae. (e) Chemical larvicide: One part of D.D.T. emulsion in thirty million parts of water is used most extensively as a spray to kill larvae, but it takes 50 hours. Planes can be used for this purpose on large areas.

4. **Elimination of breeding places.** For those mosquitoes which breed in rain-filled containers and cisterns, like *Aedes,* emptying of water is effective. For large ponds and swamps digging a sloping ditch removes large volumes of water. Small ponds can be filled up with mud. In India cycles of 5 wet days followed by 2 to 4 dry days were found to be highly effective in controlling *Anopheles* in fields

5. **Preventive medicine.** Daily doses of quinine are effective against mosquito bites, but a successful vaccine has yet to be found for yellow fever.

REVISION QUESTIONS

1. Give an account of the external structures of either *Culex* or *Anopheles*.
2. Describe the life cycle of a mosquito.
3. 'Mosquitoes are related to various diseases', discuss. Write a note on their control measures.
4. Discuss the mouth parts of male and female *Culex* and *Anopheles* mosquitoes. How will you identify them considering their mouth parts only ?

76

Musca: The Housefly

The houseflies of genus *Musca* are cery common in human dwellings, they are specially abundant and very active during summer and rainy season. In winter most of them die, but many survive in warm places, but the cold makes them slow and sluggish. They rest at night on ceilings, walls, and fixtures like electric wires. There are many species of *Musca*, such as *Musca nebulo,* the commonest housefly in India ; *Musca domestica* in Europe and America ; *Musca vicina* is common in all oriental countries; *Musca autumnalis* is found in Europe and Southern Asia; *Musca sorbens* from the Mediterranean throughout warmer Asia.

MUSCA NEBULO

SYSTEMATIC POSITION

Phylum	.....	**Arthropoda**
Subphylum	.....	**Mandibulata**
Class	.....	**Insecta**
Subclass	.....	**Pterygota**
Division	.....	**Endopterygota**
Order	......	**Diptera**
Genus	......	*Musca*
Species	......	*nebulo*

EXTERNAL FEATURES

Musca nebulo, the common Indian housefly is a heavily built insect and is about 8 mm in length. The colour of the body is gray. The body is distinctly divided into head, thorax and abdomen.

1. **Head.** The head is large and freely mobile. It is as broad as the thorax. It bears two large reddish-brown compound eyes, each having about 4,000 ommatidia. On the dorsal side of the head

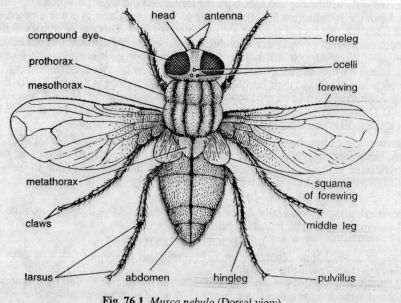

Fig. 76.1. *Musca nebulo* (Dorsal view).

there are three ocelli or simple eyes on a triangular ocellar plate. Between the compound eyes the dorsal region of the head has a vertex, below which is a frons. In front of the head is a depression bounded by a Ω-shaped frontal suture or ptilinal suture. In the depression is a pair of small three-jointed antennae, the last joint being the largest. The antennae can be raised in front of the head or can be withdrawn into the depression. On the last segment of the antenna is a bristle which is plumose to the tip, it is an arista. Above the bases of antennae is a small crescentic sclerite known as frontal lunule. Below each compound eye is a lateral gena. Below the depression is a membranous ridge called the epistome.

Mouth parts. The mouth parts are of sponging type, *i.e.,* they are adapted to suck the liquid food. The mouth parts comprise a fleshy and retractile proboscis which lies under the head. The proboscis is formed of three parts, a basal rostrum, a middle haustellum, and a distal pair of labella. The rostrum is cone-shaped and has a clypeus in front. Morphologically the rostrum is a part of the head and it bears a pair of one jointed maxillary palps. Inside the rostrum is a chitinous fulcrum which encloses the pharynx. Under the lower end of the fulcrum is a small chitinous hyoid sclerite which serves to keep the lumen of the pharynx distended. Hinged to the rostrum is a haustellum formed by a highly modified labium, the posterior part of the haustellum has a weakly chitinized theca or mentum. The front side of the haustellum has a deep oral groove enclosing a labrum-epipharynx and a hypopharynx. The hypopharynx has a salivary duct. The labrum-epipharynx is grooved, the goove is closed below by the hypopharynx to form a tube or food canal. The mandibles and maxillae are absent. The distal labella are large lobes fused in the middle, their outer surface has a series of channels called pseudotracheae which are kept open by a series of incomplete chitinous rings which make them look like tracheae. The pseudotracheae open externally by a double row of tiny holes

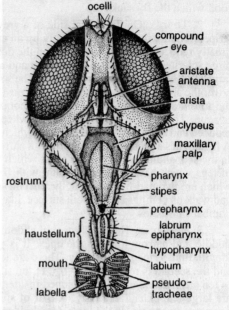

Fig. 76.2. Housefly. Head and mouth parts (Dorsal view).

through which liquid food is taken in. The pseudotracheae converge into a mouth lying betweeen the two labella. Near the mouth are very small prestomal teeth which are used for rasping solid food. The proboscis can be retracted below the head and it folds between the rostrum and haustellum.

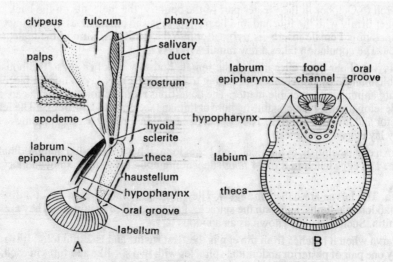

Fig. 76.3. Housefly. A—Proboscis in lateral view ; B—T.S. proboscis through haustellum.

Feeding. The housefly feeds on any organic fluid, its mouth parts are modified for lapping up liquid food. The proboscis is extended and the labella are placed on the fluid, the labella can smell and taste the food. By the suctorial action of the pharynx fluid food and very fine solid particles are sucked up into the pseudotracheae from where they go into the mouth, and then into the food canal formed by labrum-epipharynx and hypopharynx, then the food enters the pharynx and goes to the alimentary canal. Houseflies also feed on solid substances, especially sugar and sweets, the fly then regurgitates a drop of liquid from the alimentary canal and saliva from salivary glands onto the solid food through the pseudotracheae. The alimentary canal fluid and saliva liquefy the solid particles of food which the fly sucks up.

2. Thorax. On the dorsal side of a grey-coloured thorax are four black-coloured longitudinal stripes. The thorax is formed mostly by an enlarged mesothorax, the prothorax and metathorax are greatly reduced and largely hidden on the dorsal side. The notum of mesothorax is formed of three large sclerites, a prescutum, a scutum and a scutellum with transverse sutures between them. The large mesohorax bears a pair of wings. The wings are almost transparent, and when folded at rest they cover the abdomen and project beyond it posterioly. On the lower inner side of the wing is a free lobe, the alula, and beyond this toward the thorax there are two other lobes called squamae which are opaque. These three lobes fold below when wings are closed. The metathoracic wings are much reduced and modified to form halteres which are balancing organs, they vibrate rapidly during flight. A haltere has a broad basal scabellum, a narrow stem or pedicel and a terminal knob, the capitellum. In the scabellum are several sensillae which are sound receptors. Below the thorax arise three pairs of legs which have normal structure with five-jointed tarsi. Each tarsus ends in two claws below which are two pad-like pulvilli, the pulvilli secrete a sticky fluid by means of which the fly can rest and walk on ceilings and smooth surface, like glass panes, without falling. The entire leg bears a large number of bristles.

3. Abdomen. The attachment of abdomen to thorax is narrow, and the abdomen is broad in the middle and narrow towards the apex. It is yellowish basally and dark yellow above with a black longitudinal stripe mid-dorsally. There are ten segments in the abdomen, but the first has atrophied and the second is reduced, the third to the sixth are well developed and visible, but segments seven to ten are reduced and lie telescoped inside the anterior segments. In the visible segments the terga are large and extend ventrally. A pair of spiracles are present in the ventral edges of the terga on segments two to six. In the female the hidden segments seven to ten form a tubular ovipositor which protrudes and can be seen when the fly is depositing eggs. The tenth segment bears a pair of cerci. In male the terminal segments are curved below and form a hypopygium or external genital organ. The ninth segment has a pair of claspers with an aedeagus between them. The tenth segment is fused with the ninth and bears a pair of cerci.

LIFE HISTORY

Copulation. The copulation takes place on earth, not in air. In breeding season which in India is from March to October in the greater part of the country, the male sits on the back of the female and grasps her firmly with the fore and middle pairs of legs and remains passive during the remaining period of operation. Female inserts its ovipositor into the genital atrium of the male, to receive the spermatozoa. The copulation takes a few minutes.

Egg-laying. Four days after mating the female housefly lays her eggs. The housefly lays her eggs in stable manure by preference, but failing to find this, it may lay in human faeces, garbage or decomposing animal and vegetable matter. The conditions required for laying eggs are moisture and a favourable temperature, hence, stable manure or human faeces should not be dry. The female extends her ovipositor and lays about 120 to 160 eggs at one time. In the course of a breeding season a single female may lay eggs 4 to 6 times.

Egg. An egg is whitish, cylindrical, and 1 mm long. It has two rib-like longitudinal thickenings on one side. The eggs hatch in 8 to 24 hours depending upon the temperature, and larvae emerge in the dung.

Larva. The larvae are called maggots. They are highly modified without a distinct head, no thoracic or abdominal limbs, and with the spiracles greatly reduced in number. They are covered with thin soft chitin. Such a larva is known as an apodous larva.

The larva when it hatches from the egg is the first instar and is 2 mm long. It is metapneustic having only one pair of posterior abdominal spiracles with two slit-like apertures in each, the spiracles are on the last segment. The first instar lasts for two to three days, then it moults to become the second instar which is larger, and besides the posterior pair of spiracles which become larger, the second instar acquires an anterior pair of spiracles also, it is, thus, amphipneustic with one pair of posterior abdominal spiracles and one pair of prothoracic spiracles. The second instar lasts for a day, then it

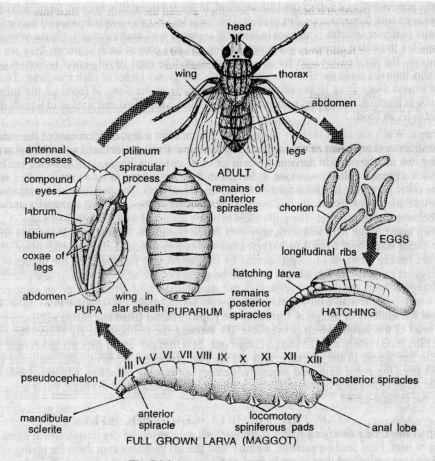

Fig. 76.4. *Musca nebulo.* Life cycle.

moults to form the third instar. The full grown larva of the third instar is 12 mm long. It has a small insignificant head which can be withdrawn, it is followed by 12 segments, the anterior end is narrow but becomes broader posterioly. The pointed anterior end has two small oral lobes which are sensory, each oral lobe has a minute sensory papilla, these sensory papillae represent reduced antennae. There

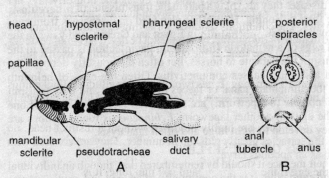

Fig. 76.5. *Musca* larva. A—Anterior end ; B—Posterior end.

is a mouth between the two oral lobes from which project a pair of hooks. The hooks are a part of secondarily developed chitinous sclerites known as cephalopharyngeal skeleton which is composed of three sclerites, a pair of hooks or mandibular sclerites which articulate posterioly with an H-shaped intermediate or hypostomal sclerite. The hypostomal sclerite has the opening of a salivary duct. Posteriorly is a large pharyngeal sclerite formed of two lamellae which unite ventrally to form a deep groove. The cephalopharyngeal skeleton is used for locomotion and for tearing up food. The third instar is amphipneustic with two pairs of spiracles, the anterior prothoracic spiracles lie in the second segment, and each has six to eight finger-like processes with openings at the tips. The posterior pair of abdominal spiracles are on the posterior dorsal side of the 12th segment, in the 3rd instar they become large, dark-coloured, and C-shaped with three sinuous slits in each. The spiracles lead into a well developed tracheal system. Below the posterior spircles is an anus in the 12th segment with anal tubercles. On the ventral side of segments six to twelve are spiny pads or pseudopods, one pair in each segment, they are used for locomotion. The third instar lasts for about 3 to 5 days. The total larval period is from 6 to 8 days, during this time the larva moults twice, and it feeds and grows larger at each moulting. The larva in feeding moves away from light into moist and dark parts of the dung, it feeds on the substance in which it was hatched, it produces enzymes by which food is liquefied and it takes in liquids and small solid particles as food.

Pupa. When the larva is ready to pupate it searches out a dry, dark crevice of the manure, the body contracts and segments are telescoped to form a pupa. Thus, the larva changes into a pupa without moulting, the last larval skin hardens to form an outer covering or puparium which encloses the pupa. Such a pupa is called coarctate. It has no chitinous covering of its own but only a soft pupal skin, the outer puparium has been formed by the last larval skin. The puparium is barrel-shaped and it becomes dark brown, externally it is segmented and shows traces of larval spiracles and spiny pads which become non-functional. The pupa takes in air by means of a pair of spine-like pupal spiracles projecting between the fifth and sixth segments of the puparium. The pupa is absolutely immobile, and the pupal stage lasts from 4 to 5 days. During this time internal changes take place, the larval organs are broken down or histolysis occurs by the phagocytes feeding upon the tissues of organs. The imaginal buds of the larva begin to form the organs of the adult, or histogenesis occurs in the pupa. Imaginal buds are dormant cells, they are stimulated by a hormone of prothoracic endocrine glands which become active only during metamorphosis and make the imaginal buds grow. By these processes the adult fly or imago is formed in the pupa. A blood-filled bag called ptilinum is formed on the head of the imago which is eversible. By forming the ptilinum the fly breaks the puparium which splits transversely and the imago comes out, its wings dry and it flies off to become sexually mature in one week. In the emergence of the fly two processes are involved, firstly the imago is liberated from the pupal skin, and secondly it emerges from the puparium which is broken by the ptilinum. After emergence of the imago the ptilinum is withdrawn into the head, but it leaves behind a mark, the ptilinal suture.

ECONOMIC IMPORTANCE OF HOUSEFLY

Apart from their annoying habits the houseflies are carriers of organisms which cause several diseases in man. Flies feed on garbage, manure, and faeces; they also visit them for laying eggs, they pick up disease germs and then come to feed on dining tables, kitchens, restaurants, and sweetshops. They pick up disease germs on their bristly legs and sticky pulvilli, then they come and brush their legs into human food. They also take in disease organisms into their alimentary canal which they transfer to human food through their faeces, and through exuding saliva and fluids of alimentary canal onto human food. Thus, houseflies are very dangerous and transmit organisms which cause human intestinal disorders, such as typhoid, paratyphoid, diarrhoea, bacillary and amoebic dysentery, and cholera. Besides these dangerous diseases they also play a part in the transmission of tuberculosis and virus of poliomyelitis, and cause food poisoning. Houseflies also feed on discharges from eyes and wounds, thus, they have been known to cause ophthalmia in Egypt and Greece, and yaws in the tropics. The larvae of housefly ingest eggs of a nematode *Habronema*, the infection is passed to the pupae and to the adult flies which transmit the parasite to horses, but often the housefly deposits the nematode larva into eyes of children and, thus, causes conjunctivitis. Often the eggs of helminth parasites of man have been found in the alimentary canal or faeces of houseflies and they transmit two such parasites, the eggs of *Hymenolepis* (a tapeworm) are transferred from the faeces of one person to infect another. Secondly, the eggs of another tapeworm *Echinococcus* found in dogs are transferred to human beings where they develop to form huge and often fatal cysts.

CONTROL OF HOUSEFLIES

In the control of houseflies and their menace it should by remembered that, though an individual may protect his house by screening and sanitation, it is the community of an area and municipalities that must co-operate. The following measures may be taken against them :

1. Control of breeding of flies. (a) Flies breed in stable manure, human faeces and garbage, these should be kept in closed cisterns, then removed by municipalities and be either buried underground or incinerated, as is done in many cantonment areas. (b) City and village garbage may be spread out in fields so that it dries quickly to prevent egg-laying. If lime is added to manure it also prevents egg-laying. In China sodium cyanide solution is put in human faeces containers and it prevents eggs-layig successfully. (c) Garbage and refuse may be treated with insecticides, such as calcium borate which kills the larvae.

2. Protection of food. If kitchens are screened and food is kept covered the flies cannot transmit disease, but this should be done on a large scale in public restaurants, in shops which sell sweets, and especially in keeping a city's milk supply free from flies.

3. Killing adult flies. Many devices can be used for killing flies in a home. (a) Fly swatters are used on dining tables, fly paper is put on windows and tables to which the flies get stuck and die. (b) Hang wires smeared with a boiled mixture of four parts of resin and one part of castor oil, the flies sit on these wires and die. (c) A few drops of 3% solution of formalin in a saucer of sweetened milk is kept in homes and restaurants, flies suck up this milk and die, but the milk should be rendered slightly alkaline to make it palatable to flies. (d) Flies can be killed most successfully by spraying of houses, barns, and privies with D.D.T., benzene hexachloride, or chlordane. Large areas of cities and villages can be sprayed from an airplane with two quarts of D.D.T. per acre, and the spraying is repeated at intervals of seven days for 21 days to ensure that all stages of houseflies are killed. (e) Other chemicals like lethane, pyrethrum, flit, B.H.C., etc., may also be used for killing the flies.

REVISION QUESTIONS

1. Describe the external features of housefly.
2. Give an account of the life history of housefly.
3. Give an account of the economic importance and control measures of housefly.

77

Apis : The Honeybee

Apis (Honeybee) is a social insect living in colonies of 50,000 or more individuals. Honeybees are mostly vegetable feeders preferably living on pollen and nectar of flowers. The larvae which have no legs are helpless and are fed by the nursing workers of the colony up to their pupation time. The adults chiefly live upon honey, while the young ones are given pure pollen or pollen mixed with honey and water to form a paste called **bees-bread.** Although these insects thrive best in gardens and forests, yet they have been noticed lapping the honey dew of some plant bugs and also seeking sugar from places other than flowers. The honeybees live in a highly organized colony wherein a perfect corporate life under strict discipline is exhibited. Excellent division of labour with the common aim of keeping the good of the society in view, make the life very harmonious and extremely busy.

In India three species of *Apis* are commonly found, *viz., Apis dorsata, Apis florea,* and *Apis indica. Apis mellifica* (European bee) occurs in the wild state in Europe. *Apis adamsoni* (African bee) is found in North Africa.

Apis dorsata (Rock bee) is the largest Indian honey bee (20 mm) and prepares large open combs (1 metre × 1.5 metre) singly on trees or caves, walls and other parts of the buildings. Several combs may occur closely in the same locality. They have a regular migratory habit of swarming in the hills during June and July but returning to plains in the middle of winter season. The workers build a fresh nest every time and this follows the swarming by the queen. A single comb of this bee may yield approximetely 25 kg of honey and crops per year. Bees-wax of this insect worth several lacs of rupees is exported from India every year.

Apis florea is the little bee of India. Their workers are very small in size but this species is non-gregarious and builds a single comb which is about 15 cm across, suspended on the branches or under caves of buildings. This does not yield much honey, hardly a few mililitres per comb.

Apis indica (Indian bee) is the common honey bee found in plains and forests throughout India. This is slightly longer than *Apis florea* and smaller than *Apis dorsata.* It builds several parallel combs about one foot across in protected places like hollow of trees, thick bushes, within caves of rocks, wells, on walls and other places of safety in buildings. This is the only Indian honey bee which is capable of domestication in artificial hives although it does not yield much honey, not more than 3 kg annually. It very readily swarms although to some extent migrates also. Various forms are met within the hills and plains.

APIS
SYSTEMATIC POSITION

Phylum	.....	**Arthropoda**
Subphylum	.....	**Madibulata**
Class	.....	**Insecta**
Subclass	.....	**Pterygota**
Division	.....	**Endopterygota**
Order	.....	**Hymenoptera**
Family	.....	**Apidae**
Genus	.....	*Apis*

CASTES

The colonies of honeybees are perennial. A good colony of Indian bees has 40 to 50 thousands individuals consisting mainly of three castes, *viz.,* **queen** or fertile female, **drones** or males and workers or sterile females. The number of workers in one colony exceeds 90 per cent of the total population.

WORKER   QUEEN   DRONE

Fig. 77.1. Castes of honeybee.

STRUCTURE OF A WORKER BEE

The body of a worker bee is densely covered with bristles having lateral barbs, unbranched bristles are found on compound eyes and legs. It is the smallest member of the colony. The colour is usually brown or black. The body is divisible into three regions, *viz.,* head, thorax, and abdomen.

1. Head. The head of honey bee is a wide and triangular structure with the apex pointed below. On the dorsolateral sides there is a pair of compound eyes and in the middle of the top there is a group of three ocelli. A pair of short but many jointed antennae are borne on the middle of the face. Each antenna consists of a long scape, a small pedicel and a flagellum which has ten segments in the female and eleven in the male. The antennae probably serve as tactile and gustatory organs.

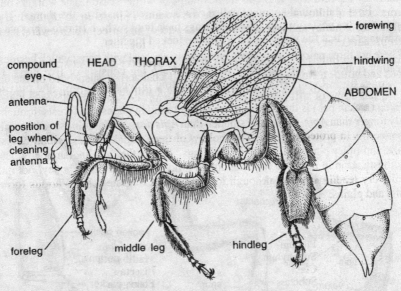

Fig. 77.2. Worker honeybee (Lateral view).

Mouth parts. The mouth parts are attached to the lower part of the head and are of chewing and lapping type. These are modified for collecting the nectar and the pollen. Mouth parts consist of labrum, epipharynx, mandibles, maxillae and labium. Labrum lies below the clypeus, below the labrum is a fleshy epipharynx which is an organ of taste. Mandibles are smooth and situated on either side of the labrum, they are used in moulding wax and making the honeycomb. The labium has submentum, mentum, paraglossa and a glossa or tongue with a long labial palp on each side. The glossa is long and can be extended, at its tip is a small labellum, the glossa is used for gathering honey, it is an organ of touch and taste. Maxillae fit over the mentum on either side, they bear small maxillary palps. The maxillae and labial palps form a tube enclosing the glossa which moves up and down to collect nectar which is forced upwards by pressing together of maxillae and labial palps.

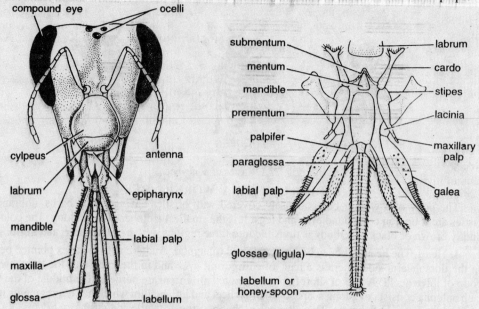

Fig. 77.3. Honeybee. Head and its appendages (Dorsal view).   **Fig. 77.4.** Honeybee. Mouth parts.

2. Thorax. First abdominal segment called propodeum is fused to the thorax. The anterior wings are larger than the posterior pair. The hindwings have hooks which fit into a groove at the rear margin of forewings so that the wings of each side are locked together.

Legs. There are three pairs of legs which are densely covered with hairs, which besides walking, help in collecting pollen and are variously modified. Each leg consists of five parts, *viz.*, coxa, trochanter, femur, tibia, tarsus (five-jointed) terminating in a pair of claws and pulvillus. Each prothoracic leg has a row of stiff bristles on tibia forming an eye brush for cleaning the compound

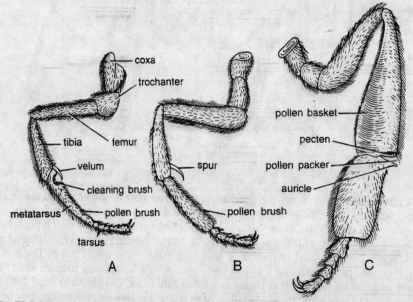

Fig. 77.5. Honeybee. Legs. A—Prothoracic leg ; B—Mesothoracic leg ; C—Metathoracic leg.

eyes, at the distal end of tibia is a movable spine, the velum which can close over a notch on the tarsus to form an antena comb through which the antenna is drawn for cleaning. Long bristles on the tarsus form a pollen brush for removing pollen from the front part of the body. Each mesothoracic leg has a pollen brush on the tarsus, the end of the tibia has a spur like a spine for removing pollen from the pollen basket and wax from abdomen. Each metathoracic leg has a large tibia with a cavity with bristles forming a pollen basket or corbicula used for storing pollen during collection, at the distal end the tibia has a row of stiff bristles called pecten below which is a flat plate, the auricle. The pecten and auricle form a wax pincher for removing wax from the abdomen of workers. The outer surface of the tarsus has a pollen brush and the inner surface has a pollen comb having rows of stiff spines, the pollen comb removes pollen from the body and fills it in the pollen basket.

3. Abdomen. Abdomen begins with the second segment, segments 2 to 7 are clearly visible but segments 8 to 10 are modified and hidden. The ovipositor is modified to form a sting (the worker being a sterile female).

Sting. The sting is made of 3 pairs of gonapophyses, one pair of segment 8, and two pairs of segment 9. The gonapophyses of segment 8 form two stylets lying parallel and enclosing a poison-canal. One pair of gonapophyses of segment 9 fuse together to form a single stylet sheath, the other pair form two stylet palps. The sting or terebra consists of two stylets articulated along their length to the hollow stylet sheath by a groove and rail arrangement. The stylets are held in place by this arrangement and they can move only up and down. The stylets and their sheath bear barbs at the tips to make a wound ; proximally the stylet sheaths have a dilated bulb, then they form arms which are associated with 3 pairs of plates bearing muscles. Attached to the stylets proximally is a median poison sac into which open two acid glands and one alkaline gland. In stinging the muscles of plates drive the stylets and stylet sheath into a victim, the secretions of two types of glands mix and pass down the poison canal into the wound. Generally the poison glands, sting and part of the intestine are pulled out in stinging and the bee dies within two days.

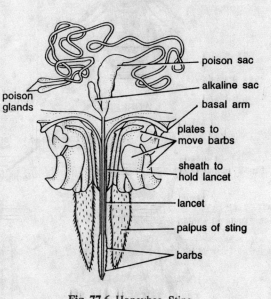

poison glands

poison sac
alkaline sac
basal arm
plates to move barbs
sheath to hold lancet
lancet
palpus of sting
barbs

Fig. 77.6. Honeybee. Sting.

DUTIES OF A WORKER

The workers attend to all duties of food collection, bringing nectar, secreting wax, tending the young, building and cleaning the comb. Consequently their mouth parts are modified for collecting nectar and moulding wax, the epidermis of abdomen for secreting wax, and their legs for collecting pollen. In queens and drones the mouth parts are shorter because they do not collect nectar, their epidermis has no wax-secreting glands, and modifications of metathoracic legs are absent.

QUEEN

General anatomy is the same as in a worker, but it is larger in size, has a longer abdomen extending behind folded wings, since it takes no part in nest making or pollen gathering. It has no wax glands or modifications on legs for pollen collection. It has notched mandibles, 12-jointed antenae and a sting which is used only to combat a rival queen, the sting can be used more than once. The queen, like the workers, is produced from fertilized eggs.

DRONE

The male or drone is larger and stouter than the worker. It has holoptic eyes which touch each other dorsally, the frontal region is reduced. It has small notched mandibles because they do not mould wax, antennae are 13-jointed, it has no sting, but the 9th sternum has 2 claspers and a membranous aedeagus. Drones are formed from unfertilized eggs.

LIFE HISTORY

When the population gets too large for the hive, then the old queen and a large number of workers swarm out to find a new colony. In the meanwhile a new queen is formed in the original colony. It takes a **nuptial flight** or **mating flight** with a number of drones. Copulation occurs in air and the new fertilized queen returns to the old hive. The spermatozoa she has received must serve for all the eggs as the queen does not copulate again. The queen can control the fertilization of eggs. Unfertilized eggs are haploid with 16 chromosomes, they produce drones, fertilized eggs are diploid with 32 chromosomes, they produce the queens and sterile female workers.

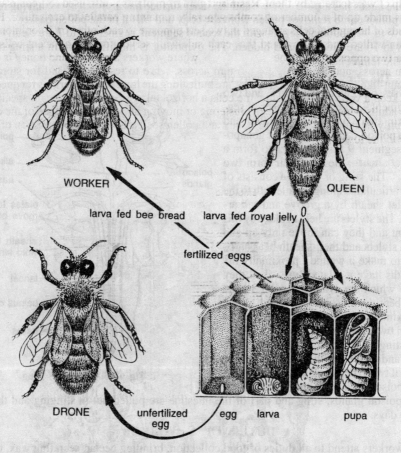

Fig. 77.7. Honeybee. Life cycle.

The queen generally lays one egg in one brood cell. The egg is pinkish, elongated, cylindrical and generally attached at the bottom of a cell at the junction of any two walls. After three days a tiny larva is developed from each egg. For two days all the larvae are fed on a protein rich **royal jelly**. Thereafter, the larvae of drone and workers are fed on honey and pollen, but larvae of queen are continuously fed on royal jelly throughout. In this way the food supply causes them to develop differently. Each larva has moults and grows; then its cell is sealed with a wax-cap. It spins a thick silken imperfect cocoon and pupates. There, as a pupa, it undergoes **complete metamorphosis** and finally cuts the cell-cap with its mandibles to emerge as a young bee. The time of development for each caste is standardized because of the temperature regulation in the hive :

Queen : egg, 3 ; larva, $5\frac{1}{2}$; pupa, $7\frac{1}{2}$ = 16 days.

Worker : egg, 3 ; larva, 6 ; pupa, 12 = 21 days.

Drone : egg, 3 ; larva, $6\frac{1}{2}$; pupa, $14\frac{1}{2}$ = 24 days.

The freshly emerged workers are first entrusted with the indoor duties for two to three weeks during which they act as nursing bees, dance attendance on the royalties, look after brood cells, build and repair the comb. Later on, they are put to outdoor duties and they are completely occupied in collection of nectar and pollen, guarding the hive, air conditioning, temperature regulation and ripening honey, etc.

HIVE

The Indian honeybees as already stated live in hives, made of combs prepared by the workers with the help of wax secreted by them. Resin and gum from plants is also used for repairs of the hive. Each hive is made up of a number of combs generally remaining parallel to each other. Each comb has thousands of hexagonal cells arranged in two sets opposite to each other on a common base. The cells are thin-walled and so arranged that each side-wall serves for two adjacent cells and each cell-base for two opposite cells. The worker cells, where workers are reared and honey is stored, are about 5 mm across, and the drone cells 6 mm across, serve to rear drones and for storage. Large vertical peanut-like queen cells, open below, are built along the lower comb margins for queen rearing. The combs keep a vertical plane, while the cells a horizontal position. There are no special cells for lodging the adults which generally keep clustering or moving about on the surface of the comb. The cells are mainly intended for storage of honey and pollen specially in the upper portion of the comb, while those in the lower part for brood rearing.

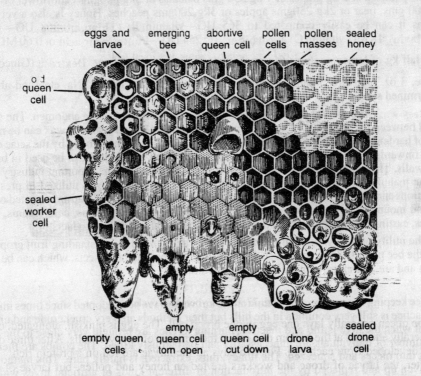

Fig. 77.8. A portion of hive showing various types of cells.

ENEMIES OF HONEYBEE

Fortunately Indian bees do not so far suffer from two severe bee diseases, *i.e.,* the isle of white disease and foul brood as commonly found on European bees. *Nosema* caused by microsporidian is decidedly injurious to bees and often colonies die from its effects, but rarely is an entire apiary destroyed.

Birds pick up a large number of bees; so also the wasps and a certain wasp (*Philanthus ramakrishnae*) very severely attack them. The common hawk moth (*Acherontia styx*) often eats away the combs and causes very serious damage. Man is probably their worst enemy.

ECONOMIC IMPORTANCE OF HONEYBEE

From the times immemorial, man has been domesticating important animals including insects to exploit them to render some service to him or to obtain the various products of their life activities. Honeybees provide honey, bees-wax to man and also help as pollinators.

Honey. Honeybees require forty to eighty thousand trips to visit several times the number of flowers for collecting one kg of honey. Each trip of the bee is two to three km long. Honey, as derived from the beehive, is not the actual nectar or sugar-bearing secretion of plants, collected by bees from flowers and stored in the minute waxen bottles in the hive. The insects swallow the nectar and carry it in their honey sac or within their crop until they are at their hive, where it is regurgitated after chemical changes due to its mixing with saliva, *i.e.,* sucrose is hydrolyzed to glucose, levulose and fructose, which are more readily assimilable by man. The water contents of nectar are mostly evaporated away by a strong current of air produced by the rapid wing beats of the workers crawling over the cells. The nectar, thus, ripens and forms honey. The cells, in which it is stored, are capped over with wax plugs to be reopened at the time of need because it is the principal food of adults and larval bees. Honey is used in many ways by man also as the chief source of natural sweet in preparing candies, cakes and bread, etc. It forms a very important food for patients of diabetes or for persons undergoing very strenuous physical exertion.

The great food value of honey can be estimated by the fact that 450gms of honey is equal to 1kg 600 gms potatoes or 2 kg grapes or 1 kg 350 gms bananas or 5kg 850gms cauliflower or cabbage or 3 kg 400 gms pear or 2kg 250gms apples or 3kg 200gms peaches. Honey is also a very powerful tonic as it can be easily compared to 365 UG—vitamin B, (Thiamin) 268 UG—vitamin G, (Riboflavin), 18 MG vitamin C (Ascorbic acid) ; 254 UG—Pantothenic acid or 0.60 MG Nicotinic acid. Half kg of honey contains $6\frac{1}{2}$ oz. Levulose (fruit sugar), $5\frac{1}{2}$ oz. Dextrose (Glucose), 9 gms Sucrose, 3 oz. moisture, 7 gms Dextrines and Gums, 1 gm of Fe, Ca, Na, etc., and about 4% of undetermined substances.

Bees-wax. The worker bees secrete wax from glands situated in the abdomen. The secretion is exuded between the segments of the underside of the abdomen and scales of wax can be noticed as a result of hardening of this secretion. These scales are detached from the body by the setae of tarsi and passed onwards to the mouth, wherein they are chewed and made plastic to be used in building the comb walls. This wax is isolated and forms an important base for an important industry concerned with the manufacture of toilet goods and cosmetics. A large quantity is utilized in pressing comb foundations and returned to the bees-hive wherever artificial methods of rearing is carried out. Several thousand mounds bees-wax is used in preparing candles, shaving creams, cold creams, cosmetics, polishes, castings of models, carbon paper cryons, electrical and other products.

The utility of honeybees is immense as can be determined by outstanding fruit crops in places where the bee population is very great. They are the only pollinating insects, which can be controlled by man and are, therefore, of great value to agriculturists.

APICULTURE

Bee keeping is a very useful pastime and is known to have been adopted since times immemorial. This practice is still very common in the hills but their methods are very cruel,crude and unscientific. At night when the hive is full and inactive, burning torches are brought very close to the hive and a large number of individuals are unnecessarily and barbarously killed. The combs are then removed and cut into pieces and squeezed. The honey, thus, extracted, is hardly pure. This method has now been given up and replaced by the introduction of different kinds of artificial hives with movable frames, in which facilities for comb-making by the bees, are provided.

An artificial hive has a large brood chamber placed on a wooden platform with slit for the entry and exit of the bees at the bottom. The chamber has a number of frames in each of which a wax sheet bearing hexagonal imprints is held up in a vertical position by a couple of wires. Along the margins of these hexagonal marks, the bess start making walls and ultimately cells. Each wax sheet called comb foundation, attracts the bees by providing the foundation for preparing combs on both of its sides. The frames are kept hanging vertically in the brood chamber, which is covered over by another frame, having a wire meshing through which workers can easily pass. Over the brood chamber is placed another chamber called super which also contains similar frames containing comb foundations to provide additional space for the expansion of hive. The wire meshing mentioned above lies between the brood chamber and super. The super is closed from above by a cover having some holes for ventilation, light and safety.

Such artificial hives are kept in kitchen gardens, fields and orchards and a queen is introduced artificially. It soon lays its first brood of eggs from which workers develop and start enhancing the colony when the hive has been active for sufficient time, the combs are removed from the frames and centrifuged as a result of which the honey is collected without disturbing the nest. The same comb can be used over and over again because it remains intact and if need arises, fresh comb foundations can be placed. The individuals are brushed aside while removing the comb for extracting honey. They again start activity on re-introduced combs. The larval stages remain uninjured. In addition to the hive, other appliances required are a smoker, a net veil, a bee-net, a pair of gloves, a knife, a brush and a centrifuge for extracting honey.

REVISION QUESTIONS

1. Give an account of the external morphology of worker honeybee.
2. Describe the life history of honeybee.
3. Write short notes on the following :
   (i) Differnt castes of honeybee;
   (ii) Mouth parts of honeybee;
   (iii) Pollen basket;
   (iv) Sting of honeybee;
   (v) Economic importance of honeybee.

78

Bombyx : The Silkworm

Bombyx mori is popularly called the Chinese silkworm or Mulberry silkworm moth. It is well known for genuine silk. The importance of silkworm in silk production was known in China during 3500 B.C. The Chinese people knew the methods for cultivating silk and of preparing cloth from it for more than 2000 years. The rearing of silk moth and production of raw silk is known as sericulture. The art of sericulture was held by Chinese a very close secret, so much so, that the leakage of any information or attempt to export eggs or living cocoons was punishable with death. Even then silk was after all introduced in Europe by two monks, who were sent to China as spies. They studied the nature, source and art of silkworm rearing and stealthily carried some eggs in their pilgrim's staff to Constantinople in 555 A.D. From this place the silkworm-rearing was spread into the Mediterranean and Asiatic countries including India, Burma, Thailand and Japan. The insect breeders have produced many races of silkworm moth by hybridization to meet the requirements of climate, rapidity of reproduction, quality, colour and yield of silk.

BOMBYX MORI
SYSTEMATIC POSITION

Phylum	.....	**Arthropoda**
Subphylum	.....	**Mandibulata**
Class	.....	**Insecta**
Subclass	.....	**Pterygota**
Division	.....	**Endopterygota**
Order	.....	**Lepidoptera**
Genus	.....	*Bombyx*
Species	.....	*mori*

HABIT AND HABITAT

Bombyx mori or the Mulberry silkworm is completely domesticated organism and is never found wild. The adult moths seldom eat and are primarily concerned with reproduction. Their larvae are voracious eaters. They feed on the leaves of mulberry trees. Some moths are single brooded or univoltine and others are many brooded or multivoltine. Owing to domestication, a large number of strains have evolved out, which produce cocoons of various shapes, sizes, weights and colours ranging from white to yellow. Only one generation is produced in one year by worms in Europe and other countries where the length of winters far exceeds the duration of summers. Some strains pass through two to seven broods and are cultivated in warm climates. In South India, particularly Mysore, Coimbatore and Salem, a strain which produces several generations, extensively utilized to produce silk.

EXTERNAL FEATURES

The adult moth is about 25.00 mm long with a wing-span of 40.00 to 50.00 mm. The female silkmoths are larger than the males. The moth is quite robust and creamy-white in colour. The body is distinctly divisible into three regions, namely head, thorax and abdomen. The head bears a pair of compound eyes, a pair of branched or feathery antennae and the mouth parts. The thorax bears three pairs of legs and two pairs of wings. The cream-coloured wings are about 25.00 mm long and are marked by several faint or brown lines. The entire body is covered by minute scales.

LIFE HISTORY OR LIFE CYCLE

The silkmoth is dioecious, *i.e.,* the sexes are separate. Fertilization is internal, preceded by copulation. The development includes a complicated metamorphosis.

Eggs. After fertilization, each female moth lays about 300 to 400 eggs. These eggs are placed in clusters on the leaves of mulberry tree. The female covers the eggs by a gelatinous secretion which glues them to the surface of the leaves. The eggs are small, oval and usually slightly yellowish in colour. The egg contains a good amount of yolk and is covered by a smooth hard chitinous shell. After laying the eggs the female moth does not take any food and dies within 4–5 days. In the univoltine (a single brood per year) they may take months because overwintering takes place in this stage but the multivoltine broods come out after 10–12 days. From the egg hatches out a larva called the caterpillar.

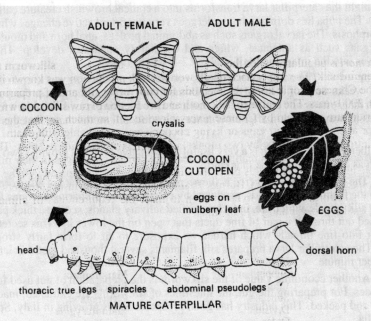

ADULT FEMALE   ADULT MALE

COCOON

crysalis

COCOON CUT OPEN

eggs on mulberry leaf

EGGS

head

dorsal horn

thoracic true legs   spiracles   abdominal pseudolegs

MATURE CATERPILLAR

Fig. 78.1. *Bombyx mori.* (Silkworm). Life history.

Larva. The larva of silkworm moth is called caterpillar larva. The newly hatched larva is about 4.00 to 6.00 mm in length. It has a rough, wrinkled, hairless and yellowish white or greyish worm-like body. The full grown larva is about 6.00 to 8.00 cm in length. The body of larva is distinguishable into a prominent head, distinctly segmented thorax and an elongated abdomen. The head bears mandibulate mouth and three pairs of ocelli. A distinct hook-like structure, the spinneret, is present for the extrusion of silk from the inner silk-gland. The thorax forms a hump and consists of three segments. Each of the three thoracic segments bears pair of jointed true legs. The tip of each leg has a recurved hook for locomotion and ingestion of leaves. The abdomen consists of ten segments of which first nine are clearly marked, while the tenth one is indistinct. The third, fourth, fifth, sixth and ninth abdominal segments bear ventrally a pair of unjointed stumpy appendages each. These are called prolegs or pseudolegs. Each leg is retractile and more or less cylindrical. The eighth segment carries a short dorsal anal horn. A series of respiratory spiracles or ostia are present on either lateral side of the abdomen.

The larva is a voracious eater and strongly gregarious. In the beginning chopped young mulberry leaves are given as food but with the advancement of age entire and matured leaves are provided as food. The caterpillar moves in a characteristic looping manner. The larval life lasts for 2–3 weeks. During this period the larva moults four times. After each moult, the larva grows rapidly. A full-grown larva is about 8.00 cm long and becomes transparent and golden brown in appearance. A pair of long sac-like silk-glands now develops into the lateral side of the body. These are modified salivary glands.

Pupa. The full-grown larva now stops feeding and hides itself in a corner under the leaves. It now begins to secrete the clear and sticky fluid of its salivary glands through a narrow pore called the spinneret situated on the hypopharynx. The sticky substance turns into a fine, long and solid thread or filament of silk into the air. The thread becomes wrapped around the body of the caterpillar larva forming a complete covering or pupal case called the cocoon. The cocoon formation takes about 3–4 days. The cocoon serves a comfortable house for the protection of the caterpillar larva for further development.

The cocoon is a white or yellow, thick, oval capsule which is slightly narrow in the middle. It is formed of a single long continuous thread. The outer threads, which are initial filaments of the cocoon, are irregular but the inner ones forming later the actual bed of the pupa, is one long continuous thread about 300 metres in length, wound round in concentric rings by constant motion of the head from one side to the other about 65 times per minute. The irregular surface threads are secreted first and the inner continuous thread later. The silk thread is secreted at the rate of 150 mm per minute. Within a fortnight the caterpillar larva transforms into a conical brownish creature called the pupa or the chrysalis. The pupa lies dormant, but undergoes very important active changes which are referred to as metamorphosis. The larval organs such as abdominal prolegs, anal horn and mouth parts are lost. The adult organs such as antennae, wings and copulatory apparatus develop. The pupa finally metamorphoses into the imago or adult in about 2–3 weeks time.

Imago or adult. The adult moth emerges out through an opening at the end of the cocoon in about 2 to 3 weeks time, if allowed to live. Immediately before emergence, the pupa secretes an alkaline fluid, that softens one end of the cocoon and after breaking its silk strands, a feeble crumpled adult squeezes its way out. Soon after emergence, the adult silkmoths mate, lay eggs and die.

ECONOMIC IMPORTANCE

The mulberry silkworm moth is a very useful and valuable insect. It provides two very important products such as silk and gut to the mankind.

1. Silk. The true silk of commerce is the secretion of the caterpillars of silkworm moth. Silk is a secretion in the form of fine threads, produced by caterpillars in preparing cocoons for their pupae. Long sac-like silk-glands, which are, in fact, modified salivary glands, secrete a thick pasty substance, which is passed out through a pair of fine ducts that open on the lower lip. This secretion is spun by the caterpillar into fine threads which harden on exposure to air to form fairly strong and pliable silk-strands. The caterpillar larva prepares silk filaments several thousand metre in length at the rate of 15.00 cm per minute.

2. Gut. Another economic value of the silkworm is the preparation of gut used for surgical and fishing purposes. For preparing the gut, the intestines of silkworms are extracted, made into strings, dried, treated and packed. This industry has good prospects and is growing in Italy, Spain, Formosa, Japan and India.

SERICULTURE

The rearing of silkworms for the production of raw silk is known as sericulture. The Chinese people knew the methods of cultivating silk and preparing cloth from it for more than 2000 years. But the art of sericulture was held by them a very close secret, so much so, that leakage of any information or attempt to export eggs or living cocoons was punishable with death. Even then silk was after all introduced in Europe by two monks, who were sent to China as spies. They studied the nature, source, and art of silk-rearing and stealthily carried some eggs in their pilgrim's staff to Constantinople in 555 A.D. From this place the silk-rearing spread into Mediterranean and Asiatic countries including India, Burma, Thailand and Japan.

Nowadays, sericulture is an important industry of several Asian and European countries, but China and Japan are the only great producers of raw-silk. No government in this world can profit by its silk-insdustry except providing employment to half a dozen people per acre of mulberry or part-time work to farmers. A rough estimate in India reveals that this industry is providing work to about 5 million people with an annual income amounting to Rs. 19 crores. The total production is about 2.5 million pounds as against a demand of about 4.2 million pounds per year. Silk industry in India has drawn the attention of the Government of India considerably. In 1934 an Imperial Sericulture Committee was formed and since 1939 an All India Sericulture Conference meets every year. Important research work is being undertaken on problems of production of silk, the processes of spinning, reeling, preparing yarn and cloth in Assam, Bengal, Madras, Punjab, Kashmir and Mysore, etc. Research is also in progress regarding the production and supply of healthy eggs, refrigeration, etiology, hybridisation and breeding studies besides the propagation and cropping of mulberry varieties.

Sericulture thrives in China, Japan and France also but not in America because this involves plenty of manual labour which is not as cheap in America as in China, Japan and India, etc., besides silk can hardly compete with synthetic fibres.

Sericulture is a regular industry in India and it has silk-producing centres in Assam, Bengal, Madras, Punjab, Kashmir and Mysore. Healthy eggs of high yielding strains are procured from sericulture research stations. The hatching of the eggs can be controlled (accelerated or postponed) artificially by proper conditions of refrigeration. The eggs are placed in paper-lined trays made of split bamboo. The trays are kept on stools, the legs of which rest in dishes containing water to make them ant-proof. The eggs are periodically stirred by a feather. Larvae are given chopped mulberry leaves 5 to 9 times per day during the larval period which lasts for 3 to 5 weeks in which larvae moult four times. The pupae are not allowed to become adult. To procure silk, the cocoons, before the emergence of the silk-moth, *i.e.,* 8 to 10 days after the cocoon formation, are dropped in hot water or subjected to steam or dry heat or fumigation. Sometimes they are killed by sunning for 4–5 days called stifling. This results in killing the pupae. After assorting the cocoons with respect to their texture and colour, they are skilfully unwound by experts. Soaking cocoons in boiling water, helps in softening the cement or adhesion of the silk-threads among themselves and in loosening the outer threads to separate freely. After the loose strands have been removed by a revolving brush, free ends from four or five cocoons are passed through eyelets and guides to twist into one thread and wound round a large wheel, from which it is transferred to spools. This is known as raw-silk or reeled silk. The raw silk is again boiled, stretched and purified by acids or by fermentation. It is then carefully washed several times to bring about the well-known silk lustre on the thread. It is then supn and woven into fabrics which we most proudly prize.

The waste outer layers or superficial threads and damaged cocoons , etc., are combed, teased and then the filaments are spun. This product is known as spun silk.

About 40 to 50 million kilograms of raw silk is consumed in the world anually. Indian consumption is estimated to be about 2 million kilograms of silk and production only 1 –1.5 million kilograms per year, the half of which is the production of Mysore only.

One cocoon yields about 300 metres of silk thread. It requires about 25,000 cocoons to prepare a half a kilogram of finished silk. An idea of the total number of cocoons sacrificed every year for the benefit of human race can be had from the fact that about 40 to 50 million kilograms of silk is consumed annualy in the world.

Diseases in Silkworms

Silkworms suffer form several diseases. Chief of these is pebrine caused by a protozoan parasite *Nosema bombycis* of the microsporidian group. In this disease the caterpillars turn pale brown and later on shrink and die. This disease is highly infectious, transmittable through eggs and responsible for very heavy economic losses. The control is brought about by a microscopic examination of the body fluids of the female, in which the parasites (pebrine corpuscles) are met with. The eggs may be discarded or retained according to the presence or absence of parasites. Other diseases are fletcherie and grasserie but of minor importance. Some times caterpillars exhibit sysmptoms like jaundice disease, *i.e.,* losing appetite, showing irregular growths, etc.

Other Silkworm Moths

There are two other silkworm moths which also yield silk. These are *Attacus receni* , B, the Eri silkworm moth and *Antherea paphia,* B, the tassar silkworm moth. Both these moths belong to the family Saturnidae are large-sized and their caterpillars are also considerably monstrous, stout and about 10.00 cm long. The Eri silkworm which lives upon castor, is a domesticated form, cultivated in warm damp places. It is found in South-East Asia. Its life history resembles that of the mulberry worm. Its cocoon has loose texture and silk is not reelable, hence, this is carded and spun. The gloss on the thread is inferior. Adults are stout dark moths with dark brown white spotted and striped wings. The tassar silkworm resembles the Eri but the caterpillars feed upon *Dalbergia, Shorea,* and *Terminalia,* etc. The cocoon is hard shell-like of the size of a hen's egg and is generally found attached to a plant by a stalk. The moth has yellowish or deep brown wings with an eye-spot on each one. It is found in China, India and Sri Lanka. Cocoon has reelable silk. This is a wild variety but can be domesticated. The silk produced by Eri silkworm and tassar silkworm is not of very good quality.

Other silkworms, *viz.,* Moon moth, Atlas moth, Cashew caterpillars and Ficus worm, although produce silk cocoons but the quality of filament produced is inferior and weak, hence, they have no economic value.

REVISION QUESTIONS

1. Give an account of the life history of silkworm you have studied and point out its economic importance.
2. Write a detailed note on sericulture.

79

Cimex : The Bedbug

The bedbug (*Cimex*) has been known to the mankind from time immemorial. It is a small ectoparasitic insect, which feeds upon human blood. Bedbug has been intimately associated with man throughout the ages and has been referred to as a "domesticated insect". It is of old world origin, and has been carried to nearly all parts of the world. It is an important household pest. There are three species which attack man. *Cimex lectularis* is cosmopolitan in distribution. *Cimex hemipterus* (formerly *Cimex rotundus*) is the Indian bedbug. It is limited to tropical and subtropical regions in distribution. *Cimex boueti* is the tropical species and is distributed in South America and Africa. All these three species of bedbug differ but very slightly from one another.

CIMEX

SYSTEMATIC POSITION

Phylum	.....	**Arthropoda**
Subphylum	.....	**Mandibulata**
Class	.....	**Insecta**
Subclass	.....	**Pterygota**
Division	.....	**Exopterygota**
Order	.....	**Hemiptera**
Genus	.....	*Cimex*

DISTRIBUTION

Bedbug is widely distributed all over the world. *Cimex lectularis* is found in America, Europe, Siberia, Northern China, Australia and Northern India. *Cimex hemipterus* (formerly called *Cimex rotundus*) occurs throughout India, Burma, Malayasia, Southern China and Central Africa.

HABIT AND HABITAT

Bedbugs are found all over the world. They inhabit dark, damp human dwellings such as old houses, buildings, hotels, hostels, rest houses, barracks, carriages and almost anywhere else. They live in cracks in the walls and floor, in crevices in the beds and furniture, under mattresses, carpets and wall paper and in similar places. The thin bodies of bedbugs are well adapted to life in narrow spaces or crevices.

Bedbugs are nocturnal, but often come out during the day. They are gregarious insects. These are sanguivorous ectoparasites. They are strongly attracted by the warmth and the odour of the body. They are incapable of flight but they migrate from one house to another along the walls, pipes or drains. They are carried from one place to another on clothing, in luggage or furniture. If not allowed to reach the beds by placing their legs in water troughs or other barriers, they climb up the wall and move along the ceiling to drop down from there on the beds. They usually suck human blood, but also attack warm blooded animals such as birds (domestic fowl) and mammals (mice, rats, rabbits, cats and dogs). They suck human blood while the man is sleeping, after which they quickly run away. Their gregarious habit results in great discomfort to mankind. Bedbugs can survive without food for several months or a year and even longer. The starving bedbugs may feed upon birds, rats, mice and rabbits and may also resort to cannibalism. Their retiring habits coupled with their power to fast for long periods make their eradication difficult. Bedbugs give out a peculiar kind of odour or foul smell due to the presence of secretion of stink gland. They are oviparous and undergo gradual metamorphosis.

EXTERNAL FEATURES

Shape, size and colour. The body of bedbug is small, oval and dorso-ventrally flattened. It measures about 5.00 mm in length and about 3.00 mm in width. The colour of bedbug is reddish-brown which changes to deep purple or red after feeding. The body is profusely covered with bristles and hairs. The body consists of three parts : the head, the thorax, and the abdomen.

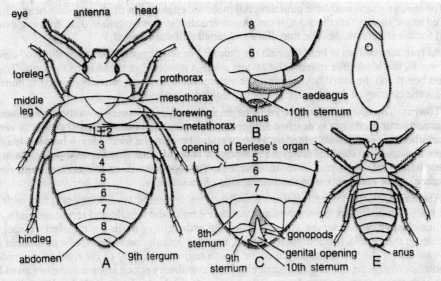

Fig. 79.1. *Cimex.* A—Adult male (Dorsal view) ; B—Genitalia of male ; C—Posterior end of abdomen of adult female (Ventral view) ; D—Egg, E—Young nymph.

Head. The short and broad head fits inside lateral extensions of prothorax. Head bears a pair of compound eyes and two short antennae. Compound eyes are well developed but ocelli are absent. The antennae are four jointed. The clypeus is distinct. On the ventral side of the head, the mouth parts form a sucking apparatus known as proboscis, beak or rostrum.

Mouth parts. Mouth parts form a pointed beak or rostrum that lies bent under the head in a ventral groove up to the first pair of legs. The mouth parts are modified for piercing the skin and sucking the blood. They consist of a labrum, labium, a pair of mandibles and a pair of maxillae. The labrum is short and it covers the mid-dorsal groove of the rostrum. The labium forms an elongated incomplete hollow tube or sheath called the rostrum. It is three-jointed and mid-dorsally grooved to enclose the four needle-shaped stylets, two mandibles and two maxillae. The mandibles are flattened and sharply pointed. The maxillae are slightly shorter and possess serrated edges. The mandibles, worked by muscles in the head, slide independently on either side of the two maxillae which do not move independently of each other. The inner maxillary surfaces are grooved so as to form two exceedingly fine channels running along their entire length. One of these is the feeding channel and is connected to the pharynx. Blood is sucked through it. Feeding channel is bigger and dorsal in

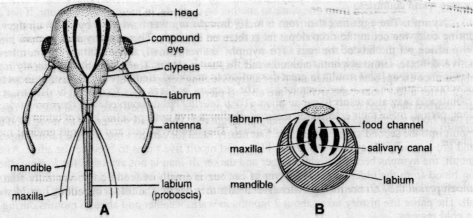

Fig. 79.2. *Cimex.* Mouth parts. A—Head and mouth parts in front view ; B—T.S. of mouth parts.

position. The other is the salivary channel joined by its ducts to the salivary glands, and is connected to a small pump beneath the pharynx. The salivary channel is smaller and ventral in position, it is used for injecting saliva into the puncture. All these are enclosed in the trough-like beak. The beak is grooved in such a way that the sides of the groove are almost close together, thus, forming a protective sheath for the stylets inside. The maxillary and labial palps are absent.

At rest, the rostrum is bent beneath the thorax. For feeding, the rostrum is directed downwards or forwards, the blade-like mandibular stylets make a puncture in the skin of the host. The jointed rostrum bends and the maxillary stylets enter the wound. The saliva runs down into the puncture and prevents the clotting of the blood which is subsequently sucked up.

Thorax. The thorax is divisible into a large prothorax, a very small mesothorax and metathorax. The pronotum of prothorax is notched anteriorly to receive the head. The mesothorax is very small. The metathorax is generally covered by a pair of stub-like vestigial forewings or hemielytra that arise from the mesothorax. The hindwings are completely absent so that flight is impossible. Each thoracic segment bears ventrally a pair of short, stout legs. The legs have three-jointed tarsi with two strong claws each. Stink glands open on the ventral side of metathorax.

Abdomen. The abdomen is flat and consists of ten segments, tenth segment is tiny with an anus. In the male, the abdomen is narrower and pointed than in the female and terminates into a curved hook-like clasper, which serves as a sheath for the aedeagus or penis for transferring spermatozoa to female. In the female, the abdomen is broad, rounded apically and possesses a prominent notch or cleft ventrally on the posterior margin of the fourth segment, slightly to the right of the middle line. This notch or cleft is the opening of a particular blind copulatory pouch known as the organ of Berlese, from which there is no opening to any other organ of the body. In the female, the eight and ninth sterna are cleft into two parts. There are no cerci. The spermatozoa are introduced into organ of Berlese by the aedeagus or penis of the male. The spermatozoa bore through the organ of Berlese and reach the ovary.

LIFE HISTORY

Before laying eggs, the female bug feeds on blood-meal and mates with the male bug. Life history of bedbug exhibits gradual metamorphosis and comprises three stages : egg, nymph and adult.

Mating. In bedbugs, the mating or copulation is quite interesting. While mating or copulating, the male bug takes up a position diagonally across the body of female bug and introduces its penis into the notch or cleft of the organ of Berlese to transfer the spermatophores. The spermatozoa bore through the wall of organ of Berlese and reach the ovary to fertilize the eggs. Thus, fertilization is internal.

Eggs. The female lays about 200 to 500 eggs, singly or in batches, 2 or 3 eggs per day, in cracks and crevices of cots and furniture, in holes, under mattresses and similar other places. The eggs of bedbugs are pearly white oval or cylindrical objects, furnished with a little cap-like lid at one end which is slightly curved to one side. The end possessing the cap-like lid bears a micropyle. The eggs are about 1.00 mm in length and are laid singly or in small batches. The eggs are laid throughout the year in warm countries.

Nymph. The eggs hatch in from 6 to 10 days during warm weather but take a longer period during cold weather as their development is retarded by cold. The young bugs or nymphs come out by pushing off the lids of the eggs. The nymphs are very small, about 1.00 to 1.50 mm long, flat, active, delicate, semitransparent creatures and are pale in colour. They resemble the parents in general appearance except being smaller and paler and possessing comparatively thicker antennae and stouter legs. After a few hours, the nymphs are able to pierce the skin of man and suck the blood, and if undisturbed they feed to repletion in about 3 or 4 minutes. They may take a meal three or four times of their body weight and become globular and bright red. They need shelter but no more food till they moult into the second stage. After their first hearty meal they have a much more robust appearance, and grow rapidly. They feed on human blood and moult five times to become the adult. After each moult, the nymphs become slightly larger and darker. If man is not available for feeding, they feed on blood from the older bugs. The nymphs can survive without feeding for 3 or 4 months during which period they do not moult. After five moults they become adult taking about 7 to 24 weeks in all. The entire life history takes about 2 months in warm weather and about 6 months during winter in cold regions.

ECONOMIC IMPORTANCE

The bedbugs are the most annoying and disgusting household pests. They feed on human blood by piercing the skin, causing in some cases only, pain and inflammation. The economic importance of bed bug can be better studied under the following heads :

1. Nuisance. The bedbugs emit foul and stinking smell due to the secretion of the stinking glands. This peculiar odour is unbearable to the human beings. When their number increases sufficiently, the sleep becomes almost impossible. Their bite causes inflammation, irritation and disturbance in sleep. Sleepless nights with constant irritation due to the introduction of saliva of bedbug in the human blood during feeding are likely responsible to contribute greatly to the ill-health of children and even of certain adult persons.

2. Diseases. The bedbugs have been suspected of transmitting many diseases from man to man. They are supposed to transfer the micro-organisms or germs of kala-azar, bubonic plague, relapsing fever, typhoid and even tuberculosis. It is doubtful, however, if they are active or chief vectors of any major disease, but they appear to possess the micro-organism of kala-azar, plague, typhoid, relapsing fever and tuberculosis and under exceptional circumstances they may become means of their dissemination and transmission. It is generally accepted now that bed bugs are not responsible for large outbreaks of epidemic diseases.

CONTROL

The following measures are suggested to control the bedbugs :

1. The houses should be well-ventilated, damp-free, and clean. This can be done by cleaning the rooms, beds, mattresses and furniture, etc.

2. Necessary precautions to prevent entrance of bedbugs from infested beddings or luggage brought after journey, should be taken.

3. Badly infested rooms and furniture may be made bug-free by washing with insecticides which will penetrate the cracks and crevices in the walls of rooms and the furniture.

4. Sprinkling of boiling water, spraying of petrol or an emulsion of kerosene, benzene and petrol and fumigation with sulphur are generally used to exterminate the bedbugs.

5. Bedbugs can be killed by the fumigation of rooms and furniture with HCN gas but this should be done with extreme precaution as the HCN gas is poisonous to man also.

6. The best method to exterminate the bedbugs is the spray of DDT (dichloro-diphenyl-trichloroethane). It can be sprayed on the indoor surface and on the furniture so as to leave residue which is lethal to bedbugs which crawl over it for many months. For small infested bed rooms all that is required is about 1.5 litres of 5 per cent DDT in kerosene. This can be sprayed on all the walls and furniture where bugs may crawl or rest.

In case of irritation and inflammation of skin by bed bug bite, a little of hydrogen peroxide or ammonia may be rubbed on the skin. This acts almost as an immediate cure.

REVISION QUESTION

1. Describe the life history of bedbug and suggest some control measures.

80

Termites : The White Ants

Termites commonly called white ants are soft-bodied, social and polymorphic insects having two pairs of similar deciduous wings and live together forming large communities. The termites, however, are among the most destructive insects so far as man is concerned but in nature they help in decomposing the dead vegetation and enriching the soil. Though the termites are called white ants but they are neither completely white in colour nor ants; one can easily differentiate these from ants by the absence of a constriction or peduncle between the thorax and the abdomen, in addition to some other morphological and behavioural characteristics. However, more than 1700 species of termites are known today. Some common genera are *Macrotermes, Mastotermes, Odontotermes, Kalotermes, Nasutitermes, Leucotermes, Coptotermes, Achotermopsis, Zootermopsis,* etc.

SYSTEMATIC POSITION

Phylum	.....	**Arthropoda**
Subphylum	.....	**Mandibulata**
Class	.....	**Insecta**
Subclass	.....	**Pterygota**
Division	.....	**Exopterygota**
Order	...	**Isoptera**
Type	..	**Termite**

DISTRIBUTION

Termites are widely distributed in the tropical and subtropical regions of world, they also occur in temperate regions.

HABIT AND HABITAT

The termites are nocturnal and they prefer to live in eternal darkness. They cannot withstand the exposure of dry air and, therefore, they construct tunnels in the earth and wood. The termites are best known nest building insects. Since, they bore through wood causing much damage, they can digest wood with the help of symbiotic flagellates, such as *Trichonympha campanula* living in their intestine and passed on from generation to generation. These are social insects forming large communities and well marked polymorphic individuals.

Primitive termites live in galleries bored in wood, dead trees, structural timbers and wooden buildings. Some termites make tunnels in the ground, they destroy roots of grasses, vegetation and crops. More advanced termites make huge maunds called termitaria which are up to 6 metres

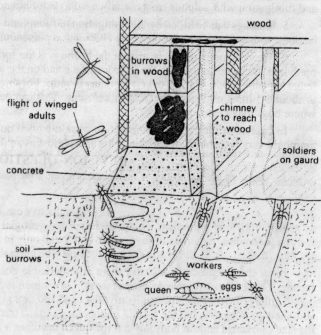

Fig. 80.1. Diagram showing the termite colony.

high, they are made of excavated mud, wood and excreta mixed with saliva, their walls become hard as rocks. Wood-eating termites (*Termopsis*) have no workers, they form galleries in decaying logs. *Calotermes, Neotermes* and *Mastotermes* bore into dry wood, such as posts, furniture and wooden buildings. *Calotermes* bores into stems of tea plants in Sri Lanka. *Leucotermes* and *Captotermes* live in the ground, and through the soil they enter the woodwork of buildings making passages of mud for concealment. Indian termite *Odontotermes* includes both underground dwellers and maund builders. Termitaria are made mostly in Africa, Sri Lanka and Australia.

In maunds and termitaria is a maze of passages, chambers, royal chamber and special cells for storing food or cultivating fungus gardens. Nocturnal foraging parties of workers go out to collect vegetable food which is stored in special cells. Workers go above to collect seeds, grass and vegetation, these are cut up and stored in special cells, or granaries.

MORPHOLOGY

Shape, size and colour. The body size is variable; from small to moderate-size. They are yellow, brown, black or pale coloured insects having weak sclerotized bodies.

Structure. The body has distinct three regions, the head, thorax and abdomen. The integument or skin covering the body is soft, delicate, thin and highly sensitive. The head bears a pair of compound eyes which are often functionless, a pair of antennae and the mouth parts are biting and chewing type with well developed mandibles. The neck has prominent lateral sclerites. Pronotum is prominent. There are two pairs of long, narrow similar wings, each with a basal suture from where the wing can be cast off. There are three pairs of walking legs; tarsi are 4-jointed with a pair of claws. Abdomen has 10 segments ending in a pair of short 2 to 6 jointed cerci, in male the ninth segment has a pair of anal stylets.

Termite community. Termites differ from other social insects in having a large number of castes. Basically, a termite community includes two forms :

1. Reproductive forms or castes. There are three types of reproductive castes which are **fertile** males and females. These are as follows :

A. Macropterous forms or winged forms or first reproductive caste are sexually perfect males and females, they are the ancestors of community from which other forms have been derived, they have two pairs of large, equal-sized wings which project beyond the abdomen at rest. Body is chitinized and dark brown. Compound eyes are well developed and there is a pair of ocelli. Brain and sex organs are larger than in others. Males and females leave the nest, lead a brief aerial life, shed their wings at the basal sutures, then they come together in pairs and mate, after which they find a place for a new nest. Each pair is a dealated king and queen or primary royal pair, they have stumps of shed wings, king and queen are permanently associated, they are monogamous. The queen becomes large by growth of its abdomen. Now, they are the originators of a new colony.

B. Brachypterous forms or short winged forms or second reproductive caste are sexually mature males and females but they are nymphal in appearance, they have short wing buds only, body is less chitinized and pale-coloured. Compound eyes are not dark, brain and sex organs are smaller. They are subterranean and do not leave the nest. If the primary king or queen dies, its place is taken by brachypterous individuals forming substitute or complemental king or queen, such queens produce fewer eggs, there may be several substitute kings and queens in one nest and they are polygamous.

C. Apterous (wingless) forms or third reproductive caste look like nymphal workers, they have no wings, cuticle is colourless, compound eyes are vestigial and ocelli are absent, they have both males and females. Apterous forms are rare and found only in lower termites, *e.g., Leucotermes*, they are known as ergatoid kings and queens, they may be several.

In all three reproductive castes there is remarkable post-embryonic growth, especially in the female. The fertilized female develops into a queen which is 5 to 7.5 cm long, the increase in size is due to enlargement of the abdomen only, the head and thorax remain normal, the terga and sterna of abdomen do not grow, but the pleural membranes expand tremendously, this is due to an increase in the size of ovaries and fat body, so that the queen becomes a large, inert, egg-laying individual. The queen formed from the macropterous female is the largest. The queen lives for 6 to 15 years and lays a million eggs in its life. It was once believed that the destruction of the queen would ultimately kill out the community but this is not so because brachypterous or apterous queens will form and continue the community.

2. Sterile forms or castes. There are two types of wingless(apterous)sterile castes. These are males and females in which sex organs are rudimentary and non-functional. These are of two types:

A. Sterile workers are apterous, sterile males and females in which sex organs have atrophied and are non-functional. A worker has its integument very little chitinized and body is pale-coloured, it looks like a nymph, head is wide pointing downwards, compound eyes are absent, and in some species ocelli are also absent. Workers may be **dimorphic,** in one the head and mandibles are larger than in the other form, *e.g.,* in *Odontotermes*. In some workers are **trimorphic** with small intermediate and larger sizes, *e.g., Termes*. The number of workers in a community is very large, and with the exception of reproduction and defence, they perform all duties, looking after eggs and the young, finding food, planting and cultivating fungi, making nests, and feeding the queen and soldiers. They also lick and groom each other. Because of their gnawing habit the workers destroy crops, wood and human belongings and cause tremendous loss to man.

B. Sterile soldiers are apterous males and females with no sex organs. A soldier has a large chitinous head, big mandibles and colour is pale. Soldiers are of two types : (a) **mandibulate soldiers** have large powerful mandibles but no frontal rostum, (b) **nasute soldiers** have small mandibles and a median frontal rostrum on the head. Soldiers defend the community, mandibulate soldiers with their mandibles and nasute soldiers by exuding a viscid repellent fluid through the frontal rostrum. At times soldiers plug the burrows with their heads.

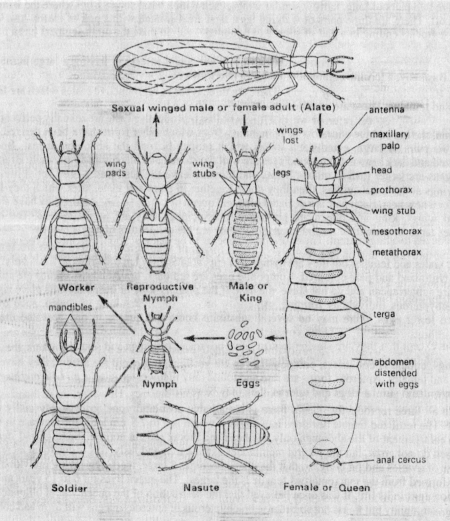

Fig. 80.2. Termites. Castes and life cycle.

Food. Food of termites consists of wood, vegetation, faecal matter of termites, cast off skins and the dead of the colony. Some termites cultivate **fungus gardens,** they are made of a reddish brown, spongy comb produced by workers form vegetable matter and excreta, on the comb fungal hyphae grow producing white patches. Fungus gardens are grown in chambers located near the centre of the nest, they communicate with a **royal chamber** in which the king and queen live. The queen is fed by workers only on saliva and fungal hyphae. The eggs and nymphs develop in fungal chambers or nurseries, workers tend and feed the nymphs on fungus and vegetable matter which are partly predigested by workers, thus, symbiotic flagellates are transferred to nymphs. The nymphs develop either into fertile males and females which can leave the nest and new colonies, or into sterile workers or soldiers.

LIFE HISTORY

The life history and the origin of caste system in termites is extremely complicated. The life history of termite can be explained as under :

1. Swarming and mating. Usually equal number of males and females of macropterous and brachypterous forms leave their nest in huge numbers or great swarms at definite times of the year, generally after the first showers of rain on the onset of rainy season. This is called **swarming.** Swarming may occur either at night or even during the day; it depends upon the species of termite. The termites are not true fliers and, hence, after a short flight they come down to the ground, their wings are shed off and they become dealated. One male and one female pair, referred to as **royal couple,** they search for a sheltered place either in wood or on the ground. After getting a suitable place, they excavate a **nuptial chamber,** where copulation takes place. The flight of termites is not a true **nuptial flight** because copulation does not take place in air unless they come to the ground. In the paired dealated individuals, male becomes the king which cohabits the female, the queen for the whole life. These individuals now become the originators of a new colony.

2. New colony. As referred to, that the royal pair copulate in the nuptial chamber. After copulation, the queen lays cluster of eggs, from these eggs nymphs are hatched out. These nymphs develop into workers. When workers are formed in large numbers, they take up different duties like feeding and attending the royal pair and enlarging the nest. Then the nymphs hatching out from the eggs develop into the soldiers. Thus, in the early months and years of the formation of a new colony workers and soldiers are only formed and then macropterous or brachypterous forms are produced.

3. Modifications. It has already been mentioned earlier that the queen undergoes drastic modifications attaining a size nearly 20 to 30 thousand times larger than the worker, the head and thorax reduced to a large extent. The entire body appears to be made of abdomen only. It becomes an egg laying individual and on an average it lays nearly 4000 eggs in a day and millions of eggs in its life time. When the power of **fecundity** (egg-laying) ceases, it dies and devoured by the other members of the colony. The king, however, undergoes less remarkable change, its body gets inflated due to well-fed condition but inert life.

4. Development. The eggs are oval, elongated, smooth and pale coloured. Development is **gradual** and **metamorphosis** is not complete. The **nymphs** which hatch out from the eggs are like the adults except that they are smaller in size, have no traces of wings and sexually immature. The nymphs undergo several **moultings** to attain adulthood.

5. Differentiation of castes and determination of sex. The formation of different castes in a community from similar eggs has been explained by various theories. However, these theories are based on complex interaction of hormones, pheromones, availability of food supply and social behaviour, etc.

So far **sex determination** is concerned, it is noticed that male gametes possess one sex-chromosome less than those of the female gametes. Thus, the genetic constitution of male may be represented as $A\ A\ X$ and that of the female as $A\ A\ X\ X$ (where, A symbolizes autosomes and X sex chromosomes). Therefore, male gametes may possess either $A\ X$ or A and female gametes possess $A\ X$ only (all ova are alike genetically). When ovum $(A\ X)$ is fertilized with male gamete having $A\ X$, a zygote with $A\ A\ X\ X$ is produced which develops into a **female** and when an ovum $(A\ X)$ is fertilized with male gamete having A, a zygote with $A\ A\ X$ is produced which develops into a **male**.

ECONOMIC IMPORTANCE

Termites are the cause of huge damage to man. Since, their main food is cellulose, hence, they injure and destroy the wood work of houses, timbers, furnitures, railway sleepers, wooden bridges, boats, telegraph poles, books, large orchard trees like mango, apple, coconut, citrus, guava, chiku and many field crops like sugarcane, groundnut, tea, coffee, cotton, potato plants, etc., are badly damaged by them.

Though termites cause a great deal of damage, they are also useful, they render service to mankind by consuming dead wood and vegetable products, they aid in agriculture by enriching the soil with their faecal matter, and by making the soil permeable to air and moisture exactly in the same way as earthworms.

In addition, they are also useful as they constitute food to several animals like birds, reptiles, rodents, etc. Natives of South East Africa consume queens of termites as a delicious dish.

Besides termites other insects also live in termite habitations, they are called **termitophilous fauna** and con t mostly of beetles. Some are treated as true guests by termites, some are indifferently tolerated guests, while others are scavengers and predators. In some cases more than one species of termites may live in the same habitation.

CONTROL OF TERMITES

The control measures of termites can be adopted as per their abode. However, following steps can be taken to control their menace :

1. In fields termitaria should be destroyed by pouring kerosene oil, carbon bisulphate, etc.

2. Nests can also be fumigated by sulphur, arsenic and kerosene oil.

3. Timbers when infected are treated by drilling holes at intervals and filling and sealing them with insecticides like sodium fluoride, calcium arsenate, etc.

4. The queen should be searched out from established colonies and killed.

5. The plantation pits should be treated by 0.2% dieldrin.

6. The orchard trees can be protected by termites by spraying 1 per cent dieldrin.

7. Crop fields should be dusted by 10 per cent BHC at the rate of 20 to 25 kg per hectare before sowing.

8. Wooden foundation, if any, should not touch the soil and, hence, should be cemented at the ground level and should be painted by some insecticides.

9. In recent days anti-termite treatment is advised to undertake at the foundation level of the buildings.

10. The affected parts of trees can be sprayed with **paris green**; trunk of trees should be banded by coal-tar or DDT from the ground level.

REVISION QUESTIONS

1. Give an account of the bionomics of termites.
2. Describe the life history of termite and give a note on its economic importance and suggest control measures.

81

Arthropoda : Characters, Classification and Types

DEFINITION

Arthropods are bilaterally symmetrical, triploblastic, metamerically segmented animals with coelom which is reduced and modified. Their body is covered externally in a chitinous exoskeleton which moults periodically and their appendages are jointed.

GENERAL CHARACTERS

1. Arthropods are triploblastic, bilaterally symmetrical, metamerically segmented animals.

2. Body is covered with a thick chitinous cuticle forming an exoskeleton.

3. Body segments usually bear paired lateral and jointed appendages.

4. Musculature is not continuous but comprises separate striped muscles.

5. Body cavity is haemocoel. The true coelom is reduced to the spaces of the genital and excretory organs.

6. Digestive tract is complete, mouth and anus lie at opposite ends of the body.

7. Circulatory system is open with dorsal heart and arteries but without capillaries.

8. Respiration through general body surface, by gills in aquatic forms, tracheae or book lungs in terrestrial forms.

9. True nephridia are absent; excretion by coelomoducts or Malpighian tubules or green or coxal glands.

10. Cilia are entirely absent from all parts of the body.

11. Sexes are generally separate and sexual dimorphism is often exhibited by several forms.

12. Fertilization is internal. Development is usually indirect through larval stages.

13. Parental care is also often well marked in many arthropods.

14. Most diversified group inhabiting the land, water and air.

CLASSIFICATION

Phylum Arthropoda and its various groups have been classified differently by different workers. But the classification of Arthropoda followed in the present text is generally based on Vandel (1949), Snodgrass (1960) and Storer (1979). Onychophora, however , was considered to be arthropod for a long time but the modern trend is to consider it as an independent group of segmented animals. Hence, this group (Onychophora) has been discussed in a separate chapter.

SUBPHYLUM I. TRILOBITOMORPHA
(Gr., *tria* = three+ lobos=lobe+ *morphe*=form)

1. Represented by fossil trilobites only.

2. Body separated by two longitudinal furrows into three lobes.

3. Except the last segment all segments bear biramous appendages.

4. All were marine forms.

5. All were bottom dwellers, *i.e.*, benthozoic and existed from Cambrian to Permian.
Examples : *Triarthrus, Dalmanites.*

SUBPHYLUM II. CHELICERATA
(Gr., *chele*=claw+*keros*=horn+*ata*=group)

1. Body divisible into cephalothorax or prosoma and abdomen or opisthosoma.

2. First pair of appendages are chelicerae which are preoral and feeding in function.

3. Second pair of appendages are pedipalpi which are postoral.

4. Antennae and true jaws not found.

5. Mostly terrestrial and predaceous.

Class 1. Merostomata

1. Exclusively aquatic, all marine.

2. Prosoma bears compound eyes placed laterally; it is broadly jointed to abdomen.
3. Five or six pairs of appendages in abdomen modified as gills or branchiae for respiration.
4. Abdomen ends in a spike-like long telson.

Subclass I. Xiphosura

1. Prosoma is convex covered by a broad horse-shoe-shaped carapace.
2. Prosoma bears six pairs of appendages.
3. Opisthosoma hexagonal consisting of six mesosomatic segments and a vestigial unsegmented metasoma with a long narrow telson.
4. Genital openings paired covered by genital operculum.
5. Respiration by lamelliform gills or book-gills attached to the abdominal appendages.
   Example : *Limulus* (King crab).

Subclass II. Eurypterida

1. Extinct (Palaeozoic) forms.
2. Large sized arthropods.
3. Cephalothorax small covered by dorsal carapace.
4. Cephalothorax followed by 12 free segments and a terminal elongated narrow telson.
5. Cephalothorax with six pairs of appendages.

Examples : *Eurypterus, Pterygotus.*

Class 2. Arachnida
(Gr., *arachne*=spider+*oid*=like)

1. Mostly terrestrial, few aquatic.
2. Prosoma bears six pairs of appendages; one pair chelicerae one pair pedipalpi and four pairs of walking legs.
3. Abdomen usually without appendages.
4. Respiratory organs either tracheae, book-lungs or book-gills.
5. Excretory organs are Malpighian tubules or coxal glands or both.
6. Sexes are separate, sexual dimorphism not conspicuous and development mostly direct.

Order 1. Scorpionida

1. Terrestrial forms found under stones in tropical and subtropical regions; true scorpions.
2. Prosoma covered dorsally by carapace and bears a pair of chelicerae, a pair of pedipalpi and four pairs of walking legs.
3. Opisthosoma divisible into mesosoma and metasoma; mesosoma is broad consisting of seven segments and metasoma is narrow consisting of five segments with a poison-sting.

4. A pair of comb-like pectines occur ventrally on the second segment of mesosoma.
5. Respiration by four pairs of book-lungs
   Examples : *Buthus, Palamnaeus.*

Order 2. Pseudoscorpionida

1. Minute false scorpions found under the bark of trees.
2. Prosoma formed of six fused segments covered dorsally by carapace.
3. Opisthosoma of ten to twelve segments.
4. Sting and telson not found.
5. A pair of spinning glands present.
6. Respiration by tracheae.
   Example: *Chelifer.*

Order 3. Palpigradi

1. Small arachnids.
2. Opisthosoma of ten segments and is jointed to the prosoma by a pedicle.
3. Telson with a long jointed flagellum.
4. Chelicerae are chelate and pedipalpi leg-like.
5. Respiration by three pairs of book-lungs.
   Example : *Koenenia.*

Order 4. Solifugae

1. Body consists of prosoma and opisthosoma.
2. Prosoma consists of three fused and last three segments.
3. Opisthosoma composed of ten segments and is not marked off from prosoma.
4. Chelicerae are large and chelate, pedipalpi are elongated and leg-like.
5. Poison glands absent.
6. Respiration by tracheae.
7. Commonly referred to as sun spiders or wind spiders.
   Example : *Galeodes.*

Order 5. Amblypygi

1. Somewhat flattened body.
2. Carapace covering the prosoma undivided.
3. Pedipalpi large and heavy, chelicerae of moderate size.
4. First pair walking legs sensory in nature.
5. Opisthosoma bears twelve segments, flagellum absent.
   Example : *Charinus.*

Order 6. Uropygi

1. Commonly referred to as whip scorpions.
2. Chelicerae two-jointed and moderate in size.
3. Pedipalpi large, heavy and usually with pincers.
4. Opisthosoma bears twelve segments, a long flagellum present in the last segment.
5. Eyes one pair.

Examples: *Thelyphonus, Mastigoproctus.*

Order 7. Araneae

1. Body consists of prosoma and opisthosoma.
2. Prosoma is unsegmented covered by cara-pace and bears six pairs of appendages.
3. Opisthosoma is usually unsegmented attached to prosoma by a narrow pedicle.
4. Chelicerae are subchelate with poison glands.
5. Pedipalps simple and six jointed.
6. Eight eyes are arranged dorsally in two rows on the carapace of prosoma.
7. Respiration either by book-lungs or book-lungs and tracheae both.
8. True spiders.

Examples : *Argiope* (Writing spider), *Aranea* (House spider) *Lycosa* (Wolf spider), *Agelena* (Funnel-web spider).

Order 8 Ricinulei

1. Body consists of prosoma and opisthosoma.
2. Prosoma with movable anterior cucullus.
3. Opisthosoma composed of nine segments and connected to prosoma by a pedicle.
4. Chelicerae and pedipalpi are chelate.
5. Respiration by tracheae.

Examples : *Cryptocellus, Ricinoides.*

Order 9. Phalangida or Opiliones

1. Spider-like in appearance.
2. Prosoma unsegmented, opisthosoma bears ten segments.
3. Pedicel absent between prosoma and opisthosoma.
4. Chelicerae chelate; pedipalpi leg-like.
5. Spinning glands not found.
6. Respiration by tracheae.

Examples : *Phalangium, Leiobunum.*

Order 10. Acarina

1. Body unsegmented in which prosoma is fused with opisthosoma.
2. Chelicerae and pedipalpi are small and associated with the mouth-parts which are adapted for biting, piercing and sucking.
3. Respiration by tracheae or by skin.
4. Free living and parasitic forms.
5. Commonly referred to as ticks and mites.

Examples : *Chorioptes* (Mite), *Sarcoptes* (Itch-mite) *Idodex* (Tick).

Class 3. Pycnogonida

1. Commonly referred to as sea spiders.
2. Very small in size.
3. Body mainly consists of cephalothorax, abdomen reduced.

4. Pedipalpi short segmented and chelicerae very small.
5. Usually eight pairs of long walking legs.
6. Mouth placed on a long proboscis.
7. Eyes simple and 4 in number.
8. Respiratory and excretory organs wanting.
9. Sexes separate (dioecious); females with a pair of ovigers for carrying eggs.

Examples : *Pycnogonum, Nymphon.*

SUBPHYLUM III. MANDIBULATA
(L., *mandibula*=mandible+*ata*=group)

1. Terrestrial and aquatic both freshwater and marine.
2. Body divisible into either **cephalothhorax** and abdomen or head, thorax and abdomen.
3. Appendages of head consist of one or two pairs of antennae, one pair of mandibles and one or two pairs of maxillae.
4. Eyes usually compound.
5. Respiration either by gills or tracheae.
6. Excretion by Malpighian tubules or green glands.
7. Sexes usually separate with sexual dimorphism.
8. Development usually involves larval stages.

Class 1. Crustacea
(L., *crusta* = a hard shell)

1. Mainly aquatic, generally marine but few freshwater and few live in moist places.
2. Generally free living but few are parasitic forms.
3. Head often fused with thorax to form cephalothorax covered dorsally by carapace.
4. Head bears a pair of compound eyes and five pairs of appendages.
5. Thorax and abdomen often with a pair of biramous appendages in each segment ; appendages modified for various purpose.
6. Respiration either by gills or general body surface.
7. Coelom greatly reduced, it is in the form of haemocoel.
8. Blood vascular system comprises a dorsal contractile heart communicating by valvular ostia with an enclosing pericardial sinus.
9. Excretory organs are modified coelomoducts which may be either maxillary glands or antennary (green) glands.
10. Sexes usually separate; sexual dimorphism is common.
11. Development includes metamorphosis with free larval stages.

Subclass I. Cephalocarida

1. Body divisible into a horse-shoe-shaped head and trunk; trunk bears 19 segments.
2. Eyes and carpace not found.
3. Head bears 2 pairs of antennae, a pair of jaws and 2 pairs of maxillae.
4. Anterior nine trunk segments bear appendages which appear triramous.
5. Monoecious forms, genital opening on the 19th segment.
6. Marine and bottom dweller forms.

    Example : *Hutchinsoniella.*

Subclass II. Branchiopoda

1. Freshwater, free-living, small-sized forms.
2. Carapace either shield-like or bivalved shell-like or even absent.
3. Thoracic appendages flattened, lobed and leaf-like provided with bristles.
4. Appendages are usually for locomotion and filter feeding; they also serve as gills.
5. Abdomen devoid of appendages but bears a pair of caudal stylets.
6. Antennules and maxillae reduced or absent.
7. Parthenogenesis is very common.
8. Larva is nauplius.

Order 1. Anostraca

1. Body elongated, carapace not developed.
2. Eyes stalked.
3. Antennae uniramous.
4. Caudal stylets unjointed.
5. Commonly called fairy shrimps.
    Examples: *Branchipus, Eubranchipus.*

Order 2. Notostraca

1. Body elongated, carapace broad shield-shaped.
2. Eyes without stalk (sessile).
3. Antennae reduced, anterior half of trunk bears 35–70 pairs of appendages.
4. Caudal stylets many-jointed.
5. Commonly called tadpole shrimps.
    Examples : *Apus, Lepidurus.*

Order 3. Diplostraca

1. Body laterally compressed.
2. Carapace usually transparent bivalved shell covering the body but not the head.
3. Eyes sessile and usually united together.
4. Antennae biramous, large and used for swimming.
5. Caudal stylets unjointed, curved, claw-like.
6. Commonly called clam-shrimps or water-fleas.
    Examples : *Daphnia, Limentis.*

Subclass III. Ostracoda

1. Small crustaceans found both in freshwater and sea.
2. Body laterally compressed not distinctly segmented.
3. Body enclosed in bivalved shell.
4. Two pairs of stout and cylindrical thoracic appendages.
5. Antennules and antennae used in swimming.
6. Mandibles are provided with palps.
7. Parthenogenesis is of common occurrence.
8. Commonly called seed-shrimps.

Order 1. Myodocopa

1. Found in sea water.
2. Carapace notched with apertures for antennae.
3. Second antennae biramous with a large basal segment.
4. Second antennae used in swimming.
    Examples : *Cypridina, Phylomedes.*

Order 2. Platycopa

1. Found in sea water.
2. Carapace not notched without apertures for antennae.
3. Second antennae uniramous.
4. Trunk appendages one pair.
5. Antennae not used in swimming.
    Example : *Cytherella.*

Order 3. Podocopa

1. Both marine and freshwater forms.
2. Carapace unnotched without apertures for antennae.
3. Second antennae uniramous, leg-like with claws at the tips.
    Examples : *Cypris, Darwinula.*

Order 4. Cladocopa

1. Found in sea water.
2. Carapace unnotched without apertures for antennae.
3. Second antennae biramous.
4. Both pairs of antennae used in swimming.
    Example : *Polycope.*

Subclass IV. Mystacocarida

1. Small-sized crustaceans with elongated body divisible into head, five-segmented thorax and six-segmented abdomen.
2. Head appendages well developed as also is the first thoracic pair (maxillipedes).
3. Abdominal appendages wanting except a pair of caudal stylets in the last segment.
4. Sexes separate.
5. Metanauplius is the earliest known larval stage.
    Example : *Derocheilocaris.*

Subclass V. Copepoda

1. Free or parasitic crustaceans found both in fresh and salt water.
2. Small bodied crustaceans ; body segmented, divisible into head, thorax and abdomen.
3. Thoracic appendages typically biramous except the first which is uniramous.
4. Abdomen without appendages but provided with a pair of caudal styles.
5. Compound eyes absent but a single median eye present.
6. Antennules and antennae are usually well developed, mandibles usually with a palp.
7. Eggs are carried in egg sac (s) by females and larva is nauplius.

Order 1. Calanoida

1. Found in freshwater lakes, ponds and also in sea water.
2. Body constricted just behind the segment bearing fifth leg.
3. Antennae biramous.
   Examples : *Calanus, Diaptomus.*

Order 2. Harpacticoida

1. Found in freshwater, salt water and brackish water.
2. Body constriction scarce between segments bearing fourth and fifth legs.
3. Antennae biramous.
   Example : *Harpacticus.*

Order 3. Cyclopoida

1. Found in freshwater lakes and ponds and also in salt water.
2. Body constriction between segments bearing fourth and fifth legs clearly apparent.
3. Antennae uniramous.
   Example : *Cyclops.*

Order 4. Monstrilloida

1. Larvae parasitic in marine polychaete worms.
2. Mouth parts and antennae not found.
   Example : *Monstrilla.*

Order 5. Caligoida

1. Ectoparasitic forms on freshwater and marine fishes.
2. Body articulation between third and fourth thoracic segments apparent in males.
3. Ectoparasites in gill-chambers of fishes.
4. Attachment to host body by antennae.
   Example: *Caligus.*

Order 6. Lernaeopodoida

1. Ectoparasitic forms on freshwater and marine fishes.

2. Body segmentation not apparent.
3. Appendages reduced or none.
4. Usually attach to the host body by second maxillae.
   Examples : *Lernaea, Salmincola.*

Subclass VI. Branchiura

1. Parasitic crustaceans living as ectoparasites on both freshwater and marine fishes.
2. Dorso-ventrally flattened body.
3. Carapace covers the cephalothorax.
4. Mouth suctorial.
5. Thoracic appendages five pairs.
6. Compound eyes present but sessile.
7. Abdomen small, unsegmented and bilobed.
8. Commonly called fish lice.
   Example : *Argulus.*

Subclass VII. Cirripedia.

1. Exclusively marine and sedentary forms.
2. Adults always fixed or may be parasitic.
3. Body segmentation poorly developed.
4. Carapace forms a pair of folds, the mantle which completely encloses the animal.
5. Compound eyes absent in adults.
6. Thoracic appendages six pairs and typically biramous.
7. Abdomen rudimentary usually having a pair of caudal styles.
8. Hermaphrodite (monoecious).
9. Commonly called barnacles.

Order 1. Thoracica

1. Non-parasitic, sedentary forms.
2. Body surrounded by calcareous shell.
3. Thoracic limbs six pairs and biramous.
4. Alimentary canal present.
   Examples : *Lepas* (Goose barnacle), *Balanus* (Acorn barnacle).

Order 2. Acrothoracica

1. Parasitic forms, bore into the shells of Mollusca and corals.
2. Body covered by large mantle.
3. Calcareous shell absent.
4. Thoracic appendages less than six pairs.
5. Alimenlary canal present.
   Examples : *Alcippe , Cryptophialus.*

Order 3. Ascothoracica

1. Parasitic forms on Anthozoa and Echinodermata.
2. Thoracic appendages six pairs.
3. Mouth appendages are modified into piercing and sucking organs.
4. Alimentary canal mostly absent.
   Examples : *Laura, Petrarca.*

Order 4. Apoda

1. Parasitic forms.
2. Body without mantle and thoracic appendages.
3. Body maggot-like.
4. Appendages and anus absent.
5. Hermaphrodite.
   Example : *Proteolepas.*

Order 5. Rhizocephala

1. Parasitic forms on decapod crustraceans.
2. Body extremely degenerated.
3. Appendages and alimentary canal absent.
4. No trace of segmentation.
5. Attachment to host by a stalk with roots which penetrate into tissues of the host.
   Example : *Sacculina.*

Subclass VIII. Malacostraca

1. Mostly large crustaceans found both in fresh and sea water.
2. Thorax comprises eight segments, while abdomen comprises six rarely seven segments.
3. Exoskeleton of head united with few or more thoracic segments to from cephalo- thoracic carapace.
4. Compound eyes are usually stalked.
5. Abdomen is devoid of caudal styles.
6. Development through zoaea stage; Nauplius stage rarely occurs.

Order 1.Nebaliacea

1. Primitive marine crustaceans.
2. Large bivalved carapace with an adductor muscle.
3. Thorax with eight pairs of leaf-like gills.
4. Abdomen contains seven segments and a telson.
5. Stalked eyes.
6. Telson with a pair of caudal style.
   Example : *Nebalia.*

Order 2. Mysidacea

1. Marine crustaceans.
2. Carapace covers almost entire thorax.
3. Eyes stalked.
4. Thoracic appendages are all biramous.
5. Uropods form broad fan-like tail fin.
   Examples : *Mysis, Hemimysis*

Order 3. Isopoda

1. Marine, freshwater, terrestrial or parasitic crustaceans.
2. Body dorso-ventrally flattened.
3. Carapace absent. Eyes sessile.
4. Abdomen is usually short.
   Examples : *Oniscus, Bopyrus.*

Order 4. Amphipoda

1. Mostly marine crustaceans.
2. Body usually laterally compressed.

3. No carapace.
4. Eyes sessile.
5. Second and third pair of thoracic appendages are nearly always modified as prehensile organs.
   Examples: *Caprella, Gammarus.*

Order 5. Stomatopoda

1. Marine forms.
2. Body elongated with broad abdomen.
3. Carapace small covering three thoracic segments.
4. Stalked eyes.
5. First five pairs of abdominal appendages are provided with gills.
6. Heart is elongated.
   Example : *Squilla.*

Order 6. Decapoda

1. Mostly marine forms.
2. Carapace covers the entire thorax.
3. Thoracic appendages are modified as three pairs of maxillipedes and five pairs of walking legs.
4. Statocyst present.

Suborder 1. Macrura

1. Abdomen well developed, elongated and extended.
2. Antennules and antennae are both large.
3. Eyes are not enclosed in orbits.
   Examples : *Palaemon, Astacus.*

Suborder 2. Anomura

1. Abdomen more or less reduced and fixed.
   Examples : *Hippa, Eupagurus.*

Suborder 3. Brachyura

1. Abdomen is greatly reduced, hard and folded beneath the body.
   Examples : *Cancer, Carcinus.*

Class 2. Chilopoda*

1. Inclu s centipedes or hundred-leggers.
2. Body flattened dorso-ventrally and elongated.
3. Body divisible into head and trunk.
4. Head bears a pair of antennae, a pair of mandibles and a pair of maxillae.
5. Each trunk segment with a pair of legs.
6. First pair of legs modified to form poison claws.
7. Carnivorous, active and predaceous.

Order 1. Scutigeromorpha

1. Legs 15 pairs and very long.
2. Much elongated antennae.
3. Spiracles unpaired, median and placed dorsally.
   Example : *Scutigera.*

Order 2. Lithobiomorpha

1. Legs 15 pairs and very short.
2. Much elongated antennae having 19–70 segments.
3. Spiracles paired and placed laterally.
   Example : *Lithobius.*

Order 3. Geophilomorpha

1. Burrowing forms having slender body.
2. Legs small, 31 to 170 pairs.
3. Spiracles paired and placed laterally.
4. Eyes absent and antennae possess 14 segments.
   Example : *Geophilus.*

Order 4. Scolopendromorpha

1. Elongated body bears 21 or 23 pairs of legs.
2. Head with or without eyes, bears 17–30 jointed antennae.
3. Spiracles paired, placed laterally but only in the anterior trunk segments
   Example : *Sclopendra.*

Class 3. Symphyla*

1. Includes garden centipedes.
2. Terrestrial but found in damp places with humus.
3. Body divisible into head and trunk.
4. Head bears one pair of antennae one pair of mandibles and two pairs of maxillae.
5. Trunk 12-segmented, bearing one pair of legs in each segment.
6. Spiracles are present in head only; eyes absent.
7. Genital apertures are situated mid-ventrally between 4th pair of legs.
   Examples : *Scutigerella, Scolopendrella.*

Class 4. Pauropoda*

1. Minute, soft-bodied arthropods found in dark damp places usually under stones, logs, fallen leaves and in soil.
2. Body divisible into head and trunk.
3. Head bears a pair of antennae, a pair of mandibles and two pairs of maxillae forming lower lip.
4. Trunk bears 11 segments and anal pygidium.
5. Nine pairs of legs in trunk segments, eyes absent.
6. Gonopores lie mid-ventrally on 3rd segment.
   Examples : *Pauropus, Decapauropus.*

Class 5. Diplopoda*

1. Includes millipedes or thousand-leggers.
2. Body cylindrical, subcylindrical, elongated and capable of being rolled up.
3. Body divisible into head, thorax and abdomen.
4. Head consists of five segments, thorax of four segments and abdomen of 20–100 segments.
5. Head possesses one pair of antennae, one pair of mandibles and one pair of maxillae.
6. Thoracic segments with one pair of legs in each, while abdominal segments bear two pairs of legs.
7. Poison claws not found.
8. Herbivorous in food habit.
9. Gonopores mid-ventrally situated on 3rd abdominal segment.

Order 1. Pselaphognatha

1. Minute, body covered with serrated bristles.
2. Trunk bears 11 or 13 segments.
3. Gnathochilarium (fused maxillae of both the sides) with a pair of palps.
4. Integument soft.
5. Stink glands absent.
   Examples : *Polyxenus, Lophoproctus.*

Order 2. Pentazonia

1. Body capable of being rolled up into a tight ball.
2. Trunk with 13–15 segments.
3. Each trunk segment with five sclerites.
4. One or two pairs of male gonopods, *i.e.,* clasping organs present.
5. Stink glands not found.
   Examples : *Glomeris, Onomeris.*

Order 3. Nematomorpha

1. Body segments 26 to 60 ; trunk segments 26 to 32.
2. Spinning glands two or three pairs.
3. Male gonopods one or two pairs on 7th segment.
4. Eyes present.
5. Commonly referred to as silk-spinning millipedes.
   Examples : *Striaria, Cleidogono.*

Order 4. Juliformia

1. Trunk with 40 or more segments, commonly called snake millipedes.

---

* These four classes, *i.e.,* Chilopoda, Symphyla, Pauropoda and Diplopoda were formerly considered together under a single class, Myriapoda.

2. Male gonopods one or two pairs on 7th segment.
3. Spinning glands not found.
4. Stink glands present on most of the trunk segments.
   Examples : *Julus, Spirobolus.*

Order 5. Colobognatha

1. Trunk with 30 to 192 flattened segments commonly called suctorial millipedes.
2. Head conical and mouth parts small.
3. Male gonopods two pairs, one pair each in segments 7th and 8th.
4. Stink glands present.
   Examples : *Polyzonium, Platydesmus.*

Order 6. Polydesmoidea

1. Trunk with 19 to 22 segments, commonly called flat-backed millipedes.
2. Male gonopods one or two pairs on 7th segments.
3. Spinning glands absent but stink glands present.
   Examples : *Polydesmus, Oxidus.*

Class 6. Insecta
(L., *insectum* = being cut into)

1. Insects are air breathing mostly terrestrial and rarely aquatic arthropods.
2. Body is divided into three distinct regions head, thorax and abdomen.
3. Head consists of six fused segments and bears a pair of compound eyes, a pair of antennae and mouth parts adapted for chewing, biting, piercing, sucking, siphoning or sponging type.
4. Thorax comprises three free segments, each bearing a pair of legs and two pairs of wings borne on the second and third segments.
5. Abdomen comprises 7–11 segments and devoid of appendages.
6. Liver is absent but salivary glands are usually present.
7. Heart is elongated, tubular and is divided into eight chambers situated in the abdomen.
8. Respiration by branched tracheae.
9. Excretion by Malphigian tubules.
10. Sexes are separate.
11. Development is sometimes direct, more usually complicated by metamorphosis.

Subclass I. Apterygota
(Gr., *a*=without *ptera*=wings)

1. Primitive wingless insects.
2. Metamorphosis is little or absent.

Order 1. Protura

1. Minute soft bodied insects.
2. Antennae and compound eyes are absent.
3. Mouth parts are biting.
4. Abdomen twelve segmented.
5. Tracheae are absent.
6. Metamorphosis little.
   Example : *Acerentomon.*

Order 2. Thysanura

1. Small primitive insects.
2. Body is elongated, flatttened and naked or scaly.
3. Mouth parts biting; antennae long and well developed.
4. Abdomen eleven segmented.
5. A pair of cerci many segmented and a median caudal filament long.
6. Primitive metamorphosis.
   Example : *Lepisma* (Silver fish)

Order 3. Aptera

1. Small, white or pale blind insects.
2. Body flattened.
3. Mouth parts biting.
4. Antennae long, many segmented.
5. Caudal filament absent.
6. Metamorphosis absent.
   Example : *Campodea.*

Order 4. Collembola

1. Minute insects; body naked or covered with hair or scales.
2. Antennae four to six segmented.
3. Eyes absent.
4. Mouth parts biting.
5. Abdomen six segmented and usually with a ventral tube, tenaculum and spring.
6. Metamorphosis absent.
   Examples : Spring tails, Snow flies.

Subclass II. Pterygota
(Gr., *ptera*=wings)

1. Wings are usually present.
2. Abdomen devoid of appendages except genitalia and cerci.
3. Metamorphosis simple or complex.

Division I. Exopterygota

1. Metamorphosis primitive or simple.
2. Young stages are nymphs.
3. Wings develop externally.

Order 5. Orthoptera

1. Medium sized to large insects.
2. Usually with a pair of narrow leathery forewings or tegmina and a pair of well developed membranous hind wings.
3. Mouth parts strong biting and chewing.

4. Compound eyes and usually two or three ocelli.
5. Short or long, simple or segmented cerci.
6. Simple metamorphosis.
   Examples : Locusts, Grasshoppers Crickets, etc.

Order 6. Grylloblattodea

1. Small thysanuriform insects.
2. Wings absent, mouth parts biting type.
3. Antennae filiform, many segmented.
4. Compound eyes are small, ocelli absent.
5. Simple metamorphosis.
   Example : *Grylloblatta.*

Order 7. Blattaria

1. Medium to large sized insects
2. Wings present or absent.
3. Antennae long, many segmented and filiform.
4. Mouth parts biting and chewing type.
5. Cerci prominent and segmented.
6. Metamorphosis simple.
   Examples : *Periplaneta, Blatta.*

Order 8. Phasmida

1. Large leaf or stick-like insects.
2. Antennae usually long, filiform and may segmented.
3. Compound eyes are small, ocelli two or three or absent.
4. Mouth parts biting type.
5. Wings present or absent.
6. Cerci small and segmented.
   Examples : *Phyllium, Carausius* (Stick insect).

Order 9. Mantodea

1. Medium to large insects.
2. Head small, triangular and bears large compound eyes with three or more ocelli.
3. Mouth parts biting type.
4. Prothorax greatly elongated.
5. Fore-legs modified for capturing and holding the prey.
6. Wings large, small or absent. Metamorphosis is simple.
   Example : *Mantis* (Praying mantis).

Order 10. Dermaptera

1. Small to medium sized insects.
2. Body is elongated with smooth or tough or chitinous covering.
3. Mouth parts biting type.
4. Abdomen is provided with forcep-like cerci at the posterior end.
5. Simple metamorphosis.
   Example : *Forficula.*

Order 11. Diploglossata

1. Very small insects.
2. Body depressed covered with short hairs.
3. Mouth parts biting type.
4. Eyes and wings absent.
5. A pair of unsegmented cerci present.
6. Simple metamorphosis.
   Example : *Hemimerus.*

Order 12. Plecoptera

1. Meidum to large sized, elongated somewhat flattened and soft bodied insects.
2. Head broad and bears a pair of long filiform 25 to 100 segmented antennae.
3. Compound eyes are moderate in size with two or three or no ocelli.
4. Mouth parts biting type.
5. Two pairs of equal many veined wings, hind pair with large anal area.
6. Abdomen eleven segmented, last segment reduced and bears long filiform multisegmented cerci.
7. Simple or hemimetabolous metamorphosis.
8. Larvae are known as naiads which are aquatic.
   Examples : Stone flies, Salmon flies.

Order 13. Isoptera

1. Social and polymorphic insects living in colonies under a caste system.
2. Small to medium sized mostly soft bodied and pale coloured insects.
3. Head small to very large, bears moniliform short or long many segmented antennae.
4. Mouth parts biting and chewing type.
5. Compound eyes vestigial with two or no ocelli.
6. Wings when present, two pairs, similar in size, shape and venation.
7. Cerci short and simple or 2–8 segmented.
8. Metamorphosis simple.
9. A colony contains both winged and wingless sexual individuals and wingless sterile workers and soldiers.
   Examples : Termites, White ants.

Order 14. Zoraptera

1. Minute winged or wingless insects.
2. Antennae moniliform, nine segmented.
3. Compound eyes and ocelli are present in winged forms, absent in wingless forms.
4. Mouth parts biting type.
5. Cerci short and unsegmented.
6. Metamorphosis simple.
   Example : *Zorotypus.*

Order 15. Embioptera

1. Small slender insects with somewhat flattened body.
2. Head large bears filiform antennae.
3. Compound eyes small in female, often large in male, ocelli absent.
4. Mouth parts biting chewing type.
5. Thorax nearly as long as abdomen.
6. First tarsal segment of fore-legs enlarged to contain glands and spinnerets.
7. Wings when present two pairs, membranous, similar in size and venation.
8. Metamorphosis simple or hemimetabolous.

   Example : *Oligotoma.*

Order 16. Corrodentia

1. Small compact winged or wingless insects.
2. Head large and free, bears short or long filiform antennae.
3. Compound eyes are usually large or without ocelli.
4. Mouth parts modified biting type.
5. Cerci absent.
6. Metamorphosis simple.

   Examples : Book lice, Bark lice, Dust lice.

Order 17. Mallophaga

1. Small wingless ectoparasitic insects.
2. Body is broad or elongated, flattened dorsally, tough and well chitinised.
3. Head hypognathus without setiform or clavate antennae.
4. Compound eyes are reduced, ocelli absent.
5. Mouth parts biting type.
6. Legs short with stout claws specialized for clasping hairs and feathers.
7. Cerci absent.

   Example : Bird lice.

Order 18. Anoplura

1. Minute to small sized, permanently ectoparasitic on mammals.
2. Body is flattened, elongated without wings.
3. Head small with short 3–5 segmented, setiform antenne.
4. Compound eyes reduced or absent, ocelli absent.
5. Mouth parts piercing and sucking type.
6. Legs short with single claw specialized for grasping hairs.
7. Cerci absent.

   Example : *Pediculus* (Human louse).

Order 19. Ephemerida

1. Small to medium sized, soft bodied delicate slender insects.
2. Antennae short setiform.
3. Mouth parts vestigial.
4. Well developed compound eyes and three ocelli present.
5. One or two pairs of fragile many veined wings.
6. Cerci are very long, filiform and multisegmented with a similar median caudal filament.
7. Metamorphosis simple or hemimetabolous.
8. Naiad (nymphs) are aquatic with abdominal tracheal gills.

   Example : *Ephemera* (May fly).

Order 20. Odonata

1. Medium sized to large, slender, swift flying predaceous insects.
2. Head mobile, bears large compound eyes and ocelli.
3. Mouth parts biting type.
4. Two pairs of similar long narrow net-veined wings.
5. Naiads (nymphs) are aquatic with or without exterior gils.
6. Metamorphosis simple or hemimetabolous.

   Examples : Dragon flies, Demsel flies.

Order 21. Thysanoptera

1. Minute, slender, terrestrial insects.
2. Body somewhat compressed dorsally or almost cylindrical.
3. Antennae short six to nine segmented.
4. Compound eyes with three ocelli present.
5. Mouth parts modified for piercing, chafing and sucking.
6. Wings when present two pairs of long and narrow with few veins.
7. Abdomen 10–11 segmented with an ovipositor.
8. Simple metamorphosis.

   Example : *Thrips.*

Order 22. Hemiptera

1. Minute to large, oval or elongated and dorso-ventrally flattened terrestrial or aquatic insects.
2. Antennae 2 to 10 or rarely 25 segmented.
3. Eyes large with or without ocelli.
4. Mouth parts piercing and sucking type.
5. Wings when present two pairs, fore pair usually thickened basally and membranous apically in Heteroptera and wholly membranous in Homoptera.
6. Cerci absent.
7. Anal respiratory filaments present in some aquatic forms and anal filaments in male coccids.
8. Metamorphosis simple.

9. Mostly phytophagous, some are predaceous.

   Examples : *Belostoma,* Aphids Cicadas, Scale insects.

Division II. Endopterygota

1. Metamorphosis is complex (complete).
2. Young stages are known as larvae.
3. Wings develop internally.

Order 23. Megaloptera

1. Medium to large sized insects.
2. Head prognathus, bears many segmented slender antennae.
3. Mouth parts biting type.
4. Wings two pairs, similar in shape, size and venation.
5. Cerci absent.
6. Metamorphosis complex including aquatic larvae.

   Examples : *Sialis, Corydalus.*

Order 24. Neuroptera

1. Minute to medium sized, mostly terrestrial insects.
2. Head hypognathus, bears large and widely separated compound eyes.
3. Antennae usually filiform.
4. Mouth parts biting type.
5. Wings two pairs, similar in shape, size and venation.
6. Cerci absent.
7. Complex metamorphosis, carnivorous.

   Example : *Chrysopa.*

Order 25. Raphidiodea

1. Small to medium sized, elongated, fragile terrestrial insects.
2. Antennae setiform, many segmented.
3. Compound eyes prominent with three or none ocelli.
4. Mouth parts biting type.
5. Two pairs of similar wings.
6. Female with long slender ovipositor.
7. Metamorphosis is complex.

   Examples : Snake flies, Serpent flies.

Order 26. Mecoptera

1. Small to medium sized, slender, predaceous insects.
2. Head usually elongaged and vertical.
3. Antennae long, filiform and many segmented.
4. Compound eyes are large and widely separated, ocelli three or none.
5. Mouth parts biting type.
6. Wings two pairs, similar in shape, size and venation.
7. Cerci short, simple or two segmented.

8. Metamorphosis complex.

   Example : *Panorpa* (Scorpion flies).

Order 27. Trichoptera

1. Small to medium sized, diurnal and nocturnal moth-like insects.
2. Antennal long, filiform and many segmented.
3. Compound eyes are well developed with three or none ocelli.
4. Mouth parts biting type.
5. Wings two pairs, covered with hairs and scales.
6. Cerci one or two segmented.
7. Metamorphosis complex or holometabolic.
8. Larva aquatic.

   Example : *Philopotamus* (Caddis fly).

Order 28. Lepidoptera

1. Medium to large sized flying terrestrial insects.
2. Body and wings are completely covered by flat overlapping, scales and hairs.
3. Antennae variable often clavate or serrate, hooked or knobbed or plumose.
4. Compound eyes large with two or no ocelli.
5. Mouth parts siphoning type with long coiled proboscis.
6. Wings two pairs, fore pair often largest.
7. Metamorphosis complex.
8. Larvae caterpillars with three pairs of thorcic legs and two to four pairs of abdominal prolegs.

   Examples : Butterflies, Moths.

Order 29. Coleoptera

1. Minute to large insects with leathery integument.
2. Antennae variable in shape and size, usually 11 segmented.
3. Eyes conspicuous but cecelli absent.
4. Mouth parts biting and chewing type.
5. Wings two pairs, fore wings or elytra similar to body texture and useless in flight.
6. Abdomen usually 10 segmented.
7. Cerci absent.
8. Metamorphosis complex.

   Examples : Beetles, Weevils.

Order 30. Strepsiptera

1. Minute free living and endoparasitic dimorphic insects.
2. Antennae short flabellate.
3. Eyes conspicuous but ocelli absent.
4. Mouth parts atrophied biting type.
5. Fore-wings small white, hind wings large fan-shaped.

6. Metamorphosis complex and hypermeta-
   morphosis.
   Example : *Stylops*.

Order 31. Hymenoptera

1. Minute to large sized, social or parasitic
   insects
2. Antennae 12 segmented in male and 13 segmented in female.
3. Ocelli generally present.
4. Mouth parts sepcialized for biting, chewing
   lapping and sucking.
5. Wings two pairs, membranous and narrow.
6. Abdomen always with basal pedicel.
7. Female with conspicuous ovipositor
   modified into saw, drill or sting.
8. Metamorphosis complex.
   Examples : Wasps Bees Ants.

Order 32. Diptera

1. Minute to medium sized, diurnal, nocturnal,
   terrestrial and aquatic insects.
2. Body slender with fragile integument.
3. Antennae variable, simple or with arista.

4. Eyes large and separate with three ocelli.
5. Mouth parts modified for sucking, lapping
   piercing and sponging.
6. Fore wings developed for flight, while hind
   wings reduced to halteres.
7. Metamorphosis complex.
8. Larvae limbless and vermiform known as
   maggots.

   Examples : Houseflies, Mosquitoes,
                  Midges.

Order 33. Siphonoptera

1. Minute to small sized insects ectoparasitic
   on birds and mammals.
2. Body laterally compressed.
3. Head small with or without eyes and ocelli.
4. Antennae short and capitate.
5. Mouth parts piercing and sucking type.
6. Cerci absent.
7. Metamorphosis complex.
   Example : Fleas.

REPRESENTATIVE TYPES OF ARTHROPODA

1. *Limulus*. *Limulus* (Fig. 81.1) is commonly known as king crab. Body consists of anterior
prosoma and a posterior opisthosoma. Prosoma is convex above with sloping sides and bears three
longitudinal ridges, one median and two lateral. A pair of simple median eyes and pair of lateral
compound eyes are placed on the dorsal surface of prosoma. Prosoma bears six pairs of appendages
grouped round the mouth, the first pair of chelate chelicerae, four pairs of chelate legs and a last pair
of non-chelate legs. Opisthosoma is hexagonal, movably articulated with prosoma and consists of
six mesosomal segments and unsegmented metasoma with long telson or caudal spines. Opisthosoma bears six pairs of appendages, first pair forms genital operculum, the remaining five pairs
carry book lungs. Respiration by book gills. Excretion by coxal or brick red glands. Larva is
trilobite. *Limulus* is a marine form found burrowing in the sand.

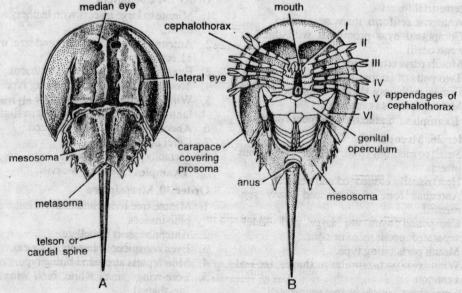

Fig. 81.1. *Limulus* (King crab) A—Dorsal view ; B—Ventral view.

2. *Spiders.* Spiders (Fig. 81.2) are the most successful Arachnida and about 35,000 species are known. Spiders have two characteristic adaptations, first they produce silk for a variety of uses and second the pedipalpi of males are modified to form copulatory organs. Body is divided into two regions, a prosoma and an opisthosoma, the two are joined by a narrow waist or pedicel, the body and limbs are thickly covered with chitinous hairs which are probably tactile. Prosoma is covered dorsally by a carapace formed by fused terga of 6 segments and ventrally by a sternum. Mid-dorsally the carapace has 4 pairs of simple eyes, the region of carapace in front of the eyes is a clypeus, posteriorly the carapace has a series of depressions. In front of the sternum is a labium, the upper lip is called a rostrum, between the lips is a small mouth. Prosoma bears 6 pairs of appendages, a pair of 2- jointed chelicerae lying in front and above the mouth, each consists of a large basal segment, the paturon which contains a poison gland and a fang-like distal segment, the unguis at whose tip the duct of the poison gland opens. There is a pair of 6 jointed pedipalpi which are non-chelate and their basal joint forms a gnathobase ; the joints are coxa, trochanter, femur, patella, tibia and tarsus. The pedipalp of a male spider is modified to form an intromittent organ lying in the tarsus and consisting of a bulb having seminal vesicle and a spirally-twisted tube through which spermatozoa are transferred to the female during copulation. There are 4 pairs of 7-jointed legs, the joints are coxa, trochanter, femur, patella, tibia, metatarsus and tarsus; the tarsus usually has 2 claws. Opisthosoma is soft and usually unsegmented but is made of 13 segments. The first or pre-genital segment forms the pedicel, its tergum is called lorum and sternum, the plagula. The second segment has the first pair of lung books, it also has a single genital aperture. The third segment bears either a second pair of lung books or a pair of spiracles. Fourth segment has an anterior pair of spinnerets and the fifth segment has one or two pairs of spinnerets, over the spinnerets is often a special cover called cribellum. The remaining opisthosomatic segments are limbless, they are fused together to form a small anal tubercle at the end of which opens an anus.

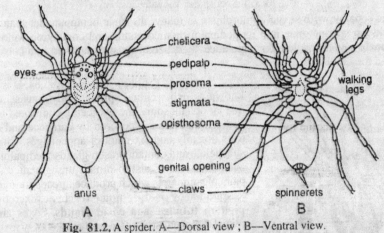

Fig. 81.2. A spider. A—Dorsal view ; B—Ventral view.

The base of each spinneret is firm but the tip is membranous having hairs and barbs; these form a spinning field. Spider have either 2 pairs or 3 pairs of spinnerets which form a spinning apparatus or arachnidium. Inside the opisthosoma are spinning or silk glands from which fine tubes open on the surface of the spinning field of the spinnerets; the secretion of glands issues through the tubes and forms silk threads. The silk is used for lining the burrows or nests or it is used for making a cocoon for the eggs or for wrapping the captured prey, or it is formed into a safety line by which the spider can hang in mid air, or in some spiders it is used for spinning a web for snaring the prey. In some spiders there are special curved spines called calamistrum on the tarsus of hind legs which are used in conjunction with spinnerets for weaving the silk into a web.

Respiratory organs consist of lung book and tracheae, their number varies in different groups of spiders, both have external openings or spiracles. In most spiders there is a pair of lung books and a pair of spiracles leading into straight, unbranched tracheae. Some spiders have two pairs of lung books, while others have only two pairs of spiracles with tracheae. Thus, spiders show all stages of replacement of lung books by tracheae.

Spiders are carnivorous feeding on insects, but some on larger animals also. The prey is killed by the poison in chelicerae, proteolytic enzymes are produced by salivary glands of lips which cause partial external digestion, liquid food is strained by bristles and sucked in by pulsations of the stomach, the chitinous remains of the prey are discarded as empty husk. The mid-gut has several **diverticula**, a main diverticulum in opisthosoma, and one pair in prosoma which send a branch into each leg. Food is stored and digestion is completed in the diverticula.

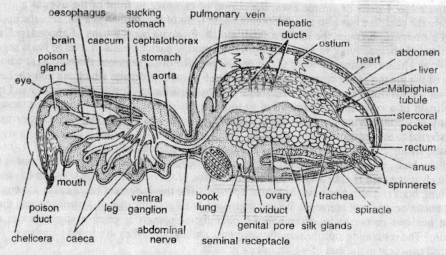

Fig. 81.3. V.S. of spider showing anatomy.

Sexes are separate with sexual dimorphism in many, the male being smaller than the female. The male sucks up spermatozoa into its pedipalpi then courtship and copulation follow. In some spiders the female eats the male after copulation. Fertilized eggs are enclosed in a cocoon spun by spinnerets.

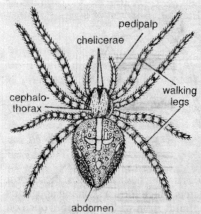

Fig. 81.4. *Aranea* (Spider).

3. *Aranea* (Spider). *Aranea* (Fig. 81.4) is commonly known as **orb webbed spider**. Body consists of prosoma and an opisthosoma, the two being connected by a narrow pedicel. **Prosoma** is covered by carapace and bears eight eyes dorsally and six pairs of appendages. Chelicerae are subchelate and contain poison glands. Pedipalpi are simple and six jointed. **Opisthosoma** is unsegmented, bears three pairs of spinnerets which produce threads for making webs. Respiration by **book-lung** and **tracheae.** Excretion by **Malpighian tubules** and **coxal glands.** Sexes are separate, sexual dimorphism is often well marked. Carnivorous. *Aranea* is found in houses and gardens.

4. **Mites.** Mites surpass all other arachnids in numbers, they are minute microscopic Acarina. The free-living mites feed on animal and vegetable matter, they are found on the ground, under dead leaves or bark and on plants on which some species form galls. Many mites are terrestrial and some are aquatic but they have no gills. About 50 per cent of mites are parasitic, they infect almost all kinds of animals, they are mostly ectoparasites of man and animals, though a few are endoparasites, *e.g., Pneumonyssus* in lungs of monkeys.

In mites the prosoma and opisthosoma are unsegmented having no division, they are so joined as to form a single ovoid body, though in some it may be elongate. The body is covered with tactile hairs or scales. Eyes may be present or absent. There are 6 pairs of appendages, chelicerae are chelate or modified for piercing and sucking, pedipalpi are leg-like with 5 joints or less, their basal joint may form a plate called **mascilla** or may unite to form a **labium.** Accessory mouth parts are often present as a **hypostome** or under lip and an **epistome** or upper lip, the lips may unite to form a **rostrum** enclosing protruding chelicerae. The chelicerae open an incision and the hypostome penetrates and liquids are sucked in. There are generally four pairs of legs. Respiratory organs are absent or there are tracheae. Sexes are separate, the young hatches as a **larva** with three pairs of legs, it feeds and rests, then moults to form a **nymph** with four pairs of legs, there may be up to three nymphal stages the final moulting produces an adult. Some common mites are described. *Eriophyes* is a gall mite it kills buds, causes leaf curl and makes large abnormal galls on twigs. *Demodex* is a follicle mite, it has an elongated body, it lives in sebaceous glands and hair follicles of man and animals and causes dermatitis.

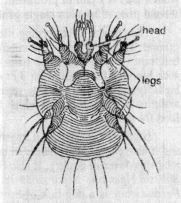

Fig. 81.5. *Sarcoptes scabiei.*

5. Sarcoptes. *Sarcoptes* (Fig. 81.5) is minute in size and microscopic. Body is oval or rounded and dorso-ventrally flattened having transverse striations and few short bristles. Mouth parts are situated anteriorly and provided with chelate chelicerae. Four pairs of legs. Anterior two legs are stronger and project beyond the body and provided with terminal stalked suckers. Posterior two legs are shorter and attached more ventrally and carry long bristles. Prosoma and opisthosoma are not distinguishable. *Sarcoptes scabiei* is an unpleasant dangerous ectoparasite which attacks man causing **scabies** which produce severe irritation that may lead to **eczema.** The parasite bores down and lives below the skin especially in soft regions.

Ticks. Ticks are large mites with leathery skin, all of them feed on vertebrate blood, they have several distensible diverticula of the gut which are filled up with blood. Their saliva contains an **anticoagulin,** as in leeches, which prevents coagulation of blood. Ticks are of two types, soft-bodied ticks without a scutum but a ventral capitulum (Argasidae) and hard-bodied ticks with dorsal shield or scutum and dorsal capitulum (Ixodidae). The scutum nearly covers the entire dorsal surface in males, but in females it is much smaller. They have a movable capitulum having a **rostrum** enclosing toothed chelicerae and toothed hypostome, pedipalpi are 3 or 4-jointed. There are 4 pairs of prominent, slender 6-jointed legs with two claws and a pad or pulvillus. They are parasites of mammals, birds and reptiles.

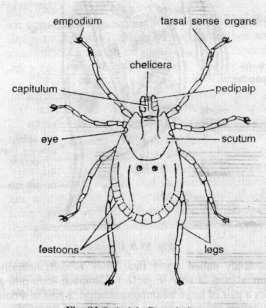

Fig. 81.6. A tick. Dorsal view.

6. Ixodes (Sheep tick). It is brown in colour and 4 mm long. There is no division into prosoma and opisthosoma. Anteriorly is an oval, movable false head or **capitulum** behind which is a body covered with leathery skin with no sign of segmentation. Capitulum has two sensory pitted areas dorsally in the female only, there are no eyes. The sternal region of capitulum is elongated in front to form a **hypostome** having many recurved hooks and a mid-dorsal groove. On each side of the hypostome is a two-jointed **chelicera** toothed at the tip. A pair of 4-jointed pedipalpi have their basal joints united to form a sheath which encloses the chelicerae and hypostome, thus, forming a blood-sucking apparatus. There are four pairs of slender legs, the legs are 7-jointed ending in two claws and sucker-like **pulvillus**. The tarsus of first pair of legs has a sensory cup-shaped **Haller's organ**. The body behind the capitulum is covered by a dorsal, chitinous **scutum** or dorsal shield, completely in the male, but only in the anterior half in the female, because of this the body of the female can be distended greatly on feeding. At the posterior ventral side is an anus. Behind the fourth pair of legs is a pair of prominent spiracles leading into convoluted tracheae. Between the first and second pairs of legs is a single genital aperture.

The female, after gorging itself with blood of sheep, copulates with a male, then drops to the ground. The male feeds after copulation. After weeks the female lays eggs near roots of grass, eggs hatch into larvae with three pairs of legs. Larvae climb upon grass and cling to any vertebrate and suck blood. After feeding for 3 or 4 days they fall off and moult to become nymphs with 4 pairs of legs. Nymphs climb up a new vertebrate host and suck blood for 5 days, then they fall to the ground and moult to become adult which find a new host. The larvae, nymphs, and adults can live without food for months.

Ixodes is a sheep tick, it transmits a virus which causes tick fever in sheep and domestic animals and it also causes encephalitis in man. *Argas* is a poultry tick, it carries a spirochaete which causes relapsing fever in poultry. It also bites man. *Margaropus* or *Boophilus* is a cattle tick, it inoculates *Babesia bigemina,* a sporozoan, into the blood which causes Texas fever in cattle which proves fatal. *Dermacentor* is a dog tick of brown colour, parasitic on domestic animals and man, it causes a dangerous tularemia and relapsing fever. *Ornithodorus* transmits a spirochaete *Rickettsia* which causes dangerous relapsing fever in man.

7. *Apus.* Apus (Fig. 81.7) is commonly known as tadpole fish. Body is elongated measuring about 20–30 mm in length. Anterior two-third of the dorsal surface is covered by a horse-shoe-shaped carapace. Head is broad and depressed and bears paired eyes, a median eye and a dorsal organ above and antennules and antennae below. Shell glands are present on the lateral surface of carapace. Anal segment bears a pair of caudal styles. Reproduction by parthenogenesis. Apus is found in freshwater in most part of the world.

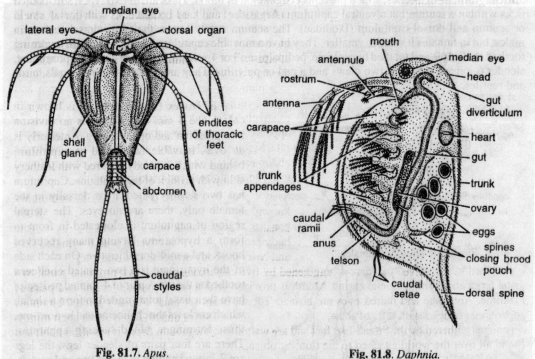

Fig. 81.7. *Apus.*   Fig. 81.8. *Daphnia.*

8. *Daphnia. Daphnia* (Fig. 81.8) is commonly called water flea. Body is soft, laterally compressed measuring 1–2 mm in length. Segmentation is very imperfect. Carapace ends into a pointed dorsal spine. Head is rounded and bears a pair of large biramous antennae, a pair of small antennules and a compound sessile eye. Large biramous antennae are the chief organs of locomotion.

Thorax bears usually five pairs of leaf-like appendages. Abdomen is devoid of appendages. Sexes are separate. Female carries eggs and embryos in a large brood pouch situated between abdomen and posterior part of the carapace. *Daphnia* is found in freshwater ponds, streams and ditches.

9. *Cypris*. Body is unsegmented and laterally compressed. The body is completely enclosed in a bivalved carapace. At the anterior end is a median eye. Compound eye and heart are absent. There are only seven pairs of appendages, *i.e.*, antennules, antennae, mandibles, first maxilla, second maxilla and two pairs of thoracic appendages. Antennules and antennae are large biramous and help in swimming. Abdomen is devoid of appendages and is terminated by a pair of small caudal

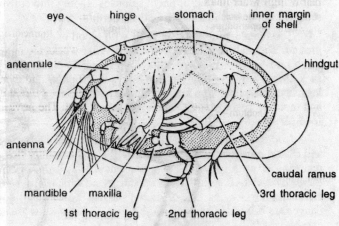

Fig. 81.9. *Cypris.*

styles. Development by parthenogenesis. *Cypris* is free swimming and occurs in freshwater stagnant ponds.

10. *Cyclops*. Body is elongated or pear-shaped measuring 1.5 to 5 mm in length. First thoracic segment is fused with the head forming the cephalothorax which is covered dorsally by carapace. Single median eye is present on the dorsal surface of the carapace. Five pairs of thoracic segments, last segment bears the genital aperture. Four abdominal segments, last segment bears, the anus dorsally and a pair of caudal styles produced into plummed setae. Antennules are very large and serve as principal organs of locomotion. Antennae are relatively short and uniramous. Abdomen is devoid of appendages except the caudal styles. Sexes are separate. Mature females carry two egg-sacs attached to the abdomen. *Cyclops* is a free swimming copepod found everywhere in fresh and brakish water.

11. *Lepas*. *Lepas* (Fig. 81.11) is commonly known as goose barnacle or ship barnacle. Body consists of a long stalk or pedicel and capitulum (the body proper). Pedicel is covered with a wrinkled skin and bears the body proper at its distal end. Capitulum

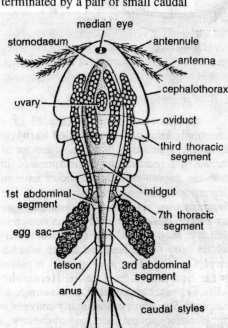

Fig. 81.10. *Cyclops* (Female).

is enclosed in a bivalved carapace strengthened by five calcareous plates, two proximal scuta, two distal terga and a single dorsal carina. Mouth is provided with a pair of mandibles and two pairs of maxillae. Antennae and paired eyes are absent. Thorax bears six pairs of many jointed biramous appendages fringed with tufts of setae. Hermaphrodite, *i.e.*, sexes united. *Lepas* feeds upon minute organisms gathered by the thread-like feet and are wafted into the mouth. *Lepas* is sessile in habit and found all over the world attached to the floating objects.

12. *Balanus*. *Balanus* (Fig. 81.12) is commonly known as rock barnacle or acorn barnacle. Peduncle is absent so the shell is directly attached to the rocks. Body is surrounded by a calcareous shell comprising of six plates, an unpaired carina, an unpaired rostrum and two pairs of lateral plates. The opening of the shell is provided with a four fold cover consisting of two scuta and two

terga. Six pairs of thoracic legs are protruded out through the opening of shell and sweep in food particles. Hermaphrodite, *i.e.*, sexes united. Larva is nauplius. *Balanus* is found attached to rocks below high water mark.

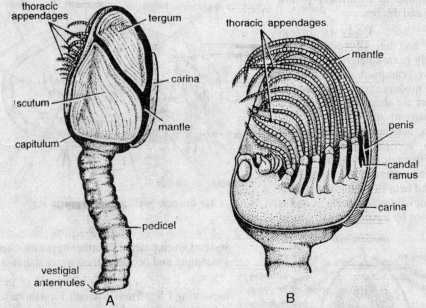

Fig. 81.11. *Lepas.* A—Entire animal; B—Carapace removed.

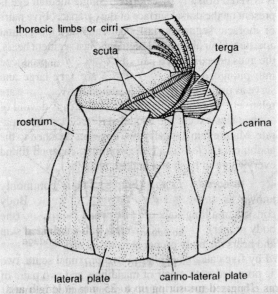

Fig. 81.12. *Balanus.*

13. *Sacculina. Sacculina* (Fig. 81.13) is commonly known as root headed barnacle. It has the appearance of a fleshy tumour attached by a peduncle to the abdomen of the crab on its ventral side. It shows extreme degeneration due to parasitic mode of life. Segmentation, appendages, mouth and anus are entirely absent. Peduncle sends numerous delicate root-like filaments which ramify within body of the host and absorb nourishment. Opening of the mantle cavity is placed at the hind end of the parasite. Hermaphrodite, *i.e.*, sexes are united. Larva is cirripede-nauplius. *Sacculina* causes many changes in the secondary sexual characters of the host, a phenomenon known as parasitic castration. *Sacculina* is found as parasite on crabs.

14. *Mysis. Mysis* (Fig. 81.14) is a small transparent shrimp-like form. Body is bilaterally compressed and elongated measuring from 2–6 mm in length. Carapace covers the entire thorax except the last two segments. Head bears antennules, antennae and a pair of stalked eyes. First pair of thoracic appendages are modified as maxillipedes and the rest are biramous serving as swimming organs. Brood pouch is attached to the posterior thoracic segments. Development takes place within the brood pouch, so there is no larval stage. *Mysis* is a marine pelagic form. It is generally confined to the surface of water.

15. *Oniscus. Oniscus* (Fig. 81.15) is commonly known as wood louse or sow bug. Body is broad, oval and dorso-ventrally flattened. Head is fused with the first segment of the thorax forming the cephalothorax which is not covered dorsally by carapace. Eyes are sessile and compound. Antennules and antennae are uniramous. It feeds upon decaying vegetation. *Oniscus* is a terrestrial crustacean found under stones logs and bark, etc.

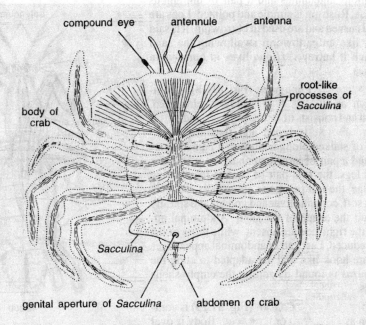

Fig. 81.13. *Sacculina* parasitizing a crab.

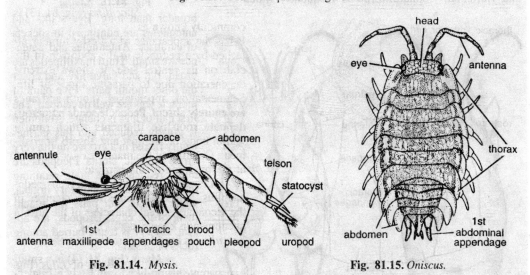

Fig. 81.14. *Mysis.*   **Fig. 81.15.** *Oniscus.*

16. Squilla. Body of *Squilla* (Fig. 81.16)is elongated measuring up to 25 mm in length and divisible into head, thorax and broad abdomen. Carapace is thin and uncalcified which leaves the last three segments uncovered. Rostrum covers the anterior head region which is divided into two distinct segments, the first bearing the stalked eyes and the second the antennules. First five pairs of thoracic appendages are turned forwards and act as maxillipedes of which the second pair is exceptionally large and sub-chelate. Remaining three thoracic appendages are slender legs. Pleopods are large and biramous, first five bear gills, the sixth forms large uropod. *Squilla* is active and predatory, it catches hold of the prey with the powerful maxillipedes. It is found in burrows in the sand or mud at the bottom of the sea.

17. *Hippa.* *Hippa* or *Emerita* (Fig. 81.17) is commonly known as **mole crab.** Body is ovate with large cephalothorax. Carapace is smooth and mouth parts are poorly developed. Head bears eyes, a pair of biramous antennules and a pair of uniramous large antennae. Rostrum is simple and pointed. Legs are flattened and curved and are used in burrowing. It is said that it feeds like an earthworm swallowing the sand through which it burrows. *Hippa* lives in burrows in sand in the sea.

18. *Eupagurus.* *Eupagurus* (Fig. 81.18) is commonly known as hermit crab. Body is elongated, asymmetrical and consists of cephalothorax and abdomen. Cephalothorax is broad and flattened. Head bears a pair of stalked elongated eyes, a pair of short antennules and a pair of large antennae. Thorax bears five pairs of legs, the first pair of chelate legs having unequal chelae, the last two pairs are usually reduced. Abdomen is soft, contains liver and gonads and spirally twisted to suit the shape of the shell. Abdominal appendages of the right side are absent, while those of the left side are reduced. Last pair of abdominal appendages or uropods are hook-like and are adapted to cling the shell. *Eupagurus* is found inhabiting the empty shells of gastropods.

19. *Cancer* (Crab) . *Cancer* (Fig. 81.19) is commonly known as rock crab or true crab. Body is oval and flattened. Cephalothorax is frequently much

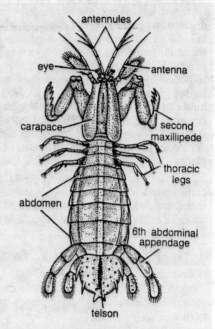

Fig. **81.16.** *Squilla.*

broader than long. Eye stalks and antennules are continued in sockets of carapace. Antennules and antennae are small. Third maxillipedes are broad, flat and valve-like and cover the other mouth parts. Five pairs of thoracic legs are well developed. The first pair of legs is chelate. Abdomen is greatly reduced and lies permanently flexed in a groove on the very broad thoracic sterna. Pleopods are much reduced, the male retaining only two pairs as copulatory organs, while female four pairs for attachment of the eggs. Uropods are absent. *Cancer* is found buried among rocks or in sand.

20. *Julus.* Body of *Julus* (Fig. 81.20) is elongated and cylindrical consisting of large number of segments. Head bears a pair of short seven jointed antennae, a pair of mandibles and a pair of maxillae forming gnathochilarium. Each trunk segment, except the first four

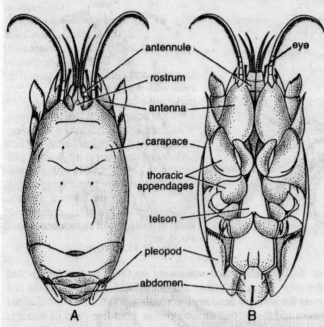

Fig. **81.17.** *Hippa.* A—Dorsal view; B—Ventral view.

and last segment, bears two pairs of legs. Poison jaws are absent. Stink glands present along the sides of the body. Genital opening on the third segment behind the head. Sexes are separate. *Julus* is found hidden usually in dark and damp places under stones or wood or in decaying leaves.

21. *Scolopendra.* Body of *Scolopendra* (Fig. 81.21) is elongated and dorso-ventrally flattened with numerous segments. Head is distinct and bears a pair of antennae, a pair of mandibles and two pairs of maxillae. Trunk segments numerous, each bearing a single pair of legs. First pair of trunk appendages or max-illipedes bears a sharp claw connected with the poison gland. Genital opening is situated at the hind end of the body. Sexes are separate. Car-nivorous, feeding on insects, spiders, worms, slugs, etc. *Scolopendra* commonly occurs un-der stones in rotten logs and in houses in damp places.

22. *Lepisma.* *Lepisma* (Fig. 81.22) is commonly known as silver fish. Body is flat-tened covered with silvery scales. Head bears a pair of many segmented antennae and a pair of ocelli. Mouth parts are biting and chewing type. Thorax bears three pairs of legs but devoid of wings. Abdomen eleven segmented with a pair of long many jointed cerci and a median caudal filament. *Lepisma* is com-monly found in damp cool places and in books.

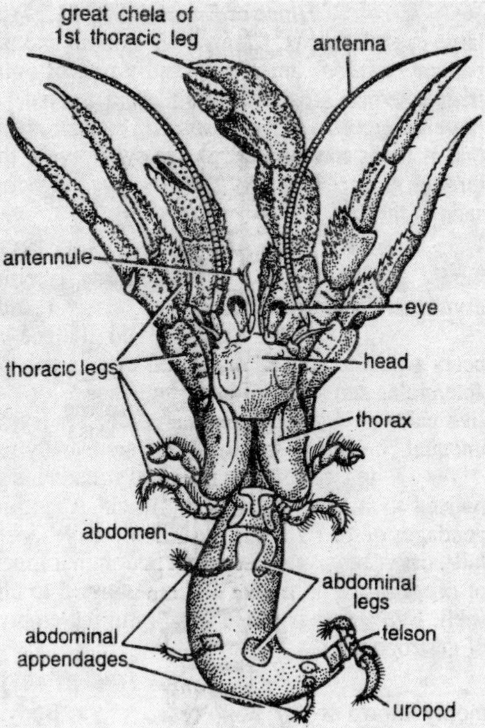

Fig. 81.18. *Eupagurus.*

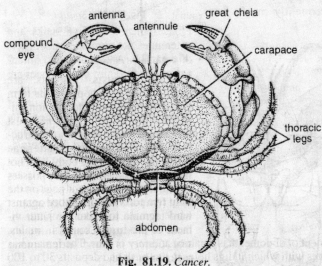

Fig. 81.19. *Cancer.*

23. Collembola. *Collembola* (Fig. 81.23) is commonly known as spring tail. Body is nearly cylindrical and divisible into head, thorax and abdomen. Head bears 4–6 segmented antennae and simple eyes. Compound eyes and trachea are absent. Mouth parts are biting and chewing type. Thorax bears three pairs of legs. Wings are absent. Abdomen is six seg-mented. On the ventral surface of first abdominal segment is a tube-like pro-jection or collophore. Fourth abdomi-nal segment bears a springing organ, the furcula, on the ventral surface. *Collembola* is found in crevices of bark, in moss, under stones, leaves and wood, etc.

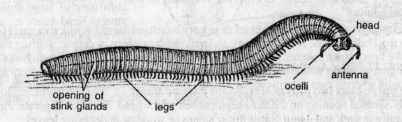

Fig. 81.20. *Julus.*

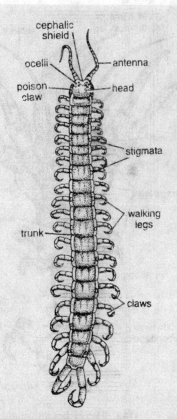

Fig. 81.21. *Scolopendra.*

Fig. 81.22. *Lepisma.*

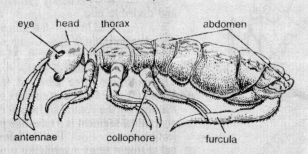

Fig. 81.23. *Collembola.*

24. Locusts. Locusts are short-horned grasshoppers, the term grasshopper is restricted to non-migratory forms, while the name locust is reserved for the migratory destructive phase. They have antennae much shorter than the body with not more than 25 segments, they possess stridulatory apparatus of pegs on the hind femurs which is rubbed against hard tegmina to make the latter vibrate to produce a sound in males, the females are noiseless; the first segment of abdomen has a pair of auditory organs. The female has a short ovipositor made of separate plates with which it digs holes in the earth and deposits 30 to 100 elongated eggs, a glutinous fluid is discharged on eggs which hardens to form a waterproof **egg-sac**, a female in one season deposits 20 such masses of eggs; the eggs hatch into nymphs which undergo 5 to 8 ecdyses to become adults. Locusts are voracious devourers of vegetation and crops both as nymphs and adults.

Lucusta migratoria is one of the chief migratory locusts of the old world, it extends from Eastern Europe to the Philippine Is. It is 5 cm long and yellowish or green in colour. *Schistocerca gregaria* is one of the best known species, it is 5 cm or more in size and has yellow non-migratory phase and pinkish migratory phase with dark patches on tegmina in both phases; it extends from North Africa to North India where it causes tremendous damage to crops. *Cyrtacanthacris succinata,* the Bombay locust is reddish, it is confined to India. *Melanoplus* and *Schistocerca americana* are confined to North America.

Phases and biology. Locusts are polymorphic, they exist in three phases : 1. A **migratory phase** or **phase gregaria**. 2. **solitary phase** or **phase solitaria**. 3. **intermediate phase** or **phase transiens**.

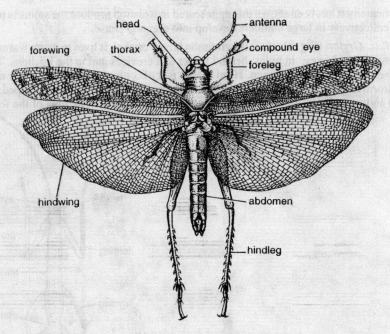

Fig. 81.24. Locust (Dorsal view).

1. **Phase gregaria** has black and yellow or orange colour in its nymphal instars which are formed in any environment, in the adult the pronotum is somewhat concave with a prominent constriction, the wings are proportionately longer, on reaching sexual maturity the colour changes, especially in the male. This phase is gregarious both as nymphs and adults ; when their number increases they form large, dense swarms and migrate from their breeding grounds. Causes of migration are not fully understood, they may be due to certain favourable ecological conditions or some gregarious instinct which bring about migration. Both pairs of wings are used in migration and they reach new grounds where they eat up all vegetation. Cessation of flight is due to physiological causes including maturation of gonads. Then they reproduce in the new grounds, and the progeny develops into phase solitaria when the environment is different from the original breeding grounds. 2. **Phase solitaria** has a convex pronotum with prominent longitudinal ridge called **carina,** there is no constriction, they

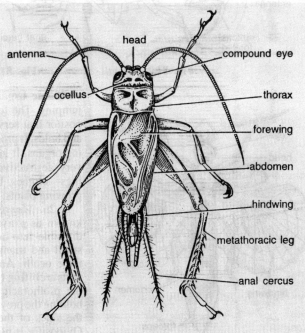

Fig. 81.25. *Gryllus.* (Dorsal view)

are not gregarious and no colour changes occur on sexual maturity. Their nymphs undergo colour changes simulating the colour of the environment. 3. Phase transiens shows a tendency towards one or the other two phases according to whether they are developing towards the solitary or gregarious condition, they are, thus, of various intermediate grades.

Experimentally it has been shown that eggs reared in isolation produce the solitaria phase, while those reared collectively in large numbers develop into gregaria phase.

25. *Gryllus. Gryllus* (Fig. 81.25) is the common house-cricket. It lives in damp warm places like under logs, stones and boxes, in holes, behind books and crevices and in the kitchens. The body is divided into head, thorax and abdomen. Head bears a pair of compound eyes and a pair of antennae which are filiform and longer than body. Mouth parts are mandibulate and well developed. Forewings are hardened and are called tegmina and hindwings are membranous. The tibia of the forelegs bear

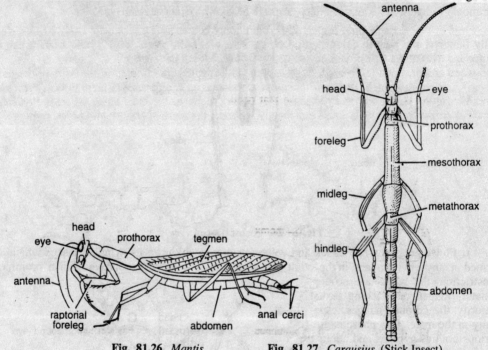

Fig. 81.26. *Mantis.*   **Fig. 81.27.** *Carausius.* (Stick Insect).

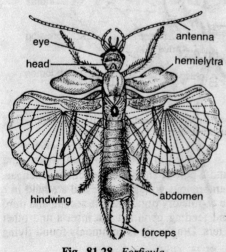

Fig. 81.28. *Forficula.*.

tympanic organ and the hindlegs are modified for jumping. The female possesses a well developed ovipositor that serves for depositing the eggs in crevices and holes. It produces familiar sound with its stridulating organs. It is nocturnal and omivourus. They are very destructive and damage the household belongings—clothes, books, food etc. They also attack the growing plants.

26. *Mantis. Mantis* (Fig. 81.26) is commonly known as praying mantis. Body is elongated and divisible into head, thorax and abdomen. Head is small and triangular bears large compound eyes and three ocelli. Antennae are long and filiform. Mouth parts are biting type. Prothorax is much elongated and the prothoracic legs are modified for grasping and holding the prey. Wings are folded flat and overlapping the sides of the body. Abdomen is ten segmented. Ovipositor is not erected. It is carnivorous feeding on other insects. Mantes lie in wait for their prey, the

forelegs are raised in an attitude of prayer, hence, the common name praying mantis.*Mantis* is found living in the area of plantation.

27. *Carausius* (Stick insect).*Carausius* (Fig. 81.27) is commonly known as stick insect.Body is elongated and slender having a stick-like appearance. Head is small and bears compound eyes and a pair of long filiform antennae. Thorax is elongated bearing three pairs of long slender legs. Wings absent. Abdomen ten segmented. They are herbivorous and eat on the leaves, etc. *Carausius* is found in tropical forests in the thick vegetation.

28. *Forficula* (Earwig). *Forficula* (Fig. 81.28) is commonly known as earwig. Body is elongated and covered by tough chitinous covering. Mouth parts are biting and chewing type.Forewings or tegmina are short, leathery and truncate but the hindwings are large, membranous. Forcep-like cerci at posterior end of abdomen. They are nocturnal and feeding on vegetation. *Forficula* is commonly found in moist places under stones in decaying vegetable matter, etc.

29. *Pediculus*.*Pediculus* (Fig. 81.29) is commonly known as human louse.Body is dorso-ventrally flattened and pale in colour with dark marking along the sides. Head small, bears a pair of compound eyes and a pair of five segmented antennae. Mouth parts are piercing and sucking type. Wings are absent. Each leg bears a large curved claw adapted for clinging to the hairs of the host. Abdomen nine segmented. *Pediculus humanus* is found as an ectoparasite of man. In fact, *Pediculus humanus capitis* is the human head-louse that occurs clung to the head hairs, whereas *Pediculus humanus corporis* is the body louse that mostly harbours the hairs of arm-pit and pelvic region.

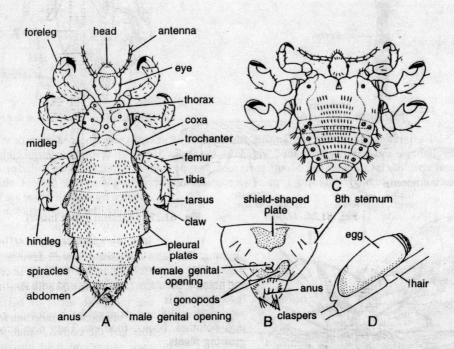

Fig. 81.29. *Pediculus* (Human lice). A—*Pediculus humanus capitis* (Human head-louse); B—Posterior end of the female head-louse ; C—*Phthirius pubis* (Human pubic louse) ; D—An egg or nit.

30. Dragon-fly. Body of dragonfly (Fig. 81.30) is slender, divisible into head, thorax and abdomen. Head bears a pair of large compound eyes and a pair of short inconspicuous antennae. Mouth parts biting and chewing type. Two pairs of membranous wings present and are held in a horizontal position. Abdomen long cylindrical with male copulatory organs on the second and third sternites. Nymphs are aquatic, breath by rectal gills and feeding upon aquatic insects and other organisms. Dragon-flies are strong fliers and strong hunters. Dragon-fly is commonly found flying in the air in the vicinity of water.

31. Belostoma. *Belostoma* (Fig. 81.31) is commonly known as giant water bug. Body is elongated covered by leathery exoskeleton, brownish in colour and reaches the length of 10 cm. Head is broad and bears eyes and small inconspicuous four segmented antennae. Mouth parts piercing and sucking type. Thorax broad, somewhat triangular or narrower anteriorly. Wings leathery, well developed and hemielytra large. Legs flat, fore pair short and raptorial, middle and hind legs serve for swimming. It is carnivorous, feeds on insects, snails, fry and tadpoles. *Belostoma* is found in ponds and lakes in tropical countries.

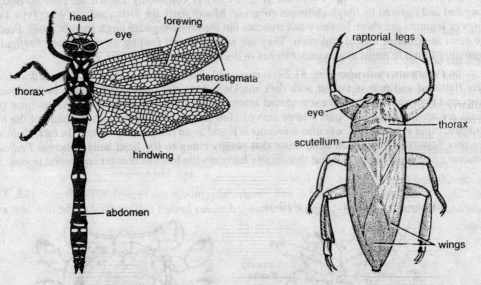

Fig. 81.30. Dragon-fly.   Fig. 81.31. *Belostoma* (Giant water bug).

32. Butterflies. Butterflies are familiar and fascinating insects generally seen in gardens. Body slender, delicate and completely clothed with hairs and scales. Head small, bears a pair of compound eyes and a pair of clavate antennae. Mouth parts sucking type with a conspicuous long coiled proboscis and are commonly called siphoning type. Two pairs of well developed wings are present which are covered by scales. Larvae are known as caterpillars. Butterflies are diurnal or day fliers and suck the nectar from the flowers. Butterflies are commonly found in gardens flying over the flowering plants.

33. Moths. Moths (Fig. 81.33) are the close allies of butterflies. Their antennae are short and feather-like and the body is stout. At rest their wings are held horizontally. Moths are nocturnal or night fliers. They come on the light during rainy season. These are very attractive insects. Examples of moths are cercopia moth, cloth moth, sphinx moth, etc. The common cloth moth is *Tinea pellionella*.

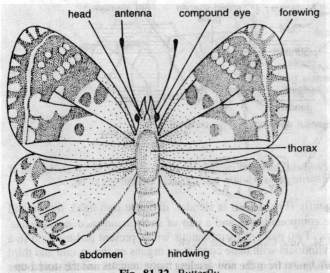

Fig. 81.32. Butterfly.

34. Ants. The best known and most numerous of insects, the ants are the dominant insects and outnumber all other land animals.

This is really the age of ants. All ants are social and no truly solitary species is known. Ants show polymorphism like honey bees and termites. They are distinguished from other insects by the presence of one or two nodes between the **propodaeum** (thorax) and **gaster** (abdomen), elbowed antennae. Typically an ant colony comprises the following types of individuals : **workers** or **ergates soldiers** or **degenerates, gyne** or **fertile female** or **queen** and **aner** or **fertile males.** The **workers** are sterile, apterous females, the smallest members of the colony and often also polymorphic. The **soldiers** are sterile females and peculiarly modified workers with enormous head and mandibles, fitted for crushing and fighting. The **gyne** or fertile females or queens are large and often enormous with wings and well-developed reproductive or-

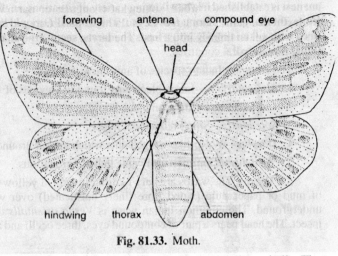

Fig. 81.33. Moth.

gans. The **aner** or fertile males possess well developed reproductive organs and male genitalia. The queen, once fertilized during the nuptial swarming, dealates herself and establishes the first nest and

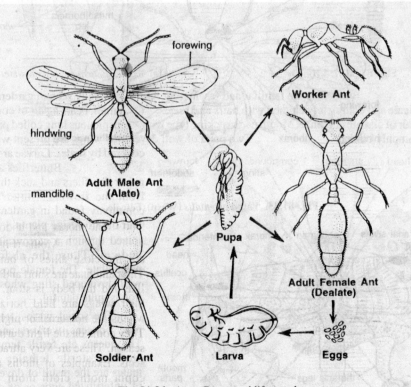

Fig. 81.34. Ants. Castes and life cycle.

rears her first brood. She draws her nourishment from the now-useless flight muscles and the stored-up fat. When the first larvae appear, they are fed by a special nutritive secretion of the salivary glands and as soon as the first workers appear, they go forth into the world, foraging. Then they can take over all the duties of the rearing of the brood, foraging, nest-building, cleaning, nursing, fighting, etc. The queen thence forward continues to lay eggs for nearly fifteen years. The population of a single colony varies considerably from a few thousand to over 500,000 individuals. The formicaria or the ant nest is established in a bewildering variety of situations, such as underground, inside hollow stems, fruits, thorns, galls, among leaves, etc. The tropical *Oecophylla smaragdina* webs leaves of various trees with silken threads into a nest. The larvae secrete the silk and are used by workers as a kind of living thread-ball.

The common Indian species of ants are as follows :

1. *Monomorium*—Large black ants found in crevices of walls, tree trunks, etc.
2. *Camponotus*—Common black house ants.
3. *Solenopsis*—Small red ants of house.
4. *Dorylus*—Wasp-like winged ants which appear around light after rains.
5. *Aenictus*—Common army ants that are gregarious. .

35. Wasps. The wasps are very familiar insects of yellow or chestnut red body. They build nest of mud or paper pulp (wood fibre finely masticated) over walls, ceilings and trees, in holes or underground. The common Indian wasp is *Vespa orientalis* (Fig. 81.35) a chestnut red coloured insect. The head bears a pair of compound eyes, three ocelli and a pair of antennae and chewing mouth

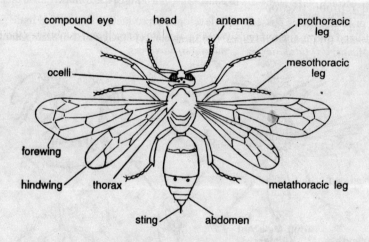

Fig. 81.35. *Vespa orientalis* (Wasp). Female.

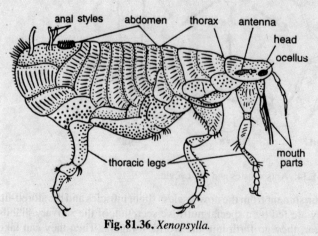

Fig. 81.36. *Xenopsylla.*

parts. The thorax and abdomen are joined through a narrow and small pedicel. Thus, the abdomen is pedicellate. The female possesses a well developed sting whose infliction is quite painful.

The social wasps are trimorphic : queens, workers and males. The queens are fertile females, the workers sterile females and the males are the result of development of unfertilized eggs or of eggs laid sometimes by the sterile workers that cannot be fertilized. The nest is made in a variety of situations such as on trees, in holes or underground. The queen starts nest building in spring and constructs a few hexagonal cells of paper pulp. The first workers then take over and enlarge the nest, until it becomes a flourishing colony. They feed on insects, meat, fruit-juices, sugar, honeydew, sweet-meat and candies, etc. *Vespa* is widely distributed. *Vespa vulgaris,V. germanica, V. cincta* and other related species are ground nesters and *V. sylvestris* suspends its nests from trees. The genus *Polistes* which suspends its nests from trees, belonging to a closely related family Polistidae, distinguised by the slender body and short petiole. *Polistes* hunts on caterpillars and also feeds on fruit-juices.

36. *Xenopsylla.* *Xenopsylla* (Fig. 81.36) is commonly called rat flea. Its body is laterally compressed without wings. Integument is heavily sclerotized, brown in colour and armed with spines and bristles. Head is closely set into thorax with front at tubercle and often with genal ctenidia. Antennae are clavate, short and concealed in grooves. Compound eyes are absent. Thorax is compact with segmentation distinct often with pronotal ctenidia on the posterior margin, prosternum is large. Walking legs are elongated, clawed and modified for jumping. Mouth parts are piercing and sucking type. The adult flea is active and slips through hair with great ease. *Xenopsylla cheopis* is an ectoparasite of mammals specially rats. It transmits the plague from rats to man.

REVISION QUESTIONS

1. Give an outline classification of phylum Arthropoda up to orders and mention at least one example of each order.
2. Give an account of the characters of phylum Arthropoda. Classify it up to classes mentioning their characteristic features and examples.
3. Give an account of the characters of either Crustacea or Insecta and classify up to orders giving their characters and examples.
4. Write short notes on the following :
   (i) *Daphnia;* (ii) *Cyclops;* (iii) *Lepas;* (iv) *Sacculina;* (v) *Eupagurus;* (vi) *Scolopendra;* (vii) Locust; (viii) *Mantis;* (ix) *Carausius;* (x) *Limulus;* (xi) *Sarcoptes.*

82

Arthropoda in General

LARVAL FORMS IN CRUSTACEA

One of the most important features of a large group of the crustaceans is the occurrence of larval forms in all the chief groups. The development of Crustacea is either direct or indirect which is always accompanied by more or less metamorphosis. The development is direct in the case of large eggs with enough yolk and indirect in the case of small eggs with a little amount of yolk. Larval forms are only met with in the case of small sized eggs, usually with metamorphosis and hatching takes place at different stages of development. Few important larval forms are described in the following account.

1. Nauplius larva. Nauplius larva is egg-shaped and unsegmented. It has a broad anterior end with a median eye, large labrum and three paired appendages. The median eye is characteristic of the nauplius larva and is often referred to as the nauplius eye, it is made usually of three but at times four ocelli which are pigmented cups with no lens, and are innervated by the protocerebrum. The median eye may degenerate or persist in the adult crustacean. The appendages are uniramous antennules having two groups of sensory cells forming frontal organs, a pair of biramous antennae, and a pair of biramous mandibles for swimming, they have gnathobases directed towards the mouth, though the gnathobases of mandibles may be absent at first. A stomodaeum with mouth, proctodaeum with anus, and a midgut are also present.

A typical crustacean hatches as a free-swimming nauplius, but in Malacostraca (except in primitive forms) the nauplius is passed over as a stage within the egg membrane. However, in certain crustaceans like Branchiopoda the nauplius metamorphoses directly into the adult but in majority of crustaceans it metamorphoses to adult through various intermediate larval stages like metanauplius, protozoaea, zoaea, cypris, mysis, megalopa, phyllosoma, alima, etc.

2. Metanauplius larva. Metanauplius larva is like a nauplius, except that it shows some segmentation of the body, and there are four pairs of additional appendages of the thorax which shows some segmentation; these appendages are two pairs of maxillae and two pairs of maxillipedes. Some Notostraca, such as *Apus,* hatch as a metanauplius larva.

3. Protozoaea larva. In marine prawns like *Penaeus* and some other decapods, the nauplius directly develops into protozoaea larva. The body of protozoaea is divisible into cephalothorax and abdomen. The cephalothorax is broad, segmented and covered with carapace. The appendages that appeared in metanauplius become well developed and functional. The rudiments of other thoracic appendages also appear. The abdomen is unsegmented, without any appendage and has a forked telson.

4. Zoaea larva. Zoaea larva has a well formed head with a long, median dorsal spine, two stalked compound eyes and one simple eye, all appendages from antennules to the last pair of maxillipedes are present, carapace is well formed and produced in front into a rostrum. Thorax is unsegmented and rudimentary at its hinder end. Abdomen is well formed and six segmented, but it has no appendages except a forked telson. It swims by its biramous maxillipedes.

In *Penaeus,* protozoaea develops into zoaea. In some Anomura the egg hatches as a zoaea which passes through a metazoaea stage to become the adult. Metazoaea is, in fact, an advanced stage of zoaea but differs from it in having uniramous rudiments of thoracic appendages behind the maxillipede. However, the third maxillipedes are biramous in hermit crab's (Anomura) metazoaea and uniramous in that of crab (Brachyura). The abdominal appendages, *i.e.,* pleopods also develop as buds. In some decapods, *e.g.,* crabs, the life history starts from zoaea stage.

   5. **Cypris larva.** Cypris larva is covered by a bivalved shell having adductor muscle. Head has compound eyes, antennules with discs on which cement glands open, antennae are lost but remaining cephalic appendages are present, thorax has six pairs of biramous limbs, there is an abdomen of four segments. It has many adult features. In Cirripedia, *e.g., Lepas,* the egg hatches as a nauplius, it changes into a cypris which gets fixed by discs of antennules with the secretion of cement glands, then it becomes a pupa which forms shell plates and rotates to assume the adult form.

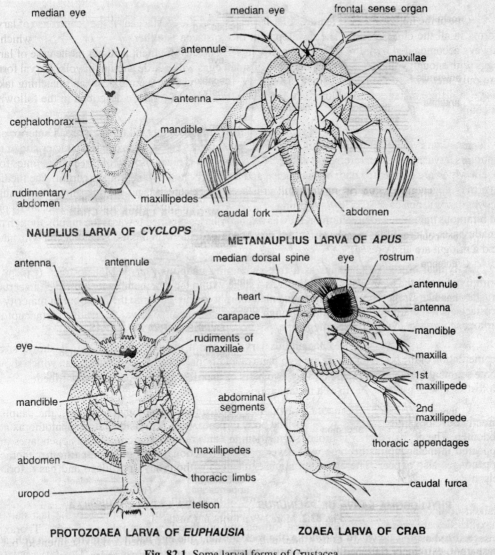

Fig. 82.1. Some larval forms of Crustacea.

   6. **Mysis or schizopod larva.** Mysis or schizopod larva resembles an adult *Mysis*. Head and thorax have a carapace, all cephalic and thoracic appendages are present, but all thoracic appendages are alike and biramous with exopodites, abdomen has five pairs of pleopods and the sixth form uropods. In some Decapoda, *e.g.,* in *Penaeus,* a marine prawn, the egg hatches as nauplius, it passes by successive moults through zoaea stage, protozoaea stage and mysis stage which changes into an adult. In some lobsters, *e.g., Homarus* both nauplius and zoaea are passed within the egg, it hatches as a mysis larva which changes into an adult.

7. Megalopa larva. Megalopa larva has a large unsegmented cephalothorax with all 13 pairs of appendages like those of a crab, abdomen is straight and in line with cephalothorax, it is like the abdomen of prawn with 6 pairs of well formed pleopods. In crabs the nauplius is passed in the egg, it hatches as a zoaea which by moulting forms the megalopa stage, the megalopa by moulting forms the adult.

In Decapoda there is a gradual abbreviation of development. Stages which are free larval forms in lower types of Crustacea are hurried through within the egg before hatching.

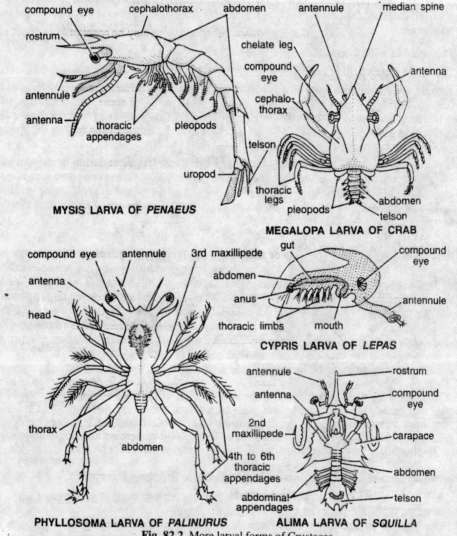

Fig. 82.2. More larval forms of Crustacea.

8. Phyllosoma larva. In *Palinurus* (the rock lobster), the egg hatches directly into a delicate, trasparent, extremely flattened leaf-like larva called phyllosoma or glass crab. This larva is large sized having three distinct regions in the body, the head, thorax and abdomen. An oval carapace covers the head and a part of thorax. It possesses a pair of stalked compound eyes placed antero-laterally in the head. Thorax bears six pairs of appendages; the first thoracic or maxillipedes are rudimentary, second are uniramous, third well formed biramous, and remaining three (4th, 5th, and 6th) pairs are biramous legs which are enlarged. Abdomen shows segmentation but appendages are absent. This larva undergoes several moultings and transforms into the adult. Phyllosoma is, however, considered to be modified mysis larva.

9. Alima larva. In some Malacostraca like *Squilla*, the egg directly hatches out in a young stage called alima larva. It is a pelagic form having slender body with a short but broad carapace. Its body is glassy and transparent. In addition to all cephalic appendages, only first two thoracic appendages are found. The abdomen has distinct six segments with four or five pairs of pleopods. The alima larva is supposed to be modified zoaea stage but it differs strikingly from zoaea in having the armature of the telson and well developed large second maxillipedes.

In addition to these, the glaucothoe larva of hermit crab resembles the megalopa larva as described earlier. Likewise, the calyptosis larva of *Euphausia* (a malacostracan) is similar to the zoaea larva in all essential features except that it possesses sessile paired eyes in place of stalked eyes.

Importance of larval stages. The importance of larval stages may be accounted as under :

1. They help in wide dispersal of the species.

2. The larval stages help in establishing relationships between various groups.

3. Occurrence of nauplius stage in all crustaceans connects the different representatives of this class together. As referred to, the nauplius establishes relationship of some obscure animals like *Sacculina* where adult has lost the characters of the class and even the phylum. In fact, it is the presence of nauplius stage in its life history that connects *Sacculina* to class Crustacea and further the presence of cypris stage relates it to subclass Cirripedia.

4. If Haeckel's law of recapitulation (which states that every organism during its development, *i.e.*, ontogeny, repeats its evolutionary history, *i.e.*, phylogeny) is considered true then it can be said that the nauplius stage represents the ancestral form of crustaceans because all crustaceans invariably pass through nauplius stage during their development. Hence, it can be concluded that present day crustaceans have evolved through nauplius stage.

MOUTH PARTS OF INSECTS

Insects constitute the largest group of animals in the Animal Kingdom. In fact, insects have undergone adaptive diversity in such a way that they have occupied nearly all possible habitats. Obviously, insects have developed different feeding habits as their food differs variously. We also know that insects inflict great damage to men and their belongings by eating or feeding and causing injuries. So, for this purpose, they have got certain appendages in their head around the mouth; these appendages together constitute the mouth parts. Since, the food and feeding habits of insects differ, hence, their mouth parts also differ considerably. The mouth parts of insects, therefore, grouped into two main categories; chewing or mandibulate type and sucking or suctorial type.

Basically, the mouth parts of insects include a pair of mandibles, a pair of labium or first maxillae and the lower lip represented by fused second pair of maxillae. In chewing type of mouth parts, the mandibles are well developed and the maxillae are simple as found in orthopterans like cockroaches and grasshoppers. These mouth parts are adapted for cutting or biting and chewing or crushing the food. In suctorial type of mouth parts, the mandibles are vestigial, *e.g.*, lepidopterans or absent, *e.g.*, housefly or blade-like, *e.g.*, honeybee or in the form of piercing needles or stylets, *e.g.*, mosquito. The maxillae, however, exhibit modifications in various ways for piercing and sucking the food.

The mouth parts of insects are, however, classified into following five types :

1. Biting and chewing type. This type of mouth parts are supposed to be the most primitive type as the other types are believed to be evolved from biting and chewing type of mouth parts. Though, this type of mouth parts have been discussed in chapters relating to cockroach and grasshopper, even then for ready reference these consist of the labrum forming upper lip, mandibles, first maxillae, second maxillae forming lower lip, hypopharynx and the epipharynx.

The labrum is median, somewhat rectangular flap-like. The mandibles are paired and bear toothed edges at their inner surfaces; they work transversely by two sets of muscles to masticate the food. The first maxillae are paired and lie one on either side of the head capsule behind the mandibles. Each possesses a five-jointed maxillary palp which is a tactile organ. The first maxillae help in holding the food. The second maxillae are paired but fused to form the lower lip. Its function is to push the masticated food into the mouth. The hypopharynx is single median tongue-like process at whose base the common salivary duct opens. The epipharynx is a single small membranous piece lying under the labrum and bears taste buds.

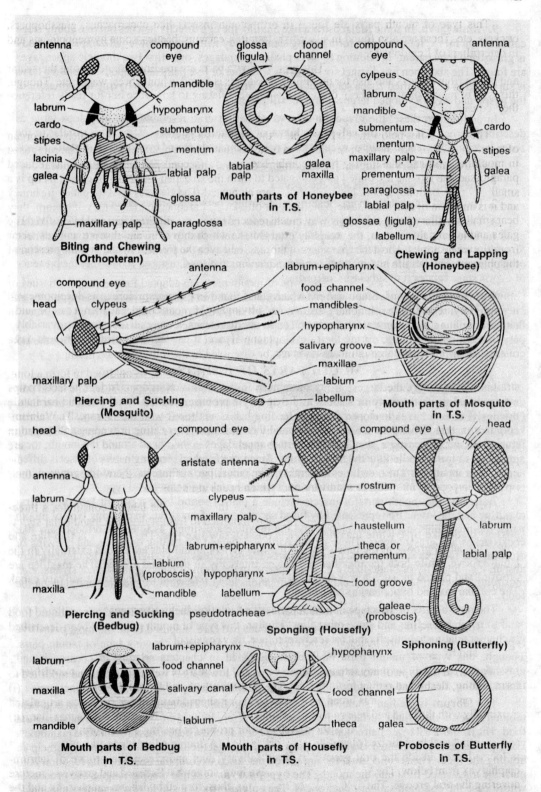

Fig. 82.3. Mouth parts of insects.

This type of mouth parts are found in orthopteran insects like cockroaches, grasshoppers, crickets, etc. These are also found in silver fish, termites, earwigs, beetles, some hymenopterans and in caterpillars of Lepidoptera.

2. Chewing and lapping type. This type of mouth parts are modified for collecting the nectar and pollen from flowers and also for moulding the wax, as is found in honeybees, wasps, etc. Though, this type of mouth parts have been discussed in chapter relating to honeybee but for ready reference they consist of the labrum, epipharynx, mandibles, first pair of maxillae and second pair of maxillae.

The labrum lies below the clypeus, below the labrum is a fleshy epipharynx which is an organ of taste. Mandibles are short, smooth and spatulated, situated one on either side of the labrum; used in moulding wax and making the honeycomb. The labium (second pair of maxillae) has reduced paraglossae, the glossae are united and elongated to form the so called retractile tongue, at its tip is a small labellum or honeyspoon. The labial palps are elongated. The glossa is used for gathering honey and it is an organ of touch and taste. The first pair of maxillae are placed at the sides of labium, they bear small maxillary palps , lacinia is very much reduced but galea are elongated and blade-like. The galea and labial palps form a tube enclosing the glossae which moves up and down to collect nectar from flower nectaries. The nectar is sucked up through the tube, so formed, by the pumping action of the pharynx. The labrum and mandibles help in chewing the food.

3. Piercing and sucking type. This type of mouth parts are adapted for piercing the tissues of animals and plants to suck blood and plant juice, and found in dipteran insects like mosquitoes and hemipteran insects like bugs, aphids, etc. Though, this type of mouth parts have been described in chapters relating to mosquito and bedbug, but for ready reference, they usually consist of labium, labrum and epipharynx, mandibles, maxillae (1st pair) and hypopharynx. However, for the sake of easy description, this type of mouth parts can be discussed in the following two headings.

(i) Piercing and sucking mouth parts of mosquitoes. The labium is modified to form a long, straight, fleshy tube, called proboscis. It has a deep labial groove on its upper side. The labial palps are modified to form two conical lobes at the tip of the proboscis, called labella which bear tactile bristles. The labrum is long needle-like. The epipharynx is fused with the labrum. The labrum-epipharynx, thus, covers the labial groove dorsally from inside. These structures appear C-shaped in transverse section having a groove, called food channel. Mandibles, maxillae and hypopharynx are modified to form needle-like stylets which are placed in the labial groove. In male mosquitoes, the mandibles are absent. The mandibles are finer than the maxillae, but both have saw-like edges on their tips. The hypopharynx possesses salivary duct which opens at its tip.

(ii) Piercing and sucking mouth parts of bugs. In bedbug, the labium constitutes a three-jointed proboscis. The mandibles and maxillae are modified to form stylets; the mandibular stylets possess blade-like tips, while maxillary stylets possess saw-like tips. The labrum is flap-like and covers the labial groove at the base only. Of the four stylets, mandibles are placed externally in the labial groove, while both the maxillae are placed internally in the labial groove. The maxillae are grooved and placed in such a way that they form an upper food channel and lower salivary canal. The epipharynx and hypopharynx are absent.

4. Sponging type. This type of mouth parts are adapted for sucking up liquid or semiliquid food and found in houseflies and some other flies. Though, this type of mouth parts have been descrtibed in chapter relating to housefly, but for ready reference, they consist of labrum-epipharynx, maxillae, labium and hypopharynx; mandibles are entirely absent.

In fact, in this type of mouth parts, the labium, *i.e.*, lower lip is well developed and modified to form a long, fleshy and retractile proboscis. The proboscis is divisible into three distinct parts : (i) rostrum or basiproboscis; it is broad, elongated and cone-shaped basal part of proboscis articulated proximally with the head and bears a pair of unjointed maxillary palps representing the maxillae, (ii) haustellum or mediproboscis; it is the middle part of proboscis bearing a mid-dorsal oral groove and a ventral weakly chitinized plate-like theca or mentum. A double-edged blade-like hypopharynx is located deep inside the oral groove; it bears salivary duct and closes the groove of labrum-epipharynx from below. The labrum-epipharynx is a long, somewhat flattened and grooved structure covering the oral groove. The food canal or channel is, thus, formed by labium-epipharynx and the hypopharynx and (iii) labella or distiproboscis; it is the distal part of proboscis and consists of two broad, flattened and oval spongy pads having a series of channels called pseudotracheae. These open externally by a double row of tiny holes through which liquid food is taken in. The pseudotracheae converge into the mouth lying between the two lobes of labella which lead into the food canal.

5. Siphoning type. This type of mouth parts are adapted wonderfully for sucking flower nectar and fruit juice, found in butterflies and moths belonging to the order Lepidoptera of class Insecta. They consist of small labrum, coiled proboscis, reduced mandibles and labium. The hypopharynx and epipharynx are not found.

The labrum is a triangular sclerite attached with the fronto-clypeus of the head. The proboscis is formed by well-developed, greatly elongated and modified galeae of maxillae. It is grooved internally to form the food channel or canal through which food is drawn up to mouth. At rest, when proboscis is not in use, it is tightly coiled beneath the head but it becomes extended in response to food stimulus. The extension of proboscis is achieved by exerting a fluid pressure by the blood. Mandibles are either absent or greatly reduced, situated on the lateral sides of the labrum. The labium is triangular plate-like bearing labial palps.

METAMORPHOSIS IN INSECTS

During the period of post-embryonic growth (after hatching) an insect undergoes a series of ecdyses or casts off its integument, by this process it attains its maximum size. The stages between ecdyses are called stadia, and the form attained by an insect in any stadium between two ecdyses is termed an instar. When it emerges from an egg it is in its first instar, at the end of this stadium it undergoes an ecdysis and assumes the second instar, and so on. The final instar is the adult or imago. The changes an insect undergoes to become an imago are collectively called metamorphosis. Insects show the following types of metamorphosis :

1. Ametabolic metamorphosis. In lower insects (Collembola, Thysanura) the young which hatches from an egg is a miniature of the adult and is called a nymph, it differs from the adult in having immature reproductive organs; by several moultings and growth it becomes an adult. These insects are primitively wingless, they are also called Apterygota, *e.g., Lepisma,* the change from young to adult is negligible, such insects are ametabolic because there is no metamorphosis.

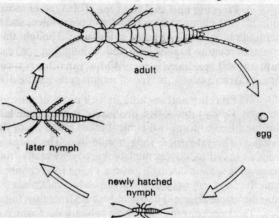

Fig. 82.4. *Lepisma* (silver-fish). Stages of life history exhibiting no metamorphosis (ametabolic metamorphosis).

2. Heterometabolic metamorphosis. In winged insects the adult differs in several respects from the young, such insects are said to undergo metamorphosis in becoming adults. The nymph which hatches from the egg has a general resemblance to the ad t in body form, type of mouth parts and possession of compound eyes, though these nymphs may nave adaptations associated with their particular habits of being aquatic, swimming or burrowing. In these the change from nymphs to adults is a gradual process in which appendages, mouth parts, antennae and legs of the nymph grow directly into those of the adult. Wings develop gradually as external outgrowths of thorax and are visible externally in the nymphal instars, because of their external wing development they are aslo called exopterygota. The reproductive organs mature gradually. Insects showing this slight change from nymph to adult are known as heterometabolic (gradual), they include Dictyoptera, Orthoptera, Isoptera, Hemiptera and Anoplura. Though nymphs of dragon flies, may flies, etc., are quite different from the adult in having special nymphal adaptations because their nymphs are aquatic, while the adults are aerial, the nymphal adaptations are shed in changing into adults, such forms with slightly greater changes are called hemimetabolic (incomplete), they include Odonata, Plecoptera and Ephemeroptera.

3. Holometabolic metamorphosis. In Lepidoptera, Coleoptera, Hymenoptera, Diptera, Siphonoptea, etc., the young which hatches from the egg is called a larva, the larva is very different from the adult in structure, body form, mouth parts, legs and in its mode of life, the larva has lateral ocelli in place of compound eyes, it feeds voraciously, grows, moves about and undergoes ecdyses. The larva is so different from the adult that it first changes into a resting, quiscent instar called a pupa which is often enclosed in a cocoon secreted by the labial glands of the larva. Great trasformation occurs in this instar, wings develop internally from pockets of the hypodermis, and they are not visible from outside. Because wings develop form internal imaginal discs these insects are also called endopterygota. Appendages are formed, muscles, tracheae and parts of the alimentary canal are replaced by corresponding organs of the imago. Such vast changes are called holometabolic metamorphosis.

In holometabolic insects there is an internal reconstruction during late larval and pupal instars. Larval organs, with the exception of central nervous system and developing reproductive organs, are disrupted, their breaking down is called histolysis, this is brought about by phagocytes which feed on the organs, and products of their digestion are then used for building new structures. The building of new structures is brought about by growth centres called imaginal buds or discs. Imaginal discs are groups of formative cells which are set aside in the larva, they are the rudiments of future organs of the imago, they form legs, mouth parts, internal organs and wings. This process of formation of organs of an imago from imaginal discs inside the pupa is known as histogenesis and it results in the formation of the imago.

Thus, two postembryonic processes occur in all insects, the first is growth in the young and the second is **metamorphosis,** in both of which moulting takes place; both processes are controlled by hormones of endocrine glands. Insects have two such endocrine glands, they are corpora allata and prothoracic glands. The juvenile hormone of corpora allata controls growth and moulting up to the end of the larval period. So long as the juvenile hormone of corpora allata is produced the final moulting into a pupa or into an adult cannot take palce. The prothoracic glands are a pair of small glands in the first thoracic segment, they produce a hormone called ecdyson which brings about moulting and development of imaginal discs and reproductive organs. When both hormones are secreted, then moulting of the larva only will take place. The result of the two hromones is supression of adult characters from appearing during larval and pupal instars. When only ecdyson is secreted, and the juvenile hormone is not produced, then the larva will moult into a pupa, and the pupa into an imago. Thus, it is seen that ecdyson is essential for each moulting, but its action is modified as long as the juvenile hormone is present. Removal of the

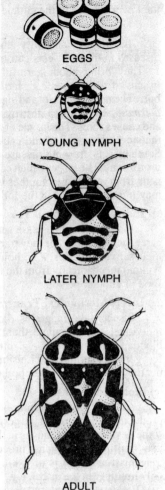

EGGS

YOUNG NYMPH

LATER NYMPH

ADULT

Fig. 82.5. Stink bug (Hemiptera). Stages of life history exhibiting heterometabolic metamorphosis or to say gradual metamorphosis.

adult

naiad emerges from water

egg

naiad

Fig, 82.6. Dragon-fly (Odonata). Stages of life history exhibiting hemimetabolic metamorphosis or to say incomplete metamorphosis.

old cuticle in ecdysis is brought about by an enzyme secreted by the hypodermis, the enzyme erodes the lower surface of the cuticle, then the hypodermis secretes a new cuticle below the old one.

INSECTS AND DISEASES

Insects are constanlty attacking man and his domestic animals by spreading various kinds of diseases in them. Insects cause diseases in two ways : 1. They bring about harmful effects by destroying tissues of their hosts, *e.g.,* larvae of a fly *Dermatobia* burrow under the skin and cause cutaneous myiasis. *Dermatophilus,* a flea destroys tissues below the skin and causes sores. The larvae of a fly *Gastrophilus* enter the stomach of horses and cause intestinal myiasis. 2. Some insects transmit disease-producing bacteria and protozoans. The insect which carries the disease organisms from one host to another is called a **vector** which may transmit disease in the following ways :

(a) Indirect Mechanical Transmission

Insects pick up disease germs on their bodies and carry them to a host, or they transfer the germs through their saliva or faeces, *e.g.,* house flies carry germs of typhoid mechanically from the faeces of a patient to the food of another person.

(b) Direct Mechanical Transmission

Insects take in germs directly from a diseased individual and inoculate them into wounds, skin or blood of another person, *e.g.,* biting fly *Stomoxys* transfers germs of anthrax and Leishmanias of oriental sores, but they carry these in their bodies only for a short time.

(c) Biological Transmission

An insect may not only be a vector of a disease-producing organism, but the germs or parasites undergo some devlopmental changes in the body of the insect or may multiply in it, such a process is called biological transmission which is of 3 kinds : (i) Disease germs only multiply in the insect, *e.g.,* plague germs in a flea. (ii) Disease germs undergo developmental changes and also multiply in the insect, *e.g.,* malarial parasites in mosquitoes. (iii) Disease organisms undergo development but do not multiply in the insects, *e.g.,* filaria larvae of elephantiasis in mosquitoes.

Important disease-producing insects are mosquitoes, flies, fleas, lice and bugs.

1. Mosquitoes. Several species of *Anopheles* are vectors of human malaria. The female *Anopheles* bites a malarial patient and takes in malarial *Plasmodium* along with human blood. *Plasmodium* multiplies and undergoes sporogony in *Anopheles* which transmits the parasite when it bites another person. There are four types of malaria. 1. *Plasmodium vivax* causes benign

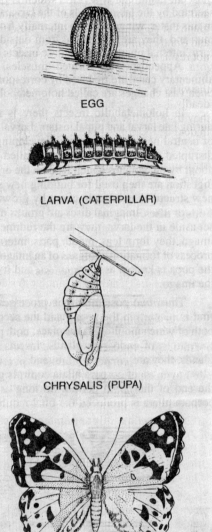

EGG

LARVA (CATERPILLAR)

CHRYSALIS (PUPA)

ADULT

Fig. 82.7. Butterfly (Lepidoptera). Stages of life hisotory exhibiting holometabolic (complete) metamorphosis.

tertian malaria in which the attacks of fever are every 48 hours. 2. *P. malariae* causes quartan malaria in which fever comes on every 72 hours. 3. *P. falciparum* causes malignant tertian malaria in which fever is more or less continuous. 4. *P. ovale* causes mild tertian malaria in which fever comes on every 48 hours. Because different species of *Anopheles* are widely distributed, malaria is very widespread. Malaria not only causes thousands of deaths annually in the tropics, but it also prevents the cultivation of the most fertile regions of the earth.

Culex transmits malaria in birds. *Culex fatigans* and *C. pipiens* are intermediate hosts and vectors of the larva of a nematode *Wuchereria bancrofti* whose adults cause elephantiasis in man. The larvae of *Wuchereria* come to the peripheral blood only at night when the *Culex* sucks blood and takes in the larvae. The larvae develop in the mosquito and are transmited to new human hosts where they mature in the lymphatic system. *Wuchereria* is also transmitted by some species of *Anopheles* and *Aedes* in warm countries. The nematode causes inflammation of arms, legs, scrotum or mammary glands of human beings. Another mosquito of genus *Mansonia* transmits *Wuchereria malayi* in India and Southeast Asia, this nematode is confined only to legs. All cases of infection by *Wuchereria* do not result in elephantiasis.

Aedes is a widespread mosquito, it bites both by day and night. *Aedes aegypti* is the vector of the virus of yellow fever. Yellow fever is widespread in South America and Africa, it is much more deadly than malaria. *A. aegypti* and other species also carry the virus of dengue or "breakbone fever", they transmit the infection from monkeys and dengue breaks out as an epidemic in warm countries; in dengue there is high tempeature, rash on the skin and pain in the bones.

2. **Flies.** Species of *Musca*, the housefly transmit germs of typhoid which are picked up on the bristles of body and legs from the excreta of a patient and trasferred to human food. They also transmit germs of trachoma, an eye disease of tropics, and the germs of cholera, dysentery and diarrhoea.

Glossina, the testse fly is the vector of *Trypanosoma* from animals to man. *G. palpalis* and *G. tachinoides* transmit *Tryponosoma gambiense* which causes Gambian sleeping sickness. *G. morsitans* transmits *Trypanosoma rhodesiense* which causes Rhodesian sleeping sicknes. The trypanosomes are injected by the fly into the blood of man from where they reach the lymph gland and cerebrospinal fluid resulting in sleeping sickness which proves fatal. Domestic and wild animals are also susceptible to sleeping sickness, *G. morsitans* is also the vector of *Trypanosoma brucei* which causes nagana in cattle and horses, nagana is similar to sleeping sickness.

Phlebotomus, a sandfly sucks the blood of reptiles and mammals, it spreads sandlfly fever in India and countries around the Mediterranean. *Phlebotomus papatasi* is the vector of snadfly fever in which there is a pain in the eyes, stiffness in the back and neck, and a reduction of white blood corpuscles. *P. papatasi* and *P. sergenti* transmit *Leishmania tropica* which causes Oriental sores in India and Eastern Asiatic countries. *P. major* in China and *P. argentipes* in India transmt *Leishmania donovani* which causes kala-azar fever in which the parasites enter the spleen, liver, bone marrrow and endothelial cells. Kala-azar occurs in epidemic forms and proves fatal for man. *P. verrucarum* transmits the bacillus of Oroya fever in South American countries.

Tabanus, a gadfly and *Stomoxys*, a stable fly are biting and blood sucking flies, they act as vectors of *Trypanosoma evansi* which causes surra, a widespread tropical disease of horses and cattle, which is fatal in horses. *Tabanus* and *Stomoxys* may also mechanically transmit *Leishmania topica* of Oriental sores, and bacillus of anthrax, a virulent disease of cattle. *Stomoxys* is the intermediate host of larvae of *Hymenolepis*, a tapeworm of poultry, and of larvae of *Habronema*, a nematode of horses.

Chrysops, the mangrove fly sucks human blood in West Africa. It is the intermediate host and vector of *Filaria loa*, a human nematode parasite which causes "Calabar swellings", the nematode wanders about in the sub-cutaneous tissues, especially around the eyes. The larvae come to the peripheral circulation by day time when *Chrysops dimidiata* sucks human blood, the larvae develop in the fly and are transmitted to new hosts. *Chrysops discalis* transmits the germs of tularaemia, a plague-like disease of rodents in America.

Hypoderma, the warble fly lays eggs on legs of cattle, in America, the larvae burrow into the skin and reach the alimentary canal. In India the larvae of *Hypoderma crossii* develop below the skin of the back of goats.

Simulium. the blackfly transmits larvae of a filarial nematode *Onchocera* which infects man and cattle in Africa, America and Europe.

3. **Fleas.** *Xenopsylla cheopis* and *X. astia* are rat fleas, they suck the blood of an infected rat and transmit the bacilli of bubonic plague to man, the infection is caused by the gut getting blocked by bacilli in rat, and sucked blood is regurgitated into a wound, or infection may be caused through infected faeces of flea being rubbed into human skin by scratching. Plague occurs in epidemic form in India. *X. cheopis* also transmits germs of endemic typhus from rats to man; it also transmits germs

of tularaemia from rats to man. *Xenopsylla* is an intermediate host of larvae of two tapeworms, *Dipylidium caninum* of dogs and cats, and *Hymenolepis* of rats and man.

4. Bugs. *Cimex,* the bed bug has been suspected of being the cause of many human diseases, but this has not been proved. In the gut of bed bugs are anti-bacterial substances which do not permit bacteria to live for long. *Cimex* may carry and transmit germs of plague and relapsing fever, this is only for short periods. Three bugs *Triatoma,* the "assassin bug," *Panstrongylus* and *Rhodnius* breed in human dwellings, they are the vectors of *Trypanosoma cruzi* which causes Chagas' disease in South America, this disease is similar to sleeping sickness, it is a wasting disease of the brain and body, it proves fatal. *Triatoma rubrofasciata* is found in India, its nymphs are common in houses hiding in crevices and under carpets, this species is concerned with transmission of kala-azar.

5. Lice. *Pediculus,* the louse sucks blood and takes in *Rickettsia* which multiply in the louse, when they are injected into human beings they cause epidemc and endemic typhus. *Pediculus* also carries *Rickettsia* which cause trench fever in man, and the spirochaetes of relapsing fever. Trench fever and relapsing fever are spread through the excreta of louse when it is rubbed into the human skin or the louse gets crushed on the human body.

ECONOMIC IMPORTANCE OF INSECTS

Man and insects have been at war for the same food and same places to live in. Insects attack man and his domestie animals by causing diseases, they destroy his property and his crops, hence, insects are of very great importance to man. Some insects are beneficial to man, but most are injurious to him directly or indirectly.

A. Beneficial Insects

Insects which produce honey, wax, lac, dyes and silk are commercially beneficial. Some insects are very helpful in destroying injurious insects.

1. Commercial products. *Apis,* the honeybees produce millions of tons of honey every year, it also gives bees wax from its combs. Benefits of bees are cosmopolitan, not only in producing honey and wax, but also in bringing about cross-pollination of many fruits and flowers without which these plants could not exist. *Tachardia,* the lac insect secretes commercial lac produced from integumentary glands as a protective covering by females, shellac is made from lac in India. *Dactylopius,* the cochineal insect of Mexico is found on cacti, dried bodies of females of this scale insect are used for making cochineal dyes. *Bombyx* and *Eupterote* are silk moths, they are reared in India, China, Japan and Europe, their larvae called silk worms spin cocoon of raw silk, the silk fibre is reeled off and used for making silk. In Asiatic countries over 25 million kilograms of silk are produced annually. Dried elytra of two beetles, *Lytta* and *Mylabris* are used for making cantharidin, a powerful aphrodisiac.

The larvae of two flies, *Lucilla* and *Phormia* are used in healing such wounds of bones which do not respond to medicines, the larvae are put in wounds of bones and bone marrow, they clear away suppurating and dead tissues, prevent bacterial growth and excrete allantoin which heals the wounds.

2. Useful predaceous insects. Some insects are predaceous, they feed upon and destroy a large number of injurious insects. *Stagomantis,* a mantis is voracious, it feeds on flies, grasshoppers and caterpillars, some of which are injurious to crops. The larvae and adults of *Chilomenes,* a lady-bird beetle, feed on aphids which infect cotton plants. *Novius,* a lady-bird bettle, destroys scale worms which are pests of orange and lemon trees. *Epicauta* is a blister beetle, it deposits eggs where locusts occur, the larvae on hatching enter egg capsules of locusts and eat up masses of eggs. *Calasoma,* a ground beetle preys upon many kinds of lepidopterous larvae whch destroy cereals and cotton.

3. Beneficial parasitic insects. Some insects parasitize injurious insects, they usually lay eggs in the bodies of larvae and adults of harmful insects ; the young on hatching from eggs finally kill their hosts. The larvae of *Tachina* and related flies are parasites of injurious lepidopterous larvae, such as army-worms which are injurious to cereals. Larvae of hymenopteran flies and carnivorous wasps devour aphids in large numbers. Chalcids and ichneumon flies are parasitic, laying eggs in cocoon and larvae of phytophagous Lepidoptera. *Apanteles,* a hymenopteran fly lays eggs in army-worms and boll worms, the parasitic larvae gnaw their way through the skin of the host.

4. Scavengers. Some insects are scavengers, they eat up dead animal and vegetable matter, thus, they prevent decay. Some ants and larvae of some flies can devour entire animal carcasses.

B. Injurious Insects

Compared with beneficial insects the number of injurious insects is very large.

1. Disease transmitting insects. Many types of mosquitoes, flies, fleas, lice and bugs transmit diseases to man and domestic animals, they have been described earlier in insects and diseases.

2. Household insects. Human food is spoiled by cockroaches, ants, flies and weevils. *Tinea, Teniola* and *Trichophaga* are clothes moths, they lay eggs on warm clothes, the larvae on hatching eat and destroy clothes, they also feed on furs, carpets and dry fruits. *Anthrenus* is a carpet beetle, it is a scavenger eating decaying animal matter, but its larvae destroy carpets and preserved biological specimens. *Tenebrio* is the mealworm beetle, its larvae are mealworms, they eat meal, flour and stored grains, such as rice. *Lepisma,* the silver fish and *Liposcelis,* the book louse live in and destroy books and old manuscripts. *Termites,* the white ants cause untold destruction of books, carpets, furniture and wood-work of buildings.

3. Injurious to domestic animals. *Glossina,* the tsetse fly transmits *Trypanosoma brucei* which causes nagana in horses. *Tabanus* and *Stomoxys,* the blood sucking flies inject *Trypanosoma evansi* into horses and cattle which causes surra in India. The larvae of *Hypoderma,* the warble fly bore below the skin of oxen and make holes for breathing, then they pass through the gullet and again pierce the skin on the sides of the spine to form swellings, they not only injure the hide but also reduce the meat and milk supply. *Gasterophilus,* the bot-fly lays eggs on hair of horse, the larvae enter the stomach in large numbers. *Melophagus,* the sheep tick and *Hippobosca,* the forest fly of cattle and horses suck blood of their hosts and often cause haemorrhage. *Menopon,* the chicken louse sucks blood and causes destruction of fowls.

4. Injurious to crops. Many insects damage forest trees, growing farm crops, fruits and stored grain, the damage they cause annually runs into millions of rupees. The number of such insects is innumerable, they are mostly Lepidoptera, Coleoptera, Diptera and Hemiptera. *Euproctis,* the brown tail moth and *Lymantria,* the gipsy moth are serious pests of shade and foliage trees, their larvae are a menace and destroy forest trees. *Myetiola,* the Hessian fly is a small sized midge, its larvae damage wheat plants. The larvae of two Lepidoptera *Chilo* in India, and *Diatraea* in America bore into stems of sugar-cane and cause a great deal of damage. *Pyrilla,* a hemipteran sugar-cane leaf hopper sucks the juice of sugar-cane, both as adult and nymph, causing great loss of sugar. *Pyrausta* is a moth found all over the world, but specially abundant in the tropics, its larvae known as corn borers are notorious for boring into stems and fruits of corn (maize). *Nephotettix,* the Indian rice leaf-hopper and *Leptocorisa,* the oriental pest of rice and millet are Hemiptera, they attack rice in very large number eating the leaves and ears. The larvae of *Schoenobius,* a moth bore into the stems of rice plants in India, they kill the plants. Nymphs and adults of *Hieroglyphus,* an orthopteran eat up the growing shoots of rice plants, thus, preventing formation of grain. *Dysdercus,* the Indian cotton bug, *Oxycarenus,* the Egyptian cotton bug, and *Anthonomous* the cotton-boll weevil are very injurious to cotton, they stain and destroy cotton-bolls, *Aphis,* a hemipteran is a serious cotton pest in India, the pests often attack cotton plants in large numbers causing the plants to wilt and die. The larvae of two Lepidoptera, *Agrotis* and *Gnorimoschema* are potato cut-worms in India, the former feeds on potato leaves and cuts off the stems, while the larvae of the latter eat the potatoes in the field and stores, larvae also attack tobacco and tomatoes. Larvae of *Agrotis* are also destructive to peas, cabbage, tobacco, ground nuts, wheat and cauliflowers. The larvae of some Coleoptera are called wire-worms, such as *Agriotis* and *Limonius,* they are root-feeders and are extremely destuctive to cereals, root crops and grasses. Many insects and their larvae destroy vegetables in India. *Siphocoryne* is an aphis which feeds on cabbage leaves; *Anasa,* the squash bug is destructive to cucurbitaceous plants; *Earias* the spotted bollworm destroys ladyfingers; *Aulacophora,* the red beetle feeds on pumpkins; the larvae of *Bruchus* , a beetle bore into pods of beans and peas killing the seed. Many insects attack fruit trees, they damage roots, trunks, stems, leaves, inflorescence and fruit. *Drosicha,* a mealy bug causes destruction of mangoes, plums, papaya, jack fruit, pears and citrus fruits in India. The nymphs and adults of *Ideocerus,* a mango leaf hopper attack the inflorescence and suck the sap, thus, they cause tremendous damage by preventing formation of mango fruit. The larvae of *Contarinia* fly feed on young pears which soon decay. *Psylla,* an apple bug, lays eggs on apple and pear tree, the nymphs on hatching damage the blossom and shoots; the larvae of *Anthonomus,* a beetle also destroy apple blossoms and prevent formation of the fruit. *Nysius,* a bug is very destructive to several kinds of fruit trees.

Many moths, caterpillars and beetle cause a great deal of damage to stored grains; two beetles *Tenebrio* and *Tribolium* have similar habits and are commonly found in stores and granaries, the former is found in all stages in meal, flour and stored goods, its larvae are known as meal worms. *Tribolium* eats stored wheat and grain. *Calandra,* a weevil bores through grains of rice and other stored grain in India.

REVISION QUESTIONS

1. Write an essay on larval forms in Crustacea and mention their importance.
2. Give an account of mouth parts in insects.
3. Describe different types of metamorphosis met within insects and mention the factors that govern the process of metamorphosis.
4. "Insects are supposed to be cause of various diseases", discuss.
5. Write an essay on economic importance of insects.

83

The onychophorans have been described as the "connecting link" between annelids and arthropods. The validity of such a statement may be questioned, but this little group of animals does have many interesting similarities to both annelids and arthropods. The group furnishes an excellent example of discontinuous distribution. Formerly the Onychophora (Gr., *onychos* = claw; *phoros*=bearing) was treated as a class and was placed as an appendix to the phylum Arthropoda, but recently it has been given the status of a separate phylum. The ten genera and seventy odd species belonging to the group Onychophora are all usually referred to as *Peripatus*. The genus *Peripatus* was established in 1826 by Guilding, who first obtained specimens of it from St. Vincent in the Antilles.

All onychophorans live in tropical regions (the East Indies, the Himalayas, the Congo, the West Indies and northern South America) or south temperate regions (Australia, New Zealand, South Africa and the Andes). No species are found north of Tropic of Cancer.

HABIT AND HABITAT

Peripatus is a terrestrial animal found living in moist places, in crevices of rocks, under bark, stones, logs and beneath fallen leaves and other dark and damp places or along stream banks. It is generally confined to humid habitats. It is nocturnal in nature and predaceous and carnivorous in feeding habit. Most species of *Peripatus* are predaceous and feed on small invertebrates, such as snails, insects and worms. A number of species display a particular preference for termites. Most species of *Peripatus* are viviparous and a single large female may produce 30 or 40 young ones in a year.

EXTERNAL MORPHOLOGY

The body of *Peripatus* is caterpillar-like. It is soft, elongated, bilaterally symmetrical and more or less cylindrical and ranges from 1.4 cm to 15.00 cm in length. The external segmentation is indistinct and marked only by the presence of paired appendages. Numerous annuli or superficial lines mark the body, but such annuli do not correspond to the segmentation. The skin covered by the

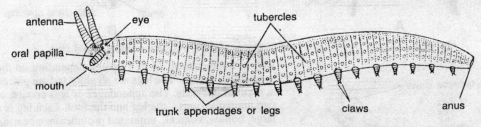

Fig. 83.1. *Peripatus.* External features in lateral view.

thin cuticle is soft and has a velvety texture and thrown into a number of fine transverse ridges bearing numerous conical papillae or tubercles armed with little chitinous spines. The colouration varies considerably in different species from dark grey to brown. The ventral surface is nearly always flesh-coloured, while the dorsal surface has a darker colour. But blue, green, red-orange or black colourations are also marked.

The entire body of *Peripatus* may be divided into an indistinctly marked off head and an elongated trunk.

1. Head. The head of *Peripatus* bears a pair of eyes, a pair of antennae, a pair of jaws or mandibles, and a pair of oral papillae.

(i) Eyes. The eyes are simple and dorsal in position. They resemble the eyes of chaetopods.

(ii) Antennae. One pair of antennae represents the first pair of appendages. The antennae are ringed and taper slightly till near their termination, where they are slightly enlarged. The rings bear a number of spines. The free end of each antenna is covered by a sheath of spiny tissue.

(iii) Jaws or mandibles. One pair of jaws or mandibles constitute the second pair of appendages. These are present deep inside the mouth cavity. Each jaw is small, muscular, stumpy and provided at its free end with a pair of sharp cutting blades. Each jaw is composed of two curved, falciform pointed chitinous plates, the inner toothed and the outer concave edge. The jaws have their convex edge directed forwards and their concave or cutting edge turned backwards. The inner cutting plate usually bears a number of cutting teeth in addition to the main tooth. The jaws appear to be used for tearing the food.

(iv) Oral papillae. Third paired appendage is a pair of oral papillae. The oral papillae are placed at the sides of the head, one on each side. On the terminal end of each oral papilla is situated an aperture of a special kind of gland called slime gland. The oral papillae possess two main rings of the projecting tissue and their extremities bear irregularly arranged papillae. **Mouth** is situated on the ventral side immediately behind the oral papillae.

2. Trunk. The trunk is devoid of exoskeletal coverings and its skin is thrown out into a number of ridges, along which wart-like papillae are placed. The trunk possesses appendages or legs which

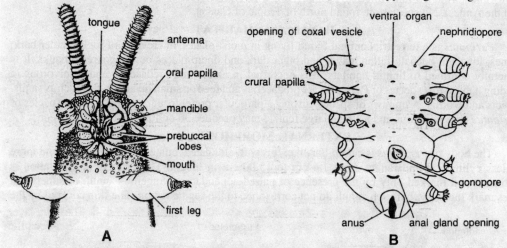

Fig. 83.2. *Peripatus.* A—Anterior end in ventral view; B—Posterior end in ventral view.

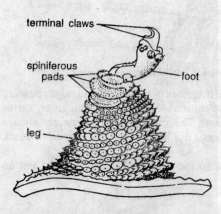

Fig. 83.3. *Peripatus.* A leg.

vary in number from 14 to 43 pairs, depending on the species and the sex. The legs are all alike and are placed at regular intervals. The appendages or legs consist of two main divisions—the leg and the foot. Each leg is a large, hollow, conical, unjointed protuberance bearing a pair of terminal claws (Fig. 83.3). At the distal end of each leg on the ventral side are three to six transverse spiniferous pads, on which the leg rests when walking. The entire surface of the leg consists of numerous papillae. The foot is attached to the distal end of the leg. It is slightly narrower at its attached extremity than at its free end. It bears two sickle-shaped claws and two, three or four papillae. The part of the foot which carries the claws is specially retractile and is generally found more or less telescoped into the proximal part. The **anus** which serves as the outlet of the alimentary canal lies at the posterior end of the body and behind the last pair of legs. The genital pore or reproductive opening is situated on the ventral surface between the last pair of legs just in front of the anus. A nephridiopore lies at the base of each leg.

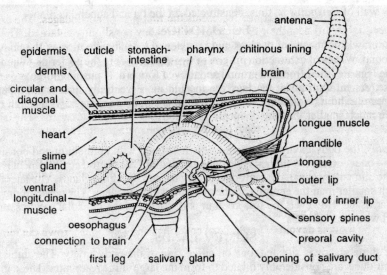

Fig. 83.4. *Peripatus.* Anterior end in sectional view.

BODY WALL

The body wall is dermo-muscular, consisting of cuticle, epidermis, dermis and muscles.

1. Cuticle. It is a thin, chitinous outer layer which covers the body surface. The cuticle of onychophorans is only one micron thick, flexible and very permeable. It is not divided into articulating plates. The absence of a rigid exoskeleton enables onychophorans to squeeze their bodies into very confining places. The cuticle is ridged and covered with microscopic small and large tubercles which give it a velvety texture which is unknown in other animals.

2. Epidermis. Beneath the cuticle is a single layer of epidermis, which overlies the dermis and muscle fibres. The epidermis is composed of a single layer of cells. It also secretes the cuticle on its outer surface.

3. Dermis. It is a thin layer comprising of connective tissue. It lies just below the epidermis.

4. Muscles. There are three layers of muscle fibres which lie beneath the dermis. The outer layer is composed of circular muscles. The inner layer consists of longitudinal muscles. Between the

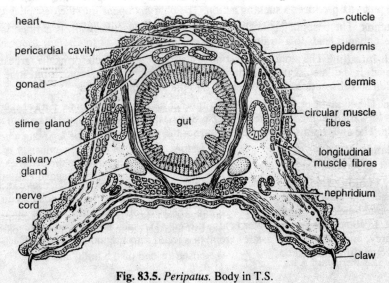

Fig. 83.5. *Peripatus.* Body in T.S.

outer and inner layers, there is a layer of diagonal muscles. The main muscles of the body wall are unstriated and divided into fibres, each invested by a delicate membrane. The muscles of the jaws are transversely striated.

The body wall of *Peripatus* is, thus, constructed on the typical annelidan plan.

LOCOMOTION

Peripatus crawls by means of the legs and by extension and contraction of the body, which is held off the ground. Waves of contraction progress from the anterior to the posterior. When a segment is extended, the legs are lifted from the ground and moved forward. A pushing force is exerted in the effective stroke, As in arthropods, the legs are located more ventrally than are the parapodia of annelids. *Peripatus* exhibits a slow movement. *Peripatus* can also easily crawl through crevices or holes which are much smaller than the diameter of its body.

BODY CAVITY

In *Peripatus,* the body cavity is a haemocoel. It is lined with epithelium and consists of four compartments—one central, two laterals and one pericardial. The central compartment is the largest and contains the alimentary canal, the reproductive organs and the slime glands. The lateral compartments are much smaller than the central and they extend within the legs. The pericardium contains a peculiar cellular tissue. However, the true coelom is restricted to the gonadial cavities and to small sacs associated with the nephridia.

SLIME GLANDS

A pair of slime glands is situated, one on either side of the body cavity. The slime glands are tubular and their ducts are considerably dilated to form the large slime reservoirs. These glands open on the terminal ends of the oral papillae and secrete an adhesive slime for entangling the prey. The secretion of the slime glands is discharged as two streams for a considerable distance as great as 50 cm. This secretion hardens very rapidly into threads in the air.

DIGESTIVE SYSTEM

The digestive system consists of alimentary canal and digestive glands.

Alimentary Canal

The alimentary canal is very simple and tube-like. It begins with the mouth and consists of foregut of a pharynx and oesophagus, the midgut composed of stomach-intestine, and the hindgut or rectum.

Mouth. The mouth is located at the base of prebuccal depression. It is enclosed by the prebuccal or oral papillae which form a preoral cavity. Within the preoral cavity lie the lateral claw-like mandibles which are used for grasping and cutting the prey. The mouth leads into a pharynx.

Pharynx. The pharynx is thick-walled and muscular. The cavity of the pharynx is lined by chitin and in cross-section it appears X-shaped. The wall of the pharynx is raised to increase the cavity. Such movement of pharynx produces a sucking action. The pharynx opens into the oesophagus.

Oesophagus. The oesophagus is short having a weak muscular wall. It is lined internally by chitin. The oesophagus leads to a straight midgut.

Stomach-intestine. The stomach-intestine is a striaght tube which forms the largest part of the alimentary canal. It is dilated soft-walled tube lined by ectoderm. The stomach-intestine is the chief site of digestion and absorption. It leads behind into the hindgut or rectum.

Rectum. The hindgut or rectum is a short tubular and narrow terminal part of the alimentary canal. It loops forward over the intestine before passing posterioly to the anus. The rectum is internally lined by chitin. The anus opens on the ventral side at the posterior end of the body.

Digestive Glands

The most important digestive gland is a pair of salivary glands.

Salivary glands. A pair of salivary glands opens into a median dorsal groove in the preoral cavity. Each salivary gland is slender, tubular and elongated. The salivary glands extend from third to tenth and sometimes up to thirty-first segment. The two salivary ducts fuse to open within the preoral cavity. In some forms, a reservoir is also present. The salivary secretions are passed into the body of the prey, and the digested tissues are then sucked into the mouth. The salivary glands are supposed to be modified nephridia.

Ingestion and Digestion of Food

Peripatus is predaceous and carnivorous and its food comprises small invertebrates, such as snails, insects and worms. A prey, when detected, is captured by the spurting of slime from the slime gland. It is then held firmly by the lips and sucking of the pharynx. The jaws split open the prey and the saliva, containing various enzymes, is poured over the prey through the slit. The soft parts of the prey are digested by the saliva. The nutritive fluids of the digested soft parts are drawn in by the sucking action of the pharynx and oesophagus. The peristaltic action of the midgut wall carries the material to pass posteriorly through its lumen. The midgut cells secrete a thin membrane around the food particles. Various juices secreted by the lining of the midgut penetrate this membrane envelope and digest the food further. The digested materials come out of the membrane and are absorbed by the absorptive cells in the midgut lining. The residual matter which remains within the membrane gradually passes to the hindgut and is finally ejected from the anus.

CIRCULATORY SYSTEM

The circulatory system consists of a single mid-dorsal tube, the heart placed on the dorsal surface of the gut. The heart is tubular and contractile, lies within the pericardial sinus. It is provided with a pair of lateral ostia in each segment. The heart extends from the segment bearing first pair of legs to the segment immediately before last. The heart propels the blood forward into the general haemocoel. The partitions between sinuses are perforated by openings that facilitate blood circulation. The pericardial sinus is separated from the general body cavity by a longitudinal partition. No other definite blood vessel is found. The blood is colourless and contains phagocytic amoebocytes.

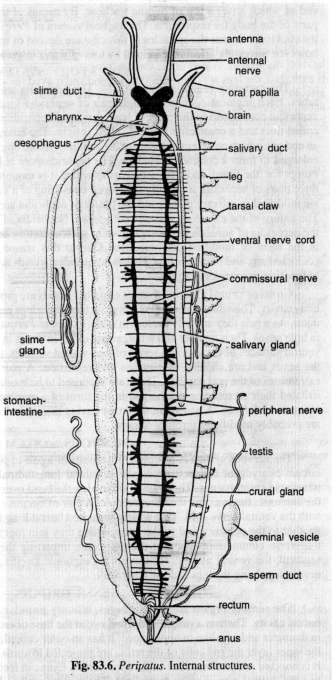

Fig. 83.6. *Peripatus*. Internal structures.

Labels: antenna, antennal nerve, oral papilla, brain, salivary duct, leg, tarsal claw, ventral nerve cord, commissural nerve, salivary gland, peripheral nerve, testis, crural gland, seminal vesicle, sperm duct, rectum, anus; slime duct, pharynx, oesophagus, slime gland, stomach-intestine.

RESPIRATORY SYSTEM

The respiratory system consists of air tubes called **tracheae** or tracheal tubes. The tracheae are delicate, unbranched or rarely branched tubes. They are lined by a thin chitinous layer exhibiting faint transverse striations. The tracheae extend throughout the body and communicate to outside through minute spiracles. The spiracles are minute openings. These are present in large numbers all over the surface of the body between bands of tubercles. The spiracle opens into a very short atrium, at the end of which arises a tuft of minute tracheae. By means of tracheal tubes the air is conveyed to all parts of the body for respiration. The tracheal system of *Peripatus* is markedly different from that of the cockroach in that the spiracles in this case are devoid of any closing mechanism. This condition, however, adversely affects the animal by loss of water in great quantity.

EXCRETORY SYSTEM

The excretory organs are nephridia. The nephridia are segmentally arranged pairs of coiled tubes. Each segment contains a single pair of nephridia located in the ventro-lateral sinuses. The nephridia correspond to the pairs of legs. A typical nephridium consists of a long ciliated funnel. a coiled duct and a contractile bladder called vesicle. The ciliated funnel and nephrostome lie within an end sac, which represent a vestige of the coelom. Before opening to the outside, the tubule becomes enlarged to form a contractile bladder. The nephridiopore is located on the inner base of each leg except for the fourth and fifth segments in which it is mounted on a more distal tubercle. The first three pairs of nephridia are poorly developed consisting of a vesicle and duct. The anterior nephridia are modified as salivary glands and the posterior nephridia are modified as gonoducts in the female. The nature of the excretory waste is not known. Nephridia of *Peripatus* are, however, analogous to the nephridia of annelids but homologous to such excretory organs of arthropods. In both, these are in the form of modified coelomoducts. Due to this reason, recent workers prefer to call them coelomoducts and not nephridia. Following peculiar glands are also found in the body of *Peripatus* to function as excretory organs.

Coxal or crural glands. A series of paired glands are present in the lateral compartments of the body cavity. Their ducts open on the lower surface of the legs just outside the apertures of the excretory ducts. As a rule they are only present in male, except in *Peripatus capensis* in which they are present in both sexes. Their number and arrangement differ in males in different species. Also opening on the ventral surfaces of the legs is a series of thin-walled vesicles, the coxal organs. These occur in both the sexes and are capable of eversion and retraction. A pair of large slime glands opens on the extremities of the oral papillae. These are supposed to be modified coxal glands. When the animal is irritated their secretion is discharged in the form of a number of fine viscid threads probably as a measure of defence. A pair of anal glands having uncertain function opens close to the anus. These are probably modified excretory organs.

NERVOUS SYSTEM

The nervous system is primitive. It consists of a pair of supra-pharyngeal ganglia or brain, two circum-pharyngeal connectives, a pair of lateral longitudinal nerve cords connected together by transverse commissures. The brain is situated in the head over the pharynx and it supplies nerves to the antennae, the eyes and the mouth region. A pair of circum-pharyngeal connectives unite the brain with the ventral nerve cord. Two widely separated lateral longitudinal nerve cords run parallel to one another to the posterior end of the body, where they join together behind the anal aperture. Several transverse commissures connect the two cords imparting them a ladder-like appearance. In each segment, the ventral nerve cords contain a ganglionic swelling and give rise to a number of paired nerves supplying the legs and the body wall.

SENSE ORGANS

The sensory organs are a pair of eyes, sensory papillae and specialized sensory cells in the buccal cavity. There is a simple and small eye at the base of each antenna. Each eye is 0.2 to 0.3 mm in diameter and cup-like in appearance. It has an outer cuticular cornea and thick lens (Fig. 83.6) In the inner layer the rod cells of the retina are projected towards the lens at one end and the other end is connected with the branches of the optic nerves. Eyes can feel the difference between light and dark and the animal moves away from light. The sensory cells which are present on the antennae are responsible to feel the way during locomotion. Numerous sensory papillae are distributed all over the body. Each papilla consists of a seta and a group of sensory cells. These papillae are responsible for determining air currents and also act as tactile receptors. Several specialized sensory cells are also present in the lining of buccal cavity. These sensory cells determine the taste of food.

REPRODUCTIVE SYSTEM

The sexes are always separate and the cavities of the reproductive organs are coelomic. The males are usualy smaller than females.

Male reproductive organs. The male reproductive organs consist of a pair of testes, a pair of seminal vesicles, a pair of vasa deferentia, an ejaculatory duct and a male gonopore. The **testes** are elongated and tubular structures. From each testis a narrow and slender **vas efferens** opens through a funnel-like aperture into the **seminal vesicle.** On each side an elongatea, narrow, slender and coiled **vas deferens** arises from the seminal vesicle and unites with its fellow from the other side to form a central tube called **ejaculatory duct.** The proximal part of the ejaculatory duct is glandular and secretes a substance which packs the sperm cells into **spermatophores.** The spermatophores are as long as 1.0 mm and are enclosed in a chitinous envelope. The ejaculatory duct opens to exterior on the ventral surface between the legs of the last pair or behind them. The male gonopore is ventral and posterior like that of the female.

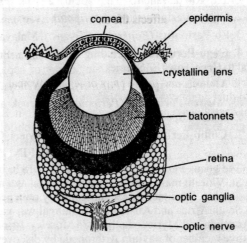

Fig. 83.7. *Peripatus.* L.S. of an eye.

Female reproductive organs. The female reproductive organs include a pair of ovaries, a pair of oviducts, a pair of uteri, a vagina, and a female genital pore. The **ovaries** are a pair of elongated tubular structures located in the posterior part of the body. Two ovaries are fused at the anterior and posterior ends. From each ovary arises an **oviduct** which runs anteriorly and then bends to form a curved **uterus.** The uteri are beaded in appearance. The two uteri unite to form a median **vagina** (or common atrium) which opens to the exterior through a common **genital pore** situated ventrally near the posterior end of the body. In some forms, a process called **ovipositor** is present near the genital aperture.

DEVELOPMENT

Onychophorans are **oviparous, ovo-viviparous,** or **viviparous.** In most species the reproduction appears to be continuous **Oviparous** forms are limited to the Australian genera, *Ooperipatus* and *Symperipatus.* The females of these genera are provided with an ovipositor. The large yolky eggs are enclosed in chitinous shells and are laid in moist places. The cleavage is superficial.

All other onychophorans are ovo-viviparous or viviparous. The fertilization is internal and the egg develops within the uterus. In the mating of South African *Peripatopsis,* which lacks seminal receptacles, the male crawls over the body of the female and deposits a spermatophore at random on her sides or back. Over a period of time a female may accumulate many spermatophores. The spermatophore stimulates blood amoebocytes and these amoebocytes dissolve the cuticle and skin (integument) of the female and that of the spermatophores. The sperms then pass from the spermatophore into the female haemolymph. They eventually reach the ovaries , where fertilization of eggs takes place. The eggs of viviparous onychophorans are small and have little yolk. The cleavage is either superficial or holoblastic. The uterine secretion provides for the nutrition of the embryo. The nutritive material is obtained by the embryo through a special embryonic membrane or through a placental connection to the uterine wall. The pattern of development varies in different forms.

GEOGRAPHICAL DISTRIBUTION

The geographical distribution of onychophorans is peculiar in a number of respects. The phylum consists of two families. Each has a wide, discontinuous distribution around the world, but neither is found in the same area with species of the other family. The family **Peripatidae** is more or less equatorial in distribution, while the family **Peripatopsidae** is limited to the Southern Hemisphere. The genus *Peripatus* is found restricted in the various places of the world such as South Africa, Australia, New Zealand, Tasmania, New Britain, South America and West Indies, Malaya, Equatorial Africa and Chile. The species of *Peripatus,* of which between 50 and 60 are known, fall into seven discontinuous geographical groups, the members of which are more closely related to each other than those of any other group. The names and distribution of these groups, together with the generic names which have been applied to them by various authors are as follows :

1. **Neo-Peripatus** (*Peripatus*). Neotropical region (West Indies and America from Mexico in the North to Rio de Janeiro in the South). 29 Species.

2. **Congo-Peripatus** (*Mesoperipatus* Evans). Congo district in West Africa. 1 Species.

3. **Eo-Peripatus** (*Eoperipatus* Evans). Malaya (Malacca and Sumatra). 4 Species.

4. **Capo-Peripatus** (including *Peripatopsis* Pocock and *Opisthopatus* Purcell). South Africa (Natal to Cape Town) 7 Species.

5. **Melano-peripatus** (*Paraperipatus* Willey). New Britain. 1 Species.

6. **Austro-Peripatus** (*Peripatoides* Pocock and *Ooperipatus* Dendy). Australia, Tasmania, New Zealand. 8 Species.

7. **Chilio-Peripatus** (*Opisthopatus* Bouvier). Chile. 1 Species.

AFFINITIES

The genus *Peripatus* was established in 1826 by Guilding, who first obtained specimens of it from St. Vincent in the Antilles. He regarded it as a mollusc, misled by its slug-like antennae and by its moist skin. Specimens were subsequently obtained from other parts of the neotropical region and from South Africa and Australia. The animal was variously assigned by the zoologists of the day to the Annelida and Myriapoda. In 1874 Moseley first of all established the position of *Peripatus* as a primitive member of phylum Arthropoda by discovering the tracheae.

Peripatus exhibits affinities with Annelida, Arthropoda and Mollusca as well as peculiarities of its own.

A. Annelidan affinities. *Peripatus* resembles the annelids in the following features :

1. Vermiform body with truncated extemities.
2. True head is absent.
3. Segmentation in both is homonymus.
4. Outer body covering is cuticle, skin is thin and flexible.
5. Musculature is smooth and muscles operate in identical way.
6. Appendages are hollow and unjointed.
7. Locomotion slow and by peristalsis as in an earthworm.
8. Simple and straight alimentary canal.
9. Paired segmentally arranged nephridia.
10. Slime glands and coxal glands correspond with similar glands of Chaetopoda.
11. Structure of the eye is same as in polychaetes.
12. Presence of cilia in the reproductive tracts.

B. Arthropodan affinities. *Peripatus* resembles the arthropods in the following characteristic features :

1. Presence of antennae.
2. Body is covered with chitinous cuticle like that of arthropods.
3. The appendages are provided with claws.
4. Jaws are modified appendages.
5. Locomotion is not annelid-like but by legs having definite musculature.
6. Presence of haemocoel.
7. Absence of perivisceral part of coelom.
8. Coelom reduced to the cavities of excretory and reproductive organs.
9. Peculiar salivary glands, supposed to be modified nephridia.
10. Presence of lateral ostia as doors between heart and pericardial sinus.

11. Presence of tracheae as respiratory organs.

12. Brain is large and resembles the brain of typical arthropod.

13. General structure of reproductive organs and the pattern of development is same as in other arthropods.

C. Molluscan affinities. *Peripatus* exhibits the following molluscan characteristics :

1. Slug-like appearance of the body.

2. Ladder-like nervous system as found in Polyplacophora and Prosobranchiata.

The above characteristics led to the inclusion of *Peripatus* among Mollusca. But according to other evidences, these are only superficial resemblances.

D. Onychophoran characteristics. The following characteristic features are peculiar to Onychophora in which they differ from other phyla :

1. Body shows no or indistinct segmentation.

2. Appearance of skin is not like that of arthropods.

3. Antennae not homologous to the antennae of other arthropods.

4. Three segmental head of *Peripatus* exhibits a condition mid-way between that of Annelida and Arthropoda.

5. Segments behind head are simple and identical.

6. Restriction of jaws to a single pair. Movement of jaws is from anteiror to the posterior end.

7. Presence of slime and coxal glands.

8. Arrangement of tracheae is not arthropod-like. Here in each segment there are numerous permanently opened spiracles.

9. Two ventral nerve cords are widely separated and without true ganglia.

10. Structure of eye is less complicated.

11. The disposition of reproductive organs.

TAXONOMIC POSITION

Peripatus is of special interest because its body exhibits certain structures characteristic of annelids and other structures found only in arthropods. Therefore, they are regarded to be an intermediate stage or connecting link between Annelida and Arthropoda. However, onychophorans appear to be more closely allied to arthropods than to the annelids. They may represent an offshoot from near the base of the arthropod line. Based on such phylogenetic considerations, Manton (1970) and other contemporary zoologists have included onychophorans within the Arthropoda as a subphylum or class. But, absence of an exoskeleton and jointed limbs and the primary annelidan characters in Onychophora present serious problems. As a matter of fact, onychophorans are neither annelids nor arthropods but possess distinctive characteristics of their own, therefore. Onychophora are nowadays considered as a separate phylum.

But the modern view is somewhat different. It is presumed that the group is very ancient and once had been more widespread and diversified containing a great variety of forms. This is supported by the discovery of eleven fossil specimens of the mid-Cambrian, *Aysheaia* which closely resembles the modern Onychophora. The latest view holds that Onychophora is not an evolutionary link between Annelida and Arthropoda but a distinct surviving branch of segmental animals.

REVISION QUESTIONS

1. Describe the habit, habitat and external morphology of *Peripatus*.
2. Describe the digestive system and process of digestion in *Peripatus*.
3. Give an account of the nervous system and reproductive system of *Peripatus*.
4. Discuss the affinities of Onychophora and suggest a suitable place for this group in the Animal Kingdom.
5. Write a note on geographical distribution of *Peripatus*.

84

Phylum Echinodermata

The name Echinodermata (Gr., *echinos* = hedgehog+*derma*=skin) appears to have originated with Jacob Klein (1734), who, however, applied it only to echinoids. Echinodermata are all exclusively marine animals living on the shore but mostly on the bottom of the sea. They are coelomate animals with pentaramous radial symmetry, that is the body can be divided into five parts arranged around a central axis, but the larva is bilaterally symmetrical. There is no head. They have an endoskeleton of calcareous ossicles made from mesoderm, there are also external spines which may be movable or fixed. A large ciliated enterocoelous coelom forms a perivisceral cavity and several intricate systems, one of which is a water vascular system from which project delicate tube feet. Respiratory organs are minute gills protruding out from the coelom. There is no definite blood vascular system, it is represented only by lacunar tissue, there are no definite excretory organs. Nervous system forms a ring around the mouth with nerves radiating from it, it is the principal nervous system and is in contact with the ectoderm, in addition there is a deeper nervous system lying in the mesoderm. Sexes are usually separate but copulation does not take place, the gonads discharge to the exterior and fertilization takes place in sea water. Echinodermata have no parasitic forms. They possess great powers of regeneration.

Echinodermata have a world-wide distribution and the phylum contains some 5,300 known species and a large number of fossil forms. The phylum is divided into two subphyla, *viz.,* Pelmatozoa and Eleutherozoa, Pelmatozoa, has only one living class Crinoidea, while Eleutherozoa has four living classes, Holothuroidea, Echinoidea, Asteroidea, Ophiuroidea.

85

Asterias : A Sea Star

Asterias is commonly known by the name of starfish. The name starfish is somewhat misleading suggesting an organism to be like a star and fish but as *Asterias* lacks in both the characteristics, therefore, recently it is renamed as sea star. There occur about 150 species of *Asterias* all of which have different geographical distribution. *Asterias rubens* occurs on the English and North European coasts, *A. vulgaris* is found on the North Atlantic coast of North America, *A. forbesi* occurs on the eastern sea shore from the Maine to the Gulf of Mexico, *A. amurensis* is found in the Behring sea, Japan and Korea, and *A. tenera* occurs on the sea shore from Nova Scotia to New Jersey. Some other common sea stars are *Pentaceros, Astropecten, Asterina, Heliaster, Solaster, Luidia*, etc. The following account will give a general idea about the anatomical organisation of the genus *Asterias*.

SYSTEMATIC POSITION

Phylum	.....	**Echinodermata**
Subphylum	.....	**Eleutherozoa**
Class	.....	**Asteroidea**
Order	.....	**Forcipulata**
Genus	.....	*Asterias*

HABIT AND HABITAT

Asterias is exclusively marine, bottom dwelling or **benthonic** animal, inhabiting various types of bottom, mainly in the littoral zone where they crawl about or may remain quiescent at times, either in the open or more or less concealed. *Asterias forbesi* is found equally abundant on hard, rocky, sandy or soft bottom, while other species have been found to prefer rocky sea bottoms. The most species of *Asterias* are generally solitary but under certain ecological conditions, such as to avoid direct sunlight or excessive drying, many individuals may gather at some place for the purpose of protection. Most of them are nocturnal, remain quiet in day time and become active during night. They move by crawling on the bottom, mostly at a rather slow rate. All sea stars are carnivorous and feed voraciously on almost any available slow moving or sessile animals, chiefly on polychaetes, crustaceans, molluscs and other echinoderms and even corpses. Many species of *Asterias* exhibit various types of biological relationships such as parasitism and commensalism, etc., with the members of different zoological groups. Sea stars, in general, exhibit remarkable power of autotomy and regeneration.

EXTERNAL FEATURES

Shape, size and colour. *Asterias* has a radially symmetrical and pentamerous body. The body consists of a central, pentagonal central disc from which radiate out five elongated, tapering, symmetrical spaced projections, the rays or arms. In some genera, the number of arms may be more than five, for example, there are 7–14 arms in *Solaster* and more than 40 arms in *Heliaster*. The size varies from 10–20 cm in diameter though some forms may be much smaller or longer. The colour is variable having shades of yellow, orange, brown and purple. The body has two surfaces, the upper convex and much darker side is called the aboral or abactinal surface. The lower surface is flat, less pigmented and is called the oral or actinal surface. The oral and aboral surfaces are not the ventral and dorsal surfaces but correspond to the left and right sides of the bilaterally symmetrical larva. The axes occupied by the arms are known as radii and the regions of the central disc between the arms are inter-radii. A well defined head is entirely absent.

Oral surface. The side of body, which in natural condition remains towards the substratum and contains the mouth or oral opening, is flat and of dark orange to purplish colour, is called oral or actinal surface. The oral sur-

face bears the following structures :

1. **Mouth.** On the oral surface, in the centre of the pentagonal central disc is an aperture, the actinosome or mouth. It is a pentagonal aperture with five angles, each directed towards an arm. The mouth is surrounded by a soft and delicate membrane, the peristomial membrane or peristome and is guarded by five groups of oral spines or mouth papillae.

2. **Ambulacral grooves.** From each angle of the mouth radiates a narrow groove called the ambulacral groove which runs all along the middle of oral surface of each arm.

3. **Tube feet or podia.** Each ambulacral groove contains four rows of locomotory,

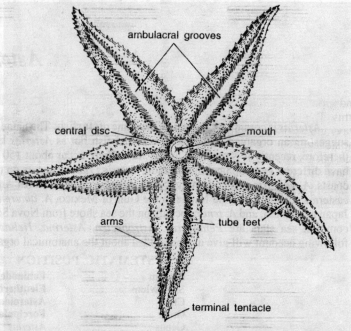

Fig. 85.1. *Asterias.* External features (Oral view).

food capturing, respiratory and sensory organs called tube feet or podia. The tube feet are soft, thin-walled, tubular, retractile structures provided with terminal discs or suckers. The suckers function as suction cups to afford a firm attachment on the surface to which they are applied.

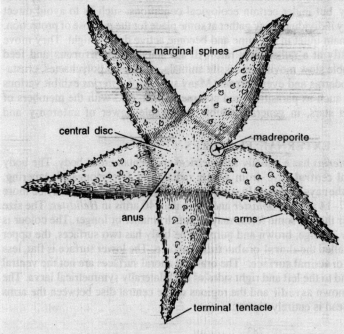

Fig. 85.2. *Asterias.* External features (Aboral view).

4. **Ambulacral spines.** Each ambulacral groove is bordered and guarded laterally by 2 or 3 rows of movable calcareous ambulacral spines which are capable of closing over the groove. Near the mouth, these spines often become larger, stouter, assemble in five groups, one at each inter-radius of disc and are called mouth papilla. Outside the ambulacral spines are three rows of stout immovable spines, beyond which occurs another series of marginal spines along the borders of the arms demarcating the oral from the aboral surface.

5. **Sense organs.** Sense organs include five unpaired terminal tentacles and five unpaired eye spots. The tip of each arm bears a small median,

non-retractile and hollow projection, the terminal tentacle. It acts as a tactile and olfactory organ. At the base of each tentacle occurs a bright red photo-sensitive eye spot made up of several ocelli.

Aboral surface. The side of the body, which remains directed upward or towards the upper surface, is convex and of light orange to purplish colour, is called aboral or abactinal surface. The aboral surface bears following structures :

1. Anus. A minute circular aperture, called the anus, is situated close to the centre of the central disc of aboral surface.

2. Madreporite. At the aboral surface of the central disc occurs a flat, sub-circular, asymmetrical and grooved plate called madreporite plate or madreporite between the bases of two of the five arms. The surface of madreporite is marked by a number of radiating, narrow, straight or slightly wavy grooves with pores in them. The madreporite is, thus, a sieve-like porous plate and it leads to the stone canal of water vascular system. The number of madreporite to an individual though remains one, but the presence of more than one madreporite in some species is due to the increase in number of arms beyond the normal number of five. The two arms having madreporite between their bases are collectively referred to as a bivium and the other three arms as a trivium. The symmetrical position of madreporite, thus, converts the radial symmetry of *Asterias* into bilateral symmetry.

3. Spines. The entire aboral surface is covered with numerous short, stout, blunt, calcareous spines or tubercles. The spines are variable in size and are arranged in irregular rows running parallel to the long axes of the arms. The spines are supported by the irregularly-shaped calcareous plates or ossicles which remain buried in the integument and form the endoskeleton.

4. Papulae or gills. Between the ossicles of integument are present a large number of minute dermal pores. Through each dermal pore projects out a very small, delicate, tubular or conical, finger-like or thread-like, thin-walled, membranous and retractile projection called the dermal branchia or gill or papula. The papulae are hollow evaginations of the body wall and their lumen remains in continuation with the coelom. They are internally lined by coelom. They have respiratory, as well as excretory functions.

5. Pedicellariae. Besides the spines and gills, entire aboral surface is covered by many whitish modified spine-like tiny pincers or jaws called pedicellariae. The oral surface also bears pedicellariae. Each pedicellaria consists of a long or short, stout, flexible stalk having no internal calcareous support. The stalk bears three calcareous ossicles or plates : a basilar piece or plate at the extremity of the stalk and jaws or valves which remain movably articulated with the basilar piece and serreted along their apposed edges. Pedicellariae having three calcareous pieces and a stalk are called forcipulate pedunculate pedicellariae. *Asterias* possesses two types of forcipulate pedunculate pedicellariae. *viz.,* (i) straight type and (ii) crossed type.

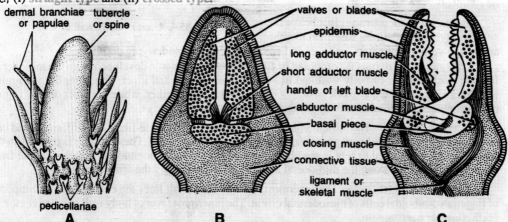

Fig. 85.3. *Asterias.* A—A cluster of pedicellariae, papulae, and tubercle ; B—Straight type pedicellaria ; C—Crossed type pedicellaria.

(i) Straight type pedunculate pedicellariae. This type of pedicellariae are simple. Their two jaws are more or less straight and attached basally to the basal piece. When closed they remain parallel and meet throughout their length. The two jaws work against one another like the blades of a forcep with the help of three pairs of muscles. There are two pairs of adductor muscles for closing the jaws and a pair of abductor muscles for opening them.

(ii) **Crossed type pedunculate pedicellariae.** In the crossed type of pedicellariae, the basal ends of the two jaws cross each other like the mandibles of a crossbill, so that the basal piece is enclosed between their crossed portions. In this type of pedicellariae, the jaws are also operated by two pairs of adductor muscles and one pair of abductor muscles.

Certain other pedicellariae having no stalk and, thus, called sessile pedicellariae are also found on the body of *Asterias*. They serve as defensive and offensive organs and provide protection to gills and general body surface by keeping the body surface free from debris and organisms like sponges and coelenterates setting on the body.

BODY WALL

The body wall of *Asterias* consists of following tissue layers :

1. **Cuticle.** The body surface is clothed with a definite cuticle consisting of two layers, an outer thick homogeneous layer and an inner delicate layer.

2. **Epidermis.** Just beneath the cuticle lies a layer of ciliated epithelium which extends over all the external appendages of body such as spines, pedicellariae, tube feet and gills, etc. The epidermis is composed of a variety of cells such as ordinary flagellated or ciliated columnar cells, neurosensory cells, mucous gland cells or goblet cells having finely granular contents, muriform gland cells filled with coarse spherules and the pigment granules which provide characteristic external colouration to the animal.

3. **Nervous layer.** Beneath the epidermis lies a nervous layer, varying in thickness in different areas and penetrated by the attenuated bases of the epidermal cells on their elastic filaments.

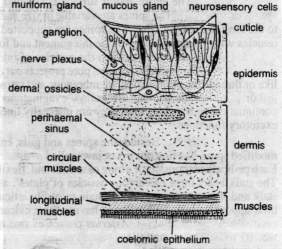

4. **Basement membrane.** Just below the nervous layer lies a delicate basement membrane which separates the nervous layer and epidermis from the underlying dermis.

Fig. 85.4. *Asterias*. Body wall in V.S.

5. **Dermis.** The dermis is composed of fibrous connective tissue developed from the mesoderm. It is the thickest layer of body wall and has two regions : outer and inner. The outer dermal region secretes and houses the endoskeletal ossicles and binds them together, while the inner dermal region contains numerous blood containing spaces called perihaemal spaces.

6. **Muscular layer.** The muscular layer consists of smooth muscle-fibres. It is differentiated into an outer circular muscle layer and inner longitudinal muscle layer. These muscle layers are on the whole weakly developed except in the aboral wall where stronger longitudinal bundles radiate from the centre of the disc along the mid-dorsal line of each arm, to bend the arms aborally.

7. **Coelomic epithelium.** The innermost layer of body wall lines the coelom and is composed of flagellated cuboidal cells of mesodermal origin. The innermost layer of body wall is called coelomic epithelium or peritoneum.

ENDOSKELETON

The rigidity of the body of *Asterias* is due to the presence of definite skeleton. In *Asterias*, the endoskeleton is unique in being mesodermal in origin instead of ectodermal as in other invertebrates. It consists of numerous calcareous ossicles. The ossicles are of various shapes and are bound together by connective tissue. They form a reticulate skeleton, leaving spaces for the emergence of groups of papulae. The ossicles have irregular arrangement on the aboral surface but have definite and regular arrangement on the oral surface. On the oral surface, they are regularly around the mouth and in the ambulacral groove. Five plate-like ossicles called oral ossicles remain arranged around the mouth. Each ambulacral groove is supported by double rows of large, transversely placed opposite rod-shaped ambulacral ossicles. The ossicles of the two opposite rows are arranged like an inverted V, their aboral ends meeting at the apex of the V, like the rafters supporting the roof of a shed and forming a conspicuous ambulacral ridge. The ambulacral ossicles do not bear any spines, tubercles or other external appendages. Because they are movably articulated in the ambulacral groove, they permit the opening or closing of the latter. Further, each ambulacral ossicle has a notch on its outer as well as inner margin. The two notches of the adjacent ossicles together form an oval aperture, the ambulacral **pore** for the passage of tube-foot. The ambulacral pores are so arranged that they form two rows on each side of the ambulacral groove. At its outer end, each ambulacral groove articulates with one admbulacral ossicle forming the edge of the groove and bearing two or three movable spines on small tubercles. Next to the adambulacral ossicle there are two rows of the ossicles called supra- and inframarignal ossicles.

SECTION OF AN ARM

The arm is covered all around by a thin two-layered cuticle, a ciliated epidermis and an underlying thick dermis which has many perihaemal spaces and ossicles. Epidermis and dermis are thinned over the projecting spines, pedicellariae and papulae but they wear off from spines. The aboral side is a thick convex arch, and the oral side is like an inverted Λ , between the two limbs of the Λ is an ambulacral groove. The arm encloses a perivisceral coelom.

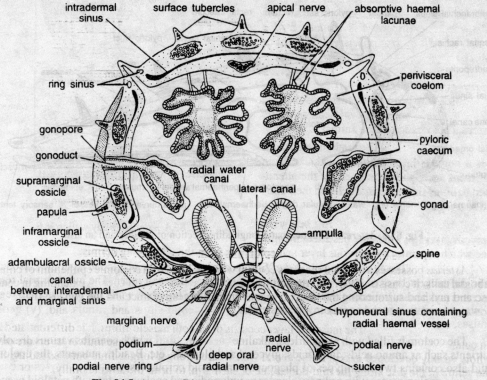

Fig. 84.5. *Asterias*. Diagrammatic transverse section of an arm.

The aboral wall has a number of irregular, fenestrated ossicles which are calcareous, on some ossicles rest projecting spines. From the aboral side dermal papulae project out, the coelom is continued into the papulae. Between the spines and attached to them are many pedicellariae. Each lateral margin of the arm has two large spines, they are a supramarginal spine and below it an inframarignal spine. Mid-dorsally the arm has a large cardinal spine.

On the oral surface the ambulacral groove is supported by two elongated ambulacral ossicles meeting at the summit of the groove, at each end of the ambulacral groove is an adambulacral ossicles and spine. The ambulacral ossicles form two columns in the oral surface of each arm and on each side there is a single column of adambulacrals. The adambulacral spine can touch the substratum or bend inwards to protect the ambulacral groove. Above the ambulacral groove runs a radial canal which is joined on each side by a podial branch to two ampullae and one tube foot. Below the radial canal is a radial hyponeural sinus enclosing a radial haemal channel.

Muscles. The median aboral side below the body wall has an apical longitudinal muscle which stretches the arm. Each pair of ambulacral ossicles has an upper and a lower transverse ambulacral muscle, the upper or superior transverse ambulacral muscle widens the ambulacral groove, and the lower or inferior transverse ambulacral muscle makes the ambulacral groove narrow. Between the adjacent ambulacral ossicles of each side is a longitudinal ambulacral muscle which shortens the arm and the ambulacral groove. The outer end of each ambulacral ossicle is connected to the adambulacral ossicle by a lateral transverse ambulacral muscle which widens the ambulacral groove.

Nerves. In the middle of the ambulacral groove is a radial nerve cord in the shape of a V. Above the radial nerve cord are two Lange's nerves. Close to the outer end of each ambulacral ossicle is a marginal nerve. Each podium has a nerve ring.

Inside the perivisceral coelom of the arm is a pair of pyloric caeca, each suspended by two longitudinal mesenteries from the aboral surface. If the section passes through the base of the arm the perivisceral coelom has a pair of gonads attached to the body wall by their ducts.

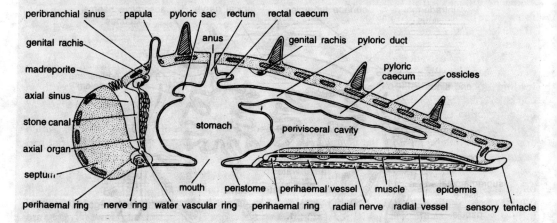

Fig. 85.6. *Asterias.* Diagrammatic longitudinal section of the disc and an arm.

COELOM

Asterias possesses a true and spacious coelom which is lined by a coelomic epithelium of ciliated cuboidal cells. It consists of various compartments, *viz.*, (i) a perivisceral coelom extending in central disc and rays and surrounding the visceral organs such as digestive tract and the gonads, (ii) coelom of water vascular system, (iii) axial sinus, (iv) perihaemal sinus and canals and, (v) genital sinuses, etc.

The coelom is filled with a colourless, alkaline coelomic fluid which contains various dissolved nutrients such as amino acids, fatty acids, glycerol and glucoses, etc. Besides nutrients, the coelomic fluid also contains two main types of phagocytic amoeboid corpuscles, the amoebocytes or coelomocytes : coelomocytes with ordinary slender pseudopodia and coelomocytes with petaloid pseudopodia. The coelomic fluid, like the haemolymph of Arthropoda, bathes the tissue of the body and performs the function of circulatory system. It distributes the nutrients to various body cells and also performs the respiratory as well as excretory functions.

DIGESTIVE SYSTEM

The digestive system of *Asterias* comprises the alimentary canal and digestive glands.
Alimentary Canal

In *Asterias,* the alimentary canal is tubular, straight, short and extends vertically along the oral-aboral axis in the central disc. It comprises the following parts :

1. Mouth. The mouth is the anteriormost aperture of alimentary canal and it is situated in the centre of the peristomial membrane of the oral surface. It is provided with a sphincter muscle and radial fibres and is capable of great expansion and retraction. The mouth leads upward into the oesophagus.

2. Oesophagus. The oesophagus is a very short, wide and vertical tube. It opens aborally in the stomach.

3. Stomach. The stomach is a broad sac and fills the interior of the disc. It is typically divided by a horizontal constriction into a voluminous oral part, the cardiac stomach and a flattened aboral part, the pyloric stomach. The cardiac stomach has a muscular, highly folded wall bulged out to form five lobes, one opposite each arm. The cardiac stomach is connected to the ambulacral ridge of each arm by ligaments of muscles and connective tissues called mesenteries or gastric ligaments which serve to anchor the cardiac stomach in place. During the feeding process, the cardiac stomach can be everted through the mouth by the contraction of muscles of body

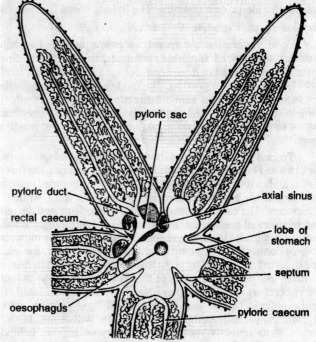

Fig. 85.7. *Asterias.* Digestive system.

wall. The retraction of cardiac stomach is brought about by five pairs of retractor muscles which arise from the lateral sides of the ambulacral ridge. The pyloric stomach is much smaller, flat and pentagonal sac. It communicates with the intestine.

4. Intestine. The intestine is a short, narrow, five sided tube that runs straight upward to open out at the anus. It gives off two or three little hollow diverticula called intestinal or rectal caeca placed inter-radially. The intestinal caeca are brown in colour and each bears several short, irregularly-shaped diverticula. The actual function of intestinal caeca is well disputed. However, they are considered as excretory organs, because, they secrete a brown fluid.

5. Anus. The intestine opens on the aboral surface by a posteriormost aperture of the alimentary canal called anus. The anus is situated eccentrically on the aboral side of central disc.

Histology of alimentary canal. Histologically the wall of the alimentary canal consists from within outwards of an enteric epithelium of columnar ciliated cells of endodermal origin, a subepidermal nervous layer, a connective tissue layer devoid of ossicles, a layer of muscles and an outermost layer of coelomic epithelium or visceral peritoneum. The thickness of the layers varies in different parts of the alimentary canal.

Digestive Glands

To the pyloric stomach are attached ten, long brownish or greenish glandular appendages variously called pyloric caeca, digestive glands, branchial caeca, hepatic caeca, etc. There are two pyloric caeca in each arm, each suspended from the aboral wall of the arm by two longitudinal mesenteries that enclose between them a coelomic space continuous at its central end with the general coelom of the disc. Each pyloric caecum consists of double series of hollow lobulated sacs that open into a central tube duct. The two ducts forming a pair of caeca of each arm unite to form a main pyloric duct that opens into the pyloric stomach at one of its angles.

Histology of digestive gland. Histologically the pyloric caeca are complex structures and are lined by ciliated columnar epithelium which is composed of four types of epithelial cells. The current producer cells bear longer flagella and maintain a steady circulation of the fluids and digested food in the cavities of the caeca; the mucous cells produce mucus; the secretory or granular cells secrete digestive enzymes to convert proteins into peptones, starch into monosaccharide sugars and fats into fatty acids and glycerol, and the storage cells store reserve food such as lipids, glycogen and polysaccharide-protein complex. The pyloric caeca function like pancreas of vertebrates.

Physiology of Digestive System

Food. *Asterias* is a carnivorous animal and feed voraciously on worms, crustaceans, snails, bivalves, small-sized starfishes, echinoderms and fishes. Sometimes, *Asterias* also feed on dead animals and under hazardous conditions may live without food for several months.

Ingestion and digestion. The mode of feeding or ingestion in *Asterias* is of most unusual type. It swallows small-sized animals directly through the mouth. The prey is held by the tube feet and cardiac stomach is everted and wrapped round it. The enzymatic secretions of pyloric caeca poured out on to the prey and when digestion is completed, stomach is withdrawn along with the digested food.

To feed shelled molluscs (bivalves), *Asterias* adopts another interesting technique. It creeps over the clam and holding it with tube feet, orients it to bring the free margins of the shell close to its mouth. It now arches its body, assuming a characteristic humped or umbrella-like posture. The more proximal tube feet firmly grip both valves of the bivalve's shell, while the more distal ones are attached to the substratum. The cardiac stomach is now everted through the mouth by the concentration of body wall and pressure of coelomic fluid. The tube feet gripping the valves of the clam's shell exert a steady pull as the muscles in the arms contract. But, because the muscles of clam cannot maintain a continuous state of contraction for a long time and sooner or later, the adductors of the mussel become fatigued or exhausted and finally relax, so that the shell opens. *Asterias,* now, inserts its already everted cardiac stomach into the mantle cavity of the clam and pours out its proteolytic enzymes. The enzymes digest the visceral organs of clam, they, thus, convert the proteins of visceral organs into peptones and amino acids, polysaccharidic carbohydrates and lipid contents into fatty acids and glycerol. When the digestion is partially completed the sea star withdraws its stomach alongwith the digested food by means of its retractor muscles and moves on leaving behind the shell of the victim. Remaining digestion of food substances occurs in cardiac stomach from which the digested food diffuses to coelomic fluid for body wide distribution and to pyloric caeca where it may be distributed to arms or stored in storage cells of epithelium of pyloric caeca. The undigested food is either egested out directly from the mouth or pass through intestine and egested out through the anus.

WATER VASCULAR (AMBULACRAL) SYSTEM

The water vascular system is a modified part of coelom and it consists of a system of sea-water filled canals having certain corpuscles. It plays most vital role in the locomotion of the animal and comprises madreporite, stone canal, ring canal, radial canal, Tiedeman's bodies, lateral canals, and tube feet.

1. Madreporite. As already stated, the madreporite is a rounded calcareous plate occurring on the aboral surface of the central disc in inter-radial position. Its surface bears a number of radiating, narrow, straight or wavy grooves or furrows. Each furrow contains many minute pores at its bottom. Each pore leads into a very short, fine, tubular pore canal which passes inward in the substance of the madreporite. There may be about 200 pores and pore-canals. The pore-canals unite to form the collecting canals which open into an ampulla beneath the madreporite.

2. Stone canal. The ampulla opens into a S-shaped stone canal. The stone

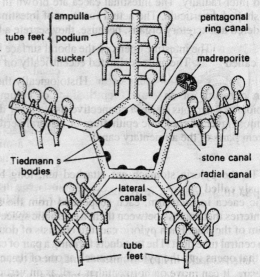

Fig. 85.8. *Asterias*. Water vascular system.

canal extends downwards (orally) and opens into a ring canal, around the mouth. The walls of stone canal are supported by a series of calcareous rings. The lumen of stone canal is lined by very tall flagellated cells. In embryonic stages and in young *Asterias,* the stone canal remains a simple tube but in adult *Asterias,* lumen of stone canal possesses a prominent ridge with two spirally rolled lamellae which by branching become more complicated in structure. During its course, the stone canal is ensheathed by a wide, thin-walled tubular coelomic sac, called axial sinus.

3. **Ring canal.** The ring canal or water ring is located to the inner side of the peristomial ring of ossicles and directly above (aboral) to the hyponeural ring sinus. It is wide and pentagonal or five sided.

4. **Tiedemann's bodies.** The ring canal gives out inter-radially nine small, yellowish, irregular or rounded glandular bodies called racemose or Tiedemann's bodies, from its inner margins. The Tiedemann's bodies rest upon the peristomial ring of ossicles. The actual function of Tiedemann's bodies is still unknown, however, they are supposed to be lymphatic glands to manufacture the amoebocytes of the water vascular system.

5. **Polian vesicles.** The ring canal gives off on its inner side in the inter-radial position one, two or four, little, pear-shaped, thin-walled, contractile bladders or reservoirs with long necks called polian vesicles. They are supposed to regulate pressure inside ambulacral system and to manufacture amoeboid cells of ambulacral system.

6. **Radial canal.** From its outer surface the ring canal gives off a radial water canal into each arm that runs throughout the length of the arm and terminates as the lumen of terminal tentacle. In the arm the radial water canal runs immediately to the oral side of the ambulacral muscles.

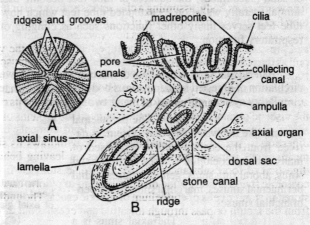

Fig. 85.9. *Asterias.* Madreporite, A—As seen from outside, B—Vertical section.

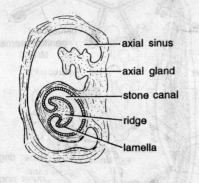

Fig. 85.10. *Asterias.* T.S. of axial complex.

7. **Lateral canals.** In each arm, the radial canal gives out two series of short, narrow, transverse branches called lateral or podial canals. Each lateral canal is attached to the base of a tube foot and is provided with a valve to prevent backward flow of fluid into the radial canal.

8. **Tube feet.** As already mentioned, there are four rows of tube feet in each ambulacral groove. A tube foot or podium is a hollow, elastic, thin-walled, closed cylinder or sac-like structure having an upper sac-like ampulla, a middle tubular podium and a lower disc-like sucker. The ampulla lies within the arm, projecting into the coelom above the ambulacral pore which is a gap between the adjacent ambulacral ossicles for the passage of the podium. The tube feet are chief locomotory and respiratory organs of *Asterias.*

LOCOMOTION

Asterias lacks in head or anterior end, therefore, capable to move in any direction according to its desire. It can move on horizontal as well as on vertical surfaces by the help of tube feet.

Locomotion on a horizontal surface. When an *Asterias* desires to move on a horizontal surface in a given direction, the arm or arms pointing in that direction is lifted. The ampullae of raised arm contract, the valve in the lateral canals close and the water of the ampullae is forced into the podia. The podia of the tube feet become extended, elongated and enlarged in the general direction of movement due to the hydrostatic pressure produced by influx of water into them. Subsequently, the terminal suckers of the tube feet become attached to the substratum and their central parts are withdrawn to form suction cups. Due to the vacuum so produced, the suckers acquire a firm grip over the substratum. Mucus secreted by the tips of the tube feet further aids in attachment. The tube feet now pivot forward on their attached suckers, assuming vertical position and thereby pushing the body forwards. The longitudinal muscles of the podia now contract and this forces their fluid back into the ampullae and releases their suckers. The ampullae then contract again and whole sequence of events is repeated.

Locomotion on a vertical surface. In climbing a vertical surface, the tube feet pull the body forward. By the alternate contraction and expansion of tube feet and by adherence of suckers of tube feet on surface *Asterias* climbs on the vertical surface.

Asterias employs its tube feet, only when, it moves on hard rocky substratum. But, on soft mud or sand (substratum) the suckers of tube feet become useless, therefore, on such soft surfaces the animal literally walks on its extended tube feet which now act like small legs. Besides locomotion, tube feet serves many other functions such as clinging of animal body to substratum, tactile and respiratory function.

CIRCULATORY SYSTEM

Asterias lacks in a true blood vascular system. However, the system which is responsible for circulation of digested food to various body organs is often termed as circulatory system. The so called circulatory system includes following two systems : 1. perihaemal system, and 2. haemal system.

1. Perihaemal system. The perihaemal system, like the water vascular system, is derived from the coelom and is composed of many tubular coelomic sinuses such as axial sinus, aboral ring sinus, genital sinuses, radial perihaemal sinuses, marginal sinuses and peribranchial sinuses.

(i) Axial sinuses. The axial sinus is a thin-walled, vertical, wide tubular coelomic cavity enclosing the stone canal and the axial gland. The three forming a well developed axial complex.

(ii) Aboral ring sinus. The aboral ring sinus is a tubular, pentagonal channel or sinus around the intestine, lying just inside the aboral wall of the central disc. It communicates with the axial sinuses.

(iii) Genital sinuses. The aboral ring sinus gives off five pairs of genital branches, one pair in each arm. The genital sinuses surround the gonads.

(iv) Oral ring sinus. At its oral end, the axial sinus opens into the inner division of a circular channel, the oral, peribuccal, perihaemal, or hyponeural ring sinus which runs around the mouth. It is a large tubular sinus and is divisible into an inner narrow and an outer wide ring by an oblique circular septum called haemal strand.

(v) Radial perihaemal sinuses. The outer division of ring sinus gives out five radial hyponeural or perihaemal sinuses, one

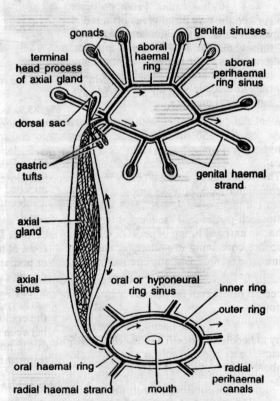

Fig. 85.11. *Asterias.* Diagrammatic representation of perihaemal and haemal systems.

of which extends through each arm between the radial nerve and the radial water canal. Like oral ring sinus, each radial sinus is also divided longitudinally into two by a vertical partition or septum, continuous with the haemal strand. The radial perihaemal sinuses also give out fine channels into the tube feet.

(vi) Marginal sinuses. In each arm, two longitudinal marginal sinuses run longitudinally on each side just aboral to the marginal nerve cord. The fine lateral channels connect the marginal channels with the radial perihaemal sinuses.

(vii) Peribranchial sinuses. The sinuses occurring as circular spaces around the basal parts of papulae or gills are called peribranchial sinuses.

2. Haemal system. The haemal or blood lacunar system of *Asterias* is reduced and is of open type like the haemocoel of Arthropoda and Mollusca. It includes inter-communicating spaces having no coelomic epithelium and are derived embryologically from the blastocoel. The haemal system is filled with coelomic fluid containing coelomocytes and is enclosed in the coelomic spaces of perihaemal system. The main haemal sinuses are as follows :

(i) Oral haemal ring. It is the circular haemal sinus, located around the mouth just below the ring canal of the water vascular system. Oral haemal ring is a fine channel or a ring of lacunar tissue which runs in the septum dividing the hyponeural sinus. The oral haemal ring is connected with aboral haemal ring through axial gland.

(ii) Radial haemal sinuses or strands. These arise radially from the oral haemal ring and one extends into each arm, along the floor of the ambulacral groove just below the radial canal of the water vascular system. The radial haemal sinuses also give off branches into the podia.

(iii) Axial complex. The perihaemal and haemal systems of *Asterias* are intimately connected by a complicated structure called axial complex. The axial complex comprises the following three parts : a thin-walled, tubular coelomic cavity called axial sinus containing the stone canal of water vascular system and axial gland, both are closely attached with the walls of axial sinus by the mesenteries.

(iv) Axial gland. This is the principal part of the haemal system. The axial gland is an elongated, fusiform, brownish or purple coloured spongy body. It is covered externally by coelomic epithelium and is called variously as heart, ovoid gland, dorsal organ, septal organ, brown gland, etc. The axial gland is connected with the oral and aboral haemal sinuses at its oral and aboral ends respectively. At its oral end the axial gland becomes thin and terminates in the septum that subdivides the hyponeural ring sinus. At its aboral end, the axial gland has an aboral extension or terminal process called head process which is lodged in a separate, closed contractile coelomic sac called dorsal sac. The dorsal sac is situated below the madreporite, close to the ampulla of the stone canal, but has no communication with the ampulla. A pair of gastric tufts also arises from the haemal sinuses in the wall of the cardiac stomach and opens into the axial gland near its aboral end. Digested food from the stomach passes into the haemal circulation through the gastric tufts. Histologically, the axial gland has an external lining of peritoneum and its interior is filled by connective tissue outlining numerous spaces containing irregularly arranged cells of the nature of coelomocytes. The axial gland has an intimate relation with the circulation of blood in perihaemal and haemal channels.

(v) Aboral haemal ring. It is a pentagonal ring canal lying beneath the aboral surface of the central disc. From the aboral haemal ring or canal extend five pairs of genital haemal strands to the gonads.

Function. The haemal system acts as a pathway for the distribution of food substances carried by the coelomocytes. The flow of fluid within it is maintained by the contractile activity of the dorsal sac. The axial gland acts as a genital stolon, producing sex-cells, which reach the gonads through the aboral haemal ring and its branches.

RESPIRATORY SYSTEM

The respiratory organs of *Asterias* are gills or papulae and tube feet. The papulae are the chief respiratory organs. They are simple, contractile, transparent, hollow outgrowths of body wall on the aboral surface having ciliated epithelium at outer and inner surfaces. They are derived from coelom and their lumen remains in direct communication with coelom. An exchange of O_2 and CO_2 takes place between sea water and body fluid of gills. The cilia of epithelial cells have vital role in movement of coelomic fluid and in creating respiratory water currents in sea water. The other thin-walled, richly vascularized and moist body parts also act as respiratory organs.

EXCRETORY SYSTEM

Asterias lacks well specialized excretory organs. The nitrogenous metabolic excretory waste usually contains ammonium compounds. They pass from various tissues into the coelomic fluid and from there they diffuse through the thin walls of the rectal caeca, tube feet and gills. The coelomocytes have significant role in the excretion of excretory wastes from the coelom.

NERVOUS SYSTEM

The nervous system of *Asterias* is of simple and primitive type. It is composed of nerve fibres and nerve nets which are closely associated with the epidermis. The nervous system comprises the following four units placed at different levels in the disc and arms.

1. Oral or ectoneural or epidermal nervous system. The oral nervous system is situated just beneath the epidermis. It is the main part of the sensory nervous system and sensory in nature. It comprises the following parts :

(i) **Nerve ring.** The nerve ring is pentagonal in shape and is circum-oral, *i.e.,* occurs around the mouth in the peristomial membrane. It supplies nerve fibres to the peristomial membrane and the oesophagus and at each radius gives off a radial nerve.

(ii) **Radial nerve.** The nerve ring gives off five radial nerves, each of which runs throughout the length of the arm in the bottom of the ambulacral groove. Each radial nerve terminates as a sensory cushion on the aboral side of the terminal tentacle. A cross section of an arm shows that the radial nerve is a thick V-shaped mass continuous on its outer side with the epidermis and separated on its inner side from the hyponeural sinus only by a thin dermis and the coelomic epithelium. The radial nerve consists of fibrillae arranged in layers and interspersed with bipolar and multipolar ganglion cells.

(iii) **Subepidermal nerve complex.** The subepidermal nerve complex is an extensive network of nerve cells and nerve fibres beneath the epidermis all over the body surface including the gills and pedicellariae, etc. It is connected with radial nerve cords by nerve fibres. The subepidermal nerve-plexus is thickened into a cord which forms (i) two **marginal nerves** each of which extends throughout the length of an arm on each side and gives off a longitudinal series of **lateral motor nerves** which supply the ossicles, muscles, coelomic epithelium of that area and (ii) a nerve ring in the suckers of each tube foot.

The ectoneural nervous system acts as the central nervous system of *Asterias*. It has sensory and motor neurons.

2. Deep or hyponeural nervous system. The hyponeural nervous system occurs in the form of a nervous layer in the lateral part of the oral wall of the hyponeural sinus, beneath the coelomic epithelium lining the sinus. This nervous layer is called **Lange's nerve.** It is separated from the lateral part of the radial nerve only by a thin layer of dermal connective tissue. Lange's nerve gives off a series of nerves along the arm into the adjacent lower transverse muscle extending between the ambulacral ossicles in the roof of the hyponeural sinus. Lange's nerve continues to the peristomial region, where it forms five inter-radial thickenings in the floor of the ring sinus that lies aboral to the main nerve ring.

3. Aboral or coelomic nervous system. The aboral or coelomic nervous system is situated just outside the parietal peritoneum on the aboral side. It consists of a nerve ring in the central disc and a nerve in each arm. This system has connection with marginal nerves by nerve fibres. It innervates the body muscles of aboral side and is motor in function.

4. Visceral nervous system. The visceral nervous system occurs in wall of the gut just outside the enteric epithelium. It innervates the muscles of alimentary canal and is connected with the visceral receptors.

SENSE ORGANS

Asterias possesses a few primitive sense organs which are as follows :

1. Eyes. The eyes are the most significant sensory organs of *Asterias*. They are simple, pigmented and occur at the base of terminal tentacles. On the oral surface, at the base of each terminal tentacle occur optic cushions which are composed of the thick epidermis with many photoreceptors or pigmented cup ocelli. Each ocellus is a cup-shaped or funnel-like pocket of ectoderm. It is covered externally by the cuticle beneath which is found in many species a lens formed by the epidermis. The wall of cup consists of epidermal cells, altered into a shorter, stouter shape and filled distally with red pigment granules and of retinal cells, disposed between the pigment cells. The retinal cells are elongated cells with a distal bulbous enlargement projecting into the cavity of the cup and a proximal fibre passing into the underlying radial nerve. The number of ocelli in one optic cushion or eyes ranges from 80 to 200 in different species. A transparent gelatinous tissue fills the cavity of ocellus. The ocelli are light-perceiving organs which can detect changes in light intesity.

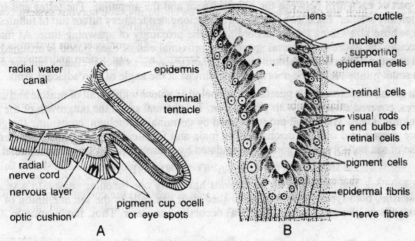

Fig. 85.12. *Asterias*. A—Section through a terminal tentacle and eyespot ; B—V.S. of a single eye-pit or ocellus.

2. Terminal tentacles. The terminal tentacles have sensory cells which are tactile and also sensitive to food and other chemical stimuli.

3. Neurosensory cells. The entire body surface or epidermis of *Asterias* is traversed by many neurosensory cells serving as both tango- and chemoreceptors. The neurosensory cells are slender cells with a fusiform body containing the nucleus, a distal thread-like process reaching to the cuticle, and a proximal fibre entering the subepidermal nerve plexus. They are especially numerous in the suckers of the podia, at the base of spines and pedicellariae and terminal tentacles.

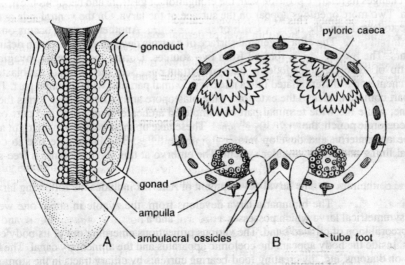

Fig. 85.13. *Asterias*. Gonads. A—An arm dissected to show gonads ; B—T.S. of an arm showing gonads.

REPRODUCTIVE SYSTEM

Most species of *Asterias* are unisexual or dioecious, *i.e.*, sexes are separate except a few species such as *Asterias rubens* which is hermaphrodite. There is no marked sexual dimorphism, however, during breeding season some sort of colour difference between both the sexes may occur. The reproductive organs of *Asterias* are of primitive type and lack copulatory organs, accessory glands, receptacles for storing ova and reservoirs for storing mature sperms. There are only gonads which act as reproductive organs.

Gonads. The male gonads are testes and female gonads are ovaries. Each sexually mature male or female individual contains five pairs of testes or ovaries, one pair is lying free laterally in the proximal part of each arm between the pyloric caeca and the ampullae. The testes and ovaries are morphologically similar. Each gonad appears as an elongated feathery tuft or tuft of tubules or bunch of grapes, whose size varies greatly according to the proximity of spawning time. At maturity the gonads occupy the entire perivisceral space. The proximal end of each gonad is attached to aboral body wall near the interbrachial septum by a very short gonoduct which is ciliated and opens laterally through a small gonopore on the aboral surface almost at the angle of two adjacent arms.

Each gonad is enclosed in a genital sac of coelomic nature with a wall of muscle and connective tissue fibres, covered externally with peritoneum. This genital sac is the outgrowth of the genital or aboral coelomic sinus. The gonad proper is lined by germinal epithelium, containing the germ cells. The mature sperms and ova are discharged by male and female *Asterias* respectively in sea water. The release of sex cells from the gonads is regulated by neurohormonal secretion of radial nerve.

LIFE HISTORY AND DEVELOPMENT

Fertilization. The most species of *Asterias* have only one breeding season in a year. During breeding season, both types of mature sexes shed their sex cells in the sea and union of male and female sex cells or gametes (sperms and ova) occurs in sea water. Thus, fertilization in *Asterias* is external.

Embryogeny. The embryological development of *Asterias* is indirect and includes various larval stages. The fertilized egg or zygote is spherical, half millimeter in diameter and contains little amount of yolk. The cleavage is holoblastic and equal and it converts the unicellular zygote into a single layered, hollow, ciliated and spherical structure called coeloblastula. The coeloblastula possesses a fluid-filled central space, called blastocoel and it swims about freely. The blastula undergoes embolic invagination and becomes two layered cup-like gastrula. The gastrulation involves the inward pushing of blastomeres of one side. The inpushing encloses a cavity called archenteron and it occupies the larger part of blastocoel which ultimately becomes obliterated. This embryonic stage is called gastrula and it has an outer ectodermal and inner endodermal germinal layers. The archenteron or gastrocoel communicates to the exterior by a wide aperture called blastopore. The blastopore changes its relative position with the elongation of gastrula and becomes the anal opening of the larva. Two more openings appear on the surface of the larva. On the ventral side, a tubular ingrowth of ectoderm forms the larval mouth or stomodaeum. Another opening occurs on the dorsal side as the dorsal pore. The cilia of general surface of gastrula degenerate and certain definite ciliary band appears. The mesoderm is formed from two sources. During the gastrular invagination, the advancing tip of archenteron (endoderm) buds off certain mesenchyme cells into the blastocoel. The growing archenteron is differentiated into a narrow proximal part and wide terminal part. The narrow proximal part communicates to the exterior by the blastopore and in later stages forms the stomach, and intestine, while the wide terminal part of completed archenteron expands and cuts off on each side into a coelomic pouch, the hydroenterocoel. These take up their position to the right and the left sides of the archenteron and develop into coelomic pouches. The latter give rise to coelom, its mesodermal lining and water vascular system. The embryo at this stage becomes a free-swimming larva.

Larval development. The larval development of *Asterias* includes the following larval stages:

Bipinnaria larva. The bipinnaria larva develops from the zygote in about one week. It is a bilaterally symmetrical larva which possesses a preoral and a postoral ciliated band, and a preoral lobe with preoral loop of ciliated band. The various projections emerging out of its body correspond to the arms. Inside the body appears the coelomic apparatus and the alimentary canal. The bipinnaria larva feeds on diatoms, etc., by creating food-bearing currents by ciliary tracts in the stomodael wall.

It swims freely by forwarding its anterior end, with a clockwise rotation, after some time the bipinnaria larva transforms into the next larval stage, the brachiolaria larva.

Brachiolaria larva. In the brachiolaria larva the side-lobes of bipinnaria increase in length to become long, slender and ciliated larval arms. The larval arms move and contract. The preoral arms also give out processes called the brachiolar arms. The arms of brachiolaria larva have coelomic prolongations and possess tips of adhesive cells. The bases of these arms surround the elevated, adhesive, glandular area performing the function of a sucker or fixation disc by which the larva becomes attached at the time of metamorphosis.

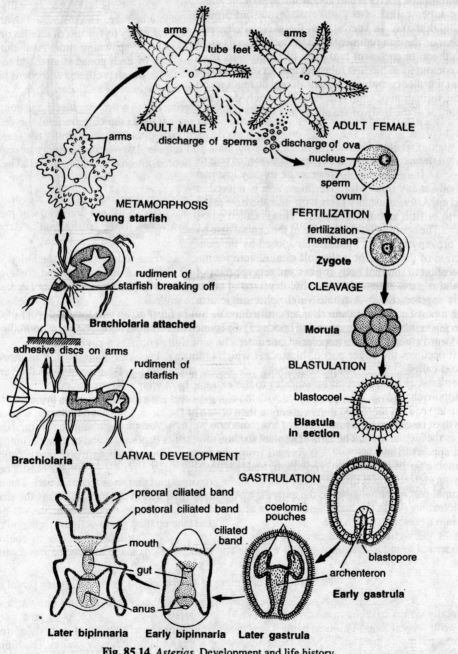

Fig. 85.14. *Asterias*. Development and life history.

METAMORPHOSIS

In about 6 or 7 weeks, the brachiolaria larva settles on the bottom or on some solid object and is fixed with that by its adhesive arms. Now the bilaterally symmetrical larva metamorphoses into a radially symmetrical adult. The larval mouth and anus close. A new mouth is formed on the left side of the larva and a new anus is developed on the right side. The left and right side of the larva, thus, subsequently differentiated into oral and aboral surfaces of the adult. Five lobes called arm rudiments grow out around oral-aboral axis. In later stages, the skeletal elements appear on the arm rudiments and the radial canals grow into them. In each arm two pairs of outgrowths from the coelom form the first tube feet and serve for attachment. Further complex reorganisational changes result in the formation of adult *Asterias*. The newly detached rudiment of the body of sea star is less than 1 mm with short stubby arms.

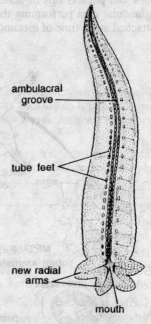

Fig. 85.15. Comet state of *Linckia*.

REGENERATION AND AUTOTOMY

Asterias possesses considerable power of regeneration. It is capable to regenerate its any lost part of body at any time. Moreover, if an arm is injured or held up, *Asterias* usually casts it off near the base at the fourth or fifth ambulacral ossicle. This is called autotomy. The opening left in the side of the central disc by the broken off arm is immediately closed by the contraction of the adjacent body wall musculature for the protection of internal body organs and regeneration of new arm starts at that place. A disc deprived of all its arms regenerates. In *Asterina vulgaris,* a single arm with a portion of disc regenerates an entire animal. But in *Linckia,* an arm totally devoid of disc can also regenerate complete animal (Fig. 85.15). Specimens with small regenerating arms at the base of the large original arm are popularly called comets.

REVISION QUESTIONS

1. Give an account of the habit, habitat and external features of starfish.
2. Describe the digestive system and mode of feeding in starfish.
3. Describe the water vascular system of starfish and mention the role of this system in the life of starfish.
4. Give an account of the circulatory system of starfish.
5. Describe the nervous system of an echinoderm you have studied.
6. Give an account of the development and life history of *Asterias*.
7. Write short notes on :
   (*i*) Madreporite; (*ii*) Pedicellariae; (*iii*) Endoskeleton of *Asterias;* (*iv*) Tube feet, (*v*) Polian vesicles; (*vi*) Axial complex; (*vii*) Bipinnaria larva.
8. Draw labelled diagrams only :
   (*i*) T.S. of an arm of starfish. (*ii*) L.S. of an arm of starfish.

86

Echinodermata : Classification, Characters and Types

DEFINITION

Echinoderms are enterocoelous coelomates with pentamerous radial symmetry, without distinct head or brain having a calcareous endoskeleton of separate plates or pieces and a peculiar water vascular system of coelomic origin with podia or tube-feet projecting out of the body.

GENERAL CHARACTERS

1. The echinoderms are exclusively marine and are among the most common and widely distributed of marine animals.

2. They occur in all seas from the intertidal zone to the great depths.

3. Symmetry usually radial, nearly always pentamerous.

4. Body is triploblastic, coelomate with distinct oral and aboral surfaces and without definite head and segmentation.

5. They are of moderate to considerable size but none are microscopic.

6. Body shape rounded to cylindrical or star-like with simple arms radiating from a central disc or branched feathery arms arise from a central body.

7. Surface of the body is rarely smooth, typically it is covered by five symmetrically spaced radiating grooves called ambulacra with five alternating inter-radii or inter-ambulacra.

8. Body wall consists of an outer epidermis, a middle dermis and an inner lining of peritoneum.

9. Endoskeleton consists of closely fitted plates forming a shell usually called theca or test or may be composed of separate small ossicles.

10. Coelom is spacious lined by peritoneum, occupied mainly by digestive and reproductive systems and develops from embryonic archenteron, *i.e.,* enterocoel.

11. Presence of water vascular or ambulacral system is the most characteristic feature. It consists of tubes filled with a watery fluid.

12. Alimentary tract is usually coiled tube extending from the mouth located on the oral surface to the anus on the aboral or oral surface.

13. Circulatory or haemal or blood lacunar system is typically present.

14. Respiration occurs through a variety of structures, *i.e.,* papulae in starfishes, peristomial gills in sea urchins, genital bursae in brittle stars and cloacal respiratory trees in holothurians.

15. Excretory system is wanting.

16. Nervous system is primitive, consisting of networks concentrated into the radial ganglionated nerve cords.

17. Sense organs are poorly developed.

18. Sexes are usually separate (dioecious) with few exceptions. Gonads are simple with or without simple ducts.

19. Reproduction is usually sexual, few reproduce asexually or by regeneration.

20. Fertilization is external, while few echinoderms are viviparous.

21. Development is indeterminate including characteristic larvae which undergo metamorphosis into the radially symmetrical adults.

CLASSIFICATION

The classification is adopted from Hyman, L. H. (1955). Only living classes and orders have been described.

SUBPHYLUM I. PELMATOZOA
(Gr., *pelmatos*=stalk+*zoon*=animal)

1. Mostly extinct echinoderms.
2. Body is attached by the aboral surface or by an aboral stalk.
3. Mouth and anal aperture present on the oral surface facing upwards.
4. Viscera is enclosed in a calcareous test. •
5. Tube feet or podia are primarily food catching and devoid of suckers.
6. Main nervous system is aboral.
7. Pelmatozoa has only one living class.

CLASS 1. CRINOIDEA
(Gr., *crinon*=lily+*eidos*=form)

1. Both extinct and living forms.
2. Living members are without stalk and free moving but extinct forms attached by a stalk.
3. Body consists of an aboral cup, the calyx and oral cover or roof, the tegmen and strongly pentamerous in structure.
4. Oral surface is directed upwards.
5. Mouth usually central, anus usually eccentric are present on the oral surface.
6. Arms movable, simple, mostly branched, usually five or ten in number with or without pinnules.
7. Ambulacral grooves are open and extend along arms and pinnules to their tips.
8. Madreporite, spines and pedicellariae are present.
9. Sexes are separate. Larva doliolaria.
10. Commonly called sea lilies or feather stars.

Order Articulata

1. Extinct and living crinoids.
2. Calyx pentamerous, flexible incorporating the lower arm ossicles.
3. Tegmen leathery containing calcareous particles or small plates.
4. Mouth and ambulacral grooves exposed
   Examples : *Antedon, Rhizocrinus, Metacrinus.*

SUBPHYLUM II. ELEUTHEROZOA
(Gr., *eleutheros*=free+*zoon*=animal)

1. Mostly living echinoderms.
2. Stem or stalk absent, usually free living forms.
3. Body structure usually pentamerous.
4. Oral surface bearing the mouth is downward or lying on one side.
5. Anus usually on the aboral surface.
6. Ambulacral grooves usually not for food

gathering and the tube feet with suckers are chiefly locomotory organs.
7. Main nervous system is oral.

CLASS 1. HOLOTHUROIDEA
(Gr., *holothurion*=water polyp+*eidos*=form)

1. Body bilaterally symmetrical, usually elongated in the oral-aboral axis having mouth at or near one end and anus at or near the other end.
2. Body surface is coarse.
3. Endoskeleton reduced to microscopic spicules or plates embedded in the body wall.
4. Mouth surrounded by a set of tentacles attached to water vascular system.
5. Podia or tube feet are usually present and locomotory.
6. Alimentary canal is long and coiled and cloaca usually with respiratory trees.
7. Sexes are usually separate and gonad single or paired tufts of tubules.
8. Commonly called sea cucumbers.

Order 1. Aspidochirota

1. Podia or tube feet are numerous.
2. Mouth is surrounded by 10–30 mostly 20 peltate or branched oral tentacles.
3. Retractor muscles of pharynx are absent.
4. A pair of well developed respiratory trees is present.
   Examples : *Holothuria, Stichopus, Mesothuria.*

Order 2. Elasipoda

1. Numerous podia or tube feet.
2. Mouth is usually ventral and surrounded by 10–20 peltate or branched tentacles.
3. Oral retractors absent.
4. Respiratory tree is absent.
   Examples : *Deima, Benthodytes.*

Order 3. Dendrochirota

1. Podia or tube feet are numerous.
2. Oral tentacles are dendritic or branched or branched like tree branches.
3. Oral retractors are absent.
4. Respiratory trees are present.
   Examples : *Thyone, Cucumaria, Phyllophorus.*

Order 4. Molpadonia

1. Podia or tube feet are absent except as anal papillae.
2. Oral tentacles are digitate or finger-shaped.
3. Oral retractors are absent.
4. Respiratory trees are present.

5. Posterior region is generally tapering into a caudal portion.
   Examples : *Molpadia, Paracaudina.*

Order 5. Apoda

1. Body vermiform having smooth or warty surface.
2. Podia or tube feet are absent.
3. Oral tentacles are 10–20, simple, digitate or pinnate.
4. Pharyngeal retractors are present in some forms.
5. Respiratory trees are absent.
6. Water vascular system is greatly reduced.
   Examples : *Synapta, Chiridoata.*

CLASS 2. ECHINOIDEA
(Gr., *echinos*=hedgehog+*eidos*=form)

1. Body is spherical, disc-like, oval or heart-shaped.
2. Body is enclosed in an endoskeletal shell or test of closely fitted calcareous plates covered with movable spines.
3. Outer calcareous plates are distinguished into five alternating ambulacral and five inter-ambulacral areas.
4. Podia or tube feet come out from the pores of ambulacral plates and are locomotory in function.
5. Mouth is centrally placed on the oral surface and surrounded by a membranous peristome. Anus is located at the aboral pole and surrounded by membranous periproct.
6. Ambulacral grooves are absent.
7. Pedicellariae are stalked and three jawed.
8. Sexes are separate. Gonads are pentamerous.
9. Development includes a free swimming echinopluteus larva.
10. Commonly called sea urchins and sand dollars.

SUBCLASS I. BOTHRIOCIDAROIDA

1. Each inter-ambulacral is with single row of plates.
2. Madreporite radially placed.
3. Typical lantern absent.
4. Includes a single extinct Ordovician genus.
   Example : *Bothriocidaris.*

SUBCLASS II. REGULARIA

1. Body is globular, mostly circular and sometimes oval in shape.
2. Symmetry is pentamerous with two rows of inter-ambulacral plates.
3. Mouth is centrally located at the oral surface and surrounded by peristome.
4. Anus is centrally placed at the aboral pole surrounded by periproct.

5. Aristotle's lantern is well developed.
6. Madreporite is ambulacral.

Order 1. Lepidocentroida

1. Test flexible with overlapping or separated plates.
2. Ambulacral plates continue up to mouth lip.
   Examples : *Phormosoma, Sperosoma.*

Order 3. Cidaroidea

1. Test is rigid and globular.
2. Two rows of long narrow ambulacral plates and two rows of inter-ambulacral plates are present.
3. Ambulacral and inter-ambulacral plates continue up to mouth lip.
4. Gills and sphaeridia are absent.
5. Five bushy Stewart's organs are present appended to the lantern.
   Examples : *Cidaris, Notocidaris.*

Order 4. Aulodonta

1. Test is symmetrical and globular.
2. Test composed of two rows each in a ambulacral and inter-ambulacral plates.
3. Ambulacral and inter-ambulacral plates reach up to the margin of peristome.
4. Gills and sphaeridia are present.
5. Teeth of Aristotle's lantern are devoid of keel.
   Examples : *Diodema, Astropyga.*

Order 6. Camarodonta

1. Test is rigid and rarely oval.
2. Epiphyses of lantern are enlarged and meeting above the pyramids.
3. Teeth are keeled.
4. All the four types of pedicellariae are present.
   Examples : *Echinus, Strongylocentrotus.*

SUBCLASS III. IRREGULARIA

1. Test is mostly flattened oval to circular.
2. Symmetry is bilateral.
3. Mouth centrally placed on the oral surface.
4. Anus is displaced posteriorly generally marginal at oral or aboral surface and lies outside the apical system of plates.
5. Podia or tube feet are not locomotory.

Order 1. Clypeastroida

1. Test is flattened, oval or rounded in shape covered with small spines.
2. Mouth and apical system are usually central and oral in position.
3. Aboral ambulacral areas petaloid.
4. Aristotle's lantern present.
5. Gills are absent.
   Examples : *Clypeaster, Laganum.*

Order 2. Spatangoida

1. Test is oval or heart-shaped.
2. Four aboral ambulacral areas petaloid, fifth not petaloid.
3. Aristotle's lantern absent.
4. Gills absent.

   Examples : *Spatangus, Lovenia, Echinocardium.*

CLASS 3. ASTEROIDEA
(Gr., *aster*=star+*eidos*=form)

1. Body is flattened, pentagonal or star-shaped.
2. Oral and aboral surfaces are distinct, the oral surface directed downwards and aboral surface upwards.
3. Five to fifty long or short rays or arms radiating symmetrically from a central disc.
4. Mouth is centrally placed at the oral surface surrounded by a membranous peristome.
5. Anus is small and inconspicuous located more or less eccentrically on the aboral surface.
6. Ambulacra form prominent grooves provided with podia or the feet.
7. Ambulacra are restricted to oral surface extending from the peristome to the tips of the arms.
8. Endoskeleton is flexible, made of separate ossicles.
9. Pedicellariae are small, movable spine-like always present.
10. Respiration by papulae.
11. Sexes separate, gonads radially arranged.
12. Development includes **bipinnaria** or **brachiolaria larva.**
13. Commonly called **starfishes** or **sea stars.**

Order 1. Phanerozonia

1. Arms are provided with two rows of conspicuous marginal plates.
2. Oral plates are infra-marginal and aboral plates are supra-marginal.
3. Pedicellariae are alveolar or sessile type.
4. Podia or tube feet are arranged in two rows.
5. Mouth frame is well developed and adambulacral type.

   Examples : *Luidia, Astropecten, Archaster, Pentaceros.*

Order 2. Spinulosa

1. Arms are generally without conspicuous marginal plates.
2. Aboral skeleton is imbricated or reticulated with single or group of spines.
3. Pedicellariae are rarely present.
4. Podia or tube feet are in two rows provided with suckers.
5. Mouth frame is of adambulacral type.
6. Ampullae single or bifurcated.

   Examples : *Aesterina, Echinaster, Hymenaster, Solaster.*

Order 3. Forcipulata

1. Marginal plates are inconspicuous or absent.
2. Aboral skeleton is mostly reticulate with conspicuous spines.
3. Pedicellariae are pedunculate type with a basal piece.
4. Podia or tube feet are arranged in four rows and provided with suckers.
5. Papulae are on both surface.
6. Mouth frame is of ambulacral type.

   Examples : *Brisingaster, Heliaster, Zoraster, Asterias.*

CLASS 4. OPHIUROIDEA
(Gr., *ophis*=serpent+*oura*=tail+*eidos*=form)

1. Body is flattened with a pentamerous or rounded central disc.
2. Oral and aboral surfaces are distinct.
3. Arms usually five rarely six or seven are long, slender, smooth or spiny.
4. Ambulacral grooves are absent.
5. Anus and intestine are absent.
6. Madreporite is on the oral surface.
7. Sexes are separate, gonads pentamerous.
8. Burase usually 10.
9. Development includes a free swimming **pluteus larva.**
10. Commonly called **brittle stars.**

Order 1. Ophiurae

1. Arms are simple, mostly five in number, moving chiefly in transverse plane.
2. Arm ossicles articulated by pits and projections.
3. Disc and arms are usually covered with distinct shields or scales.
4. Spines on arms are borne laterally and are directed outward or toward the arm tips, not downwards.
5. Single madreporite.

   Examples : *Ophioderma, Ophioscolex, Ophiothrix, Ophiolepie.*

Order 2. Euryalae

1. Arms are simple or branched , long and flexible, capable of coiling around objects and of rolling up in vertical plane.
2. Ossicles of arms are articulated in streptospondylus manner.
3. Disc and arms are without or poorly developed scales or shields.
4. Spines are directed downward often forming hooks or spiny clubs.
5. One madreporite in each inter-radius.

   Examples : *Asteronyx, Astrophyton, Astoporpa*

REPRESENTATIVE TYPES OF ECHINODERMATA

1. *Antedon*. *Antedon* (Fig. 86.1) is commonly known as feather star. Body consists of a central disc or calyx and a series of five radiating arms. Central disc or calyx is differentiated into an upper oral surface and lower aboral surface. Oral surface is covered with a soft and lethery skin, the tegmen bearing the central mouth and the anus on a papilla in an inter-radius. Aboral surface bears several slender curved jointed cirri supported by small ossicles which serve for attachment. Each arm divided at its base into two, so that there are ten long slender flexible arms, bearing lateral pinnules. Five ambulacral ciliated grooves radiate from the mouth towards the arms, where each divides into two and the branches extend along the oral surface of the arms. Tube feet or podia without suckers are present along the edges of ambulacral grooves. Sexes are separate, gonads contained in the dilated bases of pinnules. Development includes a pentacrinoid larva with jointed stalk. *Antedon* is marine, found at moderate depths attached to the rocks and stones.

2. *Holothuria*. Body of *Holothuria* (Fig. 86.2) is elongated, bilaterally symmetrical bearing the mouth and anus at opposite ends. Body bears numerous podia or tube feet, locomotory on the ventral surface and papilliate on the dorsal surface. Body wall is leathery having a skeleton of minute ossicles. Mouth is anteriorly placed, surrounded by 15–30 peltate tentacles. Respiratory tree is well developed. Cuverian tubules are also present. Madreporite is

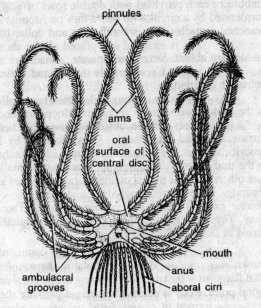

Fig. 86.1. *Antedon.*

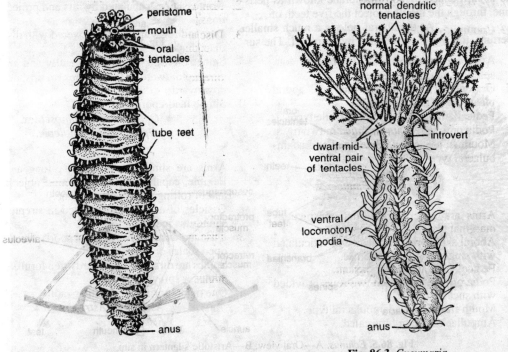

Fig. 86.2. *Holothuria.*   **Fig. 86.3.** *Cucumaria.*

internal. Sexes are separate, gonad single tuft attached to left side of the dorsal mesentery. Development includes auricularia larva. *Holothuria* feeds by pushing sand containing organic food into mouth with the help of tentacles. *Holothuria* is found in shallow tropical seas.

3. *Cucumaria*. *Cucumaria* (Fig. 86.3) is commonly known as sea cucumber. Body is elongated, cylindrical with mouth and anus at opposite ends. The body is five-side bearing five longitudinal ambulacra each provided with double rows of podia or tube feet. Oral end bears the large mouth surrounded by a circular lip and a thin peristomial membrane. Mouth bears ten highly dendritic or branched tentacles. The smooth, thin and collar-like region at the base of tentacles is known as introvert. Anus is terminal and placed at the aboral end. Respiratory trees are present. Cuverian tubules are absent. Sexes are separate, gonads are arranged in two tufts. Development includes an auricularia larva. *Cucumaria* is marine and cosmopolitan in distribution.

4. *Thyone*. Body is elongated, somewhat swollen in the middle with mouth and anus at opposite ends. Podia or tube feet are distributed over the entire body surface. Oral end bears the mouth surrounded by 10 dendritic or branched tentacles. Two tentacles attached to the mid-ventral ambulacral area, are much smaller than others. Anus is placed on the aboral end. Sexes are separate. Development includes auricularia larva. *Thyone* exhibits great power of regeneration and autotomy. *Thyone* is marine and found being completely buried in sandy and muddy bottom.

5. *Echinus*. *Echinus* (Fig. 86. 5) is commonly known as sea urchin. Body is globular in shape, somewhat flattened at the two poles forming distinct oral and aboral poles. Body is enclosed in a rigid globular shell or corona formed of closely fitted calcareous plates. Entire surface of the animal except the peristome and periproct is covered with spines articulated to the shell. Pedicellariae with three jaws and sphaeridia are present among the spines. Mouth lies in the centre of oral pole and is surrounded by soft membrane known as peristome, through the mouth project the five teeth of Aristotle's lantern. At the aboral pole is a much smaller aperture, the anus surrounded by periproct. The sur-

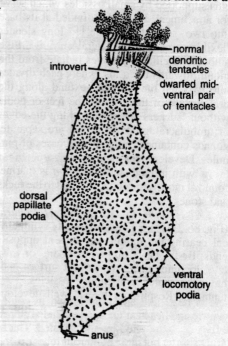

Fig. 86.4. *Thyone*.

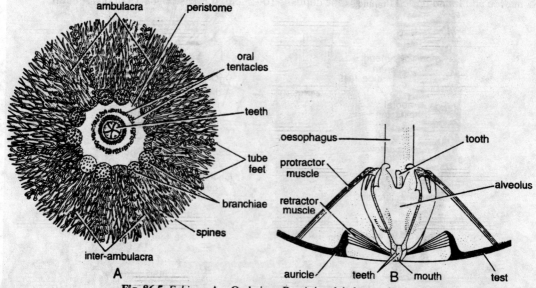

Fig. 86.5. *Echinus*. A—Oral view; B—Aristotle's lantern in situ.

face of the shell is divided into alternating ambulacral and inter-ambulacral areas. Numerous podia or tube feet project from the surface among the spines. These are arranged in five double rows in ambulacral areas. Sexes are separate. Gonads are five large masses. Development includes a free swimming echinopluteus larva. *Echinus* is marine, found in the sea in the rocky places.

6. *Echinarachinus.* *Echinarachinus* (Fig. 86.6) is commonly known as sand dollar. The body is almost circular disc-like and dorso-ventrally flattened. The test is covered with numerous very small, soft and delicate spines. Mouth is centrally placed, surrounded by five petaloid ambulacra. Peristome bearing the anus, lies on one edge. The aboral ambulacral areas are petaloid and with open ends. *Echinarachinus* is found buried in the sandy soil in the coastal line of North Atlantic and North Pacific Oceans.

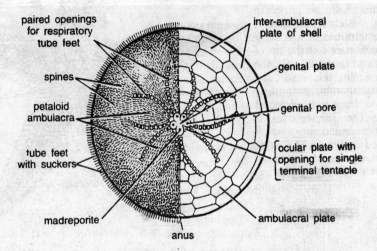

Fig. 86.6 *Echinarachinus.*

7. *Echinocardium.* *Echinocardium* (Fig. 86.7) is commonly known as heart urchin. The body shape is heart-like and light brown in colour. Peristome is transversely elongated and mouth is eccentric and lies near the anterior end. The periproct having anus lies at the hinder end. Ambulacra are five, petaloid and aborally situated. The anterior median ambulacrum is the largest and deepest bearing shorter but more numerous tube feet. Inter-ambulacral areas bear long, curved spines, while ambulacral areas bear only short, thin spines. Aristotle's lantern and teeth are absent. *Echinocardium* is marine and found buried in sand at the depth of 10–15 cm. It is cosmopolitan in distribution.

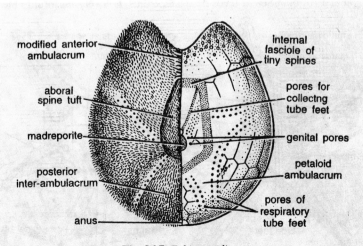

Fig. 86.7. *Echinocardium.*

8. *Astropecten*. *Astropecten* (Fig. 86.8) is a large, flat, five pointed sea star. The body is star-shaped, consisting of a central disc prolonged radially into five flexible triangular arms with tapering tips. The body is markedly flattened, with two distinct surfaces, a lower oral surface and an upper aboral surface. On the oral surface, the mouth opens in the centre surrounded by a soft membranous area, the peristome. Five broadly opened ambulacral grooves extend from the mouth and pass each along the entire length of one of the arms. Tube feet project in two rows along each ambulacral groove. The terminal tube foot or tentacle, which stands at the tip of each arm, has a pigmented spot, the eye at its base. The skin is soft and somewhat transparent, permitting the internal skeleton to be detected from outside. The skeleton consists of calcareous rods and plates which are embedded in the dermal layer and leave interspaces of soft tissue through which tube feet penetrate. Pedicellariae project around the spines. On the aboral surface, near the periphery of the disc and opposite the angle between two arms, is a small circular grooved plate, the ma-

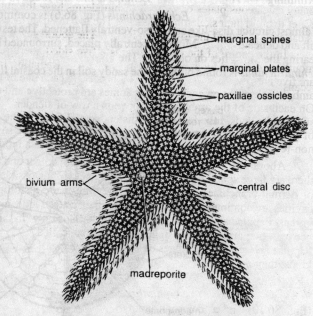

Fig. 86.8. *Astropecten*. (Aboral view).

dreporite which is perforated by numerous pores which lead into the water vascular system. The anus is absent. The armature on the aboral surface consists of short blunt spines projecting in bundles known as paxillae. The spines in each paxilla are arranged in a circle around a basal vertical stalk. Very small soft finger-like dermal branchiae arise between the paxillae, specially on the disc, as hollow outgrowths from the skin. *Astropecten* is found in our seas from below the tide line to great depths. It creeps about very slowly on the sea-bottom, but at rest it lies partly buried in sand with the central part of its body raised into a cone above the sand.

9. *Pentaceros*. *Pentaceros* (Fig. 86.9) is not regarded as a separate genus, but it is now included in genus *Oreaster*. It is found commonly in the Indo-Pacific Ocean and around the West Indies; in the Bay of Bengal and Arabian Sea, it feeds on oysters, thus, it is very harmful to the pearl industry.

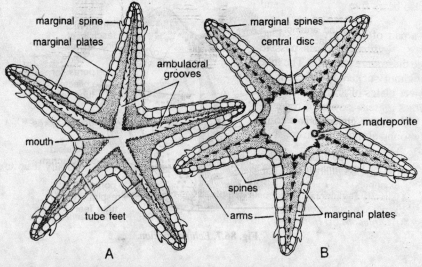

Fig. 86.9. *Pentaceros*. A—Oral view; B—Aboral view.

It has a diameter of about 25 cm, the body is very thick and regular star-shaped. It has a central disc and five tapering arms or rays, the arms are not sharply demarcated from the central disc, the disc is large and arms are short with broad bases, this shape is termed stellate. The axes of arms are called radii, and the spaces between them are inter-radii. The animal has a hard integument containing many calcareous plates or ossicles, echinoderms have the ability to use calcium carbonate from sea water to build their skeleton of ossicles. The two main surfaces are really lateral, but the upper surface is called aboral and the lower one is oral. The aboral surface is convex and oral surface is flat.

In the centre of the oral surface is a five sided aperture called actinostome which encloses a mouth surrounded by a membranous peristome. Radiating from the actinostome into the five arms are five narrow ambulacral grooves, bordering each one of these grooves are two rows of movable ambulacral spines on each side, the spines are protective and can close over the ambulacral grooves. On each side of the ambulacral groove is a row of slender tube feet or podia, they are tubular with sucker-like ends, tube feet can be distended and fixed to the substratum for locomotion. At the end of each ambulacral groove is a bright red eye made of several ocelli, above the eye is a small non-retractile sensory tentacle which is olfactory, it is a modified tube foot with no ampulla.

Aboral surface is yellow to reddish-brown in colour and has many stout spines in irregular rows, there are large spines on the margins, all spines rest on ossicles. Between the spines of papulae (gills or dermal branchiae) project singly, they are made histologically of thinned body wall and their cavities are continuous with the coelom, they are retractile and function as respiratory and excretory organs. Papulae are confined to the aboral surface only. In the centre is a minute anus, near the anus between two arms is a flat light coloured plate called madreporite lying asymmetrically. Near the papulae and around the spines on both oral and aboral surfaces are microscopic pedicellariae of two kinds, they are either stalked or sessile.

10. *Ophiothrix*. *Ophiothrix* (Fig. 86.10) is a common spiny brittle star. It has a small rounded central disc and five slender jointed arms arising from the lower surface of the disc. The arms are covered on all sides by the plates or shields and fringed with spines. The ambulacral grooves, dermal branchiae and pedicellariae are entirely absent. The oral surface bears a madreporite and a mouth possessing five movable plates serving as jaws. The oral surface also bears five oral shields and podial pores. The base of each arm bears a pair of deep grooves, called bursal slits through which pass to outside the mature sex cells. The tube feet without suckers are present on the lower plates of arms. *Ophiothrix* possesses a great power of regenerating its lost arm. *Ophiothrix* is commonly found along Atlantic coast.

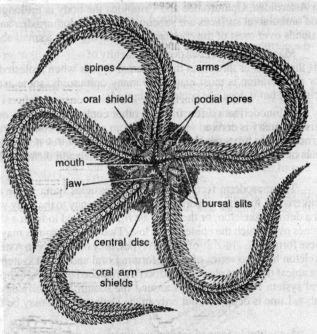

Fig. 85.10. *Ophiothrix*. (Oral view).

REVISION QUESTIONS

1. Give an account of the characters of Phylum Echinodermata and classify it up to orders giving examples.
2. Classify Phylum Echinodermata up to orders giving characters and examples.
3. Write short notes on :
   (i) *Antedon;* (ii) *Holothuria;* (iii) *Pentaceros;* (iv) *Echinus;* (v) *Ophiothrix.*

87

Echinodermata in General

Echinodermata form a well defined and successful group of marine animals existing since the Palaeozoic, they live at the bottom of all seas creeping about slowly, though some can swim. They exhibit great diversity of form and habit, and form a peculiar group. The body is made of 10 principal divisions which radiate from a main axis, they are five radii and five inter-radii. The surface having a mouth is oral or ambulacral, and the opposite surface is aboral or adambulacral. Tube feet project from the ambulacral surface forming radial bands called ambulacra. In Asteroidea and Crinoidea the tube feet of each ambulacrum project on either side of an ambulacral groove at the bottom of which lies a radial nerve cord, but in other classes the ambulacral groove is closed, so that it forms an epineural canal enclosing the nerve cord. Main axis of the body passes between these two surfaces, and the length of the axis determines the shape of the body. The axis is short in starfishes with a lower aboral surface; in others the axis is long, in sea cucumbers the oral surface with the mouth is anterior and the animal lies with the main axis parallel to the ground, in sea lilies oral surface is uppermost. In Asteroidea, Ophiuroidea and Crinoidea the body is prolonged into arms in the direction of radii, and ambulacral surfaces are subequal, but in Holothuroidea and Echinoidea the ambulacral surface extends over most of the compact body leaving only a small aboral area opposite the mouth.

Many Echinodermata possess a faculty of self-mutilation or autotomy by which they can break off their arms or throw out their internal organs when molested, this faculty along with the capacity for regeneration is most marked in many ophiuroids, some asteroids, some holothurians and some crinoids, but it does nor occur in echinoids.

Echinodermata differ from all other coelomate animals mainly due to their radial symmetry, this symmetry is derived secondarily from a bilateral condition and it distorts all their systems. Some structures are bilateral, but externally the symmetry is never quite perfect because a madreporite or anus or a genital opening makes one of the interradii different from others.

SKELETON IN ECHINODERMATA

The mesoderm forms a skeleton of ossicles lying in the dermis, the ossicles may be few and scattered so that they impart a leathery consistency to the body wall, or they may be united by muscles as a definite skeleton, or they may be firmly jointed to form a shell. Some ossicles usually project as spines over which the epidermis is lost. Two or three spines may be arranged so as to work as pincers, these form pedicellariae of various types, they occur only in Asteroidea and Echinoidea. The primitive skeleton had two series of plates forming oral and apical systems, but in present day Echinodermata the apical plates are absent or reduced or replaced by accessory plates, e.g., corona of sea urchins. The oral system forms five plates around the mouth, it is fully developed only in Crinoidea forming a calyx. Lime is deposited not only in the skeleton but it may be found in any organ of the body.

COELOM IN ECHINODERMATA

A coelom is formed from paired pouches which arise as lateral outpushings of the embryonic archenteron, thus, the coelom is enterocoelic. The pouches undergo a constriction so that each forms an anterior and a posterior sac, the posterior sacs grow and form coelomic cavities and the anterior sacs become the rudiments of a water vascular system, they are called hydrocoel sacs. The left hydrocoel sac acquires a stone canal which communicates with the body wall, the right hydrocoel sac disappears, but recent evidence shows that the right hydrocoel sac is represented by the dorsal sac of the axial sinus. Thus, the entire water vascular system is formed from the left hydrocoel and it assumes a radial arrangement of its parts.

Besides the water vascular system the coelomic cavities form a perivisceral cavity containing the main viscera, a perihaemal system which encloses a vascular system, and its aboral sinus extension enclosing the gonads, and an axial sinus of varied development in different classes, but it has an opening forming a madreporite.

RELATIONSHIP OF ECHINODERMATA

The free Eleutherozoa have been derived from attached pelmatozoic ancestors. Echinodermata show no close relationship to any invertebrates, except with Hemichordata and Pogonophora. These three phyla have a number of common features, among which are the formation of coelom by enterocoely, retention of blastopore as the site of the future anus, in having a dipleurula-like larva at some stage, and in having a heart vesicle which may represent the right anterior coelom. The larvae of some echinoderms (auricularia larva of holothurians) closely resemble the tornaria larva of *Saccoglossus*. But they are closely related to hemichordates because of the following reasons : 1. The mesoderm is derived from cells around the lips of the blastopore. 2. They possess a mesodermal endoskeleton, whereas the invertebrates have an ectodermal exoskeleton. 3. The blastopore becomes the adult anus as in chordates, in invertebrates (annelids, molluscs) the blastopore becomes the mouth. 4. Mouth arises as a new structure from the ectodermal stomodaeum as in chordates. 5. The coelom is formed from paired lateral diverticula of the archenteron and is enterocoelic.

The many resemblances between echinoderms and hemicordates are neither accidental nor due to convergent evolution, but because the two phyla are closely related and both arose from some common ancestor. Hemichordates are closer to this common ancestor, while echinoderms have deviated greatly because they have arisen as a blind branch from the ancestral type.

REVISION QUESTIONS

1. Write notes on :
   (i) Symmetry in Echinodermata;
   (ii) Skeleton in Echinodermata;
   (iii) Coelom in Echinodermata;
   (iv) Relationship of Echinodermata.

88
Phylum Hemichordata

Hemichordata or Adelochordata are tongue worms which have been included for long as a subphylum or class of Phylum Chordata in the lower chordates or Protochordata, but now they are placed as an independent phylum of invertebrates, since their supposed affinities with chordates are doubtful. Hemichordata are a small group of marine, solitary or colonial, worm-like, enterocoelous animals, most of which live in tubes. The soft, fragile body breaks readily in collecting. The body and enterocoelous coelom are divisible into three unequal regions, *viz.*, proboscis, collar and trunk. In most forms one to several pairs of gill-clefts lead from the pharynx to the exterior. Nervous system is a network of nerve cells and fibres on the surface of the body, embedded in the epidermis. They have no bony tissue, but a buccal diverticulum is present in the preoral region, which is often regarded as a notochord, There is no tail. Development is direct in some, while in others there is a tornaria larva. The phylum has 100 species.

TYPE : *BALANOGLOSSUS*

Balanoglossus (Gr., *balano*=acorn; *glossa*=tongue) belongs to class Enteropneusta which have a straight digestive tube with mouth and anus at opposite ends. They have numerous gill-clefts but have no anus. They are burrowing animals ranging in size from about 2 cm to 50 cm. *Balanoglossus* has about 20 species.

HABIT AND HABITAT

Balanoglossus is a burrowing and exclusively marine animal. It is found in shallow waters between tide marks along the coast of warm and temperate oceans. *Balanoglossus* is world-wide in distribution. *Balanoglossus* is tubicolous living in U-shaped burrows excavated in the sandy bottom. The walls of the tube are lined with mucus secreted by the mucous gland of the animal. The burrows are open at both ends, and spiral coils of faeces like the castings of earthworms may be seen at the posterior opening. In its burrow *Balanoglossus* lies in a twisted condition but its anterior and posterior extremities are straight. Knight Jones (1952) reported that the animal moves in its burrow with the help of cilia present all over the body.

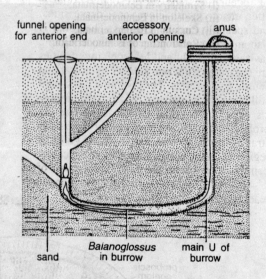

Fig. 88.1. *Balanoglossus* in U-shaped burrow. (After Young, 1962).

EXTERNAL MORPHOLOGY

The body of *Balanoglossus* is soft, elongated, cylindrical, being richly ciliated all over and covered with mucus. The length of animal varies from 2 cm to 2.5 meters. Most forms are drab coloured, though reddish tints are present, several species are luminiscent due to mucus. They have an offensive odour. The body is bilaterally symmetrical and divided into three regions, *viz.*, proboscis or protosome, collar or mesosome, and trunk or metasome.

Proboscis. The proboscis forms the anterior part of the body and is either rounded or conical in shape. It is continued posteriorly into a short, narrow neck or proboscis stalk. The proboscis is hollow and has thick muscular walls. Its cavity opens to the outside by means of a small opening called the proboscis-pore. In certain cases there are two proboscis-pores. In some species the proboscis-pore does not communicate with the proboscis-coelom, but terminate blindly, and may send off a narrow tubular diverticulum which opens into the neurocoel. The proboscis sits in the collar somewhat like an acorn in its cup, a character that has given the name "acorn worms" to the group. The mouth, which is always wide open and incapable of closing completely, lies on the ventral side and its lips are the ventral edges of the collar region.

Collar. The collar lies posterior to the proboscis and anterior to the trunk. It is a short cylinder usually about as wide as long and mostly shorter than the proboscis although sometimes longer. The funnel-like anterior part of the collar, the collarette, embraces the proboscis stalk and usually also the posterior part of the proboscis. Posteriorly the collar is sharply demarcated from the trunk by a circular indentation. The surface of the collar is often marked with elevations, depressions, and specially circular grooves. The collar is also muscular and possesses two coelomic cavities. The right and left coelomic cavities are separated from one another by dorsal and ventral mesenteries. The coelomic cavities of collar are completely cut off from the proboscis cavity. The collar cavity as well as the proboscis cavity are crossed by numerous strands of connective tissue which give the region a spongy appearance. The collar cavity communicated with the exterior by a pair of collar-pores, and short ciliated tubes (canals) leading into the first gill-pouches.

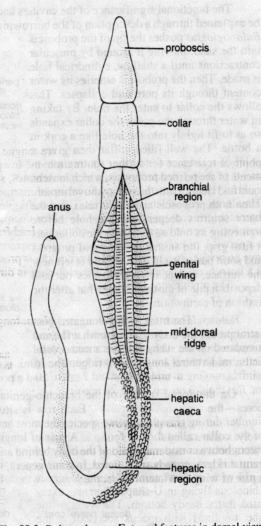

Fig. 88.2. *Balanoglossus*. External features in dorsal view.

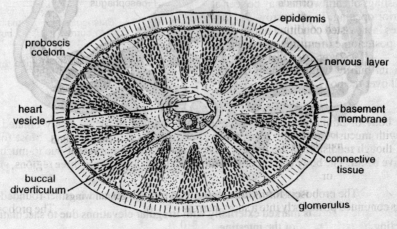

Fig. 88.3. *Balanoglossus*. T.S. of proboscis.

The functional significance of the cavities and water pores in the proboscis and collar may best be explained through a description of the burrowing habits. When on the surface of the sandy bottom *Balanoglossus* pushes the tip of the proboscis into the sand, moving it around by muscular contractions until a shallow, cylindrical hole is made. Then the proboscis empties its water content through its pore and collapses. This allows the collar to enter the hole. By taking in water through the pores the collar expands so as to fit lightly into the hole like a cork in a bottle. The well-filled collar then gives a point of resistance for further rooting movements of the refilled proboscis, which loosens sand and stows it into the scoop-shovel mouth. Then both proboscis and collar relax and the latter squirms deeper into the hole before tightening its hold again. Once the collar gets a firm grip, the animal makes rapid progress and soon buries itself. The tail end is left near the surface, and at intervals comes out and deposits a pile of castings somewhat after the fashion of earthworms.

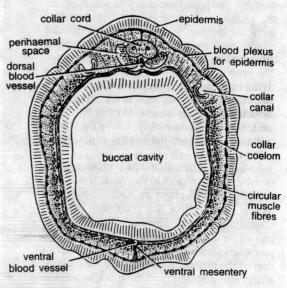

Fig. 88.4. *Balanoglossus.* T.S. of collar.

Trunk. The trunk is the elongated posterior part of the body. It is somewhat flat and annulated on the surface. It has a mid- dorsal and a mid-ventral longitudinal ridge. The trunk is divisible into three parts, an anterior branchio-genital region, a middle hepatic region, and a posterior abdominal or post-hepatic region.

On the dorsal surface of the branchio-genital region of the trunk is a double row of small pores—the branchial apertures. Each row is situated in a long furrow. These pores increase in number during growth. In some species the most anterior are overlapped by a posterior prolongation of the collar called the operculum. A pair of longitudinal genital ridges or genital wings extends throughout a considerable part of the body behind and in the region of the branchial apertures. In these genital ridges, gonads are situated. In some genera, the genital ridges are so prominent that they form a pair of wing-like lateral folds, the genital wings, but in other genera folds are absent.

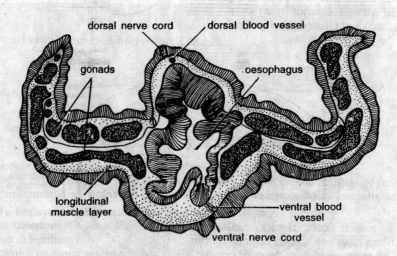

Fig. 88.5. *Balanoglossus.* C.S. through genital wings.

The hepatic region is marked externally with irregular elevations due to sacculations produced by projecting hepatic caeca of the intestine.

The abdominal region is longest and cylindrical. It tapers gradually and has a terminal anus. The coelom of the trunk is divided into two lateral closed cavities by vertical partition.

BODY WALL

The body wall of *Balanoglossus* is made up of an outer epidermis and an inner musculature.

1. Epidermis. It consists of a single layer of epithelial cells. The epithelial cells are of tall columnar type and have their nuclei near their broader bases. These cells are mainly of two types : (i) ciliated epidermal cells are more numerous and each bears cilia at its free end; (ii) gland cells are lying interspersed between the ciliated epidermal cells and are further of three kinds : (a) goblet cells are flask-shaped and secrete mucus; (b) reticulate cells are long cells with vacuolated cytoplasm which also secrete mucus; (c) mulberry cells are long cells containing coarse cytoplasmic granules and, hence, are also called granular gland cells. They secrete amylase. The mucus, secreted by gland cells, covers the animal and lines its burrow. The mucus has an obnoxious smell. In addition to these cells, the body wall of proboscis and anterior part of the collar also contain neurosensory cells which take darker stain than the rest. There is no dermis.

Immediately below the epidermis is a thick nervous layer consisting of bipolar and quadripolar nerve cells and fibres which form a network lying in close contact with the epidermal cells. This layer is traversed by the filamentous bases of the epidermal cells that are connected with the basement membrane. The fibres of sensory epidermal cells synapse with the fibres of nerve cells.

Below the nervous layer is a thick basement membrane made up of two lamellae pressed together. The basement membrane supports the epidermis and serves for attachment of underlying muscles.

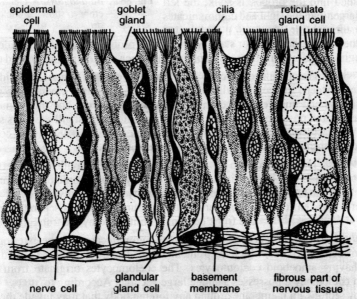

Fig. 88.6. *Balanoglossus.* V.S. of body wall.

2. Musculature. The musculature of typical body-wall and gut-wall is greatly reduced and more or less replaced by muscles arising from the coelomic epithelium. The muscle fibres are smooth and of circular, longitudinal and diagonal types. The muscle layer lies below the basement membrane.

The proboscis musculature comprises a thin layer of circular muscle fibres and a thick layer of longitudinal muscle fibres. The longitudinal muscles fibres obliterate the proboscis coelom and some of the fibres cross one another diagonally. The collar musculature is confined to the collarette and consists of an inconspicuous layer of circular fibres and prominent bands of longitudinal and diagonal fibres. The longitudinal and diagonal fibres, along with connective tissue, also traverse the collar coelom in a criss-cross pattern. The trunk musculature consists mainly of moderately developed longitudinal muscle fibres which are better developed on the ventral side. The muscle layer is interrupted by the dorsal and ventral mesenteries and the lateral septa. Several radial muscle fibres are also found in the trunk region. The radial muscle fibres extend between the digestive tract and the body wall and traverse the trunk coelom.

COELOM

The coelom is enterocoelous having been formed as outgrowths of the enteron. Corresponding with the three body regions the coelom is divided into three portions which are completely separated from each other by septa. The coelom is lined with coelomic epithelium or peritoneum. But enteropneusts are peculiar in that their coelomic epithelium has connective tissue and muscle fibres which fill much of the original coelomic cavities, and a distinct peritoneal lining has disappeared, moreover the coelomic musculatre largely replaces the body wall muscles. The three parts of the coelom are an unpaired proboscis coelom, a pair of collar coeloms, and a pair of trunk coeloms.

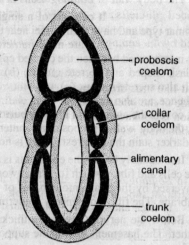

Fig. 88.7. *Balanoglossus*. Diagram of tripartite embryo showing coelomic cavities.

1. Proboscis coelom. The proboscis coelom or **protocoel** is a single space in the proboscis which is largely occupied by muscles and connective tissue and a few structures like buccal diverticulum, glomerulus and central sinus or heart. Dorsally, towards the posterior side, the proboscis coelom is divided by a dorsal mesentery into right and left dorso-lateral compartments which extend into the proboscis stalk; the left compartment is larger than the right and communicates with the exterior through the **proboscis pore** situated mid-dorsally at the base of the posterior stalk. Ventrally the proboscis coelom is divided by a ventral mesentery into right and left ventro-lateral compartments which are continuous behind the mesentery.

2. Collar coelom. The collar coelom or **mesocoel** has two cavities lying side by side in the collar, one on each side between the collar wall and buccal cavity. The two cavities are partitioned by incomplete mid-dorsal and mid-ventral mesenteries. The collar coelom does not communicate with the proboscis coelom, but posteriorly, its each cavity opens into the first gill sac of its side by a canal called **collar canal.** Each collar coelom opens to the exterior by a **collar pore.** The collar coelom is greatly obliterated by the collar musculature and connective tissue.

3. Trunk coelom. The trunk coelom or **metacoel** has two closed cavities lying between the body wall and alimentary canal. The two cavities are separated by an incomplete dorsal and a complete ventral mesentery . In the branchio-genital region each cavity is further divided by a **lateral septum** into a dorso-lateral and ventro-lateral compartment. The trunk coelom is separated from the collar coelom by a **collar-trunk septum.** The trunk coelom is obliterated by the trunk musculature.

Coelomic fluid. The proboscis and collar coeloms communicate with the exterior and get filled with sea water through their pores, which keeps them turgid. The trunk coelom is filled with a watery coelomic fluid having amoeboid coelomocytes. The coelomocytes originate from the coelomic epithelium. Each coelomocyte possesses a single large vacuole. According to **Spengel,** they behave like leucocytes by secreting a membrane around any foreign body that may invade the animal.

ENDOSKELETON

In *Balanoglossus* there is no definite endoskeleton but there are four structures of a supporting nature, they are a **buccal diverticulum, proboscis skeleton, branchial skeleton,** and a **pygochord.**

1. Buccal diverticulum. Buccal diverticulum is a hollow preoral outgrowth, extending from the roof of the buccal cavity into the proboscis. It was for a long time also called a **notochord** or a **stomochord** on the assumption that it represents the anterior portion of the notochord of chordates. The buccal diverticulum extends forward in some enteropneusts as a slender **vermiform process** or **appendix.** The buccal diverticulum is neither analogous nor homologous with the chordate notochord, histologically it is identical with the wall of the buccal cavity, it is apparently nothing more than a pre-oral extension of the gut.

2. Proboscis skeleton. Proboscis skeleton or nuchal skeleton is formed by the basement membrane becoming thick to form a laminated plate from which arise two thin horns or cornua, the plate usually has a mid-ventral keel. The proboscis skeleton lies in the proboscis stalk, while its horns extend into the roof of the buccal cavity.

3. Branchial skeleton. The walls of the U-shaped gill-clefts are supported by skeletal rods called primary and secondary gill-rods formed by thickening of the basement membrane.

4. Pygochord. Pygochord is longitudinal rod-like structure extending from the ventral side of the intestine to the body wall, its function is not known but it may support the soft abdominal region.

DIGESTIVE SYSTEM

Alimentary Canal

In *Balanoglossus*, the alimentary canal is a straight tube. Its anterior opening, the mouth, is wide and circular and situated on the ventral side in a groove between the proboscis stalk and collarette. The mouth remains open costantly. The posterior opening

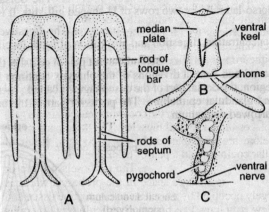

Fig . 88.8. *Balanoglossus.* Skeletal elements. A—Branchial skeleton; B—Proboscis skeleton; C—Pygochord.

or the anus is a circular aperture at the extreme posterior end of the trunk. Between the mouth and anus, the alimentary canal can be distinguished into four regions : buccal tube, pharynx, oesophagus, and intestine. Their walls are composed of ciliated epithelium lined externally by basement membrane and devoid of muscle fibres.

1. Buccal tube. The mouth leads into a buccal tube or cavity in the collar region. Its epithelial wall contains glandular goblet cells. The dorsal wall of buccal tube forms a short, stiff and hollow buccal diverticulum that projects into the proboscis coelom. It extends up to the collar-trunk septum behind which it continues into the pharynx.

2. Pharynx. The wall of the roof of the buccal tube opens into the pharynx lying in the branchial region of the trunk. Its wall bears a longitudinal constriction along each lateral side. These lateral

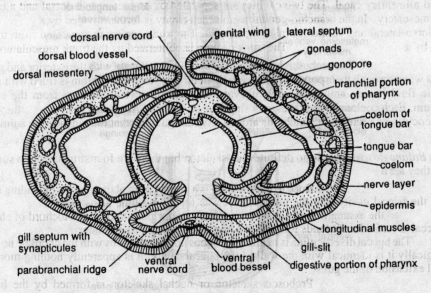

Fig. 88.9. *Balanoglossus.* T.S. through pharyngeal or branchiogenital region.

constrictions project into its lumen as ridges, called parabranchial ridges consisting of tall columnar cells. These ridges and constrictions incompletely divide the pharynx into a dorsal branchial portion (pore pharynx) and a ventral digestive portion (digestive pharynx).

(i) **Branchial portion of pharynx.** The dorsal branchial portion of pharynx is perforated dorso-laterally by two rows of U-shaped gill-slits. It is concerned with respiration.

(ii) **Digestive portion of pharynx.** The digestive portion of pharynx is concerned with the food concentration, digestion and absorption of food. Its ciliated epithelial wall contains gland cells.

3. **Oesophagus.** Behind the last pair of gill-slits the pharynx continues into the oesophagus. The dorsal and ventral divisions of the pharynx continue for some distance into the oesophagus; in this region, the dorsal part of the oesophagus is called postbranchial canal which possesses thick, folded and glandular epithelium. The posterior part of the oesophagus reduce in diameter and has deeply furrowed epithelium.

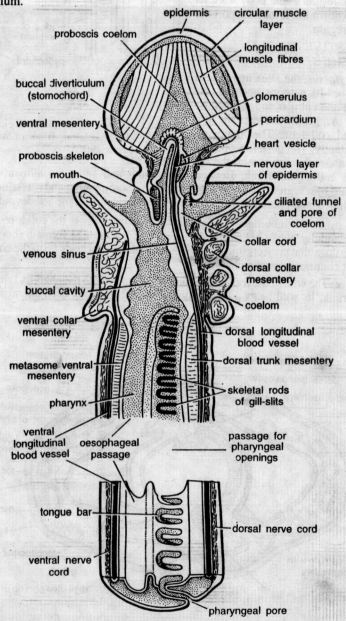

Fig. 88.10. *Balanoglossus.* M.L.S. of anterior region to show the alimentary canal.

4. Intestine. Behind the oesophagus is an intestine, It occupies the hepatic and post-hepatic regions of the trunk. The **hepatic region** of the intestine is highly vascular. Its epithelial cells are dark green or dark brown and its dorsal wall forms numerous prominent sacculations called **hepatic caeca** which push the body wall outwards and are, thus, visible externally. The **post-hepatic region** of the intestine is connected with the ventral body wall by the pygochord. The intestine has the form of a simple tube and bears a pair of dorso-lateral grooves lined by tall epithelial cells bearing long cilia. The intestine opens out through the **anus** situated at the extreme hind end of the body. The anus often possesses sphincter muscles.

Food, Feeding and Digestion

Balanoglossus is a "**ciliary feeder**". Its food comprises microscopic organisms and minute organic particles present in water and mud or bottom sand in which it makes its burrows. The lateral cilia lining the gill-slits set up a current of water directed backward which enters through the mouth, takes its course through the buccal tube, pharynx, gill-slits and branchial sacs, and leaves through gill-pores.

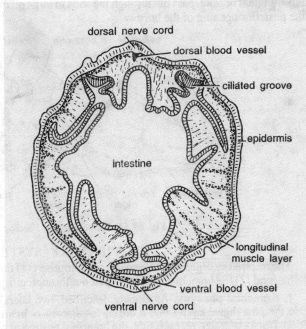

Fig. 88.11. *Balanoglossus.* T.S. through post-hepatic intestine.

This is called **respiratory-cum-food current.** Some food particles directly enter the mouth with this current, while some come in contact with the proboscis and are entangled in the mucus that covers it. The mucus is secreted by the gland cells of the proboscis epithelium. Cilia covering the proboscis direct the mucous string, containing food particles towards the pre-oral ciliary organ at the base of the proboscis. From here the mucous string is passed back into the mouth by the action of the proboscis cilia, assisted by the main water current entering the mouth. Organic particles present in the mud or sand are ingested directly along with mud or sand at the time of burrowing.

At the base of the proboscis, on the ventral side, there is a U-shaped depression bordered by long epidermal cells bearing long cilia. This structure is called the **pre-oral ciliary organ.** It tests the quality of food and the water entering the mouth. Undesirable substances are prevented from entering the mouth by the ventral part of the collarette which does so by covering the mouth. Thus, the rejected particles, instead of entering the mouth, pass back over the collar.

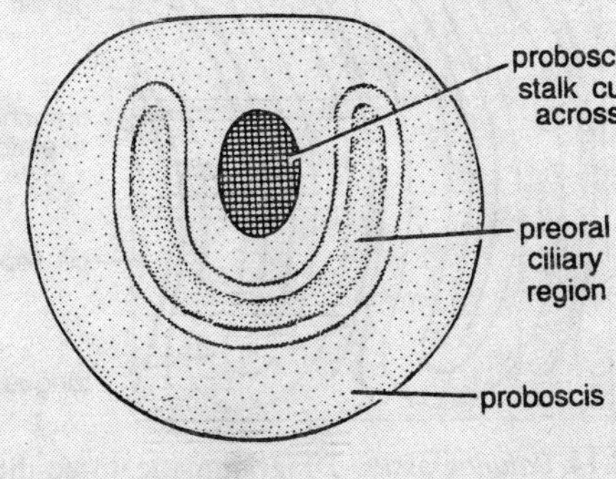

Backward movement of food through the alimentary canal is maintained by the cilia lining its walls. In the pharynx, the food passes through the ventral digestive portion. The exact process of digestion in *Balanoglossus* is not known with certainity, however, the digestion of food is brought about by the enzymes secreted by proboscis, gland cells of the pharynx, oesophagus and hepatic region of the intestine. Proboscis secretes mucus, which contains amylase, is ingested with the food. The gland cells of pharynx and oesoph-

Fig. 88.12. *Balanoglossus.* Posterior view of proboscis showing the preoral ciliary organ.

agus also secrete enzymes. It is also claimed that hepatic caeca secrete amylase, maltase, lipase and weak protease. The enzymes digest the organic particles in the mud or sand. Undigested substances, along with mud or sand, pass out through the anus in large quantities which forms piles of "castings" at the posterior opening of the burrow.

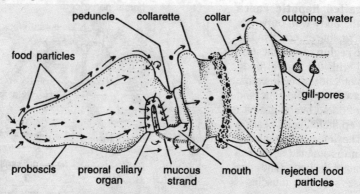

Fig. 88.13. *Balanoglossus.* Feeding current.

RESPIRATORY SYSTEM

The respiratory organs of *Balanoglossus* comprise : (1) the branchial portion of pharynx bearing gill-slits, and (2) the branchial sacs that open out through gill-pores.

1. Branchial pharynx. As already described, two lateral longitudinal para-branchial ridges divide the pharyngeal cavity into a dorsal respiratory or branchial portion and a ventral digestive portion. Dorso-laterally, on each side, the branchial portion of pharynx is perforated by a longitudinal series of numerous U-shaped openings, the gill-slits. The number of gill-slits varies and increases as the animal grows older. Each gill-slit is a broad oval slit in the beginning, but later, a hollow projection of dorsal pharyngeal wall, called tongue bar, grows into the slit making it U-shaped. The hollow tongue bars enclose coelomic cavity and do not touch the ventral side of the gill-slits. The portions of the pharyngeal wall between two adjacent U-shaped gill-slits are called gill-septa. The gill-septa are solid and do not enclose coelom. A tongue bar is connected with its adjacent gill-septa by longitudinal connections are called synapticula. The tongue-bars and gill-septa are supported by M-shaped skeleteal rods. The middle arm of an M-shaped rod is bifurcated at the free end and lies in a gill-septum, while its outer arms lie in adjacent tongue bars. Thus, each tongue bar contains two arms of two adjacent skeletal rods. Each U-shaped gill-slit is richly lined by cilia, called lateral cilia.

2. Branchial sacs. Gill-slits do not open directly to outside. Each gill-slit opens into a gill-pouch called branchial sac which lies between the body wall and the pharynx. Each branchial sac in turn opens to the exterior by a small, independent gill-pore. However, in *Balanoglossus misakiensis* the first four branchial sacs become united to open by a common gill-pore to outside. The collar coelom also communicates with the common branchial sac of its side through a collar canal. The gill-pores are visible externally in two longitudinal rows, one on each side of the mid-dorsal ridge in the branchiogenital region of the trunk.

Mechanism of respiration. The lateral cilia lining the gill-slits create a current of water (food-cum-respiratory current) that enters the pharynx through mouth, then passes through gill-slits into the branchial sacs and

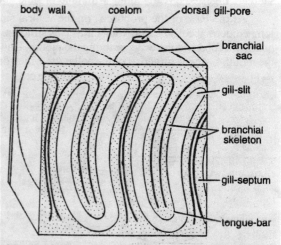

Fig. 88.14. *Balanoglossus.* Diagrammatic three-dimensional view of two gill-slits and two branchial sacs.

finally leaves through the gill-pores. The tongue bars are richly supplied with blood capillaries and take part in respiration. The blood of their capillary networks takes up oxygen dissolved in water and diffuses carbon dioxide to it.

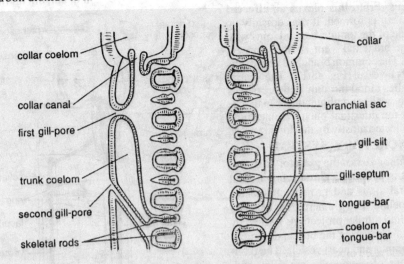

Fig. 88.15. *Balanoglossus misakiensis.* H.L.S. of branchial portion of pharynx showing first four gill-slits opening by a common gill-pore.

BLOOD VASCULAR SYSTEM

The blood vascular system of *Balanoglossus* consists of closed vessels, lacunar spaces and a definite pulsating organ, generally known as the heart. The blood is colourless and has no or very few corpuscles; it may contain a few detached endothelial cells; it has no respiratory pigment. Most of the blood vascular system is located between the lamellae of the basement membrane and the leaves of the mesentery.

There are two main longitudinal vessels, the dorsal and ventral vessels, running along the length of the body. The dorsal vessel is situated just below the dorsal nerve cord and above the alimentary canal and runs through the dorsal mesentery. The blood flows anteriorly through the dorsal vessel. The ventral vessel is located in the ventral mesentery and the blood flows posteriorly in it. These two vessels are highly contractile and their walls are composed of an inner endothelium surrounded by muscle layer.

The dorsal vessel extends from the anus to the collar where it occupies a median position between two perihaemal cavities. The dorsal vessel is dilated at the front of the collar, forming a venous sinus which passes anteriorly into a central sinus or heart. The central sinus is situated above the buccal diverticulum. Immediately above the central sinus there is a triangular contractile epidermal sac called heart vesicle. Blood from the central sinus enters the glomerular sinuses of the proboscis complex. In glomerulus the blood is cleared of nitrogenous wastes. From the glomerulus, the blood is collected by four vessels. These vessels are regarded as the arteries because the blood leaving the glomerulus is considered to be purified. These arteries are : (i) a mid-dorsal proboscis artery, (ii) a mid-ventral proboscis artery and two efferent glomerular arteries. The mid-dorsal and mid-ventral proboscis arteries supply blood to the proboscis. The efferent glomerular arteries run backward along the two sides of the buccal diverticulum. These vessels then run ventrally to encircle the buccal tube as the peribuccal arteries. The peribuccal arteries unite together ventrally to form a single longitudinal ventral vessel.

The ventral vessel runs up to the posterior end of the body through the ventral mesentery. On its way, the ventral vessel gives out a ventral collar vessel to supply the collar. The collar tissue contains two distinct lacunar networks which communicate posteriorly with a ring vessel. The ring vessel is located in the collar-trunk septum. It arises from the ventral vessel and is connected with the dorsal vessel. A lateral phryngeal vessel appears in the lacunar plexus at the junction of the two pharyngeal regions. The ventral vessel continues up to the anus and gives off lacunar networks all along the alimentary canal. The ventral vessel gives out an afferent branchial artery to each gill-septum which bifurcates to supply the two adjacent tongue-bars. Thus, each tongue-bar receives two afferent branchial arteries which break up into a plexus. From this plexus an efferent branchial vein is formed. It runs dorsally up to the middle of the tongue-bar and joins with the efferent branchial vein of the adjacent tongue-bar. The common branchial vein opens into the dorsal vessel (Fig. 88.17). The ventral vessel supplies blood through lacunar plexus to the body wall and alimentary canal. The blood from the intestinal plexus in the trunk region is collected mostly by the dorsal vessel.

EXCRETORY SYSTEM

In *Balanoglossus*, the excretory organ is glomerulus or proboscis gland lying in front of the central sinus and projecting into the proboscis coelom. The glomerulus is made up of several blind tubular projections formed by the peritoneum covering the buccal diverticulum, central sinus and heart vesicle. The tubular projections of glomerulus are filled with blood which is confluent with the blood of the central sinus. The covering of the glomerulus is composed of excretory peritoneal cells. The excretory peritoneal cells of glomerulus contain yellow or brown granules, probably of excretory substances. The excretory waste substances from the glomerulus pass on into the proboscis coelom from where they finally pass out to the exterior through the proboscis pore.

NERVOUS SYSTEM

The nervous system of *Balanoglossus* is of a very primitive type resembling that of coelenterates and echinoderms. Nervous sys-

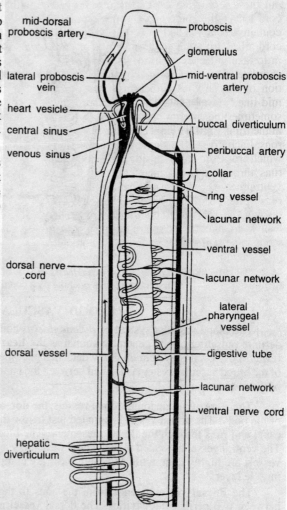

Fig. 88.16. *Balanoglossus*. Blood vascular system in anterior end in lateral view.

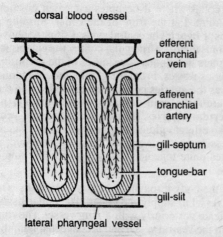

Fig. 88.17. *Balanoglossus*. Branchial vessels in portion of the branchial wall.

tem consists primarily of an epidermal plexus or a layer of nerve cells and nerve fibres lies just below the epidermis. Thread-like processes of the epidermal cells contribute to the network or nerve net. The nervous layer is composed of longitudinal nerve fibres with bipolar and multipolar nerve cells at the margin. The nervous layer becomes thickened along definite strands to form two main nerve cords, one **mid-dorsal** and the other mid-ventral, which run along the entire length of the trunk. Ventral cord extends up to collar-trunk septum where it is connected with the dorsal cord by a circular strand, called **circumenteric nerve ring**.

Dorsal cord extends anteriorly up to the base of proboscis where it is connected with another circular strand called anterior nerve ring. From the anterior nerve ring longitudinal nerve fibres are given out, these nerve fibres are called subsidiary longitudinal cords of proboscis. In the collar region, dorsal cord leaves the epidermis and projects into the collar coelom as the collar cord. The collar cord contains a cavity called neurocoel. The collar cord arises from the epidermis, but has sunk in to take a deeper position. Its similarity to chordate nerve ford, formed by the invagination of the nervous ectoderm at the dorsal mid-line, is evident. The collar cord and sometimes the anterior part of the dorsal cord in the trunk or nerve ring, contains giant neurons. Each gives off a single large nerve fibre which crosses to the other side of the body and runs through the circumenteric ring to the ventral nerve cord. The number of giant neurons varies from about 10 to 160. They are responsible for rapid conduction of stimuli leading to quick retraction of body parts. Although the collar cord is the most complex part of the nervous system, it is no more than a conduction path and the site of giant neuron formation.

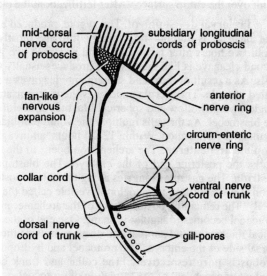

Fig. 88.18. *Balanoglossus.* Nerve cords in the anterior region of the body.

SENSE ORGANS

In *Balanoglossus* the sense organs are poorly developed. In the epidermis are numerous neurosensory cells which are connected to the nerve net, they are more numerous on the proboscis. It is claimed that in some species a few neurosensory cells form photoreceptors sensory to light. On the ventral side of the base of the proboscis is a U-shaped depression called a preoral ciliary organ. It has ciliated cells joined to the nerve net, it is a chemoreceptor.

REPRODUCTIVE SYSTEM

In *Balanoglossus,* the sexes are separate and are indistinguishable externally except in case of the colour of the ripe gonads shown through the body wall in the living animal. The gonads occur in one or more longitudinal rows to the sides of the alimentary canal lying within the genital pleurae in the anterior part of the trunk. Gonads develop from the coelomic wall, though they have no connection with coelom in the adult. The gonads are generally sacciform bodies but may be elongated or lobulated and secondary gonads may arise by subdivision of the primary ones through lobulation. Each gonad is a sac, it continues into a short ductule which opens to the exterior by a gonopore. The gonopores are generally located to the lateral (external) side of the gill-pores in the same branchio-genital groove. The saccular gonads are lined with germinal epithelium which is continuous with the ectoderm. By the proliferation of cells from the germinal epithelium sperms or **ova** are produced. The mature sperms and ova are discharged outside through the genital pores. The sperm has a rounded head and a flagella-like tail but the ova are of two types. The small ovum measures about 0.06 mm in diameter and undergoes indirect development with a pelagic larva known as tornaria larva, while the larger ovum measures about 0.4 mm in diameter and undergoes direct development without larval stage. The mature sperms and ova are shed into the burrows where fertilization takes place, *i.e.,* the fertilization is external.

DEVELOPMENT

In *Balanoglossus,* the development is indirect, *i.e.,* the development is followed by the metamorphosis of a well developed larval form, the tornaria larva.

Fertilization. During breeding season (May to June) mature ova and sperms are discharged in the surrounding water where fertilization takes place. First the ova, egg-mass, are discharged by the female from its burrow and then the sperms are discharged by the male from its burrow. The number of eggs discharged at a time varies from few dozens to more than a thousand. Normally one to three hundred eggs are shed at a time. According to available evidences maturation starts some four hours before ovulation and that the egg is generally in the metaphase of the first meiotic division when shed. It is at this condition the egg is fertilizable. Fertilization of eggs within 6 to 7 hours after shedding yields a high percentage of normal development. The spermatozoon is able to enter the eggs at any point over the entire surface. After fertilization, the cleavage starts.

Prelarval development. The zygote, produced as a result of fertilization, undergoes cleavage. The cleavage is holoblastic, almost equal and mostly of the radial type. The first cleavage starts about two hours after fertilization and produces two generally, but not invariably, equal cells. The second cleagave is like the first and produces usually (but not invariably) four approximately equal cells. As a result of third and subsequent cleagaves a sphere of equal blastomeres is produced, it is called morula. The morula undergoes the reorganisation of its blastomeres and takes the form of a single-layered hollow and spherical blastula or coeloblastula. Its central fluid-filled cavity is called the blastocoel. As the cells multiply the volume of blastula increases. Blastula results in about 6–15 hours after fertilization. Within 12–24 hours, an invagination starts in the blastula which deepens to form the archenteron. The archenteron opens to the outside through a blastopore. The blastopore marks the posterior end of the embryo. The blastopore soon closes and the embryo now called gastrula. The gastrula elongates along the antero-posterior axis. Now the anterior tip of the archenteron is differentiated as a coelomic vesicle called the protocoel Thus, origin of coelom is entero-coelic. The remaining posterior part of the archenteron marks the future gut or alimentary canal. The protocoel becomes triangular in shape. One end of the protocoel gets attached to the underside of the apical thickening and another end opens to outside through an aperture, the hydropore, towards the dorsal side of the embryo. The protocoel and hydropore represent the future proboscis coelom and proboscis pore respectively. The collar and trunk coelom develop as solid invaginations of the hindgut, independent of the formation of protocoel.

Larval development. After the formation of the protocoel, the inner end of the early gut moves towards the ventral surface and opens to the outside through a mouth. The gut is now differentiated into the oseophagus, stomach and intestine. The intestine opens to outside through an anus, formed at the place of closed blastopore. By this time (after a day or so) the embryo becomes uniformly ciliated and escapes from fertilization membrane to lead a free swimming larval life. It is called tornaria larva.

Tornaria larva. Tornaria larva was first of all discovered by J. Muller in 1850 and was considered by him as the larva of echinoderms. Later on in 1869 it was Metschnikoff who established that it is a larva of *Balanoglossus clavigerus*. The name tornaria is given to it because of its habit of rotating in circles. Tornaria larva is usualy oval in shape and is excessively transparent. The size of tornaria larva varies from 1 mm to 3 mm. It has a ventral mouth near the equatorial plane of the body, a posterior terminal anus and gut differentiated into an oesophagus, stomach and intestine. The cilia form two bands on the body surface. The anterior ciliary band or circumoral band takes up a winding course over the preoral surface and forms a postoral loop. Its cilia are short and serve to collect the food. The posterior ciliated band or circumanal ring or telotroch lies as a ring in front of the anus. The cilia in this band are long, powerful and act as chief locomotor organ of tornaria. A ciliary wave passing along the telotroch causes the larva to rotate constantly in swimming. At the anterior end is an apical plate of thickened epidermal cells. The apical plate bears a pair of eye spots or ocelli and a tuft of sensory cilia called apical tuft or ciliary organ. The protocoel (proboscis coelom) is present in the form of a thin-walled sac and opens to the exterior through a hydropore (proboscis pore). To the right of the hydropore lies a pulsating heart vesicle which develops in the later stages of tornaria larva. The collar and trunk coeloms appear in the older larva.

Metamorphosis. The tornaria larva swims freely, leads a planktonic life feeding on minute organisms. After swimming for some time the tornaria larva sinks to the bottom and metamorphoses into an adult. During metamorphosis, the size of larva is reduced probably due to loss of water. Transparency, ciliary bands, sensory cilia and eye spots are lost. The body elongates and is distinguished into proboscis, collar and trunk by the appearance of two constrictions, and the trunk region is elongated. The hydropore persists as proboscis pore. Simultaneously the buccal diverticulum and gill-slits appear as outgrowth of the alimentary canal. The reproductive organs make their appearance, probably from the mesoderm. Thus, the larva gradually changes into the adult. The adult leads a benthonic life.

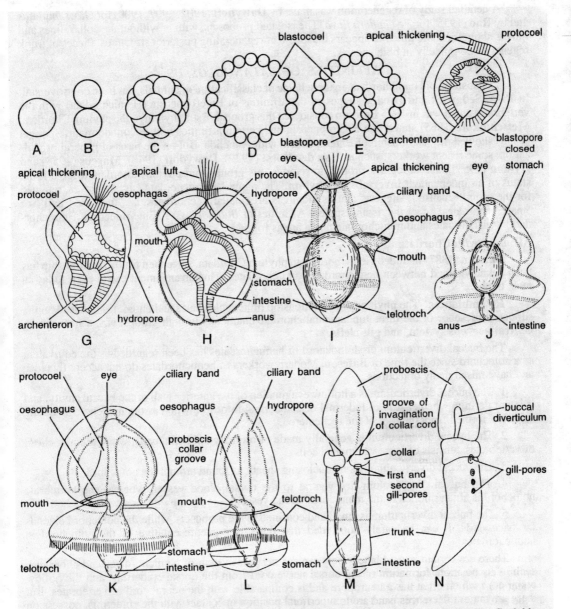

Fig. 88.19. *Balanoglossus.* Stages of development. A—Zygote ; B—2-Cell stage ; C—Morula; D—Coeloblastula ; E—Gastrulation ; F—Gastrula ; G—Early tornaria ; H—Young tornaria in section, I—Young tornaria ; J—Fully formed tornaria ; K to N—Metamorphosis of tornaria into a young *Balanoglossus.*

ASEXUAL REPRODUCTION

Asexual reproduction is known to occur in *Balanoglossus capensis* (Gilchrist, 1923). During summer the juvenile phase of this, at first considered a distinct species for it lacks hepaic sacculations, reproduces by cuting off small pieces from the tail end forward. These regenerate completely into the adult sexual type found in winter.

REGENERATION

Balanoglossus has great power of regeneration, small pieces are constricted from the posterior end, each of which regenerates into a complete individual. Other broken pieces of the animal also regenerate into new individuals.

A detailed study of regeneration was made by Dawydoff (1902, 1907, 1909) for *Gloss. minutus* and by Rao (1955) for *Ptychodera flava*. The isolated proboscis, with or without the collar, lines and moves about for some time but appears incapable of regenerating posterior structures. Pieces of trunk regenerate completely in both species.

AFFINITIES OF *BALANOGLOSSUS*

The position of Hemichordata, in the scheme of classification of animals, has been controversial. In 1814, Sedgwick and Huxley suggested the affinities of Enteropneusta (Hemichordata) with the vertebrates and it was in 1885 Bateson considered this group as a subphylum of the phylum Chordata. Metschnikoff (1865) stated that Enteropneusta had certain affinities with Echinodermata. Spengel (1893) showed the relationship of Enteropneusta with Annelida. But on the basis of general organization, some recent workers, such as Van der Horst (1939), Dawydoff (1948), Marcus (1958) and Hyman (1959) have thought it proper to remove this group from phylum Chordata to give it the status of an independent invertebrate phylum. The name "Hemichordata" is, however, retained for the group because it suggests that its members are related to chordates, *i.e.*, they are "half" or "part" chordates, a fact that is undisputed. Affinities of *Balanoglossus* (Enteropneusta, Hemichordata) with chordates and non-chordate phyla are as follows :

Affinities with Chordata

Bateson (1887) included Hemichordata in phylum Chordata, since then a close relationship has been acknowledged between hemichordates and chordates. This arrangement exists even today in most books.

Resemblances. The phylogenetic relationship of hemichordates and chordates in based on the supposed presence of the three fundamental chordate characters in both groups, *viz.*, a notochord, central nervous system, and gill-clefts.

The buccal diverticulum or stomochord of hemichordates has been regarded as the equivalent of a notochord since the time of Bateson. Modern workers of hemichordates do not accept this idea and have raised many objections :

1. The buccal diverticulum is a hollow evagination of the anterior wall of the buccal cavity, and it is not definite whether it is endodermal or ectodermal in origin, whereas the notochord is a long solid rod formed from the roof of the archenteron.

2. The buccal diverticulum is generally made of ordinary epithelial cells, while the notochord of vertebrates consists of large vacuolated cells.

3. The buccal diverticulum has no enclosing sheath as found around the notochord.

4. The buccal diverticulum lies ventral to the dorsal blood vessel, whereas the vertebrate notochord is always dorsal to the main dorsal blood vessel.

5. The buccal diverticulum is small and confined to the proboscis, while the notochord extends far backwards. It can be safely concluded that there is no representative of the notochord in hemichordates.

There are certain resemblances between the nervous system of hemichordates and chordates, such as its position, formation of the dorsal nerve cord from the dorsal epidermis, and the hollow collar cord which often has a neuropore and is comparable with the neural cord of vertebrates. But there are major differences, such as its superficial position in contact with the epidermis, possession of a main ventral nerve cord, and a circumenteric nerve ring, in these features the nervous system is distinctly invertebrate. Thus, the invertebrate features of the nervous system of hemichordates outweigh its chordate characters.

The chief link between the hemichordates and chordates lies in the pharynx and its gill-clefts. The details of the branchial apparatus having tongue bars, M-shaped skeletal rods and synapticula are exactly like those of *Amphioxus*. But the endostyle and epibranchial groove are absent from the pharynx of hemichordates. Such similarity can be only due to common ancestry, and phylogenetic relationship of hemichordates and chordates cannot be denied.

Differences. But the inclusion of hemichordates in phylum Chordata cannot be justified on the basis of a few similarities which are more than outweighed by important differences. The main differences are :

1. Chordates do not have the body and coelomic regions corresponding to those of hemichordates.

2. The circulatory and nervous systems of hemichordates are like those of invertebrates.

3. There is no post-anal tail in hemichordates.

4. Chordates are metamerically segmented animals, this segmentation is clearly shown by the muscular, nervous, circulatory, and excretory systems, whereas there is a total absence of segmentation in hemichordates.

Affinities with Annelida

Resemblances. The main resemblances of Hemichordata with Annelida are as follows :

1. The general body form and burrowing habit of tubicolous forms are alike and mud is ingested in burrowing. It is passed out from the anus as castings.

2. The vascular system of most hemichordates is like that of annelids with blood flowing anteriorly in the dorsal vessel and posteriorly in the ventral vessels.

3. The hemichordate tornaria larva appears like a modified trochosphere larva of polychaete worms.

Differences. The differences between two groups are so great that there can be no phylogenetic relationship between them. The differences are as follows :

1. Gill-slits are absent in annelids.

2. Paired nerve cords are present in annelids.

3. The larva of Hemichordata and Annelida also differ in the following ways :

(i) Nephridia are absent in tornaria larva.

(ii) Pre-oral coelom is absent in trochosphere larva.

(iii) In trochosphere blastopore becomes the mouth, while in tornaria it becomes the anus.

Affinities with Echinodermata

The adult hemichordate and adult echinoderm are so different that one cannot suspect any relationship between them, the only anatomical similarity between them is their nervous system which in both cases consists of nerve net lying near the surface embedded in the epidermis. But there is a strong affinity between the two phyla on embryological evidence, the method of formation of the gastrula and the coelom is very similar in the two phyla and for years the tornaria larva was considered to be the larva of an echinoderm. The tornaria larva shows a very striking resemblance with the auricularia larva and specially with bipinnaria of Asteroidea.

Resemblances. The resemblance extends into the following details :

1. The ciliated band is identical and follows the same course in the tornaria and the auricularia and bipinnaria, though the telotroch and eye spots of the tornaria are absent in echinoderm larvae.

2. The alimentary canal has the same shape and the same divisions into foregut, stomach, and intestine in hemichordate and echinoderm larvae.

3. In both groups the blastopore becomes larval anus.

4. The cleavage and gastrulation follow the same pattern in both.

5. The greatest and the most convincing resemblance lies in the method of formation and arrangement of coelomic cavities. In both the coelom is of enterocoelous origin and it divides into three antero-posterior parts, which in hemichordates are called proboscis coelom (protocoel), collar coelom (mesocoel), and trunk coelom (metacoel), while in echinoderms the three parts of the coelom are axocoel, hydrocoel, and somatocoel. Moreover the proboscis coelom and collar coelom of hemichordates open to the exterior by pores through short hydroporic canals, as does the hydrocoel in echinoderms.

6. The heart vesicle of hemichordates is related to the proboscis coelom and is homologous with the madreporic vesicle of echinoderm larvae, and both these structures are closely connected to the glomerulus of hemichordates and the axial gland of echinoderms which combine the vascular and excretory functions.

Differences. There are following differences between two groups :

1. Eye spot is absent in bipinnaria.

2. The apical plate and telotroch are absent in bipinnaria.

3. The protocoel is paired in echinoderms, while unpaired in tornaria larva.

The many embryonic resemblances between hemichordates and echinoderms cannot possibly be accidental or due to convergent evolution. The only infallible conclusion is that the two groups are closely related and that they arose from a common ancestor. Echinoderms have deviated greatly from the ancestral type, while hemichordates are closer to it. The common ancestor gave rise to echinoderms as a blind side branch, while the main line of evolution produced the hemichordates and chordates.

Conclusion. The above affinities have led to the conclusion that echinoderms, hemichordates and chordates have arisen from a common ancestral stock, the dipleura larva. Further, the echinoderms deviated greatly from the ancestral stock and formed blind branch in the main line of evolution. The main line of evolution continued to give rise to hemichordates and chordates.

It appears most reasonable to place them in the invertebrates as an independent phylum which has arisen from an ancestral stock that has given rise, on the one hand, to echinoderms and, on the other hand, to hemichordates and chordates.

REVISION QUESTIONS

1. Give an account of habit, habitat and external features of *Balanoglossus.*
2. Describe the internal anatomy of *Balanoglossus.*
3. Describe the digestive system of *Balanoglossus.*
4. Give an account of the circulatory system of *Balanoglossus.*
5. Describe the structure of tornaria larva and its metamorphosis.
6. Discuss the affinities of *Balanoglossus.*
7. Draw only labelled diagrams of the following :
   (i)   T.S. *Balanoglossus* through proboscis;
   (ii) T.S. *Balanoglossus* through collar;
   (iii) T.S. *Balanoglossus* through genital wings;
   (iv) M.L.S. of *Balanoglossus.*

89

Hemichordata : Characters, Classification and Types

DEFINITION

Usually vermiform, solitary or colonial enterocoelous coelomate animals with intra-epidermal nervous system and a pre-oral gut with or without gill-slits and without typical nephridia.

GENERAL CHARACTERS

1. Solitary and colonial, mostly tubicolous, exclusively marine.
2. Body soft, fragile, vermiform and divisible into proboscis, collar and trunk.
3. Body wall with a single-layered epidermis.
4. Coelom enterocoelous, divisible into protocoel, mesocoel and metacoel.
5. Buccal diverticulum, earlier considered as notochord, present in the proboscis.
6. Digestive tract complete; in the form of straight or U-shaped tube.
7. Gill-slits, when present, are paired and one to numerous.
8. Circulatory system simple and well developed; closed type; usually with a contractile heart vesicle and two longitudinal vessels, one dorsal and one ventral, interconnected by lateral vessels and sinuses.
9. Excretion by a single glomerulus situated in the proboscis.
10. Nervous system primitive comprising mainly of an intra-epidermal nerve plexus.
11. Reproduction mostly sexual. Sexes separate or united. Gonads one to several pairs.
12. Fertilization external. Development mostly indirect through a free swimming tornaria larva. Direct development is also found in some forms.

CLASSIFICATION

Phylum Hemichrodata has been divided into following four classes :

CLASS 1. ENTEROPNEUSTA

1. Commonly known as "acorn" or "tongue worms."
2. Solitary and burrowing worm-like marine animals.
3. Body consists of proboscis, collar and trunk; collar without tentaculated arms.
4. Alimentary canal straight; mouth and anus at opposite ends.
5. Numerous pairs of U-shaped gill-slits.
6. Two pairs of hepatic caeca present in the middle of the trunk.
7. Sexes separate; gonads numerous, sac-like.
8. Development with or without tornaria larva.

Examples : *Balanoglossus, Saccoglossus (=Dolichoglossus), Ptychodera.*

CLASS 2. PTEROBRANCHIA

1. Sedentary, solitary or colonial, tubicolous marine animals.
2. Proboscis with ciliated tentacles to produce ciliary feeding currents of water.
3. Collar with two or more tentaculated arms bearing tentacles.
4. One pair of gill-slits or none, never U-shaped.
5. Alimentary canal U-shaped with dorsal anus situated near the mouth at the same end.

6. Sexes separate or united; single or one pair of gonads.
7. Development direct, may or may not include a free swimming larval stage.
8. Asexual reproduction by budding in some.

Order 1. Cephalodiscida

1. Solitary or several individuals living unconnected in a common gelatinous house.
2. Collar with several tentaculated arms.
3. Gill-slits single pair.
4. Gonads single pair.
   Examples : *Cephalodiscus, Atubaria.*

Order 2. Rhabdopleurida

1. Colonial, zooids connected by a stolon.
2. Collar with two tentaculated arms.
3. Gill-slits absent.
4. Gonad single.
   Example : *Rhabdopleura* (Single genus).

REPRESENTATIVE TYPES

1. *Saccoglossus* (=*Dolichoglossus*).
Saccoglossus (Fig. 89.1) is a typical enteropneust very much similar to *Balanoglossus* in habits, habitat and structure. It is a marine, slender soft-bodied tongue worm living in spirally twisted furrows. Body is divisible into proboscis, collar and a trunk. Proboscis or protosome is exceptionally elongated and pointed than in other tongue worms. Collar slightly overhangs the beginning of the trunk covering first three or four pairs of gill-pores. Trunk is differentiated into anterior branchial region and posterior branchial region. Genital wings and hepatic caeca are absent. Alimentary canal is straight and anus lies at the posterior end of the body. Mature gonads are yellow in male and gray in female and their position is marked externally by dorso-lateral genital folds in the middle part of the trunk. Synapticula are absent so that tongue bars hang freely in their gill-slits. Sexes are separate and fertilization is external. Development is direct without a free-swimming tornaria larva. *Saccoglossus* is found in the Indo-Pacific Atlantic coasts, New Zealand and Australia.

2. *Ptychodera*. *Ptychodera* (Fig. 89.2) bears a close resemblance to *Balanoglossus* in habits, habitat and structure. It is soft-bodied, slender marine burrowing animal. The general colour of the animal is yellowish. Its body is elongated and divisible into proboscis, collar and trunk. Proboscis and collar are short, while trunk is quite elongated. Gonads are

CLASS 3. PLANCTOSPHAEROIDEA

This class is represented by a few small rounded, transparent and pelagic larvae, supposed to be specialized tornaria of some unknown hemichordate *Planctosphaera pelagica*. The larva has branching arborescent ciliated bands on the surface. The alimentary canal of larva is U-shaped. The adult form is yet unknown.

CLASS 4. GRAPTOLITA

These are extinct colonial hemichordates, mainly known from the fossil structures of their tubes. Each animal is housed in a zooid. These were abundant in the Ordovician and Silurian periods.

Example : *Dendrograptus.*

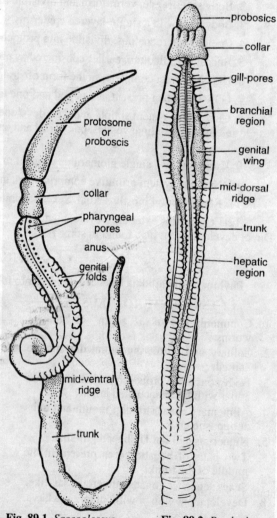

Fig. 89.1. *Saccoglossus.* **Fig. 89.2.** *Ptychodera.*

situated in the genital wings. Hepatic caeca are distinct. Sexes are separate. Development is indirect involving a free-swimming tornaria larva. It exhibits bioluminescence. *Ptychodera* is found in the sea of tropical and subtropical regions.

    3. *Cephalodiscus. Cephalodiscus* (Fig. 89.3) individuals or zooids occur together in large aggregations attached to objects on the sea bottom in tropical and temperate oceans. The zooids live in separate tubes embedded in a common matrix called a coenoecium but the various zooids are free from each other.

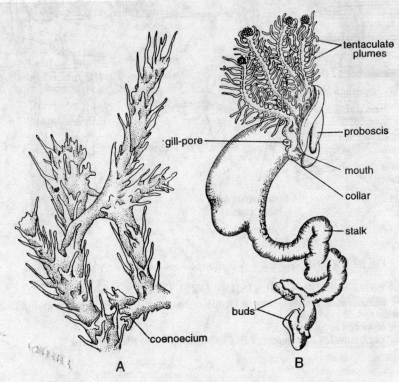

Fig. 89.3. *Cephalodiscus.* A—A part of colony; B—An individual zooid.

    A zooid of *Cephalodiscus* has a general structure like that of *Balanoglossus*. The body has a proboscis, collar and trunk borne on a hollow muscular stalk. The proboscis is a ventrally bent disc. The collar bears several hollow branched arms in two rows, they bear tentacles and are spoken of as tentaculated arms, the arms bear cilia which drive a food laden current of water into the mouth. The trunk is a plump sac having a U-shaped alimentary canal with a ventral mouth and a dorsal anus. In the anterior part of the trunk is a single pair of gill-clefts. Sexes are separate, each has a pair of gonads opening by separate gonopores situated dorsally on the front part of the trunk. Fertilization and direct development with no larval stage occur in the coenecium. The original individual is produced sexually, on its trunk is a peduncle bearing buds, the buds become free and each forms a zooid which secretes a tube.

    4. *Rhabdopleura. Rhabdopleura* (Fig. 89.4) is a true colonial form. The colonies are attached to stones, corals, and sessile marine animals mostly in the North Atlantic. The colony has a thin horizontal branching tube called a coenecium from which short erect tubes arise, each containing a zooid. A zooid is minute, its general structure is like an enteropneust with a proboscis, collar and trunk, attached to the trunk is a stalk. On the collar is a pair of hollow branching arms having cilia which collect the food of the animal. Alimentary canal is U-shaped so that the anus lies close to the mouth. There are no gill-clefts and a glomerulus is lacking.

    Sexes are separate, each sex has a single gonad with a gonopore on the right side. Large yolky eggs are laid. An original individual is produced sexually, on its trunk is a peduncle which bears buds, the buds do not become free and each forms a zooid. Each zooid secretes its own ringed vertical tube or case which is formed ring by ring. The horizontal part of each tube has a black stolon which connects the various zooids to the parent so that a colony of connected zooids is formed.

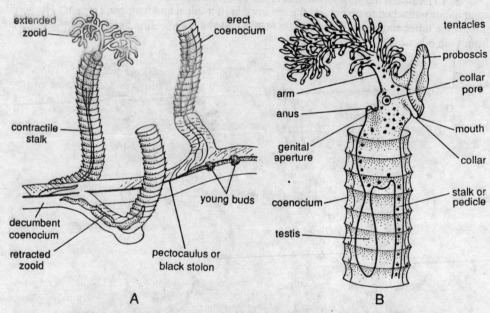

Fig. 89.4. *Rhabdopleura.* A—A portion of a colony ; B—An individual zooid.

REVISION QUESTIONS

1. Give an account of the characters of Hemichordata. Classify it up to orders giving characters and examples.
2. Write notes on the following :
   (i) *Saccoglossus;* (ii) *Ptychodera*; (iii) *Cephalodiscus*; (iv) *Rhabdopleura.*

Glossary

Abdomen. In arthropods, the body region posterior to the thorax.

Abductor. A muscle that draws a part away from the median line or centre of the body.

Aboral. Opposite the mouth.

Absorption. The taking in of fluids or other substances by cells or tissues.

Acanthocephala. A phylum of spiny-headed parasitic worms; pseudocoelomate.

Acarina. The order of arachnids to which mites and ticks belong.

Acclimatize. To become habituated or accustomed to a new environment.

Acentric. Having no centre; specially a type of mitosis in which a centriole is absent.

Acetylcholine. A substance liberated at nerve endings. It is involved in conduction across synapses and is associated with many parasympathetic nerves.

Achromatic figure. Metaphase plate chromosomal line-up.

Acicula. Needle-like bristle within parapodium of polychaete.

Acellular. Without cellular organisation.

Acinus. One of the small terminal sacs in a multicellular gland.

Acoelomate. Animals without a coelom.

Acrosomal cap. Covering over the head of a sperm, derived from Golgi complex.

Acrosome. Structure at the tip of a sperm head that makes contact with the ovum at the time of fertilization.

Active transport. Movement of a substance through a membrane with the help of a carrier. Carrier in this case bonds to substance.

Adambulacral. Pertaining to the side, towards or upon ambulacral groove.

Adaptation. The fitness of an organism for its environment.

Adductor. A muscle that draws a structure toward the median line.

Adenine. A purine component of nucleic acids and nucleotides.

Adenosine. Phosphorylated organic compounds that function in intercellular energy transfers.

Adipose tissue. Fat tissue, composed of polygonal or rounded cells. Mostly for energy storage.

ADP. Adenosine diphosphate. ATP with one less phosphate. Of lower energy than ATP.

Adsorption. Adhesion of a very thin layer of liquid, dissolved substance or gas molecules to a solid surface.

Aerial. Inhabiting or frequenting the air.

Aerobe. Organism that is able to live and grow in the presence of free oxygen.

Afferent. A vessel or structure leading to or toward a certain region.

Agamete. An asexual structure in the embryogeny that develops into a complex individual.

Agamogony. A method of asexual reproduction.

Agamont. A gamete producing parent body.

Alimentary. Pertaining to digestion or digestive tract.

Alternation of generation. Alternate succession of sexual (haploid) and asexual (diploid) generations in the life cycle of an organism.

Ambulacral groove. A groove in the arm of an echinoderm lined by tube feet.

Ambulacrum. Grooves lined with tube feet in certain echinoderms.

Amitosis. Direct nuclear division in which the nucleus constricts and separates into two portions without formation of condensed chromosomes or spindle fibres.

Ammonotelic. An organism whose nitrogenous excreta is mainly ammonia.

Amoebocyte. Amorphous independently mobile cell.

Amoeboid. Cell movements resembling those of the amoeba.

Amphibious. Capable of living on land as well as in water.

Amphiblastula. Blastula-like sponge larva; large-celled vegetal pole, small-celled flagellated animal pole; free-swimming.

Amphimixis. Union of male and female gametic nuclei to form a zygote nucleus.

Ampulla. A small bladder-like sac.

Anabolism. The constructive phase of metabolism in which the cells build protoplasm from food materials.

Anaerobic. Able to live and grow without the presence of air or free oxygen.

Analogous. Body parts with similar functions but usually genetically dissimilar.

Anaphase. A stage in mitosis when chromosomes move from the equatorial plate to opposite ends of the mitotic spindle.

Anastomosis. A union or joining together, as of two or more blood vessels, nerves or other structures.

Anatomy. Study of the structure of animals and plants.

Angstrom. One thousand of a micron.

Anion. Negatively charged ion.

Anisogamy. Sexual fusion in which male and female gametes are of unequal size.

Annelida. Phylum to which the segmented worms such as the earthworms belong.

Annulus. Any ring or ring-like structure.

Antennae. Tactile sense organs on the heads of arthropods.

Antennules. Many-jointed feelers found on some arthropods and located near the antennae; sometimes called the first antennae.

Anterior. Pertaining to the front or head end of an animal or the forward-moving end of an animal.

Anticoagulant. A substance that prevents the coagulation of blood.

Anus. The posterior opening of the digestive tract.

Aorta. The large artery carrying blood away from the heart.

Aperture. Orifice or opening.

Apical. At the top or apex.

Apopyle. Pore leading from the chambers into the central cavity or spongocoel in sponges.

Appendage. Portion of the body that projects and has a free end such as limbs.

Apterous. Without wings or wingless.

Aquatic. Pertaining to water or living in water.

Arachnida. A class of the Arthropoda including the spiders, ticks, mites and scorpions.

Arboreal. Pertaining to trees as tree-living.

Archenteron. Primitive digestive tract of a metazoan embryo, formed during gastrulation.

Archeocyte. Amoeboid cell which receives, digests and transports food, may also produce other cells, *e.g.*, reproductive cells.

Areolar. Containing minute air-filled spaces.

Aristotle's lantern. In most Echinoidea, complex pentagonal apparatus made of muscle, connective tissue and bony tissue. Used in feeding and locomotion.

Arthropoda. A phylum of segmented invertebrates with jointed appendages like, prawns and insects.

Articulation. A joint between two segments or structures.

Artificial classification. Classification based on characters of convenience without relation to phylogenetic significance.

Aschelminthes. A phylum of pseudocoelomate worms.

Asconoid. Type of sponge structure in which canals pass directly from the ostia to the spongocoel, which is lined with collar cells.

Asexual reproduction. Reproduction without involving gametes.

Assimilation. Process by which digested food and other materials are changed into protoplasm.

Aster. A star-like figure formed during mitosis and composed of the centrosome and the lines radiating from it.

Asymmetry. Condition in which opposite sides of an animal are not alike, without symmetry.

Atoll. Horse shoe or ring-like island consisting of a belt of coral reef surrounding a central lagoon.

ATP. Adenosine triphosphate, an energy rich molecule formed in cellular respiration.

Auditory. Pertaining to the organ or sense of hearing.

Auricle. Ear-like projection or lobe-like appendage, *e.g.*, lateral flap near planarian eye.

Auricularia. Larva of holothuroid Echinodermata.

Autotomy. Self-mutilation; the automatic "voluntary" breaking off a part of the body of an animal.

Autotrophic nutrition. Process of nutrition in which an organism manufactures its own food.

Avicularium. Polymorphic individual, shaped like a bird's head, within an ectoproct colony, having a protective function.

Axon. Nerve fibre that conducts nerve impulses away from the cell body.

Barnacle. A crustacean.

Barrier reef. Reef separated from shore by wide deep channel.

Basal disc. Foot of some Cnidaria which is flattened and attaches to a substratum by secretion of a sticky substance.

Behaviour. Reactions of the whole organism to the environment.

Benthos. Organisms living on or in the bottom, either of the ocean or freshwater from the edge of water to the greatest depths.

Bilateria. The metazoans with bilateral symmetry.

Bilateral cleavage. Unequal-sized blastomeres are confined to separate areas in the morula, yields a bilaterally symmetrical morula.

Bilateral symmetry. The arrangement of the body parts so that the right and left halves are mirror images of each other.

Binary fission. The type of asexual reproduction by means of which the organism divides into two approximately equal halves.

Binomial nomenclature. The international system of naming animals whereby two names are used. The first is generic, the second is specific.

Biology. The science of life, it includes botany, zoology and all the fields of study associated with life.

Bioluminescence. The emission of light by living organisms.

Blepharoplast. Basal granule at the base of a flagellum or a cilium.

Bipinnaria. Larva of asteroid Echinodermata.

Biradial symmetry. Condition in which an animal has radially arranged parts that lie half on one side and half on the other side of a median longitudinal plane. Example Ctenophora.

Biramous. Crustacean appendage with protopodite, endopodite and exopodite, each of the two branches is segmented, some branch may be absent.

Bivalent. The pachynema stage of meiosis, the four chromatids formed from two homologous chromosomes, all joined by a common centromere. Also called a tetrad.

Blastocoel. Cavity of the blastula.

Blastoderm. Blastodisc or its outgrowth. Also in superficial cleavage (*e.g.*, in insects) the outer cellular layer of blastula.

Blastopore The opening into the archenteron of the gastrula.

Blastula. The early embryo in which the cells form a hollow ball.

Body cavity. Cavity located between body wall and internal organs of an animal.

Book lungs. Paired respiratory structures present in various arachnids.

Brackish. Water intermediate in salt content between sea water and freshwater.

Branchiostegite. Portion of the exoskeleton that covers the gills in higher crustaceans.

Bronchiole. A tiny air tube in the lung.

Bronchus. One of the two main air passages on the trachea.

Brownian movement. Movement of the cytoplasm due to the intercellular molecular collisions. Especially visible in *Amoeba*.

Bryozoa. A phylum of sea weed-like invertebrates; moss animals.

Buccal. Pertaining to the mouth or oral cavity.

Bud. Developing lateral branch of an organism.

Budding. Production of offspring by development of a lateral branch from part of the body. It is a form of asexual reproduction.

Byssus. Silk-like threads secreted by mussels for attachment to rock surfaces.

Calcareous. Containing lime or calcium.

Calciferous glands. Structures that lie at the sides of the oesophagus of some annelids, *e.g.*, earthworms.

Captaculum. A tentacle-like food capture structure growing out from head of tooth shell mollusc.

Carapace. Hard covering of the crustacean cephalothorax.

Carnivorous. Eating or living on other animals.

Castings. Undigested solids containing soil.

Castration. The act of removing the sex glands, usually from males.

Catabolism. Breaking down or destructive phase of metabolism; the metabolic processes in which chemical breakdown occurs, for example respiration.

Cation. Positively charged ion.

Caterpillar. Larval stage in the metamorphosis of butterflies and moths.

Caudal. Pertaining to the tail or posterior part of the body.

Cell. Small mass or unit of protoplasm surrounded by a cell membrane and containing one or more nuclei.

Cellular. Pertaining to or consisting of cells.

Central nervous system. The brain and the spinal cord including the dorsal root ganglion. Abbreviated CNS.

Centriole. Cytoplasmic organelle which forms the spindle pole during mitosis and meiosis.

Centromere. A point where the spindle fibre is attached; a constricted region of the chromosome not coloured by the usual chromosomal stains.

Centrosome. A small differentiated area of a cell containing the centriole.

Cephalic. Pertaining to or situated near the head.

Cephalization. The tendency toward the centralization of important parts, as the sense organs in the head or in the head region.

Cephalothorax. Body division formed by the fusion of the head and thorax in some arthropods.

Cercaria. A free-swimming larval stage of a trematode parasite, which encysts in a fish.

Cervix. Neck-like structure.

Chelate. Claw possessing appendage.

Chelicera. An anterior pair of appendages in arachnids such as spiders and related forms.

Cheliped. A crustacean appendage having a pincer-like claw distally, such as the first and second walking legs of a *Palaemon*.

Chemoreceptor. Organ or neuron sensitive to specific chemical changes or gradients.

Chemotaxis. A movement response to chemical stimulus.

Chemotherapy. Study of the use of drugs and other substances of chemical nature in the treatment of specific diseases.

Chiasmata. Crossover loci on chromosomes during mitosis and meiosis.

Chitin. A complex organic substance or a polysaccharide protein horny substance, forming the exoskeleton of arthropods and some other animals.

Chlorocruorin. Green blood pigment present in plasma of certain annelids.

Chlorogogue. Excretory cell of certain invertebrates including annelids, carrying wastes from body fluids to epidermis.

Chloroplast. A chromatophore containing chlorophyll.

Choanocyte. Flagellated collar cells found in sponges.

Chromatin. The stainable protoplasmic substance in the nucleus of a cell that gives rise to the conspicuous chromosome during mitosis.

Chromomere. Individual chromatin granule in a chromosome.

Chromonema. Thread-like strands of chromatin visible in the nucleus during mitosis and in some cells during interphase.

Chromosomes. Deeply staining rod-shaped bodies within the nucleus and conspicuously visible during cell division. They contain the genes.

Chrysalis. The pupal stage of butterfly.

Cilia. Microscopic hair-like projections from certain cells which vibrate causing movement.

Cirrus. Small and movable projection from a cell or body surface.

Classification, Artificial. Grouping on basis of resemblance in structure, colour, habit, etc.

Classification, Natural. Taxonomic scheme utilizing evolutionary, adaptational and anatomical considerations as discriminational basis.

Cleavage. Series of early divisions of an egg into many cells.

Clitellum. A thickened glandular portion of the body of an earthworm or other annelid, used in the formation of cocoon.

Cloaca. A common receptacle for digestive, excretory wastes and reproductive cells.

Clypeus. Rectangular sclerite ventral to the frons of an insectan head.

Cnidaria or Coelenterata. Phylum of animals all possessing cnidoblast structures.

Cnidoblast. Type of cell in which nematocyst is found.

Cnidocil. Hair-like processes projecting from the outer margin of the cnidoblast.

Cocoon. A protective covering for eggs, larvae, pupae or adult animals.

Coelom. The body cavity lined with tissue of mesodermal origin in which the digestive and other organs lie.

Coelomoduct. Duct of mesodermal origin that conveys gametes and/or excretory products from coelom to exterior of body.

Colloblast. The type of cell in ctenophore tentacles capable of adhesion.

Colony. Group of individuals, unicellular or multicellular, of the same species, which have developed from a common parent and remain organically attached or held together.

Commensalism. An association of individuals of two different species in which at least one is benefited and the other is neither benefitted nor harmed.

Commissure. A group of connective nerve fibres uniting two like structures in the two sides of the brain or spinal cord or similar cords connecting nerve centres elsewhere.

Community. A more or less complex group of plants and animals that occupy a particular area.

Compound eye. An eye (in arthropods) with numerous ommatidia.

Conjugation. A method of sexual reproduction in which two unicellular animals unite, exchange nuclear material and then divide as in the *Paramecium*.

Contractile vacuole. A space in the cytoplasm of certain species of Protozoa where fluids collect before being periodically discharged to the outside.

Copulation. Sexual union of two individuals involving the transference of sperms from the male to the female body.

Corona. A ring or circle of tentacles.

Corpora allata. In insects, structures containing neurosecretory cells which secrete juvenile hormone.

Corpus allatum. Endocrine gland behind the brain in insect head which secretes hormones responsible for larval moult.

Cortex. Outer portion of a structure.

Cranial. Pertaining to brain or skull such as cranial nerves.

Crinoid. Class of Echinodermata to which sea lilies belong.

Crop. Expanded portion of the anterior part of a digestive tract specialized for storage.

Cross fertilization. Fertilization of an egg produced by one individual, with a sperm produced by another individual.

Crossing over. Process in which homologous chromosomes break and exchange corresponding segments.

Ctenophora. Radiate phylum of animals possessing comb-plates such as comb-jellies.

Cuticle. Thin non-cellular outermost covering secreted by the underlying epidermis.

Cyclosis. Circular streaming movement of cytoplasm in certain cells.

Cydippid. Ctenophora larva.

Cyphonautes. Ectoproct larva.

Cyst. The stage of an organism where it is enclosed in a resistant wall.

Cysticercus. Bladderworm; larva containing an invaginated scolex. Tapeworm larva.

Cytokinesis. Cleavage of cells during telophase of mitosis and meiosis. Starts with invagination of equatorial plate.

Cytology. Science that deals with the structure of cells.

Cytopharynx. Pharynx or gullet of a protozoan such as *Paramecium*.

Cytoplasm. Protoplasm of a cell exclusive of the nucleus.

Cytosine. Nitrogen base found in nucleic acids and nucleotides.

Cytostome. Cell mouth, for example in *Paramecium*.

Dactylozooid. Sensory polyp of Hydrozoa.

Daughter cells. Two cells formed by the division of one cell.

Decapod. Ten footed animal such as decapod crustacean.

Defecation. Passage of waste material from the digestive tract of an animal.

Degenerate. To lose generative ability.

Dendrite. Fibre of a nerve cell that conducts impulses toward the nerve cell body.

Deoxyribose. Component of deoxyribonucleic acid (DNA).

Dermal. Pertaining to the skin.

Dermis. The inner layer of the skin, lying below the epidermis.

Desiccation. Drying, dehydration.

Deuterostomia. Animals in which blastopore forms anus, second embryonic opening forms mouth opposite anus.

Dextral. Coiling clockwise.

Diakinesis. In meiosis, the stage where all cytoplasmic divisions occur.

Diapause. Inactive stage of an insect during pupal stage.

Diffusion. Movement of molecules from a region of high concentration to one of lower concentration brought about as a consequence of their kinetic energy.

Digestion. Conversion of complex substances of food into simple soluble forms which can be absorbed.

Dimorphism. Difference in size, structure, form, colour, etc., between two types of individuals of the same species.

Dioecious. Having the male and female reproductive organs in separtate individuals.

Dipleurula. Developmental stage of echinoderms and hemichordates; hypothetical ancestor of most deutero-stomes.

Diploblastic. Derived from two embryonic germ layers, ectoderm and endoderm.

Diploid. Referring to the number of chromosomes in somatic cells; double the number of chromosomes that occur in the mature egg or sperm.

Diplonema stage. In meiosis, stage where chromosomes of each bivalent split. Chiasmata may appear.

Distal. Away from the point of attachment, for example, the hand is the distal part of the arm.

Diurnal. Petaining to the time of day light. It is opposed to nocturnal, which pertains to the time of night.

Diverticulum. Sac-like projection of a tubular organ.

DNA. Deoxyribose nucleic acid (deoxyribonucleic acid).

DNA polymerase. An enzyme affecting DNA synthesis.

Dorsal. Pertaining to the back, opposed to ventral in a bilaterally symmetrical animal.

Duct. A tube for the flow of a fluid.

Ecdysis. Moulting; the shedding of the outer cuticular covering of an arthropod.

Ecdyosone. Insect hormone which initiates metamorphic activity.

Echinodermata. Animal phylum characterized by spiny skin to which sea urchins and sea stars belong.

Echiuroidea. Schizocoelomate, worm-like phylum characterized by hind-end spines.

Ecology. The science studying the inter-relations between living organisms and their environment.

Ectocommensal. Pertaining to an organism that lives on the external surface of another organism, the host, without either benefiting or injuring it.

Ectoderm. Outer layer of cells in the gastrula. This layer gives rise to the epidermis, sense organs and nervous system.

Ectoparasite. A parasite that lives on the outside of the body of its host.

Ectoplasm. Layer of cytoplasm nearest the surface of the cell.

Ectoprocta. Coelomate, sessile phylum with U-shaped intestine, mouth surrounded by lophophore, and opening outside lophophore.

Ectosarc. Structure in a protozoan composed of ectoplasm.

Effector. Any part of the body, such as a muscle or gland, transforming motor impulses into motor action.

Efferent. Conveying outward or away from a structure. Opposite of afferent.

Egest. To discharge unusable food or residues from the digestive tract.

Electron micrograph. Enlarged photograph of an object taken by attaching a camera to an electron microscope.

Electron microscope. Optical instrument in which a beam of electrons focussed by means of magnetic field (magnectic lens) is used to produce an enlarged image of a minute object on a fluorescent screen or a photographic plate.

Elephantiasis. Human lymphatic disease caused by a nematode (*Filaria bancrofti*). Lymph ducts become clogged, new ducts are formed along with new connective tissue.

Eleutherozoa. Subphylum of Echinodermata composed of all extinct classes except crinoids.

Embryo. Young animal that is passing through its developmental stages, usually within the egg membranes or within the maternal uterus.

Embryogeny. The development of an organism.

Embryology. The study of the development of an organism.

Encyst. To become enclosed in a sac (cyst).

Encystment. Process whereby an animal becomes enclosed in an impermeable envelope.

Endoderm. Innermost layer of the early embryo which gives rise to the lining of the digestive tract.

Endoparasite. A parasite living within the body of its host.

Endoplasm. Within a cell, the cytoplasm that is surrounded by ectoplasm.

Endoplasmic reticulum. Complex system of inter-connecting channels within a cell made up of unit membranes.

Endopodite. Principal internal (medial) branch of a biramous appendage of a crustacean.

Endoskeleton. A supporting framework on the inside of an animal, whether it be cartilaginous, bony, or of other material.

Endosome. The central mass, consisting largely of chromatin material, in the nucleus of certain Protozoa.

Enteron. Digestive tract, especially in Cnidaria.

Entomology. Study of insects.

Entoprocta. Pseudocoelomate, sessile phylum with U-shaped intestine, mouth surrounded by circle of ciliated tentacles, and opening within circle.

Enzyme. An organic substance (protein) that produces a specific chemical change.

Ephyra. Stage of free-swimming larva in scyphozoan coelenterates.

Epiboly. Posterior growth of a fold of the blastoderm over the surface of an embryo in the process of forming the enteron during gastrulation.

Epicranium. Largest sclerite of the head in the grasshopper and related forms.

Epicuticle. During moulting, these epidermal cells secreted under the old exoskeleton.

Epidermis. Outer cellular layer of cells covering the external surface of the body.

Epipodite. A long slender structure, fastened to the protopodite of the walking leg of a crustacean.

Epithelium. Usually a sheet of cells covering either external or internal surface of the body.

Erythrocyte. Red blood corpuscle.

Ethology. The study of animal behaviour based on comparisons, the observation of patterns and the consideration of environmental adaptations.

Evagination. An outpocketing from any surface by growth, especially a cavity.

Excretion. Discharge of metabolic wastes; also the substances discharged.

Exopodite. External branch of a typical biramous appendage of a crustacean.

Exoskeleton. A supporting structure on the outside of an animal body. The skeleton of an invertebrate is usually an exoskeleton.

Extensor. Any muscle that straightens out or extends a part of the body such as foot.

Extracellular. Outside of the cell or cells.

Exumbrella. Convex, aboral surface of the medusae.

Fauna. Animal life of a given period or region.

Faeces. The indigestible, unabsorbed residue of digestion.

Fertilization. Union of a mature ovum and a mature sperm to form zygote.

Filopodium. Filamentous pseudopodium of sarcodine protozoans.

Fission. Asexual method of reproduction by division into two or more parts approximately equal in size.

Fissure. Furrow, cleft, or slit.

Flagellum. A long whip-like cytoplasmic organelle.

Flame cell. Terminal invertebrate excretory cell containing a group of beating cilia.

Food vacuole. Intra-cellular digestive organelle.

Fossil. Remains or other indications of prehistoric forms of life.

Free-living. Capable of independent existence.

Fringing reef. Coral ridge build up from ocean bottom.

Frons. Anterior portion of an insect head.

Fundus. Base of a hollow structure or the part farthest from the opening.

Gamete. A mature reproductive or germ cell either ovum, sperm or other type of reproductive cell.

Gametocyte. Parental gametes of some merozoites which, as long as they remain in host, undergo no further development. Harmless in man, but if sucked into a mosquito , become active.

Gametogenesis. Process of development of gametes.

Ganglion. Group of mass of nerve cell bodies, usually, located within the central nervous system in invertebrates.

Gastrocoel. Primitive digestive cavity of metazoan embryo formed by gastrulation.

Gastrodermis. Lining of coelenterate digestive cavity.

Gastropoda. Class of Mollusca to which snails and slugs belong.

Gastrotricha. Tiny, aquatic, pseudocoelomate with ventral cilia-like bristles.

Gastrovascular. Serving the function of both digestion and circulation.

Gastrula. An embryonic stage with two germ layers, ectoderm and endoderm.

Gastrulation. Process by which a gastrula is formed; invagination of the blastula.

Gemmule. Multicellular vegetative bud of certain sponges.

Gena. Lateral portion of an insect's head.

Gene. A functional segment of DNA containing hereditary informations.

Genetics. The science of heredity and variations.

Genital. Pertaining to the reproductive organs of either sex.

Genus. The taxonomic sub-division of a family. A genus is usually composed of several species.

Gill. Type of respiratory organ for aquatic organisms.

Gizzard. Muscular part of the digestive tract, as in earthworms and insects, used for grinding the ingested food.

Gland. One or many associated cells that secrete or excrete one or more special substances.

Glochidium. A bivalve larva of mussel and clam.

Glycolysis. The metabolic conversion of sugars into simpler compounds.

Golgi apparatus. A cytoplasmic organelle for the storage of cellular secretions.

Gonad. Reproductive organ, either ovary, testis or ovotestis in which gametes are produced.

Gonangium. Reproductive individual of a hydroid colony.

Gonotheca. Firm external covering of a gonangium.

Gonozooid. Reproductive polyp of Hydrozoa.

Green gland. Somewhat modified nephridium, functional in crabs and prawns.

Gregarious. Living in groups, as in flocks and herds.

Gynandromorph. Individual showing a condition where part of an animal may be male and another part female.

Habitat. Environment in which an animal lives.

Haploid. With a single set of chromosomes as normally present in a mature gamete.

Haemocoel. The coelom filled with blood (haemolymph). It functions as a part of the circulatory system as in arthropods.

Hepatic. Pertaining to the liver.

Herbivorous. Feeding chiefly on plants.

Hermaphrodite. An individual possessing both male and female reproductive organs.

Hibernation. Passing of the winter in a dormant inactive state.

Hindgut. Posterior portion of the digestive tract in arthropods.

Histology. Branch of anatomy that deals with the microscopic structure of tissues and organs.

Holoblastic. Cleavage in which an entire egg cell divides.

Holophytic. Type of nutrition, found in green plants and in some mastigophores, which involves photosynthesis.

Holothuroidea. Class of Echinodermata to which the sea cucumbers belong.

Holozoic. Type of nutrition found in most animals, that involves ingestion and digestion of organic material.

Host. Organism that provides food, shelter, or other benefits to another organism.

Host cells. In Cnidaria, the epitheliomuscular cells which house the cnidoblasts.

Hydranth. Expanded end of a branch of a hydroid colony specialized for vegetative function.

Hydrocaulus. Main stalk-like stem of a hydroid colony.

Hydrorhiza. Basal portion of a hydroid colony often branched and root-like, used for attachmentt to substratum.

Hydrotheca. Transparent membrane that extends from the perisarc and surrounds the main part of the hydranth.

Hyperparasitism. Condition where parasites are parasitized by other parasites. May be secondary, tertiary, etc.

Hypostome. Region surrounding the mouth in coelenterates.

Imago. An adult insect.

Ingestion. The act of taking the food into the mouth.

Insecticide. Chemical agent that kills insects.

Insectivorous. Insect eating animal.

Instar. Period between consecutive insect moults.

Integument. Outer covering, specially the skin.

Inter-cellular. Between cells.

Intra-cellular. Within cells.

Introvert. Narrow anterior part of a sipunculid which may be muscularly withdrawn inward. Also distal end of Bryozoan bearing lophophore.

Invagination. Infolding of any part; infolding of a layer of tissue in gastrulation.

Invertebrate. Any animal without vertebral column or backbone.

Involution. The process of rolling or turning in of cells over a rim during gastrulation.

Irradiation. Exposure to ultraviolet or other types of rays.

Irritability. Ability to respond to stimuli.

Isogamy. Sexual reproduction involving fusion of two similar gametes but from opposite sexes.

Jelly-fish. Coelenterate belonging to class Scyphozoa.

Joint. A place of union between two hardened structures.

Juvenile hormone. Hormone produced by corpora allata in insects. Its presence prevents an imaginal moult.

Karyoplasm. The nucleus, including the nuclear membrane and all it encloses.

Kinetosome. The basal body of a flagellum or cilium.

Kinorhyncha. Pseudocoelomate class of Aschelminthes.

Labial. Pertaining to the lips.

Labium. A lip, specifically the lower lip of an insect's mouth part structures.

Labrum. Upper lip of the insect's mouth. Dorsal to the mouth opening.

Lamella. A thin leaf-like layer.

Lappet. Flap-like projection, as on each side of tentaculocysts or on planarians' head.

Larva. An immature, free-living stage in the life cycle of various animals, which reach the adult form by undergoing metamorphosis.

Lateral. The side of the body. At each side of the median line.

Leptonema stage. In meiosis, the stage resembling mitotic prophase, chromosomes become visible.

Littoral. Floor of the sea from the shore to the edge of the continental shelf.

Locomotion. Movement involving the organism as a whole.

Lophophore. Anterior tentacle-bearing area of certain coelomates; serves in food capture.

Lorica. Protective covering secreted by certain organisms, *e.g.*, some ciliate protozoans.

Lumen. Internal cavity within a body or structure such as the lumen of the intestine, a gland duct or a blood vessel.

Luminescence. Production of light as a result of chemical reactions in cells.

Lysosome. Sub-cellular digestive organelle which contains enzymes.

Macronucleus. Large nucleus of Ciliophora; controls all activities except reproduction.

Madreporite. Strainer-like cover of the opening to the water vascular system in echinoderms.

Maggot. Worm-like legless larva of a fly.

Mandible. A jaw, either jaw of an arthropod.

Mantle. Fold of the body wall that encloses the soft structures of an animal such as a mollusc and which secretes the shell.

Manubrium. A structure projecting from the middle of the sub-umbrellar surface of the medusa and bearing the mouth at its free end.

Mastication. Chewing food with the mouth parts as in many insects.

Maxilla. One of the several mouth part structures of the *Palaemon*.

Maxillipede. One of the three pairs of thoracic appendages in the Crustacea.

Meiosis. Last stages in the development of gametes, characterised by two divisions, in which the number of chromosomes is reduced by half to the haploid number.

Merozoite. Mature trophozoite after mitotic division.

Mesoderm. The middle layer of embryonic cells, between the ectoderm and endoderm.

Mesogloea. Non-cellular jelly-like substance lying between the ectoderm and endoderm in coelenterates.

Mesothorax. Middle portion of thorax.

Metagenesis. Alternation of sexual with an asexual generation in reproduction in the life cycle of a coelenterate such as *Obelia*.

Metamerism. Condition where the body of an animal is made up of a succession of homologous parts (metameres).

Metamorphosis. Marked structural change or transformation during development, for example as from larva to adult.

Metanephridium. Tubular organ of excretion, such as that found in the earthworm, leading to the exterior from the coelom.

Metaphase. Stage of mitosis during which the chromosomes are lined up in the equatorial plane of the spindle.

Metathorax. Posterior portion of the thorax.

Metazoa. All multicellular animals in which there is a differentiation of the body cells as opposed to the unicellular animals.

Micron. The one thousandth part of a millimetre.

Micronucleus. In organisms with micronuclei, smaller nucleus most useful in reproductive activity.

Midgut. In arthropods, middle portion of digestive tract, not lined with cuticle.

Migration. Movement of a part of a population of a species (usually in groups) from one region to another.

Mimicry. Adaptive resemblance of certain animals to others or surroundings resulting in protection for the mimic from predators.

Miracidium. Larval stage of a fluke, develops from an egg, gives rise to sporocyst larva.

Mitochondria. Small spherical or rod-like cytoplasmic organelles, associated with important metabolic reactions in a cell such as Krebs cycle; the powerhouse of the cell.

Mitosis. Cell division during which chromosomes appear to become doubled longitudinally, the halves of each one passing into separate daughter cells.

Mollusca. Non-segmented, schizocoelomate phylum.

Moult To cast off the exoskeleton. To shed portions of the skin.

Monoecious. Having both male and female reproductive organs.

Morphogenesis. Development of form and size.

Morphology. Study that deals with the form and structure of organisms.

Morula. Solid ball of cells resulting from egg cleavage.

Mucron. In Sporozoa, an anterior structure in some individuals which is a modification of a portion of the ectoplasm.

Multiple-fission. Type of asexual reproduction in which the nucleus performs several mitotic divisions before any cytokinesis.

Mutualism. An association of two species which is beneficial to both of them.

Myocyte. Contractile cell surrounding pores and oscula, able to close them.

Myoneme. Type of contractile fibril in certain Protozoa.

Myriapoda. Collective term for chilopod, diplopod, pauropod and symphyla arthropod.

Naiad. An aquatic gill-breathing nymph.

Natural parthenogenesis. Development of an egg without fertilization during the normal life cycle of an animal, as in aphids.

Nauplius. First larval stage of crustaceans.

Necrosis. Death.

Nekton. All animals that swim in the ocean water.

Nematocyst. One of the stinging capsules found in the coelenterates; each is produced by a single cell; a cnidoblast.

Nematoda. Round worms of the phylum Aschelminthes.

Nemertina. An acoelomate phylum of ribbon worms, also called Rhynchocoela.

Nephridiopore. External opening of an excretory tubule or nephridium.

Nephridium. Tubular excretory structure characteristic of many invertebrates, such as the animals.

Nephromixium. Reproductive excretory structure of certain polychaetes.

Nerve. Bundle of nerve fibres, located outside the central nervous system.

Nerve cord. Cord of neurons and ganglia forming part of a central nervous system.

Nerve net. Epidermal motor and sensory nerve matrix (network) in cnidarians.

Neural. Pertaining to the nervous system.

Neuron. A nerve cell, including the cell body and all its processes.

Nidamental. Pertaining to gland in female cephalopods which secretes a protective egg capsule.

Nocturnal. Active at night.

Nucleic acids. Molecules made up of joined nucleotide complexes, primarily DNA and RNA.

Nucleolus. A spherical well defined body found within the nucleus of many kinds of cells.

Nucleoprotein. Molecular complex made up of nucleic acid and protein.

Nucleotide. A molecule that consists of a joined phosphate, five carbon sugar, and purine or a pyrimidine.

Nucleus. A specialized protoplasmic body within the cell which contains chromosomes.

Nurse cell. In female Porifera, amoebocyte or choanocyte which transfers a sperm cell to the site of the ovum, then releases it. Also a cell which probably nourishes an ovum.

Nutrient. Any substance used in metabolism either inorganic or organic.

Nutrition. Sum of the processes concerned in the growth, maintenance and repair of the living body as a whole or of its constituent parts.

Objective. The lens or combination of lenses of a microscope nearest the object under observation.

Observation. A perception, either quantitative or qualitative, of a set of phenomena.

Ocellus. A simple type of eye as in many invertebrates especially in insects or other arthropods.

Ocular. Eye piece of the microscope; pertaining to the eye.

Olfactory. Pertaining to the sense of smell.

Ommatidium. One of the elongated rod-like units of a compound eye of an arthropod.

Omnivorous. Eating all kinds of food, both plants and animals.

Ontogeny. Entire developmental history of the individual organism.

Onychophora. A phylum of caterpillar-like animals, structurally intermediate between annelids and arthropods.

Oocyst. Swelling in stomach wall caused by implantation of sporozoites.

Oocyte. Egg mother cell from which are produced, by the first maturation division, the secondary oocyte and the first polar body.

Oogenesis. Process of formation of ova.

Oogonium. The primordial cell which gives rise to the ovarian egg.

Ookinite. Movable zygote (fertilized egg) of a gametocyte, within a mosquito or suitable host.

Operculum. Structure serving to cover the opening of some snail shells.

Ophiuroidea. Class of Echinodermata to which brittle stars belong.

Ophthalmic. Pertaining to eye.

Optic. Pertaining to the eye or to sight.

Optic nerves. Nerves from the eye to the brain.

Oral. Pertaining to the mouth.

Organ. A group of tissues associated to perform one or more functions.

Organelle. A specialized part within a single celled animal, differentiated to perform a certain function.

Organism. Any living individual, plant or animal.

Organogeny. Process of the formation of specialized tissues and organ systems during embryonic development.

Osculum. Relatively large external opening of the central cavity (spongocoel) through which water leaves a sponge.

Osmosis. Diffusion through a semi-permeable membrane.

Osmotic pressure. The aquatic force exerted because of different solute concentrations in water solvent.

Osphradium. Sensory area in incurrent siphon of some mollusc, such as *Pila*.

Ostium. An opening to a passage or to a canal system in sponges.

Otic. Pertaining to the ear.

Ovary. Female gonad in which the egg (ova) multiply and develop.

Oviduct. A tube that conveys eggs from ovary to uterus or to exterior.

Oviparous. Producing eggs that hatch outside the body of the mother, egg-laying animals.

Ovipositor. Organ of female insects that helps in depositing of eggs.

Ovoviviparous. Producing eggs that are retained and hatched within the mother's body.

Ovulation. Release of eggs from the ovary.

Ovum. An egg, a non-motile female gamete.

Oxidation. Chemical change in which a molecule loses one or more electrons; sometimes involves combining oxygen. Usually an exothermic reaction.

Oxyhaemoglobin. The molecule formed when haemoglobin combines with oxygen.

Pachynema stage. In meiosis, the stage where the homologous chromosomes twist around each other, followed by splitting of the synapsed chromosome, leading to four chromatids.

Palaeontology. The science that deals with ancient life of the earth as revealed by fossils, impressions and other remains found in the earth's surface layers.

Palpus. Palp that is a process of an appendage as in insects.

Papilla. Any small nipple-shaped projection or elevation.

Paramylum. Starch-like substance; reserve food material.

Parapodium. Flattened, movable, paired appendage on the body segments of many polychaete annelids.

Parasite. Organism that lives during the whole or phase of its life cycle upon or within another organism (host) and from which it derives nourishment.

Parthenogenesis. The production of offspring from unfertilized eggs.

Paternal. Pertaining to father.

Pathogenic. Disease-producing.

Pathology. Study of abnormal (diseased) structures and abnormal functioning of life processes.

Pedal. Pertaining to the feet.

Pedicellaria. Small pincer-like processes on the surface of certain echinoderms.

Pedicle. Narrow waist between cephalothorax and abdomen in spiders.

Pedipalp. Either of the second pair of appendages in Arachnida; often sensory and sometimes used in seizing prey as in scorpions.

Pelagic. Inhabiting the open water, away from shore, as in the ocean.

Pelecypoda. Class of Mollusca to which the clams and oysters belong.

Pellicle. The protective layer on the surface of some protozoans, for example, *Paramecium*.

Pelmatozoa. Subphylum of Echinodermata to which crinoids are the only extant members.

Pen. Feather-shaped skeleton of a squid.

Penetrant. Largest type of cnidarian nematocyst, containing a coiled tube and spines, used in prey capture.

Penis. Male organ of copulation for conveying sperms to the female genital tract.

Periostracum. Distal chitinous layer in mollusc shells; protective.

Peristalsis. Type of smooth muscle contraction in which a wave of contraction follows a wave of relaxation passing along a hollow organ, especially the digestive tract.

Peristome. Region around the mouth of a radially symmetrical animal such as hydra.

pH. Symbol for relative concentration of hydrogen ions in a solution; values go from 0 to 14 , the lower the value, the more the hydrogen ions.

Phagocyte. Type of white blood cell that engulfs and digests bacteria and other foreign materials.

Phagocytosis. Engulfment of food particle because of membrane invagination proximal to particle and subsequent membrane closure over particle.

Phagosome. Result of phagocytosis, a food vacuole.

Pharynx. Anterior portion of the digestive tract between the mouth cavity and the oesophagus.

Pheromone. A substance secreted by an organism to the external environment which influences the behabiour of the members of the same species.

Photoreceptor. Light sensitive cell or organ.

Phototaxis. The movement response of an organism to light.

Phylogeny. Ancestral or evolutionary history of an organism.

Phylum. Any of the main taxonomic divisions into which the animal kingdom is divided.

Physiology. Science dealing with functions in organisms.

Pinnule. A feather-like structure as in crinoid arm pinnules.

Pinocytosis. Cellular drinking or intake of fluid.

Planarian. Free-living flatworm.

Plankton. Floating or drifting aquatic organisms, mostly microscopic.

Planula. The ciliated free-living larval form of most coelenterates.

Plasma membrane. External membrane formed by cytoplasm of a cell.

Plasmagel. Relatively rigid cytoplasm.

Plasmolysis. Decrease in inter-cellular pressure. Cell shrinks. Occurs if cell is placed in hypertonic solution.

Plasmasol. Relatively liquid cytoplasm.

Plastid. A cytoplasmic body found in certain cells, often containing pigment.

Platyhelminthes. Phylum that includes the flatworms such as planaria.

Pleuteus. Echinoid and ophiuroid larva.

Plexus Network, chiefly of nerves or blood vessels.

Pneumatophore. Air-filled float of siphonophoran hydroids.

Polar body. Small non-functional cell thrown off during the meiosis of the egg cell.

Polyclad. An order of free-living flatworms characterised by many branched digestive cavity.

Polyembryony. One egg producing many larvae.

Polymorphism. Occurrence of several forms in a single species.

Polyp. A tubular coelenterate form.

Porifera. Phylum to which sponges belong.

Porocyte. Water intake cell of certain sponges, characterized by canal passing through it.

Posterior. Toward the hind or rear end.

Predator. Animal that preys upon other animals for its food.

Prehensile. Adapted for holding and grasping.

Primitive. Early stage or type unspecialized.

Proboscis. Tubular extension of the nose, lips or pharynx. The extended beak-like mouth parts of insects.

Proctodaeum. Terminal part of digestive tract, near anus lined with ectoderm.

Proglottid. Tapeworm segment.

Pronotum. Dorsal surface, including sclerites, of an insect's prothorax.

Prophase. Any one of the first stages of mitosis during which chromosomes become distinctly visible.

Prosopyle. One of the surface pores opening into a sponge chamber.

Prostomium. Anterior portion of the first segment of the annelids such as the earthworm, overhanging the mouth region.

Protandry. Production of sperm, and then ova, by the same gonad.

Prothoracic gland. In insects, a gland which secretes ecdyosone during moulting.

Prothorax. Anterior portion of the thorax.

Protonephridium. Excretory organ of certain invertebrates with closed inner end branched or with one terminal cell.

Protopodite. The basal portion, usually composed of two segments of a biramous appendage of a crustacean such as *Palaemon*.

Protozoa. A phylum of acellular animals.

Proximal. Near the point of attachment of an organ.

Pseudocoel. A body cavity not completely lined with mesoderm as found in round worms.

Pseudopodia. Blunt temporary protoplasmic projections found in amoeba or in some amoeba-like cells.

Pupa. Developmental stage in the complete metamorphosis of an insect.

Pyloric caeca. Digestive glands.

Pyloric valve. Valve at the posterior end of the stomach.

Pyrenoid. In some chloroplasts, a centre for the formation of a starch-like substance called paramylum.

Queen. Reproductive female of social insects, as in bees and ants.

Quinine. The drug used in the treatment of malaria.

Radial canal. A canal radiating from the disc of sea stars and related animals.

Radial cleavage. Cleavage in which successive tiers of equal-sized blastomeres lie directly above and below one another; cleavage is indeterminate.

Radial symmetry. The condition in which similar parts are arranged about a common centre like the spokes of a wheel.

Radiata. Eumetazoan grade of animals such as coelenterates with primary and secondary radial symmetry.

Radiolaria. Protozoans with shells of silicon.

Radula. Horny rasping organ in alimentary tract of certain molluscs.

Recapitulation theory. Theory that the individual in its development passes through the ancestral history of the species. Ontogeny repeats phylogeny.

Receptor. A sensory end organ.

Rectum. Posterior intestinal region in some higher invertebrates.

Redia. One of the several types of larvae found in the life cycle of most trematodes.

Reduction division. Maturation division in which the homologous pairs of chromosomes are separated to form daughter cells.

Reflex. Simple involuntary action in response to a stimulus.

Regeneration. Replacement by growth of a part of the body that has been lost.

Renal. Pertaining to the kidney.

Renette. In some nematodes, an excretory cell with short tube attached.

Reproduction. Production by an organism of others of its kind.

Respiration. Use of oxygen by the cell, this is usually termed cellular or internal respiration.

Response. Reaction to a stimulus, either internal or external.

Reticulum. Network of filaments, fibrils or fibres within cytoplasm.

Retina. Light sensitive layer of an eye.

Rhabdites. Rod-like bodies in the epidermis of certain flatworms, as in the planaria.

Rhabdome. A rod-like structure formed of the inner surface of the adjacent sensory cells in the ommatidium of a compound arthropod eye.

Rhabdomere. Receptor area of a retinal cell, one of the component parts of the rhabdome.

Rheotaxis. A movement in response to air and water current.

Ribosome. DNA containing cytoplasmic organelle and site of protein synthesis.

RNA. Ribonuleic acid. Helps in protein sythesis.

Rostrum. The anteriorly projecting beak as in *Palaemon*.

Rotifera. Phylum of microscopic pseudocoelomate animals.

Rudimentary. Pertaining to a body part not completely developed.

Sagittal. In a bilaterally symmetrical animal, pertaining to the antero-posterior plane.

Saliva. Secretion of the salivary gland.

Salivary. Pertaining to the saliva-secreting glands of the mouth.

Saprotroph. An organism that lives on dead organic matter.

Saprozoic. Pertaining to an animal that lives on dead organic matter.

Scaphopoda. A class of Mollusca having shell like a tooth.

Schizocoel. The coelom formed by the splitting of embryonic mesoderm.

Schizogony. Asexual multiple fission in Protozoa.

Scientific name. Binomial or trinomial designation of an animal.

Sclerite. Hardened body wall plate bounded by sutures, as in the arthropods.

Scleroblast. Amoebocyte-like cells in sponges which secrete spicules.

Scolex. Small knob-like head at the anterior end of the tapeworm.

Secondary spermatocytes. In meiosis, the cells formed after the first cytoplasmic division during diakinesis.

Secretion. Substances produced in the body by a cell or multicellular gland.

Sedentary. Staying in one place.

Segment. One part of a metameric animal.

Self-fertilization. Fertilizing an egg by a sperm from the same individual.

Sense organ. An organ sensitive to a particular type of stimulus.

Sensory cell. Cell that is very sensitive to stimuli, receptor.

Septum. Partition that separates two cavities or two structures.

Sessile. Attached, not free-moving, sedentary.

Setae. Bristles such as those embedded in the body wall of the earthworm.

Sexual dimorphism. Phenomenon of two sexes of a given species differing in secondary characters.

Sexual reproduction. Reproduction involving the gametes.

Siliceous. Containing silicon dioxide or silica.

Sinistral. Coiling counter-clockwise.

Sinus. A thin-walled cavity.

Sinus gland. In some arthropods, gland at the base of eye-stalk controlling chromatophore dispersion. Under influence of X-gland.

Siphon. Tube that draws in or expels fluids.

Siphonoglyph. Ciliated groove in sea anemone which serves to create a current of water into the gastrovascular cavity.

Siphonozooid. Specialized polymorphic form which produces water currents to help in breathing in certain coelenterate colonies.

Siphuncle. Gas-filled canal that passes through the coiled chambered *Nautilus* shell.

Solitary. Living alone, not a member of the colony or group.

Somite. One of the sessile segments or metameres of a metameric animal, an organ or organ rudiment.

Species. A population of inter-breeding individuals.

Sperm. A mature male reproductive cell or gamete.

Spermatheca. Seminal receptacle in some female insects.

Spermatogenesis. Process of formation of spermatozoa.

Spicule. One of many solid structures that composed the structural framework of a sponge.

Spinnerets. Structures present on the abdomen of spiders.

Spiracle. In insects, an external opening of the tracheal or respiratory system.

Spongin. Chemical used in fibres of poriferan skeletons. Secreted by spongioblasts.

Spongocoel. Paragastric or central cavity of a sponge.

Spore. Special reproductive body of lower organisms.

Sporocyst. Larval stage in the life cycle of fluke, develops from miracidium larva and gives rise to numerous rediae.

Sporozoite. Young infective sporozoan.

Sporulation. Process of forming spores, reproduction by multiple fission.

Statoblast. Chitinous shell secreted by, for example, certain freshwater Bryozoa.

Statocyst. Organ of equilibrium in animals such as *Palaemon*.

Statolith. Solid body within a statocyst.

Stigma. A sensitive pigment or eye spot in certain Protozoa.

Stimulus. Changes in the external or internal environment of an animal that brings about a response.

Stolon. A branch upon which colonial individuals may bud upright.

Stomodaeum. Anterior portion of the alimentary canal lined with ectoderm. It is also called foregut.

Strobilation. Budding in segments of sessile scyphozoan coelenterate larvae resulting in cutting off following free-swimming ephyral larvae.

Subumbrella. Concave oral surface of medusae.

Symbiosis. An association of two individuals of two different species for mutual benefit.

Synapsis. In meiosis, during zygonema stage of prophase, the pairing of homologous chromosomes.

Syncytium. Undivided mass of cytoplasm containing many nuclei; a product of nuclear division with cell division.

Syngamy. Union of gametes in sexual reproduction forming a zygote.

System. Group of organs concerned with the same general function as circulation or digestion.

Tactile. Pertaining to the sense of touch.

Taxis. A movement response.

Taxon. Category of animal classification.

Taxonomy. Science that deals with the classification of organisms.

Telophase. Any of the final phases of mitosis in which the cell divides and the daughter nuclei are formed.

Telson. Terminal extension of the last abdominal appendage of a crustacean such as the *Palaemon*.

Tentacle. A flexible arm-like extension from the body of many invertebrates such as hydra ; used in grasping and movement.

Tentaculocyst. Sense organs of some cnidarians.

Tergum. Dorsal portion of the exoskeleton of any body segment in the arthropods, such as the grasshopper.

Terrestrial. Living on the ground.

Test. Shell.

Testis. Male reproductive gland (gonad) in which sperms are formed.

Thermotaxis. Behavioural response of an organism to contact.

Thigmotaxis. A movement response to touch.

Thorax. Major division of an animal just posterior to the neck or to the head if no neck is present.

Tissue. Group of cells of similar structure, with inter-cellular substances, if any, which perform a specialized function.

Tornaria. Larva of particular enteropneust haemichordates.

Trachea. The respiratory tube of an arthropod.

Trichocyst. An adhesive cytoplasmic organelle of ciliate Protozoa.

Trilobite. Extinct marine arthropod of Palaeozoic.

Triploblastic. Derived from three primary germ layers–ectoderm, mesoderm, and endoderm.

Trochanter. Second segment of the insect leg between the coxa and the femur.

Trochophore. Free-swimming marine ciliated larva.

Trophozoite. Sporozoite in the phase of its life cycle where its principal activity is nutrition and growth.

Tube feet. Tubular organs of locomotion found in the ambulacral grooves of sea stars and other echinoderms.

Turbellaria. Free-living flatworm class.

Typhlosole. A median dorsal internal fold in the intestine of several types of animals, including the earthworm.

Umbo. Elevation near the hinge of a bivalve shell.

Uniramous (appendage). Arthropod appendage with longitudinal segmental morphology.

Uracil. An RNA base which is analogous to DNA's thymine.

Ureotelic. Animal whose nitrogenous excreta contains mainly urea.

Uricotelic. Animal whose nitrogenous excreta contains mainly uric acid.

Urogenital. Pertaining to organs of both the urinary and reproductive systems taken collectively.

Uropod. Flattened abdominal appendage in *Palaemon*.

Vacuole. Small structure consisting of a cavity in the cytoplasm filled with a liquid /and or other products.

Valve. Any structure that limits or closes an opening.

Vas deferens. Duct that carries sperms away from the testis.

Veliger. Larval stage of many molluscs.

Ventral. Pertaining to the belly, away from the back. Opposite of dorsal.

Ventriculus. In insects, the stomach.

Vestibule. An outer cavity with an entrance to a (usually) larger, deeper cavity.

Vestigial. Degenerate structure that was better developed or functional in more primitive or ancestral groups.

Viviparous. Giving birth to living young that develop from egg within the body of the mother.

Water expulsion vesicle. New term for contractile vacuole. Osmoregulatory apparatus which can secrete water from the cytoplasm.

Wax. A form of lipid useful in organism protection.

X-gland. In some arthropods, endocrine gland passing secretions (hormones) along axons to sinus gland at the base of eye-stalk.

Xiphosura. Class of arthropods to which king-crab belongs.

Yolk. Stored nutritive material for nourishment of the embryo.

Zoaea. A kind of crustacean larva.

Zoogeography. Branch of zoology dealing with the geographic distribution of animals.

Zooid. One of the members of a hydroid or siphonophore colony.

Zoology. Science that deals with animal life.

Zygonema stage. In meiosis, a stage where synapsis occurs.

Zygote. The product of the union of two gametes of any type.

Selected References

Allen, R.D., 1962, *Amoeboid movement,* Scientific American, 206, 112–122.

Al-Hussaini, A.H., and Demian, E.S., 1967, *Practical Animal Morphology,* Macmillan and Company Ltd., London, U.K.

Bahl, K.N., 1943, *Pheretima,* The Indian Zoological Memoirs, Lucknow Publishing House, Lucknow, India.

Baker, J.R., 1969, *Parasitic Protozoa,* Hutchinson, London.

Baini Prasad, 1932, *Pila,* The Indian Zoological Memoirs, Lucknow Publishing House, Lucknow, India.

Barnes, R.D., 1980, *Invertebrate Zoology,* W.B. Saunders Company, Philadelphia and London.

Barrington, E.J.W., 1974, *Invertebrate Structure and Function,* Thomas Nelson and Sons Ltd., London.

Bayer, F.M. and Owre, H.B., 1968, *The Free Living Lower Invertebrates,* The Macmillan Co., New York.

Berril, N.J., 1957, *Indestructible Hydra,* Scientific American, December, 1957.

Berril, N.J., 1966, *Biology in Action,* Heinemann Educational Books Ltd., London, U.K.

Bhatia, M.L., 1941, *Hirudinea,* The Indian Zoological Memoirs, Lucknow Publishing House, Lucknow, India.

Borradaile L.A., F.A. Potts and L.E.S. Estham, 1962, *The Invertebrata,* Asia Publishing House, Bombay, India.

Brown Jr., F.A., 1956, *Selected Invertebrate Types,* John Wiley and Sons, New York, U.S.A.

Buchsbaum, R., 1963, *Animals without Backbones,* Chicago University Press, Chicago, U.S.A.

Buffaloe, N.D., 1964, *Principles of Biology,* Prentice Hall of India Pvt. Ltd. New Delhi, India.

Bullough, W.S., 1958, *Practical Invertebrate Anatomy,* Macmillan and Company Ltd., London, U.K.

Burke, J.D., 1970, *Cell Biology,* Scientific Book Agency, Calcutta, India.

Cain, A.J., 1966, *Animal Species and their Evolution,* Hutchinson University Library, London.

Carter, G.S., 1961, *A General Zoology of the Invertebrates,* Sidgwick and Jackson Ltd., London, U.K.

Chandler, A.C., and C.P. Read, 1961, *Introduction to Parasitology,* W.B. Saunders Company, Philadelphia and London.

Cheng, T.C., 1964, *The Biology of Animal Parasites,* W.B. Saunders Company, Philadelphia and London.

Cheng. T.C., 1973, *General Parasitology,* Academic Press, New York.

Cockraum, E. and W.J. McCauley, 1965, *Zoology,* W.B. Saunders Company, Philadelphia, London.

Corfton, H.B., 1966, *Nematodes,* Hutchinson University Library, London.

Cornwel, P.B., 1968, *The Cockroach,* Vol. I. Hutchinson and Co. Ltd., London.

Dales, R., Phillips, 1963, *Annelids,* Hutchinson University Library, London.

Darwin, C., 1962, *The Structure and Distribution of Coral Reefs,* University of California Press, Berkely.

Dawes, B., 1956, *The Trematoda,* Cambridge University Press, London.

De Bruyn, P.P.H., 1947, *Theories of amoeboid locomotion*, Quart. Rev. Bio. 22 : 1– 14

De Robertis, E.D.P. and De Robertis Jr., E.M.F., 1987, *Cell and Molecular Biology*, Lea and Febiger, Philadelphia, U.S.A.

Diller, W.F., 1963, *Nuclear reorganization process in Paramecium aurelia with description of autogamy and hemixis*, J. Morphol., 59 : 11– 67.

Dellinger, O., 1906, *Locomotion of Amoeba and Allied forms*, J. Exp. Zool., 3 : 337 – 358.

Dogiel, V.A., 1965, *General Protozoology*, Clarendon Press, Oxford.

Edwards, C.A. and Lofty, J.R., *Biology of Earthworm*, Chapman and Hall, London.

Ehret, C.F., and Powers, E.L. 1959, *The Cell Surface of Paramecium*, Int. Rev. Cytol. 8 : 97 – 133.

Elliot, A., 1968, *Zoology*, Appleton-Century-Crafts, Division of Meredith Corporation, New York, U.S.A.

Erasmus, D.A., 1972, *The Biology of Trematodes*, Edwin Arnold (Publishers) Ltd., London.

Frost, S.W., 1942, *General Entomology*, McGraw Hill Book Company, New York, U.S.A.

Fry, W.G. (Ed.), 1970, *The Biology of the Porifera*, Academic Press, Inc. New York.

Gardiner, M.S., 1972, *The Biology of Invertebrates*, McGraw Hill Book Company, New York.

Gray, J. and Lissman, H.W., 1938, *Studies of Animal Locomotion*, VII., *Locomotory reflexes in the Earthworm*, J. Exp. Biol., 15 : 506 – 517.

Green, J. 1961, *A Biology of Crustacea*, Quadrangle Books, Chicago.

Grell, K.G., 1973, *Protozoology*, Springer-Verlag, Berlin, New York.

Groove, A.J., G.E. Newel and J.D. Carthy, 1962, *Animal Biology*, University Tutorial Press Ltd., London, U.K.

Hall, R.P., 1953, *Protozoology*, Prentice Hall Inc. Englewood Cliffs, N.J., U.S.A.

Harmer, S.F. and A.E. Shipley, 1958, *Crustacea*, The Cambridge Natural History, Vol. IV. Macmillan & Co., London, U.K.

Harmer, S.F., and A.E. Shipley 1959, *Insects*, Part II, The Cambridge Natural History, Vol., VI Macmillan & Co. Ltd., London, U.K.

Hegner, R.W., and J.G. Engemann, 1968, *Invertebrate Zoology*, Macmillan and Company Ltd., New York, U.S.A.

Hickmann, C.P., 1961, *Integrated Principles of Zoology*, The C.V. Mosby Co., St. Louis.

Hickmann, C.P., 1973, *Biology of the Invertebrates* The C.V. Mosby Co., St. Louis.

Hirschfield, H.I., 1962, *The Biology of the Amoeba*, Annals of the New York Academy of Sciences, Vol. 78, Art 2, pp. 401 – 704.

Honigberg, B.M., *et al.*, 1964, *A Revised Classification of Phylum Protozoa*, J. Protozool, 11 : 7 – 20.

Hyman, L.H., 1940, *The Invertebrates, Protozoa through Ctenophora* Vol. I, McGraw Hill Book Company, New York U.S.A.

Hyman, L.H., 1951, *The Invertebrates, Platyhelminthes and Rhynchocoela*, Vol. II, McGraw Hill Book Company, New York, U.S.A.

Hyman, L.H., 1951, *The Invertebrates, Acanthocephala, Aschelminthes* and *Entoprocta*, Vol. III, McGraw Hill Book Co., New York, U.S.A.

Hyman, L.H., 1955, *The Invertebrates, Echinodermata*, Vol. IV, McGraw Hill Book Co., New York, U.S.A.

Hyman, L.H., 1959, *The Invertebrates, Smaller Coelomate Groups,* Vol. V, McGraw Hill Book Co, New York, U.S.A.

Hyman L.H., 1967, *The Invertebrates, Mollusca I,* Vol. VI, McGraw Hill Book Company, New York, U.S.A.

Imms, A.D., Richards, O.W., and Davies, R.G., 1957, *A General Text Book of Entomology*, Methuen and Company Ltd., London, U.K.

Jennings, H.S., 1906, *Behaviour of Lower Organisms,* Columbia University Press, New York.

Kennedy, D., 1965, *The Living Cell,* Readings from Scientific American, Freeman, San Francisco. Kimbell, R.F., 1943, Mating Types in the Ciliate Protozoa, Quart. Rev. Biol., 18 : 30 – 45.

Kudo, R.P., 1966, *Protozoology,* Thomas Springfield, Illinois, U.S.A.

Lanan, F., 1967, *Euglenoid Flagellates,* Prentice Hall, Englewood Cliffs, New Jersey.

Laverack, M.S., 1963, *The Physiology of Earthworms,* The Macmillan Company, New York.

Leedale, G.F., 1964, *Pellicle Structure in Euglena*, British Phycol. Bull., 2 : 291 – 306.

Leedale, G.F., 1966, *Euglena :* A new look with the electron microscope, Adv. of Science, Vol. 23.

Little, V.A., 1967, *General and Applied Entomology,* Oxford and I.B.H. Publishing House, Calcutta, India.

Mann, K.M., 1962, *Leeches* (Hirudinea) Pergamon Press, New York, U.S.A.

Manwell, R.D., 1961, *Introduction to Protozoology.* Edwin Arnold Publishers Ltd., London, U.K.

Mast, S.O., 1931, *Locomotion in Amoeba proteus*, Protoplasma, 14 : 321 – 330.

Mayr, E., 1963, *Animal Species and Evolution,* Harward University Press, New York.

Meglitsch, P.A., 1972, *Invertebrate Zoology,* Oxford University Press, New York, U.S.A.

Mercer, E.H., 1959, *An Electron Microscopic Study of Amoeba proteus,* Proc. R. Soc. London B. 150 : 216 – 232.

Morton, J.E., 1967, *Molluscs,* Hutchinson University Library, London.

Nichols, D., 1967, *Echinoderms,* Hutchinson University Library, London.

Parker, T.J. and William, A. Haswell Edited by A.J., Marshall and W.D. Williams. (7th edition), 1972, *A Text Book of Zoology: Invertebrates,* English Language Book Society and Macmillan Company, London.

Patton, R.L., 1963, *Introductory Insect Physiology,* W.B. Saunders Co., Philadephia.

Patwardhan, S.S., 1958, *Palaemon,* The Indian Zoological Memoirs, Lucknow Publishing House, Lucknow, India.

Pitelka, D., 1962, *The Electron Microscopic Structure of Protozoa,* Pergamon Press, New York.

Pon, R.D., 1968, *The Biology of Mollusca,* Pergamon Press, New York.

Russel-Hunter, W.D., 1968, *A Biology of Lower Invertebrates,* The Macmillan Co., New York

Russel-Hunter, W.D., 1969, *A Biology of Higher Invertebrates,* The Macmillan Co., New York.

Saxena, B.B., 1955, *Physiology of excretion in the common Indian apple snail, Pila globosa,* J. Anim. Morph. and Physiol., 2 : 87 – 95.

Sedgewick, A., 1966, *A Student Text Book of Zoology.* I, III, Central Book Depot, Allahabad.

Simpson, G.G., 1961, *Principles of Taxonomy,* Columbia University Press, New York.

Sleigh, M., 1975, *The Biology of Protozoa,* Edwin Arnold (Publishers) Ltd., London.

Smyth, J.C., 1966, *The Physiology of Trematodes,* W.H. Freeman & Co., San Francisco.

Snodgrass, R.E., 1952, *A Text Book of Arthropod Anatomy,* Comstock Publishing Associates, Ithaca, New York, U.S.A.

Soulsby, E.J.L., 1976, *Helminths, Arthropods and Protozoa of Domesticated Animals,* The English Language Book Society, London.

Stephenson, J. 1930, *The Oligochaeta,* Oxford University Press, London.

Stiles, K.A., R.W. Hegner, and R.A. Boolootian, 1969, *College Zoology,* Amerind Publishing Co., Pvt. Ltd., New Delhi, Bombay, Calcutta, India.

Storer, T.I., and R.L. Usinger, 1965, *General Zoology,* McGraw Hill Book Company, New York, London.

Tuzet, O., 1963, *The Physiology of Sponges,* In E.C. Dougherty (ed.) *The Lower Metazoa,* University of California Press, Berkely.

Verma, P.S., 1993, *A Manual of Practical Zoology Invertebrates,* S. Chand & Co. Ltd., New Delhi, India.

Verma, P.S., and V.K. Agarwal, 1993, *Cell Biology, Genetics and Ecology,* S. Chand & Co. Ltd., New Delhi, India.

Verma P.S., and V.K. Agarwal, 1993, *Cytology,* S. Chand & Co. Ltd., New Delhi, India.

Weisz, P.B., 1966. *The Science of Biology,* McGraw Hill Book Company, New York, U.S.A.

Vickerman, K., 1966, *Genetic System in Unicellular Animals,* Science Progress, Vol. 54, pp. 13 – 26.

Vickerman, K and Cox, F.E.G., 1967, *The Protozoa,* John Murray, London.

Waterman, T.H., (ed.) 1960-61, *The Physiology of Crustacea (2 Vols.),* Academic Press, New York.

Wigglesworth, V.B., 1965, *The Principles of Insect Physiology,* English Language Book Society and Methuen and Company Ltd., London, U.K.

Wilmoth, James H., 1967, *Biology of Invertebrates,* Prentice Hall, Inc. Englewood Cliffs, New Jersey.

Wilson, H.V., 1907, *On some phenomena of coalescence and regeneration in sponges,* J. Exp. Zool., 5 : 245 – 257.

Winchester, A.M., and H.B. Lovell, 1961, *Zoology,* D. Van Nostrand Company, Inc. Princeton, New Jersey, New York.

Wichterman, R., 1955, *The Biology of Paramecium,* The Blakiston Company. Inc. Toronto, New York, U.S.A.

Index

SOME SELECTED BOOKS FOR DEGREE STUDENTS

BOTANY

B.R. Vashishta

BOTANY FOR DEGREE STUDENTS : ALGAE

The new edition includes life histories of a few more types such as Ulva, Enteromorpha, Prot siphen, Pleurococcus and Mougeotia.

03 011   8/e, Rep. 1998   pp 464

B.R. Vashishta

BOTANY FOR DEGREE STUDENTS : FUNGI

Reflects recent advances in the field of Mycology. Gives a vivid account of the various aspects of Botany.

03 012   10/e Rep. 1998   pp 528

B.R. Vashishta

BOTANY FOR DEGREE STUDENTS : BRYOPHYTA

Contains the latest research material and includes the life history of Notothylus. Gives a clear picture of the pattern of Alternation of Generations.

03 013   8/e Rep. 1998   pp. 368

P.C. Vashishta

BOTANY FOR DEGREE STUDENTS : PTERIDOPHYTA

Present edition incorporates new chapters on life cycles of Isoetes, Salvinia and Azolla. Good many diagrams are given to illustrate important aspects of morphology and development.

03 014   5/e Rep. 1998   pp 520

P.C. Vashishta

BOTANY FOR DEGREE STUDENTS : GYMNOSPERMS

It makes a detailed study of morphology and reproduction of both living and fossil forms.

03 015   2nd/e Rep. 1998   pp. 512

B.P. Pandey

COLLEGE BOTANY (Vol.I & II)

These two volumes are compilation work which embodies a fairly comprehensive tre tment of the fundamental facts of the subject to the beginners in this field. Simple language, self-explanatory labelled diagrams with detailed legends are some of the salient features of this elementary text for the Degree students of Botany.

Vol. I — Algae, Fungi & Bryophyta

03 151   5/e Rep. 1997   pp.936

Vol. II — Pteridophyta, Gymnosperms

& Palaeobotany

03 152   7/e1998   pp 216

Also available in parts by B.P. Pandey :

A TEXT-BOOK OF BOTANY : ALGAE

03 092   5/e Rep. 1994   pp 280

A TEXT-BOOK OF BOTANY : FUNGI

03 213   5/e Rep. 1994   pp. 416

A TEXT-BOOK OF BOTANY : BRYOPHYTA

03 214   5/e Rep. 1994   pp. 224

A TEXT-BOOK OF BOTANY : PTERIDOPHYTA

03 215   5/e Rep. 1994   PP. 176

A TEXT-BOOK OF BOTANY : GYMNOSPERMS

03 216   5/e Rep. 1994   PP. 208

(All these parts are also available in Hindi)

B.P. Pandey

PLANT ANATOMY

This book provides the fundamental facts of plant Anatomy for the graduate and post-graduate students of Botany with detailed facts, terminology and internal structures of common plants. This book may safely be used as laboratory guide also.

03 016   5 /e Rep. 1998   pp 656

B.P. Pandey

INTRODUCTION TO PLANT ANATOMY

This book embodies a comprehensive treatment of the various aspects of plant Anatomy. The text deals mainly with the anatomy of vascular plants. Emphasis has been given on the anatomical study of the Angiosperms.

03 072   1/e (Rep)1993   pp. 318
03 161   1/e Hindi 1993   pp. 390

B.P. Pandey

A TEXT-BOOK OF BOTANY: ANGIOSPERMS

Dealing primarily with Taxonomy, Anatomy, Economic Botany & Embryology of Angiospermic plants, this book also covers Pharmacognosy Morphogenesis and is profusely illustrated with self-explanatory and well-labelled diagrams.

03 118   4 /e Rep. 1998   pp. 830

B.P. Pandey

TAXONOMY OF ANGIOSPERMS (SYSTEMATIC BOTANY)

In all sixty-five families have been discussed in detail, forty-nine from Dicots and sixteen from Monocots. The families have been arranged according to the phylogenetic system of classification propounded by John Hutchinson.

03 149   6/e 1997   pp. 610

B.P. Pandey

A TEXT-BOOK OF PLANT PATHOLOGY
(Pathogen and Plant Diseases)

This text embodies a fairly comprehensive treatment of the fundamental facts and aspects of plant pathology, and also serves as a laboratory manual. This book will also serve as an introduction to plant pathology to the beginners in this field.

03 253   3/e 1997   pp. 512

Purekar, Singh & Deshmukh

PLANT PHYSIOLOGY AND ECOLOGY

In a compact size, this book present a very comprehensive and up to date knowledge regarding Plant Physiology, Ecology and Phytogeography and cover the syllabus of many Indian universities.

03 054   2/e 1992   pp. 390

R.S. Shukla & P.S. Chandel

PLANT ECOLOGY

In this book the chapter on Environment has been upgraded. The chapter on Ecosystem contains more information and better diagrams. Chapters on Autecology and Ecological Genetics of Population has been re-written. Similarly there are better diagrams and additional matter in the chapter on Synecology.

03017   8/e Rep. 1998   pp. 334

R.S. Shukla & P.S. Chandel

PLANT ECOLOGY AND SOIL SCIENCE

Since the Ecology courses at Undergraduate and Post-graduate levels have been substantially revised in all the Indian Universities, this book has been revised keeping in view the requirements of the students.

03 018   8/e Rep. 1998   pp. 421

B.P. Pandey

ECONOMIC BOTANY

Several new topics and photographs have been added in this thoroughly revised edition.

03 021   5/e Rep. 1997   pp. 527

V.K. Jain

FUNDAMENTALS OF PLANT PHYSIOLOGY

Great emphasis has been laid in this book on basic fundamentals with simultaneous incorporation of most up- to-date information in sufficient details. The subject-matter has been splitted into 'typical questions' to make it more meaningful to the students.

03 020   6/e Rep. 1997   pp. 456

R.S. Shukla & P.S. Chandel

CYTOGENETICS, EVOLUTION AND

PLANT BREEDING

This book is suitable for biology and agriculture students at the under-graduate and graduate level. The subject matter is systematically arranged and illustrated with easy diagrams. Each topic is discussed in the light of recent researches.

03 019   3rd/e Rep. 1998   pp. 568

CYTOGENETICS AND EVOLUTION

03 073   2/e 1989   pp. 346

J.L. Jain

FUNDAMENTALS OF BIOCHEMISTRY

There have been several new discoveries in biochemistry which had necessitated revision of almost all chapters of this book. Five new chapters concerning 'Bio-energetics and Metabolism' have been added, incorporating the latest information on the subject.

03 115   4/e Rep. 1992   pp. 673

J.L. Jain

ELEMENTARY BIOCHEMISTRY

Contains the basic concept of biochemistry written in a manner suited to the broad spectrum of the college students and providing them an insight at a molecular level all those materials which are considered to be hidden secrets of life.

03 095   2/e 1990   pp. 372

R.C. Dubey

TEXT-BOOK OF BIOTECHNOLOGY

Bringing forth the current information on different areas of Biotechnology, this book also provides the details of the researches being carried out in all the aspects in India and abroad. In seventeen chapters which form the five parts this petite book contains illustrations, diagrams, figures and tables.

03 217   1/e 1993   pp. 290

B.P. Pandey

TANNINS AND DYES

This work presents a comprehensive account dealing with plants yielding tannins and dyes from their different parts. Both Tannins and Dyes have been classified according to the morphological nature, distribution and usage.

03 119   1/e 1981   pp. 141

J.F. Southey, Ed.

PLANT NEMATOLOGY

Reveals the various important aspects of Nematology. Conveys the subject-matter in a lucid and comprehensive manner.

03 121   2/e   pp. 282

ZOOLOGY

E.L. Jordan & P.S. Verma

INVERTEBRATE ZOOLOGY

The new edition has a separate section on 'Minor Phyla'. Provides good many illustrations on Ctenophora, Endoprocta, Nemertinea, Acanthocephala, Rotifera, Ectoprocta Brachiopoda and Phoronida. It contains latest material obtained from the recent researches.

03 027   14/e Rep. 1998   pp. 880
03 048   2/e Hindi 1993   pp. 1160

E.L. Jordan & P.S. Verma

CHORDATE ZOOLOGY AND ANIMAL PHYSIOLOGY

Incorporates the Morphology and Physiology of Chordate types. Has new figures at appropriate places.

03 028   10/e 1991   pp. 1163
03 088   2/e Hindi 1993   pp.1247

P.S. Verma,
V.K. Agarwal & B.S. Tyagi
CHORDATE EMBRYOLOGY
Gives a lucid, well-illustrated and up-dated account of the subject. Contains new chapters such as Gradient Theory, Embryonic Inductions, Metamorphosis, regeneration and differentiation.

| 03 026 | 10/e Rep. 1998 | pp. 426 |

Verma, Tyagi & Agarwal
ANIMAL PHYSIOLOGY AND ECOLOGY
This book provides the students of B.Sc. and M.Sc. a better understanding of the functions of different organ systems of animals, the inter-relationship & co-existence between animals, plants and microbes and interactions occurring between organisms and their environments.

| 03 031 | 4/e 1996 | pp.724 |

ANIMAL PHYSIOLOGY

| 03 030 | 6/e Rep. 1998 | pp. 448 |

Agarwal, Srivastava & Kumar
ANIMAL PHYSIOLOGY AND BIOCHEMISTRY
The book emphasizes in depth the knowledge of physiology which have assumed gigantic proportions in modern times. However, in this compact book only the central concept such as various biological molecules and physiology of different organs-systems have been dealt in detail.

| 03 087 | 3/e Rep. 1998 | pp. 452 |

P.S. Verma & V.K. Agarwal
ENVIRONMENTAL BIOLOGY
The thoughtless exploitation of various natural resources by man has resulted in a very critical state of existence. To forestall this, the science of Ecology has come forward to human rescue to save them from this state of self-destruction, dilemma and Paradox. Visualising this, the book has been especially prepared for the B.Sc. & M.Sc. students of different Indian universities of Biology as well as Environmental science.

| 03 171 | 4/e 1998 | pp. 600 |

P.S. Verma & V.K. Agarwal
CYTOLOGY
The book provides a lucid, simple, detailed and well illustrated account of cell biology and molecular biology.

| 03 022 | 8/e 1998 | pp. 584 |

P.S. Verma & V.K. Agarwal
CELL BIOLOGY, GENETICS, MOLECULAR BIOLOGY, EVOLUTION & ECOLOGY
The present edition contains several new illustrations and new chapters such as inbreeding, outbreeding, hybrid vigour in Genetics.

| 03 024 | 14/e 1998 | pp. 1116 |

P.S. Verma & V.K. Agarwal
CONCEPT OF MOLECULAR BIOLOGY

| 03 255 | 1/e 1998 | pp. 160 |

CONCEPT OF EVOLUTION

| 03 256 | 1/e 1998 | pp. 160 |

CONCEPT OF CELL BIOLOGY

| 03 250 | 1/e 1998 | pp. 336 |

CONCEPT OF GENETICS, HUMAN GENETICS AND EUGENICS

| 03 254 | 1/e 1998 | pp. 240 |

CONCEPT OF ECOLOGY

| 03 250 | 1/e 1998 | pp. 272 |

P.J. Bentley
COMPARATIVE VERTEBRATE ENDOCRINOLOGY
This book is a suitable text for senior undergraduate/graduate courses in vertebrate endocrinology and comparative endocrinology and as a background reading for courses in comparative animal physiology. It is also useful for First-year medical students and endocrinology researchers.

| 03 129 | 2/e 1990 | pp. 415 |

P.S. Verma & V.K. Agarwal
GENETICS
All the chapters of this book have been thoroughly revised in keeping pace with the rapid progress in the field of life sciences.

| 03 023 | 8/e 1998 | pp. 592 |

L.R. Patki, B.L. Bhalchandra & I.H. Jeevaji
AN INTRODUCTION TO MICROTECHNIQUE
This small and compact book contains all the aspects of mircotechnique in a fair Quantum in the right sequence, which makes it very useful and important for the students working in Biological and Pathological laboratories, as well as the practitioners in any laboratory using Mircotechnique.

| 03 047 | 2/e 1992 | pp. 167 |

Jawaid Ahsan & Subhas Prasad Sinha
A HANDBOOK ON ECONOMIC ZOOLOGY
This hand-book is a practical guide to applied Zoology in which science of fisheries, Sericulture, lac culture, Apiculture, Sponge culture and pearl formation has been dealt with an economic point of view.

| 03 128 | 8/e Rep. 1998 | pp. 178 |

S.N. Prasad & Vasantika Kashyap
AN INTRODUCTION TO TOXICOLOGY
This book provides useful details of toxic chemicals which are widely used for different purposes especially in agriculture where the benefits are manifold which outweigh the risks.

| 03 203 | 1/e 1991 | pp. 200 |

CHEMISTRY

B.S. Bahl, G.D. Tuli & Arun Bahl
ESSENTIALS OF PHYSICAL CHEMISTRY
The book has completed 50 years of its successful and useful existence. The text has been re-written and enlarged so as to make it modern in approach. The

latest trends have been integrated with the fundamental con- cepts and the matter has been made up-to-date.

| 04 028 | 24 /e 1998 | pp. 880 |
| 04 030 | Hindi Edition | pp. 790 |

N.Kundu & S.K. Jain

PHYSICAL CHEMISTRY

This highly understandable, up-to-date, comprehensive text presents theoretical as well as the experimental aspects of modern physical chemistry. The emphasis has been laid on the development of a conceptual approach to the chemical systems with the aid of mathematical modelling without letting the latter to overshadow the former.

| 04 049 | I /e Rep. 1996 | pp. 1134 |

D.N. Bajpai

ADVANCED PHYSICAL CHEMISTRY

For B.Sc. Part III students of chemistry, this book covers newly revised syllabi of almost all the Indian universities. The subject matter is treated in simple and easily comprehensible language.

| 04 170 | 2 /e 1998 | pp. 1056 |

G.D. Tuli & P.L. Soni

REFRESHER COURSE IN B.Sc. PHYSICAL CHEMISTRY

With two new chapters in this thoroughly revised and enlarged edition viz., The Solid State and Electro-motive Force, this book has been universally recognised by the students of Indian universities a pass-port for success for the last 37 years.

| 04 079 | 13 /e 1993 | pp. 408 |

W.U. Malik, G.D. Tuli & R.D. Madan

SELECTED TOPICS IN INORGANIC CHEMISTRY

Most of the topics deal with the theoretical aspects of Inorganic Chemistry. The book elucidates the fundamentals and the approach to discussion is modern throughout.

| 04 039 | 6 /e 1993 | pp. 696 |

R.D. Madan & Satya Prakash

MODERN INORGANIC CHEMISTRY

This book explains the chemistry of elements on the basis of the latest theories of Chemistry. First few chapters of the book are devoted to the study of fundamentals of chemistry and others describe the extraction properties of elements alongwith the preparation, properties, uses and structure of their important compounds. Every chapter is followed by a large number of descriptive and objective type questions.

| 04 097 | 2 /e Rep. 1998 | pp. 1552 |

Satya Prakash, G.D. Tuli, S.K. Basu & R.D. Madan

ADVANCED INORGANIC CHEMISTRY VOL. I & II

Thoroughly revised and updated, this edition contains several new topics in addition to latest university questions at the end.

| 04 231 | Vol. I | 17 /e1998 | pp. 1156 |
| 04 232 | Vol. II | 17/e 1998 | pp. 5o4 |

H.D. Mathur & O.P. Tandon

CHEMISTRY OF RARE ELEMENTS

This book has been written to meet the requirements of the M.Sc. and B.Sc. (Hons.) students of all the Indian universities in the study of rare elements and their compounds.

| 04 133 | 3 /e 1989 | pp. 262 |

B.S. Bahl & Arun Bahl

ADVANCED ORGANIC CHEMISTRY

The book has now been substantially rewritten and enlarged. A good deal of new material has been added. The book retains its functional group approach while treating the chemistry of Aliphatic and Aromatic compounds.

| 04 024 | 3 /e Rep. 1998 | pp. 1376 |

B.S. Bahl & Arun Bahl

A TEXT-BOOK OF ORGANIC CHEMISTRY

This book has been written with the student in mind. The language is simple, explanations clear, and presentation very systematic. The salient features include functional group approach and separate treatment of aliphatic and aromatic compounds, a new chapter on spectroscopy and the latest solved and unsolved University Questions.

| 04 023 | 15 /e Rep. 1998 | pp. 876 |
| 04 025 | Hindi /e | pp. 1070 |

B.S. Bahl

REFRESHER COURSE IN B.Sc. ORGANIC CHEMISTRY

This book follows a self-teaching ap- proach. The language in this examination-oriented book is simple and presentation systematic. Explanations are brief and to-the-point.

| 04 045 | 2 /e 1993 | pp. 816 |

G.D. Tuli & P.L. Soni

REFRESHER COURSE IN B.Sc. INORGANIC AND ANALYTICAL CHEMISTRY

Provides an up-to- date and systematically ar- ranged account of the important aspects of Inorganic and Analytical chemistry for the B.Sc. student of Indian universities.

| 04 034 | 13 /e Reprint 1994 | pp.520 |

J.N. Gurtu & R. Kapoor

ORGANIC REACTIONS AND REAGENTS

This book deals with the fundamental principles of organic chemistry, organic reaction mechanisms and organic reagents and is suitable for degree and post-graduate students.

| 04 150 | 2 /e 1991 | pp. 648 |

P.R. Singh & S.K. Dikshit

MOLECULAR SPECTROSCOPY :

Principles and Chemical Applications

Besides dealing with the introduction, instrumentation, principles and application, each chapter presents a problem set at the end.

| 04 072 | 1 /e 1990 | pp. 125 |

Y.R. Sharma

ELEMENTARY ORGANIC SPECTROSCOPY

Methods based on relationships between structural

features and physical properties are not only making an ever increasing contribution but also have altered the scope and pace of organic chemistry due to the new technique of spectroscopy. The book as such deals with application of these methods on selected representative molecules which provides insight into the subject for Honours and Post-graduate students of organic chemistry.

| 04 073 | 2 /e Rep. 1997 | pp. 310 |

V.K. Srivastava & K.K. Srivastava
INTRODUCTION TO CHROMATOGRAPHY

The separation of a complex mixtures or compounds often pose very difficult proposition, which, however, was finally settled to rest and with immaculate result by means of chromatography method which has been widely used in different fields, science as well as arts, to the greatest advantage of mankind.

| 04 111 | 4 /e 1991 | pp. 144 |

A.K. Srivastava & P.C. Jain
ELEMENTS OF NUCLEAR CHEMISTRY

This book is suitable for B.Sc. (Hons.) and post-graduate students. It describes the basic principles of nuclear chemistry—structure of nucleus, fission and fusion, separation methods, uses of radio isotopes etc.

| 04 042 | 2 /e 1989 | pp. 176 |

S.S. Dara
A TEXT-BOOK OF ENGINEERING CHEMISTRY

This book is written exclusively for students of various branches of engineering keeping in view their practical life. It contains 12 chapters which are of basic importance in the curriculum of engineering chemistry for all branches of engineering. Each chapter consists of a methodical introduction, historical background, dis- cussion of basic physico-chemical principles involved and practical applications and significance. This is a book which is universally recommended for the students as well as the chemical engineers.

| 10 092 | 6 /e Rep. 1998 | pp. 752 |

S.S. Dara
A TEXT-BOOK OF ENVIRONMENTAL CHEMISTRY AND POLLUTION CONTROL

It provides a basic knowledge about environmental chemistry and pollution control which form an essential component of science and engineering curriculum at Graduate and Post-graduate level. This book has brought with it the ways and methods of preserving the earth's environment and its biological diversities.

| 04 189 | 1 /e Rep 1998 | pp. 214 |

MEDICAL SCIENCE

S. Subrahmanyam & K. Madhavan Kutty
A TEXT BOOK OF HUMAN PHYSIOLOGY

This book is now a standard work not only for graduate students but also for the post-graduate students. It expresses the fundamental principles and the physiological basis of modern medicine in a clear, lucid style.

| 22 001 | 5/e 1994 | pp. 708 |

F.S.K. Barar
ESSENTIALS OF PHARMACOTHERAPEUTICS

This book brings together the basic concepts of pharmacology as a whole aiming at safe and effective use of drugs in the treatment of disease. Scope includes medical students, residents, teachers and pharmacologists.

| 22 013 | 2/e 1994 | pp. 1056 |

T.S. Ranganathan
MULTIPLE CHOICE QUESTIONS IN ANATOMY

The objective type of questions (multiple choice) have become a compulsory part of the question papers in many university examinations and the entrance examinations for the Post-graduate courses in Medicine are also no exception of it. These questions are different from stereotyped. Keeping it in mind, the book has been prepared to provide a good exercise to the students in Anatomy to answer objective type of questions.

| 06 044 | 1/e 1993 | pp. 112 |

T.S. Ranganathan
A TEXT BOOK OF HUMAN ANATOMY

An attempt has been made in this book to present the details in an organised and methodical way as well as in a simple easily understandable style. All the relevant aspects of a topic like gross anatomy, histology, embryology, surface anatomy and applied anatomy are given cogently so that the students need not have to hunt for the material in different text-books. There are 431 line diagrams which will help easily in understanding and remembering the anatomy facts without taxing the memory.

| 22 010 | 8/e Rep. 1998 | pp. 804 |

OTHER IMPORTANT BOOKS

BOTANY

Mandahar, C.L.
03 102 Introduction to Plant Viruses
2/e 1987

Pandey, B.P.
Modern Practical Botany
Vol. I & II

ZOOLOGY

Verma, P.S. & Srivastava, P.C.
(B.Sc. F.Y. Zoology Unified
Course M.P.)

03 190 Non-chordate & Cell Biology
Paper I 2/e 1993

03 193 Chordate & General Biology
Paper II 2/e 1993

Jordan, E.L. & Verma, P.S.
03 028 Chordate Zoology and Animal
Physiology
10/e 2nd reprint 1993

Jajurley, Puranik & Thakur
03 080 Invertebrate Zoology 2/e 1992

**Sambasiviah, Kamalakara
Rao & Augustine Chellappa**
03 029 Animal Physiology and
Ecology 2/e

03 077 Animal Ecology

Verma, P.S.
03 032 A Manual of Practical Zoology :
Invertebrates 12/e 1997

03 033 A Manual of Practical Zoology
Chordates 10/e 1997

Verma, P.S. Srivastava, P.C.
03 222 Advanced Practical Zoology
3/e 1998

MEDICAL SCIENCE

Kumud P. Tamaskar
22 018 A Text- Book of Gynaecology
1/e 1986

**Lala Surajnandan Prasad &
L. Kulczycki (Eds)**
22 009 Paediatric Problems

Raju, G. Ramakrishanam
22 021 Text -Book of Obstetrics
2/e 1990

Gupta, Laha & Gupta
22 012 A Handbook of Medicine 1/e

Domingo M. Aviado Krantz & Carr's
22 004 Pharmacologic Principles of
Medical Practice 8/e

John V. Basmajian Grant's
22 002 Method of Anatomy 10/e

**Sangham Lal, Balakrishna Rao, B.N. &
Anand, S.S. (Ed.)**
22 007 Text -Book of Surgery 2/e

Behl, P.N. & Captain, R.M.
22 008 Skin-irritant And Sensitizing
Plants Found In India 2/e

CHEMISTRY

**Madan R.D., Tewari J.S. &
Mundhara, G.L.**
04 181 FY Chemistry (Inorganic,
Organic & Physical) 2/e 1993

Prasad, Sidhanti & Sastry
04 153 B.Sc Chemistry Vol. I 1/e 1991

Vyawahar & Palsokar
04 176 Modern Organic Chemistry
Part I 5/e 1993

Khanna, Krishnan
01 102 Fundamentals of Environmental
Pollution 11/e 1991

Vyawahare, A.R.
04 199 Modern Organic Chemistry
Part III 1/e 1997

B.S.Bahl & Arun Bahl
04 025 Snatak Karbanik Rasayan
2/e 1997

Madan, R.D.
04 161 B.Sc. Inorganic Chemistry Part I
1/e 1990

Ratolikar & Nimdeoker.
04 175 Modern Inorganic Chemistry
Part I 6/e 1992

Nimdeokar, N.M.
04 182 Modern Inorganic Chemistry
Part II 6/e 1993

Ratolika & Palsokar
04 179 Modern Physical Chemistry
Part I 6/e 1992

Ratolikar, V.G.
04 186 Modern Physical Chemistry
Part II (Nagpur) 6/e 1993

04 163 Modern Physcial Chemistry
Part III 2/e 1994

Gurtu J.N. & Kapoor R.
Advanced Experimental
Chemistry
04 116 Vol. I : Physical Chemistry
4/e 1992

04 117 Vol. II : Inorganic Chemistry
3/e 1990

04 118 Vol. III : Organic Chemistry
4/e 1991

**Giri, S., Bajpai, D.N. &
Pandey, O.P.**
04 033 Practical Chemistry 7/e 1996